COMPREHENSIVE RENEWABLE ENERGY

COMPREHENSIVE RENEWABLE ENERGY

EDITOR-IN-CHIEF
Ali Sayigh
Chairman of WREC, Director General of WREN, and Chairman of IEI, Brighton, UK

VOLUME 8
OCEAN ENERGY

VOLUME EDITOR
AbuBakr S. Bahaj
University of Southampton, Southampton, UK

ELSEVIER

AMSTERDAM BOSTON HEIDELBERG LONDON NEW YORK OXFORD
PARIS SAN DIEGO SAN FRANCISCO SINGAPORE SYDNEY TOKYO

Elsevier
Radarweg 29, PO Box 211, 1000 AE Amsterdam, The Netherlands
The Boulevard, Langford Lane, Kidlington, Oxford OX5 1GB, UK
225 Wyman Street, Waltham, MA 02451, USA

Copyright © 2012 Elsevier Ltd. All rights reserved.

4.04   Hydrogen Safety Engineering: The State-of-the-Art and Future Progress
Copyright © 2012 V Molkov

5.16   Renewable Fuels: An Automotive Perspective
Copyright © 2012 Lotus Cars Limited

The following articles are US Government works in the public domain and not subject to copyright:
1.19   Cadmium Telluride Photovoltaic Thin Film: CdTe
1.37   Solar Power Satellites
4.02   Current Perspective on Hydrogen and Fuel Cells
5.02   Historical Perspectives on Biofuels

No part of this publication may be reproduced, stored in a retrieval system or transmitted in any form or by any means electronic, mechanical, photocopying, recording or otherwise without the prior written permission of the publisher

Permissions may be sought directly from Elsevier's Science & Technology Rights Department in Oxford, UK: phone (+44) (0) 1865 843830; fax (+44) (0) 1865 853333; email: permissions@elsevier.com. Alternatively you can submit your request online by visiting the Elsevier web site at http://elsevier.com/locate/permissions, and selecting *Obtaining permission to use Elsevier material*

Notice
No responsibility is assumed by the publisher for any injury and/or damage to persons or property as a matter of products liability, negligence or otherwise, or from any use or operation of any methods, products, instructions or ideas contained in the material herein. Because of rapid advances in the medical sciences, in particular, independent verfication of diagnoses and drug dosages should be made.

British Library Cataloguing in Publication Data
A catalogue record for this book is available from the British Library

The Library of Congress Control Number: 2012934547

ISBN: 978-0-08-087872-0

For information on all Elsevier publications
visit our website at books.elsevier.com

Printed and bound in Italy

11 12 13 14 10 9 8 7 6 5 4 3 2 1

Working together to grow
libraries in developing countries

www.elsevier.com | www.bookaid.org | www.sabre.org

ELSEVIER   BOOK AID International   Sabre Foundation

Editorial: Gemma Mattingley, Joanne Williams
Production: Edward Taylor, Maggie Johnson

EDITOR-IN-CHIEF

Professor Ali Sayigh, BSc, DIC, PhD, CEng, a British citizen, graduated from Imperial College London and the University of London in 1966. He is a fellow of the Institute of Energy, a fellow of the Institution of Electrical Engineers, and is a chartered engineer.

From 1966 to 1985, Prof. Sayigh taught in the College of Engineering at the University of Baghdad and at King Saud University, Saudi Arabia, as a full-time professor, and also at Kuwait University as a part-time professor. From 1981 to 1985, he was Head of the Energy Department at the Kuwait Institute for Scientific Research (KISR) and expert in renewable energy at the Arab Organization of Petroleum Exporting Countries (AOPEC), Kuwait.

He started working in solar energy in September 1969. In 1984, he established links with Pergamon Press and became Editor-in-Chief of his first international journal, *Solar & Wind Technology*. Since 1990 he has been Editor-in-Chief of *Comprehensive Renewable Energy* incorporating *Solar & Wind Technology*, published by Elsevier Science Ltd., Oxford, UK. He is the editor of several international journals published in Morocco, Iran, Bangladesh, and Nigeria.

He has been a member of the International Society for Equitation Science (ISES) since 1973, founder and chairman of the ARAB Section of ISES since 1979, chairman of the UK Solar Energy Society for 3 years, and consultant to many national and international organizations, among them, the British Council, the Islamic Educational, Scientific and Cultural Organization (ISESCO), the United Nations Educational, Scientific and Cultural Organization (UNESCO), the United Nations Development Programme (UNDP), the Economic and Social Commission for Western Asia (ESCWA), and the United Nations Industrial Development Organization (UNIDO).

Since 1977 Prof. Sayigh has founded and directed several renewable energy conferences and workshops in the International Centre for Theoretical Physics (ICTP) – Trieste, Italy, Canada, Colombia, Algeria, Kuwait, Bahrain, Malaysia, Zambia, Malawi, India, the West Indies, Tunisia, Indonesia, Libya, Taiwan, UAE, Oman, the Czech Republic, Germany, Australia, Poland, the Netherlands, Thailand, Korea, Iran, Syria, Saudi Arabia, Singapore, China, the United States, and the United Kingdom.

In 1990 he established the World Renewable Energy Congress (WREC) and, in 1992, the World Renewable Energy Network (WREN), which hold their Congresses every 2 years, attracting more than 100 countries each time. In 2000, he and others in UAE, Sharjah, founded the Arab Science and Technology Foundation (ASTF) and regional conferences have been held in Sweden, Malaysia, Korea, Indonesia, Australia, UAE, and Libya, to name but a few. Prof. Sayigh has been running an annual international seminar on all aspects of renewable energy since 1990 in the United Kingdom and abroad. In total, 85 seminars have been held.

Prof. Sayigh supervised and graduated more than 34 PhD students and 64 MSc students at Reading University and the University of Hertfordshire when he was a professor from 1986 to 2004.

He has edited, contributed, and written more than 32 books and published more than 500 papers in various international journals and conferences.

In 2000–09, he initiated and worked closely with Sovereign Publication Company to produce the most popular magazine at annual bases called *Renewable Energy*, which was distributed freely to more than 6000 readers around the world. Presently, he is the editor-in-chief of *Comprehensive Renewable Energy*, coordinating 154 top scientists', engineers', and researchers' contributions in eight volumes published by Elsevier Publishing Company, Oxford, UK.

VOLUME EDITORS

Dr. Wilfried G. J. H. M. van Sark graduated from Utrecht University, the Netherlands, with an MSc in experimental physics in 1985, and with an MSc thesis on measurement and analysis of I–V characteristics of c-Si cells. He received his PhD from Nijmegen University, the Netherlands; the topic of his PhD thesis was III–V solar cell development, modeling, and processing. He then spent 7 years as a postdoc/senior researcher at Utrecht University and specialized in a-Si:H cell deposition and analysis. He is an expert in plasma chemical vapor deposition, both radio frequency and very high frequency. After an assistant professor position at Nijmegen University, where he worked on III–V solar cells, he returned to Utrecht University, with a focus on (single-molecule) confocal fluorescence microscopy of nanocrystals. In 2002, he moved to his present position as assistant professor at the research group Science, Technology and Society of the Copernicus Institute at Utrecht University, the Netherlands, where he performed and coordinated research on next-generation photovoltaic devices incorporating nanocrystals; for example, luminescent solar concentrators, as well as photovoltaic performance, life cycle analysis, socioeconomics, and policy development. He is member of the editorial board of Elsevier's scientific journal *Renewable Energy*, and member of various organizing committees of the European Union, the Institute of Electrical and Electronics Engineers (IEEE), and the SPIE PV conferences. He is author or coauthor of over 200 peer-reviewed journal and conference paper publications and book chapters. He has (co-)edited three books, including the present one.

Professor John K. Kaldellis holds a mechanical engineering degree from the National Technical University of Athens (NTUA) and a business administration diploma from the University of Piraeus. He obtained his PhD from NTUA (Fluid Sector) sponsored by Snecma–Dassault, France, and Bodossakis Foundation, Greece. He is currently the head of the Mechanical Engineering Department and since 1991 the director of the Soft Energy Applications and Environmental Protection Laboratory of the Technological Education Institute (TEI) of Piraeus. Prof. Kaldellis is also the scientific director (for TEI of Piraeus) of the MSc in Energy program organized by Heriot-Watt University and TEI of Piraeus. His scientific expertise is in the fields of energy and the environment. His research interests include feasibility analysis of energy sector applications; technological progress in wind, hydro, and solar energy markets; hybrid energy systems; energy storage issues; social attitudes toward renewable energy applications; and environmental technology–atmospheric pollution. He has participated in numerous research projects, funded by the European Union, European/Greek Industries, and the Greek State. Prof. Kaldellis has published six books concerning renewable energy applications and environmental protection. He is also the author of more than 100 scientific/research papers in international peer-reviewed journals and more than 300 papers for international scientific conferences. During the last decade, he was also a member of the Scientific Committee of the Hellenic Society of Mechanical–Electrical Engineers as well as a member of the organizing and scientific committee of several national and international conferences. He is currently a member of the editorial board of the *Renewable Energy International* journal and reviewer in more than 40 international journals in the energy and environment sector. He is the editor of the book *Stand-Alone and Hybrid Wind Energy Systems: Technology, Energy Storage and Applications* that has recently been published.

Dr. Soteris A. Kalogirou is a senior lecturer at the Department of Mechanical Engineering and Materials Science and Engineering at the Cyprus University of Technology, Limassol, Cyprus. He received his Higher Technical Institute (HTI) degree in mechanical engineering in 1982, his MPhil in mechanical engineering from the Polytechnic of Wales in 1991, and his PhD in mechanical engineering from the University of Glamorgan in 1995. In June 2011, he received the title of DSc from the University of Glamorgan.

For more than 25 years, he has been actively involved in research in the area of solar energy and particularly in flat-plate and concentrating collectors, solar water heating, solar steam generating systems, desalination, and absorption cooling. Additionally, since 1995, he has been involved in pioneering research dealing with the use of artificial intelligence methods, such as artificial neural networks, genetic algorithms, and fuzzy logic, for the modeling and performance prediction of energy and solar energy systems.

He has 29 books and book contributions and published 225 papers, 97 in international scientific journals and 128 in refereed conference proceedings. To date he has received more than 2550 citations on this work. He is Executive Editor of *Energy*, Associate Editor of *Renewable Energy*, and Editorial Board Member of another 11 journals. He is the editor of the book *Artificial Intelligence in Energy and Renewable Energy Systems*, published by Nova Science Inc.; coeditor of the book *Soft Computing in Green and Renewable Energy Systems*, published by Springer; and author of the book *Solar Energy Engineering: Processes and Systems*, published by Academic Press of Elsevier.

He has been a member of the World Renewable Energy Network (WREN) since 1992 and is a member of the Chartered Institution of Building Services Engineers (CIBSE), the American Society of Heating Refrigeration and Air-Conditioning Engineers (ASHRAE), the Institute of Refrigeration (IoR), and the International Solar Energy Society (ISES).

Dr. Andrew Cruden, a British citizen, was born in 1968. He obtained his BEng, MSc, and PhD in electrical engineering from the University of Strathclyde and CEng, MIEE Dr. Cruden is a past member of BSI GEL/105 Committee on Fuel Cells and Committee member of the IET Scotland Power Section. He is Director of the Scottish Hydrogen and Fuel Cell Association (SHFCA; www.shfca.org.uk) and Director of Argyll, Lomond and the Islands Energy Agency (www.alienergy.org.uk).

Dr. Cruden has been active in the field of hydrogen and fuel cells since 1995, when he acted as a consultant for Zevco Ltd., providing assistance with power electronic interfaces for early fuel cell systems. Later in 1998, he helped found the Scottish Fuel Cell Consortium (SFCC), supported by the Scottish Enterprise Energy Team, which ultimately developed a battery/fuel cell hybrid electric vehicle based on an AC Cobra kit car. The experience and contacts from the SFCC eventually gave rise to the formation of the Scottish Hydrogen and Fuel Cell Association (SHFCA), a trade body for the industry to promote and commercialize Scottish expertise in this field. Dr. Cruden was the founding chairman of the SHFCA.

Dr. Cruden is currently investigating alkaline electrolyzers in terms of improving their part load efficiency and lifetime when powered by variable renewable power sources, for example, wind turbines, as part of a £5 million EPSRC Supergen project on the 'Delivery of Sustainable Hydrogen' (EP/G01244X/1). He is also working with a colleague within Electronic and Electrical Engineering (EEE) at Strathclyde, studying the concept of vehicle-to-grid energy storage, as a mechanism not only to allow controlled load leveling on the power system, but also to potentially 'firm' up renewable energy generation. This work is supported by two research grants, an international E.On Research Initiative 2007 award and an ESPRC grant (EP/F062133/1).

Dr. Cruden is a senior lecturer within the Department of Electronic and Electrical Engineering at the University of Strathclyde. His current fields of research are modeling fuel cell and electrolyzer systems, fuel cell combined heat and power (CHP) systems, power electronic devices for interfacing both vehicular and stationary fuel cell systems, condition monitoring systems for renewable energy sources (i.e., wind turbines as part of EPSRC Supergen on Wind Energy Technologies, EP/D034566/1), and energy management systems for hybrid electric vehicles.

His areas of expertise include hydrogen-powered fuel cells and electrolyzers, energy storage for electric vehicles, and renewable energy generation.

Professor Dermot J. Roddy, BSc, PhD, CEng, FIET, joined Newcastle University as Science City Professor of Energy in 2008 after a period of some 20 years in the energy industry and petrochemical sectors. He is also Director of the Sir Joseph Swan Centre for Energy Research, which integrates energy research across Newcastle University and links with a powerful external industrial base in the energy sector. Outside of the university he is Chairman of Northeast Biofuels, Finance Director of the UK Hydrogen Association, and Vice-President of the Northern England Electricity Supply Companies Association. Prior to coming to Newcastle University, he was Chief Executive of Renew Tees Valley Ltd. – a company which he set up in 2003 to create a viable and vibrant economy in the Tees Valley based on renewable energy and recycling – where he was instrumental in a wide range of major renewable energy and low-carbon projects relating to biomass, biofuels, hydrogen, carbon capture and storage, wind, and advanced waste processing technologies. From 1998 to 2002, he ran the crude oil refinery on Teesside as a site director for a $5 billion turnover facility before moving to the Netherlands to work on Petroplus' international growth plans. Roddy's experience in the petrochemical industry began in 1985, involving a variety of UK and international roles in operations, engineering, and technology with ICI and others. Prior to that he developed leading-edge technology at Queen's University, Belfast, for optimization and control in aerospace applications.

André G. H. Lejeune was born on 2 August 1942 in Belgium. He was graduated in 1967 as a civil engineer, in 1972 as doctor in applied sciences (PhD), and in 1973 as master in oceanography in the University of Liège in Belgium. He was appointed full-time professor in the same university in 1976, and was visitor professor at the UNESCO–IHE Institute for Water Education in the Netherlands and Ecole Polytechnique Fédérale de Lausanne (EPFL) in Switzerland. Within the framework of his activities of professor, director of the Hydraulic Constructions and Hydraulic Research Laboratory, and expert, he took part in studies of dams and hydraulic structures and went on site in more than 90 countries of the world. In particular, he was for the last 6 years the chairman of the Technical Committee on Hydraulics for Dams in ICOLD (International Commission of Large Dams). He is a member of the Belgian Royal Academy of Sciences. He made his PhD thesis in hydraulic numerical modelization. This thesis received the Lorenz G. Straub Award in Minneapolis, USA (H. Einstein Jr. was a member of the Jury), and was used in particular by Chinese colleagues in the Three Gorges Project. Due to his practice and experience, he has a very complete knowledge of the hydraulic phenomena modelizations through both numerical and physical means.

With his wife, he has 3 children and 11 grandchildren. He likes books, tennis, and diving.

Thorsteinn I. Sigfusson is an internationally recognised physicist, educated in Copenhagen, Denmark, and Cambridge, UK. He is Director-General of the Innovation Center, Iceland and Professor of physics at the University of Iceland. He has been a visiting professor at Columbia University, New York, and he is currently the lead scientist in a prize-winning energy technology project performed at Tomsk Polytechnic University in Tomsk, Russia.

He has been a key figure in the introduction of new ideas and opportunities in the further greening of Icelandic society through the energy industry, and instrumental in the challenge of saving imported hydrocarbons by focusing on hydrogen from renewable energy.

He has started over a dozen start-up companies from research in Iceland and chaired various international societies in alternative energy. Among his achievements in geothermal energy is the construction of the world's largest solid-state thermoelectric generator powered with geothermal steam in southern Iceland. At the Innovation Center, Iceland, efforts are made to develop materials to withstand erosion in geothermal environments.

AbuBakr S. Bahaj is Professor of Sustainable Energy at the University of Southampton. After completing his PhD, he was employed by the University, progressing from a researcher to a personnel chair of Sustainable Energy. Over the past 20 years, Prof. Bahaj has established the energy theme within the University and directed his Sustainable Energy Research Group (SERG, www.energy.soton.ac.uk), which is now considered to be one of the United Kingdoms's leading university-based research groups in renewable energy and energy in buildings. He initiated and managed research in ocean energy conversion (resources, technologies, and impacts), photovoltaics, energy in buildings, and impacts of climate change on the built environment in the University. This work has resulted in over 230 articles published in academic refereed journals and conference series of international standing (see www.energy.soton.ac.uk).

Prof. Bahaj is the head of the Energy and Climate Change Division (ECCD) within the highly rated Faculty of Engineering and the Environment – Civil Engineering and the Environment – (www.civil.soton.ac.uk/research/divisions/divlist.asp?ResearchGroupID=1) (second in the United Kingdom, Research Assessment Exercise in 2008, with 80% of research judged to be either 'World Leading' or 'Internationally Excellent'). The aims of the Division and SERG are to promote and execute fundamental and applied research and preindustrial development in the areas of energy resources, technologies, energy efficiency, and the impact of climate change.

Prof. Bahaj is an experienced research team director and has many internationally focused research projects including collaborative projects in China, the European Union, the Middle East, and Africa. He also coordinated (2006–10) the United Kingdom's Engineering and Physical Sciences Research Council (EPSRC), Ecoregion Research Networks that aim to develop research themes and projects to study eco-city development encompassing resource assessment, technology pathways for the production and conservation of energy, planning, and social and economic studies required in establishing eco-regions in China and elsewhere (http://www.eco-networks.org). He is a founding member of the Sino-UK Low Carbon City Development Cooperation (LCCD) which aims to promote and undertake research into pathways for low-carbon development in Chinese cities. His work also encompasses an ongoing multimillion pound program in Africa, 'Energy for Development' for promoting and implementing village electrification systems, addressing villager's needs, and establishing coherent approaches to the commercial sustainability of the projects. This program is funded by the Research Councils and the UK Department for International Development (DFID; www.energyfordevelopment.net).

Prof. Bahaj is the editor-in-chief of the *International Journal of Sustainable Energy* and associate Editor of the *Renewable & Sustainable Energy Review*. He was on the editorial boards of the journals *Sustainable Cities and Society* and *Renewable Energy* (2005–11), and the United Kingdom's Institute of Civil Engineering journal *Energy* (2006–09). He was a member of the Tyndall Centre for Climate Change Research Supervisory Board (2005–10), and from 2001 to 2007 he was a member of the UK Government Department of Business, Enterprise and Regulatory Reform (now Department for Business Innovations and Skills, BIS), Technology Programmes Panels on Water (including ocean energy) and Solar Energy, now being administered by the Technology Strategy Board (TSB). Prof. Bahaj was the chair of the Technical Committees of the World Renewable Energy Congress – held in Glasgow (July 2008) and in Abu Dhabi (September 2010). He was a member of the Technical Committee of the 27th International Conference on Offshore Mechanics and Arctic Engineering (OMAE, 2008), a member of the management and technical committees of the European Wave and Tidal Energy Conferences (EWTEC, Porto, Portugal, September 2007; and Uppsala, Sweden, September 2009). He is also a member of the British Standards Institution (BSI) Committee GEL/82 on PV Energy Systems. Recently, at the invitation of the International Energy Agency, he has completed the 2008 status report on tidal stream energy conversion and in September 2009 was elected to chair the next EWTEC conference in the series – EWTEC2011 which was held in Southampton, 5–9 September 2011, and attended by around 500 participants.

To address training in the areas of energy and climate change Prof. Bahaj has coordinated and developed a set of MSc programs under the banner 'Energy and Sustainability' that address Energy Resources and Climate Change and Energy, Environment and Buildings.

CONTRIBUTORS FOR ALL VOLUMES

P Agnolucci
Imperial College London, London, UK

EO Ahlgren
Chalmers University of Technology, Gothenburg, Sweden

D Aklil
Pure Energy Center, Unst, Shetland Isles, UK

D-C Alarcón Padilla
Centro de Investigaciones Energéticas Medioambientales y Tecnológicas (CIEMAT), Plataforma Solar de Almeria, Almeria, Spain

K Alexander
University of Canterbury, Christchurch, New Zealand

S Alexopoulos
Aachen University of Applied Sciences, Jülich, Germany

A Altieri
UNICA – Brazilian Sugarcane Industry Association, São Paulo, Brazil

A Anthrakidis
Aachen University of Applied Sciences, Jülich, Germany

E Antolín
Universidad Politécnica de Madrid, Madrid, Spain

P Archambeau
University of Liège, Liège, Belgium

H Ármannsson
Iceland GeoSurvey (ISOR), Reykjavík, Iceland

MF Askew
Wolverhampton, UK

A Athienitis
Concordia University, Montreal, QC, Canada

G Axelsson
University of Iceland, Reykjavik, Iceland

V Badescu
Polytechnic University of Bucharest, Bucharest, Romania

AS Bahaj
The University of Southampton, Southampton, UK

P Banda
Instituto de Sistema Fotovoltaicos de Concentración (ISFOC), Puertollano, Spain

VG Belessiotis
'DEMOKRITOS' National Center for Scientific Research, Athens, Greece

P Berry
ADAS High Mowthorpe, Malton, UK

F Bidault
Imperial College London, London, UK

D Biro
Fraunhofer Institute for Solar Energy Systems, Freiburg, Germany

G Boschloo
Uppsala University, Uppsala, Sweden

C Boura
Aachen University of Applied Sciences, Jülich, Germany

E Bozorgzadeh
Iran Water and Power Resources Development Company (IWPCO), Tehran, Iran

CE Brewer
Iowa State University, Ames, IA, USA

M Börjesson
Chalmers University of Technology, Gothenburg, Sweden

RC Brown
Iowa State University, Ames, IA, USA

F Bueno
University of Burgos, Burgos, Spain

K Burke
NASA Glenn Research Center, Cleveland, OH, USA

LF Cabeza
GREA Innovació Concurrent, Universitat de Lleida, Lleida, Spain

L Candanedo
Dublin Institute of Technology, Dublin, Ireland

YG Caouris
University of Patras, Patras, Greece

UB Cappel
Uppsala University, Uppsala, Sweden

JA Carta
Universidad de Las Palmas de Gran Canaria, Las Palmas de Gran Canaria, Spain

P Chen
Dalian Institute of Chemical Physics, Dalian, China

DG Christakis
Wind Energy Laboratory, Technological Educational Institute of Crete, Crete, Greece

DA Chwieduk
Warsaw University of Technology, Warsaw, Poland

J Clark
University of York, York, UK

G Conibeer
University of New South Wales, Sydney, NSW, Australia

AJ Cruden
University of Strathclyde, Glasgow, UK

MC da Silva

B Davidsdottir
University of Iceland, Reykjavík, Iceland

O de la Rubia
Instituto de Sistema Fotovoltaicos de Concentración (ISFOC), Puertollano, Spain

E Despotou
Formerly of the European Photovoltaic Industry Association, Brussels, Belgium

BJ Dewals
University of Liège, Liège, Belgium

AL Dicks
The University of Queensland, Brisbane, QLD, Australia

R DiPippo
University of Massachusetts Dartmouth, Dartmouth, MA, USA

E Dunlop
European Commission DG Joint Research Centre, Ispra, Italy

NM Duteanu
Newcastle University, Newcastle upon Tyne, UK;
University 'POLITEHNICA' Timisoara, Timisoara, Romania

LM Eaton
Oak Ridge National Laboratory, Oak Ridge, TN, USA

H-J Egelhaaf
Konarka Technologies GmbH, Nürnberg, Germany

T Ehara
Mizuho Information & Research Institute, Tokyo, Japan

B Erable
Newcastle University, Newcastle upon Tyne, UK;
CNRS-Université de Toulouse, Toulouse, France

S Erpicum
University of Liège, Liège, Belgium

G Evans
NNFCC, Biocentre, Innovation Way, Heslington, York, UK

AFO Falcão
Instituto Superior Técnico, Technical University of Lisbon, Lisbon, Portugal

G Faninger
University of Klagenfurt, Klagenfurt, Austria; Vienna University of Technology, Vienna, Austria

GA Florides
Cyprus University of Technology, Limassol, Cyprus

ÓG Flóvenz
Iceland GeoSurvey (ISOR), Reykjavík, Iceland

RN Frese
VU University Amsterdam, Amsterdam, The Netherlands

Þ Friðriksson
Iceland GeoSurvey (ISOR), Reykjavík, Iceland

VM Fthenakis
Columbia University, New York, NY, USA; Brookhaven National Laboratory, Upton, NY, USA

M Fuamba
École Polytechnique de Montréal, Montreal, QC, Canada

A Fuller
University of Canterbury, Christchurch, New Zealand

LMC Gato
Instituto Superior Técnico, Technical University of Lisbon, Lisbon, Portugal

R Gazey
Pure Energy Center, Unst, Shetland Isles, UK

TA Gessert
National Renewable Energy Laboratory (NREL), Golden, CO, USA

MM Ghangrekar
Newcastle University, Newcastle upon Tyne, UK; Indian Institute of Technology, Kharagpur, India

M Giannouli
University of Patras, Patras, Greece

EA Gibson
University of Nottingham, Nottingham UK

A Gil
Hydropower Generation Division of Iberdrola, Salamanca, Spain

SW Glunz
Fraunhofer Institute for Solar Energy Systems, Freiburg, Germany

JC Goldschmidt
Fraunhofer Institute for Solar Energy Systems ISE, Freiburg, Germany

R Gottschalg
Loughborough University, Leicestershire, UK

MA Green
The University of New South Wales, Sydney, NSW, Australia

J Göttsche
Aachen University of Applied Sciences, Jülich, Germany

J Guo
China Institute of Water Resources and Hydropower Research (IWHR), Beijing, China

A Hagfeldt
Uppsala University, Uppsala, Sweden

B Hagin
Ingénieur-Conseil, Lutry, Switzerland

K Hall
Technology Transition Corporation, Ltd., Tyne and Wear, UK

O Hamandjoda
University of Yaounde, Yaounde, Republic of Cameroon

AP Harvey
Newcastle University, Newcastle upon Tyne, UK

JA Hauch
Konarka Technologies GmbH, Nürnberg, Germany

D Heinemann
University of Oldenburg, Oldenburg, Germany

V Heller
Imperial College London, London, UK

GP Hersir
Iceland GeoSurvey (ISOR), Reykjavík, Iceland

T Heyer
Technical University of Dresden, Dresden, Germany

P Hilger
Aachen University of Applied Sciences, Jülich, Germany

B Hillring
Swedish University of Agricultural Sciences, Skinnskatteberg, Sweden

T Hino
CTI Engineering International Co., Ltd., Chu-o-Ku, Japan

LC Hirst
Imperial College London, London, UK

B Hoffschmidt
Aachen University of Applied Sciences, Jülich, Germany

H Horlacher
Technical University of Dresden, Dresden, Germany

N Hughes
Imperial College London, London, UK

SL Hui
Bechtel Civil Company, San Francisco, CA, USA

D Husmann
University of Wisconsin–Madison, Madison, WI, USA

JTS Irvine
University of St Andrews, St Andrews, UK

D Jacobs
Freie Universität Berlin, Berlin, Germany

Y Jestin
Advanced Photonics and Photovoltaics Group, Bruno Kessler Foundation, Trento, Italy

A Jäger-Waldau
Institution for Energy Transport, Ispra, Italy

S Jianxia
Design and Research Institute, Yangzhou City, Jiangsu Province, China

E Johnson
Pure Energy Center, Unst, Shetland Isles, UK

HF Kaan
TNO Energy, Comfort and Indoor Quality, Delft, The Netherlands

JK Kaldellis
Technological Education Institute of Piraeus, Athens, Greece

SA Kalogirou
Cyprus University of Technology, Limassol, Cyprus

HD Kambezidis
Institute of Environmental Research and Sustainable Development, Athens, Greece

M Kapsali
Technological Education Institute of Piraeus, Athens, Greece

M Karimirad
Norwegian University of Science and Technology, Trondheim, Norway

T Karlessi
National and Kapodistrian University of Athens, Athens, Greece

SN Karlsdóttir
Innovation Center Iceland, Iceland

D Al Katsaprakakis
Wind Energy Laboratory, Technological Educational Institute of Crete, Crete, Greece

O Kaufhold
Aachen University of Applied Sciences, Jülich, Germany

CA Kaufmann
Helmholtz Zentrum für Materialien und Energie GmbH, Berlin, Germany

KA Kavadias
Technological Education Institute of Piraeus, Athens, Greece

LL Kazmerski
National Renewable Energy Laboratory, Golden, CO, USA

A Kazmi
University of York, York, UK

K Kendall
University of Birmingham, Birmingham, UK

J Kenfack
University of Yaounde, Yaounde, Republic of Cameroon

R Kenny
European Commission DG Joint Research Centre, Ispra, Italy

HC Kim
Brookhaven National Laboratory, Upton, NY, USA

L Kloo
KTH—Royal Institute of Technology, Stockholm, Sweden

G Knothe
USDA Agricultural Research Service, Peoria, IL, USA

FR Kogler
Konarka Technologies GmbH, Nürnberg, Germany

D Kolokotsa
Technical University of Crete, Crete, Greece

K Komoto
Mizuho Information & Research Institute, Tokyo, Japan

E Kondili
Technological Education Institute of Piraeus, Athens, Greece

H Kristjánsdóttir
University of Iceland, Reykjavík, Iceland

LA Lamont
Petroleum Institute, Abu Dhabi, UAE

GA Landis
NASA Glenn Research Center, Cleveland, OH, USA

JGM Lee
Newcastle University, Newcastle upon Tyne, UK

G Leftheriotis
University of Patras, Patras, Greece

A Lejeune
University of Liège, Liège, Belgium

T Leo
FuelCell Energy Inc., Danbury, CT, USA

E Lester
The University of Nottingham, Nottingham, UK

E Lorenz
University of Oldenburg, Oldenburg, Germany

JW Lund
Geo-Heat Center, Oregon Institute of Technology, Klamath Falls, OR, USA

A Luque
Universidad Politécnica de Madrid, Madrid, Spain

BP Machado
Intertechne, Curitiba, PR, Brazil

EBL Mackay
GL Garrad Hassan, Bristol, UK

T-F Mahdi
École Polytechnique de Montréal, Montreal, QC, Canada

GG Maidment
London South Bank University, London, UK

A Malmgren
BioC Ltd, Cirencester, UK

C Manson-Whitton
Progressive Energy Ltd., Stonehouse, UK

Á Margeirsson
Magma Energy Iceland, Reykjanesbaer, Iceland

A Martí
Universidad Politécnica de Madrid, Madrid, Spain

M Martinez
Instituto de Sistema Fotovoltaicos de Concentración (ISFOC), Puertollano, Spain

S Mathew
University of Brunei Darussalam, Gadong, Brunei Darussalam

PH Middleton
University of Agder, Grimstad, Norway

R Mikalsen
Newcastle University, Newcastle upon Tyne, UK

D Milborrow
Lewes, East Sussex, UK

H Müllejans
European Commission DG Joint Research Centre, Ispra, Italy

V Molkov
University of Ulster, Newtownabbey, Northern Ireland, UK

M Moner-Girona
Joint Research Centre, European Commission, Institute for Energy and Transport, Ispra, Italy

PE Morthorst
Technical University of Denmark, Roskilde, Denmark

N Mortimer
North Energy Associates Ltd, Sheffield, UK

E Mullins
Teagasc, Oak Park Crops Research Centre, Carlow, Republic of Ireland

P Mulvihill
Pioneer Generation Ltd., Alexandra, New Zealand

DR Myers
National Renewable Energy Laboratory, USA

D Nash
University of Strathclyde, Glasgow, UK

GF Nemet
University of Wisconsin–Madison, Madison, WI, USA

H Nfaoui
Mohammed V University, Rabat, Morocco

T Nikolakakis
Columbia University, New York, NY, USA

X Niu
Changjiang Institute of Survey, Planning, Design and Research, Wuhan, China

B Norton
Dublin Institute of Technology, Dublin, Ireland

A Nuamah
The University of Nottingham, Nottingham, UK; RWE npower, Swindon, UK

B O'Connor
Aachen University of Applied Sciences, Jülich, Germany

O Olsson
Swedish University of Agricultural Sciences, Skinnskatteberg, Sweden

V Ortisi
Pure Energy Center, Unst, Shetland Isles, UK

H Ossenbrink
European Commission DG Joint Research Centre, Ispra, Italy

AG Paliatsos
Technological Education Institute of Piraeus, Athens, Greece

A Pandit
VU University Amsterdam, Amsterdam, The Netherlands

E Papanicolaou
'DEMOKRITOS' National Center for Scientific Research, Athens, Greece

A Paurine
London South Bank University, London, UK

N Pearsall
Northumbria University, Newcastle, UK

RJ Pearson
Lotus Engineering, Norwich, UK

RD Perlack
Oak Ridge National Laboratory, Oak Ridge, TN, USA

H Pettersson
Swerea IVF AB, Mölndal, Sweden

GS Philip
KCAET, Malapuram, Kerala, India

S Pillai
The University of New South Wales, Sydney, NSW, Australia

M Pirotton
University of Liège, Liège, Belgium

BG Pollet
University of Birmingham, Birmingham, UK

D Porter
Association of Electricity Producers, London, UK

A Pouliezos
Technical University of Crete, Hania, Greece

R Preu
Fraunhofer Institute for Solar Energy Systems, Freiburg, Germany

CM Ramos

C Rau
Aachen University of Applied Sciences, Jülich, Germany

AA Refaat
Cairo University, Giza, Egypt

TH Reijenga
BEARiD Architecten, Rotterdam, The Netherlands

AHME Reinders
Delft University of Technology, Delft, The Netherlands; University of Twente, Enschede, The Netherlands

G Riley
RWE npower, Swindon, UK

DJ Roddy
Newcastle University, Newcastle upon Tyne, UK

S Rolland
Alliance for Rural Electrification, Brussels, Belgium

A Roskilly
Newcastle University, Newcastle upon Tyne, UK

F Rubio
Instituto de Sistema Fotovoltaicos de Concentración (ISFOC), Puertollano, Spain

F Rulot
University of Liège, Liège, Belgium

L Rybach
GEOWATT AG, Zurich, Switzerland

M Santamouris
National and Kapodistrian University of Athens, Athens, Greece

J Sattler
Aachen University of Applied Sciences, Jülich, Germany

M Sauerborn
Aachen University of Applied Sciences, Jülich, Germany

TW Schmidt
The University of Sydney, Sydney, NSW, Australia

N Schofield
University of Manchester, Manchester, UK

REI Schropp
Utrecht University, Utrecht, The Netherlands

K Scott
Newcastle University, Newcastle upon Tyne, UK

SP Sen
NHPC Ltd., New Delhi, India

TI Sigfusson
Innovation Center, Reykjavik, Iceland

L Sims
Konarka Technologies GmbH, Nürnberg, Germany; Universität Augsburg, Augsburg, Germany

C Smith
NNFCC, Biocentre, Innovation Way, Heslington, York, UK

K Sæmundsson
Iceland GeoSurvey (ISOR), Reykjavík, Iceland

BK Sovacool
Vermont Law School, South Royalton, VT, USA

J Spink
Teagasc, Oak Park Crops Research Centre, Carlow, Republic of Ireland

JN Sørensen
Technical University of Denmark, Lyngby, Denmark

T Stallard
The University of Manchester, Manchester, UK

GS Stavrakakis
Technical University of Crete, Chania, Greece

R Steim
Konarka Technologies GmbH, Nürnberg, Germany

BJ Stokes
CNJV LLC, Washington, DC, USA

L Sun
KTH—Royal Institute of Technology, Stockholm, Sweden; Dalian University of Technology (DUT), Dalian, China

L Suo
Science and Technology Committee of the Ministry of Water Resources, Beijing, China

DT Swift-Hook
Kingston University, London, UK; World Renewable Energy Network, Brighton, UK

A Synnefa
National and Kapodistrian University of Athens, Athens, Greece

S Szabo
Joint Research Centre, European Commission, Institute for Energy and Transport, Ispra, Italy

MJY Tayebjee
The University of Sydney, Sydney, NSW, Australia

A Tesfai
University of St Andrews, St Andrews, UK

P Thornley
The University of Manchester, Manchester, UK

Y Tripanagnostopoulos
University of Patras, Patras, Greece

L Tsakalakos
General Electric – Global Research Center, New York, NY, USA

JWG Turner
Lotus Engineering, Norwich, UK

E Tzen
Centre for Renewable Energy Sources and Saving (CRES), Pikermi, Attica, Greece

T Unold
Helmholtz Zentrum für Materialien und Energie GmbH, Berlin, Germany

J van der Heide
imec vzw, Leuven, Belgium

P van der Vleuten
Free Energy Consulting, Eindhoven, The Netherlands

F Van Hulle
XP Wind Consultancy, Leuven, Belgium

GC van Kooten
University of Victoria, Victoria, BC, Canada

WGJHM van Sark
Utrecht University, Utrecht, The Netherlands

I Waller
FiveBarGate Consultants Ltd, Cleveland, UK

I Walsh
Opus International Consultants Ltd., New Zealand

Y Wang
Newcastle University, Newcastle upon Tyne, UK

T Wizelius
Gotland University, Visby, Sweden; Lund University, Lund, Sweden

LL Wright
University of Tennessee, Knoxville, TN, USA

H Xie
Changjiang Institute of Survey, Planning, Design and Research, Wuhan, China

M Yamaguchi
Toyota Technological Institute, Tempaku, Nagoya, Japan

P Yianoulis
University of Patras, Patras, Greece

EH Yu
Newcastle University, Newcastle upon Tyne, UK

H Yu
Newcastle University, Newcastle upon Tyne, UK

DP Zafirakis
Technological Education Institute of Piraeus, Athens, Greece

G Zaragoza
Centro de Investigaciones Energéticas Medioambientales y Tecnológicas (CIEMAT), Plataforma Solar de Almeria, Almeria, Spain

M Zeman
Delft University of Technology, Delft, The Netherlands

PREFACE

Comprehensive Renewable Energy is the only multivolume reference work of its type at a time when renewable energy sources are increasingly in demand and realistically sustainable, clean, and helping to combat climate change and global warming. Renewable energy investment has exceeded US$10 billion per year during the past 5 years. The World Renewable Energy Network (WREN) predicts that this figure is set to increase to US$20 billion per year by 2015.

As Editor-in-Chief, I have assembled an impressive world-class team of 154 volume editors and contributing authors for the eight volumes. They represent policy makers, researchers, industrialists, financiers, and heads of organizations from more than 80 countries to produce this definitive complete work in renewable energy covering the past, explaining the present, and giving the ideas and prospects of development for the future. There are more than 1000 references from books, journals, and the Internet within the eight volumes. *Comprehensive Renewable Energy* is full of color charts, illustrations, and photographs of real projects and research results from around the world. Each chapter has been painstakingly reviewed and checked for consistent high quality. The result is an authoritative overview that ties the literature together and provides the user with reliable background information and a citation resource.

The field of renewable energy research and development is represented by many journals that are directly and indirectly concerned with the field. But no reference work encompasses the entire field and unites the different areas of research through in-depth foundational reviews. *Comprehensive Renewable Energy* fills this vacuum, and is the definitive work for this subject area. It will help users apply context to diverse journal literature, aiding them in identifying areas for further research and development.

Research into renewable energy is spread across a number of different disciplines and subject areas. These areas do not always share a unique identifying factor or subject themselves to clear and concise definitions. This work unites the different areas of research and allows users, regardless of their background, to navigate through the most essential concepts with ease, saving them time and vastly improving their understanding so that they can move forward, whether in their research, development, manufacturing, or purchase of renewable energy.

The first volume is devoted to Photovoltaic Technology and is edited by Mr. Wilfried G. J. H. M. van Sark from the Netherlands. It consists of 38 chapters, written by 41 authors from Europe, the United States, Japan, China, India, Africa, and the Middle East. The topics covered range from the smallest applications to MW projects. A brief introduction and history is followed by chapters on finance and economics, solar resources, up- and downconversion, crystalline photovoltaic (PV) cells, luminescent concentrators, thin-film and multiple-junction plastic solar cells, dye-sensitized solar cells, bio-inspired converters, application of micro- and nanotechnology, building integrated photovoltaics (BIPV) application in architecture, and very large-scale PV systems. Without doubt, this is an impressive tour of an immense field.

Volume 2 is devoted to Wind Energy and is edited by Professor John K. Kaldellis from Greece. It consists of 22 chapters written by 22 authors, again from various parts of the world, covering all aspects of wind energy from small wind mills to very large wind farms. The volume includes chapters on the history of wind power, the potential of wind power, wind turbine development, aerodynamic analysis, mechanical and electrical loads, control systems, noise and testing, onshore and offshore wind systems, policy, industry, and special wind power applications.

Volume 3 is devoted to Solar Thermal Applications and the editor is Professor Soteris A. Kalogirou from Cyprus. It consists of 19 chapters written by 17 authors. All aspects of solar thermal energy and its applications are covered. The volume begins with solar energy as a source of heat and goes on to describe the history of thermal applications, low-temperature and high-temperature storage systems, selective coating, glazing, modeling and simulation, hot water systems, space heating and cooling, water desalination, industrial and agricultural applications, concentration power, heat pumps, and passive solar architecture. The authors have looked at the Sun from the thermal energy aspect and put together a very informative and up-to-date volume from which every interested person, no matter what their level of knowledge, can benefit.

Volume 4 is on Fuel Cells and Hydrogen Technology and is edited by Dr. Andrew Cruden from the United Kingdom. It consists of 14 chapters covering the following topics: introduction and perspectives on hydrogen and fuel cells; theory and application of alkaline fuel cells; application of proton exchange membrane (PEM) fuel cells; molten carbonate fuel cells; solid oxide fuel cells; microbial and biological fuel cells; storage of compressed gas and hydrogen; the economy and policy of hydrogen technology; hydrogen safety engineering and future progress; the use of hydrogen for transport; and hydrogen and fuel cell power electronics. The 14 chapters were written by 16 authors. All aspects of practice, innovative technology, and future guidelines for researchers and industry have been addressed in this definitive volume.

Volume 5 deals with the huge field of Biomass and Biofuels and is edited by Professor Dermot J. Roddy from the United Kingdom. This work consists of 21 chapters written by 23 authors, again covering all aspects of biomass and biofuels, including their past, present, and future. The volume explains the history and prospective future of biofuels; bioethanol development in Brazil; power generation from biomass; biomass co-firing stations; biomass world market; a critical assessment of biomass – combined heat and power (CHP) energy systems; the ethics of biofuel production – issues, constraints, and limitations; greenhouse gases life cycle analysis; six different solutions from gasification and pyrolysis; new processes in biomass-to-liquid technology; new processes in biofuel production; biofuels from waste materials; novel feedstocks and woody biomass; feedstocks with the potential of yield improvement; renewable fuels – an automotive prospective; and novel use of biofuels in a range of engine configurations. Under Expanding the Envelope, there are chapters on biochar, extracting additional value from biomass, and biomass to chemicals. Finally, the chapter on bioenergy policy development concludes the volume.

Volume 6 is concerned with Hydro Power and is edited by Professor André G. H. Lejeune from Belgium. This is the oldest of all the renewable energy applications and has progressed over the ages from pico-hydro of a few hundred watts to large- and mega-scale dams generating more than 3000 MW with innovative civil engineering capability. This volume consists of 18 chapters prepared by 21 authors. It contains introduction – benefits and constraints of hydropower, recent developments and achievements in hydraulic research in China, and the management of hydropower and its impacts through construction and operation. The volume then assesses nine hydropower schemes around the world: the Three Gorges Project in China; large hydropower plants of Brazil; hydropower in Iran – vision and strategy; the recent trend in developing hydropower in India; the evolution of hydropower in Spain; hydropower in Japan; hydropower in Canada; an overview of institutional structure reform of the Cameroon power sector and assessment; and hydropower reliability in Switzerland. Other important issues are covered: pumped storage power plants; simplified generic axial-flow microhydro turbines; the development of a small hydroelectric scheme at Horseshoe Bend, Teviot River, New Zealand; concrete durability in dam design structure; and long-term sediment management for sustainable hydropower.

Volume 7 deals with Geothermal Energy. The editor of this volume is Professor Thorsteinn I. Sigfusson from Iceland. The volume consists of 10 chapters, which are written by 15 different authors. It covers the following areas: introduction and the physics of geothermal resources and management during utilization; geothermal shallow systems – heat pumps; geothermal exploration techniques; corrosion, scaling, and material selection in geothermal power production; direct heat utilization of geothermal energy; geothermal power plants; geochemical aspects of geothermal utilization; geothermal cost and investment factors; and the role of sustainable geothermal development.

Volume 8 is devoted to Generating Electricity from the Oceans, edited by Professor AbuBakr S. Bahaj from the United Kingdom. It consists of six chapters written by five authors. The volume covers the historical aspects of wave energy conversion, resource assessment for wave energy, development of wave devices from initial conception to commercial demonstration, air turbines, and the economics of ocean energy.

One chapter is totally devoted to Renewable Energy Policy and Incentives. It is included in the first volume only. The author of this chapter is Mr. David Porter, Chief Executive of the Association of Electricity Producers in the United Kingdom, an author who has had vast experience of dealing with electricity generation in the United Kingdom over many years. He has advised the British Government on how to meet supply and demand of electricity and coordinate with all electricity producers regarding their sources and supply. The chapter outlines the types of mechanisms used to promote renewable energy and their use, the impact on their deployment, ensuring investor certainty, the potential for harmonizing support schemes, and the conclusion.

In short, my advice to anyone who wants to acquire comprehensive knowledge concerning renewable energy, no matter which subject or application, is that they should acquire this invaluable resource for their home, research center and laboratory, company, or library.

Professor Ali Sayigh BSc, DIC, PhD, FIE, FIEE, CEng
Chairman of WREC (World Renewable Energy Congress)
Director General of WREN (World Renewable Energy Network)
Chairman of IEI (The Institution of Engineers (India))
Editor-in-Chief of *Renewable Energy*
Editor-in-Chief of *Renewable Energy Magazine*

CONTENTS

Editor-in-Chief	v
Volume Editors	vii
Contributors for All Volumes	xi
Preface	xix

Volume 1   Photovoltaic Solar Energy

Renewable Energy

1.01	Renewable Energy Policy and Incentives *D Porter*	1

Photovoltaic Solar Energy

1.02	Introduction to Photovoltaic Technology *WGJHM van Sark*	5
1.03	Solar Photovoltaics Technology: No Longer an Outlier *LL Kazmerski*	13
1.04	History of Photovoltaics *LA Lamont*	31

Economics and Environment

1.05	Historical and Future Cost Dynamics of Photovoltaic Technology *GF Nemet and D Husmann*	47
1.06	Feed-In Tariffs and Other Support Mechanisms for Solar PV Promotion *D Jacobs and BK Sovacool*	73
1.07	Finance Mechanisms and Incentives for Photovoltaic Technologies in Developing Countries *M Moner-Girona, S Szabo, and S Rolland*	111
1.08	Environmental Impacts of Photovoltaic Life Cycles *VM Fthenakis and HC Kim*	143
1.09	Overview of the Global PV Industry *A Jäger-Waldau*	161
1.10	Vision for Photovoltaics in the Future *E Despotou*	179

| 1.11 | Storage Options for Photovoltaics VM Fthenakis and T Nikolakakis | 199 |

Resource and Potential

| 1.12 | Solar Radiation Resource Assessment for Renewable Energy Conversion DR Myers | 213 |
| 1.13 | Prediction of Solar Irradiance and Photovoltaic Power E Lorenz and D Heinemann | 239 |

Basics

| 1.14 | Principles of Solar Energy Conversion LC Hirst | 293 |
| 1.15 | Thermodynamics of Photovoltaics V Badescu | 315 |

Technology

1.16	Crystalline Silicon Solar Cells: State-of-the-Art and Future Developments SW Glunz, R Preu, and D Biro	353
1.17	Thin-Film Silicon PV Technology M Zeman and REI Schropp	389
1.18	Chalcopyrite Thin-Film Materials and Solar Cells T Unold and CA Kaufmann	399
1.19	Cadmium Telluride Photovoltaic Thin Film: CdTe TA Gessert	423
1.20	Plastic Solar Cells L Sims, H-J Egelhaaf, JA Hauch, FR Kogler, and R Steim	439
1.21	Mesoporous Dye-Sensitized Solar Cells A Hagfeldt, UB Cappel, G Boschloo, L Sun, L Kloo, H Pettersson, and EA Gibson	481
1.22	Multiple Junction Solar Cells M Yamaguchi	497
1.23	Application of Micro- and Nanotechnology in Photovoltaics L Tsakalakos	515
1.24	Upconversion TW Schmidt and MJY Tayebjee	533
1.25	Downconversion MJY Tayebjee, TW Schmidt, and G Conibeer	549
1.26	Down-Shifting of the Incident Light for Photovoltaic Applications Y Jestin	563
1.27	Luminescent Solar Concentrators JC Goldschmidt	587
1.28	Thermophotovoltaics J van der Heide	603
1.29	Intermediate Band Solar Cells E Antolín, A Martí, and A Luque	619
1.30	Plasmonics for Photovoltaics S Pillai and MA Green	641
1.31	Artificial Leaves: Towards Bio-Inspired Solar Energy Converters A Pandit and RN Frese	657

Applications

1.32	Design and Components of Photovoltaic Systems *WGJHM van Sark*	679
1.33	BIPV in Architecture and Urban Planning *TH Reijenga and HF Kaan*	697
1.34	Product-Integrated Photovoltaics *AHME Reinders and WGJHM van Sark*	709
1.35	Very Large-Scale Photovoltaic Systems *T Ehara, K Komoto, and P van der Vleuten*	733
1.36	Concentration Photovoltaics *M Martinez, O de la Rubia, F Rubio, and P Banda*	745
1.37	Solar Power Satellites *GA Landis*	767
1.38	Performance Monitoring *N Pearsall and R Gottschalg*	775
1.39	Standards in Photovoltaic Technology *H Ossenbrink, H Müllejans, R Kenny, and E Dunlop*	787

Volume 2 Wind Energy

2.01	Wind Energy – Introduction *JK Kaldellis*	1
2.02	Wind Energy Contribution in the Planet Energy Balance and Future Prospects *JK Kaldellis and M Kapsali*	11
2.03	History of Wind Power *DT Swift-Hook*	41
2.04	Wind Energy Potential *H Nfaoui*	73
2.05	Wind Turbines: Evolution, Basic Principles, and Classifications *S Mathew and GS Philip*	93
2.06	Energy Yield of Contemporary Wind Turbines *DP Zafirakis, AG Paliatsos, and JK Kaldellis*	113
2.07	Wind Parks Design, Including Representative Case Studies *D Al Katsaprakakis and DG Christakis*	169
2.08	Aerodynamic Analysis of Wind Turbines *JN Sørensen*	225
2.09	Mechanical-Dynamic Loads *M Karimirad*	243
2.10	Electrical Parts of Wind Turbines *GS Stavrakakis*	269
2.11	Wind Turbine Control Systems and Power Electronics *A Pouliezos*	329
2.12	Testing, Standardization, Certification in Wind Energy *F Van Hulle*	371
2.13	Design and Implementation of a Wind Power Project *T Wizelius*	391
2.14	Offshore Wind Power Basics *M Kapsali and JK Kaldellis*	431

2.15	Wind Energy Economics D Milborrow	469
2.16	Environmental-Social Benefits/Impacts of Wind Power E Kondili and JK Kaldellis	503
2.17	Wind Energy Policy GC van Kooten	541
2.18	Wind Power Integration JA Carta	569
2.19	Stand-Alone, Hybrid Systems KA Kavadias	623
2.20	Wind Power Industry and Markets PE Morthorst	657
2.21	Trends, Prospects, and R&D Directions in Wind Turbine Technology JK Kaldellis and DP Zafirakis	671
2.22	Special Wind Power Applications E Kondili	725

Volume 3 Solar Thermal Systems: Components and Applications

Solar Thermal Systems

3.01	Solar Thermal Systems: Components and Applications – Introduction SA Kalogirou	1
3.02	Solar Resource HD Kambezidis	27
3.03	History of Solar Energy VG Belessiotis and E Papanicolaou	85

Components

3.04	Low Temperature Stationary Collectors YG Caouris	103
3.05	Low Concentration Ratio Solar Collectors SA Kalogirou	149
3.06	High Concentration Solar Collectors B Hoffschmidt, S Alexopoulos, J Göttsche, M Sauerborn, and O Kaufhold	165
3.07	Thermal Energy Storage LF Cabeza	211
3.08	Photovoltaic/Thermal Solar Collectors Y Tripanagnostopoulos	255
3.09	Solar Selective Coatings P Yianoulis, M Giannouli, and SA Kalogirou	301
3.10	Glazings and Coatings G Leftheriotis and P Yianoulis	313
3.11	Modeling and Simulation of Passive and Active Solar Thermal Systems A Athienitis, SA Kalogirou, and L Candanedo	357

Applications

3.12	Solar Hot Water Heating Systems G Faninger	419
3.13	Solar Space Heating and Cooling Systems SA Kalogirou and GA Florides	449
3.14	Solar Cooling and Refrigeration Systems GG Maidment and A Paurine	481
3.15	Solar-Assisted Heat Pumps DA Chwieduk	495
3.16	Solar Desalination E Tzen, G Zaragoza, and D-C Alarcón Padilla	529
3.17	Industrial and Agricultural Applications of Solar Heat B Norton	567
3.18	Concentrating Solar Power B Hoffschmidt, S Alexopoulos, C Rau, J Sattler, A Anthrakidis, C Boura, B O'Connor, and P Hilger	595
3.19	Passive Solar Architecture D Kolokotsa, M Santamouris, A Synnefa, and T Karlessi	637

Volume 4 Fuel Cells and Hydrogen Technology

4.01	Fuel Cells and Hydrogen Technology – Introduction AJ Cruden	1
4.02	Current Perspective on Hydrogen and Fuel Cells K Burke	13
4.03	Hydrogen Economics and Policy N Hughes and P Agnolucci	45
4.04	Hydrogen Safety Engineering: The State-of-the-Art and Future Progress V Molkov	77
4.05	Hydrogen Storage: Compressed Gas D Nash, D Aklil, E Johnson, R Gazey, and V Ortisi	111
4.06	Hydrogen Storage: Liquid and Chemical P Chen	137
4.07	Alkaline Fuel Cells: Theory and Application F Bidault and PH Middleton	159
4.08	PEM Fuel Cells: Applications AL Dicks	183
4.09	Molten Carbonate Fuel Cells: Theory and Application T Leo	227
4.10	Solid Oxide Fuel Cells: Theory and Materials A Tesfai and JTS Irvine	241
4.11	Biological and Microbial Fuel Cells K Scott, EH Yu, MM Ghangrekar, B Erable, and NM Duteanu	257
4.12	Hydrogen and Fuel Cells in Transport K Kendall and BG Pollet	281
4.13	H_2 and Fuel Cells as Controlled Renewables: FC Power Electronics N Schofield	295
4.14	Future Perspective on Hydrogen and Fuel Cells K Hall	331

Volume 5 Biomass and Biofuel Production

Biomass and Biofuels

5.01 Biomass and Biofuels – Introduction 1
DJ Roddy

5.02 Historical Perspectives on Biofuels 11
G Knothe

Case Studies

5.03 Bioethanol Development in Brazil 15
A Altieri

5.04 Biomass Power Generation 27
A Malmgren and G Riley

5.05 Biomass Co-Firing 55
A Nuamah, A Malmgren, G Riley, and E Lester

Issues, Constraints & Limitations

5.06 A Global Bioenergy Market 75
O Olsson and B Hillring

5.07 Biomass CHP Energy Systems: A Critical Assessment 87
M Börjesson and EO Ahlgren

5.08 Ethics of Biofuel Production 99
I Waller

5.09 Life Cycle Analysis Perspective on Greenhouse Gas Savings 109
N Mortimer

Technology Solutions – New Processes

5.10 Biomass Gasification and Pyrolysis 133
DJ Roddy and C Manson-Whitton

5.11 Biomass to Liquids Technology 155
G Evans and C Smith

5.12 Intensification of Biofuel Production 205
AP Harvey and JGM Lee

5.13 Biofuels from Waste Materials 217
AA Refaat

Technology Solutions – Novel Feedstocks

5.14 Woody Biomass 263
LL Wright, LM Eaton, RD Perlack, and BJ Stokes

5.15 Potential for Yield Improvement 293
J Spink, E Mullins, and P Berry

Technology Solutions – Novel End Uses

5.16 Renewable Fuels: An Automotive Perspective 305
RJ Pearson and JWG Turner

5.17 Use of Biofuels in a Range of Engine Configurations 343
A Roskilly, Y Wang, R Mikalsen, and H Yu

Expanding the Envelope

5.18	Biochar *CE Brewer and RC Brown*	357
5.19	Extracting Additional Value from Biomass *MF Askew*	385
5.20	Biomass to Chemicals *A Kazmi and J Clark*	395
5.21	Bioenergy Policy Development *P Thornley*	411

Volume 6 Hydro Power

Hydro Power

6.01	Hydro Power – Introduction *A Lejeune*	1

Constraints of Hydropower Development

6.02	Hydro Power: A Multi Benefit Solution for Renewable Energy *A Lejeune and SL Hui*	15
6.03	Management of Hydropower Impacts through Construction and Operation *H Horlacher, T Heyer, CM Ramos, and MC da Silva*	49

Hydropower Schemes Around the World

6.04	Large Hydropower Plants of Brazil *BP Machado*	93
6.05	Overview of Institutional Structure Reform of the Cameroon Power Sector and Assessments *J Kenfack and O Hamandjoda*	129
6.06	Recent Hydropower Solutions in Canada *M Fuamba and TF Mahdi*	153
6.07	The Three Gorges Project in China *L Suo, X Niu, and H Xie*	179
6.08	The Recent Trend in Development of Hydro Plants in India *SP Sen*	227
6.09	Hydropower Development in Iran: Vision and Strategy *E Bozorgzadeh*	253
6.10	Hydropower Development in Japan *T Hino*	265
6.11	Evolution of Hydropower in Spain *A Gil and F Bueno*	309
6.12	Hydropower in Switzerland *B Hagin*	343

Design Concepts

6.13	Long-Term Sediment Management for Sustainable Hydropower *F Rulot, BJ Dewals, S Erpicum, P Archambeau, and M Pirotton*	355
6.14	Durability Design of Concrete Hydropower Structures *S Jianxia*	377
6.15	Pumped Storage Hydropower Developments *T Hino and A Lejeune*	405

6.16	Simplified Generic Axial-Flow Microhydro Turbines A Fuller and K Alexander	435
6.17	Development of a Small Hydroelectric Scheme at Horseshoe Bend, Teviot River, Central Otago, New Zealand P Mulvihill and I Walsh	467
6.18	Recent Achievements in Hydraulic Research in China J Guo	485

Volume 7   Geothermal Energy

7.01	Geothermal Energy – Introduction TI Sigfusson	1
7.02	The Physics of Geothermal Energy G Axelsson	3
7.03	Geothermal Energy Exploration Techniques ÓG Flóvenz, GP Hersir, K Sæmundsson, H Ármannsson, and Þ Friðriksson	51
7.04	Geochemical Aspects of Geothermal Utilization H Ármannsson	95
7.05	Direct Heat Utilization of Geothermal Energy JW Lund	169
7.06	Shallow Systems: Geothermal Heat Pumps L Rybach	187
7.07	Geothermal Power Plants R DiPippo	207
7.08	Corrosion, Scaling, and Material Selection in Geothermal Power Production SN Karlsdóttir	239
7.09	Geothermal Cost and Investment Factors H Kristjánsdóttir and Á Margeirsson	259
7.10	Sustainable Energy Development: The Role of Geothermal Power B Davidsdottir	271

Volume 8   Ocean Energy

8.01	Generating Electrical Power from Ocean Resources AS Bahaj	1
8.02	Historical Aspects of Wave Energy Conversion AFO Falcão	7
8.03	Resource Assessment for Wave Energy EBL Mackay	11
8.04	Development of Wave Devices from Initial Conception to Commercial Demonstration V Heller	79
8.05	Air Turbines AFO Falcão and LMC Gato	111
8.06	Economics of Ocean Energy T Stallard	151
Index		171

8.01 Generating Electrical Power from Ocean Resources

AS Bahaj, The University of Southampton, Southampton, UK

© 2012 Elsevier Ltd.

8.01.1	Introduction	1
8.01.2	Wave Energy Conversion	1
8.01.3	Marine Current Energy Conversion	2
8.01.4	Technology Development Assessment	3
8.01.5	Prototype Device Development and Commercial Farms	4
8.01.6	Future Prospects	5
Acknowledgments		6
References		6

8.01.1 Introduction

The current global energy needs, their associated security of supply, and price fluctuations are at the forefront of the energy debate. In addition, environmental issues associated with the current energy generation, which is centered on the utilization of fossil fuels especially for the production of our electricity needs, and the impact of climate change will require new thinking in terms of energy efficiency and implementation of policies to exploit nonpolluting natural resources. Inherently, the utilization of such resources implies the development of low carbon technologies, which can also be perceived as the current cornerstone in many of the developed and developing countries aimed at reducing our dependence on fossil fuels. This reduces emissions and creates new jobs (green revolution). Nevertheless, such aims will need strong support in terms of investment and policies targeting support to enhance energy-generating capacities through the development of low carbon technologies, especially those from renewable resources. It is also clear that the current economic climate offers a window of opportunity for new growth through targeted elements of the various stimuli packages initiated by many governments around the world for the expansion of renewable energy technologies.

Ocean energy resources derived from wind, waves, tidal, or marine currents can be utilized and converted to large-scale sustainable electrical power. Conversion systems are easily adaptable and can be integrated within the current utility power supply infrastructure and networks. However, in the development of renewable energy technologies, many countries have embarked on policies that are highly reliant on the expansion of large-scale offshore wind energy to electrical power, with only little attention being directed at other areas of renewable energy. Although this is understandable, as wind technologies are far more mature, it is important not to marginalize the utilization of other ocean resources by concentrating effort on and diverting the available financial resources to offshore wind only.

Ocean energy has many forms – tides, surface waves, ocean circulation, salinity, and thermal gradients. The focus of this volume of *Comprehensive Renewable Energy* is dedicated to two of these. Those found in tidal or marine currents, driven by gravitational effects, and wind-driven waves, derived ultimately from solar energy. Globally, tidal dissipation on continental shelves has been estimated at 2.5 TW [1]. The United Kingdom, which is currently considered the world's leader in the technological conversion of ocean energy resources, has estimated shoreline resources of approximately 10% (0.25 TW) of the global tidal resource. If one-tenth of this figure could be tapped for power generation (which would undoubtedly require a very large capital investment), tidal stream or marine current power could deliver around 220 TWh a^{-1}, which roughly equates to half of the United Kingdom's current electricity consumption. Whilst most of the incident wave energy is dissipated in deep water, where economic exploitation is yet to be demonstrated, there is nevertheless a significant nearshore resource estimated at 1.3 TW globally by the European Thematic Network on Wave Energy, with a technically exploitable resource of 100–800 TWh a^{-1} [2]. In addition, the United Kingdom is also one of the countries that has one of the most energetic of wave climates, which could provide up to 50 TWh a^{-1} [3].

This volume of *Comprehensive Renewable Energy* gives an analysis of the current state of art of generating electricity from wave and tidal currents (termed ocean energy). This chapter gives an overview of ocean wave and marine current energy conversion with more emphasis on the latter; Chapters 8.02, 8.03, 8.04, and 8.05 address the history of wave energy, wave resource assessment, wave device development, and air turbines, respectively; and Chapter 8.06 reviews the economics of ocean energy.

8.01.2 Wave Energy Conversion

Wave energy is inherently stochastic, being a consequence of airstreams or wind energy. Wave energy stems from wave motion and as can be seen below, its power is related to the wave height and period. There are many technological variants, each of which is aimed at exploiting the various properties of wave action. Deep-water sea waves offer large energy fluxes under predictable conditions over periods of days.

The power P per unit width of a wavefront is given by

$$P = \left(\frac{1}{64}\right)\left(\frac{\rho g^2}{\pi}\right)(H_s^2 T_e^2) \quad [1]$$

where P is in $(W\,m^{-1})$, ρ is the density of sea water $(kg\,m^{-3})$, g is the acceleration due to gravity $(m\,s^{-1})$, H_s is the significant wave height (m), and T_e is the wave period (s^{-1}) [4]. More in-depth theoretical analysis of the fundamentals can be found in the now standard textbook on wave energy conversion [5].

The conversion of wave energy into usable energy is extremely complex due to the hydrodynamic processes present in the diffraction and radiation of the waves as they propagate to shore. In essence, the conversion to electrical power is subject to hugely varying energy fluxes and time scales (few seconds in wave action and hour or days in sea states) that the conversion technology needs to cope with and, once conversion occurs, conditioning the generated power to the 50 or 60 Hz of the electrical utility grid is also challenging. The conversion is established through what is known as a power take-off (PTO) system, such as an air turbine, power hydraulics, electrical generator, and other variants that can be exploited for the production of usable energy. Wave energy conversion has its roots in our response to the oil crises of 1973 (see Chapter 8.02) and consequently this area is much older than the relatively new marine current energy conversion. An in-depth review of the status of energy conversion technologies is given in Reference 6.

It should be noted that both wave energy and marine current converters (Section 8.01.3) will need to be designed not only to generate power but also to ensure survivability of the device. The designs will need to withstand the most severe conditions expected in their lifetime. For instance, the concepts being developed vary greatly and since it is not possible to predict with great accuracy the severity of a storm at a certain location, a probabilistic approach will be needed to determine design conditions and the acceptable level of risk for the device being developed [6].

8.01.3 Marine Current Energy Conversion

Marine currents are a form of kinetic energy and are generally diffuse, but concentrated at a number of potential sites around the world where sea flows are channeled around or through constraining topographies (e.g., islands and straits). The tides, which drive such currents, are highly predictable, being a consequence of the gravitational effects of the planetary motion of the earth, the moon, and the sun. Such characteristics offer marine current energy converters (MCECs) an advantage over other renewable energy resources – such as wind or wave energy [7, 8]. This is because power generation from developed projects that rely on marine currents will have quantifiable and firmly foreseeable future energy yields that can be planned for and managed appropriately within the normal utility grid. Additionally, the quantifiable long-term energy yields offer a particular advantage to project developers for negotiating, with electrical utility companies, a better power purchasing agreement compared with other renewables.

The utilization of marine currents is akin to that of wind energy resource conversion; that is, the kinetic energy of the moving fluid can similarly be extracted and applied using a suitable type of turbine rotor. It does not, therefore, require water-impounding structures such as dams used in conventional hydropower but some sort of anchoring system within the flow stream. In addition, and in most cases, the fundamental understanding needed has similar basis as those used to predict the energy in a moving fluid as employed in wind energy conversion. The analysis offered for the consideration of wind turbines can be extended to marine current turbines. The power P_o (W) available from a stream of water (in the absence of significant changes in depth or elevation) is given by

$$P_o = \frac{1}{2}\rho A v_o^3 \quad [2]$$

where ρ $(kg\,m^{-3})$ is the density of fluid, A (m^2) is the cross-sectional area of the rotor under consideration, and v_o $(m\,s^{-1})$ is the unperturbed fluid speed.

As can be seen from Reference 2, P_o is proportional to the cube of the fluid velocity; hence, the energy produced is highly sensitive to variations in the fluid velocity. In addition, the power in the flow is also proportional to the fluid density, which for water is about 800 times that of air. This indicates that the power density or flux $(kW\,m^{-2})$ for marine current energy resource will be appreciably higher than that produced by wind energy when considered at appropriately rated speeds for both technologies [7]. The consequence of this is that smaller and hence more manageable MCECs can be installed to exploit local conditions, such as water depth or bathymetry where they are favorable. However, water depth in practice places a constraint on the maximum rated power of a marine current turbine. Such a constraint does not exist for wind turbines.

If one considers technology variants that are similar or related to those of wind energy conversion (although other unique design philosophies are being pursued), estimation of energy capture can be undertaken. For instance, the classic analysis of power extraction which stems from a wind front intercepted by an actuator disk [9] can be used. In the case of a horizontal axis turbine, the analysis states that the maximum power that can be extracted by a single turbine in an unconstrained flow is the fraction 16/27 (=0.59) of the kinetic energy flux through the actuator (rotor) disk area, and the power, in the case of no extraction, is given by eqn [2]. In general, this fraction is known as the power coefficient C_p, defined by

$$C_p = \left(\frac{P}{P_o}\right) = \frac{P}{(1/2)\rho A v_o^3} \quad [3]$$

where *P* is the power developed by the rotor. For all wind turbines currently in operation, $C_p < 0.59$; however, more sophisticated design methods allowing for the effects of finite numbers of blades predict for typical designs, maximum values of C_p in the range 0.4–0.5 [9, 10]. Such analysis also applies to the case of similar turbines in marine current sites or tidal stream channels, provided these are wide and deep compared with the rotor disk diameter and that there is only a small change in free surface elevation across the turbine location [10, 11]. In eqn [3], C_p can be thought of as the effectiveness of a device in generating power, regardless of flow speed or capture area of the device.

In must be noted that there are major differences in the engineering of marine current turbines as compared with those operating in wind energy. This is particularly due to the higher density of water compared with air, the closer proximity of the free surface, and the much slower speed of flow and cavitation. Furthermore, installations of such converters in fast-flowing seas will clearly present structural engineering challenges for both system integrity and the foundations of the submerged structure [12].

8.01.4 Technology Development Assessment

There is a plethora of concepts with different designs targeting energy extraction from wave and marine current resources. It is therefore unrealistic to establish a common approach that can arrive at an assessment of the various concepts being developed. Nevertheless, one can arrive at a common characterization of operating principles which could be used to establish a class of technology within wave or marine current energy conversion. In both cases, energy capture is achieved through a structure that converts the resource into mechanical energy and then through conventional rotating or linear generators – known as the PTO – into electrical power for supply to an electrical grid. In wave energy, air, water turbines, as well as hydraulic motors can be used to provide the mechanical coupling that converts the alternate motion of the waves into a continuous one-directional motion (Chapter **8.02** and Reference 6). In marine currents, a rotor such as in a horizontal axis turbine can be used. Rotor design encompasses blade design, in which the mechanical motion is transferred to a type suitable for input to a stage where electrical power is produced. This subsystem may include a gearbox, a set of lever arms and pistons driving hydraulic fluid, and/or an electrical generator of a fixed or variable speed type. In most cases, the generated electricity is conditioned and transmitted to the grid through a subsystem which includes power electronics, transformers, circuit breakers, and cables.

In order for the technology to succeed, progress will need to span from research and development to project-scale implementation. Currently, there is a global community involved in various phases of wave and marine current energy device and project development. To date, there are only a handful of devices that can be classified to be at the commercial pilot demonstration stage, and much effort is concentrated at research and development and testing at scale stages at various sea test sites such as the European Marine Energy Centre (EMEC) [13]. However, it is recognized that there are large numbers of concepts being considered or developed and that these efforts seem to dilute the already scarce financial support. Hence, there is a need for some consolidation.

Nevertheless, development of wave and marine current technologies will need to consider the appropriate steps needed to establish reliable devices and coherent projects. In **Figure 1**, such steps are highlighted in terms of their relationship both to the technology (device) and to the project development (site and any associated environmental impacts). The former is related to the conception of the original idea and its development whilst the latter is more related to deployment at a pilot/commercial scale in the sea. For instance, in order to provide reliability of the systems being developed, conversion devices will need to be subjected to technology readiness level (TRL) or assessment protocols [14–17]. An introduction to TRLs and the step-by-step development of WECs are addressed in Chapter **8.04**. Further analysis of the various sections of **Figure 1** can be found in Reference 12.

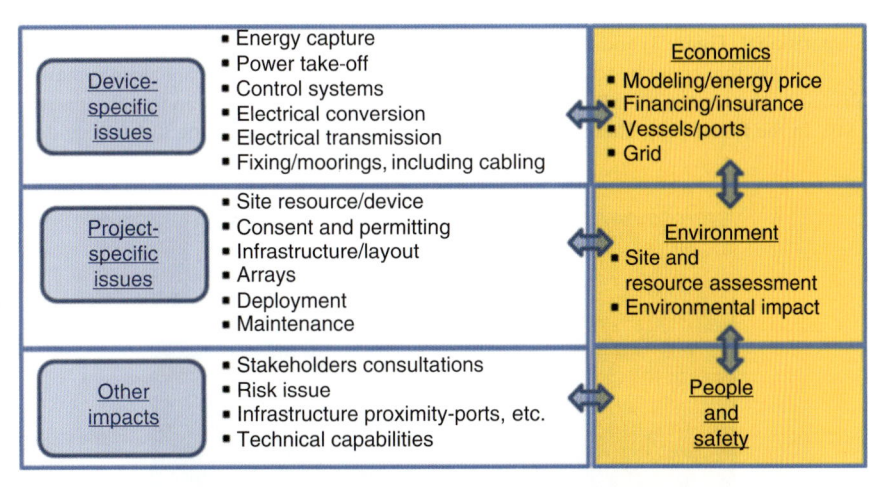

Figure 1 Developmental issues for wave and marine current energy conversion technologies spanning device and project development. Adapted from Bahaj AS (2011) Generating electricity from the oceans. *Renewable and Sustainable Energy Reviews* 15(7): 3399–3416.

The technology can be considered to be mature when multiple devices at the tens of megawatts are deployed in the sea and the full reliability of the systems and their maintenance needs are quantified. Such deployment will require a developer to identify a project site, undertake the various steps needed to obtain consent, and permit and have a robust plan for deployment and maintenance. The investment in such a site is dependent on the perceived energy production. This in turn will depend on the intensities of the resources, be it wave characteristics or water flow velocities. Generally, and as can be seen from **Figure 1**, the overall cost of an ocean energy project – wave or a marine current – will be likely dominated by capital and operating costs including upfront cost of consenting, surveys, and so on (Chapter **8.06**). Since the revenue is mainly dependent on the flow or wave conditions, the profitability of a project is highly dependent on a clear understanding of site conditions including wave and flow field characteristics. Hence, resource and site assessments will be crucial in any economic analysis of the viability of an ocean energy project. In addition, there are many factors which also need consideration: weather windows for deployment, understanding of seabed conditions, availability of vessels, proximity to a grid connection, and ports. In most cases, especially in the United Kingdom, the grid connection issue is similar to that encountered with other renewable energy technologies such as offshore wind and hence will not be discussed here.

8.01.5 Prototype Device Development and Commercial Farms

In both wave and marine current energy conversion, there is currently, to the author's knowledge, no commercially operated capacity in the world. However, in terms of prototypes operating at anticipated future commercial device capacities, there are notable installations within the United Kingdom and elsewhere. A survey of publicly available information on prototype device development and deployment as well as commercial aspirations can be found in Reference 12.

What will underpin the expansion of commercial activities in wave and marine current energy conversion will be the deployment and installation at array or farm scale. Currently, there are no such farms or arrays of multiple devices deployed and operating in the sea. However, a notable exception has been the installation in northern Portugal in 2008 of a set of three Pelamis P1 wave energy devices representing the world's first grid-connected wave farm having a capacity of 2.25 MW (**Figure 2**). This Aguçadoura wave energy project was supported by a generous feed-in tariff of approximately €0.23 kWh^{-1}, but was unfortunately abandoned for various reasons attributed mainly to the financial collapse of one of the partners in the project [18, 19]. Nevertheless, the technology developer Pelamis Wave Power Ltd [20] is currently progressing with the testing of their P2 converter at EMEC, and plans for larger projects of farms within the United Kingdom are underway [12, 20].

For technology progression and for gaining operational experience in the sea, it will be imperative that the next phase in the development of wave and marine current energy devices is at the multimegawatt scale of multiple devices in array or farm configurations. This is a necessary step that will allow project developers to

1. gain the required experience at all stages of deployment;
2. quantify the production of power at farm scale; and
3. provide the economic evidence of the scale effects (deployment, installation, connectivity, maintenance within the operating environment, etc.) that are deemed necessary for cost reductions in this important field of renewable energy conversion.

An approach that has been developed around the world, which is hoped to provide seamless project development in wave energy conversion, is the creation of infrastructure zones in the sea to provide facilities to developers. These provisions take away from developers the prolonged and costly aspects associated with all the difficulties of permitting, consenting, and planning needed for operation in the ocean. Such marked and confined 'ocean zones' in effect offer 'deploy-and-plug' facilities in which all device-specific issues are taken care of [12]. Currently, there are only two globally available zones, one in the United Kingdom – Wave Hub – which is operational (**Figure 3**) and the other in Portugal – Wave Pilot Zone (WPZ). The United Kingdom's Wave Hub has an initial capacity of 20 MW that could be scaled up to 50 MW in the future, and plans are afoot to have its first array in 2013 [21]. The WPZ, established on the west coast of Portugal about 130 km north of Lisbon, has an initial capacity of 80 MW that could be expanded to 250 MW in the future [22]. These sites will undoubtedly help in progressing technology development and allow

Figure 2 World's first wave farm of three Pelamis P1-A machines of 750 kW each installed at Aguçadoura, Portugal. Image courtesy of PWP Ltd. [18].

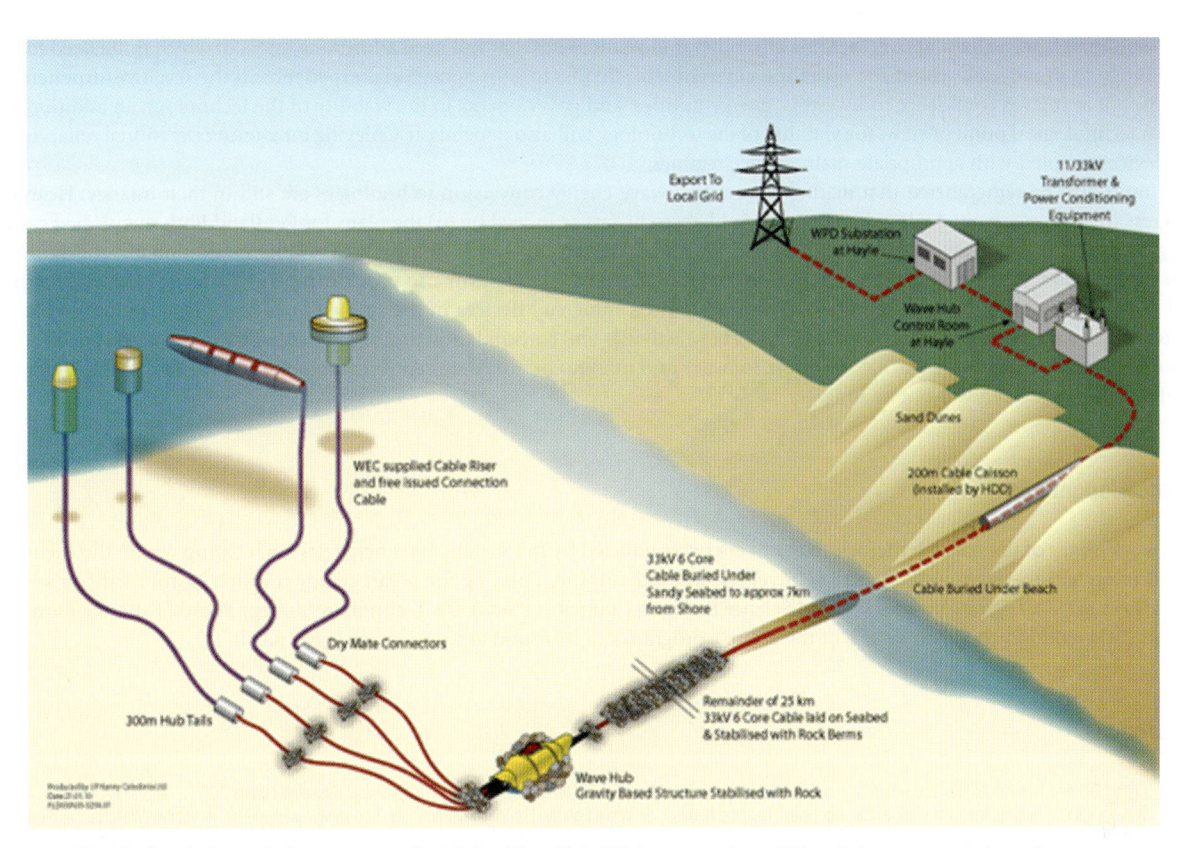

Figure 3 World's first deploy-and-plug ocean zone installed at Wave Hub, UK. Image courtesy of Wave Hub, www.wavehub.co.uk.

experience to be gained at both the deployment and the installation phases. Overtime, technical, operational, and maintenance data will be generated that will help with the development of second-generation devices.

8.01.6 Future Prospects

It is clear from current planned activities in wave and marine current energy conversion that the impact of the economic crises has not been as disastrous as for other sectors. The impetus for deployment at farm scale is gathering pace. Scotland, with support from its independent executive, seems to provide the necessary support to enhance technology prospects for deploying at the required scale. Over the past 2 years, several developers and electrical generation utilities have jointly been preparing for commercial-scale deployment projects in the Scottish Pentland Firth. In the United Kingdom, the Crown Estate owns the seabed around the coast and has been offering site options and leases for projects for offshore wind and now wave and marine current energy conversion. The recent results, specifically for the latter, announced by the Crown Estate for Round 1 Pentland Firth and Orkney waters have created ambitious plans to install up to 1.6 GW of multiple devices in farms. These plans encompass an initial 10 demonstration and commercial projects totaling 1.2 GW of potential capacity covering different technologies. These are divided as 600 MW wave energy capacity and 600 MW marine current capacity having an estimated total cost of approximately £4.2 billion (US$7 billion) and are planned to be installed by 2020 [23]. In addition, the highlighted projects will need a new electrical grid or strengthening of the existing electrical grid and other infrastructure costing around £1 billion (US$1.5 billion). The extra investment is proposed to be covered from public sources to develop and build not only new grid connections but also harbors and other infrastructure in Orkney and Caithness.

The idea behind the above venture is similar to that proposed for the development of specific 'ocean zones' for technology installation mentioned earlier. The Crown Estate being a project partner will in effect be offering seamless support transcending bottleneck issues such as permitting, consenting, and in this case including financial support. However, a lot more will need to be in place, for example, the long-term incentives needed from the government to bridge the financial investment gap in such projects [12, 24, 25].

Another issue that is a major barrier for the wave and marine current energy conversion technologies is the cost per megawatt installed. This is estimated to be in the range £7–10 million (US$11–15 million) per megawatt installed, with the lower value for multimegawatt installations and the higher one for a single commercial prototype. This will need to be surmounted not only by industry but also the required government support mechanisms to at least achieve parity with offshore wind currently costing around £3 million MW^{-1} installed.

In summary, given all the above, there are also other important issues that will need addressing, most of which is the need for the technology to prove itself within the operating environment, that is, to gain operational experience in the sea. This experience is paramount as it gives confidence to investors, energy utilities, and governments in the viability of the technology. In addition and from a technological point of view, the viability of the technology will also depend on achieving long-term operational reliability of the devices coupled with appropriate maintenance regimes.

It must also be remembered that marine current and wave energy conversion technologies are still in their infancy. However, progress to multimegawatt deployment in farms is likely to be fast as judged by (a) the plans for Pentland Firth mentioned earlier, (b) global activities such as those in Korea and Canada, and (c) the recent entry to the this area of China. Additionally, this notion is also supported by the prepared 'ocean zones' – Wave Hub and WPZ – which will also provide impetus for technology deployment and the deployment of four grid-connected, large-scale precommercial devices in the sea at EMEC and plans for large-scale test centers in Canada, the United States, and Sweden. These activities and consolidation provided by the entry to the market of electrical utilities provide further evidence that the future for wave and marine current energy conversion looks bright and that the large-scale road technology rollout will not be long.

Acknowledgments

This work is part of the research themes on ocean energy conducted by the Sustainable Energy Research Group within the Faculty of Engineering and the Environment at the University of Southampton. Funding for ocean energy research is from various sources including the UK's Engineering and Physical Science Research Council (EPSRC), the Technology Strategy Board (TSB), the European Union (EU), and industry. Full details of the group's program can be found at www.energy.soton.ac.uk.

References

[1] Egbert GD and Ray RD (2003) Semi-diurnal and diurnal tidal dissipation from TOPEX/Poseidon altimetry. *Geophysical Research Letters* 30(17): OCE 9-1–OCE 9-4.
[2] Wavenet(2003) Results from the work of the European Thematic Network on Wave Energy. European Community. http://www.waveenergy.net/Library/WaveNet%20Full%20Report(11.1).pdf
[3] Thorpe TW (1999) A brief review of wave energy. *Technical Report ETSU-R120*, May.
[4] Twidell J and Weir T (2006) *Renewable Energy Resources*, 2nd edn. London; New York: Taylor & Francis.
[5] Falnes J (2002) *Ocean Waves and Oscillating Systems*. Cambridge: Cambridge University Press.
[6] de Falcão AFO (2010) Wave energy utilization: A review of the technologies. *Renewable and Sustainable Energy Reviews* 14: 899–918.
[7] Bahaj AS and Myers LE (2003) Fundamentals applicable to the utilisation of tidal current turbines for energy production. *Renewable Energy* 28(14): 2205–2211.
[8] Fraenkel PL (1999) New developments in tidal and wave power technologies. In: *UK-ISES Proceedings C73*, pp. 137–145.
[9] Betz A (1966) *Introduction to the Theory of Flow Machines*. Oxford: Pergamon Press.
[10] Burton A, Sharpe D, Jenkins N, and Bossanyi E (2001) *Wind Energy Handbook*. Chichester, UK: Wiley.
[11] Blunden LS (2009). New Approach to Tidal Stream Energy Analysis at Sites in the English Channel. PhD Thesis, University of Southampton.
[12] Bahaj AS (2011) Generating electricity from the oceans. *Renewable and Sustainable Energy Reviews* 15(7): 3399–3416.
[13] www.emec.org.uk
[14] Bahaj AS, Blunden LS, and Anwar AA (2008) Formulation of the tidal-current energy device development and evaluation protocol. *Sustainable Energy Series, Report 5*. August.
[15] Department for Business, Enterprise and Regulatory Reform (2008) *Tidal-Current Energy Device Development and Evaluation Protocol. URN 08/1317*. http://www.berr.gov.uk/files/file48401.pdf
[16] http://www.emec.org.uk/national_standards.asp
[17] OCEAN ENERGY (2003) *Development & Evaluation Protocol, Part 1: Wave Power*. HMRC. September.
[18] http://www.pelamiswave.com/our-projects/agucadoura
[19] http://www.guardian.co.uk/environment/2009/mar/19/pelamis-wave-power-recession.
[20] www.pelamiswave.com
[21] http://www.wavehub.co.uk/news/press_releases/wave_hub_plugged_in_and_open.aspx
[22] http://www.wavec.org/client/files/10_02_02_Madrid_Ana_Brito_Melo.pdf
[23] www.thecrownestate.co.uk/energy/wave-and-tidal
[24] http://www.ofgem.gov.uk/Sustainability/Environment/RenewablObl/Pages/RenewablObl.aspx
[25] http://www.decc.gov.uk/en/content/cms/what_we_do/uk_supply/energy_mix/renewable/policy/renew_obs/renew_obs.aspx

8.02 Historical Aspects of Wave Energy Conversion

AFO Falcão, Instituto Superior Técnico, Technical University of Lisbon, Lisbon, Portugal

© 2012 Elsevier Ltd. All rights reserved.

8.02.1	Introduction	7
8.02.2	The Wave Energy Resource	8
8.02.3	Wave Energy Technologies	8
8.02.4	Conclusion	9
References		9

8.02.1 Introduction

The possibility of converting wave energy into usable energy has inspired numerous inventors: more than 1000 patents had been registered by 1980 [1] and the number has increased markedly since then. The earliest such patent was filed in France in 1799 by a father and son named Girard [2].

Yoshio Masuda (1925–2009) (**Figure 1**), a former Japanese naval officer, may be regarded as the father of modern wave energy technology, with studies in Japan since the 1940s. He developed a navigation buoy powered by wave energy, equipped with an air turbine, which was in fact what was later named a (floating) oscillating water column (OWC) device. These buoys were commercialized in Japan since 1965 (and later in the United States) [3]. Later, in Japan, Masuda promoted the construction, in 1976, of a much larger device: a barge (80 m × 12 m), named Kaimei, used as a floating testing platform housing several OWCs equipped with different types of air turbines [4]. Probably because this was done at an early stage when the science and the technology of wave energy conversion were in their infancy, the power output levels achieved in the Kaimei testing program were not a great success.

The oil crisis of 1973 induced a major change in the renewable energy scenario and raised the interest in large-scale energy production from waves. In 1975, the British Government started an important research and development program in wave energy [5], followed shortly afterwards by the Norwegian Government. The first conferences devoted to wave energy took place in England (Canterbury, 1976; Heathrow, 1978).

While the Government funding of the British program markedly declined in 1982, the activity in Norway went on to the construction, in 1985, of two full-sized (350 and 500 kW rated power) shoreline prototypes at Toftestallen, near Bergen. In the following years, until the early 1990s, the activity in Europe remained mainly at the academic level, the most visible achievement being a small (75 kW) OWC shoreline prototype deployed on the island of Islay, Scotland (commissioned in 1991) [6]. In 1990, two OWC prototypes were constructed in Asia: a 60 kW converter integrated into a breakwater at the port of Sakata, Japan [7], and a bottom-standing 125 kW plant at Trivandrum, India [8].

The wave energy absorption is a hydrodynamic process of considerable theoretical difficulty, in which relatively complex diffraction and radiation wave phenomena take place. This explains why a large part of the work on wave energy published in the second half of the 1970s and early 1980s was on theoretical hydrodynamics, in which several distinguished applied mathematicians took leading roles, with special relevance to Johannes Falnes, in Norway, and David V. Evans, in the United Kingdom.

In the development and design of a wave energy converter, the energy absorption may be studied theoretically/numerically or by testing a physical model in a wave basin or wave flume. Stephen Salter is widely regarded as the pioneer in model testing of wave energy converters. In 1974, he started the experimental development of the 'duck' concept in a narrow wave flume at the University of Edinburgh. Salter's experimental facilities were greatly improved with the construction, in 1977, of the 10 m × 27.5 m × 1.2 m 'wide tank' equipped with 89 independently driven paddles that made Edinburgh the leading center for the experimental development in wave energy conversion. Later, as the development of wave energy converter concepts progressed toward the prototype construction stage, the need of larger-scale testing required the use of very large laboratory facilities. This was the case, in Europe, of the large wave tanks in Trondheim (Norway), Wageningen (The Netherlands), and Nantes (France).

The situation in Europe was dramatically changed by the decision made in 1991 by the European Commission of including wave energy in their R&D program on renewable energies. The first projects started in 1992. Since then, more than 30 projects on wave energy have been funded by the European Commission involving a large number of teams active in Europe. A few of these projects took the form of coordination activities, namely, one in 2000–03 with 18 partners and, more recently (2004–07), the *Coordination Action in Ocean Energy*, with 40 partners. Also sponsored (and in some cases partly funded) by the European Commission were a series of European Wave Energy Conferences (the more recent ones including also tidal energy).

In 2001, the International Energy Agency established an Implementing Agreement on Ocean Energy Systems (IEA-OES, presently with 18 countries as contracting parties) whose mission is to facilitate and coordinate ocean energy research, development, and demonstration through international cooperation and information exchange. Surveys of ongoing activities in wave energy worldwide can be found in the IEA-OES annual reports [9].

In the last few years, growing interest in wave energy is taking place in northern America (the United States and Canada), involving the national and regional administrations, research institutions and companies, and giving rise to frequent meetings and conferences on ocean energy [10, 11].

Figure 1 Commander Yoshio Masuda (right) with Dr. A. W. Lewis, in 2001. Courtesy: A. W. Lewis, University College Cork.

8.02.2 The Wave Energy Resource

The assessment of the wave energy resource is a basic prerequisite for the strategic planning of its utilization and for the design of wave energy devices. The characterization of the wave climate had been done before for other purposes, namely, navigation and harbor, coastal, and offshore engineering (where wave energy is regarded as a nuisance), for which, however, the required information does not coincide with what is needed in wave energy utilization planning and design. The studies aiming at the characterization of the wave energy resource, having in view its utilization, started naturally in those countries where the wave energy technology was developed first. In Europe, this was notably the case in the United Kingdom [12, 13]. When the European Commission decided, in 1991, to start a series of 2-year (1992–93) 'Preliminary Actions in Wave Energy R&D', a project was included to review the background on wave theory required for the exploitation of the resource and to produce recommendations for its characterization [14]. The WERATLAS, a 'European Wave Energy Atlas', also funded by the European Commission, was the follow-up of those recommendations. The WERATLAS remains the basic tool for wave energy planning in Europe.

8.02.3 Wave Energy Technologies

Unlike large wind turbines, there is a wide variety of wave energy technologies, resulting from the different ways in which energy can be absorbed from the waves and also depending on the water depth and on the location (e.g., shoreline, nearshore, offshore). Several methods have been proposed to classify wave energy systems, according to location (e.g., shoreline, nearshore, offshore), to working principle (e.g., OWCs, oscillating bodies, overtopping devices), and to size ('point absorbers' vs. 'large' absorbers). Recent reviews identified about 100 projects at various stages of development. The number does not seem to be decreasing as new concepts and technologies replace or outnumber those that are being abandoned.

In most cases, the final product is the electrical energy to be supplied to a grid. This energy has to be generated in some kind of electrical machine, either a more or less conventional rotating generator (as in small hydro and wind applications) or a direct-drive linear generator. In the former case, there has to be a mechanical interface that converts the alternative motion (of the oscillating-body or body-pair or of the OWC) into a continuous one-directional motion. The most frequently used or proposed mechanical interfaces are water turbines (low and high head), air turbines, and hydraulic motors (high-pressure oil driven). The power equipment is possibly the single most important element in wave energy technology, and underlies many (possibly most) of the failures to date.

Air turbines equipped most of the early (small and large) wave energy converters and are still the favored power take-off system for many development teams. Conventional turbines are not appropriate for reciprocating flows, and so new types of turbines had to be devised and developed, the best known being the Wells turbine invented by Alan A. Wells in 1976. Self-rectifying air turbines were probably the object of more published papers than any other piece of equipment for wave energy converters.

More or less, conventional low-head hydraulic turbines are used in overtopping devices, whereas high-head (in general Pelton) turbines are an alternative to hydraulic motors in oscillating-body devices. High-pressure oil circuits, with rams, gas accumulators, and hydraulic motors, have been used in several oscillating-body wave energy converter prototypes. This may be regarded as an unconventional use of conventional equipment. Although linear electrical generators have been proposed since the late 1970s for wave energy devices with translational motion and have indeed equipped several devices tested in the sea, they are still at the prototype development stage.

Energy storage capacity is a highly desirable feature in a wave energy converter and can be provided in a variety of manners, as is the case of the flywheel effect in air turbines, water reservoirs in run-up devices, and gas accumulators in high-pressure hydraulic (water and oil) circuits. The use of large electrical capacitors in connection with linear generator technology is being envisaged.

8.02.4 Conclusion

In general, the development of wave energy converters, from concept to commercial stage, has been found to be a difficult, slow, and expensive process [15]. Although substantial progress has been achieved in the theoretical and numerical modeling of wave energy converters and of their energy conversion chain, model testing in wave basin – a time-consuming and considerably expensive task – is still essential. The final stage is testing under real-sea conditions. In almost every system, optimal wave energy absorption involves some kind of resonance, which implies that the geometry and size of the structure are linked to wavelength. For these reasons, if pilot plants are to be tested in the open ocean, they must be large structures. For the same reasons, it is difficult, in the wave energy technology, to follow what was done in the wind turbine industry (namely, in Denmark): relatively small machines were developed first and were subsequently scaled up to larger sizes and powers as the market developed. The high costs of constructing, deploying, maintaining, and testing large prototypes under sometimes very harsh environmental conditions, has hindered the development of wave energy systems; in most cases, such operations were possible only with substantial financial support from governments (or, in the European case, from the European Commission).

References

[1] McCormick ME (1981) *Ocean Wave Energy Conversion*. New York: Wiley.
[2] Ross D (1995) *Power from Sea Waves*. Oxford, UK: Oxford University Press.
[3] Masuda Y (1971) Wave-activated generator. In: *Proceedings of the International Colloq Exposition Oceans*. France: Bordeaux.
[4] Masuda Y (1979) Experimental full-scale results of wave power machine Kaimei in 1978. In: Berge H (ed.) *Proceedings of the First Symposium on Wave Energy Utilization*, pp. 349–363. Gothenburg, Sweden.
[5] Grove-Palmer COJ (1982) Wave energy in the United Kingdom: A review of the programme June 1975 to March 1982. In: Berge H (ed.) *Proceedings of the 2nd International Symposium on Wave Energy Utilization*, Trondheim, Norway, pp. 23–54.
[6] Whittaker TJT, McIlwaine SJ, and Raghunathan S (1993) A review of the Islay shoreline wave power station. In: Elliot G and Caratti G (eds.) *Proceedings of First European Wave Energy Symposium*, Edinburgh, UK. East Kilbride: National Engineering Laboratory, pp. 283–286.
[7] Ohneda H, Igarashi S, Shinbo O, *et al.* (1991) Construction procedure of a wave power extracting caisson breakwater. In: Durschoff W (ed.) *Proceedings of the 3rd Symposium on Ocean Energy Utilization*, Patras, Greece. Germany: University of Hannover, pp. 171–179.
[8] Ravindran M and Koola PM (1991) Energy from sea waves: The Indian wave energy program. *Current Science* 60: 676–680.
[9] Annual Report (2008) International Energy Agency Implementing Agreement on Ocean Energy Systems; 2009. http://www.iea-oceans.org/_fich/6/Annual_Report_2008_(1).pdf (accessed 14 November 2011).
[10] Bedard R, Previsic M, Hagerman G, *et al.* (2007) North American ocean energy status: March 2007. In: *Proceedings of 7th European Wave Tidal Energy Conference*, Porto, Portugal. Lisbon: Instituto de Engenharia Mecânica.
[11] Previsic M, Moreno A, Bedard R, *et al.* (2009) Hydrokinetic energy in the United States: Resources, challenges and opportunities. In: *Proceedings of the 8th European Wave Tidal Energy Conference*, Uppsala, Sweden. Uppsala: Uppsala University, pp. 76–84.
[12] Mollison D (1980) The prediction of device performance. In: Count B (ed.) *Power from Sea Waves*, pp. 135–172. London, UK: Academic Press.
[13] Mollison D (1986) Wave climate and the wave power resource. In: Evans DV and de Falcão AFO (eds.) *Hydrodynamics of Ocean Wave Energy Utilization*, pp. 133–167. Berlin, Germany: Springer.
[14] Pontes T, Mollison D, Borge JC, *et al.* (1993) Evaluation of the wave energy resource. In: *Proceedings of the Workshop Wave Energy R&D*, pp. 1–8. Cork, Ireland. European Commission Report No. EUR 15079 EN.
[15] de Falcão AFO (2010) Wave energy utilization: A review of the technologies. *Renewable and Sustainable Energy Reviews* 14: 899–918.

8.03 Resource Assessment for Wave Energy

EBL Mackay, GL Garrad Hassan, Bristol, UK

© 2012 Elsevier Ltd. All rights reserved.

8.03.1	Introduction	12
8.03.2	**Mathematical Description of Ocean Waves**	12
8.03.2.1	Regular Waves	12
8.03.2.1.1	The Airy wave equations	12
8.03.2.1.2	The dispersion relation, phase speed, and group speed	13
8.03.2.2	Irregular Waves	13
8.03.2.2.1	The wave spectrum	13
8.03.2.2.2	Height and period parameters	14
8.03.2.2.3	Directional parameters	15
8.03.2.2.4	Standard shapes for the frequency spectrum	15
8.03.2.2.5	Standard shapes for the directional distribution	18
8.03.2.2.6	Examples of sea surface elevation for standard spectral shapes	19
8.03.3	**Estimating WEC Power**	20
8.03.4	**Wave Measurements and Modeling**	23
8.03.4.1	Wave Measurements from Moored Buoys	23
8.03.4.1.1	Instrumental characteristics	24
8.03.4.1.2	Estimation techniques for buoy data	24
8.03.4.1.3	Quality checks for buoy data	28
8.03.4.1.4	Sampling variability for temporal averages	28
8.03.4.1.5	Presentation of wave climate data from buoy measurements	31
8.03.4.2	Wave Measurements from Satellite Altimeters	31
8.03.4.2.1	Instrumental characteristics	34
8.03.4.2.2	Quality checks for altimeter data	36
8.03.4.2.3	Sampling variability for spatial averages	37
8.03.4.2.4	Calibration and validation of altimeter wave measurements	37
8.03.4.2.5	Mapping the wave resource	41
8.03.4.3	Numerical Wave Models	45
8.03.4.3.1	Brief introduction to spectral wave models	45
8.03.4.3.2	Sources of error in wave models	46
8.03.4.3.3	Qualitative description of model errors	47
8.03.4.3.4	Calibration of model data against *in situ* measurements	47
8.03.4.3.5	Uncertainties in WEC power estimated from model data	50
8.03.5	**Variability and Predictability of WEC Yield**	50
8.03.5.1	Sampling Variability	51
8.03.5.2	Synoptic and Seasonal Variability	51
8.03.5.3	Interannual and Climatic Variability	51
8.03.6	**Estimation of Extremes**	52
8.03.6.1	Introduction	52
8.03.6.2	Short-Term Distributions of Wave and Crest Heights	52
8.03.6.2.1	The short-term distribution of crest-to-trough wave heights	52
8.03.6.2.2	The short-term distribution of crest heights	53
8.03.6.3	Long-Term Distributions of Extreme Sea States	54
8.03.6.3.1	Overview of methods for estimating extreme H_s	54
8.03.6.3.2	The POT method	55
8.03.6.4	Combining Long-Term and Short-Term Distributions	70
8.03.6.4.1	The distribution of the maximum wave or crest height in a storm	71
8.03.6.4.2	The equivalent triangular storm	71
8.03.6.4.3	The long-term distribution of the maximum wave or crest height	72
References		73

8.03.1 Introduction

The assessment of the wave energy resource is an important step in the planning of a wave energy project. The process can be split into two stages. The first stage is comparative: to select the best sites for development. There are many factors other than the wave resource that influence site selection, such as availability of a grid connection, proximity to ports, or appropriate seabed conditions. These factors can often be limiting, but without an adequate wave resource a project is not viable.

The second stage is quantitative: to accurately determine the resource at a given site. A detailed understanding of the wave energy resource is necessary to assess the economic viability of a wave energy project. Like other sources of renewable energy, ocean waves are a variable resource, impossible to predict precisely. This increases the risk associated with the development of a wave energy farm, since the upfront cost is large and the return is variable and imprecisely known. It is therefore necessary to calculate the average power produced, the variability in power production, and the confidence bounds on these estimates.

Another important issue for wave energy developers is survivability. Wave energy converters (WECs) must be designed to withstand the most severe conditions expected in their lifetime. Since it is not possible to predict the severity of a storm at a certain location more than a few days in advance, a probabilistic approach must be taken to determine design conditions that represent an acceptable level of risk.

The aim of this chapter is to provide information on the wave resource so that the reader understands

- how sea states are described,
- how energy yield is estimated from wave data,
- the available sources of wave data and their characteristics,
- the variability and predictability of energy yield, and
- the methods for the estimation of extreme wave conditions.

8.03.2 Mathematical Description of Ocean Waves

To understand the concepts and definitions used to describe ocean waves, it is useful to be aware of the mathematics used to describe wave motion. The full solution to the hydrodynamic equations describing water wave motion is quite complicated and involves nonlinear terms. Fortunately, a linear approximation to the full solution, where it is assumed that the wave height is negligible compared with the wave length, is a good model for ocean waves in many situations. In particular, most of the terminology used for resource assessment can be understood in terms of linear theory. Nonlinear aspects become important for steep waves and shallow water and are essential for understanding the evolution of the wave spectrum as waves are generated, propagate, and dissipate. However, even when nonlinear aspects cannot be considered insignificant, much of the terminology based on linear theory used to describe the sea state is still applicable.

The section begins by discussing the equations that describe the motion of regular, low-amplitude waves and then goes on to discuss how a sea state can be described as a linear superposition of a large number of regular sinusoidal components using the concept of the wave spectrum.

8.03.2.1 Regular Waves

8.03.2.1.1 The Airy wave equations

The linear solutions to the hydrodynamic equations that describe ocean wave motion were first presented by Sir George Biddell Airy in 1845. They are often referred to simply as the Airy wave equations. It is easiest to work in two dimensions to begin with, with x as the horizontal coordinate and z as the vertical coordinate, positive upward and with the origin at the mean sea level. Hence, in water of depth h, $z = -h$ at the seabed. Then, the Airy wave equations can be presented as follows.

Let χ and ζ be the horizontal and vertical displacement of a water particle from its rest position (x, z), respectively. At time t,

$$\chi = a \frac{\cosh\ k(z+h)}{\sinh\ kh} \cos(kx - \omega t - \phi)$$
$$\zeta = a \frac{\sinh\ k(z+h)}{\sinh\ kh} \sin(kx - \omega t - \phi) \quad [1]$$

where a is the wave amplitude; ϕ, the phase; $\omega = 2\pi f$, the angular frequency of the water particles; f, the frequency; $k = 2\pi/\lambda$, the wave number; and λ, the wavelength.

In deep water, where $h \to \infty$, the equations reduce to

$$\chi = a \exp(kz) \cos(kx - \omega t - \phi)$$
$$\zeta = a \exp(kz) \sin(kx - \omega t - \phi) \quad [2]$$

Figure 1 shows the orbits of a water particle described by eqn [1]. The water particles move forward in the wave crests and backward in the troughs. The orbits become increasingly elliptical with depth, until at seabed the motion is purely oscillatory. In deep water, the orbits are circular at any depth, with the size of the orbit decreasing exponentially with depth. Deep water can be considered as depths for which h/λ is greater than ½.

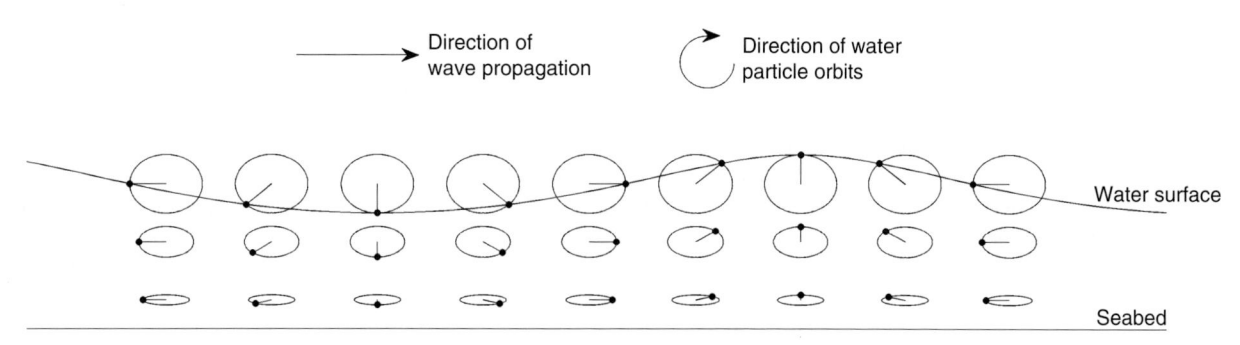

Figure 1 Motion of water particles in an Airy wave in finite depth. Ellipses show complete orbits and lines show displacement from rest positions.

8.03.2.1.2 The dispersion relation, phase speed, and group speed

The equation that governs the relationship between wavelength and period is called the dispersion relation. It is given by

$$\omega^2 = gk \tanh kh \quad [3]$$

where g is the acceleration due to gravity. For deepwater waves, $\tanh kh \to 1$ and we have

$$\omega^2 = gk \quad [4]$$

Substituting $\omega = 2\pi/T$ and $k = 2\pi/\lambda$, we see that for deep water

$$\lambda(\text{deep}) = \frac{gT^2}{2\pi} \quad [5]$$

For finite values of water depth, h, it is not possible to solve eqn [3] analytically for k in terms of ω, and numerical methods must be used to find the wavelength for a given period and water depth.

The speed at which wave crests pass a fixed point is called the phase speed and is denoted c_p. It is given by

$$c_p = \frac{\lambda}{T} = \frac{\omega}{k} \quad [6]$$

Substituting eqn [3] gives

$$c_p = \left(\frac{g}{k} \tanh kh\right)^{1/2} \quad [7]$$

For deep water, $\tanh kh \to 1$, and the phase speed is given by

$$c_p(\text{deep}) = \sqrt{\frac{g}{k}} \quad [8]$$

For very shallow water, $\tanh kh \to kh$ and the phase speed is given by

$$c_p(\text{shallow}) \approx \sqrt{gh} \quad [9]$$

The speed at which the energy propagates is known as the group speed and is denoted c_g. It is given by

$$c_g = \frac{d\omega}{dk} \quad [10]$$

Substituting eqn [3] and rearranging gives

$$c_g = \frac{1}{2} c_p \left(1 + \frac{2kh}{\sinh 2kh}\right) \quad [11]$$

For deep water, this reduces to

$$c_g(\text{deep}) = \frac{c_p}{2} \quad [12]$$

Equation [3] is called the dispersion relation because it governs how waves of different periods and wavelengths disperse from a fixed point. From eqns [6] and [11], it is clear that the group speed increases with wavelength. From eqn [9], we see that in very shallow water, the phase speed is no longer dependent on wavelength. In this case, we say that the waves are nondispersive.

8.03.2.2 Irregular Waves

8.03.2.2.1 The wave spectrum

Waves in the ocean generally look very different from the monochromatic sinusoidal form shown in **Figure 1**. For many purposes, we can think of the sea surface elevation, η, as a linear superposition of a large number of sine wave components with different amplitudes, periods, and directions:

$$\eta(x,y,t) = \sum_{n=1}^{\infty} a_n \sin[k_n(x\cos\theta_n + y\sin\theta_n) - \omega_n t + \phi_n]$$ [13]

where θ_n is the direction of the nth component.

It is normally assumed that phases are distributed randomly over [0 2π] with a uniform probability density. Under these assumptions, the sea surface elevation follows a Gaussian distribution.

The directional variance spectrum $S(f,\theta)$ describes how the energy in the wave field is distributed with frequency and direction. For small δf and $\delta\theta$, we have

$$\sum_{f}^{f+\delta f}\sum_{\theta}^{\theta+\delta\theta}\frac{1}{2}a_n^2 = S(f,\theta)\delta f\,\delta\theta$$ [14]

That is, the spectral density is the sum of the variances of the individual sinusoidal components over a given frequency and directional range.

The directional spectrum can be decomposed into two functions, one representing the total energy at each frequency and the other describing how the energy at each frequency is distributed with direction:

$$S(f,\theta) = S(f)D(f,\theta)$$ [15]

$S(f)$ is called the omnidirectional spectrum or frequency spectrum and is related to the directional spectrum by

$$S(f) = \int_0^{2\pi} S(f,\theta)\,\mathrm{d}\theta$$ [16]

$D(f,\theta)$ is the directional spreading function or directional distribution and satisfies two properties:

1. $\displaystyle\int_0^{2\pi} D(f,\theta)\,\mathrm{d}\theta = 1$ [17]

2. $D(f,\theta) \geq 0$ over [0 2π] [18]

It is a slight abuse of notation to use S to denote both directional and omnidirectional spectral density, but it is usually clear from the context which function S denotes.

8.03.2.2.2 Height and period parameters

The wave spectrum can be summarized to a reasonable accuracy using a small number of parameters. The most important are a measure of average wave height and period, followed by descriptors of directional properties. Wave height and period parameters are defined in terms of moments of the omnidirectional spectrum. The nth moment of the spectrum is defined as

$$m_n = \int_0^{\infty} f^n S(f)\,\mathrm{d}f$$ [19]

Wave height and period parameters are defined as follows:

$$\text{Significant wave height}\quad H_s = 4\sqrt{m_0}$$ [20]

$$\text{Energy period}\ T_e = \frac{m_{-1}}{m_0}$$ [21]

$$\text{Mean period}\ T_m = \frac{m_0}{m_1}$$ [22]

$$\text{Zero-crossing period}\ T_z = \sqrt{\frac{m_0}{m_2}}$$ [23]

$$\text{Peak period}\ T_p = \frac{1}{f_p}$$ [24]

where f_p is the peak frequency, that is, the frequency at which $S(f)$ takes its maximum value.

These definitions have a natural interpretation: m_0 is the variance of the sea surface elevation, and hence H_s as defined in eqn [20] is 4 times the root mean square (RMS) displacement of the sea surface. The factor 4 arises for historical reasons. The term significant wave height was originally introduced to correspond to the visual estimate made by a 'trained observer' and was defined as the average height of the highest 1/3 zero up- or down-cross waves. In narrow-band seas, the height of the average highest 1/3 of the waves is equal to $4.01\sqrt{m_0}$. For neatness, the 0.01 has been dropped from the definition of H_s. Some authors use the symbols $H_{1/3}$ and H_{m0} to distinguish between the two definitions of significant wave height. In this chapter, H_s always denotes the spectral definition given in eqn [20].

The mean period is simply the reciprocal of the mean frequency of the spectrum. The zero-crossing period is approximately equal to the average time between waves crossing the mean sea level in an upward direction. This was first shown by Rice [1, 2] for the case of a random Gaussian signal, which is a good approximation for ocean waves.

The definition of the energy period stems from the formula for wave power in deep water. For a unidirectional wave system, the power transported forward per meter of crest length is

$$P = \rho g \int_0^\infty c_g(f) S(f) \mathrm{d}f \qquad [25]$$

where ρ is the density of seawater, usually taken as $1025\,\mathrm{kg\,m^{-3}}$. In deep water, using eqns [5], [8], and [12], we have

$$\begin{aligned} P_{\mathrm{deep}} &= \frac{\rho g^2}{4\pi} \int_0^\infty f^{-1} S(f) \mathrm{d}f \\ &= \frac{\rho g^2}{4\pi} m_{-1} \end{aligned} \qquad [26]$$

So from the definition of energy period

$$P_{\mathrm{deep}} = \frac{\rho g^2}{64\pi} H_s^2 T_e \qquad [27]$$

8.03.2.2.3 Directional parameters

Directional parameters are defined as follows. The mean direction, $\theta_m(f)$, at each frequency is given by

$$\theta_m(f) = \mathrm{ATAN2}\left[\int_0^{2\pi} D(f,\theta)\sin(\theta)\mathrm{d}\theta,\ \int_0^{2\pi} D(f,\theta)\cos(\theta)\mathrm{d}\theta\right] \qquad [28]$$

where ATAN2(y, x) is the four-quadrant inverse tangent function, which uses logic on the signs of x and y to resolve the 180° ambiguity in direction. There are two commonly used definitions of the spread of energy about the mean direction at each frequency, defined in terms of either line moments or circular moments (denoted with the subscripts 'l' and 'c', respectively):

$$\sigma_l(f) = \left[\int_0^{2\pi} D(f,\theta)(\theta - \theta_m)^2 \mathrm{d}\theta\right]^{1/2} \qquad [29]$$

$$\sigma_c(f) = \left[\int_0^{2\pi} D(f,\theta)\left[2\sin\left(\frac{\theta - \theta_m}{2}\right)\right]^2 \mathrm{d}\theta\right]^{1/2} \qquad [30]$$

The circular moment definition approximates the line moment definition for narrow directional bandwidths since $2\sin(x/2) \approx x$ for small values of x. Moreover, as will be discussed in Section 8.03.4.1.2(ii), σ_c can be calculated directly from measured data without the need to estimate the directional spreading function $D(f, \theta)$.

An average direction and spread over the whole spectrum can be defined as follows:

$$\mathrm{MDIR} = \mathrm{ATAN2}\left[\int_0^\infty S(f)\sin(\theta_m(f))\mathrm{d}f,\ \int_0^\infty S(f)\cos(\theta_m(f))\mathrm{d}f\right] \qquad [31]$$

$$\mathrm{SDIR} = \frac{1}{m_0}\int_0^\infty S(f)\sigma(f)\mathrm{d}f \qquad [32]$$

8.03.2.2.4 Standard shapes for the frequency spectrum

For calculations, it is often useful to assume a standard form for the shape of the frequency spectrum and directional distribution. In deep water, the shape of the spectrum is controlled by the balance between the wind input, dissipation from whitecapping (the breaking of wave crests due to wind forcing), and nonlinear interactions between wave components. During active wave growth, when the waves are relatively steep, nonlinear interactions play a central role in controlling the shape of the spectrum, forcing it toward 'standard' unimodal shapes and smoothing local deviations (see Reference 3). The part of the wave spectrum under active input from the local wind is known as the wind sea.

If the wind drops or the waves propagate away from their generation area, they are referred to as swell. Without input from the wind, the steepness of the waves will decrease (due to frequency and direction dispersion) and the nonlinear interactions will decrease accordingly. In this case, the spectral shape will depend upon the history of the individual wave components, and a 'standard' shape will not necessarily be applicable. This can result in spectra with multiple peaks, from one or more swells possibly together with a local wind sea. In these cases, parametric descriptions of the frequency spectrum can be formed as the sum of two or more standard unimodal spectra.

The most commonly used forms of unimodal spectra for deepwater applications belong to the family given by

$$S(f) = \alpha f^{-r} \exp(-\beta f^{-s}) \gamma^{\delta(f)} \quad \text{for } \alpha, \beta, r, s > 0 \text{ and } \gamma \geq 1 \quad [33]$$

where

$$\delta(f) = \exp\left(-\frac{1}{2}\left(\frac{f - f_p}{\sigma f_p}\right)^2\right) \quad [34]$$

and it is usually assumed that

$$\sigma = \begin{cases} 0.07 & \text{for } f < f_p \\ 0.09 & \text{for } f \geq f_p \end{cases} \quad [35]$$

The parameters r and s control the shape of the spectrum, α is the scale parameter, β is the location parameter (in terms of frequency), and γ is known as the peak enhancement factor. The peak frequency of the spectrum is given by

$$f_p = \left(\frac{s\beta}{r}\right)^{1/s} \quad [36]$$

The high-frequency (HF) tail of the spectrum is proportional to f^{-r}. There is some debate on whether the spectral tail follows an f^{-4} shape or an f^{-5} shape. Most recent theoretical and empirical evidence suggests that an f^{-4} shape is more appropriate (see Reference 4 for a review). However, the most commonly used spectra in ocean engineering have an f^{-5} tail. For practical purposes though, the difference appears to be small.

The family of spectra given by eqn [33] has five free parameters. To describe the sea state with fewer variables, some of these parameters can be fixed, whereas the others are left free. The most commonly used families of spectra with one, two, and three free parameters are summarized in **Table 1**. Fixing $r = 5$, $s = 4$, and $\gamma = 1$ gives the commonly used form proposed by Bretschneider [5]. A special form of the Bretschneider spectrum for 'fully developed' seas was proposed by Pierson and Moskowitz [6], where α is fixed and the energy in the spectrum depends on the value of β only (equivalently H_s is in a fixed ratio to T_p). The Joint North Sea Wave Project (JONSWAP) form [7] was a further generalization of Bretschneider spectra, which accounted for the more peaked spectral shapes observed in fetch-limited wind seas. The term 'Ochi spectra' has been used here for the case where $s = 4$, $\gamma = 1$, and r is a free parameter, after the use of this type of spectrum by Ochi and Hubble [8]. Finally, the term 'Gamma spectra' is used by some authors to describe the form where $\gamma = 1$, r is a free parameter, and $s = r - 1$. Obviously, for this type of spectrum, it could have been written equivalently that s is free and r is fixed as $s + 1$.

For shallow water applications, the commonly used spectral forms include the TMA spectrum [9] or the form proposed by Young and Babanin [10].

Examples of the JONSWAP, Ochi, and Gamma families are shown in **Figure 2** for fixed H_s and f_p and a range of the third free parameter. In each case, the Bretschneider spectrum is a special case and is indicated with a bold line. For the JONSWAP family, the Bretschneider spectrum is the limiting form, corresponding to the most broad-banded member, whereas both Gamma and Ochi can take more broad-banded forms.

When $\gamma = 1$, the moments of the spectra defined by eqn [33] can be expressed as explicit functions of α, β, r, and s:

$$m_n = \frac{\alpha}{s} \beta^{(n-r+1)/s} \Gamma\left(\frac{r - n - 1}{s}\right) \quad \text{for } n < r - 1 \quad [37]$$

Table 1 Free and fixed parameters for families of unimodal spectra given by eqn [33]

Name	α	β	r	s	γ
Pierson–Moskowitz	5.0×10^{-4}	Free	5	4	1
Bretschneider	Free	Free	5	4	1
JONSWAP	Free	Free	5	4	Free
Ochi	Free	Free	Free	4	1
Gamma	Free	Free	Free	$r - 1$	1

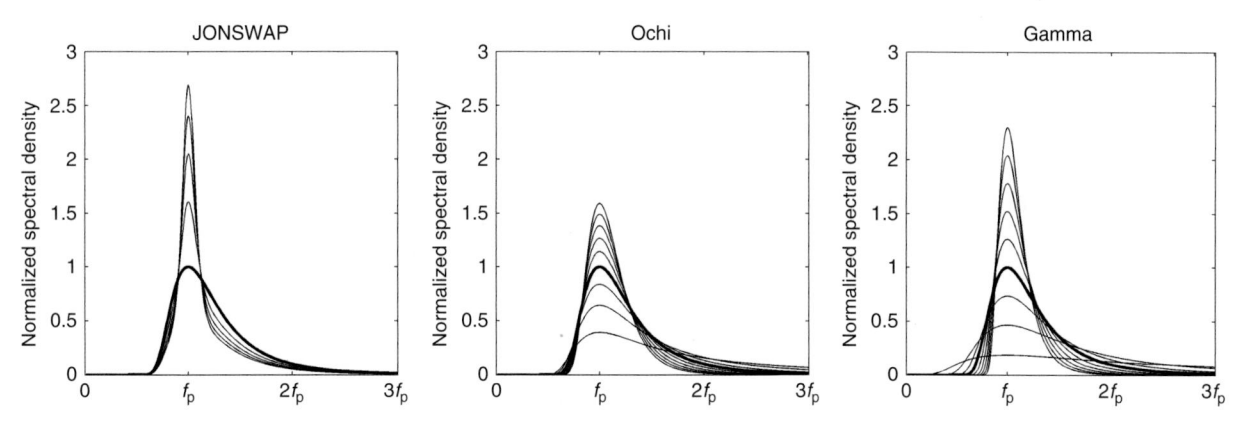

Figure 2 Examples of JONSWAP spectra for $\gamma = 1–5$ and Ochi and Gamma spectra for $r = 2–10$. Spectral densities have been normalized by the peak spectral density of a Bretschneider spectrum with the same H_s and f_p. In each plot, the Bretschneider spectrum is shown in bold.

where Γ is the Gamma function, defined by

$$\Gamma(z) = \int_0^\infty t^{z-1} e^{-t} dt \quad [38]$$

If $\gamma \neq 1$, then numerical integration must be used to compute the moments and hence the relationships between the spectral parameters. Functions of γ can be defined so that the parameters α and β can be expressed in terms of height and period parameters as follows:

$$\alpha = g_h(\gamma) H_s^2 \beta$$
$$\beta = \frac{5}{4} T_p^{-4}$$
$$T_p = g_e(\gamma) T_e$$
$$= g_m(\gamma) T_m$$
$$= g_z(\gamma) T_z \quad [39]$$

Note that the relation between β and T_p is independent of the value of γ. The values of g_h, g_e, g_m, and g_z for $1 \leq \gamma \leq 10$ are shown in **Table 2** (the values for $\gamma = 1$ correspond to the Bretschneider spectrum). The mean value of γ found in the JONSWAP spectrum was 3.3. This is sometimes referred to as the 'standard' JONSWAP spectrum and is often used to model extreme sea states.

The most commonly used multimodal spectral forms are formulated as the summation of JONSWAP, Gamma, or Ochi spectra. Ochi and Hubble [8] proposed a six-parameter spectrum formed as the sum of two Ochi spectra. However, each of the six free parameters was given as a function of H_s (together with 10 spectra representing a 95% confidence interval), so in essence this is a one-parameter spectrum. Guedes Soares [11] proposed a bimodal spectrum formed as the sum of two JONSWAP spectra, but with γ fixed as 2 for both components, resulting in a four-parameter spectrum. Torsethaugen [12] and Torsethaugen and Haver [13] have proposed a form consisting of two JONSWAP spectra. However, the values of the parameters of each spectrum are determined by the values of H_s and f_p, so the number of free parameters is reduced from 6 to 2. Finally, Boukhanovsky and Guedes Soares [14] modeled multimodal spectra as the summation of Gamma spectra, imposing no restrictions on the parameter values, resulting in a true six-parameter spectrum.

Table 2 Values of the height and period ratio functions for the JONSWAP spectrum

γ	$g_h(\gamma)$	$g_e(\gamma)$	$g_m(\gamma)$	$g_z(\gamma)$
1	0.250	1.167	1.296	1.405
2	0.201	1.132	1.240	1.338
3	0.171	1.112	1.206	1.295
3.3	0.164	1.107	1.198	1.285
4	0.150	1.098	1.183	1.264
5	0.135	1.088	1.165	1.240
6	0.122	1.080	1.151	1.221
7	0.112	1.074	1.140	1.206
8	0.104	1.069	1.130	1.193
9	0.097	1.064	1.122	1.181
10	0.091	1.061	1.115	1.172

8.03.2.2.5 Standard shapes for the directional distribution

There are several commonly used forms of the directional distribution. One of the most popular forms is due to Cartwright [15], who suggested using

$$D(\theta, f) = F(s) \cos^{2s} \frac{1}{2}(\theta - \theta_m) \qquad [40]$$

where $F(s)$ is a factor to satisfy condition 1 of eqn [17] and is given by

$$F(s) = \frac{1}{2\sqrt{\pi}} \frac{\Gamma(s+1)}{\Gamma(s+1/2)} \qquad [41]$$

The circular moment definition of directional spread (eqn [30]) is related to the index s by

$$\sigma_c^2 = \frac{2}{1+s} \qquad [42]$$

Another commonly used formulation is the wrapped normal distribution:

$$D(\theta, f) = \frac{1}{\sigma_l(f)\sqrt{2\pi}} \sum_{k=-\infty}^{\infty} \exp\left[-\frac{1}{2}\left(\frac{\theta - \theta_m(f) - 2\pi k}{\sigma_l(f)}\right)^2\right] \qquad [43]$$

This formulation directly includes the line moment spread parameter σ_l (eqn [29]). The summation over k in eqn [43] is to ensure that energy outside the interval $[0\ 2\pi]$ is added back in. In practice, the summation can be taken over the range $k = -2,...,2$. For $\sigma < 30$, the 'cosine-2s' and wrapped normal distributions have very similar shapes.

For fetch-limited sea states, the directional distribution is bimodal at frequencies greater than about twice the peak frequency (see, e.g., References 16–18). Ewans [16] has proposed the use of a double Gaussian distribution to model this bimodality. It can be written as

$$D(f, \theta) = \frac{1}{\sigma(f)\sqrt{8\pi}} \sum_{k=-\infty}^{\infty} \left\{ \exp\left[-\frac{1}{2}\left(\frac{\theta - \theta_1(f) - 2\pi k}{\sigma(f)}\right)^2\right] + \exp\left[-\frac{1}{2}\left(\frac{\theta - \theta_2(f) - 2\pi k}{\sigma(f)}\right)^2\right] \right\} \qquad [44]$$

where

$$\theta_1(f) = \frac{\theta_m + \Delta\theta(f)}{2}$$

$$\theta_2(f) = \frac{\theta_m - \Delta\theta(f)}{2}$$

and $\Delta\theta$ is the separation between the peaks of the two modes. Note that the parameter σ in eqn [44] no longer corresponds to the directional spread. The values of $\Delta\theta$ and σ are given as functions of frequency:

$$\Delta\theta = 14.93 \quad \text{for } f < f_p \qquad [45]$$

$$\Delta\theta = \exp\left[5.453 - 2.750\left(\frac{f}{f_p}\right)^{-1}\right] \quad \text{for } f \geq f_p \qquad [46]$$

$$\sigma = 11.38 + 5.357\left(\frac{f}{f_p}\right)^{-7.929} \quad \text{for } f < f_p \qquad [47]$$

$$\sigma = 32.13 - 15.39\left(\frac{f}{f_p}\right)^{-2} \quad \text{for } f \geq f_p \qquad [48]$$

The resulting distribution is unimodal for $f < 2f_p$ and becomes bimodal at higher frequencies. This formulation results in a directional distribution that is qualitatively the same as in earlier studies (e.g., References 19–21) in the way that the spread varies with frequency. However, earlier studies made the *a priori* assumption that the distribution was unimodal. Mitsuyasu *et al.* [21] and Hasselmann *et al.* [20] also suggested that the distribution was dependent on the wave age (a function of the wind speed and phase speed of the waves), whereas no such dependence was noted in later studies. The shape of the distribution is shown in **Figure 3**.

The directional distribution of swell was examined by Ewans [22]. Less evidence of bimodality in the directional distribution was found than for wind seas. The use of the wrapped normal distribution (eqn [43]) was therefore proposed, with

$$\sigma_l(f) = 6 + 4\left(\frac{f}{f_p}\right)^{-5} \quad \text{for } f < f_p \qquad [49]$$

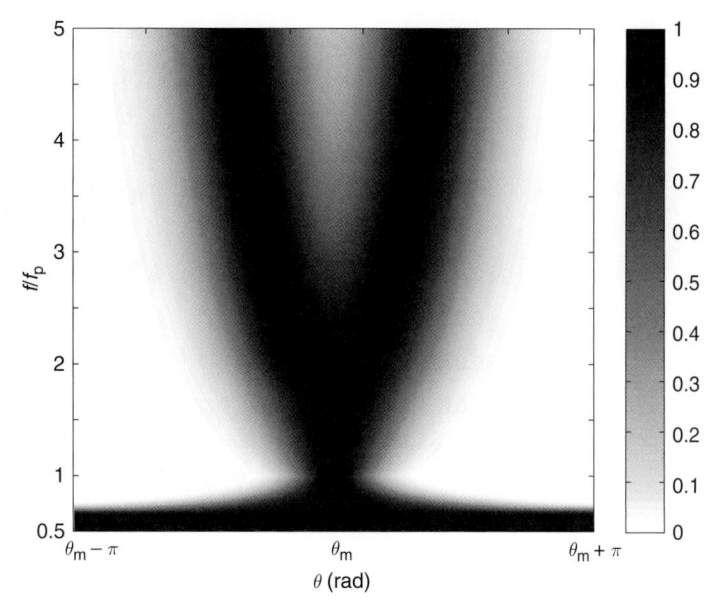

Figure 3 Directional distribution specified by Ewans [16]. Levels have been normalized to have a maximum value of 1 at each frequency.

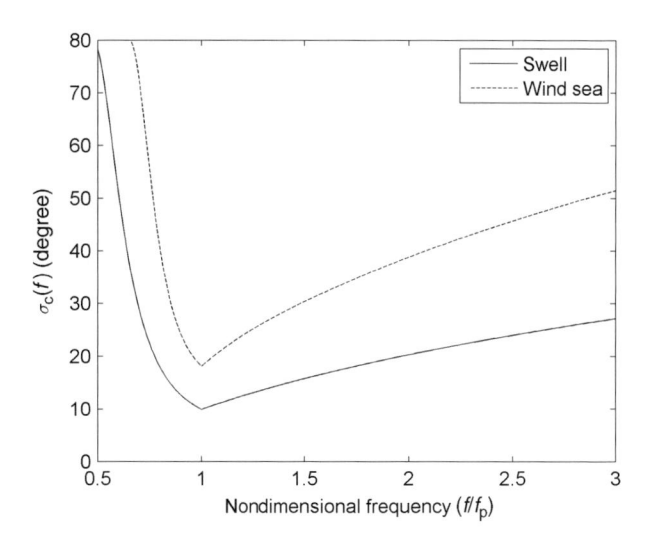

Figure 4 Comparison of directional spreading with frequency for the swell and wind sea directional distributions proposed by Ewans [16, 22].

$$\sigma_1(f) = -36 + 46\left(\frac{f}{f_p}\right)^{-0.3} \quad \text{for } f \geq f_p \qquad [50]$$

A comparison of the directional spread (circular moment definition) as a function of frequency for the wind sea and swell distributions proposed by Ewans [16, 22] is shown in **Figure 4**.

8.03.2.2.6 Examples of sea surface elevation for standard spectral shapes

It is useful to visualize how the standard spectral shapes discussed in the previous sections relate to waves that would be observed in the ocean, by simulating the sea surface elevation for various theoretical spectra. The examples in this section are chosen for comparison with the measured spectra presented in Section 8.03.4.1.5. **Figure 5** shows the polar plot of a typical swell spectrum. The polar plot shows how the energy is distributed with frequency and direction. In this case, the frequency increases radially from the center, the directions are those from which the energy is coming, and color denotes the spectral density in square meter per hertz per degree. The spectrum shown is a JONSWAP spectrum with a wrapped normal directional distribution for $H_s = 1.25$ m, $T_p = 13$ s, $\gamma = 1.5$, $\theta_m = 270°$, and the directional distribution for swell proposed by Ewans [22]. **Figure 5** also shows a simulation of the instantaneous sea surface elevation from this spectrum over an area of 2.5 km × 2.5 km. The sea surface elevation has been simulated from the spectrum using eqns [13] and [14] and assigning a random phase to each sine wave component. Note the relatively large spatial scale of the waves shown here, with the crests of the larger waves extending for over 500 m in the y-direction.

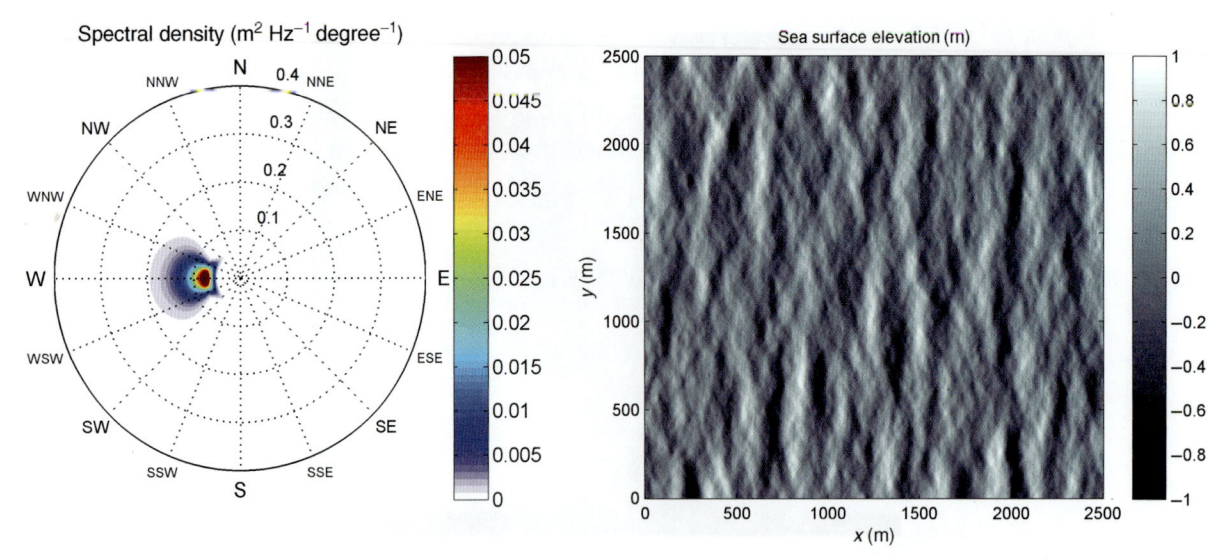

Figure 5 Example of a swell wave system (see text for details). Left: Polar spectral density plot. Right: Simulated sea surface elevation.

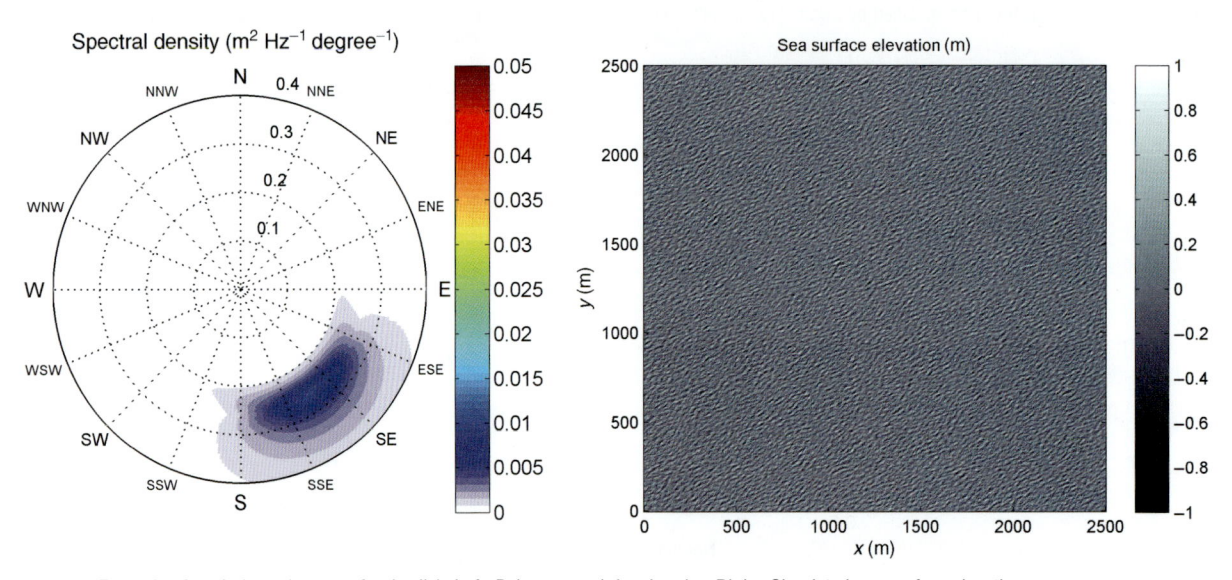

Figure 6 Example of a wind sea (see text for details). Left: Polar spectral density plot. Right: Simulated sea surface elevation.

The wavelength corresponding to the peak period is $\lambda_p = gT_p^2/2\pi = 264$ m, but the higher-frequency waves with greater directional spread are also visible as a shorter-scale roughness over the larger waves.

Figure 6 shows a spectrum and simulated sea surface elevation typical of a wind sea. This time, a JONSWAP frequency spectrum with $H_s = 1$ m, $T_p = 4$ s, and $\gamma = 1.5$ has been used, together with the Ewans [16] directional distribution with $\theta_m = 145°$. The same color scale has been used as in **Figure 5**. In this case, the wavelengths are much shorter than the swell spectrum shown in **Figure 5**, with $\lambda_p = 25.0$ m.

A mixed sea, which is the sum of the swell and wind sea spectra illustrated in **Figures 5** and **6**, respectively, is shown in **Figure 7**. Even though the total energy in each component is similar, the swell shows a much higher peak in spectral density, since the energy is more focused in both frequency and direction. Due to the large difference in the wavelengths of the swell and wind sea components, the wind sea is clearly discernable over the swell.

8.03.3 Estimating WEC Power

The response of a WEC is dependent on the full directional spectrum. However, for the purposes of estimating the energy yield, it is useful to describe the response in terms of a small number of parameters. Currently, few manufacturers of WECs publish details of the response of their device, partly for commercial reasons and partly because many devices are still at the developmental stage. For

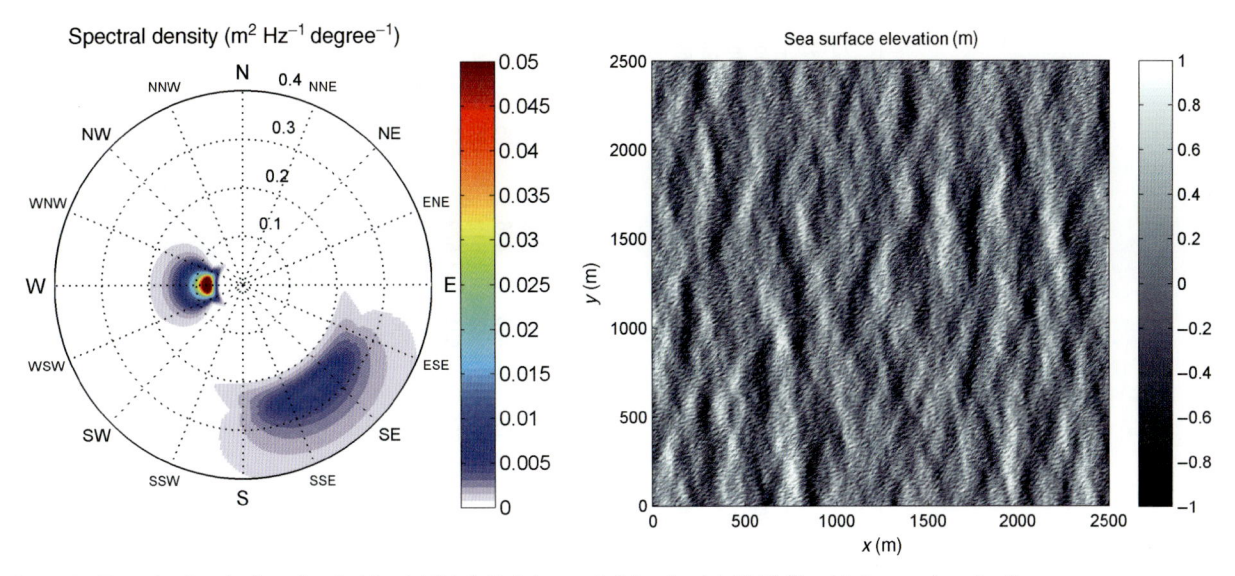

Figure 7 Example of a mixed sea (see text for details). Left: Polar spectral density plot. Right: Simulated sea surface elevation.

those manufacturers that have published details of the power produced by their machine, it has become common practice to specify it in terms of H_s and T_e in a 'power matrix'. Wave height and period parameters are natural choices for the initial parameterization of the device response. The energy period is used in preference to other period parameters since in deep water the mean power of the sea state is a function of H_s and T_e (see Section 8.03.2.2.2). Also, T_e is less sensitive than T_m and T_z to the HF end of the spectrum at which there is little useful energy. And while T_p is a useful parameter to describe theoretical spectra, it is less stable than integral parameters when estimated from measured data.

An example of a power matrix for an early version of the Pelamis is given in **Table 3**. The power response was calculated from a numerical model of the Pelamis in waves simulated from Bretschneider spectra and validated using a combination of scale-model tank tests and sea trials with a full-scale prototype. The blank cells in the table correspond to sea states that are not observed in practice due to steepness limitations.

For real wave spectra, there can be a wide range of spectral shapes for a given H_s and T_e. This can result in a significant variation in the power produced by a WEC relative to the value listed in the power matrix. An axisymmetric point absorber-type device may be relatively insensitive to directional effects, but the shape of the frequency spectrum may still have some effect. In contrast, the Pelamis has both a pitch and sway response to incoming waves and therefore may be more sensitive to directional effects.

Various approaches have been proposed to address this inherent limitation of the power matrix. In the Department of Trade and Industry (DTI) preliminary wave energy device performance protocol [23], it is suggested that several tables could be used to describe the response of the machine, specifying the mean, standard deviation, and minimum and maximum power for each cell of the power matrix. This approach has the advantage that it is relatively simple. However, the distribution of spectral shapes with a given H_s and T_e is likely to vary with location and water depth, so a set of tables will have to be generated for each site of interest.

An alternative to this approach is to include further parameters to describe the power response. Several studies have examined the sensitivity of power production to various spectral bandwidth parameters (e.g., References 24 and 190). These studies suggest that three-dimensional power matrices could be used to describe a device's power response, binned by H_s, T_e, and the spectral bandwidth. The results presented in these studies showed that whereas the use of certain bandwidth parameters can improve the accuracy of predicted performance of certain WECs at certain locations over certain ranges of conditions, there was no single bandwidth parameter that was effective at predicting performance of all WEC types at all locations over all conditions.

A slightly different approach was proposed by Kerbiriou *et al.* [25], where the measured spectra are partitioned into separate wave systems, each represented by a JONSWAP spectrum. The power response is then calculated as the sum of the contributions from each component wave system. This method was shown to significantly improve the accuracy of the energy yield assessment, but at the expense of using six parameters to describe the omnidirectional characteristics of the spectrum. Introducing further parameters will improve the accuracy of the description of the shape of the wave spectra and therefore the WEC response. However, the disadvantage of using more parameters is that a larger number of points are required to cover the parameter space, which describes the full range of sea states at a site.

There is, as yet, no consensus on a standard method for parameterizing the power response of a WEC. The most appropriate method may well be dependent on WEC itself, since the responses of different devices may be sensitive to different parameters.

Table 3 Power matrix for an early version of the Pelamis

	T_e (s)																
		5.0	5.5	6.0	6.5	7.0	7.5	8.0	8.5	9.0	9.5	10.0	10.5	11.0	11.5	12.0	12.5	13.0
H_s (m)	0.5	Idle	Idle	Idle	Idle	Idle	Idle	Idle	Idle	Idle	Idle	Idle	Idle	Idle	Idle	Idle	Idle	Idle
	1.0	Idle	22	29	34	37	38	38	37	35	32	29	26	23	21	Idle	Idle	Idle
	1.5	32	50	65	76	83	86	86	83	78	72	65	59	53	47	42	37	33
	2.0	57	88	115	136	148	153	152	147	138	127	116	104	93	83	74	66	59
	2.5	89	138	180	212	231	238	238	230	216	199	181	163	146	130	116	103	92
	3.0	129	198	260	305	332	340	332	315	292	266	240	219	210	188	167	149	132
	3.5		270	354	415	438	440	424	404	377	362	326	292	260	230	215	202	180
	4.0			462	502	540	546	530	499	475	429	384	366	339	301	267	237	213
	4.5			554	635	642	648	628	590	562	528	473	432	382	356	338	300	266
	5.0				739	726	731	707	687	670	607	557	521	472	417	369	348	328
	5.5				750	750	750	750	750	737	667	658	586	520	496	446	395	355
	6.0					750	750	750	750	750	750	711	633	619	558	512	470	415
	6.5					750	750	750	750	750	750	750	743	658	621	579	512	481
	7.0						750	750	750	750	750	750	750	750	676	613	584	525
	7.5							750	750	750	750	750	750	750	750	686	622	593
	8.0								750	750	750	750	750	750	750	750	690	625

Values in kilowatts.

8.03.4 Wave Measurements and Modeling

The types of wave data that are commonly used at present can be split into three main categories: *in situ* measurements, satellite remote sensing, and numerical wave models. Each type of data has different characteristics and is subject to certain limitations. The wave resource varies spatially and temporally on multiple scales. *In situ*, satellite, and model data all provide information about different scales of the resource. *In situ* measurements typically provide a temporal average of waves at a point or over a small area, satellite measurements provide a near-instantaneous average of waves over an area of several square kilometers, and wave models provide an estimate of the wave spectrum which can be interpreted as an average over both area and time.

An overview of the different types of *in situ* instruments is given by Tucker and Pitt [26]. Of the many types of *in situ* instruments capable of measuring waves, we focus on wave buoys here. Although instruments mounted on fixed platforms can provide high-quality wave data, they are less likely to be deployed at a wave energy site, due to the cost of installing a suitable platform to mount the device. Details of a recent intercomparison study of fixed platform instruments are given by Forristall *et al.* [27].

The use of acoustic Doppler current profilers (ADCP) is also gaining popularity for wave monitoring at wave energy sites. ADCPs are installed below the surface of the water and make measurements of surface waves and the current profile through the water column. The surface elevation is measured using an echo-ranging technique from an acoustic pulse emitted from a vertically oriented sensor. The water column velocity is inferred from the Doppler shift of an acoustic pulse emitted by sensors inclined at an angle to the vertical (usually three or four sensors inclined at around 25°). Newer ADCPs can make nondirectional wave measurements in depths up to 100 m. Directional properties are estimated from the near-surface velocity measured in the inclined beams. The distance between the beams at the surface is a function of the water depth and the angle of the beam. Aliasing due to the separation of the measurements imposes an upper frequency limit for directional measurements. For an ADCP with three beams at an angle of 25° to the vertical, the cutoff is 0.32 Hz at a depth of 20 m. Mounting an ADCP on a subsurface buoy has been suggested as a solution, but this method is in the experimental stage at present [28].

Various types of radar systems such as the HF radar or X-band marine radar can also be used for wave measurements. An overview of these is given by Kahma *et al.* [29]. These can provide high-resolution directional measurements over a wide area, although the accuracy of the measurements is dependent on the ratio between the wave frequency and the radar frequency. Radar systems are also typically much more expensive than a wave buoy, with a land-based HF radar costing upward of £100 000 to install compared with around £20 000 for a small wave buoy.

There are two types of satellite-borne instruments used to measure waves: the radar altimeter and the synthetic aperture radar (SAR). Of the two types of remote sensing data, SAR provides the only direct source of spectral and directional information. Several inversion schemes exist to extract wave spectra and parameters from the SAR data (e.g., References 30–32). However, SAR can only measure the low-frequency part of the wave spectrum. Violante-Carvalho *et al.* [33] note that the HF cutoff is sea state dependent, but in general, waves shorter than 150–200 m (around 0.1 Hz for deepwater linear waves) propagating parallel to the satellite track are not mapped directly by SAR. Moreover, the SAR data are sparse both temporally and spatially, with data acquired over areas of about 5 km × 5 km at intervals of 200 km along track for the ERS-1, ERS-2, and ENVISAT satellites. Nevertheless, the SAR spectra are useful for constraining the output of wave models and are routinely assimilated into operational models at meteorological agencies (e.g., Reference 34). The sparse nature of the data limits their usefulness for wave energy studies and they will not be considered further here.

In contrast to SAR, altimeter data are collected continuously as the satellite orbits, giving higher spatial resolution. Altimeters are capable of making accurate measurements of H_s and a reasonable estimate of wave period, but they do not provide any information on spectral shape or directional properties of the wave field and they cannot measure close to the coast (although future missions may not have this restriction). However, the global coverage and long record of measurements make altimeter data a valuable source of wave information.

Data from numerical wave models are estimates rather than measurements. Nonetheless, the current generation of wave models is of sufficient accuracy that modeled wave data can be used to calculate accurate wave energy statistics. Global hindcasts over long periods at high spatial and temporal resolution are available from several meteorological institutions and commercial companies. Hindcast data are likely to be used as the long-term data set for many wave resource studies. However, quantifying the errors and uncertainties in model data is an important and nontrivial problem, with model biases and random errors nonstationary in both space and time.

Finally, a source of wave data that is not considered here, but deserves mentioning, is voluntary observing ship (VOS) data. Officers aboard VOSs have provided visual estimates of wave parameters worldwide since 1856. These data are useful for long-term climatological studies (e.g., References 35 and 36), but are much less appropriate for calculating wave energy statistics. The data are reasonably dense along major shipping routes, but the coverage is poor outside these areas, particularly in the Southern Ocean. Moreover, they are subject to larger uncertainties and biases than other sources of wave data. Comparisons with altimeter data show that even for well-sampled regions, the occurrence of high waves is underestimated in the VOS data, since ships intentionally avoid rough seas [37].

8.03.4.1 Wave Measurements from Moored Buoys

Measurements from buoys are often taken as a 'standard' to which other measurements are compared. Buoys are capable of making accurate measurements of waves, but are subject to certain limitations and it is important to be aware of these limitations. The sea surface displacement can be inferred from the motions of the buoy, measured by accelerometers, tilt sensors, and compasses. The accuracy of the inferred wave motions is dependent on the buoy response, the accuracy of the transfer function (from buoy motion to wave motion), and the sensor accuracy. One advantage of using buoys to measure waves is that the sea surface is usually well defined – it is the point at which the buoy floats (although in high seas it is possible for the buoy to be dragged through or around wave crests). In rough conditions, spray in the air or bubbles in the water can cause problems with devices that measure the waves from below or above the surface, such as ADCPs or laser altimeters.

There are also some innate differences in the measurements of waves made by buoys compared with a fixed instrument. Small wave buoys essentially follow the particle motions of the water surface, whereas fixed instruments such as laser sensors or capacitance wire gauges measure the spatial profile of the waves. Particle-following and fixed measurements are known as Lagrangian and Eulerian measurements, respectively, referring to the frame of reference in which measurements are made. For low-amplitude waves, the differences between Lagrangian and Eulerian measurements are small, but in steep waves the differences can be significant [38, 39]. There are pros and cons to both types of measurements. A Lagrangian device measuring the orbital motions of a water particle at a particular frequency will attribute all the wave energy to this frequency, whereas an Eulerian device will distribute some of the energy among the harmonics of the orbital frequency [40, 41]. On the other hand, Lagrangian devices are not capable of measuring some nonlinear aspects of the wave profile [42, 43]. However, for the purposes of assessing WEC yield, this is not important.

8.03.4.1.1 Instrumental characteristics

8.03.4.1.1(i) Buoy response

The buoy response is governed by the size and shape of the buoy and its mooring. The designs of buoys vary, with dimensions ranging from small spherical buoys less than 1 m in diameter to large rectangular hulled buoys around 12 m in length. Small buoys have the best surface-following properties, with a spherical buoy 2 m or less in diameter having effectively unity response for waves up to about 0.5 Hz [26]. For larger buoys, the response to shorter wavelengths is damped and the wave motions must be indirectly estimated through the response amplitude operator (RAO) of the buoy (see, e.g., References 44 and 45). Meteorological institutions implementing wave measurement programs often require simultaneous measurements of winds (and other parameters) with waves; therefore, the buoy size will be a compromise between a compact shape for good surface-following properties and stability required for mounting an anemometer.

8.03.4.1.1(ii) Moorings

Moorings can affect the response of the buoy by restricting its range of motion. If the mooring does not have sufficient flexibility, it is possible for the buoy to be dragged through or around wave crests [46]. Joosten [40, 47] discusses the need for elastic moorings for wave buoys. He shows that for waves above the mass-spring resonance frequency, f_0, of the rubber cord and buoy combined, the buoy motions are not restricted by mooring forces, but for frequencies lower than f_0, the buoy does not perfectly follow the wave and heave energy is spread over a wide range of frequencies. For a Waverider buoy with the manufacturer's specified elastic mooring, f_0 is around 0.05 Hz, where there is very little energy in most wave spectra.

Steele [48] discusses Doppler effects on moored buoy measurements in the presence of currents. He notes that significant wave height is not affected, but there can be shifts in spectral energy at high frequencies and changes in mean wave direction, relative to that which would be observed in a frame of reference relative to the current.

8.03.4.1.1(iii) Sensors

Several types of sensors are commonly used in wave buoys to measure heave, tilt, and direction. These range from vertically stabilized accelerometers such as Datawell's HIPPY sensor, solid-state accelerometers such as the motion reference unit (MRU) manufactured by Seatex, to accelerometers that infer their motion from Doppler shifts in Global Positioning System (GPS) signals. Until recently, the industry standard for offshore recording has been Datawell's HIPPY sensor. Krogstad *et al.* [49] note that the MRU has several advantages over Datawell's HIPPY sensor: it has no moving parts, is small in size and of low weight, and is not sensitive to rapid rotations during transport or to low temperatures. They compare measurements made by an MRU and a HIPPY sensor in the same buoy and show that the recorded heave and slope time series are indistinguishable. De Vries *et al.* [50] compare measurements from a HIPPY and a GPS sensor in the same buoy. They note that the sensors give close to identical heave measurements, with a correlation of 0.999 94 in H_s, but the GPS sensor can give much more accurate measurements of low-frequency components of the spectrum than the HIPPY accelerometer.

8.03.4.1.2 Estimation techniques for buoy data

8.03.4.1.2(i) Estimation of the omnidirectional spectrum

The omnidirectional spectrum is usually estimated from the time series of surface elevation using the fast Fourier transform (FFT). An introduction to the FFT in the context of ocean wave analysis is given by Tucker and Pitt [26].

A less commonly used alternative to the FFT is the maximum entropy method (MEM), in which an autoregressive model is fitted to the time series and used to estimate the spectral density (see, e.g., Reference 51). This method has the advantage that the frequency resolution is very high even for short records. However, there are some problems in the implementation of the method as there is no universal criterion for the selection of the order of the autoregressive model.

In recent years, the wavelet transform has started to gain popularity for the analysis of ocean wave records (see, e.g., Reference 52). The wavelet transform has the advantage that in addition to the frequency spectrum, a time–frequency representation of the record can be presented, illustrating the way in which both wave heights and periods change with time.

8.03.4.1.2(ii) Estimation of directional properties

The case for the directional spectrum is more complicated. As discussed in the following sections, there is not enough information contained in the buoy motions to completely determine the directional spectrum. In fact, none of the instruments used today can provide all the information needed to make a robust estimate of the complete directional spectrum. In the case of buoy measurements, only the first four Fourier coefficients of the directional distribution are obtainable at each frequency. The mean direction and spread at each frequency can be obtained without making any assumptions, but estimation of the directional distribution requires the use of stochastic methods. An introduction to the various analysis methods available is given by Benoit et al. [53] and more details can be found in Kahma et al. [29]. For buoy data, the most popular methods for obtaining the directional distribution are the maximum likelihood method (MLM) and the MEM. This section starts by describing the relationship between cross-spectra, the directional distribution, and the Fourier coefficients of the directional distribution. We then describe how these are used to form model-free parametric descriptions of the directional distribution and the MLM and MEM estimates of the directional distribution.

8.03.4.1.2(ii)(a) The cross-spectral matrix Wave buoys record three signals: either heave, pitch, and roll, or heave and two horizontal displacements. We denote these three signals as P_1 (heave), P_2 (east–west slope or displacement), and P_3 (north–south slope or displacement). The cross-spectra, G_{mn}, between signals P_m and P_n are estimated using an FFT. It can be shown that G_{mn} and G_{nm} are complex conjugates, so cross-spectra need to be computed for only $m \leq n$. The cross-spectra can be decomposed into real and imaginary parts: $G_{mn} = C_{mn} + iQ_{mn}$, where C_{mn} is the coincident spectral density function or cospectrum and Q_{mn} the quadrature spectral density function or quad-spectrum.

Within the framework of linear theory, cross-spectra are related to the directional spectrum by

$$G_{mn}(f) = E(f) \int_0^{2\pi} H_m(f,\theta) H_n^*(f,\theta) D(f,\theta) d\theta \quad [51]$$

where H_m is the transfer function between the surface elevation and the signal P_m and * denotes the complex conjugate. For heave, pitch, and roll measurements, the transfer functions are given by

$$H_1 = 1 \quad [52]$$

$$H_2 = ik \cos\theta \quad [53]$$

$$H_3 = ik \sin\theta \quad [54]$$

For heave, north, and west measurements, the transfer functions are given by

$$H_1 = 1 \quad [55]$$

$$H_2 = i \coth(kd) \cos\theta \quad [56]$$

$$H_3 = i \coth(kd) \sin\theta \quad [57]$$

From eqns [51]–[57], we can see that the autospectra G_{nn} are positive real quantities, the cross-spectra G_{12} and G_{13} are purely imaginary quantities, and the cross-spectrum G_{23} is a real quantity. So for buoy measurements, the cross-spectral matrix can be written as

$$G = \begin{pmatrix} C_{11} & 0 & 0 \\ 0 & C_{22} & C_{23} \\ 0 & C_{23} & C_{33} \end{pmatrix} + i \begin{pmatrix} 0 & -Q_{12} & -Q_{13} \\ Q_{12} & 0 & 0 \\ Q_{13} & 0 & 0 \end{pmatrix} \quad [58]$$

The three autospectra are related by

$$C_{22}(f) + C_{33}(f) = k^2 C_{11}(f) \quad [59]$$

Therefore, it is possible to estimate only five independent coefficients at each frequency, of which $C_{11}(f)$ is an estimate of the frequency spectrum $E(f)$ and the other four are used to estimate the directional distribution.

8.03.4.1.2(ii)(b) Fourier series decomposition The directional spectrum can be described by a Fourier series representation:

$$D(f,\theta) = \frac{1}{\pi}\left\{\frac{1}{2} + \sum_{n=1}^{\infty}\left[a_n(f)\cos(n\theta) + b_n(f)\sin(n\theta)\right]\right\} \quad [60]$$

where the coefficients are given by

$$a_n(f) = \int_0^{2\pi} D(f,\theta)\cos(n\theta)d\theta \qquad [61]$$

$$b_n(f) = \int_0^{2\pi} D(f,\theta)\sin(n\theta)d\theta \qquad [62]$$

For buoy measurements, only the first four Fourier coefficients can be computed from the cross-spectra. From eqn [51], after some algebra, we see that

$$a_1 = \frac{Q_{12}}{\sqrt{C_{11}(C_{22}+C_{33})}} \qquad [63]$$

$$b_1 = \frac{Q_{13}}{\sqrt{C_{11}(C_{22}+C_{33})}} \qquad [64]$$

$$a_2 = \frac{C_{22}-C_{33}}{C_{22}+C_{33}} \qquad [65]$$

$$b_2 = \frac{2C_{23}}{C_{22}+C_{33}} \qquad [66]$$

It is possible to estimate the directional distribution in terms of a truncated Fourier series using the first four coefficients; however, this can result in negative values, violating the definition given in eqn [18]. As a solution to this problem, Longuet-Higgins *et al.* [54] proposed the use of a weighting function to ensure that the estimate of $D(f,\theta)$ is always positive. However, this results in diffusion of energy with direction and artificially broadens the distribution. This method is therefore not recommended. However, the relations between the Fourier coefficients and cross-spectra can be used to infer directional information as described in the following sections.

8.03.4.1.2(ii)(c)   Model-free directional parameters   The MLMs and MEMs described below lead to slightly different estimates of the directional spectrum. The mean direction usually agrees reasonably well between methods, but the estimates of directional spread can vary slightly depending on the method used. Kuik *et al.* [55] note that the use of these methods may suggest a misleadingly high directional resolution for buoy measurements. As an alternative, they proposed a method to estimate directional parameters directly from the cross-spectra, without fitting a directional distribution. These parameters are model-free, in that they do not assume a particular form of the directional distribution and can be expressed analytically in terms of the cross-spectra and are thus much faster to compute than MLM and MEM estimates.

The directional parameters defined by Kuik *et al.* [55] are

$$\theta_m = \text{ATAN2}\left(\frac{b_1}{a_1}\right) \qquad [67]$$

$$\sigma_c = [2(1-m_1)]^{1/2} \qquad [68]$$

$$\gamma_c = \frac{-n_2}{[(1-m_2)/2]^{3/2}} \qquad [69]$$

$$\delta_c = \frac{6-8m_1+2m_2}{[2(1-m_1)]^2} \qquad [70]$$

where m_1, m_2, and n_2 are the centered Fourier coefficients of the directional distribution, given by

$$m_1 = \int_0^{2\pi} D(f,\theta)\cos(\theta-\theta_m)d\theta = a_1\cos(\theta_m) + b_1\sin(\theta_m) = (a_1^2+b_1^2)^{1/2} \qquad [71]$$

$$m_2 = \int_0^{2\pi} D(f,\theta)\cos(2(\theta-\theta_m))d\theta = a_2\cos(2\theta_m) + b_2\sin(2\theta_m) \qquad [72]$$

$$n_2 = \int_0^{2\pi} D(f,\theta)\sin(2(\theta-\theta_m))d\theta = b_2\cos(2\theta_m) - a_2\sin(2\theta_m) \qquad [73]$$

The definitions of θ_m and σ_c given in eqns [67] and [68] are consistent with those given in eqns [28] and [30], respectively. The parameters σ_c, γ_c, and δ_c can be interpreted as circular moment analogues to the line moment definitions of RMS spread (eqn [29]), skewness, and kurtosis of the directional distribution, respectively. They show that for narrow directional distributions (σ_1 less than about 40°), these definitions closely match their line moment equivalents.

The skewness and kurtosis on their own are not especially useful descriptions of the directional distribution. However, they can be combined to give an indication of bimodality in the directional distribution. Kuik *et al.* [55] show that the directional distribution is likely to be unimodal and symmetric if

$$\begin{aligned} \delta &> 2 + |\gamma| \quad \text{for } |\gamma| \leq 4 \\ \delta &> 6 \quad \text{for } |\gamma| > 4 \end{aligned} \quad [74]$$

If δ does not meet this criterion, then this can be interpreted as a warning against the assumption of a unimodal symmetric distribution.

8.03.4.1.2(ii)(d) Maximum likelihood methods

The MLM estimate of the directional spectrum is given by

$$\hat{D}_0(f,\theta) = \frac{\kappa}{\sum_{m,n} H_m(f,\theta) G_{mn}^{-1}(f,\theta) H_n^*(f,\theta)} \quad [75]$$

where G_{mn}^{-1} are the elements of the inverse of G and κ is determined by the condition in eqn [17].

The cross-spectra computed from the MLM estimate are not consistent with the cross-spectra from the wave signals. Pawka [56], Oltman-Shay and Guza [57], and Krogstad *et al.* [58] have suggested iterative methods to improve the MLM estimate so that the cross-spectra are consistent. Of these, the iterative scheme of Krogstad *et al.* [58] is the simplest, whereby iterative improvements to the MLM estimate are given by

$$\hat{D}_i(f,\theta) = \hat{D}_{i-1}(f,\theta) + \gamma \left(\hat{D}_0(f,\theta) - \Delta_{i-1}(f,\theta) \right) \quad [76]$$

where $\Delta_{i-1}(f,\theta)$ is the MLM estimate calculated from the cross-spectra of $\hat{D}_{i-1}(f,\theta)$. Krogstad *et al.* [58] show that the number of iterations required for convergence depends on the value of γ, with the range $0.5 < \gamma < 1.5$ giving the best performance. Lower values of γ have a slower convergence rate, but reduce the possibility of the estimates diverging.

8.03.4.1.2(ii)(e) Maximum entropy methods

MEMs for buoy data have been proposed by Lygre and Krogstad [59] and Kobune and Hashimoto [60]. The two methods use different definitions of entropy. Lygre and Krogstad [59] define an estimate of the directional distribution that maximizes the Burg definition of entropy:

$$H_B(D) = -\int_0^{2\pi} \ln(D(\theta)) d\theta \quad [77]$$

whereas Kobune and Hashimoto [60] define an estimator that maximizes the Shannon definition of entropy:

$$H_S(D) = -\int_0^{2\pi} D(\theta) \ln(D(\theta)) d\theta \quad [78]$$

The MEM estimate of Lygre and Krogstad [59] can be expressed as an analytical function of the measured cross-spectra and is therefore very quick to compute. However, it has been shown by numerous authors to produce double peaks in cases of unimodal directional distributions (see, e.g., References 61 and 62). The MEM estimate of Kobune and Hashimoto [60] is more computationally intensive, but has been shown to produce more robust estimates of the directional distribution. Kobune and Hashimoto [60] showed that the estimate that maximizes eqn [78] has the form

$$\hat{D}(f,\theta) = \exp\left(-\sum_{j=0}^{4} \lambda_j(f) a_j(\theta) \right) \quad [79]$$

where $a_0(\theta) = 1$, $a_1(\theta) = \cos(\theta)$, $a_2(\theta) = \sin(\theta)$, $a_3(\theta) = \cos(2\theta)$, and $a_4(\theta) = \sin(2\theta)$. The λ_j's are Lagrange multipliers, found by solving the system of nonlinear equations given by equating the Fourier coefficients calculated from the measured data and the estimated directional distribution. This system of equations can be written as

$$\int_0^{2\pi} \exp\left(-\sum_{j=0}^{4} \lambda_j(f) a_j(\theta) \right) a_j(\theta) d\theta = \phi_j(f), \quad j = 0,\ldots,4 \quad [80]$$

where $\phi_0(f) = 1$, $\phi_1(f) = a_1(f)$, $\phi_2(f) = b_1(f)$, $\phi_3(f) = a_2(f)$, and $\phi_4(f) = b_2(f)$. This formulation was proposed by Nwogu *et al.* [63] and includes λ_0 as an iteration parameter to improve convergence for narrow spreading functions. This differs slightly from the formulation proposed by Kobune and Hashimoto [60], who expressed λ_0 as a function of the other four λ_j's.

The system of equations given in eqn [80] can be solved by standard numerical methods. Occasionally, there are convergence problems when trying to solve these equations. Kim *et al.* [62] proposed an approximation scheme that can be used when this occurs. They showed that by expanding the exponential term in eqn [80] to second order, the λ_j's can be expressed as

$$\lambda_0 = \ln\left[\int_0^{2\pi} \exp\left(\sum_{j=1}^{4} \lambda_j a_j(\theta)\right) d\theta\right] \quad [81]$$

$$\lambda_1 = 2\phi_1\phi_3 + 2\phi_2\phi_4 - 2\phi_1\sum_{j=0}^{4}\phi_j^2 \quad [82]$$

$$\lambda_2 = 2\phi_1\phi_4 - 2\phi_2\phi_3 - 2\phi_2\sum_{j=0}^{4}\phi_j^2 \quad [83]$$

$$\lambda_3 = \phi_1^2 - \phi_2^2 - 2\phi_3\sum_{j=0}^{4}\phi_j^2 \quad [84]$$

$$\lambda_4 = 2\phi_1\phi_2 - 2\phi_4\sum_{j=0}^{4}\phi_j^2 \quad [85]$$

Kim et al. [62] showed that this approximation scheme produces estimates close to those from eqn [80] and gives reasonable results for both unimodal and bimodal distributions, although with a slight tendency to reduce the directional width. These approximations can also be used as an initial guess for the λ_j values when solving eqn [80].

Because numerical methods are needed to solve eqn [80] for each frequency, this method is considerably slower than the iterated MLM method. Moreover, it also produces very similar results. It is therefore recommended that this method is used as a comparison to the iterated MLM estimate only if the user is suspicious of the results.

8.03.4.1.3 Quality checks for buoy data

A useful summary of real-time and postprocessing quality control tests for wave data can be found in References 64 and 65. These can be summarized as follows:

The time series of sea surface elevation can be checked for irregularities such as the following:

- Flat episode – data are rejected if N consecutive values are unchanged
- Equal peaks – data are rejected when N consecutive peaks or troughs exhibit the same values
- Spikes – points greater than N standard deviations from the mean are considered spikes
- Acceleration – data are rejected where accelerations exceed N times gravitational acceleration
- Mean crossing – data are rejected if more than N% of a time series does not cross the mean

Values of N are left to the discretion of the user.

Slamming or shock loads from breaking waves can cause spikes in the acceleration time series. The acceleration signals recorded by the buoy are double-integrated using a digital filter to give the displacement values as the convolution of the acceleration signal and the filter. Therefore, a spike in the acceleration signal will amplify the filter pattern in the displacement signal. Faults of this kind can be identified by testing for cross-correlation of the displacement signal with the filter pattern.

8.03.4.1.3(i) Postprocessing

Processed data (spectra and spectral parameters) can be compared with the preceding values for consistency or with climatological values or other meteorological measurements such as wind. Tests include

- continuity with previous values,
- swell direction consistent with the buoy location,
- wind speed consistent with the HF wave energy,
- wind direction consistent with the HF wave direction, and
- wave height consistent with period.

8.03.4.1.4 Sampling variability for temporal averages

Any measurement of the sea surface is finite in extent, both in the area and in the duration of measurement, and therefore records only a finite number of waves from a theoretically infinite population. This means that derived wave statistics have an associated uncertainty, known as sampling variability. The longer the duration of a record or the larger the area it covers, the closer the measured value will be to the true value. To complicate matters, wave conditions are nonstationary, so averaging periods or areas are a compromise between the statistical stability of an estimate and the adequate sampling of the changes in wave conditions.

Understanding the sampling properties of wave parameters is important for understanding the scatter observed in the inter-comparison of wave measurements or the verification of WEC performance. This section considers only the uncertainty that arises from the statistical variability of the sea surface. There are other factors that affect the stability of the spectral parameters such as the HF cutoff of the spectrum and the method of spectral estimation. The HF cutoff is important for T_z, but less so for T_m and T_e. For example, in the case of a Pierson–Moskowitz (PM) spectrum with a cutoff of 0.4 Hz (typical of larger wave buoys), T_z will be overestimated 16% for a peak frequency of 0.2 Hz, 4% for a peak frequency of 0.1 Hz, and 1% for a peak frequency of 0.05 Hz. For T_e, the overestimate is 4% for a peak frequency of 0.2 Hz and 0.3% for a peak frequency of 0.1 Hz. Numerical factors are much less important than sampling variability for integral parameters but can have a significant effect on T_p (see Reference 51 and references therein for details).

8.03.4.1.4(i) Theoretical results

Sampling variance for spectral parameters of theoretical spectra can be calculated from the covariance of spectral moments. This is given by [66]

$$m_{rs} = \text{cov}(\hat{m}_r, \hat{m}_s) = \frac{1}{\tau} \int_0^\infty f^{r+s} S^2(f) df + O(N^{-2}) \qquad [86]$$

where τ is the record length, N is the number of points in the time series, and the caret '^' is used to denote an estimator $\hat{a}$ of parameter a. Using a Taylor series expansion, the variances of estimates of spectral parameters are given by

$$\text{var}(\hat{H}_s) = \text{var}\left(4\sqrt{\hat{m}_0}\right) = 4\frac{m_{00}}{m_0} \qquad [87]$$

$$\text{var}(\hat{T}_e) = \text{var}\left(\frac{\hat{m}_{-1}}{\hat{m}_0}\right) = \left(\frac{m_{-1}}{m_0}\right)^2 \left(\frac{m_{-1-1}}{m_{-1}^2} - 2\frac{m_{-10}}{m_{-1}m_0} + \frac{m_{00}}{m_0^2}\right) \qquad [88]$$

$$\text{var}(\hat{T}_m) = \text{var}\left(\frac{\hat{m}_0}{\hat{m}_1}\right) = \left(\frac{m_0}{m_1}\right)^2 \left(\frac{m_{00}}{m_0^2} - 2\frac{m_{01}}{m_0 m_1} + \frac{m_{11}}{m_1^2}\right) \qquad [89]$$

$$\text{var}(\hat{T}_z) = \text{var}\left(\sqrt{\frac{\hat{m}_0}{\hat{m}_2}}\right) = \frac{1}{4}\left(\frac{m_0}{m_2}\right)\left(\frac{m_{00}}{m_0^2} - 2\frac{m_{02}}{m_0 m_2} + \frac{m_{22}}{m_2^2}\right) \qquad [90]$$

Note that m_0 is the variance of the sea surface elevation, whereas m_{00} is the variance of the estimate of m_0.

For commonly used theoretical spectra, the coefficients of variation (defined as the standard deviation divided by the mean) for spectral parameters can be calculated using the above equations. For the Bretschneider spectrum (see Section 8.03.2.2.4), the coefficients of variation are

$$\text{COV}(\hat{H}_s) = 0.475\sqrt{\frac{T_p}{\tau}} \qquad [91]$$

$$\text{COV}(\hat{T}_e) = 0.201\sqrt{\frac{T_p}{\tau}} \qquad [92]$$

$$\text{COV}(\hat{T}_m) = 0.214\sqrt{\frac{T_p}{\tau}} \qquad [93]$$

$$\text{COV}(\hat{T}_z) = 0.220\sqrt{\frac{T_p}{\tau}} \qquad [94]$$

Formulas in terms of other period parameters can be found by substituting the relationships implied by eqn [33]. For a JONSWAP spectrum with $\gamma > 1$, it is not possible to calculate a formula analytically, but the results can be calculated by integrating the spectrum numerically. For the mean value of the peak enhancement factor found by Hasselmann et al. [7], $\gamma = 3.3$, we have

$$\text{COV}(\hat{H}_s) = 0.616\sqrt{\frac{T_p}{\tau}} \qquad [95]$$

$$\text{COV}(\hat{T}_e) = 0.169\sqrt{\frac{T_p}{\tau}} \qquad [96]$$

$$\text{COV}(\hat{T}_m) = 0.214\sqrt{\frac{T_p}{\tau}} \qquad [97]$$

$$\text{COV}(\hat{T}_z) = 0.244\sqrt{\frac{T_p}{\tau}} \qquad [98]$$

Formulas in terms of other period parameters can be found by substituting the relationships implied by eqn [39]. The variability of H_s is greater for JONSWAP spectra than for PM spectra because narrower-banded spectra give longer wave groups and thus larger variation in results over a given sample duration. In contrast, the variability of period parameters increases with bandwidth. In the limiting case, if the bandwidth is infinitely narrow, then the surface elevation is the sum of waves with the same frequency and can therefore be expressed as a single sinusoidal wave, giving zero variation in period.

The distribution function of H_s has been discussed by Donelan and Pierson [67], Carter and Tucker [68], and Young [69]. Forristall *et al.* [70] note that for practical purposes the distribution can be approximated with a Gaussian. Sampling properties of directional parameters are discussed by Kuik *et al.* [55].

8.03.4.1.4(ii) Empirical results

When estimating the sampling variability of wave parameters from measured spectra, the random variability of the spectral estimates cannot be ignored. The spectral estimates $\hat{S}(f)$ have a chi-square distribution with $v = 2M$ degrees of freedom, where M is the number of Fourier harmonics over which the estimates are averaged. Krogstad *et al.* [49] note that the expected value of the squared spectral density is dependent on the level of smoothing with $E(\hat{S}^2(f)) \approx (1 + 2/v)S^2(f)$. So substituting $\hat{S}^2(f)$ in place of $S^2(f)$ in eqn [86] can lead to a bias of a factor of 2 in the case that spectral estimates are not smoothed at all. The correct formula to use when estimating the covariance of moments for measured spectra is

$$\hat{m}_{rs} = \frac{1}{\tau(1 + 2/v)} \int_0^\infty f^{r+s} S^2(f) \mathrm{d}f \qquad [99]$$

8.03.4.1.4(iii) Implications for WEC performance assessment

Practical constraints can limit the proximity of a measuring device to a WEC. For instance, a buoy must be moored a sufficient distance from a WEC to ensure that they do not collide. It is possible to deploy an ADCP on the seabed close to a floating WEC, but in deep water this may not be practical. If a buoy is used to measure the wave field incident on a WEC or an array of WECs, then sampling variability will limit the precision to which the performance of a WEC can be assessed. The uncertainty due to sampling variability will vary with the separation of the measurements from the WEC. The instantaneous sea surface elevation is correlated over several wavelengths, with the correlation length related to the spectrum by the Wiener–Khinchin theorem. However, after several wavelengths, correlation is effectively zero and the waves at the measuring device and the WEC can be considered as independent realizations of the same underlying sea state.

In order to calculate the sampling variability of WEC power, we need to know the joint distribution of H_s, T_e, and any other parameters that affect power production (see Section 8.03.3). A simple way to estimate the sampling variability is to compare estimates of WEC power from measurements made by two devices located close to each other. The European Marine Energy Centre (EMEC) in the Orkney Islands, Scotland, has two Datawell Waverider buoys moored 1.5 km apart in approximately 50 m water depth, with the same exposure to the predominant wave direction. We shall use these data together with the Pelamis power table shown in **Table 3** to illustrate the effect of sampling variability on the estimated WEC power. The data comprise 19 414 concurrent hour-long records from the two buoys over the period October 2002–July 2007. **Figure 8** shows the RMS difference in the power

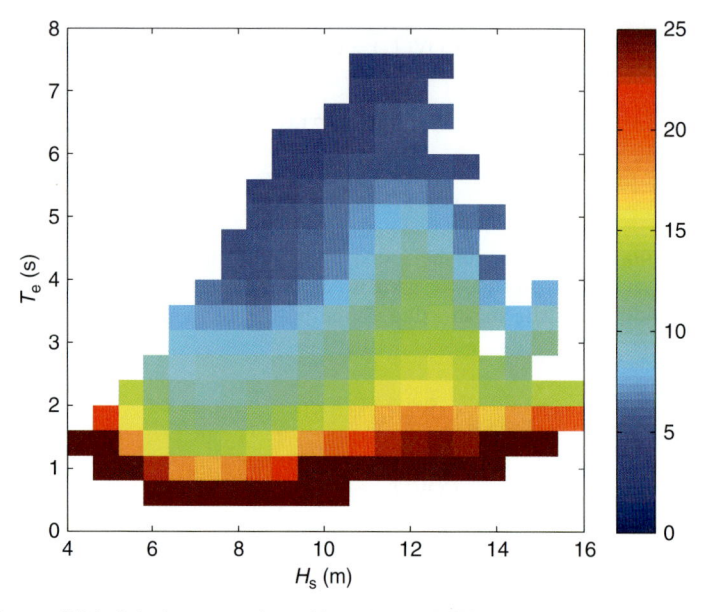

Figure 8 Normalized RMS difference (%) in Pelamis power estimated from the two EMEC buoys.

estimated from each buoy, normalized by the average power and binned by the average H_s and T_e. Since there are only a small number of data in some bins, the values have been smoothed using a Gaussian kernel. For values H_s and T_e close to the cut-in power level, the normalized RMS difference is actually much higher than 25%, but the color scale has been chosen to highlight the trends over the entire plot. It is evident that even by using measurements averaged over 1 h, sampling variability can place serious limitations on the accuracy to which WEC performance can be assessed.

8.03.4.1.5 Presentation of wave climate data from buoy measurements

Wave buoys can potentially record a large volume of information about the wave climate at a site and the question arises as to how best this information can be summarized. Typically, spectra are processed with the parameters described in Sections 8.03.2.2.2 and 8.03.2.2.3 and these can then be plotted as time series or histograms of relative occurrence or processed with mean values over various periods.

It is also informative to examine the temporal evolution of the sea state by plotting the time series of the wave spectra themselves. Since there is too much information in the full directional spectrum to plot as a two-dimensional time series, several plots can be displayed showing the omnidirectional spectral density with frequency and the mean direction and spread at each frequency. An example of this type of plot is shown in **Figure 9** using data recorded by one of the EMEC Waverider buoys. A logarithmic scale has been used for the spectral density so that the shapes of the spectra can be discerned over a wide range of H_s. The model-free directional parameters defined in Section 8.03.4.1.2(ii)(c) are used to estimate the mean direction and spread directly from the measured cross-spectra.

Examination of the frequency spectra time series tells a story that would not be evident from the plots of the integrated parameters alone. The occurrence of several distinct swell and wind sea conditions is clear both at the beginning of the month and from the 19th onward. The frequency dispersion in the swells is also clear, with the lowest frequency components arriving before the higher-frequency components, due to the increase in group velocity with period (see Section 8.03.2.1.2). This is clearly visible in the three distinct swells arriving from the 16th to the 18th, the 19th to the 21st, and the 22nd to the 27th. Throughout the month, the direction of swell components with periods greater than 10 s is consistently around 270° (west). In contrast, the wind sea direction is variable, but still clearly discernable from the swell. For example, from the 19th to the 29th, a southeasterly wind blows over the swell from the west.

A consistent pattern in the directional spread is also clear, with the spread being lowest at the spectral peak and increasing away from the peak and at points where the swell and wind sea directions cross. For example, from the 11th to the 14th, the spread is high in the HF end of the spectrum, due to a wind sea crossing the swell, whereas from the 15th to the 17th, the spread is much lower in this part of the spectrum as the swell from the west drops off and a wind sea from the north dominates.

Another interesting point to note from **Figure 9** is the tidal modulation of wave height and frequency. This is most clearly visible toward the end of the month, where the varying current causes a banding in the HF end of the spectrum as these waves propagate over an alternately opposing and following current. The effect of the current on the lower frequency end of the spectrum is smaller as the ratio of the current velocity to the wave group velocity is lower.

Some examples of directional spectra from the same month are shown in **Figure 10**. The spectra have been averaged over a 1 h period, with the directional distribution estimated using the iterated MLM (see Section 8.03.4.1.2(ii)(d)). The corresponding omnidirectional spectra are also shown in the right-hand plots, together with fitted standard spectral shapes. The lower plot shows the spectrum at 00:00 on the 8th, close to the peak of the storm. The measured spectra have parameters $H_s = 5.39$ m and $T_e = 10.7$ s, and a Bretschneider spectrum with the same parameters provides a good fit. The upper plot shows a mixed wind sea and swell condition from 21:00 on the 20th. The swell is of quite a low frequency with a peak period around 13 s, whereas the wind sea is of a relatively high frequency, with a peak around 4 s. However, the spectrum has an energy period of 8.3 s, at which there is little energy from either the swell or the wind sea. The spectrum is reasonably well fit by two JONSWAP spectra, with $H_s = 1.24$ m, $f_p = 0.077$ Hz, and $\gamma = 1.55$ for the swell and $H_s = 0.99$ m, $f_p = 0.26$ Hz, and $\gamma = 1.46$ for the wind sea.

The wave climate at a site is often summarized using a bivariate histogram of the joint distribution of H_s and T_e. This information can be combined directly with the power matrix of a WEC to get an estimate of the average energy yield. An example of a bivariate histogram is shown in **Figure 11**. The distribution is heart-shaped, with the highest waves tending to a narrow range of periods and the longest period sea states tending to a small range of H_s. Contours of constant wave power and steepness have also been added to the diagram. The red lines indicate constant power, using the formula for deep water given in eqn [27], for powers of 10, 30, 100, and 300 kW m^{-1}. The average steepness of the waves is usually defined in terms of T_z and is referred to as the significant steepness: $s = H_s/\lambda_z = 2\pi H_s/gT_z^2$, where λ_z is the wavelength given by eqn [5] that corresponds to T_z. In **Figure 11**, steepness has been calculated with T_e substituted in place of T_z. Contours are shown for s values between 0.01 and 0.05 at intervals of 0.01.

8.03.4.2 Wave Measurements from Satellite Altimeters

Measurements of waves from satellite radar altimeters provide an important complement to *in situ* measurements. Whereas *in situ* measurements provide time series of measurements at one location, satellite altimeters provide spatial series of measurements over the entire globe, with a continuous record dating back to 1991.

In general, *in situ* instruments measure the displacement of the water surface at a fixed point with respect to time. Satellite altimeters provide measurements while the satellite orbits the earth. They interrogate an area or 'footprint' of about 5 km diameter

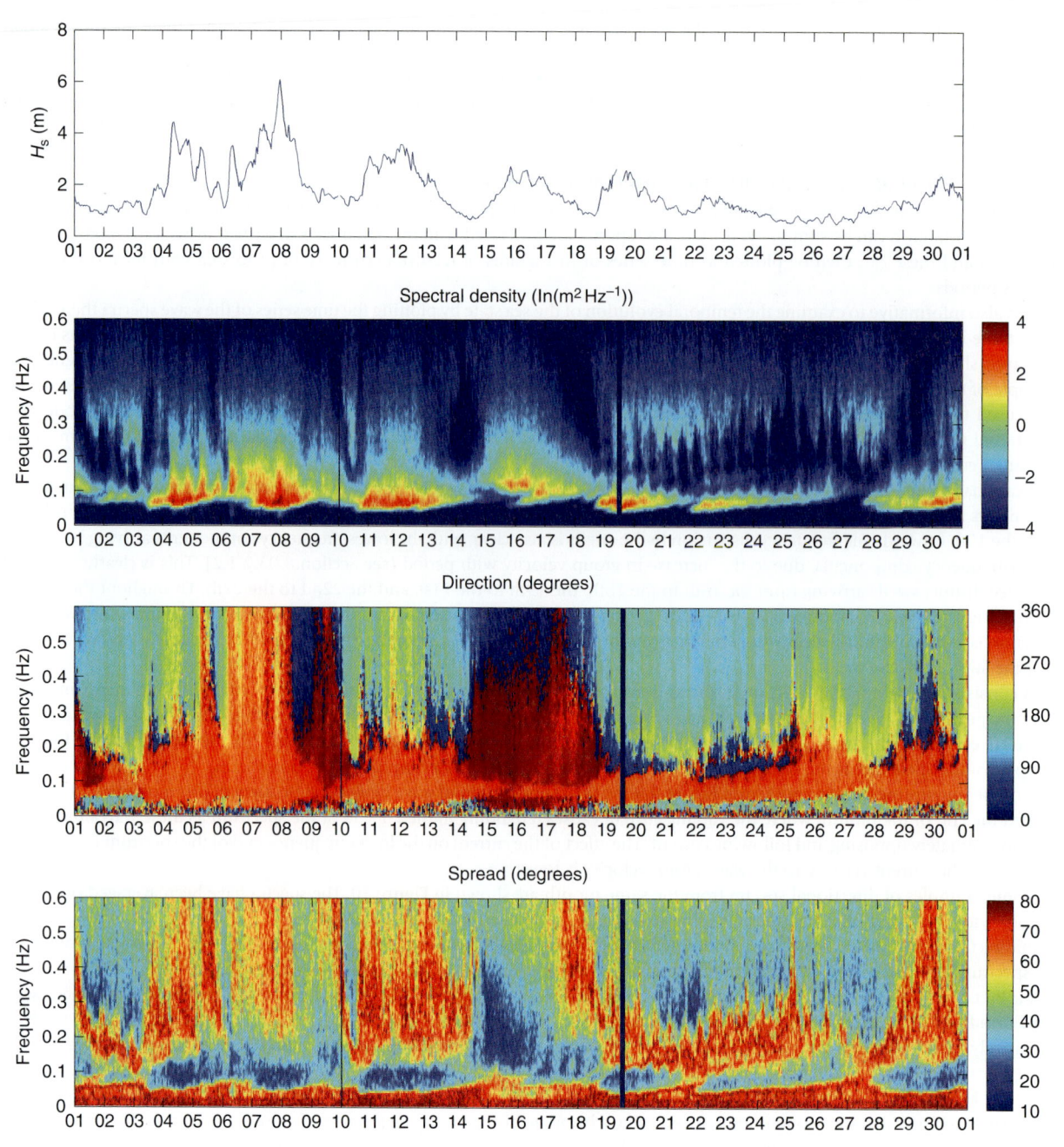

Figure 9 Time series of H_s, spectral density, mean direction, and spread recorded by a Waverider buoy at EMEC over a period of 1 month.

and report a measure of the average wave conditions over the whole area. Data are reported at 1 Hz, in which time the footprint of the altimeter will have moved about 6.5 km.

Satellite altimeters orbit the earth following a fixed path relative to the ground. The orbits are divided into passes, cycles, and phases. A pass spans half an orbital revolution around the Earth and is either ascending (south–north) or descending (north–south). A cycle is completed once the satellite returns to the same location above the Earth. The time taken to complete one cycle is known as the repeat period. If a satellite is moved into a new orbit, this is denoted by a new phase, for example, A and B. **Figure 12** shows a three-dimensional view of the first 5 passes of a cycle and a full cycle of 254 passes for the TOPEX phase A orbit.

There is an inherent compromise in the choice of orbit between the regularity of measurements at a point on the ocean surface and the spatial resolution of the satellite's coverage. For example, although the TOPEX/Poseidon (T/P) and Jason missions have a repeat period of approximately 10 days, there is a relatively large distance between adjacent crossover points. In contrast, the ERS and ENVISAT missions have a much smaller distance between crossover points of the ground tracks but a longer repeat period of

Resource Assessment for Wave Energy   33

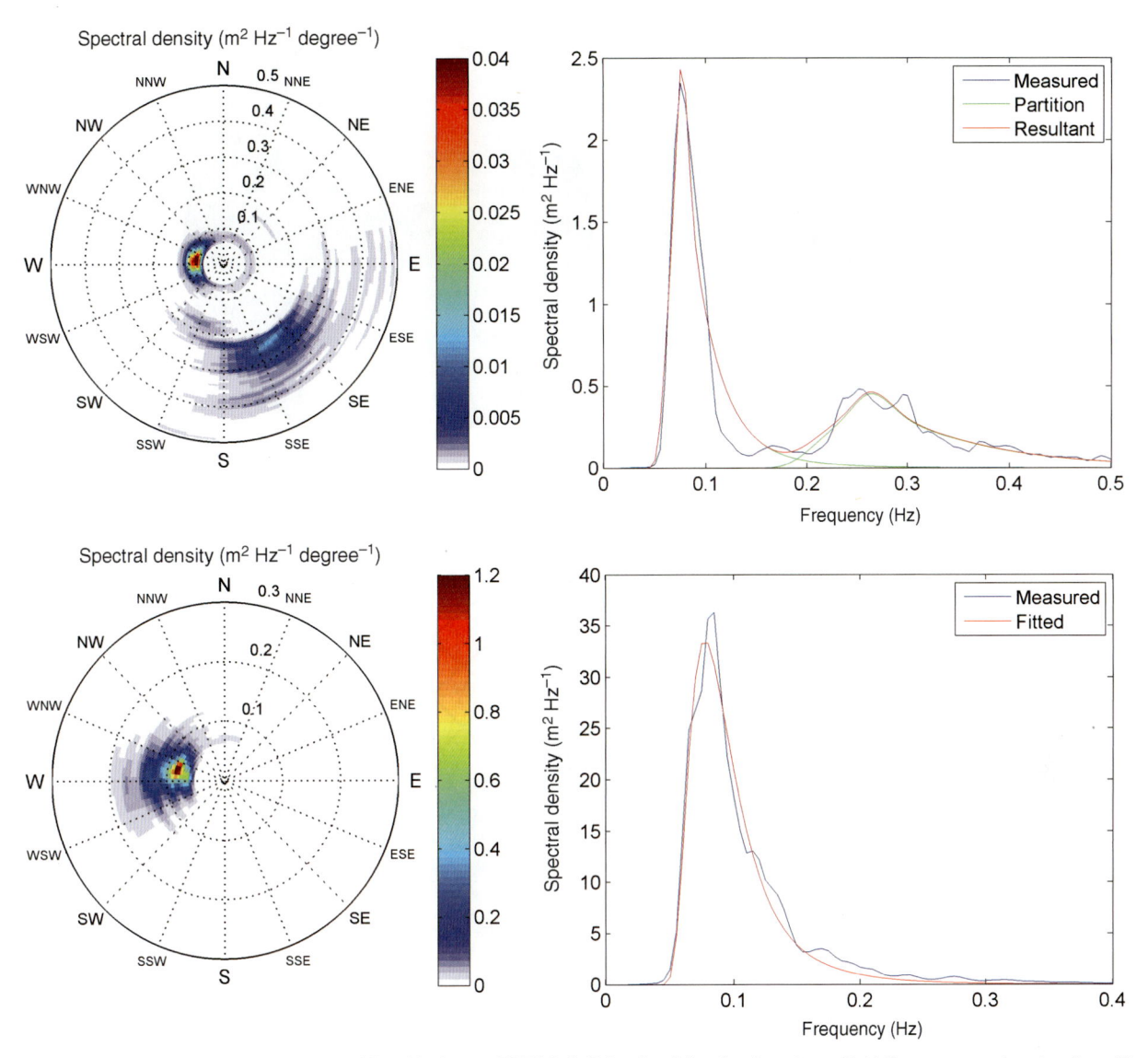

Figure 10 Examples of spectra recorded by a Waverider buoy at EMEC. Left: Polar plot of directional spectrum. Right: Frequency spectrum together with fitted JONSWAP spectra.

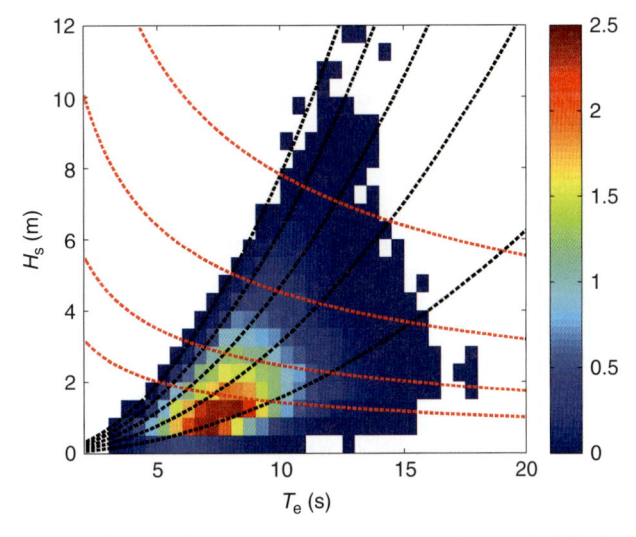

Figure 11 Bivariate histogram of H_s and T_e. Color scale denotes percentage occurrence in bins of size 0.5 m by 0.5 s. Black dashed lines indicate constant steepness and red dashed lines constant power.

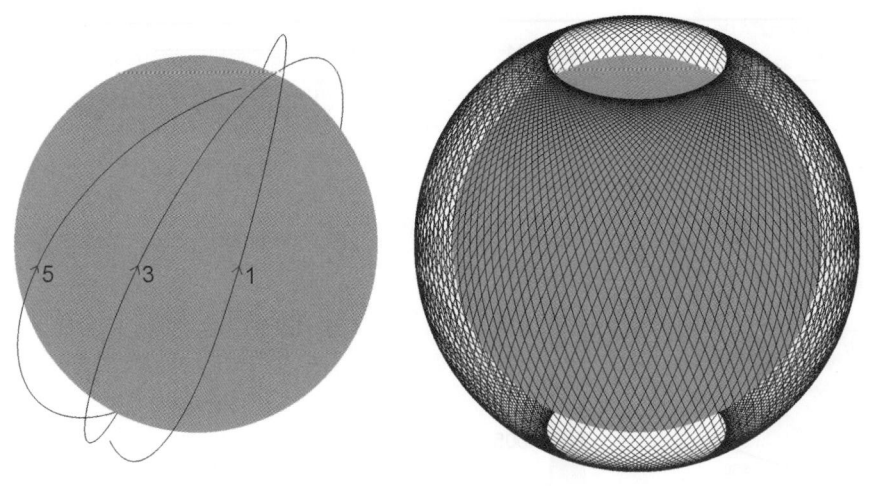

Figure 12 Three-dimensional view of TOPEX phase A orbit. Left: First five passes of a cycle. Right: A full cycle of 254 passes.

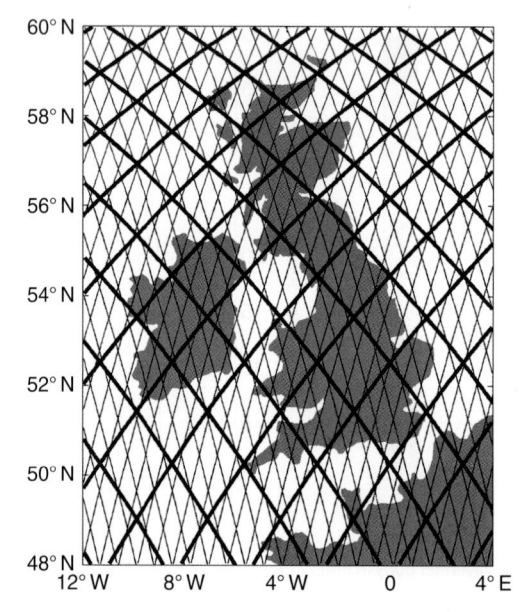

Figure 13 Altimeter passes in the vicinity of the United Kingdom. Thick lines indicate T/P/Jason (phase A) and thin lines ERS/ENVISAT.

35 days. The GEOSAT and GEOSAT Follow-On (GFO) missions have a repeat period in between that of the T/P and ERS missions of 17 days. Ground tracks of the T/P and ERS missions in the vicinity of the United Kingdom are shown in **Figure 13** and a summary of the altimeter missions to date is given in **Table 4**.

8.03.4.2.1 Instrumental characteristics

The satellite altimeter is a radar oriented at a near-vertical incidence angle to the sea surface. It measures the return signal from specular (mirror-like) reflection from the sea surface. A brief overview of the principles of radar altimetry is given in this section. For a more detailed description and extensive references, the reader is referred to Reference 71.

Altimeters operate within the microwave frequency range where graybody emission of electromagnetic radiation from the sea surface is very weak and the reflectivity of water is high, thus allowing easy distinction of the radar return from natural emission. All altimeters flown to date have carried a Ku-band (10.9–22.0 GHz) altimeter, but the TOPEX, Jason, and ENVISAT altimeters also made simultaneous measurements at a lower frequency. Both TOPEX and Jason have a dual-frequency altimeter that operates simultaneously at 13.6 GHz (Ku-band) and 5.3 GHz (C-band), and ENVISAT has a dual-frequency altimeter that operates at 13.6 GHz (Ku-band) and 3.2 GHz (S-band). Most studies of wave measurements from altimeter data have used the Ku-band data, since these data have been extensively studied and validated.

Measurements of the ocean surface are made as follows: the altimeter sends a pulse of radar energy to the ocean surface and records the return pulse. Wave height, wave period, and wind speed are inferred from the shape of the return pulse, and the distance

Table 4 Details of altimeter missions

Satellite	Data coverage	Orbit altitude (km)	Latitude/longitude coverage	Direction of travel
GEOSAT	30 September 1986–30 December 1989	800	72° N/S	Westward
GFO	7 January 2000–26 November 2008	800	72° N/S	Westward
T/P	25 September 1992–8 October 2005	1336	66° N/S	Eastward
Jason-1	15 January 2002–present	1336	66° N/S	Eastward
Jason-2	4 July 2008–present	1336	66° N/S	Eastward
ERS-1	1 August 1991–2 June 1996	785	81.5° N/S	Westward
ERS-2	29 April 1995–present	785	81.5° N/S	Westward
ENVISAT	24 September 2002–present	785	81.5° N/S	Westward

from the altimeter to the sea surface is calculated from the time taken to receive the return pulse. The technique used to transmit the pulse of radar energy and interpret the return signal is known as pulse compression, whereby an altimeter transmits a relatively long pulse with a short-frequency modulation called a chirp. The return signal is processed in a way that is equivalent to transmitting a short pulse and measuring the time history of the returned power. The equivalent pulse length is equal to the reciprocal of the chirp bandwidth. A detailed account of the use of pulse compression in satellite altimetry is given by Chelton et al. [72]. Since it is more intuitive to understand how waves affect the time history of a short pulse of radar energy, we will use this interpretation in the following sections.

8.03.4.2.1(i) The effect of waves on the return pulse

The power in the radar return pulse is proportional to the area illuminated by the radar energy on the sea surface. At the first instant a pulse reaches the surface, it illuminates a small circular region nadir to the altimeter. At successive times, the same narrow pulse illuminates annular regions with ever-increasing diameters. Despite the increasing diameters, the illuminated area remains constant. This is due to the curvature of the Earth's surface (see Appendix A1 of Reference 72). **Figure 14** illustrates this for the case of a flat sea surface.

Waves on the sea surface change the shape of the waveform that the altimeter receives. The leading edge of the returned waveform is stretched as a result of the earlier returns from wave crests and later returns from wave troughs. The higher the waves, the greater the time between the arrivals of successive returns from the crests and troughs of the waves and the more stretched the return pulse. This stretching of the shape of the return pulse can be related quantitatively to the variance of the sea surface and hence to the significant wave height H_s. A detailed description of how the presence of waves on the sea surface alters the shape of the returned waveform is given by Fu and Cazenave [71].

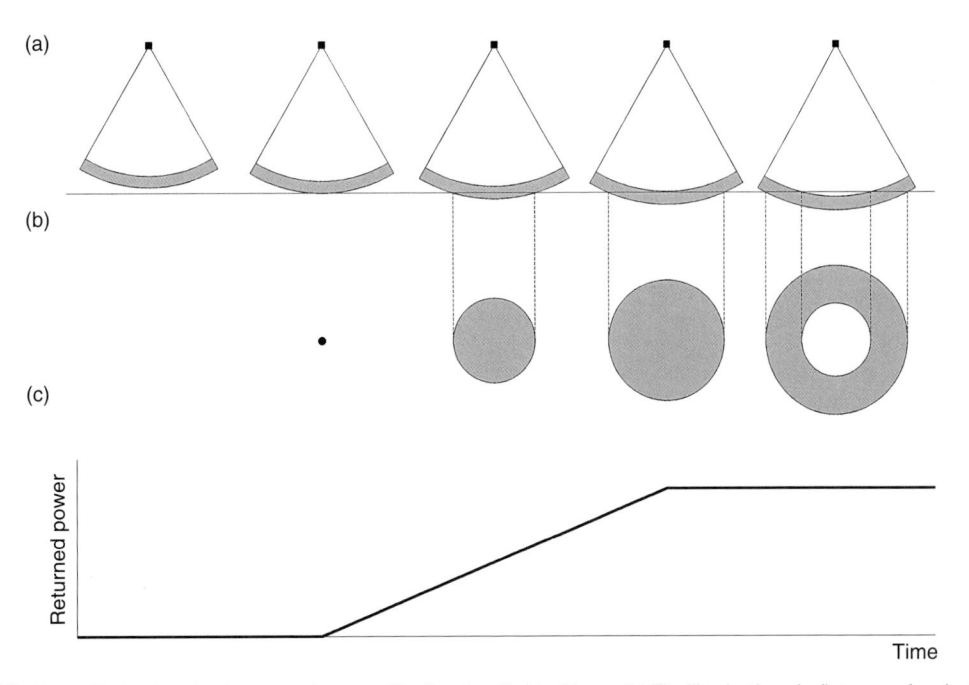

Figure 14 (a) The transmitted pulse of radar energy from an altimeter at vertical incidence. (b) The illumination of a flat sea surface by the radar pulse shown in (a). (c) The evolution of returned power received at the altimeter for a single pulse.

8.03.4.2.1(ii)   The normalized radar cross section

Another key parameter of the reflected waveform received by the altimeter is σ_0, a dimensionless quantity referred to as the normalized radar cross section or backscatter coefficient. It is a measure of the ratio between the transmitted power and the power of the return pulse received by the altimeter. It can be shown that the returned power and hence σ_0 depend only on the radar scattering characteristics or 'roughness' of the target area. The sea surface roughness increases with wind speed. At small incidence angles relevant to satellite altimetry, returned power and therefore σ_0 decrease monotonically with increasing roughness. The backscatter coefficient σ_0 can therefore be used together with the measurement of H_s to estimate wind speed and wave period.

The backscatter coefficient is corrected for the effects of atmospheric attenuation. At the Ku-band frequency of 13.6 GHz, the clear-sky one-way transmittance at normal incidence angles is rarely less than 0.96 even in a moist tropical atmosphere. The corresponding two-way attenuation is therefore generally less than 8%. At C-band and S-band frequencies, the attenuation is much less. The clear-sky attenuation of σ_0 can be accurately corrected using transmittance values derived from meteorological models. Cloud attenuation can also be accurately corrected for and is estimated using a multifrequency microwave radiometer onboard the satellite.

Rain has a much greater effect on radar signal than clouds, water vapor, or dry gases. Because of the difficulties in obtaining rain rate profiles from satellite data, no attempt is made to correct for rain attenuation of σ_0. Rather, rain-contaminated altimeter observations are flagged and excluded. However, measurements at lower frequencies are less affected by rain and can be used to maintain data coverage through severe storms [73, 74].

8.03.4.2.1(iii)   Estimation of wave period

Several models have been proposed relating the altimeter H_s and σ_0 to wave period. The backscatter coefficient, σ_0, is a measure of the roughness of the sea surface, with higher values of σ_0 corresponding to higher returned power from smoother seas and hence longer period waves. However, σ_0 is most sensitive to short wavelengths on the sea and does not give much information about the presence of swell. Measurements of σ_0 at the lower C-band or S-band frequencies are slightly more sensitive to longer wavelengths on the sea, so the use of measurements from dual-frequency altimeters can marginally improve the accuracy of estimates of period. Essentially though, wave period estimates from altimeter data are a function of the total energy in the spectrum (H_s) and the energy in the HF end of the spectrum (σ_0). Nevertheless, a reasonable accuracy can be achieved. Quilfen *et al.* [75] proposed a model using dual-frequency measurements from the TOPEX and Jason-1 missions, which gives T_z with an RMS error of 0.5 s. Mackay *et al.* [76, 77] proposed an algorithm using only Ku-band measurements, which gives T_z with an RMS error of 0.6 s and T_e with an RMS error of around 1.0 s. Further information on the accuracy of altimeter estimates of wave period is given in Section 8.03.4.2.4(ii).

8.03.4.2.1(iv)   Noise on the return signal

The time series of returned power shown in **Figure 14(c)** actually represents the time evolution of the illuminated area averaged over a hypothetical infinite ensemble of realizations. Any particular realization will be very noisy owing to the random nature of the phases of the various components of the wave field over the antenna footprint that contribute to the radar return at any particular two-way travel time. Also, as the altimeter moves along the satellite orbit, the path lengths to the specular reflectors on the various wave facets change, resulting in pulse-to-pulse fluctuations in the returned power. To reduce the effect of this, the pulses, which are transmitted at repetition rates of 1000–4000 Hz, are averaged to give one estimate every 0.1 s, and 10 of these 10 Hz values are averaged again to give the 1 Hz values that are distributed by the space agencies as the Geophysical Data Records (GDRs). The standard deviation of the ten 10 Hz values comprising each 1 Hz value is also given in the GDRs as an indicator of the data quality.

8.03.4.2.2   Quality checks for altimeter data

Errors can occur in the measured data for a number of reasons. These errors can be identified by a visual inspection of the plots of the raw data, but this is not practical for large data sets. There is no simple solution to the problem of quality checking of altimeter data. Criteria can be set based on various statistical parameters, but the limiting values are subjective.

8.03.4.2.2(i)   Factors affecting the quality of measurement

8.03.4.2.2(i)(a)   Rain effects   Radar signals are attenuated by raindrops from both absorption and scattering. In addition to reducing the measured value of σ_0, rain cells that are smaller than the illuminated area of the antenna footprint distort the shape of the radar signal that is returned from the sea surface, which can corrupt measurements of H_s. The effects of rain contamination are often apparent from erratic variation of H_s and σ_0. In some cases, however, the effects of rain contamination can lead to more subtle but significant errors in these quantities. It is therefore important to identify records for which rain contamination is highly probable.

Rain flags are distributed by the space agencies as part of the GDRs, based on the integrated columnar liquid water content. Since rain attenuation is an order of magnitude greater at the Ku-band than at the C-band or S-band, rain-contaminated observations from the dual-frequency altimeters can usually be identified as an abrupt decrease in Ku-band σ_0 relative to C-band or S-band σ_0.

8.03.4.2.2(i)(b)   Mispointing effects   The algorithms used to derive H_s and σ_0 from the return pulse assume that the radar points vertically downward toward the ocean surface. The slope of the return pulse, and hence the altimeter estimate of H_s, is not greatly affected by mispointing, but the estimate of σ_0 is more sensitive, since the returned power decreases with increased two-way travel time. Carter *et al.* [78] note that mispointing was a serious problem for GEOSAT. Moreover, estimation of the mispointing angle (also called the off-nadir or attitude angle) for GEOSAT was not good and was not measured directly.

8.03.4.2.2(i)(c)   Loss of tracking   After the altimeter sends a pulse of radar energy, it 'listens' for the return pulse within a certain interval determined by a tracking loop. In order to calculate H_s, σ_0, and two-way travel time correctly, the altimeter return signal has to be centered in the tracking loop window. Strong returns from ships, sea ice, and other objects or nonuniform attenuation from patchy rain cells can cause the leading edge of the waveform to become distorted and lead to errors in the tracking algorithm. After a period of bad returns, the wave measurements may continue to be faulty until the altimeter return signal has been reacquired and centered in the tracking loop window.

There is a similar delay when the altimeter starts making measurements again after moving over land to water. The waveform is distorted if there is land within the footprint. The footprint is about 5–10 km in diameter, depending on H_s and the altitude of the satellite orbit. When the satellite moves from land to sea, it can travel about 30 km before regaining lock on the sea surface. Often no data are obtained, but sometimes spurious measurements are recorded, which require careful quality checking of the individual measurements. GEOSAT had a particular problem in locking on to the sea surface as it came off the land, but subsequent satellites have provided more data in coastal regions.

8.03.4.2.2(ii)   Quality checking criteria
The tests developed for each altimeter depend on the parameters provided by the space agencies. Quality flags are usually issued by the data provider, but additional checks can improve the data quality. The main criteria used can be summarized as follows:

- Land flags indicating whether the altimeter is over land
- Number of 10 or 20 Hz values used to obtain 1 Hz average
- Attitude angle
- Standard deviation of the range, H_s and σ_0
- Difference between measurements at Ku-band and C-band or S-band

If the standard deviation of the 10 or 20 Hz range values about the 1 Hz value is unusually high, this can indicate that the return waveform is not properly centered in the tracking loop, caused, for example, by rain cells or passage over land. Differences between H_s or σ_0 at each frequency can indicate corruption of the measurement by rain, as the higher frequency Ku-band measurement will suffer greater attenuation.

Several authors have proposed quality checks based on various statistical relationships of data points to their neighbors. Challenor *et al.* [79] use a method to screen GEOSAT data based on a linear fit to the five previous 1 Hz values. Young and Holland [80] use a procedure to check GEOSAT data based on the standard deviation of blocks of 50 consecutive 1 Hz values. In the presence of outliers, the mean and standard deviation can be poor descriptors of the location and spread of the data. In this case, these tests can discard entire blocks where one large outlier biases the standard deviation. It may therefore be more appropriate to use the median and interquartile range.

Close to the coast, automated quality controls may fail because of along-track smoothing. In some cases when the altimeter moves from the land to the sea, a good measurement may be smoothed in with a preceding corrupt measurement. The standard deviations of the 10 and 20 Hz measurements are not smoothed, so tests based on these criteria will not catch these smoothed-in points. When using altimeter data close to land, it is recommended that a cutoff point is set by visual inspection of the data.

8.03.4.2.3   Sampling variability for spatial averages
It is more difficult to give precise estimates of the sampling variability of altimeter measurements. Krogstad *et al.* [66] established a theoretical lower bound for the sampling variability of an estimate of H_s from an instantaneous spatial average of wave conditions. However, in practice, the sampling variability of altimeter measurements of H_s contains a nonnegligible component from instrumental noise. Tournadre [81] estimated that the standard deviation of 1 Hz measurements of H_s was $0.06 + 0.03H_s$ for GEOSAT. Subsequent missions have had slightly better performance, but the exact values of sampling variability are difficult to determine due to along-track smoothing of measurements. Roughly speaking though, except at low H_s, the sampling variability of altimeter measurements of H_s is at a level similar to that of buoy measurements averaged over about 30 min.

8.03.4.2.4   Calibration and validation of altimeter wave measurements
8.03.4.2.4(i)   Significant wave height
The accuracy of significant wave height from satellite altimeters has been well documented over the years (e.g., References 78 and 82–86). The general consensus is that with the application of a linear calibration, altimeter measurements of H_s can be considered as accurate as buoy measurements.

A common approach to assess the accuracy of altimeter measurements is to make a direct comparison of near-coincident altimeter and buoy measurements. Since it is unlikely that an altimeter ground track will pass directly over a buoy, the two measurements will be separated spatially. Buoys commonly only report wave conditions averaged over 20–40 min once per hour;

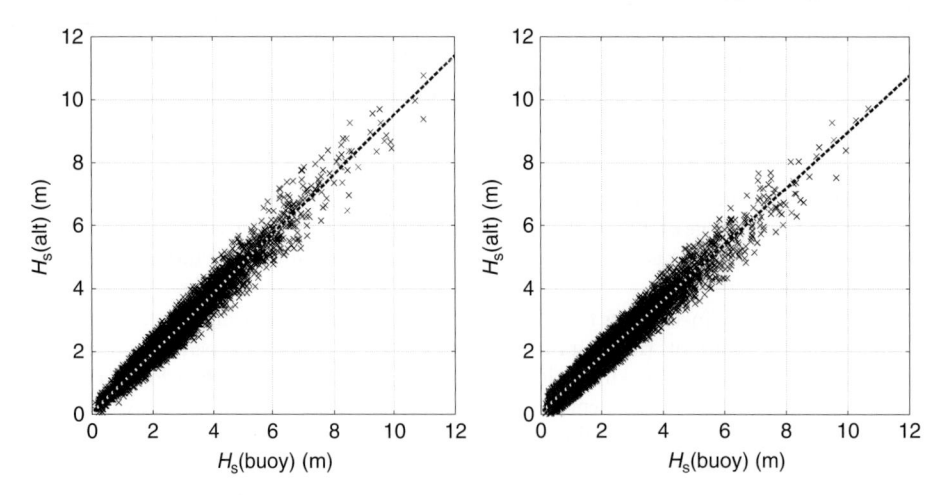

Figure 15 Orthogonal regression of altimeter H_s on buoy H_s for TOPEX (left) and ERS-2 (right).

therefore, altimeter and buoy measurements are likely to be separated temporally as well. This spatial and temporal separation introduces a random error to the comparison in addition to the sampling variability of each instrument.

An example of a comparison between collocated altimeter and buoy measurements is shown in **Figure 15**. The buoy data comprise measurements from 28 buoys operated by the US National Data Buoy Center (NDBC), detailed in Reference 76. A maximum spatial separation of 100 km and time separation of 30 min have been chosen to define a coincident measurement. For each altimeter pass by a buoy, the nearest 1 Hz value of H_s within 100 km of the buoy has been used. The collocation criteria are a compromise between the assumption that the wave conditions are stationary and the number of points included. In the open ocean, it is a reasonable assumption that conditions are stationary over this distance, although in shallow water or close to the coast, there can be considerable variability on these scales.

To obtain a calibration for the altimeter measurements, orthogonal distance regression [87] has been used, which accounts for errors in both the data sets. Ordinary least squares regression assumes that the variable on the x-axis is measured without error, which is inappropriate in this case, since the buoy measurements are subject to sampling variability and the effects of spatial and temporal separation from the altimeter measurements. Tolman [88] notes that using ordinary least squares regression and ignoring the errors in the buoy data can underestimate the slope of the regression line. Calibrations for each altimeter are given in **Table 6** in the form $H_s(\text{buoy}) = a + bH_s(\text{alt})$.

The values given in **Table 5** differ slightly from some published results, since slightly different lengths of data have been used. Krogstad and Barstow [89] note that the various calibrations presented in the literature for TOPEX give more or less the same correction for low to medium sea states. However, there is a 0.5 m difference in the range of calibration functions at $H_s = 10$ m, since typically there are far fewer data at this level, leading to greater uncertainty in the estimation.

Another reason for differing calibrations is that buoy networks operated by different countries have slightly different calibrations. Challenor and Cotton [83] calibrated altimeter H_s measurements from GEOSAT, ERS-1, ERS-2, TOPEX, and Poseidon against the NDBC buoy network to obtain a data set that is internally consistent and also consistent with the NDBC buoy network. They then used this merged altimeter data set to check the calibrations of three other buoy networks operated by the UK Met Office (UKMO), the Japan Meteorological Agency (JMA), and the Meteorological Service of Canada (MSC). They noted significant differences between the buoy networks in terms of their slopes (UKMO, MSC) or intercept (JMA), with the UKMO buoys reading about 4% high compared with NDBC, MSC to be 5% low, and the JMA buoys to have a bias of about 30 cm. However, it should be stressed that these are relative measures and it is not possible to say which calibration is correct.

Table 5 Linear calibrations of altimeter H_s against NDBC buoy data

	a	b
TOPEX	−0.07	1.06
Poseidon	−0.19	1.07
Jason-1	−0.08	1.08
ERS-2	−0.08	1.12
ENVISAT	−0.23	1.08
GFO	0.06	1.09

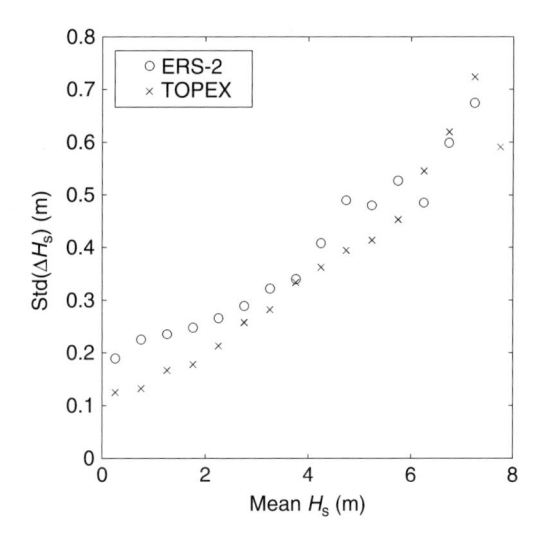

Figure 16 Standard deviation of differences in H_s from altimeter and buoy measurements.

The standard deviation of the differences in the altimeter and buoy measurements of H_s is shown in **Figure 16**. The differences are slightly higher for ERS-2 than for TOPEX. This is a result of the along-track smoothing of measurements performed onboard TOPEX which reduces the effects of sampling variability and spatial variation in wave conditions. For higher sea states, the standard deviations for the two altimeters are similar and are comparable with the differences that would be expected between two buoys.

8.03.4.2.4(ii) Wave period

In comparison with significant wave height and wind speed, the estimation of wave period from altimeter measurements has received relatively little attention. As mentioned in Section 8.03.4.2.1(iii), the accuracy of altimeter wave period estimates is limited by the insensitivity of the backscatter coefficient to low-frequency components of the wave spectrum. The most accurate algorithm for Ku-band measurements that has been proposed to date is that of Mackay *et al.* [76]. Their algorithm takes the form

$$T = \frac{1}{\beta} \ln\left[\frac{1}{\alpha}\left(\frac{c}{H_s + \gamma}\right)\right] \quad [100]$$

where

$$c = \begin{cases} \sigma_0 - A & \text{if } \sigma_0 \leq \delta \\ \delta - A & \text{if } \sigma_0 > \delta \end{cases}$$

and α, β, γ, δ, and A are empirically determined constants listed in **Tables 6** and **7**.

Figure 17 shows scatter plots of estimates of T_z and T_e from the TOPEX altimeter against buoy measurements, using the data described by Mackay *et al.* [76]. The accuracy of the altimeter estimate of T_z is better than that of T_e, with a lower level of scatter observed in the plot. This better performance is due to the sensitivity of the backscatter coefficient to the HF parts of the spectrum, to which T_z is more sensitive.

From eqn [100], it can be seen that when the altimeter measurement of σ_0 is above the threshold level δ, the period algorithm depends only on the value of H_s. This means that it cannot properly reproduce the joint distribution of H_s and T_z (or T_e) for σ_0 in this range. **Figure 18** shows the joint distributions of H_s and T_z measured by the buoys and altimeter for $\sigma_0 \leq \delta$. The altimeter reproduces the joint distribution with reasonable accuracy, but the minimum steepness shown by the altimeter estimates is slightly higher than

Table 6 Constants used in algorithm for T_z

	A	α	β	γ	δ
TOPEX	17.11	−4.054	−0.1558	1.658	12.87
Poseidon	19.40	−2.831	−0.1090	3.496	12.81
Jason-1	17.68	−4.094	−0.1488	1.851	12.95
ERS-2	17.42	−3.906	−0.1422	2.072	12.39
ENVISAT	16.28	−4.248	−0.1630	1.314	12.29
GFO	17.16	−4.550	−0.1648	1.669	12.88

Table 7 Constants used in algorithm for T_e

	A	α	β	γ	Δ
TOPEX	15.80	−3.373	−0.1232	1.384	12.48
Poseidon	18.22	−2.380	−0.0802	3.309	12.58
Jason-1	16.34	−3.191	−0.1126	1.701	12.50
ERS-2	16.05	−3.225	−0.1098	1.784	12.08
ENVISAT	15.37	−3.253	−0.1181	1.251	11.98
GFO	15.87	−3.940	−0.1332	1.338	12.54

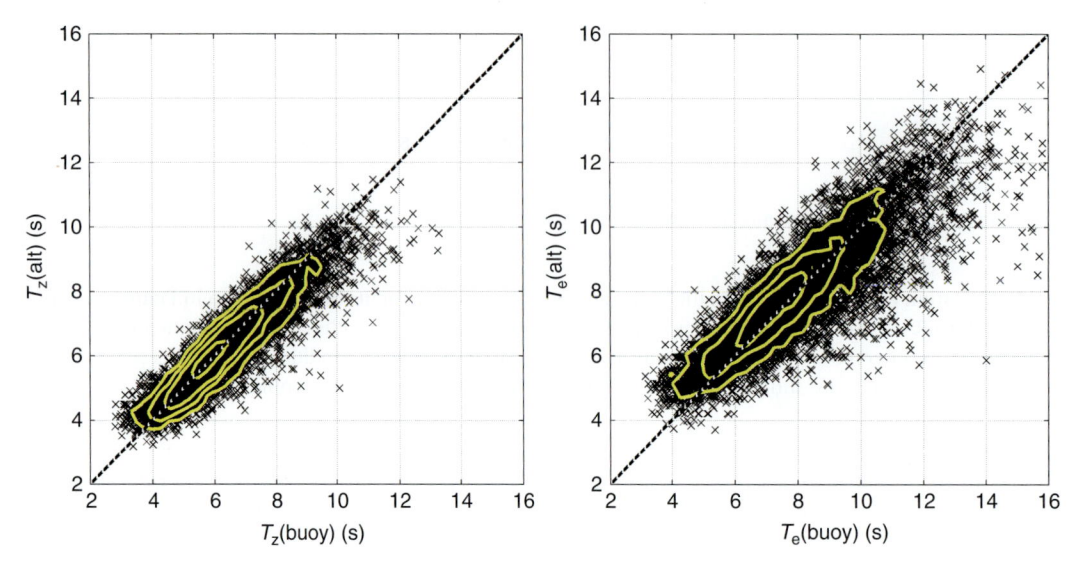

Figure 17 Scatter plots of altimeter T_z and T_e against buoy measurements. Contours show lines of equal probability density.

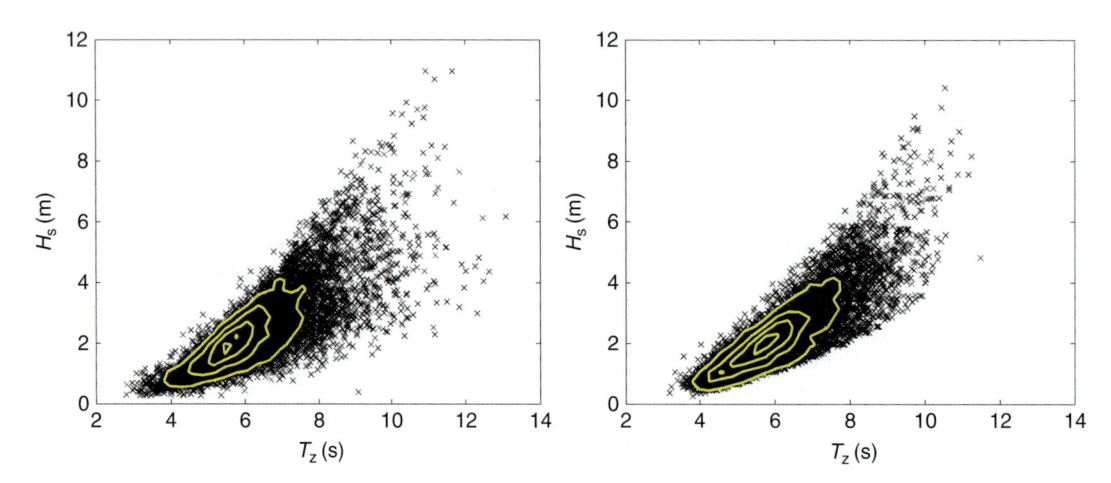

Figure 18 Joint distribution of H_s and T_z when $\sigma_0 \leq \delta$ for buoy measurements (left) and altimeter measurements (right). Crosses show individual measurements and contours indicate density.

that observed in the buoy data. Although the altimeter is not able to reproduce the joint distribution of H_s and T_z for $\sigma_0 > \delta$, it is able to match the mean value of T_z for a given H_s, as shown in **Figure 19**.

Measurements with high σ_0 correspond to times of low wind speed ($\sigma_0 = 13$ dB $\Leftrightarrow U_{10} \approx 4$ m s^{-1}) or, equivalently, swell conditions. Since the period algorithm is based on H_s alone when $\sigma_0 > \delta$, this gives a model in which all swell has the same steepness for a given H_s. However, this limitation is not too severe. From **Figure 19**, we can see that the range of steepness is in fact quite small for $\sigma_0 > \delta$. The information that σ_0 is above the threshold is sufficient to infer that the wave conditions are swell dominated and that the period can be reasonably estimated from H_s alone.

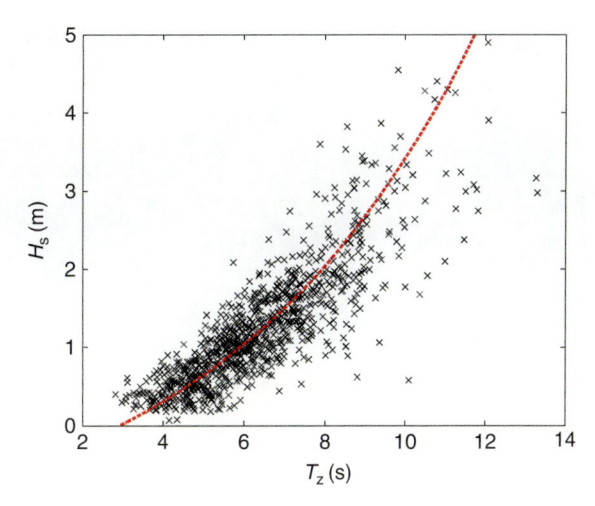

Figure 19 Scatter plot of H_s and T_z when $\sigma_0 > \delta$ for buoy measurements. The red line shows ratio given by altimeter.

8.03.4.2.5 Mapping the wave resource

One of the great advantages of the satellite altimeter is that it provides data over the entire globe. This makes it well suited to spatial mapping of oceanographic properties. The use of altimeter data for mapping wave climate in terms of H_s has been demonstrated by numerous authors (e.g., References 79 and 90–93). With the addition of estimates of T_e, altimeter data can also be used to map wave power and WEC yield. Mackay *et al.* [77] showed that altimeter measurements of H_s and T_e can be used to estimate the long-term energy yield of the Pelamis to a reasonable accuracy. Comparisons of individual estimates showed a high level of scatter, but the altimeter was able to correctly reproduce the distribution of power produced by the Pelamis. They demonstrated that by averaging data along sections of the altimeter ground track, it is possible to gauge the spatial variability of the resource in nearshore areas, with a resolution of the order of 10 km. Although measurements along individual tracks are temporally sparse, the long record of altimeter measurements enables the long-term mean power to be estimated reasonably precisely. In this section, we will concentrate on the mapping of wave power rather than the power produced by a specific WEC, but the methodology is essentially the same.

Individual estimates of wave power from altimeter measurements have quite a high level of scatter when compared with estimates from buoy measurements. **Figure 20** shows a scatter plot of altimeter against buoy estimates of power. In this example, wave power has been estimated using the formula for deep water given in eqn [27], and the altimeter measurements have been calibrated using the values given in Section 8.03.4.2.4. The orthogonal regression line shown on the plot has almost a zero intercept and a slope close to unity. The distribution of power is also reproduced correctly, as shown in the quantile plot on the right of **Figure 20**. The slight discrepancies in the quantiles above 250 kW m^{-1} correspond to probabilities exceeding 0.99, for which the uncertainty in a sample of this size (8983 data points) is quite high.

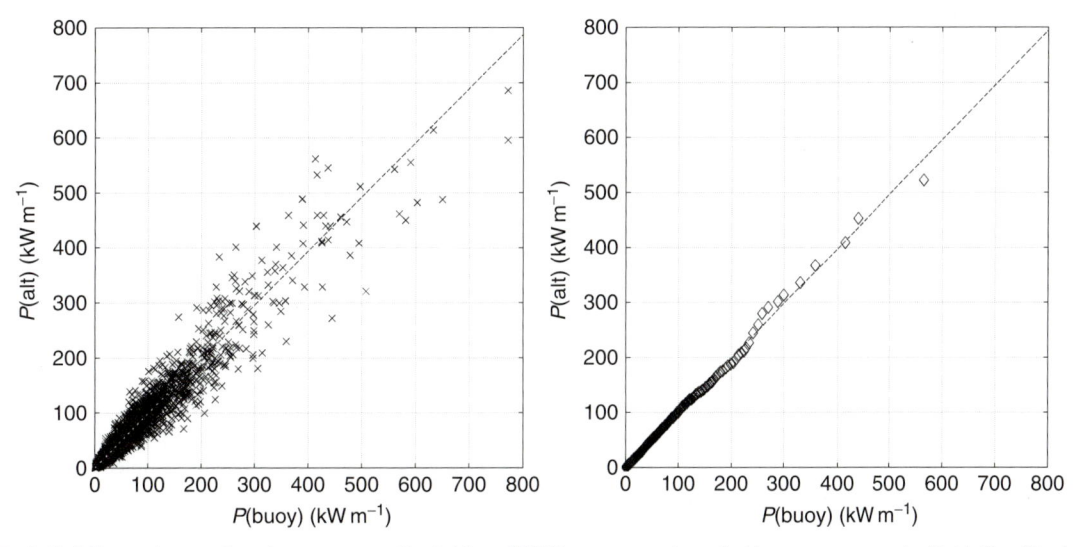

Figure 20 Left: Orthogonal regression of wave power estimated from TOPEX measurements against buoy measurements. Right: Quantile plot.

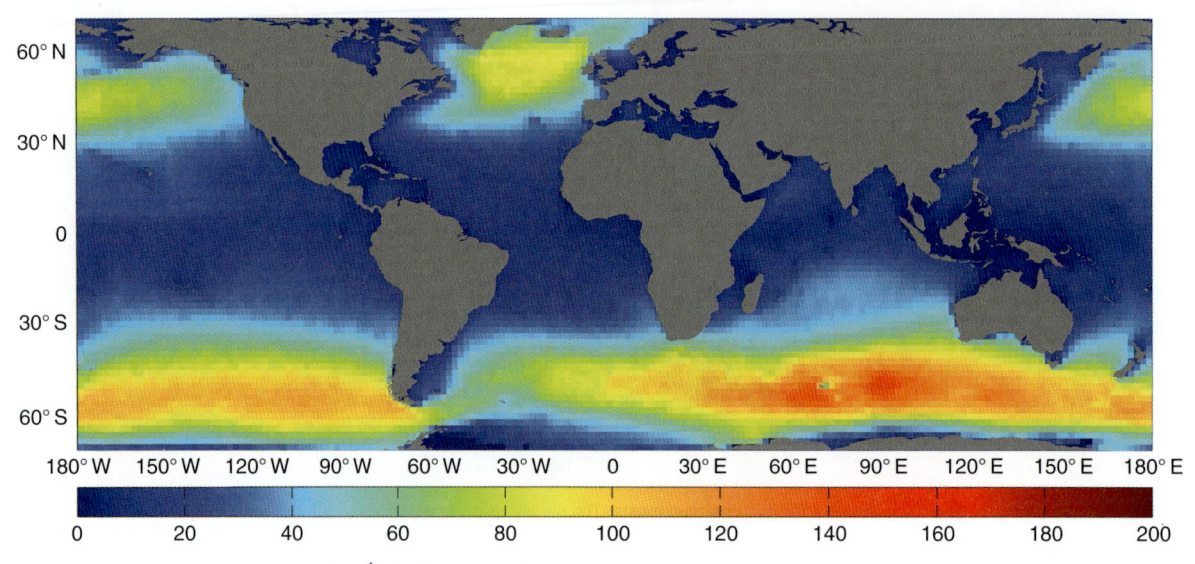

Figure 21 Annual mean wave power (kW m^{-1}) for the period 1996–2007 from combined altimeter measurements.

Global-scale maps of the monthly and annual mean wave power can be created by binning the altimeter measurements in squares of size 2° latitude by 2° longitude.

Cotton and Carter [191] showed that the monthly mean H_s calculated from five or more altimeter transects of a 2° × 2° square compares well with continuous measurements made by a buoy, with an RMS error of around 0.2 m. From 1992 onward, there have been at least two altimeters flying at all times. The sampling rate of a given geographic area depends on the latitude, the number of satellites operating at that time, and the relative phasing of the various satellite orbits. Using the combined data from TOPEX, Poseidon, Jason, ERS-2, ENVISAT, and GFO, a minimum of seven transects per month through each 2° × 2° square on the ocean can be obtained. The mean number of transects per month is 21, with only 1.5% of squares having less than 10 passes per month. Mackay et al. [77] showed that this gave a correlation between altimeter and buoy estimates of monthly mean WEC power greater than 0.95.

Figure 21 shows the annual mean wave power calculated in 2° × 2° squares over a 12-year period from 1996 to 2007. The map has been produced using the method described by Mackay et al. [77]. First, the data are quality controlled and calibrated and the median value of wave power from each altimeter pass over a 2° × 2° square is found. Data from the tandem missions are very close together in time and effectively represent duplicate measurements. From its launch, ENVISAT has been flying along the same ground tracks as ERS-2, leading by about 30 min. Similarly, Jason-1 flew in the same orbit as T/P, leading by 1 min, until TOPEX was maneuvered into its phase B orbit. Therefore, the average of the data from the tandem missions has been used so as not to bias the estimate of the mean values. In the case of TOPEX–Jason tandem mission, some additional information is gained after TOPEX was moved into its phase B orbit when the phase B ground track falls within the square and the phase A track does not.

From **Figure 21**, it is immediately obvious that the most energetic areas are in the Southern Ocean, followed by the North Atlantic and the North Pacific. These areas are situated between latitudes of about 40° and 60° N/S, where low-pressure systems generate large and powerful storms. There is a strong mean westerly flow over these areas, which creates an eastward-propagating wave field, increasing in size toward the east of these ocean basins. This effect is clearly visible in **Figure 21**, where the average wave power increases from the western to the eastern sides of the Pacific and the Atlantic. In the Southern Ocean, in the so-called Roaring Forties, there is little landmass, and consequently, wave fields can build up over large fetches.

Although the annual mean power levels in the North Pacific, North Atlantic, and Southern Ocean are comparable, the seasonal variability in the Northern Hemisphere is much stronger. **Figures 22** and **23** show the mean wave power over the periods December–February and June–August, respectively. In the Northern Hemisphere, during winter, the mean power levels in the central North Pacific and the central North Atlantic are in excess of 150 kW m^{-1} as a result of the large anticyclones that develop. In contrast, in the summer months, the average power levels decrease to less than 25 kW m^{-1} in the central North Pacific and the central North Atlantic. Another striking seasonal feature is the high power levels in the Arabian Sea, caused by the monsoon winds.

Figure 24 shows another measure of seasonality in the resource, calculated as the standard deviation of the climatological monthly mean powers divided by the annual mean power. This map exhibits slightly higher uncertainty than the maps of mean levels, and a certain amount of 'trackiness' is visible. Trackiness refers to the effect of large storms being sampled by some altimeter tracks, but not by adjacent tracks. It results in an unrealistic striped effect, most evident in the South Atlantic and the South Pacific in this figure. Nevertheless, the overall trends are still easily discernable. The Arabian Sea has the highest variability, as a result of the strong monsoon winds. The monsoon winds also cause high variability in the Bay of Bengal and the China Sea. On the whole,

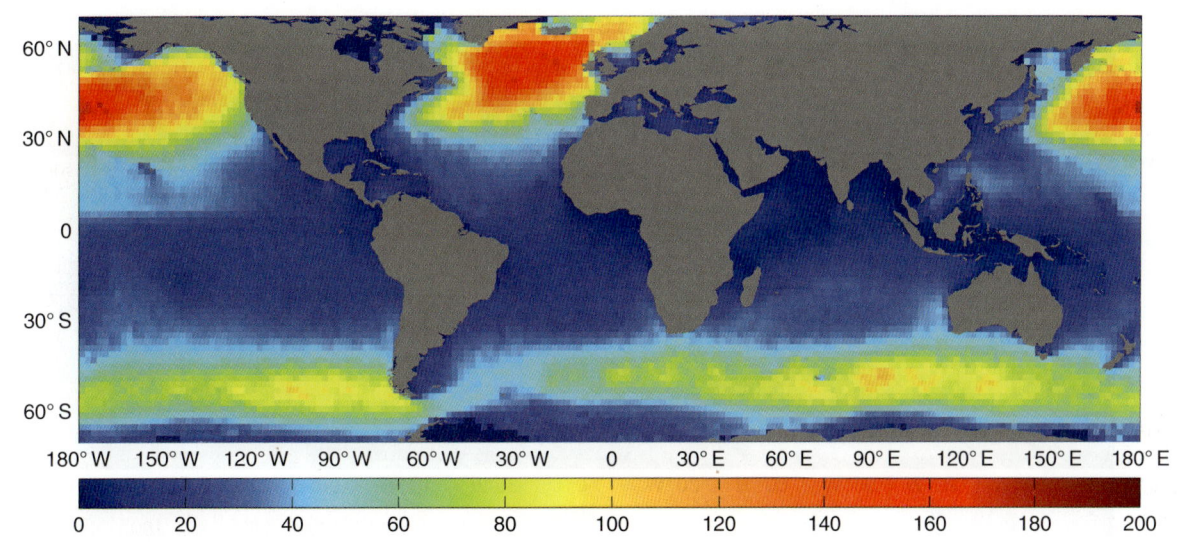

Figure 22 December–February mean wave power (kW m^{-1}) for the period 1996–2007 from combined altimeter measurements.

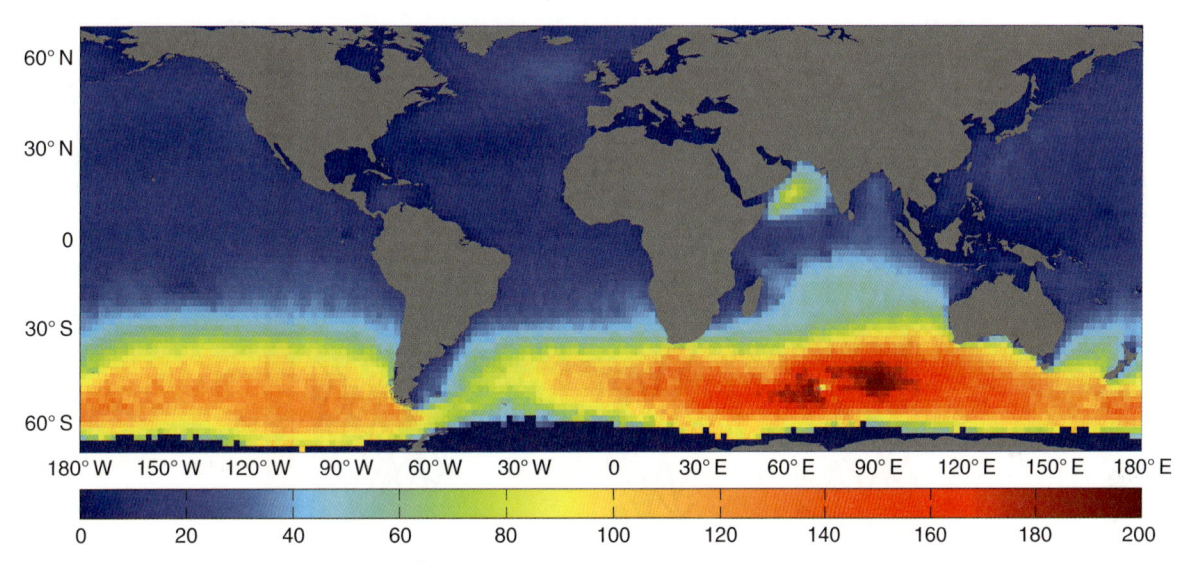

Figure 23 June–August mean wave power (kW m^{-1}) for the period 1996–2007 from combined altimeter measurements.

seasonal variability is much higher in the Northern Hemisphere than in the Southern Hemisphere, with the Southern Ocean showing remarkably little variability.

Of course, at present, it is not feasible to install a wave energy project in the middle of the ocean. However, the resource closer to the coast is dependent on the energy arriving from the open ocean, so understanding the offshore resource is a good way to start when assessing the viability of a potential project.

Maps of the wave climate in 2° × 2° squares are useful for locating areas of interest for wave energy development on large scales. However, in coastal areas, there is considerable spatial variability over smaller scales, so it is beneficial to analyze data along individual satellite passes to give finer resolution. Measurements along individual tracks are sparse, with T/P and Jason on a 10-day repeat orbit, GFO 17 days, and ERS-2 and ENVISAT 35 days, but there are many years of data for each satellite. Mackay et al. [77] showed that this enables the long-term along-track average to be estimated to a reasonable precision, and investigated the effect of sampling rate on accuracy.

Figure 25 shows the annual mean wave power in the vicinity of the United Kingdom and Ireland, calculated from along-track averages of altimeter measurements. The map shows the combined tracks of T/P/Jason-1 (phase A), ERS-2/ENVISAT, and GFO. The data have been quality controlled and missing data have been interpolated for gaps of less than three samples (~20 km). The mean value of wave power is then calculated at intervals along the ground track. Again, data from the tandem missions have been averaged

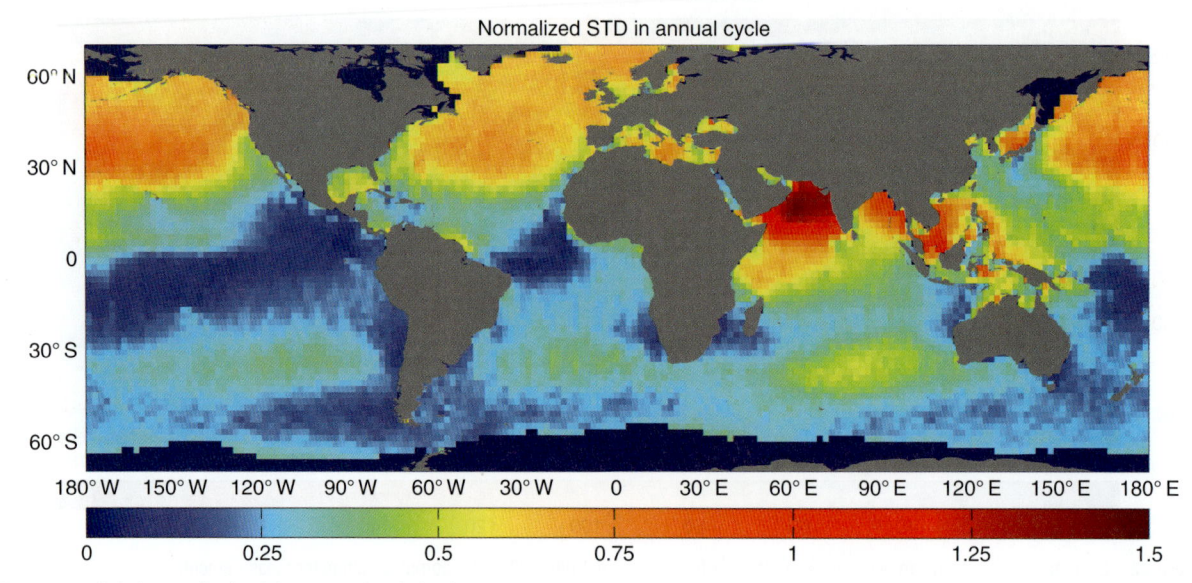

Figure 24 Relative amplitude of the seasonal variation in wave power.

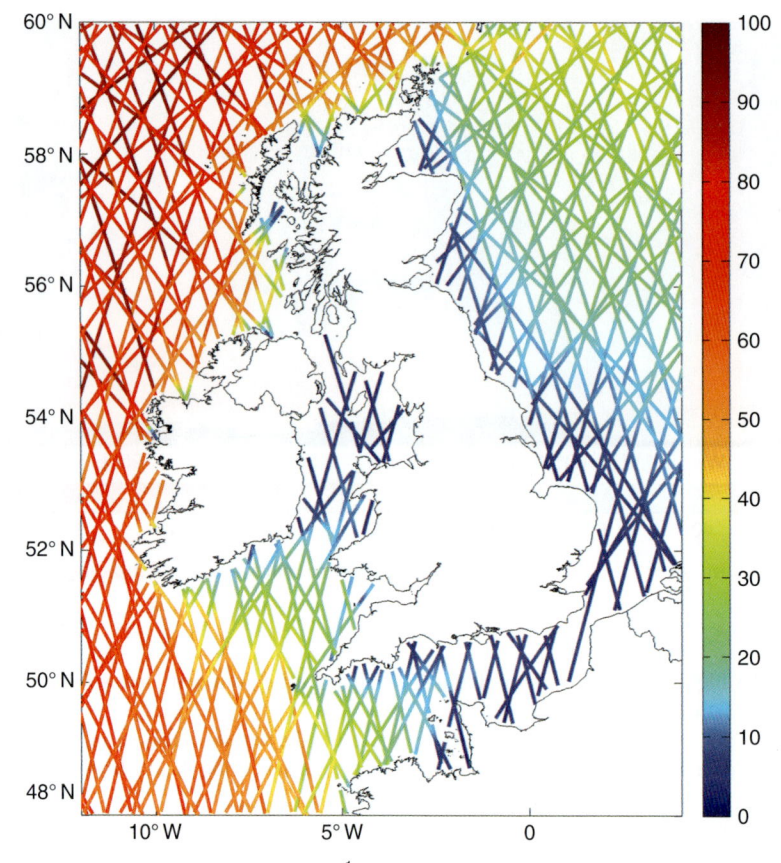

Figure 25 Annual mean wave power per meter crest length (kW m^{-1}) in the vicinity of the United Kingdom and Ireland. From combined TOPEX, Poseidon, Jason-1, ERS-2, ENVISAT, and GFO measurements.

to avoid biasing estimates of the mean values. The uncertainty in the estimates of the annual mean wave power is higher in these maps than in the offshore gridded maps. This is to be expected, since in the case of ERS-2 and ENVISAT, measurements are made only once every 35 days. This can lead to some discrepancies in the estimates of wave power between adjacent tracks and at crossover points if greater or lesser proportions of storms are sampled along one track. The uncertainty in the estimates of along-track power as a function of the sampling period and the level of variability in the sea state is discussed further by Mackay *et al.* [77].

Despite the uncertainty in the estimates of along-track mean power, patterns of the spatial variation in the wave resource on scales finer than 2° are clearly visible from **Figure 25**. The mean wave power levels on the western-facing coasts follow the patterns expected from topographic sheltering from North Atlantic storms. Power levels in the North Sea decrease from north to south as both the water depth and the mean wind speeds decrease.

In the case of the United Kingdom and Ireland, there are existing studies of the wave resource, using data from numerical wave models (e.g., References 94 and 95), so this type of map may be less useful (although the altimeter map does indicate higher power levels to the north of Scotland than in the DTI Atlas). However, in other areas of the world where model data are readily available only at coarse resolution, this type of map can give a useful initial indication of the wave resource on finer scales. Ultimately, the resolution of altimeter maps is limited by the separation between altimeter ground tracks and the inability of satellite altimeters to measure close to land, whereas the accuracy of the maps is limited mainly by the limited temporal sampling. Altimeter maps similar to the one shown in **Figure 25** can be used as a first-pass study, to give an initial estimate of the wave resource and decide if it is worth investing further time and money in a more detailed study to quantify the nearshore resource more accurately.

Apart from their use for producing spatial maps, altimeter data will still play a significant role in wave resource studies in areas that lack long records of *in situ* measurements. As discussed in the next section, wave energy statistics derived from model data can exhibit large biases. Because altimeter measurements are available globally, they can be used to calibrate offshore model data in areas where there are no *in situ* measurements available. The offshore model data can then be used as boundary conditions for a higher resolution nearshore model. However, due to the limited temporal sampling from altimeters and their lack of information on the shape of the wave spectrum, a detailed calibration is not possible using altimeter data.

8.03.4.3 Numerical Wave Models

Estimates of wave conditions produced from numerical wave models are an important complement to *in situ* and remotely sensed observations. The usefulness of *in situ* observations is limited by the sparseness of their deployment and lengths of records available, whereas altimeter observations are limited by spatial and temporal sampling, lack of spectral and directional information, and problems in measuring close to the coast. Model data can be produced with dense resolution in space and time and can provide long records of data for assessing interannual and climatic variability.

Essentially, there are two approaches used to model the evolution of waves over water: phase-resolving and phase-averaged (spectral) models. Phase-resolving models include those that solve the mild-slope equations for linear waves over slowly varying seabed and Boussinesq models for weakly nonlinear waves (see, e.g., Reference 96). In a phase-resolving model, the surface elevation is explicitly computed over a finite domain. Due to the large computational requirements needed to do this, they are more suited to coastal applications. In a phase-averaged model, the evolution of the sea surface is calculated only in a statistical sense, in the form of the wave spectrum. Spectral wave models can be implemented on multiple scales from oceanic down to small coastal domains and are widely used to generate data used in wave energy studies. For the remainder of this section, only spectral wave models will be considered.

The main focus of this section is on the use of data from spectral wave models, rather than an in-depth description of how spectral wave models work. We start by giving a brief introduction to spectral wave models and briefly discuss the factors that can affect the accuracy of their predictions. We then give a qualitative description of the error structure of model data. Understanding the errors in model data is vital for the calculation of uncertainty of derived wave energy statistics, and as will be shown, the description of model errors is a nontrivial problem.

8.03.4.3.1 Brief introduction to spectral wave models

Wave models attempt to replicate the growth, propagation, and decay of ocean waves based on the winds over the area in question. The fundamental concept underpinning spectral wave modeling is the energy balance equation. This states that the evolution of the wave spectrum is the sum of three source terms describing the input of energy from the wind, the nonlinear transfer of energy within the spectrum, and the dissipation of energy from breaking or shallow water processes. It can be written as

$$\frac{dE(f,\theta)}{dt} = S_{in} + S_{nl} + S_{ds} \quad [101]$$

where $E(f, \theta)$ is the wave variance spectrum, S_{in} is the wind input, S_{nl} are nonlinear interactions, and S_{ds} is the dissipation source term. In slowly varying conditions such as nonsteady currents or water depth, wave action density (defined as the variance spectrum divided by the intrinsic angular frequency – the frequency measured in a frame of reference moving with the current) is conserved rather than wave energy. When eqn [101] is rewritten in terms of wave action, it is known as the action balance equation. A detailed derivation of the energy and action balance equations is given by Komen *et al.* [97].

In the first generation of wave models, nonlinear interactions were not computed. The second generation of wave models resulted from a better understanding of energy transfer processes, but due to limitations in computer power at that time, nonlinear interactions were computed in a simple parameterized form. The third generation of wave models, used at present, computes an explicit representation of all three source terms and the step-by-step evolution of the wave spectrum, without *a priori* assumptions about the spectral shape.

There are currently two third-generation wave models run operationally at meteorological agencies for global domains: the WAM model [97, 98] and the WaveWatch III (WW3) model [99]. As well as using information on the wind field, wave observations from *in situ* measurements, satellite altimeters, and SAR can be routinely assimilated into both analyzed and hindcast wave fields (see, e.g., References 100 and 101). Model runs with assimilated data have been shown to significantly reduce errors in modeled wave parameters.

For coastal waters, different physical processes become significant compared with deep water, and it is usually necessary to run a dedicated shallow water model. Depth-induced refraction and shoaling of waves can be computed using linear ray-tracing models, but certain nonlinear processes also become important as waves move into shallower water. In deep water, quadruplet wave–wave interactions are the dominant type of nonlinear interaction, whereas in very shallow water (just outside the surf zone), triad interactions also become important. Quadruplet interactions are largely responsible for the progressive shift of energy to lower frequencies with fetch and for the characteristic decay of the HF spectral tail [3]. Triad interactions give rise to bound harmonics of wave components, which cause waves to have sharper peaks and shallower troughs and spectra to exhibit higher harmonics of the spectral peak [102]. Dissipation processes also change as waves propagate into shallower water. In deep water, the primary source of energy dissipation is whitecapping, whereas in shallow water, depth-induced breaking and bottom friction become significant as well. Wave–current interactions also become increasingly important as waves propagate into shallower water. An excellent introduction to all these shallow water processes is presented by Holthuijsen [4]. At present, the most commonly used shallow water spectral models are the open-source models SWAN [4, 103] and TOMAWAC [104] and the commercial code MIKE21 [105].

8.03.4.3.2 Sources of error in wave models

An in-depth review of the present state of the art and limiting factors in the physics and numerics of wave modeling is made by Cavaleri *et al.* [106]. In the following, we give a brief overview of error sources in the modeled data.

8.03.4.3.2(i) Input data

The error sources in the estimates produced by wave models can be viewed as either internal or external to the model. The internal sources of error are the formulation of source terms or 'model physics' and the numerical scheme, whereas external errors refer to errors in the input data, primarily in the wind field. In validation studies, it is common practice to assess the quality of the wind input at the same time as the wave estimates, in order to estimate the relative importance of internal and external errors. However, in general, it is not straightforward to separate internal from external errors. Janssen [107] has presented a simple model for the error in H_s resulting from wind speed errors, and has shown that they are proportional to the square of the error in wind speed. Rogers *et al.* [108] have shown that in contrast to previous studies, the errors in the wind fields used at the Fleet Numerical Meteorology and Oceanography Center (FNMOC) are no longer the dominant source of errors in wave estimates from WW3. However, this is not to say that the quality of the wind forcing is no longer important for accuracy. Recently, Feng *et al.* [109] have tested the sensitivity of WW3 to four different wind input fields and have shown that the accuracy is critically sensitive to the choice of the wind field product. Other input fields such as currents, bathymetry, or bottom conditions are less important in the open ocean but become significant in shallower coastal waters.

8.03.4.3.2(ii) Numerics

Describing a continuous physical process such as wave growth, propagation, and dissipation with a discrete model can lead to significant errors. The resolution of the geographic grid, the time step for integration, and the spectral resolution (number of frequency and direction bins) all affect accuracy. The propagation of swell on a grid with discrete directional resolution can lead to the disintegration of a continuous swell field into discrete packets. This is known as the 'garden sprinkler effect' and is discussed by Tolman [110]. The accuracy of swell propagation is also affected by blockage by small islands and ice, which are not resolved in the spatial grid [111, 112]. Furthermore, coarse geographic and temporal resolution can also lead to small intense systems being subject to some smoothing, resulting in systematic underestimation of peak wind speeds and hence peak wave heights [113].

8.03.4.3.2(iii) Model physics

There remain many open questions about the formulation of source terms in spectral wave models. Among the most important ones are the methods used to estimate nonlinear interactions, spectral dissipation in deep water, and air–sea momentum transfer at high wind speeds. At high wind speeds, many of the assumptions about the processes involved are stretched to their limit. Moreover, observations of wave growth in extreme conditions are, by their nature, limited. Rogers *et al.* [108] stress that

> given the necessary reliance on approximations in today's state-of-the-art wave models, it may be especially difficult for these models to have 'universal' tuning. In particular, tuning for applications at one scale may inevitably degrade performance at another scale. For example, tuning to short-fetch empirical growth curves probably will not produce a skilful global model.

There is also some growing concern in the wave modeling community that there may be an intrinsic limit to the accuracy achievable from the spectral approach [114, 115]. Liu *et al.* [115] show that even when working with accurate, carefully evaluated wind fields, wave model outputs show a scatter not justified by the known uncertainties in the input information. Nevertheless, some improvements in model accuracy can be expected in the future from improvements in both model physics and numerics.

8.03.4.3.3 Qualitative description of model errors

The performance of models in terms of integral parameters such as H_s and T_e is, on the whole, fairly good. However, Cavaleri [114] notes that the comparison between modeled and measured spectra is often unsatisfactory, not only in the details but sometimes also in the general structure. In this study, we will only consider the accuracy of integral parameters.

As noted before, modeled wave spectra can be considered as an estimate of the average conditions over the grid spacing and time step used in the model. Typically, global- or oceanic-scale wave models will be run with a grid spacing somewhere between 0.5° and 3° (about 50–300 km) with a time step of 3 or 6 h. Measured data are usually obtained over a smaller scale, with buoys representing a point average over time (between 20 min and 1 h) and altimeter data representing an instantaneous spatial average over an area 5–10 km in diameter. The spatial and temporal variability of wave conditions will therefore result in differences between measurements and modeled data. These differences are sometimes referred to as 'representativeness errors' and the error is assigned to the measured data [85].

The errors in modeled parameters exhibit short-term temporal correlation. That is, an overestimate or underestimate in H_s or other parameters will typically persist for a number of hours. For instance, models will tend to overpredict or underpredict the intensity of an entire storm, which leads to correlation of errors for up to a few days.

Additionally, errors in different parameters can be correlated. At high sea states, since wave spectra tend toward standard type forms, an overestimate in the model H_s will result in an overestimate of the period as well. This correlation of errors in different parameters means that one needs to be careful when calibrating model data, since adjusting model parameters independently may lead to changes in the shape of their joint distribution.

Errors in modeled parameters can be thought of as having a mean or bias and also a random component. Both the mean and bias components will have a complex dependence on the actual wave conditions. For instance, the bias of a model estimate of H_s may have a dependence on the actual H_s, period, spectral shape, swell age, and so on. Moreover, it has been shown by numerous authors that biases change with both location and time. This is due to the way in which errors occur in models and their propagation through the model domain.

Janssen [116] presents a particularly clear illustration of the nonstationary biases in the European Centre for Medium-Range Weather Forecasts (ECMWF) WAM model spectra. A plot of the bias in spectral energy binned by frequency shows that the model tends to overpredict energy at lower frequencies in the (Northern Hemisphere) summer and much less in the winter time. Moreover, the magnitude of this bias and its dependence on both frequency and time of year change from year to year. He notes that the main reasons for the changing biases are that large swells generated in the Southern Ocean in the Southern Hemisphere winter time are not well modeled due to unresolved islands and atolls (mainly in the Pacific) and the formulation of the dissipation source term.

This goes to show that it is difficult to define and adjust for a 'mean error component' since varying conditions lead to varying amounts of internal and external errors occurring and aggregating over the model domain. Therefore, errors in wind seas and young swells can be expected to have different characteristics to older swells that have propagated further, increasing uncertainties.

A further reason for nonstationary biases in model data is changes made to the models themselves. This is more of an issue for archived data from operational models than for hindcasts. However, despite the fact that hindcasts are run with a constant model setup, the quality of the input wind fields and assimilated wave data may be varying.

Finally, we note that modeled data may be subject to temporal offsets, with the model predicting that a storm arrives slightly earlier or later than it actually does. This type of error is sometimes referred to as a 'jitter error'. Jitter errors are not so important when calculating long-term mean statistics from modeled data, but are important for validation purposes when concurrent modeled and measured data are compared.

To summarize, the main features of the errors in model data are as follows:

- The bias and variance of modeled parameters may depend on multiple factors such as H_s, T_e, and swell age.
- The bias and variance of modeled parameters may be nonstationary with both time and location.
- Errors in parameters will exhibit short-term autocorrelation.
- There may also be correlation of errors between parameters; for example, errors in H_s and T_e may be correlated.
- There may be temporal offsets or jitter errors in modeled parameters.

8.03.4.3.4 Calibration of model data against in situ measurements

8.03.4.3.4(i) Techniques for estimating errors and trends

Model errors are usually estimated by comparing collocated modeled and measured parameters. Calibration against altimeter data is appropriate for offshore locations, where the limited spatial sampling of the altimeter is not a problem. However, closer to the coast where wave conditions change more rapidly and the present generation of altimeters has problems in measuring, it is necessary to calibrate models against *in situ* measurements (although future satellite altimeters may be able to measure much closer to the coast). There is a large volume of literature on model validation studies. Some examples of techniques that have been proposed to estimate errors in the model data are listed below.

If there is reason to believe that the model bias may be a linear function of a model parameter, then linear regression can be used (e.g., References 99 and 117). To test for nonlinearities, the bias and standard deviation can be estimated as a function of integrated parameters such as H_s and T_p or for discrete frequency bands (e.g., References 108 and 116). This is known as a bin-average analysis.

If three or more concurrent data sets are available, then a multiple collocation technique can be used to explicitly calculate the bias relative to one data set and the error variance of each data set (e.g., References 82 and 85). Another approach is to compare the distribution functions of modeled and measured parameters via quantile–quantile plots (e.g., Reference 118). Using distribution functions has the advantage that the effects of random errors and temporal offsets (jitter errors) are smoothed out.

8.03.4.3.4(ii) A note on the interpretation of results

In model validation studies, the objective is usually to determine the model response for a given sea state. For the purposes of estimating WEC yield, we would like to know what the actual sea state is for a given modeled estimate. These two problems are subtly different. It may seem logical to determine the mean value reported by a buoy for a given model estimate, since this is what we want to know. However, this method will lead to a calibration that is dependent on the distribution of the parameter of interest during the calibration period. Consider a comparison of H_s from an idealized model with a buoy. Suppose that the model has normally distributed errors with zero mean and a standard deviation of $0.2 + 0.1 H_s$. We assume that sampling errors in the buoy data are minimal (a reasonable assumption for 3 or 6 h averages) and simulate buoy and model data for theoretical summer and winter distributions of H_s. The distribution in both summer and winter is assumed to be lognormal with a mean of 1.5 m in summer and 3.0 m in winter and a variance of $0.7\,\text{m}^2$ in summer and $2.0\,\text{m}^2$ in winter. The distributions are shown in **Figure 26**.

We compare the model and buoy data in three different ways. First, we calculate the mean model H_s binned by buoy H_s; second, we calculate the mean buoy H_s binned by model H_s; and third, we compare quantiles of equal probability. **Figure 27** shows these

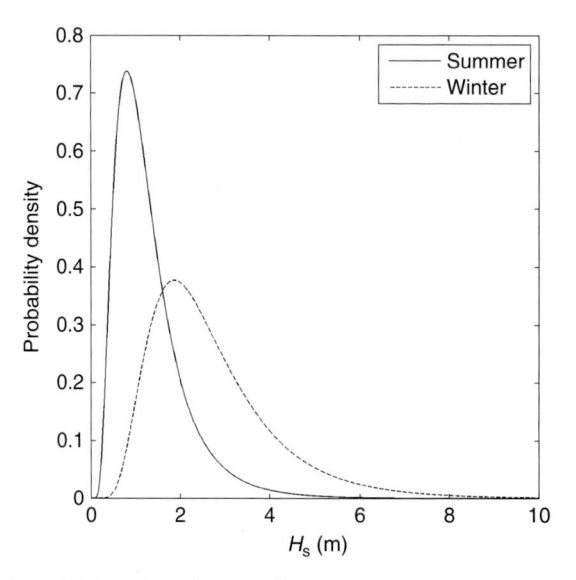

Figure 26 Summer and winter distributions of H_s for a theoretical example.

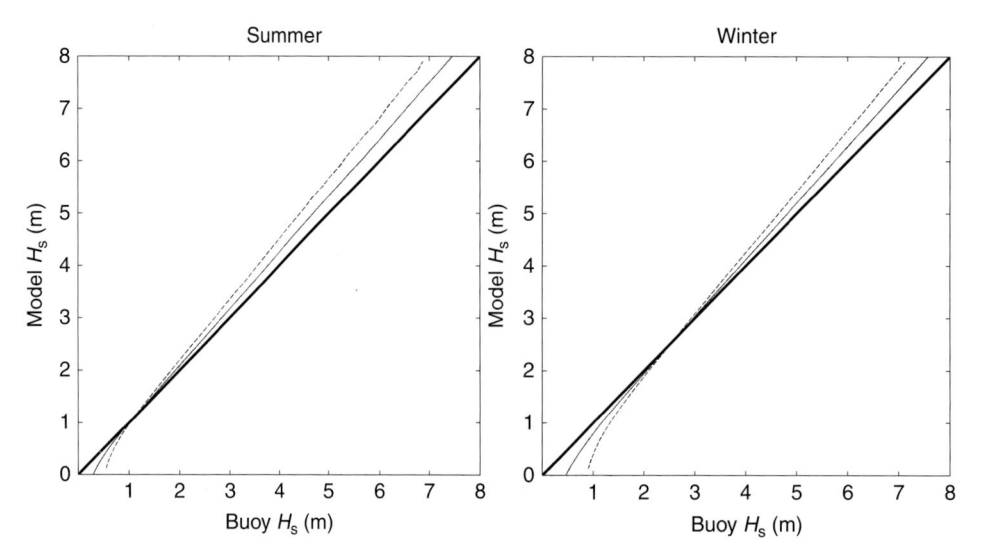

Figure 27 Comparison of calibrations for distributions of H_s shown in **Figure 26**. Bold line, mean model binned by buoy H_s; dashed line, mean buoy H_s binned by model H_s; thin line, quantile–quantile plot.

three comparisons for both the summer and the winter data. Since the errors in our idealized model have zero mean, the mean value of model H_s binned by buoy H_s is equal to the buoy H_s (assuming that we use sufficiently small bins) and the line is straight. However, it can be seen that the mean value of the buoy H_s for a given model value differs from summer to winter, with a larger bias for low H_s in winter and the location at which the lines cross differing in summer and winter. Similarly, the shape of the quantile plots is also dependent on the distribution of buoy H_s. This is because the distribution of the model H_s is a convolution of the model error distribution with the true distribution of H_s. So, despite the fact that we have considered an unbiased model with constant calibration, this example demonstrates that it can appear to change the calibration throughout the year. An in-depth investigation of this effect is presented by Tolman [88].

8.03.4.3.4(iii) The calibration problem

A further problem arises when a calibration is applied to the model data. Again, we can consider a simple hypothetical situation to illustrate the problem. Suppose we have a modeled estimate X_m of a real variable X and that

$$X_m = X + \varepsilon \qquad [102]$$

and

$$\varepsilon \sim N(\mu(X), \sigma(X)) \qquad [103]$$

where ε is a normally distributed error, whose mean and variance are dependent on X. Suppose that $\mu(X)$ and $\sigma(X)$ are stationary in time and can be determined from a bin-average analysis. In this case, a functional relationship, g, can be defined between the real and modeled values:

$$\begin{aligned} X_m &= X + \mu(X) + \delta \\ &= g(X) + \delta \end{aligned} \qquad [104]$$

where

$$g(X) = X + \mu(X) \qquad [105]$$

and

$$\delta \sim N(0, \sigma(X)) \qquad [106]$$

We then calibrate the model by applying the inverse function:

$$\begin{aligned} Y &= g^{-1}(X_m) \\ &= g^{-1}(g(X) + \delta) \end{aligned} \qquad [107]$$

where Y denotes the calibrated model values. We need to determine whether the mean of the calibrated model, Y, is equal to the mean of the real variable X. In the case that g is a linear function, $g = aX + b$, we have $Y = X + \delta/a$. So the mean of X is equal to the mean of Y, since δ has zero mean. However, if g is nonlinear, then the situation is more complicated. For instance, if g is a quadratic function, then it is simple to demonstrate that the mean value of Y is not necessarily equal to the mean of X, the difference being dependent on both the distribution of X and the error distribution.

If instead we calibrate the model using the mean value of X for a given X_m, then by definition the mean values of X and Y will be equal within the calibration data set. However, we are left with the problem that the mean value of X for a given X_m is dependent on the distribution of X, so if the distribution of X changes outside the calibration period, then the mean values of X and Y will not be equal. The differences in the mean value of X and Y introduced by calibrating using a nonlinear function g are normally quite small. Moreover, in practice, the model performance is dependent on multiple parameters, so these arguments become somewhat academic. Nevertheless, they illustrate that some care needs to be taken when determining and applying a calibration to a model.

8.03.4.3.4(iv) Calibration of estimates of WEC power from model data

A number of approaches could be taken to calibrate estimates of WEC power from model data. The pros and cons of various approaches are listed below.

8.03.4.3.4(iv)(a) Method A Estimates of WEC power from measured and modeled data are compared directly. This approach has the advantage that only one variable is involved. However, the calibration will be dependent on the joint distribution of H_s and T_e (and any other parameters that effect power capture) during the calibration period. For example, the power response of a WEC will reach a maximum at some given H_s; hence, if the proportion of time that the WEC is operating at maximum power is different outside the calibration period, then a calibration based on model power alone may not be appropriate.

8.03.4.3.4(iv)(b) Method B This method is used to define a look-up table of the value of WEC power estimated from the buoy binned by model H_s and T_e. This would be a more flexible approach than calibrating by power alone, but suffers from the problems of estimating the mean buoy value for a given model value described in Section 8.03.4.3.4(ii).

8.03.4.3.4(iv)(c) Method C This method is used to calibrate the model H_s and T_e independently using a bin-average method (binned by buoy values). This method is still susceptible to problems when applying nonlinear calibrations, as described above, but these effects are relatively small. The other point to be aware of is that errors in H_s and T_e may be correlated, so adjusting parameters independently may change the shape of their joint distribution and hence the estimated WEC power.

8.03.4.3.5 Uncertainties in WEC power estimated from model data

Mackay et al. [119] investigated the uncertainty in monthly, annual, and long-term mean power produced by the Pelamis, estimated from calibrated model data. They compared measurements from two hindcasts for the EMEC test center in Orkney with buoy measurements made on-site. One hindcast was produced using SWAN, with boundary conditions from an archive of operational data from the ECMWF WAM model, and the other was produced using a nearshore model that accounted for refraction, shoaling, and depth-induced breaking only, with boundary conditions obtained from a hindcast using WW3.

The third method described above (method C) was used to calibrate the models. Both models exhibited all the error characteristics summarized in Section 8.03.4.3.3, with seasonal changes in biases particularly evident in the WAM–SWAN hindcast. Model estimates of H_s were calibrated using a quadratic relationship, derived from a bin-average analysis, and a linear correction was applied to model T_e. The power produced by the Pelamis was estimated using the power matrix shown in **Table 3**, using both the calibrated and uncalibrated model data. Before calibration, estimates of the long-term mean power produced by the Pelamis from the two hindcasts differed by 20%, with the difference reduced to 5% after calibration.

Uncertainties in mean power from the calibrated models were estimated by simulating the temporal evolution of the error (relative to the buoy estimates) using an autoregressive moving average (ARMA) time series model. The ARMA simulations of the model error agreed with the observed errors for the WW3 hindcast, but underestimated the errors observed in the WAM–SWAN hindcast. The underestimation was due to the seasonal and interannual changes in the WAM–SWAN model bias, which it was not able to reproduce using a low-order ARMA model. In this exercise for the EMEC site, there were 2 years of buoy data concurrent with the hindcasts. Even using this relatively long calibration data set, it was not possible to properly account for variations in model performance throughout the year. This goes to show that it is imperative to source the highest quality model data for use in wave energy studies, in order to minimize biases that cannot be removed using simple calibration procedures.

Calibrating wave model data is a pragmatic solution to wave resource assessment using data that are currently available. The calibrations are difficult to justify from a physical point of view, but given the level of empiricism already present in the model setup, a further empirical calibration is not completely unreasonable. Improving the performance of the input wave models would be preferable to calibrating the outputs, but this is a much larger task. The wave modeling community continually improves the performance of their models (see, e.g., Reference 116), so some improvements can be expected in the future.

In Section 8.03.5, we discuss how the interannual and climatic variability in wave conditions affects the predictability of WEC yield and how this compares with the uncertainty in the historic data. It is shown that uncertainty resulting from variability in the resource is of a similar magnitude to uncertainty in the historic data. Therefore, improvements in the accuracy of the historic data will result in improvements in the accuracy of the predicted energy yield.

8.03.5 Variability and Predictability of WEC Yield

The factors that limit the accuracy of predictions of the energy yield from a wave farm can be split into three categories:

1. Uncertainty in future wave conditions
2. Uncertainty in conversion from wave energy to electrical energy
3. Uncertainty in the availability of machines

This section focuses on the uncertainty in future wave conditions, but it is worth making some notes on the other sources of uncertainty as well. The uncertainties that arise from parameterizing the WEC response in terms of H_s and T_e were discussed in Section 8.03.3, and a method to incorporate this into estimates of the long-term energy yield was proposed by Mackay et al. [119]. Interactions between WECs within arrays will cause differences in the power absorbed compared with an isolated device. This introduces a further level of uncertainty into the conversion from wave energy to electrical energy. There has been a considerable amount of work on the theoretical aspects of WEC interaction effects (see Reference 120 for a brief overview), but the use of spectral wave models has also been proposed to examine array effects (see, e.g., Reference 121). There is currently wide interest in modeling energy losses within arrays (e.g., the Energy Technologies Institute (ETI)-funded PerAWaT project), and a better understanding of these effects can be expected in the next few years.

The third category of uncertainty mentioned above is perhaps the most difficult to quantify. Mechanical failures are inherently unpredictable in a new technology. As operational experience is gained, maintenance requirements will be better understood and it will be possible to estimate the availability of machines. At present, it is difficult to put a realistic figure on this type of uncertainty.

Estimates of future wave conditions are based on historic conditions. The accuracy is limited by the accuracy of the historic data and the variability in the resource. The accuracy of the estimates of historic energy yield from wave model data was discussed in Section 8.03.4.3.5 (and in more detail by Mackay et al. [119]). In this section, we consider the effect that variability in the resource has on the accuracy of predictions of future energy yield. The wave resource is variable on multiple scales relevant to wave energy production: wave-to-wave (sampling variability), synoptic (weather systems), seasonal, interannual, and climatic. This variability imposes limitations on the accuracy to which the future resource can be predicted over a given timescale. For instance, the mean power produced by a WEC over a given month will vary from year to year. Similarly, the annual mean power varies between years. Moreover, it is well documented that the wave climate exhibits variability on decadal scales (see Reference 122 and references therein). Such changes in wave climate can have a significant impact on the estimation of energy yield of a potential wave farm that is based on historic data and assumes that long-term climatic mean levels are stationary. To assess the impact that variability in the wave climate can have on WEC yield, we shall consider the effects on the representative scales of variability listed above.

8.03.5.1 Sampling Variability

The shortest scale of variability in wave conditions is sampling variability. The effect of this on the performance assessment of WECs is given in Section 8.03.4.1.4(iii). In this section, we will consider the effect of sampling variability on the accuracy of monthly mean WEC power. Suppose we have a long record of accurate *in situ* measurements, say from a buoy, for a potential site of a wave farm. If a WEC had been placed close to the buoy, but not in the exact location, sampling variability will cause the power generated by the WEC to differ from that estimated from the buoy, even if we knew the exact response of a WEC to that sea state. In Section 8.03.4.1.4(iii), it was shown that the sampling variability in estimates of WEC power averaged over 1 h is considerable. However, we would expect the differences to average out over a period of about a month.

Mackay [123] simulated sampling errors for a 10-year hindcast in order to investigate the distribution of errors in monthly mean power. Sampling errors were estimated in a similar manner to that described in Section 8.03.4.1.4(iii) and were shown to be well described by a Student's t-distribution with shape parameter (degrees of freedom) $\nu = 3.855$ and a scale parameter dependent on H_s and T_e. It was shown that the standard deviation of the error in the estimated monthly mean WEC power was between 0.5% and 1%. This is an order of magnitude lower than the accuracy that is currently achievable from modeled data and demonstrates that for the purposes of long-term yield estimates, sampling variability can be neglected.

8.03.5.2 Synoptic and Seasonal Variability

Synoptic variability refers to the short-term variations in sea state caused by weather systems, on the scale of a few hours to several days. The intensity of these weather systems varies throughout the year, and most stochastic models for synoptic variability in sea state parameters include terms to model seasonal variability as well. Modeling synoptic and seasonal variability in wave conditions and WEC power production is important for the integration of wave energy into the electrical grid. It is also necessary for planning operations and maintenance schedules.

There is a considerable amount of literature on stochastic modeling of synoptic variability in sea state parameters. A recent review is presented by Monbet *et al.* [124]. A common approach is to assume that the process under consideration, $\{X(t)\}$, admits the representation $X(t) = \mu(t) + \sigma(t)W(t)$, where $\mu(t)$ and $\sigma(t)$ are deterministic time-dependent periodic functions, with a period of 1 year, representing the seasonal mean and standard deviation of the process, respectively, and $\{W(t)\}$ is a zero-mean stationary stochastic process, referred to as the residual stochastic process (e.g., Reference 125). The residual process $\{W(t)\}$ can then be modeled using conventional techniques such as ARMA models [126, 127], resampling methods [128], or artificial neural networks [129, 130].

8.03.5.3 Interannual and Climatic Variability

Interannual variability refers to the changes in monthly or annual mean values from year to year. Much of the interannual variability can be explained by purely random fluctuations caused by synoptic variability (sometimes called 'climate noise' in this context), but there is evidence that longer-term climatic changes cause interannual variability that is greater than that which would be expected as a result of synoptic variability alone. In this section, we use the term 'climatic variability' to refer to changes in multiyear average values. When modeling climatic variability, two challenges need to be addressed. The first is to establish a model for the 'natural' climatic variability in wave conditions. The second is to estimate what effect forcing on the climate system from anthropogenic emissions of greenhouse gases (GHGs) may have on wave climate and hence WEC yield.

It remains uncertain whether the observed changes in wave and storm climates in the latter part of the twentieth century are part of natural long slow variations or a result of anthropogenic forcing on the climate system (see Reference 122 for a review of studies on anthropogenic influence on the wave climate). The consensus at the moment is that there is likely to be an increase in storm frequency and intensity with GHG emissions, with a slight poleward shift in storm tracks. This will lead to an increase in wave energy at higher latitudes. However, the magnitude and speed of this change is very difficult to predict with the current generation of climate models. Mackay *et al.* [122] used the relationship between the North Atlantic Oscillation (NAO) and the wave climate, demonstrated by Woolf *et al.* [131], in order to investigate the impact of climate change on WEC yield for a site in the north of Scotland. Projections of the behavior of the NAO under climate change scenarios are highly uncertain at present, but even using the highest projected changes, Mackay *et al.* [122] demonstrated that any changes in wave climate resulting from climate change are likely to be undetectable over the lifetime of a wave energy project (~20 years) relative to the natural climatic variability. This is not to say that climatic variability is negligible, rather that the natural component of the climate variability is dominant over the timescales relevant to planning and operating a wave energy project.

Mackay et al. [122] noted that the 20-year mean power level could change by around ±10% between consecutive 20-year periods. This is about 3 times higher than would be expected if the annual power anomalies were uncorrelated noise (i.e., the result of synoptic variability only). In relation to a 10% uncertainty in the predicted mean power over a 20-year period resulting from variability in the resource, a 5% uncertainty in the historic data is still significant. Whether it is worth investing further time and money to improve estimates of the historic resource will depend on the sensitivity of the economics of a wave farm project to uncertainty in the predicted yield.

8.03.6 Estimation of Extremes

8.03.6.1 Introduction

In severe storms, the forces exerted by ocean waves can be enormous. WECs must be designed to utilize the available power from the waves under normal operating conditions while withstanding the forces in the most severe storms. Generally speaking, the larger the forces that a WEC must be designed to cope with, the more expensive it will be. Therefore, machines are designed to survive the most extreme conditions expected in their lifetime, but no more than this.

The problem of estimating extreme wave conditions can be split into three stages. The first stage is to establish a model for the distribution of wave heights for a given sea state, sometimes referred to as the short-term distribution. The second stage is to estimate the long-term distribution of sea states. Finally, the long-term and short-term distributions are combined in order to estimate the distribution of the maximum wave anticipated in the lifetime of the WEC.

The estimation of extreme wave conditions is a large and ongoing area of research. This section is intended to give an overview of the main results and an outline of the methods used to predict extremes.

8.03.6.2 Short-Term Distributions of Wave and Crest Heights

The appropriate measure of the size of a wave for design considerations will differ depending on the type of wave energy device. For floating devices, the maximum crest-to-trough wave height may be more important than the maximum crest height. For fixed offshore structures, the maximum crest elevation above the mean water level may be more important. Under the assumption that the wave amplitude is low in comparison with the wavelength and water depth, the sea surface can be assumed to be a linear superposition of sinusoidal waves and the crest height is simply half the wave height. In extreme sea states, the amplitude of the waves can no longer be considered negligible and nonlinear effects must be taken into account. Nonlinearities cause the surface elevation to become skewed, with wave crests being higher and sharper than in the linear approximation and troughs being flatter and wider. Therefore, wave and crest height distributions need to be considered separately.

8.03.6.2.1 The short-term distribution of crest-to-trough wave heights

Wave heights are commonly modeled as following a Rayleigh distribution. This was first proposed by Longuet-Higgins [132], who demonstrated that in the case of linear waves with a narrow-band frequency spectrum, wave heights are Rayleigh distributed. Both Tayfun [133] and Longuet-Higgins [134] have shown that second-order nonlinear effects do not change the wave height distribution, since both the crest and the trough are elevated from the mean water level by the same amount on average. Higher-order nonlinearities can increase the distribution of wave heights in some cases of steep, long-crested waves. However, ocean waves are typically short-crested (i.e., they exhibit directional spreading) in storms, which tends to reduce the effects of higher-order nonlinearities (see, e.g., References 135 and 136), and linear models are capable of explaining wave height distributions observed in the ocean. Both Forristall [137] and Tayfun and Fedele [138] have noted that an unusually large or 'freak' wave in a short record that does not seem to follow an established probability law can usually be explained as a relatively rare occurrence in a longer record.

Finite bandwidth affects the distribution slightly and serves to reduce the heights of the highest waves compared with the narrow-band approximation. Various distributions have been proposed that account for finite bandwidth effects. A recent review is presented by Tayfun and Fedele [138]. They compare several theoretical distributions with both simulated and observed data and show that a Rayleigh distribution that includes a bandwidth parameter is capable of accurately modeling the highest waves. This distribution can be written as follows: if we denote the crest-to-trough wave height as H, then the probability that a wave height is less than a given value h is

$$\Pr\{H \leq h\} = 1 - \exp\left[-\frac{4}{1+\psi}\left(\frac{h}{H_s}\right)^2\right] \qquad [108]$$

A commonly used definition of the parameter ψ, originally proposed by Boccotti [139], is the absolute value of the first minimum of the autocorrelation function of the surface elevation. However, Tayfun and Fedele [138] show that this definition slightly underestimates the wave heights at low probability levels, and that it is more appropriate to define it as the value of the envelope of the autocorrelation function at time $T_m/2$ (where $T_m = m_0/m_1$ as in Section 8.03.2). The autocorrelation function, ρ, and its upper (+) and lower (−) envelopes, ±r, are given by

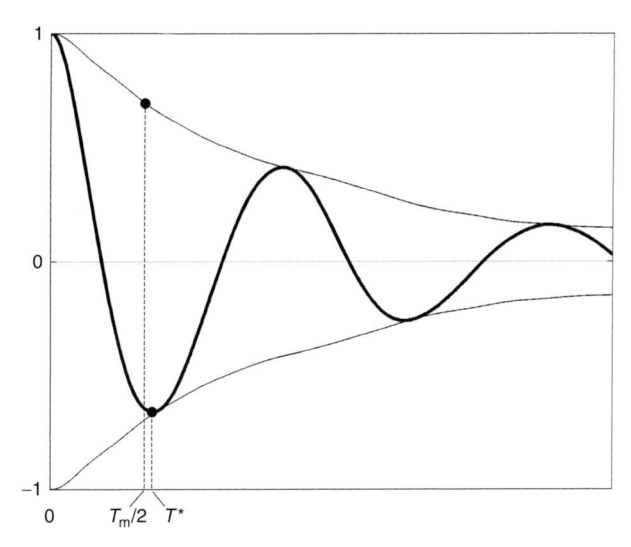

Figure 28 Autocorrelation function of surface elevation (bold line) and its upper and lower envelopes (thin lines).

$$\rho(t) = \frac{1}{m_0}\int_0^\infty S(f)\cos(2\pi f t)\mathrm{d}f \quad [109]$$

$$\hat{\rho}(t) = \frac{1}{m_0}\int_0^\infty S(f)\sin(2\pi f t)\mathrm{d}f \quad [110]$$

$$\pm r(t) = \pm\sqrt{\rho^2(t) + \hat{\rho}^2(t)} \quad [111]$$

where $\hat{\rho}$ is the Hilbert transform of ρ. The functions $\rho(t)$ and $r(t)$ are illustrated in **Figure 28**. If we define T^* as the time that $\rho(t)$ takes its first minimum, then it is clear from **Figure 28** that Boccotti's definition $\psi = |\rho(T^*)|$ is very close to $r(T_\mathrm{m}/2)$. Tayfun and Fedele [138] note that $r(T_\mathrm{m}/2) \geq |\rho(T^*)|$ with equality only in the case of zero bandwidth, when both are equal to 1. In wind–wave spectra, $r(T_\mathrm{m}/2)$ typically ranges between 0.65 and 0.75. For the purpose of estimating extremes, if there are no spectral data available to estimate $r(T_\mathrm{m}/2)$, using a value of $\psi = 0.75$ will give conservative estimates.

8.03.6.2.2 The short-term distribution of crest heights

Crest height is defined as the maximum surface elevation on a wave trace between two zero-crossing points. The alternative definition of a crest as the height of a local maximum between two troughs is not as useful for engineering applications, since broad-banded spectra can give rise to waves with several small crests and troughs between zero-crossing points.

In contrast to wave height distributions, nonlinear effects are important in wave crest distributions and there is significant departure from the linear approximation, where the sea surface elevation follows a Gaussian distribution. When the wave amplitude becomes large compared with the wavelength or water depth, the distribution of the sea surface elevation becomes positively skewed, with wave crests becoming higher and sharper and troughs becoming flatter and wider.

There is now a growing consensus that ocean wave crest distributions can be modeled by considering second-order nonlinearities only. As with wave heights, higher-order nonlinearities can increase crest heights in steep unidirectional waves, but these conditions are rarely observed in practice and second-order models agree well with observations (see, e.g., References 27 and 138).

A number of second-order crest height models have been proposed in recent years (e.g., References 42, 43, 140, 141, and 143). All are in good agreement but vary somewhat in their parameterization. The model of Forristall [42] has a simple formulation and is often used in the literature as a reference to which other distributions are compared. The model is based on the crest height distribution observed from simulations of waves with second-order nonlinearities, finite bandwidth, and infinite depth. From the results of many simulations with varying wave steepness and water depth, an empirical Weibull fit to the crest height distributions was obtained, with parameters that vary with wave steepness and water depth. Simulations were run for both two-dimensional and three-dimensional waves (where the directional spread is modeled as in Reference 16), giving two slightly different fits. In general, the two-dimensional runs gave higher crests, except for cases of very steep waves in deep water.

Forristall's model can be written as follows: if we denote the crest height as η_c, then the probability that a crest is less than a given height η is

$$\Pr\{\eta_c \leq \eta\} = 1 - \exp\left[-\left(\frac{\eta}{\alpha H_s}\right)^\beta\right] \quad [112]$$

The parameters α and β are expressed in terms of a steepness parameter

$$S = \frac{2\pi H_s}{gT_m^2} \quad [113]$$

and a depth parameter (the Ursell number)

$$Ur = \frac{H_s}{k_m^2 d^3} \quad [114]$$

where d is the water depth and k_m is the wave number corresponding to the mean frequency $1/T_m$ (see eqn [22]). Note that in deep water, $Ur \to 0$.

The parameters for the two-dimensional simulations are given by

$$\begin{aligned}\alpha_2 &= 0.3536 + 0.2892S + 0.1060Ur \\ \beta_2 &= 2 - 2.1597S + 0.0968Ur^2\end{aligned} \quad [115]$$

The parameters for the three-dimensional simulations are given by

$$\begin{aligned}\alpha_3 &= 0.3536 + 0.2568S + 0.0800Ur \\ \beta_3 &= 2 - 1.7912S - 0.5302Ur + 0.284Ur^2\end{aligned} \quad [116]$$

For comparisons with measured data, it should be noted that although buoys are capable of measuring the wave height accurately, they cannot measure nonlinear wave crests accurately. This is a result of the buoy following the motion of the water particles. As a wave crest approaches, a buoy will move forward with the crest and then backward in the trough (see illustration of water particle motions in **Figure 1**). This means that a buoy will spend more time in a crest and less time in a trough than a fixed measuring device. The result is that the distribution of surface elevation measured by a buoy is less skewed than that measured by a fixed instrument. Since crest height is measured relative to the mean water level, crests measured by a buoy will be lower than those measured by a fixed device. An analytical treatment of this problem can be found in References 38 and 39, and examples of these effects in buoy measurements are presented by Prevosto *et al.* [43].

8.03.6.3 Long-Term Distributions of Extreme Sea States

Although the distribution of wave and crest heights can be predicted accurately for a given sea state, the sea state cannot be predicted accurately more than a few days in advance. This usually necessitates the use of a probabilistic approach for estimating the distribution of possible future extreme conditions. The distribution of possible future extreme conditions is estimated from the historic extreme conditions and usually requires extrapolation outside the observed range of the historic data. For example, it may be required that a WEC is designed to have a 95% chance of survival within its lifetime. If the anticipated lifetime of a WEC is 20 years, then the device must be designed to withstand the most severe conditions in 95% of the possible future 20-year periods. If it is assumed that annual maxima (AM) are independent, then we can make the following calculation. Let X denote the annual maximum H_s and let $F(x) = \Pr\{X \leq x\}$ be the distribution function of X. Let Y denote the maximum H_s in a 20-year period and $G(x) = \Pr\{Y \leq x\}$ be the distribution function of Y. Then, since we are assuming that AM are independent, $G(x) = \Pr\{X_1 \leq x\}\Pr\{X_2 \leq x\}\cdots\Pr\{X_{20} \leq x\} = F(x)^{20}$. So the value of H_s that is exceeded in only 5% of 20-year periods corresponds to the value x for which $G(x) = 0.95$, or equivalently the x for which $F(x) = 0.95^{1/20} = 0.9974$. This is a value that is exceeded on average every $1/(1-0.9974) = 390.4$ years (return values are discussed further in Section 8.03.6.3.2(iii)).

There are no historic data sets of this length. Therefore, extrapolation outside the observed range of values is required in this example. This can be done on either a physical or a statistical basis. In energetic sites, it may not be possible to rule out the possibility of very large waves on physical grounds alone, making a probabilistic approach necessary. In this section, we start by discussing the probabilistic methods that have been proposed to estimate extreme values of H_s and present a motivation for the peaks-over-threshold (POT) method that is commonly used at present. The application of the POT method for estimating extreme values of H_s is then discussed in detail.

8.03.6.3.1 Overview of methods for estimating extreme H_s

The aim of this section is to describe the motivation for the POT method for estimating extreme H_s. The use of the POT method is justified by results from asymptotic extreme value theory. An excellent introduction to this topic is given by Coles [142]. For brevity, the mathematical details have been omitted from this section, and the reader is referred to Reference 142 for these.

Before the advent of long-term wave data sets, a popular approach for estimating extremes was to fit a parametric distribution to the entire data set and extrapolate into the tail. This is sometimes referred to as the initial distribution (ID) method. There are numerous problems with this approach for wave data. First, it is normally assumed that the data are independent and identically distributed, which is not the case for wave data. Consecutive measurements are highly correlated (in the case of *in situ* or model data) and therefore not independent. Also, conditions generally exhibit seasonal variability, meaning that data are not identically distributed during the year. Most importantly though, a fit based on the bulk of the data does not necessarily imply a good fit to the highest values in which we are interested.

This point has been well illustrated by Ferreira and Guedes Soares [144]. In extreme value theory, there is a theorem which states that the tail of any distribution that satisfies certain regularity conditions will tend to one of three forms. Ferreira and Guedes Soares [144] model the distribution of H_s using Beta and Gamma distributions that include the three limiting forms of tail behavior (see Section 8.03.6.3.2(ii)). The Gamma distribution has an exponential tail (type I) and the Beta distribution can have either long tails (type II) or short tails (type III). They show that all three types of distribution fit H_s data from the Portuguese coast very well. Kolmogorov–Smirnov tests for goodness of fit do not reject any of the distributions as not fitting the data. The three distributions are very close to each other over the range of the bulk of the data but differ remarkably at high probability quantiles. This leads to estimates of return values differing by over 5 m between the two types of the Beta model. Since there is no *a priori* reason to suppose that H_s follows one distribution rather than another, the ID method is not recommended for predicting extreme H_s [145].

Extreme value theory does not require assumptions about the distribution of the bulk of the data. Roughly speaking, the theory states that the distribution of the maximum of a sample of n independent, identically distributed observations will tend to one of three types of distribution as $n \to \infty$ (corresponding to the three tail types mentioned above). These three families of distributions are all members of the generalized extreme value (GEV) distribution. For a large enough sample size, n, this suggests the use of the GEV family for modeling extremes. This is referred to as a 'block maxima' method since it is used to model the maximum value in a 'block' of fixed size such as a year or a month (or alternatively over a fixed unit of length).

By definition, extreme conditions are rare. Therefore, making maximal use of the data is of great importance. Block maxima methods where only one value is used per block are a waste of data. For instance, several large (and independent) storms may occur in a year that are all more severe than storms in another year. The rth largest order statistic models come some way to address this problem, by using the 1st, 2nd,..., rth largest measurements in each block (see, e.g., References 146 and 147 for applications of this method to wave data). A more complete description of the upper tail of a distribution is given by a threshold model. In a threshold model, the data are not separated into blocks, but instead extreme events are defined as exceedances of some high threshold. The analysis of data exceeding a threshold is known as the POT method.

Threshold analyses of extremes and analyses based on block maxima are consistent with each other, but threshold analyses have the advantage that they use a greater proportion of the data. Again, roughly speaking, if block maxima have an approximating distribution in the GEV family, then excesses of a 'large enough' threshold will have an equivalent approximating distribution within the generalized Pareto family. The issue of choosing a 'large enough' threshold is nontrivial and is analogous to the choice of block size for the block maxima method. Too small a threshold will mean that approximation by the asymptotic limit model is likely to be poor, leading to bias in estimation and extrapolation. Too large a threshold gives fewer data, leading to large estimation variance. Threshold selection is discussed in Section 8.03.6.3.2(v).

Van Vledder *et al.* [148] and Guedes Soares and Scotto [149] have compared the use of AM and POT methods using a data set for a location on the Norwegian continental shelf. They conclude that POT is to be preferred to AM since it uses a greater number of data points. It is now common practice to use the POT method for the estimation of extreme H_s. Examples can be found in References 145 and 150–156.

Both block maxima and threshold models are special cases of point process models. The point process model provides an elegant formulation of the extreme value behavior of process. However, it does not lead to anything new in terms of statistical models, since any inference made using a point process method could equally be made using a threshold or a block maxima method. For simplicity of the exposition, we will therefore not consider the point process formulation further. Examples of the use of point process models for the estimation of extreme wave conditions can be found in References 157 and 158.

8.03.6.3.2 The POT method

In this section, details are presented on the application of the POT method to wave data. To justify the use of the method, it is important to verify that the assumptions made in the derivation of the model are satisfied by the data. The first assumption we consider is that the data are independent. This is clearly not true for wave data since wave conditions are strongly correlated over several hours. However, the assumption of independence can be relaxed by requiring independence of extremes that are sufficiently separated in time (see Reference 159). This is entirely plausible for wave data, with the occurrence of storms separated by several days being roughly independent. Short-term dependence is dealt with by declustering. That is, we consider only the maximum value in a single storm, rather than all data points within a storm above the threshold. The declustering of wave data, necessary for the application of the POT model, is discussed in Section 8.03.6.3.2(i).

In Section 8.03.6.3.2(ii), the generalized Pareto distribution (GPD) is defined, which is used to model the distribution of threshold exceedances. In Section 8.03.6.3.2(iii), we introduce the concept of return values and explain how they should be interpreted. The estimation of GPD parameters from the data is discussed in Section 8.03.6.3.2(iv).

The POT/GPD model for extremes is developed using asymptotic arguments and care is needed in its application to finite samples. The asymptotic argument used to justify the use of the POT/GPD model is difficult to verify directly. If it is shown that the GPD is a good fit for the data, then it can be argued that at least the asymptotic argument is not unreasonable. Therefore, it is important to verify that the model is a good fit for the data and that the choice of threshold is appropriate. Threshold selection and model diagnostics are discussed in Sections 8.03.6.3.2(v) and 8.03.6.3.2(vi), respectively.

Another important assumption made in the derivation of the POT model is that the data are identically distributed. This assumption is not strictly valid since the distribution of H_s is dependent on other variables, known as covariates, such as the direction of origin of a storm or the season in which the storm occurs. Covariate effects are discussed in Section 8.03.6.3.2(vii).

In Section 8.03.4.3, we saw that data from wave models were subject to considerable uncertainty at high values of H_s. The effect this has on estimates of extremes is discussed in Section 8.03.6.3.2(viii).

8.03.6.3.2(i) Preparation of data

In the POT method, the GPD is used to model the distribution of maxima between threshold crossings, referred to as threshold exceedances. If measured data are used to estimate the distribution of the maximum H_s in a storm, then it is necessary to consider the effects of sampling variability on threshold exceedances. Consider a hypothetical situation where the sea state is constant over a number of hours. If we measure the sea state in fixed periods of say 30 min, we can assume that each wave record gives an unbiased estimate of H_s. However, the maximum of these records is likely to be higher than the true value of H_s over the interval. So in a real situation, if there are several samples of waves recorded near the peak of a storm, then the maximum of the estimates of H_s from these records is likely to be higher than the expected value of H_s at the peak of the storm. Forristall et al. [70] examined the effect of this on estimates of the distribution of the maximum H_s in a storm and demonstrated that sampling variability causes estimates to be highly biased. Averaging the data over longer periods reduces sampling variability and therefore minimizes this effect. They recommend that data are smoothed using a 3 h moving average filter. The period of 3 h is chosen as a compromise between statistical stability and adequate sampling of changes in sea state. The treatment of uncertainties in modeled data is discussed in Section 8.03.6.3.2(viii).

After the data have been smoothed, the next task is to identify independent storms. The notion of a storm has a direct physical interpretation: a peak in the time history of H_s at a particular location is associated with winds generated by a weather system. In practice, winds may vary as the weather system evolves, causing several peaks over a number of days. If synoptic pressure charts were available, it may be relatively easy to see that several consecutive peaks in a record were the result of a single storm, but this may not be so clear from the time history of H_s alone. From a physical point of view, a pressure system that causes a large peak in the H_s record will generally be large in extent and persist for a number of days. It is therefore unlikely that peaks close to each other come from separate storms. Moreover, if two separate storms occur in close proximity, then it may not be realistic to assume that their characteristics are independent. This leads to some authors defining a minimum separation in time, τ, between peaks. Tawn [160] uses a separation of 30 h between storms in the southern North Sea, whereas Anderson et al. [158] use an interval of 24 h for a location in the northern North Sea. Tromans and Vanderschuren [161] proposed using an additional criterion to identify separate storms by specifying that the minimum values of H_s between two peaks must be less than a fraction p of the lower peak. In their study, they used $p = 0.8$.

The choice of criteria for declustering data is usually a compromise between leaving peaks which appear to be from the same storm and removing peaks which are from independent storms, and it is difficult to use a rigorous method to select appropriate criteria. Testing the independence of storm peaks is complicated by the temporal variation of their distribution. Seasonal variability causes a periodic correlation in peak wave heights, and any climatic variability will also result in a small, but potentially significant, correlation in peak wave heights. Mackay [123] examined the correlation between storm peak heights using data from 14 buoys in the North Pacific, with record lengths all in excess of 20 years and up to 30 years in some cases. In order to remove the seasonal signal from the declustered data, the time series were normalized using the method of Athanassoulis and Stefanakos [125], mentioned in Section 8.03.5.2. First, the mean and standard deviation are calculated for each day of the year, using a moving window of width 10 days. The functions $\mu(t)$ and $\sigma(t)$ are defined as low-order Fourier expansions of the daily mean and standard deviation, respectively. The normalized series is defined as $W(t) = (H_s(t) - \mu(t))/\sigma(t)$. The procedure is illustrated with an example using data from NDBC buoy 46002, located 500 km from the coast of Oregon, for the period 1978–2008. **Figure 29(a)** shows the

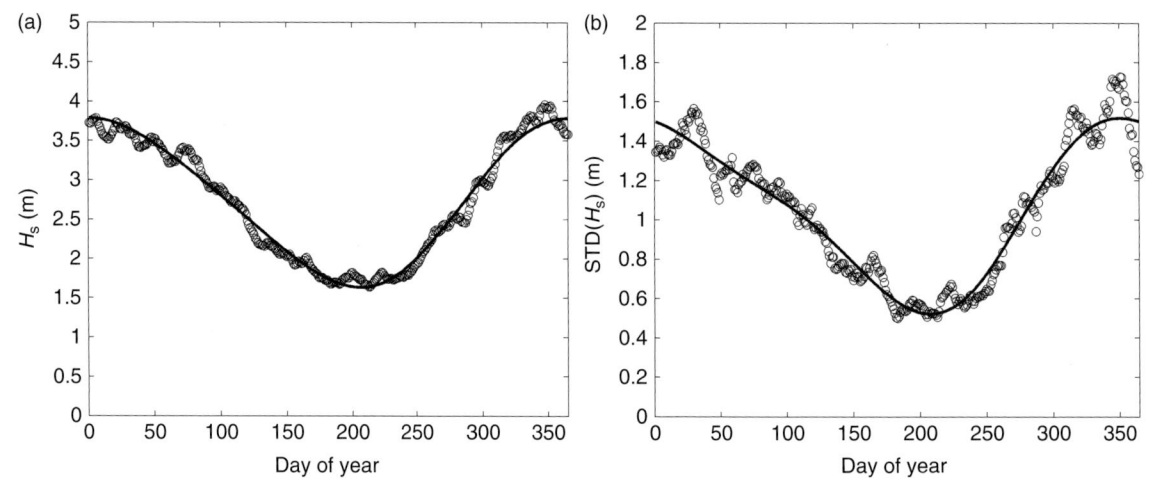

Figure 29 Fourier representation of seasonal variation in wave climate. (a) Daily mean H_s (circles) and Fourier expansion of daily mean (line). (b) Daily standard deviation in H_s (circles) and Fourier expansion of daily standard deviation (line).

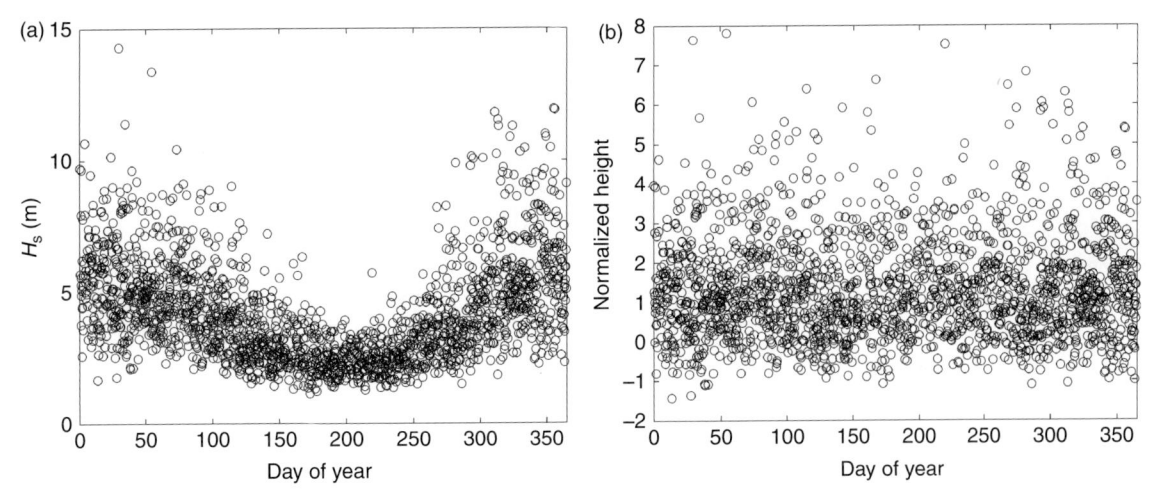

Figure 30 (a) Storm peaks identified using declustering criteria $p = 0.75$ and $\tau = 1.5$ days. (b) Normalized values of storm peaks from (a).

daily mean H_s and its Fourier expansion $\mu(t)$. **Figure 29(b)** shows the daily standard deviation and its Fourier expansion $\sigma(t)$. Second-order Fourier expansions were found to be adequate for both the mean and the standard deviation.

Figure 30(a) shows the storm peaks identified using the criteria $p = 0.75$ and $\tau = 1.5$ days. If we denote these peaks as $X_1, \ldots, X_n$, occurring at times $t_1, \ldots, t_n$, then we can define normalized storm peaks as $Y_i(t_i) = (X_i(t_i) - \mu(t_i))/\sigma(t_i)$. It should be emphasized that the data are declustered in their original form and the normalization is applied afterward. The normalized storm peaks are shown in **Figure 30(b)**. Their distribution appears to be reasonably stationary throughout the year. This is quite remarkable since the storm peaks have been normalized by the mean and standard deviation of all the data. Stefanakos and Athanassoulis [162] have suggested that this normalized series could be used to estimate extreme wave heights, but in the present author's opinion, more rigorous statistical tests would be required to show that this normalized distribution can be considered stationary.

The correlation of storm peaks that exceed a high threshold was examined using a variable threshold, set as the second-order Fourier expansion of the 90th percentile of all the data. Data for each buoy were declustered using values of p between 0.5 and 1 and of τ between 0 and 5 days. It was shown that there is little reduction in the correlation for $p < 0.7$ or $\tau > 1.5$. In addition, a visual inspection of the time series of H_s showed that making the declustering criteria stricter than this removes peaks that appear to be separate storms. Conversely, peaks that appear to be from the same storm are observed when the criteria are less strict. It was found that using criteria of $p = 0.75$ and $\tau = 1.5$ provided a good compromise between achieving a low correlation and unnecessarily removing peaks from distinct storms that occur in close proximity. The highest peaks in each season will remain for any choice of declustering criteria, but ultimately the choice of which of the lower peaks to include is somewhat subjective and will vary depending on the location.

8.03.6.3.2(ii) The generalized Pareto distribution

The cumulative distribution function (CDF) of the GPD is defined as follows. Let Y be a random variable and $X = Y - u$ be the exceedances of Y over some high threshold u. Then, X has a GPD if and only if the distribution function of X, conditional on Y exceeding u, is

$$F(x) = \Pr\{X \leq x \mid Y > u\} = \begin{cases} 1 - \left(\dfrac{1 + \xi x}{\sigma}\right)^{-1/\xi} & \text{for } \xi \neq 0 \\ 1 - \exp\left(\dfrac{-x}{\sigma}\right) & \text{for } \xi = 0 \end{cases} \quad [117]$$

for $\sigma > 0$. When $\xi \geq 0$, the support (range of validity) is $0 \leq x < \infty$, and when $\xi < 0$, the support is $0 \leq x \leq -\sigma/\xi$. The density function is given by

$$f(x) = \frac{dF(x)}{dx} = \begin{cases} \sigma^{-1}\left(\dfrac{1 + \xi x}{\sigma}\right)^{-(1 + 1/\xi)} & \text{for } \xi \neq 0 \\ \sigma^{-1}\exp\left(\dfrac{-x}{\sigma}\right) & \text{for } \xi = 0 \end{cases} \quad [118]$$

The parameters σ and ξ are called the scale and shape parameters, respectively. The family of GPD contains the uniform distribution when $\xi = -1$ and the exponential distribution when $\xi = 0$. The density functions of the GPD for various values of ξ are shown in **Figure 31**. The three cases $\xi = 0$, $\xi < 0$, and $\xi > 0$ are the three types of tail behavior referred to in Section 8.03.6.3.1. When $\xi = 0$, the distribution has an exponential tail (type I). When $\xi < 0$, the distribution has a finite endpoint and is referred to as 'short-tailed' (type III). When $\xi > 0$, the distribution is unbounded from above and is referred to as 'heavy-tailed' or 'long-tailed' (type II).

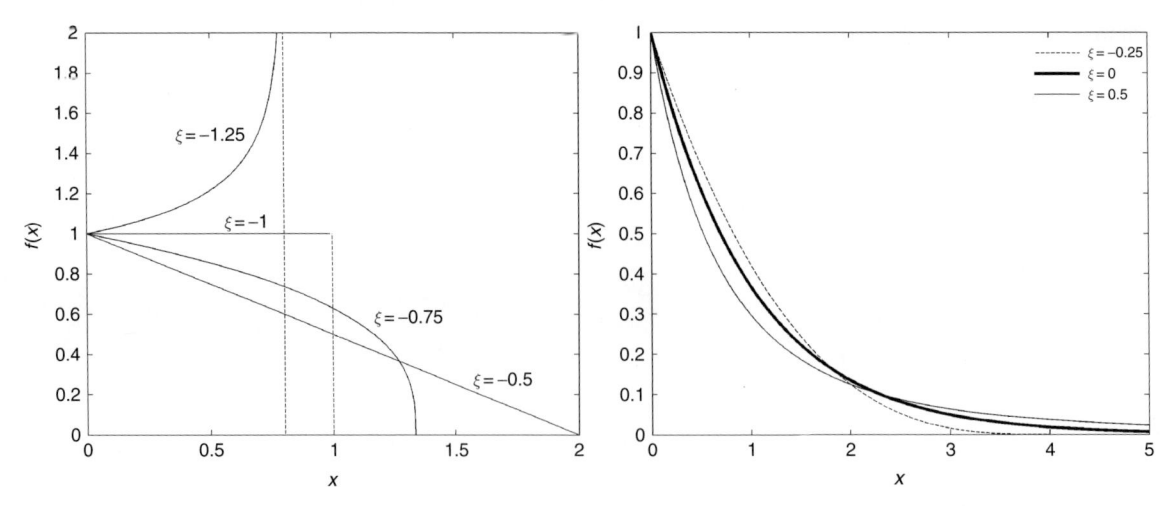

Figure 31 Probability density function of the GPD for scale parameter $\sigma = 1$ and various values of shape parameter ξ.

The mean and variance of the distribution are given by

$$E(X) = \frac{\sigma}{1-\xi} \qquad [119]$$

and

$$\text{var}(X) = \frac{\sigma^2}{(1-\xi)^2(1-2\xi)} \qquad [120]$$

Note that when $\xi \geq 1$ the mean is not defined and when $\xi \geq 1/2$ the variance is not defined. In general, for $\xi > 0$, the rth central moment exists only if $r < 1/\xi$.

8.03.6.3.2(iii) Return values

The N-year return value is the value that is exceeded once every N years on average. Or more precisely, it is the level that is exceeded in a given year with probability $1/N$. If X is a Generalized Pareto (GP) variable, the N-year return level for $Y = X + u$ is the solution of

$$\frac{1}{Nm} = \Pr\{Y > x_N\} \qquad [121]$$

where m is the number of observations per year. We have that

$$\Pr\{Y > x_N \mid Y > u\} = 1 - F(x_N - u) \qquad [122]$$

So

$$\Pr\{Y > x_N\} = \Pr\{Y > u\}(1 - F(x_N - u)) \qquad [123]$$

If we equate eqn [123] with eqn [121], substitute eqn [117], and rearrange, this gives

$$x_N = \begin{cases} u + \dfrac{\sigma}{\xi}\left[(Nm\zeta_u)^\xi - 1\right] & \text{for } \xi \neq 0 \\ u + \sigma \log(Nm\zeta_u) & \text{for } \xi = 0 \end{cases} \qquad [124]$$

where $\zeta_u = \Pr\{Y > u\}$. For dependent data, such as time series of wave height, ζ_u is estimated by n_c/n, where n_c is the number of clusters above u and n is the total number of samples.

Return values are a useful single parameter to gauge the risk associated with a particular distribution. However, they should not be confused with the largest value that is expected in a given period. In fact, for large N, the probability of exceeding x_N in an N-year period is about 0.63. To see this, we can consider, without loss of generality, the AM. Each year is a random trial with the probability of exceeding the return value $p = 1 - 1/N$. The probability that x_N is not exceeded in N years is p^N, so the probability that x_N will be exceeded at least once in N years is $1 - p^N$. But $p^N = (1 - 1/N)^N \to 1/e$ as $N \to \infty$, so $1 - p^N \to 1 - 1/e \approx 0.63$.

8.03.6.3.2(iv) Parameter estimation

The GPD is somewhat unusual, in that the parameters are usually estimated for a range of thresholds and the threshold is selected based on the estimated parameters, as discussed in the next section. First, we will discuss the estimation of the parameters from the data. Throughout this section, a caret '^' will be used to denote an estimate of the true parameter. We will denote a sample of

n observations as $x_1,\ldots, x_n$ and denote the order statistics as $x_{(1)} \leq x_{(2)} \leq \cdots \leq x_{(n)}$. Note that the x values are the exceedances of the threshold, that is, $x_i = H_{si} - u$.

Many methods have been proposed to estimate the parameters of GPD. A review of many of these methods has been presented by de Zea Bermudez and Kotz [163]. It is desirable for parameter and quantile estimators to have the following properties:

- always exist
- supports inferred from the estimates should contain all the observations
- easy and fast to compute
- low bias and variance
- low sensitivity to threshold choice

The first two properties would seem like minimum requirements for an estimator, but they are not satisfied by all the estimators that are commonly used. The maximum likelihood (ML) estimator is asymptotically efficient, but Hosking and Wallis [164] showed that the ML estimates do not display this asymptotic property for sample sizes up to 500. They also noted that sometimes the solutions to the ML equations do not exist and that at other times when the solutions do exist there can be convergence problems with the algorithm they used to find them. Hosking and Wallis [164] introduced the probability-weighted moment (PWM) estimator for the GPD and compared it with the method of moments (MOM) and ML estimators. They showed that the MOM and PWM estimators have lower bias and variance than ML estimators for sample sizes less than 500. However, both methods are sensitive to threshold choice and sometimes result in nonfeasible estimates, in that the support (range of validity) inferred from the estimates should contain all the observations (i.e., $\hat{\xi} < 0$ and $x_{(n)} > -\hat{\sigma}/\hat{\xi}$, violating the definition given in eqn [117]). Dupuis and Tsao [165] introduced hybrid MOM and PWM estimators that are always consistent with the data, but these are still sensitive to the choice of threshold.

Mackay *et al.* [166] have compared the performance of many of the estimators that have been proposed for the GPD. They showed that a modified version of the likelihood moment (LM) estimator, introduced by Zhang [167], has one of the best performances. Mackay *et al.* [166] extended the results of Zhang [167] to show that the LM estimator using the hybrid PWM estimate as the first guess performs well over all sample sizes and values of the shape parameter. The bias and RMS error of the LM estimator are consistently the lowest or close to the lowest of all the estimators tested. For larger sample sizes, the bias and variance are very close to those of the ML estimator, but the LM estimator has the advantage that it is easier to compute.

The first step in calculating the LM estimates is to calculate the PWM estimates of the GPD parameters. The PWM estimates are given by

$$\hat{\sigma}_{\text{PWM}} = \frac{2a_0 a_1}{a_0 - 2a_1} \quad [125]$$

$$\hat{\xi}_{\text{PWM}} = 2 - \frac{a_0}{a_0 - 2a_1} \quad [126]$$

where

$$a_r = \frac{1}{n} \sum_{j=1}^{n} (1 - P_j)^r x_{(j)} \quad [127]$$

and $P_j = (j - 0.35)/n$ is the empirical nonexceedance probability of $x_{(j)}$. (Note that this differs from the definition of empirical nonexceedance probability discussed in Section 8.03.6.3.2(vi), but the difference makes negligible difference to the results.) If $\hat{\xi}_{\text{PWM}} < 0$ and $x_{(n)} > -\hat{\sigma}_{\text{PWM}}/\hat{\xi}_{\text{PWM}}$, then the hybrid PWM estimate is defined to be

$$\hat{\xi}_{\text{HPWM}} = \frac{-\hat{\sigma}_{\text{PWM}}}{x_{(n)}} \quad [128]$$

The next step is to find the root of the equation

$$g(b) = \frac{1}{n} \sum_{j=1}^{n} (1 - b x_j)^q - \frac{1}{1 + \hat{\xi}_0} \quad [129]$$

where

$$q = \frac{-\hat{\xi}_0 n}{\sum_{j=1}^{n} \log(1 - b x_j)} \quad [130]$$

and $\hat{\xi}_0$ is either the PWM estimator if it is consistent or the hybrid PWM estimator otherwise. Zhang [167] shows that the roots of $g(b)$ are simple to compute since it is a smooth monotone function of b with a unique solution in $(-\infty, 1/x_{(n)})$, unless $\hat{\xi}_0 = 0$ or $x_1 = x_2 = \cdots = x_n$. He notes that a Newton–Raphson method will usually converge within 4–6 iterations to a margin of relative error less than 10^{-6}. Having found b, the LM parameter estimates are given by

$$\hat{\tilde{\xi}}_{\text{LM}} = -\frac{1}{n}\sum_{j=1}^{n}\log(1-bx_{j}) \qquad [131]$$

$$\hat{\sigma}_{\text{LM}} = \frac{\hat{\tilde{\xi}}_{\text{LM}}}{b} \qquad [132]$$

It is worth noticing that when the distribution parameters are estimated as smoothly varying functions of covariates (see Section 8.03.6.3.2(vii)), the ML estimators are much easier to work with, even though they do not have the lowest bias or variance for finite sample sizes. The reader is referred to Reference 142 for details of estimation for covariate models.

8.03.6.3.2(v) Threshold selection

It is possible to use statistical techniques to estimate the threshold from the data; however, the method preferred by most practitioners is to estimate parameters for a range of thresholds and examine the variation of certain statistics with the threshold. The disadvantage of this approach is that it makes threshold choice somewhat subjective. However, this method gives an indication of whether the GPD provides a good fit and can highlight the uncertainty in the threshold choice.

If Y is a random variable and $X_0 = Y - u_0$ has a GPD with scale parameter σ_{u_0} and shape parameter ξ, it can be shown that (see, e.g., Reference 142) for any $u > u_0$, $X = Y - u$ has a GPD with the same value of ξ and

$$\sigma_u = \sigma_{u_0} + \xi(u - u_0) \qquad [133]$$

Therefore, the variable

$$\sigma^* = \sigma_u - \xi u \qquad [134]$$

is constant with respect to u. Therefore, if we plot estimates of ξ and σ^* against u, we should observe a minimum threshold u_0 above which the parameter estimates are constant. In practice, finite sampling effects lead to variability of these parameters with threshold, so it is rare to see a completely straight line with threshold. Moreover, as the threshold increases, the number of samples will decrease, thus increasing the variance of the estimates. It is also useful to plot the estimated return values against u, since if the GPD is a valid model for the data for threshold u_0, then the estimated return values should also tend to a constant value for $u > u_0$.

From eqns [119] and [133], we have that

$$E(X) = \frac{\sigma_{u_0} + \xi u}{1 - \xi} \qquad [135]$$

So if the GPD is a valid model for exceedances over u_0, then the mean of the exceedances over threshold $u > u_0$ is a linear function of u with slope $\xi/(1-\xi)$ and intercept $\sigma_{u_0}/(1-\xi)$. This provides another diagnostic tool for choosing the threshold level, known as the mean residual life plot. The threshold is then chosen as the lowest value for which estimates of ξ, σ^*, and return values approach constant values and $E(X)$ satisfies eqn [135].

To aid the identification of a valid threshold, a bootstrap method can be used to account for the uncertainty inherent in the data. An introduction to the bootstrap method is given by Efron and Tibshirani [168]. When using a bootstrap technique, it is assumed that the data represent a realization of the underlying population. If it is further assumed that the data are independent and identically distributed, then it follows that a random sample of the data, drawn with replacement, is an equally likely realization of the same process. By resampling the data a large number of times, we can estimate the effect of sampling variability on estimates of ξ, σ^*, return values, and the mean exceedance. This can be used to add confidence bounds to the threshold plots.

Resampling alone does not smooth the threshold plots, since the mean bootstrap estimate tends to the original nonbootstrapped estimate. Incorporating information about the uncertainty of each estimate of storm peak H_s can smooth the plots to a certain extent. The distribution of the estimate of maximum H_s in a storm has been discussed in detail by Forristall et al. [70]. Their results show that the COV in the storm peak H_s for 3 h averages is around 3%. This information is incorporated into the bootstrap in the following way. For each trial, we draw a random sample $X_{(j,1)}, \ldots, X_{(j,n)}$ from the original data $X_1, \ldots, X_n$ and generate n standard normal variables $e_1, \ldots, e_n$. The bootstrap sample is defined to be $X_{(j,1)}(1 + 0.03e_1), \ldots, X_{(j,n)}(1 + 0.03e_n)$. This is a natural extension of the bootstrap method, since samples generated in this way are an equally likely realization of the underlying process.

The use of this modified bootstrap technique is illustrated in **Figure 32**, using data from NDBC buoy 46002. The mean bootstrap estimate is considerably smoother than the original nonbootstrapped estimates. Bootstrapping cannot rectify any inherent bias in the empirical distribution (i.e., differences between the shape of the sample distribution and the underlying population distribution), but uncertainty can be gauged through the confidence bounds.

From these plots, the threshold has been selected as 6.2 m. After this point, the mean exceedance becomes approximately linear, with slope -0.11 and intercept 2.2. From eqn [135], this is equivalent to $\hat{\xi} = -0.12$ and $\hat{\sigma}_{u_0} = 2.5$. The estimates of ξ and σ^* display stability from around 6.2 m until around 7.5 m, with values consistent with those from the mean excess plot. The variability displayed after this point is likely to be due to decreasing sample size. Despite the variability in the estimates of ξ and σ^* above 7.5 m, the estimate of the 50-year return value of H_s is reasonably constant from 6.2 m onward.

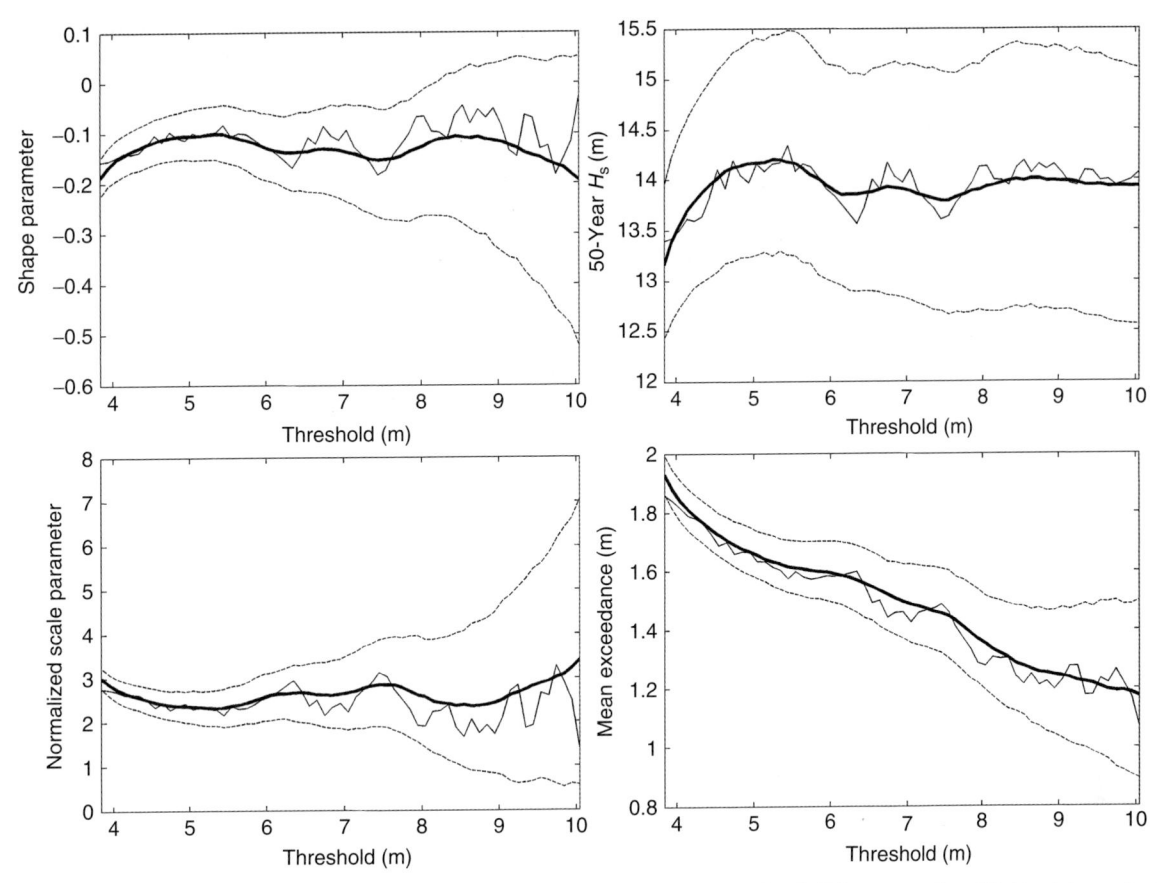

Figure 32 Threshold plots for data from buoy 46002. Thin solid line, estimates without resampling; bold line, mean of modified bootstrap estimates; dotted line, 95% confidence bounds from modified bootstrap trials.

It should be noted that introducing a zero-mean random error into the data can introduce a positive bias in the return values, as discussed in Section 8.03.6.3.2(viii). However, for the random error of 3% that we are using here, the bias is generally of the order of a few centimeters and therefore negligible in relation to the uncertainty resulting from natural variability.

8.03.6.3.2(vi) Model diagnostics

Once a threshold has been chosen, it is important to check that the GPD provides a good fit to the data. If a model does not provide a good fit to the extremes that have been observed so far, then there is little hope that it will accurately model future conditions. Probability plots, quantile plots, and return value plots are useful diagnostic tools for checking the fit of a model. They provide a graphical comparison of the estimated distribution $\hat{F}$ with the empirical distribution $\tilde{F}$. Before describing how diagnostic plots are produced, it is necessary to define how the empirical distribution function is defined.

8.03.6.3.2(vi)(a) The empirical distribution function The empirical distribution function is the nonexceedance probability assigned to the order statistics. It is also referred to as the plotting position because of its use in graphical diagnostic techniques. There has been a lot of debate in the literature about how to define the empirical distribution function. The problem can be described as follows: consider a sample $x_1, \ldots, x_n$ of observations from a common population with unknown distribution function F, and let $x_{(1)} \leq x_{(2)} \leq \cdots \leq x_{(n)}$ denote the order statistics. For the largest sample in the set, $x_{(n)}$, there are $n-1$ samples that are less than or equal to it, so we could assign it the probability $\Pr\{X \leq x_{(n)}\} = (n-1)/n$. Conversely, zero observations are larger than it, so we could assign it the probability $\Pr\{X > x_{(n)}\} = 0$, which is clearly nonsensical unless the distribution is bounded at $x_{(n)}$. As $n \to \infty$, the difference in these two approaches tends to zero, but for finite samples both approaches will introduce bias. The most appropriate definition of the empirical distribution function depends on the context in which it is used. In the case of probability plots, it is the mean value of the nonexceedance probability of the order statistics $\langle F(x_{(i)}) \rangle$ that is of interest, whereas for quantile plots and return value plots, it is the nonexceedance probability of the mean value of the order statistics $F(\langle x_{(i)} \rangle)$ that is of interest, where $\langle \cdot \rangle$ denotes the mean value. In general, $\langle F(x_{(i)}) \rangle \neq F(\langle x_{(i)} \rangle)$, so the same definition of the empirical distribution function cannot be used in both contexts. For lower-order statistics, the difference between $\langle F(x_{(i)}) \rangle$ and $F(\langle x_{(i)} \rangle)$ is small, but for the highest order statistics, the differences are significant and can affect how well the estimated distribution is perceived to fit. Appropriate definitions to use are discussed in the following sections.

8.03.6.3.2(vi)(b) Probability plots A probability plot compares the estimated distribution function $\hat{F}$ with the empirical distribution function $\tilde{F}$. It consists of the points

$$\{(\tilde{F}(x_{(i)}), \hat{F}(x_{(i)})) : i = 1, \ldots, n\} \qquad [136]$$

If $\hat{F}$ is a good model for the data, then the points should lie close to the unit diagonal. Finite sampling effects will cause some departure from this line, but substantial deviations indicate that the model does not describe the data well.

Gumbel [169] showed that the mean value of the distribution function evaluated at $x_{(i)}$ is independent of the distribution and is given by

$$\langle F(x_{(i)}) \rangle = \frac{i}{n+1} \qquad [137]$$

So for a probability plot, the appropriate way to define the empirical distribution function $\tilde{F}$ is

$$\tilde{F}(x_{(i)}) = \Pr\{X \leq x_{(i)}\} = \langle F(x_{(i)}) \rangle = \frac{i}{n+1} \qquad [138]$$

So if $\hat{F}$ is an unbiased estimator of F, then $\langle \hat{F}(x_{(i)}) \rangle = \langle F(x_{(i)}) \rangle = \tilde{F}(x_{(i)})$ and the points on the probability plot should lie on a straight line.

We can give a more precise definition of a 'substantial' deviation by considering the sampling variability of probability estimates. Note that although $x_{(i)}$ is a random variable, $\tilde{F}(x_{(i)})$ is not – for any sample $\tilde{F}(x_{(i)}) = i/(n+1)$. However, $\hat{F}(x_{(i)})$ is a random variable. The probability density function of $F(x_{(i)})$ is given by [169]

$$g_i(F(x_{(i)})) = \frac{n!}{(n-i)!(i-1)!} [F(x_{(i)})]^{i-1} [1 - F(x_{(i)})]^{n-i} \qquad [139]$$

The moments of $F(x_{(i)})$ follow from the properties of the Beta function, as

$$\langle (F(x_{(i)}))^m \rangle = \int_0^1 t^m g_i(t) \mathrm{d}t$$
$$= \frac{n!(m+i-1)!}{(i-1)!(m+n)!} \qquad [140]$$

This yields the mean as given in eqn [138] and the standard deviation as

$$\mathrm{std}(F(x_{(i)})) = \frac{1}{n+1}\sqrt{\frac{i(n-1)+1}{n+2}} \qquad [141]$$

Note that the standard deviation of $\hat{F}(x_{(i)})$ will be larger than this since $\hat{F}$ has been estimated from the data, but we can use eqn [141] to indicate whether deviations in the probability plots are significant or not. An example is shown in **Figure 33** using the fit found

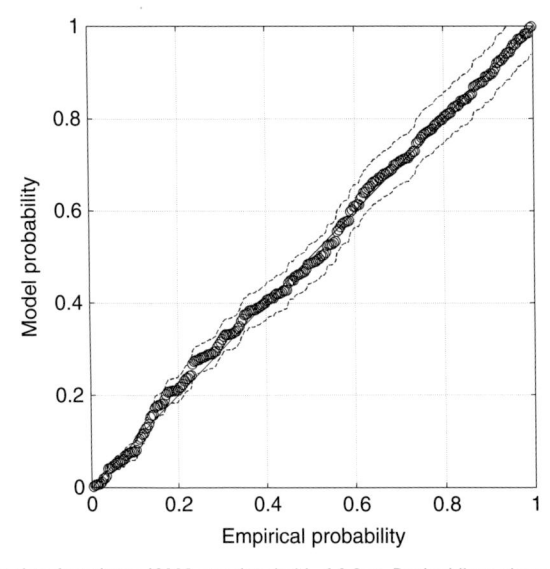

Figure 33 Probability plot for GPD fit to data from buoy 46002 at a threshold of 6.2 m. Dashed lines show ±1 standard deviation of the model probability.

for the buoy data described in the previous section, using a threshold of 6.2 m. The dashed lines show ±1 standard deviation of the model probability calculated using eqn [141] and $n = 271$. It is clear that the GPD provides a good fit to the data, with the model probability always within ±1 standard deviation of the empirical probability.

8.03.6.3.2(vi)(c) Quantile plots A quantile plot compares the estimated quantiles with the empirical quantiles. It consists of the points

$$\left\{ \left(x_{(i)}, \hat{F}^{-1}\left(\tilde{F}(x_{(i)}) \right) \right) : i = 1, \ldots, n \right\} \quad [142]$$

It provides the same information as a probability plot, but on a different scale. In a quantile plot, most of the points are bunched toward the lower quantiles, giving a better view of the fit of the model to the higher quantiles, whereas in a probability plot, the points are spread evenly between 0 and 1. Both plots provide useful information, since a fit that looks reasonable on one scale may look poor on the other.

In this case, it makes sense to define the empirical distribution function so that $\langle x_{(i)} \rangle = F^{-1}\left(\tilde{F}(x_{(i)}) \right)$, that is, $\tilde{F}(x_{(i)}) = F(\langle x_{(i)} \rangle)$. The probability density function of the ith order statistic is given by [169]

$$h_i(x) = \frac{n!}{(n-i)!(i-1)!} [F(x)]^{i-1} [1 - F(x)]^{n-i} f(x) \quad [143]$$

where f is the probability density function of X. As would be expected, the density function h depends on the parent distribution F, so no general formula for the empirical distribution function can be given in this context. Most definitions of the empirical distribution function in this context are of the form $\tilde{F}(x_{(i)}) = (i+a)/(n+b)$ (see, e.g., Reference 170). For the GPD using $a = 0$ and $b = 0.53 - 0.50\xi$, there is negligible bias in model quantiles for $\xi \le 0$, a small positive bias of 3% for the largest quantile when $\xi = 0.25$, and a bias of 7% in the largest quantile when $\xi = 0.5$.

In contrast to the probability plot, both the ordinate and the abscissa in quantile plots are random variables. The COV (defined as the standard deviation divided by the mean) for the largest observation $x_{(n)}$ in n samples from a GPD is shown in **Figure 34** for various values of n and shape parameter ξ. For values of ξ around −0.1 that are commonly observed for distributions of storm peak H_s, the COV varies from about 25% for a sample size of 25 to about 12% for a sample size of 500.

The distribution function of the model quantiles is harder to define and is dependent on the estimator used for the GPD parameters. Moreover, the unbiased plotting position depends on the distribution of the data, which is not known *a priori*. **Figure 35** shows the COV of $\Delta_n = \hat{F}^{-1}\left(\tilde{F}(x_{(n)}) \right) - x_{(n)}$, where $\tilde{F}(x_{(i)}) = i/(n + 0.53 - 0.50\hat{\xi})$ and the GPD parameters are estimated using the LM method (see Section 8.03.6.3.2(iv)). The results are based on 10 000 simulations for each value of ξ. Note that the COV of Δ_n is actually smaller than that of $x_{(n)}$, since the values of the model quantiles are dependent on the value of the empirical quantiles. Also for $\xi > 0$, the COV increases with the sample size.

An example of a quantile plot is shown in **Figure 36** using fit to the data from buoy 46002 as above. The fit of the model appears very good from this plot, with deviation only in the highest quantiles. For this example, $n = 271$ and $\hat{\xi} = -0.140$, with a 95% confidence interval of (−0.27, −0.04) estimated using the bootstrap technique. The largest empirical quantile is 14.29 m and the largest model quantile is 13.58 m, giving an underestimate of 5%, which is within the bounds expected from **Figure 35**, indicating that the deviation is not significant.

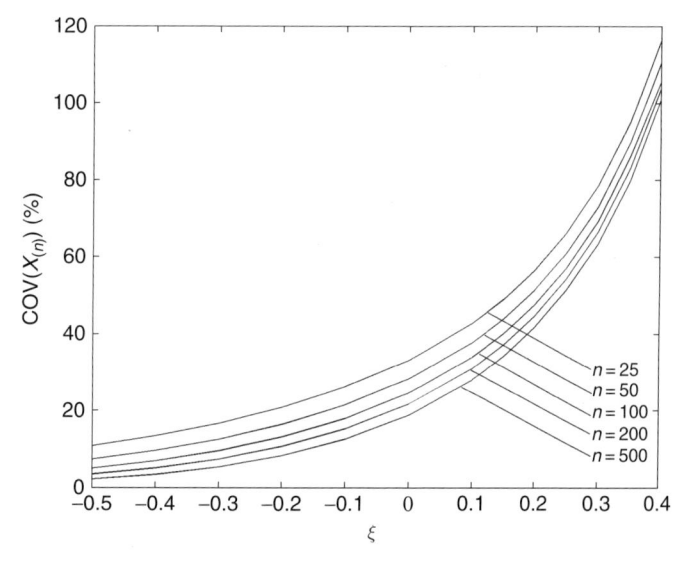

Figure 34 COV of the largest observation in n samples from a GPD for various values of n and shape parameter ξ.

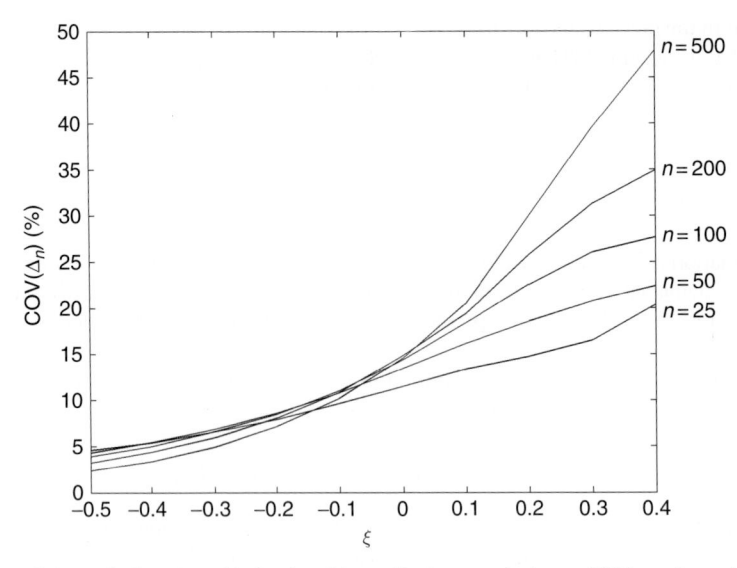

Figure 35 COV of the difference between the largest empirical and model quantiles in *n* samples from a GPD for various values of *n* and shape parameter ξ.

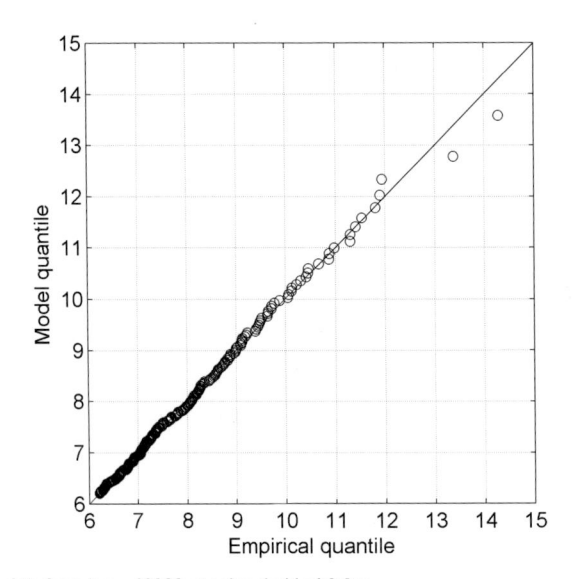

Figure 36 Quantile plot for GPD fit to data from buoy 46002 at a threshold of 6.2 m.

8.03.6.3.2(vi)(d) Return value plots A return value plot compares the empirical return values with the modeled return values. The abscissa is the return period and the ordinate is the return value. The empirical plot consists of the points

$$\left\{ \left(\tilde{N}(x_{(i)}), x_{(i)} \right) : i = 1, \ldots, n \right\} \quad [144]$$

where

$$\tilde{N}(x_{(i)}) = \left[v \left(1 - \tilde{F}(x_{(i)}) \right) \right]^{-1} \quad [145]$$

and v is the mean number of storms per year. As for the quantile plots, it is appropriate to define the empirical distribution function to be the nonexceedance probability that corresponds to the mean value of the order statistics. The difference in this case is significant. If the empirical distribution function is defined in the form $\tilde{F}(x_{(i)}) = (i+a)/(n+b)$, then the return period assigned to the largest observation in N years is $\tilde{N} = N(n+b)/(n(b-a))$. Consider the example with $v = 5$, $N = 20$, and $n = vN = 100$. If the empirical distribution function is defined in the same way as for the probability plots with $\tilde{F}(x_{(i)}) = i/(n+1)$, then $\tilde{N} = 20.2$ years, whereas if it is defined in the same way as the quantile plots with $\tilde{F}(x_{(i)}) = i/(n + 0.53 - 0.50\xi)$, then $\tilde{N} = 30.7$ for $\xi = -0.25$, $\tilde{N} = 37.9$ for $\xi = 0$, and $\tilde{N} = 49.6$ for $\xi = 0.25$. This may seem strange that the largest value observed in 20 years can be assigned a return period much greater than 20 years. However, in Section 8.03.6.3.2(iii), it was pointed out that there is an ~63% probability that the *N*-year return value is exceeded in *N* years. It therefore makes sense to define the empirical distribution function such that the return value of the largest observation is equal to the return value of the mean value of the largest sample.

The plot of modeled values consists of the points

$$\{(N, \hat{x}_N) : N \in [0, T]\} \qquad [146]$$

where $\hat{x}_N$ is given by eqn [124] with the GPD parameters substituted with their estimates. Note that for both the empirical and model plots, it is the ordinate that is the random variable (assuming that the observation period is long enough for v to be estimated reasonably precisely). In practice though, confidence bounds are not added to the empirical return values because the distribution F is not known. However, confidence bounds can be added to the modeled return values using a bootstrap method. An example is shown in **Figure 37** for the data from buoy 46002. As with the other diagnostic plots, a good agreement is observed between the model and empirical values, with the empirical return values all falling within the 95% confidence bounds for the model. In this example, the observation period was 23.5 years, with a mean value of 11.5 storms per year at this threshold level. The estimated GPD shape parameter was $\hat{\xi} = -0.140$. The return value of the largest observation was therefore set at 39.2 years. The estimated 95% confidence interval of the shape parameter is (−0.27, −0.04), which puts the mean return period of the largest observation between 35.4 and 44.4 years. Conversely, from **Figure 34**, the COV of the largest observation is around 10–15%.

8.03.6.3.2(vii)   The effect of seasonality, directionality, and other covariates
The POT/GPD model for extremes assumes that threshold crossings and the values of the exceedances are independent and identically distributed. For wave data, the assumption of identically distributed exceedances is not valid, since the distribution of H_s varies with other variables, known as covariates, such as the time of year and direction of origin of the storm, or climatic variables such as the NAO index. A lot of practitioners ignore covariate effects and use a stationary model to estimate extremes, but it is also possible to use statistical models that take into account covariate effects.

The simplest approach to modeling seasonal or directional effects is to analyze the data in discrete seasons or directional sectors over which the distribution can be considered approximately stationary (e.g., Reference 157). Alternatively, one can assume that the distribution parameters vary smoothly with season or direction and use a Fourier expansion to describe the variation (e.g., References 158 and 171). Threshold selection is problematic when estimating the variation of parameters using a Fourier expansion. When the data are split into separate seasons or directional sectors, the methods described in Section 8.03.6.3.2(v) can be used to select an appropriate threshold for each season or directional sector. As far as the present author is concerned, no objective method has been proposed for selecting a threshold when the parameters are modeled as varying smoothly throughout the year. Anderson *et al.* [158] chose arbitrarily to set the threshold as the 90th percentile of the data for each month. Jonathan and Ewans [172] used a variable threshold, estimated for each day of the year as the 50th or 80th percentile of the nearest 300 storm peaks (in terms of season). However, they note that the effect of the choice of threshold appears more influential than the incorporation of seasonally varying extreme value parameters. Moreover, there is no *a priori* reason to assume that the threshold for which the GPD can be considered a reasonable fit will correspond to the same percentile of the data or storm peaks in each season.

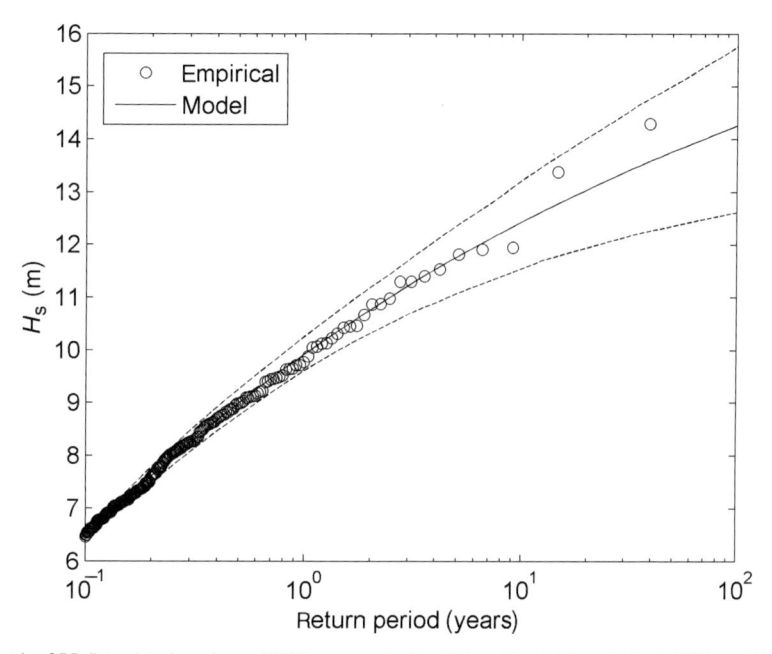

Figure 37   Return value plot for GPD fit to data from buoy 46002 at a threshold of 6.2 m. Dashed lines indicate 95% confidence bounds from bootstrap trial model fit.

Another approach to modeling the seasonality of extreme sea states has been taken by Stefanakos and Athanassoulis [162]. They use the normalization described in Section 8.03.6.3.2(i) to remove the seasonal cycle from the data and estimate extreme conditions from the normalized series. However, they do not show whether the extremal properties of their fitted model are actually a good match to those of the original data, so it is not possible to comment on the accuracy of this method.

There has been some debate in the literature about whether it is preferable to use covariate models rather than stationary models. It has been suggested by several authors (e.g., References 157, 158, and 173) that covariate models will give more accurate results since they explain more of the variability in the data and because the data violate assumptions made in the stationary model. In studies that compare estimates of extremes from stationary and nonstationary models using real data, the true return values are not known, so it is not possible to determine which models are more accurate, only that the results differ. Jonathan et al. [173] have used simulated directional data where the true return values are known and compared results from directional and nondirectional models. In their study, data come from two separate distributions, representing storms from two directions, but which could equally be interpreted as storms from different seasons. They demonstrate that in the cases they consider, the nondirectional models underestimate the return values. However, the examples presented in this study are rather artificial since in real situations the distribution of storm peak wave height will vary smoothly with direction, season, or other covariates, rather than changing sharply at the boundary of two sectors.

To address the question of whether it is preferable to use discrete seasonal and directional models in real situations, Mackay et al. [174] constructed more realistic simulations, where the distribution of storm peak wave height varies smoothly throughout the year. The simulations were based on the seasonal variation observed from long records of data (20–30 years) from 14 wave buoys in the Northeast Pacific. The data from the simulations were analyzed using both seasonal and nonseasonal models. The seasonal analyses were conducted using seasons of length 1, 2, and 3 months. The simulations showed the following results:

- The nonseasonal analyses performed at least as well as the seasonal analyses and in the majority of cases performed significantly better, with lower bias and RMS error.
- Of the seasonal analyses, the 3-month season models had the best performance, followed by the 2-month season models, with the 1-month season models consistently having the highest bias and RMS error.
- For the nonseasonal analyses, the bias in the estimate of the return value was small and remained roughly constant with the return period, whereas for the seasonal analyses, the bias increases with the return period.

Despite using more data points in total than the nonseasonal models, the seasonal models had a higher RMS error at high return periods. This was caused by the partitioning of the data into smaller sets. For each season, the smaller sample size results in greater uncertainty in the estimates of model parameters. The seasonal models with longer seasons had larger sample sizes and therefore lower RMS errors.

The reason for the positive bias of the seasonal models can be explained in terms of maxima. Let M denote the annual maximum and M_i denote the maximum in season i. Denote the distribution function of the annual maximum as $F(x) = \Pr\{M < x\}$, the distribution function of the seasonal maxima as $F_i(x) = \Pr\{M_i < x\}$, and estimates of these with a '^' as usual. Then, assuming that the maxima in each season are independent, $F(x) = \prod F_i(x)$. Consider a simple example of a two-season year, where for some high value x, $F_1(x) = F_2(x) = 0.99$ and $F(x) = 0.99^2 = 0.98$. Suppose that when the seasonal distributions are estimated from the data, the nonexceedance probability $\hat{F}_1(x)$ is underestimated, $\hat{F}_1(x) = 0.95$ say, but $\hat{F}_2(x)$ is either accurate or overestimated, $\hat{F}_2(x) \geq 0.99$. Then, $\hat{F}(x) \leq 0.95$. So the effect of an overestimate of the probability of exceeding a high value in one season is not compensated for by underestimates of the probability of exceeding that high value in the other season. Moreover, the sensitivity of the annual distribution to estimates in individual seasons will increase at higher quantiles, as $F_i(x) \to 1$. Therefore, the more seasons the year is divided into, the greater the chance that there will be an overestimate in one season. Since this overestimate is not compensated for by the estimates in other seasons, the annual distribution becomes highly biased at high quantiles.

From the results of Mackay et al. [174], it can be concluded that discrete seasonal or directional analyses should not be used to determine annual or omnidirectional return values, and that stationary models give more accurate results. If estimates of return values are required for separate seasons or direction sectors, then a model that estimates the parameters of the distribution as a smoothly varying function of direction or time could be used (e.g., References 158 and 172). However, the present author is not aware of any simulation studies that demonstrate the accuracy of smoothly varying covariate models and compare them with the accuracy of a stationary model.

8.03.6.3.2(viii) The effect of uncertainties in hindcast wave data

Errors in numerical model data can be large at high wave heights. Numerous authors have noted the tendency of models to underestimate H_s in extreme conditions (see, e.g., References 175 and 176). Even if the bias in the model data can be removed by calibration against *in situ* or satellite measurements, the random error can still result in a bias in the estimated distribution of extremes. This is because the distribution observed in the model data is the convolution of the true distribution of wave heights with the error distribution, which results in the tail of the model distribution being stretched. If we denote the true distribution of storm peaks as f, the distribution inferred from the model data as g, and the error distribution as δ, then we have

$$g(x) = \int_{-\infty}^{\infty} f(z)\delta(x-z \mid z)dz \qquad [147]$$

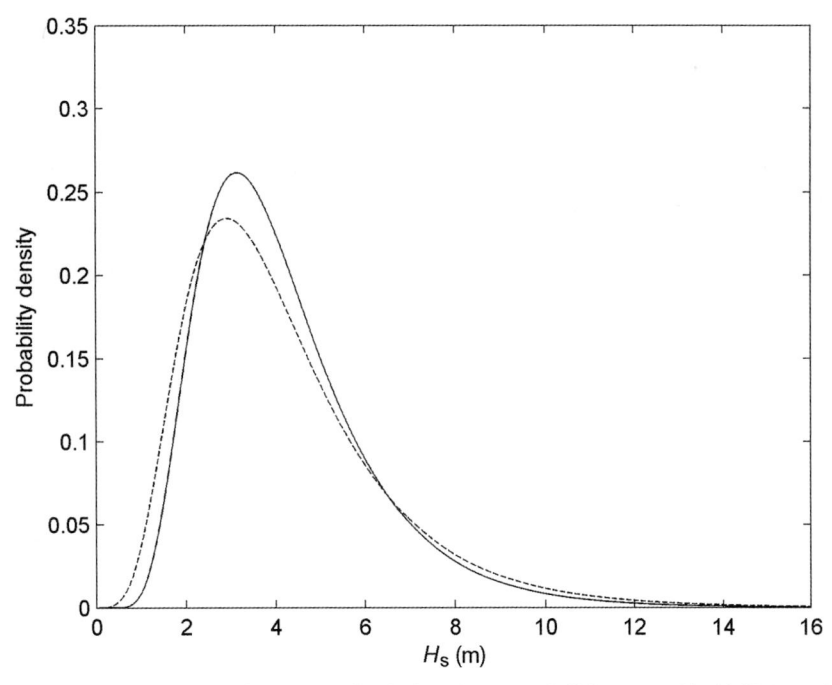

Figure 38 Solid line, distribution of storm peak H_s; Dashed line, distribution of storm peak H_s from a model with 25% standard error.

Note that the error distribution is conditional on z, since the error variance usually increases with wave height. An example of the effect of this convolution is shown in **Figure 38**. The true distribution is assumed to be lognormal with parameters $\mu = 1.34$ and $\sigma = 0.44$, and density function

$$f(x) = \frac{1}{x\sigma\sqrt{2\pi}} \exp\left(\frac{-(\ln(x) - \mu)^2}{2\sigma^2}\right) \quad [148]$$

These parameters have been chosen to approximate the distribution of storm peak wave heights observed from NDBC buoy 46002, used as an example throughout this section. The error distribution is assumed to be normal, with zero mean and standard deviation equal to $0.25H_s$. A 25% error is larger than usually observed in practice, but is used here to illustrate the effect of the convolution. **Figure 38** shows the true density function f together with the model distribution g, calculated using eqn [147]. The effect of the convolution is to stretch the tails of the model distribution relative to the true distribution and to reduce the mode of the distribution.

Hindcast uncertainty increases both the bias and the uncertainty of estimated return values. To illustrate its significance in relation to the uncertainty from finite sampling effects, **Figure 39** shows the bias and uncertainty in the estimates of the 100-year

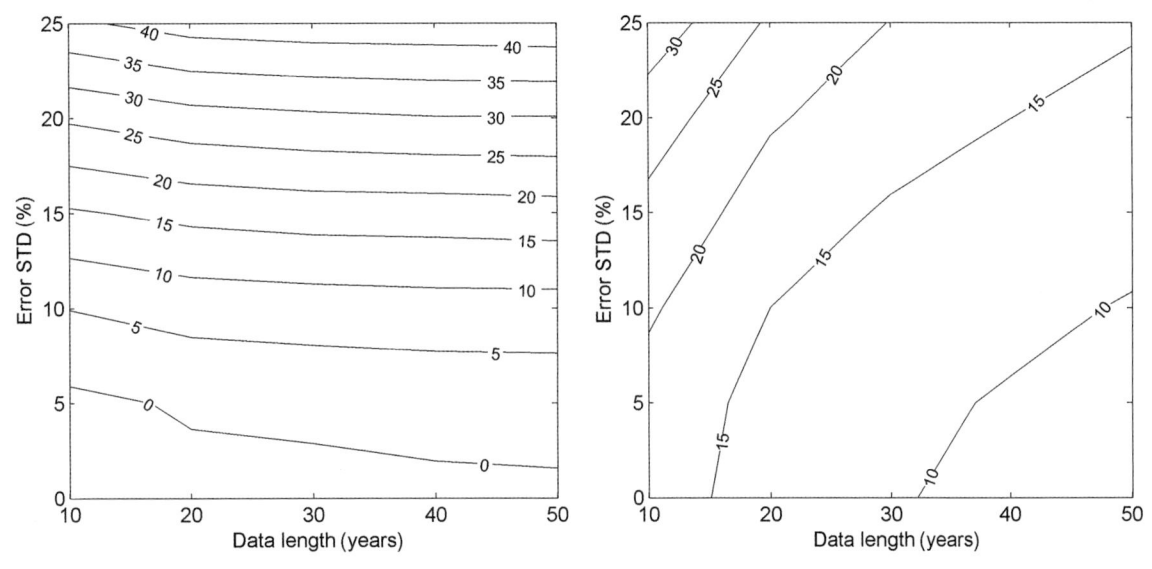

Figure 39 Bias (left) and uncertainty (right) in estimates of the 100-year return value (RV) as a function of data length and error STD (see text for simulation parameters).

return value as a function of the number of years of data and standard error in modeled storm peaks. In this example, it has been assumed that data come from a GPD with $u = 5$ m, $\sigma = 1$, $\xi = 0$, and a mean rate of 5 storms above the threshold per year. For each combination of data length and error standard deviation (STD), 10 000 simulations have been conducted as follows:

- Independent random variables $x_1,..., x_n$ are generated from a GPD where $n = 5N$ and N is the data length in years.
- Independent random variables $e_1,..., e_n$ are generated from the standard normal distribution.
- The modeled data are defined as $y_i = x_i(1 + se_i)$, where s is the standard error of the model data.
- The GPD is fit to $y_1,..., y_n$ using the LM method (see Section 8.03.6.3.2(iv)) and the 100-year return value is estimated.

The bias and standard deviation in the estimates of the 100-year return are then calculated over the 10 000 simulations. It is clear that the bias does not decrease significantly with the length of data. For the cases with zero model error, there is a small negative bias that decreases with sample size. This is a feature of the LM estimators, but in comparison with other estimators, this bias is relatively small (see Section 8.03.6.3.2(iv)). The bias from the hindcast uncertainty is significant in relation to the standard deviation of the estimates. For example, for a 20-year record length (100 samples) and standard error in the model data of 15%, the bias in the 100-year return value is 16.3% and the standard deviation is 17.5%. The values of the bias and standard deviation in estimates will change with different GPD parameters, but the example illustrates the significance.

Brooker et al. [177] discuss the problem of estimating the true distribution f from the model distribution g and error distribution δ. They propose an MLM in which the parameters of f are estimated directly from the convolution integral in eqn [147]. In the example they present, it is assumed that the tail of the distribution follows a two-parameter Weibull distribution, but they note that the method appears not to work very well with the GPD. This *a priori* assumption of the form of the distribution can lead to significant errors, as described in Section 8.03.6.3.1.

A slightly different approach was proposed by Mackay [178], which utilizes the POT/GPD framework described in the preceding sections. The first step involves fitting the GPD to threshold excesses, as described above. A parametric model is then fitted to all the declustered storm maxima and an iterative procedure is used for deconvolution of the true distribution from the error distribution. It was demonstrated that the choice of parametric distribution used to model all the storm peaks does not influence the estimates of extremes. First, we present an example of how the deconvolution procedure works.

The iterative procedure for deconvolution works by estimating the difference between the model distribution and the true distribution. We denote this difference as

$$\varepsilon(x) = g(x) - f(x) = \left[\int_{-\infty}^{\infty} f(z)\delta(x-z|z)\mathrm{d}z \right] - f(x) \qquad [149]$$

As a first guess, we can assume that the effect of the convolution of the true distribution with the error distribution is approximately equal to the effect of the convolution of the model distribution with the error distribution, that is,

$$\varepsilon_0(x) = \left[\int_{-\infty}^{\infty} g(z)\delta(x-z|z)\mathrm{d}z \right] - g(x) \qquad [150]$$

So the first estimate of the true distribution is given by

$$f_1(x) = g(x) - \varepsilon_0(x) \qquad [151]$$

Iterative improvements can be made to this estimate by inserting the new estimate of f back into eqn [150], so that

$$\varepsilon_i(x) = \left[\int_{-\infty}^{\infty} f_i(z)\delta(x-z|z)\mathrm{d}z \right] - f_i(x) \qquad [152]$$

$$f_{i+1}(x) = g(x) - \varepsilon_i(x) \qquad [153]$$

Depending on the distribution, there can be convergence problems with this algorithm if the initial error estimate ε_0 is too large. This problem can be addressed by slowing the rate of change between iterations, by including a function $\gamma(i)$ that controls the convergence speed:

$$f_{i+1}(x) = g(x) - \gamma(i+1)\varepsilon_i(x) \qquad [154]$$

The precise definition of γ is not critical and $\gamma(i) = \tanh(i/2)$ is usually a reasonable choice. Consider the example described above of a lognormal distribution, convolved with normal errors with a standard deviation of 25%. **Figure 40** shows the ratio of f_i/f for the first 20 iterations. The density function f_0 is just the model density function g and shows a large positive bias for low and high H_s, as was observed in **Figure 38**. The first iteration shows a small improvement, but by the fifth iteration, the distributions are approximately equal for $H_s < 15$ m, and by the 20th iteration, the ratio is almost unity for the entire range. Note that there is some instability in the ratio f_i/f for $H_s < 1$ m. This occurs because the value of f is very close to zero in this range – much more so than in the right tail – so the ratio f_i/f exhibits large oscillations. However, the value of f_i remains close to zero and improves with further iterations.

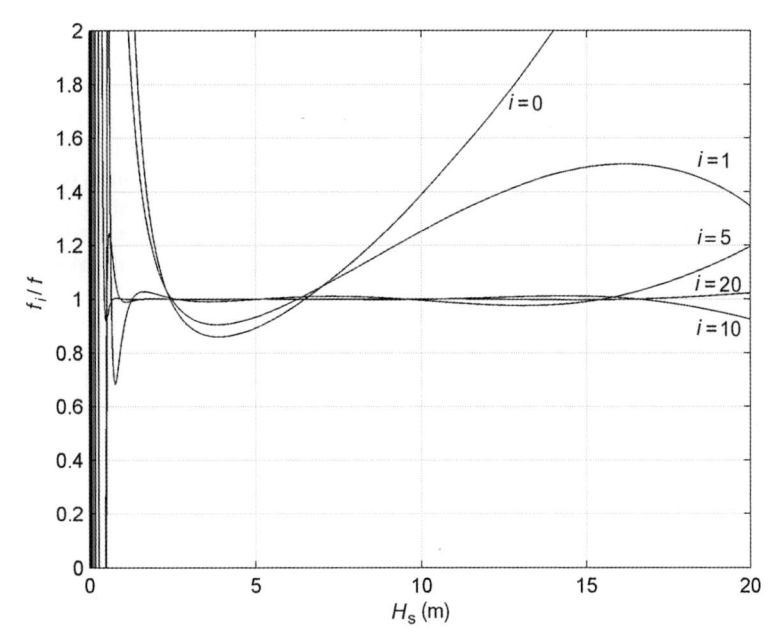

Figure 40 Ratio of density function estimated from iterative deconvolution procedure, f_i, to true density function, f.

If we assume that storms occur at an average rate of once every 5 days, we can calculate the effect that the errors in the model distribution can have on the estimated return values. The 50- and 100-year return values for the true distribution are 17.47 and 18.93 m, respectively (rather higher than the return values estimated in Section 8.03.6.3 for this location, which emphasizes the drawbacks with the ID method). The bias in the return values as a function of the number of iterations is shown in **Figure 41**, with the zeroth iteration representing the initial model distribution. The initial biases in the 50- and 100-year return values are 2.93 and 3.30 m, respectively. It is perhaps worth reiterating here that this bias was caused by the effect of a zero-mean random error (although with a standard error of 25%, which is somewhat larger than would be expected in practice). The first iterative estimate of the true density function produces return values that are too low, since the effect of the convolution is overestimated at first. However, after 20 iterations, the bias is less than 1 cm for both the 50- and 100-year return values. In practice, where the true return values are not known, the iterations can be terminated when the return values converge to a desired precision.

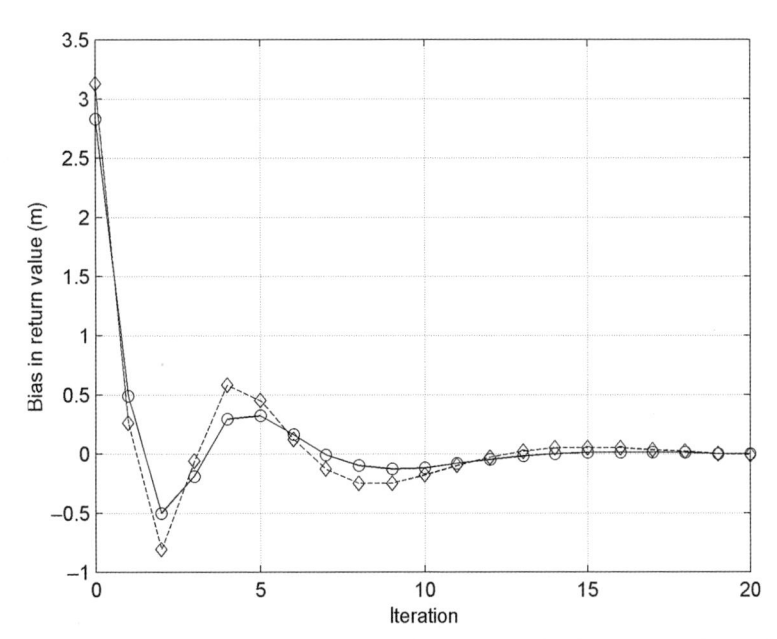

Figure 41 Bias in return value for iterative estimates of the density function. Solid line is bias in 50-year return value and dashed line is bias in 100-year return value.

In the example presented above, we have assumed that the model distribution is fitted over the entire range of the data. In practice, however, the GPD is only fitted for exceedances over a high threshold and we do not model the distribution of the bulk of the data. This can be overcome by fitting a distribution to the bulk of the data and adjusting it so that the density function matches the GPD at the threshold value. The choice of distribution for the bulk of the data is not important, as the far right tail is only affected by the convolution with the GPD part of the tail. However, to avoid numerical instabilities in the deconvolution procedure, it is necessary to ensure that the density function has smooth transition between the distribution of the bulk of the data and the GPD. A method to achieve this was proposed by Mackay [178] and it produced reasonable results. The algorithm converged in all trials with error STDs less than 15%, but diverged in around 20% of the trials with an error STD of 20% and diverged in over half of the trials for error STDs of 25%. Despite the convergence problems, the algorithm still reduced the bias to less than 1% in trials with error STDs up to 20% and around 2% in trials with an error STD of 25%.

For error STDs less than about 5%, it does not seem worthy of using the deconvolution procedure as the bias is not significant and may indeed be offset if an estimator with negative bias in estimates of high quantiles is used such as the LM or ML estimators (although note that estimators such as the PWM and moment estimators give positive bias for small sample sizes). However, the use of a deconvolution procedure can significantly reduce the bias when the hindcast has a high error STD.

8.03.6.4 Combining Long-Term and Short-Term Distributions

After the short-term and long-term distributions have been estimated, they can be combined to estimate the distribution of the maximum wave or crest height in a given period. The problem of how to do this correctly is rather subtle and the answer you get depends on the question you ask. The problem is asking the correct question. For the design of wave farms, the most relevant question is likely to be: "What is the probability that a storm will occur in a given period in which at least one wave exceeds a given size?"

The 'classic' method for combining long-term and short-term distributions involves modeling the long-term distribution of sea states and then calculating the distribution of individual wave or crest heights for the most severe r-hour sea state (where r is typically 3 or 6) in an N-year period. This neglects the probability that the highest wave will occur in a lower sea state. Carter and Challenor [179] showed that this can lead to a significant underestimation in estimates of extremes, since there will be several r-hour periods with H_s close to the most severe value, either within the same storm or in separate storms.

Forristall [180] has compared the various methods that address the shortcoming of the 'classic' method. Battjes [181] proposed a method (subsequently refined by Tucker [182]) to calculate the distribution of the maximum wave in each r-hour period. Another method was proposed by Krogstad [183], where the distribution of all wave heights in an N-year period is given by integrating the short-term distribution over the probability density function of significant wave height. Forristall [180] demonstrated that the Krogstad method gives significantly higher estimates of return values for individual waves than the Battjes method. He explains that the reason for this discrepancy is that when a storm occurs in which the H_s exceeds the N-year return value, there can be many very large individual waves during that interval. All of these individual waves go into the distribution given by Krogstad [183], whereas the Battjes method only counts the highest wave in each r-hour interval. Forristall goes on to note that the Battjes method gives higher estimates than methods that only consider the highest wave in each storm, since there can be several high waves in separate r-hour periods within each storm. Or as Arena and Pavone [184] put it, "the number of crests exceeding a fixed threshold η is greater than the number of storms in which the maximum crest height exceeds η".

As noted above, it seems more important for engineering purposes to know the probability that a single storm occurs in which a wave exceeds a given size. If such a storm occurs, usually it does not matter if that wave height is exceeded more than once within that storm. Therefore, in this section, we consider methods to calculate the distribution of the maximum wave in a random storm. (Although more recently, Arena and Pavone [185] have given formulas for the probability of occurrence of a storm in which k waves exceed a threshold.)

The first approach to estimating this distribution may be to perform a POT analysis on the maximum wave in each storm. However, records of individual wave heights that are long enough to estimate the long-term distribution do not exist. The most probable maximum in each storm can be calculated using the method described in Section 8.03.6.4.1, but fitting the GPD to the most probable highest wave in each storm neglects the chance that the highest wave may exceed the most probable.

Forristall [180] demonstrated that the method of Tromans and Vanderschuren [161] gives the correct solution to this problem and recommends that their method should be used to combine long-term and short-term distributions. The method of Tromans and Vanderschuren [161] combines the distribution of most probable maximum wave heights in a storm, with the distribution of the maximum wave height, conditional on the most probable wave height. The method presented in the remainder of the section is based on the equivalent triangular storm (ETS) method of Boccotti [186], later simplified by Arena and Pavone [184]. It is similar to Tromans and Vanderschuren's approach and ends up at the same answer. Both methods make some approximations to end up at a solution, but it is easier to understand how the approximations come about in the ETS method and to demonstrate that the approximations do not affect the end result. We start in Section 8.03.6.4.1 by showing how the distribution of the maximum wave in a storm is calculated. In Section 8.03.6.4.2, we show how this distribution is closely matched by an ETS. Finally, in Section 8.03.6.4.3, we show how the distribution of storm peak wave heights can be combined with the short-term distribution of wave or crest heights, using the concept of the ETS. Throughout this section, we will use notation referring to wave heights rather than crest heights, but the theory is applicable to either of these.

8.03.6.4.1 The distribution of the maximum wave or crest height in a storm

If it is assumed that individual wave or crest heights are independent, then the probability that the maximum does not exceed a level h in an interval Δt is simply the product of the probability that each individual wave does not exceed h. In the interval Δt, there are $\Delta t/T_z$ waves, so

$$\Pr\{H_{\max} \leq h \,|\, H_s\} = [\Pr\{H \leq h \,|\, H_s\}]^{\Delta t/T_z} \tag{155}$$

In reality, consecutive wave and crest heights are correlated, with the largest waves occurring in groups. However, the assumption of independence in eqn [155] is not restrictive. Krogstad and Barstow [187] note that for Gaussian processes, there is an analytical theory for the distribution of the maximum value during a given period of time, and that this theory gives identical results to eqn [155]. They argue that this observation makes it reasonable to use eqn [155] in the case of nonlinear waves, where in general no analytical theory exists.

During a storm, the value of H_s will vary over time. Battjes [181] and Borgman [188] developed a method to calculate the distribution of the maximum wave in a storm with time-varying H_s at roughly the same time, but the method is now usually referred to as the Borgman integral. Given a storm s with time-varying significant wave height $H_s(t)$, the probability that the maximum wave in the storm does not exceed a value h is the product of the probabilities that it does not exceed h within each interval t_i, $i = 1,\ldots, k$, during the storm:

$$\Pr\{H_{\max} \leq h \,|\, s\} = \prod_{i=1}^{k} [\Pr\{H \leq h \,|\, H_s(t_i)\}]^{\Delta t/T_z(t_i)}$$

$$= \exp\left(\sum_{i=1}^{k} \frac{\Delta t}{T_z(t_i)} \ln[\Pr\{H \leq h \,|\, H_s(t_i)\}]\right) \tag{156}$$

As $\Delta t \to 0$, eqn [156] can be expressed as an integral

$$\Pr\{H_{\max} \leq h \,|\, s\} = \exp\left(\int_0^D \frac{1}{T_z(t)} \ln[\Pr\{H \leq h \,|\, H_s(t)\}]\,\mathrm{d}t\right) \tag{157}$$

where D is the duration of the storm. The integral in eqn [157] needs to be evaluated over the interval where $H_s(t) \geq 0.8\max(H_s(t))$ as values outside this range do not affect the distribution of the maximum. Tucker and Pitt [26] showed that eqn [157] is 16 times more sensitive to changes in the peak H_s than T_z. This means that $T_z(t)$ can be replaced by a mean value for a given H_s, denoted $\bar{T}_z(H_s)$, without affecting the calculation. In the absence of measured data, it is usually assumed that the significant steepness of the storm, defined as $s = 2\pi H_s/gT_z^2$, is 1/18, which gives $T_z \approx 3.40\sqrt{H_s}$.

8.03.6.4.2 The equivalent triangular storm

When evaluating the summation in eqn [156], the order in which each value of H_s occurs does not matter, but only the duration at each level of H_s matters. Therefore, the intervals t_i could be reordered to give an equivalent storm, symmetric about the peak H_s, in which $H_s(t_i)$ increases monotonically to the peak value. This reordered shape can be approximated by a triangular storm, for which the expected maximum wave or crest height is equal to the value from eqn [156]. This is known as the ETS. More recently, Fedele and Arena [189] have proposed a generalization of this method, known as the equivalent power storm, where H_s is assumed to vary as a power law of time, rather than the linear assumption made in the ETS method. The reader is referred to this article for details.

The distribution of the maximum wave in a triangular storm can be calculated using the Borgman integral. Consider an isosceles triangle of height a and base b. The H_s in this storm is given by $H_s(t) = 2at/b$ for $0 < t \leq b/2$ and $H_s(t) = 2a - 2at/b$ for $b/2 < t \leq b$. Noting that $|\mathrm{d}H_s/\mathrm{d}t| = 2a/b$, the Borgman integral for this storm can be written as

$$\Pr\{H_{\max} \leq h \,|\, a,b\} = \exp\left(\frac{b}{a}\int_0^a \frac{1}{\bar{T}_z(H_s)} \ln[\Pr\{H \leq h \,|\, H_s\}]\,\mathrm{d}H_s\right) \tag{158}$$

The value of a for the ETS is simply the peak H_s in the measured storm, but the value of b must be found by numerical methods. First, the expected value of the maximum wave in the measured storm, denoted $E(H_{\max})$, is computed as

$$E(H_{\max}) = \int_0^\infty h \frac{\mathrm{d}}{\mathrm{d}h}[\Pr\{H_{\max} \leq h \,|\, s\}]\,\mathrm{d}h \tag{159}$$

Now, if we define

$$Q(h) = \frac{1}{a}\int_0^a \frac{1}{\bar{T}_z(H_s)} \ln[\Pr\{H \leq h \,|\, H_s\}]\,\mathrm{d}H_s \tag{160}$$

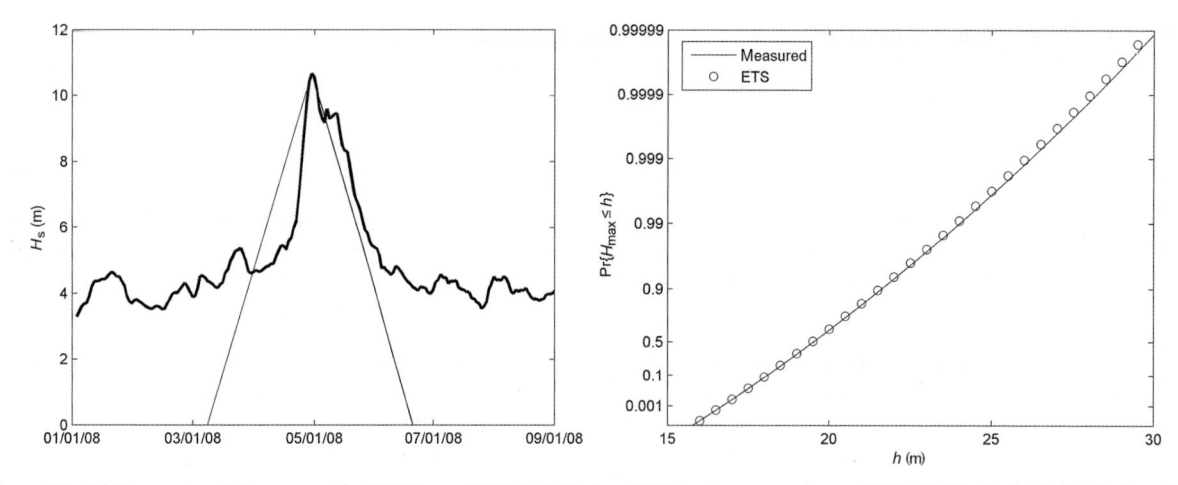

Figure 42 (a) Time series of H_s measured by NDBC buoy 46002 (bold line) and ETS to storm occurring on 05/01/08 (thin line). (b) Distribution of the maximum wave in the storm calculated from measured H_s and ETS.

then b is found by solving

$$0 = g(b) = E(H_{\max}) - \int_0^\infty h \frac{d}{dh}[\exp(b \cdot Q(h))]dh \qquad [161]$$

It is clear that $g(b)$ is a smooth monotonic function, with a unique solution in $(0, \infty)$, and thus readily amenable to numerical solution. Moreover, the function $Q(h)$ needs to be computed only once. Typically, it is sufficient to compute the integral over the range $a \leq h \leq 3a$.

An example of the ETS to a storm measured by NDBC buoy 46002 on 5 January 2008 is shown in **Figure 42(a)**. The storm has a peak H_s of 10.67 m (after taking a 3 h moving average) and the ETS has a duration of $b = 82.0$ h. The distribution of wave heights has been computed using eqn [108] with $\psi = 0.75$. To illustrate that eqn [157] is not sensitive to the precise value of T_z used, we have computed the distribution of the maximum wave in the storm using the measured values of T_z and the distribution for the ETS using $T_z = 3.40\sqrt{H_s}$. In this case, the measured T_z at the peak of the storm was 10.8 s and the peak value used in the ETS calculation is 11.1 s, so the difference is quite small. A comparison of the two distributions is shown in **Figure 42(b)**. A double-logarithmic scale is used on the y-axis to emphasize the fit at very low exceedance probabilities. The distribution from the ETS is a good match to the distribution calculated from the measured data, over the entire range. The distribution of the maximum wave from the ETS usually provides a good fit to the distribution from the measured storm, even if the 'reordered' shape of the storm is not exactly triangular. Further examples of the performance of the ETS model are presented in the work of Boccotti [186] and Arena and Pavone [184].

Under the double-logarithmic scale used in **Figure 42(b)**, a Gumbel distribution would appear as a straight line. It can be seen that the distribution of the maximum wave height in the storm is very close to a Gumbel distribution. Borgman [188] and Tromans and Vanderschuren [161] proposed the use of a Gumbel distribution to model the distribution of the maximum wave height in a storm. The example presented here lends support to the assertion made in the introduction to this section that the ETS method is in close agreement with Tromans and Vanderschuren's method. However, it is easier to understand the motivation for the ETS method, since it does not require asymptotic arguments. Moreover, it is simple to verify that the approximations made in the ETS method do not affect the results.

8.03.6.4.3 The long-term distribution of the maximum wave or crest height

To calculate the distribution of the maximum wave in N years, we first need to calculate the distribution of the maximum wave in a random storm. This can be calculated by integrating the distribution of the maxima from the ETS over the density functions of the triangle heights and bases:

$$\Pr\{H_{\max} \leq h \mid r.s.\} = \int_0^\infty \int_0^\infty p_A(a) p_B(b \mid a) \Pr\{H_{\max} \leq h \mid a, b\} da\, db \qquad [162]$$

where $p_A(a)$ is the density function of the triangle heights and $p_B(b \mid a)$ is the density function of the triangle bases, conditional on a, and r.s. denotes a random storm. The effect of changes in the ETS duration b is actually very small and the above equation can be calculated using an approximation where b is constant for a given value of a, $\bar{b}(a)$.

$$\Pr\{H_{\max} \leq h \mid r.s.\} = \int_0^\infty p_A(a) \Pr\{H_{\max} \leq h \mid a, \bar{b}(a)\} da \qquad [163]$$

The function $\bar{b}(a)$ can be estimated by regression of b on a. Usually, the regression is of the form $\bar{b} = x\exp(-ya)$, where $x, y > 0$ so that $\bar{b}(a)$ is always positive, which may not be the case if linear regression is used.

The distribution of the maximum wave in N years is then given by the distribution of the maximum wave in a random storm, raised to the expected number of storms in N years:

$$\Pr\{H_{\max} \leq h \mid N\} = [\Pr\{H_{\max} \leq h \mid r.s.\}]^{vN} \qquad [164]$$

where v is number of storms exceeding threshold per year.

Finally, the return period, $N(h)$, for a given wave height is given by

$$N(h) = \frac{1}{v \cdot \Pr\{H_{\max} > h \mid r.s.\}} \qquad [165]$$

So to summarize, the procedure to follow to arrive at an estimate of the distribution of the maximum wave or crest height in N years can be broken down into the following steps:

1. Identify storm maxima.
2. Calculate Borgman integral for each storm and find ETS.
3. Estimate $\bar{b}(a)$ and $\bar{T}_z(H_s)$ from the data, using regression.
4. Estimate $p_A(a)$ using POT.
5. Calculate distribution of the largest wave or crest height in a random storm.
6. Calculate distribution of the largest wave or crest height in N years.

References

[1] Rice SO (1944) The mathematical analysis of random noise. *Bell Systems Technical Journal* 23: 282–332.
[2] Rice SO (1945) The mathematical analysis of random noise. *Bell Systems Technical Journal* 24: 46–156.
[3] Young IR and van Vledder GP (1993) A review of the central role of nonlinear interactions in wind-wave evolution. *Philosophical Transactions of the Royal Society of London A* 342: 505–524.
[4] Holthuijsen LH (2007) *Waves in Oceanic and Coastal Waters*. Cambridge, UK: Cambridge University Press.
[5] Bretschneider CL (1959) Wave variability and wave spectra for wind generated gravity waves. Technical Memorandum No. 118. Washington, DC: Beach Erosion Board, US Army Corps of Engineers.
[6] Pierson WJ and Moskowitz L (1964) A proposed spectral form for fully developed wind seas based on the similarity theory of S. A. Kitaigorodskii. *Journal of Geophysical Research* 69(24): 5181–5190.
[7] Hasselmann K, Barnett TP, and Bouws E (1973) Measurements of wind wave growth and swell decay during the Joint North Sea Wave Project (JONSWAP). *Deutsche Pharmazeutische Gesellschaft* A8: 1–95.
[8] Ochi MK and Hubble EN (1976) Six-parameter wave spectra. In: *Proceedings of the 15th Coastal Engineering Conference*, pp. 301–328. Honolulu, HI: ASCE.
[9] Bouws E, Gunther H, Rosenthal W, and Vincent CL (1985) Similarity of the wind wave spectrum in finite depth. Part 1: Spectral form. *Journal of Geophysical Research* 90(C1): 975–986.
[10] Young IR and Babanin AV (2006) The form of the asymptotic depth-limited wind wave frequency spectrum. *Journal of Geophysical Research* 111: C06031.
[11] Guedes Soares C (1984) Representation of double-peaked sea wave spectra. *Ocean Engineering* 11: 185–207.
[12] Torsethaugen K (1993) A two peak wave spectrum model. In: *Proceedings of the 12th International Conference on Offshore Mechanics and Arctic Engineering*, vol. 2, pp. 175–180. New York: ASME.
[13] Torsethaugen K and Haver S (2004) Simplified double peak spectral model for ocean waves. *Proceedings of the 14th International Offshore and Polar Engineering Conference*. Toulon, France.
[14] Boukhanovsky AV and Guedes Soares C (2009) Modelling of multipeaked directional wave spectra. *Applied Ocean Research* 31: 132–141.
[15] Cartwright DE (1963) The use of directional spectra in studying output of a wave recorder on a moving ship. In: *Ocean Wave Spectra: Proceedings of a Conference (National Academy of Sciences)*, pp. 203–219. 23–28 May 2004. Englewood Cliffs, NJ: Prentice Hall.
[16] Ewans KC (1998) Observations of the directional spectrum of fetch-limited waves. *Journal of Physical Oceanography* 28: 495–512.
[17] Hwang PA, Wang DW, Walsh EJ, et al. (2000) Airborne measurements of the wavenumber spectra of ocean surface waves. Part II: Directional distribution. *Journal of Physical Oceanography* 30(11): 2768–2787.
[18] Young IR, Verhagen LA, and Banner ML (1995) A note on the bimodal directional spreading of fetch-limited waves. *Journal of Geophysical Research* 100(C1): 773–778.
[19] Donelan MA, Hamilton J, and Hui WH (1985) Directional spectra of wind-generated waves. *Philosophical Transactions of the Royal Society of London A* 315: 509–562.
[20] Hasselmann DE, Dunckel M, and Ewing JA (1980) Directional wave spectra observed during JONSWAP 1973. *Journal of Physical Oceanography* 10: 1264–1280.
[21] Mitsuyasu H, Tasai F, Suhara T, et al. (1975) Observations of the directional spectrum of ocean waves using a cloverleaf buoy. *Journal of Physical Oceanography* 5(4): 750–760.
[22] Ewans KC (2001) Directional spreading in ocean swell. In: *Proceedings of the Ocean Wave Measurement and Analysis*, pp. 517–529. San Francisco, CA: ASCE.
[23] DTI (2007) Preliminary wave energy performance protocol. DTI Report 07/807. London: DTI.
[24] Smith GH, Venugopal V, and Falsham J (2006) Wave spectral bandwidth as a measure of available wave power. *Proceedings of the 25th International Conference on OMAE 2006*. Hamburg, Germany, 4–10 June.
[25] Kerbiriou MA, Prevosto M, Maisondieu C, et al. (2007) Influence of sea-states description on wave energy production assessment. *Proceedings of the 7th European Wave and Tidal Energy Conference*. Porto, Portugal, 11–13 September 2007.
[26] Tucker MJ and Pitt EG (2001) *Waves in Ocean Engineering*. London: Elsevier Science Ltd.
[27] Forristall GZ, Barstow SF, Krogstad HE, et al. (2004) Wave crest sensor intercomparison study: An overview of WACSIS. *Journal of Offshore Mechanics and Arctic Engineering* 126(1): 26–34.
[28] Pedersen T and Siegel E (2008) Wave measurements from subsurface buoys. In: *Proceedings of the IEEE/OES/CMTC 9th Working Conference on Current Measurement Technology*, pp. 224–233. Charleston, NC: IEEE.
[29] Kahma K, Hauser D, Krogstad HE, et al. (2005) Measuring and analysing the directional spectra of ocean waves. EU COST Action 714, EUR 21367, ISBN 92-898-0003-8.

[30] Collard F, Ardhuin F, and Chapron B (2005) Extraction of coastal ocean wave fields from SAR images. *IEEE Journal of Oceanic Engineering* 30(3): 526–533.
[31] Schulz-Stellenfleth J, Konig T, and Lehner S (2007) An empirical approach for the retrieval of integral ocean wave parameters from synthetic aperture radar data. *Journal of Geophysical Research* 112: C03019. doi: 10.1029/2006JC003970.
[32] Schulz-Stellenfleth J, Lehner S, and Hoja D (2005) A parametric scheme for the retrieval of two-dimensional ocean wave spectra from synthetic aperture radar look cross spectra. *Journal of Geophysical Research* 110: C05004. doi: 10.1029/2004JC002822.
[33] Violante-Carvalho N, Robinson IS, and Schulz-Stellenfleth J (2005) Assessment of ERS synthetic aperture radar wave spectra retrieved from the Max-Planck-Institut (MPI) scheme through intercomparisons of 1 year of directional buoy measurements. *Journal of Geophysical Research* 110: C07019. doi: 10.1029/2004JC002382.
[34] Abdalla S, Bidlot JR, and Janssen P (2006) Global validation and assimilation of Envisat ASAR wave mode spectra. *Proceedings of SEASAR 2006: Advances in SAR Oceanography from Envisat and ERS Missions*. Frascati, Italy: European Space Agency. 24–26 January 2006.
[35] Gulev SK and Grigorieva V (2004) Last century changes in ocean wind wave height from global visual wave data. *Geophysical Research Letters* 31: L24302. doi: 10.1029/2004GL021040.
[36] Gulev SK and Grigorieva V (2006) Variability of the winter wind waves and swell in the North Atlantic and North Pacific as revealed by the voluntary observing ship data. *Journal of Climate* 19: 5667–5685.
[37] Gulev SK, Grigorieva V, Sterl A, and Woolf D (2003) Assessment of the reliability of wave observations from voluntary observing ships: Insights from the validation of a global wind wave climatology based on voluntary observing ship data. *Journal of Geophysical Research* 108: 3236. doi: 10.1029/2002JC001437.
[38] James ID (1986) A note on the theoretical comparison of wave staff and wave rider buoys in steep gravity waves. *Ocean Engineering* 13: 209–214.
[39] Longuet-Higgins MS (1986) Eulerian and Lagrangian aspects of surface waves. *Journal of Fluid Mechanics* 173: 683–707.
[40] Joosten HP (2006) Wave buoys and their elastic mooring. *International Ocean Systems* 10(3): 18–21.
[41] Rademakers PJ (1993) Waverider–wavestaff comparison. *Ocean Engineering* 20(2): 187–193.
[42] Forristall GZ (2000) Wave crest distributions: Observations and second-order theory. *Journal of Physical Oceanography* 30(8): 1931–1943.
[43] Prevosto M, Krogstad HE, and Robin A (2000) Probability distributions for maximum wave and crest heights. *Coastal Engineering* 40: 329–360.
[44] Barrick DE, Lipa BJ, and Steele KE (1989) Comments on theory and application of calibration techniques for an NDBC directional wave measurements buoy: Nonlinear effects. *IEEE Journal of Oceanic Engineering* 14(3): 268–272.
[45] Steele KE, Lau J, and Hsu YH (1985) Theory and application of calibration techniques for an NDBC directional wave measurements buoy. *Ocean Engineering* 10(4): 382–396.
[46] Allender J, Audunson T, Barstow SF, et al. (1989) The WADIC project: A comprehensive field evaluation of directional wave instrumentation. *Ocean Engineering* 16(5–6): 505–536.
[47] Joosten HP (2006) Directional wave buoys and their elastic mooring. *International Ocean Systems* 10(4): 18–21.
[48] Steele KE (1996) Ocean current kinematic effects on pitch–roll buoy observations of mean wave direction and nondirectional spectra. *Journal of Atmospheric and Oceanic Technology* 14: 278–293.
[49] Krogstad HE, Barstow SF, Aasen SE, and Rodriguez I (1999) Some recent developments in wave buoy measurement technology. *Coastal Engineering* 37: 309–329.
[50] de Vries J, Waldron J, and Cunningham V (2003) Field tests of the new Datawell DWR-G GPS wave buoy. *Sea Technology* 44(12): 50–55.
[51] Rodríguez G, Guedes Soares C, and Machado U (1999) Uncertainty of the sea state parameters resulting from the methods of spectral estimation. *Ocean Engineering* 26: 991–1002.
[52] Massel SR (2001) Wavelet analysis for processing of ocean surface wave records. *Ocean Engineering* 28: 957–987.
[53] Benoit M, Frigaard P, and Schaffer HA (1997) Analysing multidirectional wave spectra: A tentative classification of available methods. *Proceedings of the IAHR Seminar: Multidirectional Waves and Their Interaction with Structures, 27th IAHR Congress*. San Francisco, CA, USA, August.
[54] Longuet-Higgins MS, Cartwright DE, and Smith ND (1963) Observations of the directional spectrum of sea waves using the motions of a floating buoy. In: *Ocean Wave Spectra: Proceedings of a Conference (National Academy of Sciences)*, pp. 111–136. Englewood Cliffs, NJ: Prentice Hall.
[55] Kuik AJ, Van Vledder GP, and Holthuijsen LH (1988) A method for the routine analysis of pitch–roll–heave buoy wave data. *Journal of Physical Oceanography* 18: 1020–1034.
[56] Pawka SS (1983) Island shadows in wave directional spectra. *Journal of Geophysical Research* 88: 2579–2591.
[57] Oltman-Shay J and Guza RT (1984) A data-adaptive ocean wave directional-spectrum estimator for pitch–roll type measurements. *Journal of Physical Oceanography* 14: 1800–1810.
[58] Krogstad HE, Gordon RL, and Miller MC (1988) High-resolution directional wave spectra from horizontally mounted acoustic Doppler current meters. *Journal of Atmospheric and Oceanic Technology* 5: 340–352.
[59] Lygre A and Krogstad HE (1986) Maximum entropy estimation of the directional distribution in ocean wave spectra. *Journal of Physical Oceanography* 16: 2052–2060.
[60] Kobune K and Hashimoto N (1986) Estimation of directional spectra from the maximum entropy principle. In: *Proceedings of the 5th International Offshore Mechanics and Arctic Engineering Symposium*, vol. 1, pp. 80–85. Tokyo, Japan: ASME.
[61] Brissette FP and Tsanis IK (1994) Estimation of wave directional spectra from pitch–roll buoy data. *Journal of Waterway, Port, Coastal, and Ocean Engineering* 120(1): 93–115.
[62] Kim T, Lin L, and Wang H (1994) Application of the maximum entropy method to the real sea data. In: *Proceedings of the 24th International Conference on Coastal Engineering*, pp. 340–355. Kobe, Japan: American Society of Civil Engineers.
[63] Nwogu OU, Mansard EPD, Miles MD, and Isaacson M (1987) Estimation of directional wave spectra by the maximum entropy method. *Proceedings of the 17th IAHR Seminar*. Lausanne, Switzerland. 1–4 September 1987.
[64] National Data Buoy Center (NDBC) (2003) Handbook of automated data quality control checks and procedures of the National Data Buoy Center. Technical Document 03-02. Hancock County, MS: Stennis Space Center.
[65] National Oceanic and Atmospheric Administration (NOAA) (2005) Second workshop report on the quality assurance of real-time ocean data. CCPO Technical Report Series No. 05-01, July 2005, Norfolk, VA, 48pp.
[66] Krogstad HE, Wolf J, Thompson SP, and Wyatt LR (1999) Methods for intercomparison of wave data. *Coastal Engineering* 37: 235–257.
[67] Donelan MA and Pierson WJ (1983) The sampling variability of estimates of spectra of wind-generated waves. *Journal of Geophysical Research* 88: 4381–4392.
[68] Carter DJT and Tucker MJ (1986) Uncertainties in environmental design criteria. *Underwater Technology* 12: 2–8, 33.
[69] Young IR (1986) Probability distribution of spectral integrals. *Journal of Waterway, Port, Coastal, and Ocean Engineering* 112(4): 338–341.
[70] Forristall GZ, Heideman JC, Leggett IM, et al. (1996) Effect of sampling variability on hindcast and measured wave heights. *Journal of Waterway, Port, Coastal, and Ocean Engineering* 122(5): 216–225. Discussion: Goda Y 124(4): 214.
[71] Fu LL and Cazenave A (2001) *Satellite Altimetry and Earth Sciences: A Handbook of Techniques and Applications*. International Geophysics Series, vol. 69. San Diego, CA: Academic Press.
[72] Chelton D, Walsh EJ, and MacArthur JL (1989) Pulse compression and sea level tracking in satellite altimetry. *Journal of Atmospheric and Oceanic Technology* 6: 407–438.
[73] Quartly GD (1997) Achieving accurate altimetry across storms: Improved wind and wave estimates from C band. *Journal of Atmospheric and Oceanic Technology* 14(3): 705–715.
[74] Quilfen Y, Tournadre J, and Chapron B (2006) Altimeter dual-frequency observations of surface winds, waves, and rain rate in tropical cyclone Isabel. *Journal of Geophysical Research* 111: C01004. doi: 10.1029/2005JC003068.
[75] Quilfen Y, Chapron B, and Serre M (2004) Calibration/validation of an altimeter wave period model and application to TOPEX/Poseidon and Jason-1 altimeters. *Marine Geodesy* 27: 535–549.
[76] Mackay EBL, Retzler CH, Challenor PG, and Gommenginger CP (2008) A parametric model for ocean wave period from Ku-band altimeter data. *Journal of Geophysical Research* 113: C03029. doi: 10.1029/2007JC004438.

[77] Mackay EBL, Retzler CH, Challenor PG, and Bahaj AS (2008) Wave energy resource assessment using satellite altimeter data. In: *Proceedings of the ASME 27th International Conference on Offshore Mechanics and Arctic Engineering (OMAE2008-57976)*. Lisbon, Portugal: ASME.
[78] Carter DJT, Challenor PG, and Srokosz MA (1992) An assessment of Geosat wave height and wind speed measurements. *Journal of Geophysical Research* 97(C7): 11383–11392.
[79] Challenor PG, Foale S, and Webb DJ (1990) Seasonal changes in the global wave climate measured by the Geosat altimeter. *International Journal of Remote Sensing* 11(12): 2205–2213.
[80] Young IR and Holland GJ (1996) *Atlas of the Oceans: Wind and Wave Climate*, 241pp. Oxford: Pergamon Press.
[81] Tournadre J (1993) Time and space scales of significant wave height. *Journal of Geophysical Research* 98(C3): 4727–4738.
[82] Caires S and Sterl A (2003) Validation of ocean wind and wave data using triple collocation. *Journal of Geophysical Research* 108(C3): 3098.
[83] Challenor PG and Cotton PD (2002) The joint calibration of altimeter and *in situ* wave heights. World Meteorological Organization Document Number WMO/TD-No. 1081, JCOMM Technical Report No. 13. Geneva, Switzerland: WMO.
[84] Gower JFR (1996) Intercalibration of wave and wind data from Topex/Poseidon and moored buoys off the west coast of Canada. *Journal of Geophysical Research* 101: 3817–3829.
[85] Janssen PAEM, Abdalla S, Hersbach H, and Bidlot JR (2007) Error estimation of buoy, satellite and model wave height data. *Journal of Atmospheric and Oceanic Technology* 24: 1665–1677.
[86] Queffeulou P (2004) Long-term validation of wave height measurements from altimeters. *Marine Geodesy* 27: 495–510.
[87] Cheng CL and Van Ness JW (1999) *Statistical Regression with Measurement Error*. London: Arnold.
[88] Tolman HL (1998) Effect of observation errors in linear regression and bin-average analyses. *Quarterly Journal of the Royal Meteorological Society* 124: 897–917.
[89] Krogstad HE and Barstow SF (1999) Satellite wave measurements for coastal engineering applications. *Coastal Engineering* 37: 283–307.
[90] Barstow S and Krogstad HE (1995) Wave climate assessment by satellite remote sensing. *Proceedings of the 5th International Offshore and Polar Engineering Conference (ISOPE '95)*. Hague, The Netherlands.
[91] Queffeulou P and Bentamy A (2007) Analysis of wave height variability using altimeter measurements: Application to the Mediterranean Sea. *Journal of Atmospheric and Oceanic Technology* 24: 2078–2092. 11–16 June 1995.
[92] Woolf DK, Cotton PD, and Challenor PG (2003) Measurement of the offshore wave climate around the British Isles by satellite altimeter. *Philosophical Transactions of the Royal Society of London A* 361: 27–31.
[93] Young IR (1994) Global ocean wave statistics obtained from satellite observations. *Applied Ocean Research* 16: 235–248.
[94] DTI (2004) Atlas of UK marine renewable energy resources: Technical report. DTI Report No. R.1106. ABPmer, Met Office, Garrad Hassan and Proudman Oceanographic Laboratory. London: DTI.
[95] ESB International (2005) Accessible wave energy resource atlas: Ireland. Report No. 4D404A-R2. Marine Institute/Sustainable Energy Ireland. Dublin, Ireland: Marine Institute.
[96] Dingemans MW (1997) *Water Wave Propagation over Uneven Bottoms. Part 1: Linear Wave Propagation; Part 2: Non-Linear Wave Propagation*. Advanced Series on Ocean Engineering, vol. 13. Singapore: World Scientific.
[97] Komen GJ, Cavaleri L, Donelan M, *et al.* (1994) *Dynamics and Modelling of Ocean Waves*. Cambridge, UK: Cambridge University Press.
[98] WAMDI Group (1988) The WAM model – A third generation ocean wave prediction model. *Journal of Physical Oceanography* 18(12): 1775–1810.
[99] Tolman HL, Balasubramaniyan B, Burroughs LD, *et al.* (2002) Development and implementation of wind-generated ocean surface wave models at NCEP. *Weather and Forecasting* 17: 311–333.
[100] Hasselmann S, Lionello P, and Hasselmann K (1997) An optimal interpolation scheme for the assimilation of spectral data. *Journal of Geophysical Research* 102(C7): 15823–15836.
[101] Lionello P, Gunther H, and Janssen PAEM (1992) Assimilation of altimeter data in a global third-generation wave model. *Journal of Geophysical Research* 97: 14453–14474.
[102] Young IR and Eldeberky Y (1998) Observations of triad coupling of finite depth wind waves. *Coastal Engineering* 33(2–3): 137–154.
[103] Booij N, Ris RC, and Holthuijsen LH (1999) A third-generation wave model for coastal regions. Part 1: Model description and validation. *Journal of Geophysical Research* 104(C4): 7649 (98JC02622).
[104] Benoit M, Marcos F, and Becq F (1996) Development of a third generation shallow-water wave model with unstructured spatial meshing. In: *Proceedings of the 25th International Conference on Coastal Engineering (ICCE 1996)*, pp. 465–478. Orlando, FL: American Society of Civil Engineers.
[105] Danish Hydraulic Institute (1996) MIKE 21, Elliptic-Mild-Slope Wave Module, Release 2.6, User Guide and Reference Manual.
[106] Cavaleri L, *et al.* (2007) Wave modelling – The state of the art. *Progress in Oceanography* 75: 603–674.
[107] Janssen PAEM (1998) On error growth in wave models. ECMWF Technical Memo 249, p. 12. Reading, UK: ECMWF.
[108] Rogers WE, Wittmann PA, Wang DWC, *et al.* (2005) Evaluations of global wave prediction at the Fleet Numerical Meteorology and Oceanography Center. *Weather and Forecasting* 20(5): 745–760.
[109] Feng H, Vandemark D, Quilfen Y, *et al.* (2006) Assessment of wind-forcing impact on a global wind-wave model using the TOPEX altimeter. *Ocean Engineering* 33: 1431–1461.
[110] Tolman HL (2002) Alleviating the Garden Sprinkler Effect in wind wave models. *Ocean Modelling* 4: 269–289.
[111] Ponce de Leon S and Guedes Soares C (2005) On the sheltering effect of islands in ocean wave models. *Journal of Geophysical Research* 110: C09020. doi: 10.1029/2004JC002682.
[112] Tolman HL (2003) Treatment of unresolved islands and ice in wind wave models. *Ocean Modelling* 5: 219–231.
[113] Tolman HL (2002) Validation of WAVEWATCH III version 1.15 for a global domain. Technical Report 213. Camp Springs, MD: NOAA National Centers for Environmental Prediction.
[114] Cavaleri L (2006) Wave modelling – Where to go in the future. *Bulletin of the American Meteorological Society* 87(2): 207–214.
[115] Liu PC, Schwab DJ, and Jensen RE (2002) Has wind–wave modelling reached its limit? *Ocean Engineering* 29: 81–98.
[116] Janssen PAEM (2008) Progress in ocean wave forecasting. *Journal of Computational Physics* 227: 3572–3594.
[117] Bidlot JR, Holmes DJ, Wittmann PA, *et al.* (2002) Intercomparison of the performance of operational ocean wave forecasting systems with buoy data. *Weather and Forecasting* 17: 287–310.
[118] Cox AT and Swail VR (2001) A 40-year global reanalysis of ocean waves 1958–1997 (GROW). *Journal of Geophysical Research* 106(C2): 2313–2329.
[119] Mackay EBL, Bahaj AS, and Challenor PG (2010) Uncertainty in wave energy resource assessment. Part 1: Historic data. *Renewable Energy*. doi: 10.1016/j.renene.2009.10.026.
[120] Falcão AF (2002) Wave-power absorption by a periodic linear array of oscillating water columns. *Ocean Engineering* 29: 1163–1186.
[121] Millar DL, Smith HCM, and Reeve DE (2007) Modelling analysis of the sensitivity of shoreline change to a wave farm. *Ocean Engineering* 34: 884–901.
[122] Mackay EBL, Bahaj AS, and Challenor PG (2010) Uncertainty in wave energy resource assessment. Part 2: Variability and predictability. *Renewable Energy*. doi: 10.1016/j.renene.2009.10.027.
[123] Mackay EBL (2009) Wave Energy Resource Assessment. PhD Thesis, University of Southampton.
[124] Monbet V, Ailliot P, and Prevosto M (2007) Survey of stochastic models for wind and sea state time series. *Probabilistic Engineering Mechanics* 22(2): 113–126.
[125] Athanassoulis GA and Stefanakos CN (1995) A nonstationary stochastic model for long-term time series of significant wave height. *Journal of Geophysical Research* 100(C8): 16149–16162.
[126] Cunha C and Guedes Soares C (1999) On the choice of data transformation for modelling time series of significant wave height. *Ocean Engineering* 26: 489–506.
[127] Guedes Soares C and Cunha C (2001) Bivariate autoregressive models for time series of significant wave height and mean period. *Coastal Engineering* 40: 297–311.
[128] Hardle W, Horowitz J, and Kreiss JP (2003) Bootstrap methods for time series. *International Statistical Review* 71(2): 435–459.

[129] Deo MC, Jha A, Chapekar AS, and Ravikant K (2001) Neural network for wave forecasting. *Ocean Engineering* 28: 889–898.
[130] Makarynskyy O (2004) Improving wave predictions with artificial neural networks. *Ocean Engineering* 31: 709–724.
[131] Woolf DK, Challenor PG, and Cotton PD (2002) The variability and predictability of the North Atlantic wave climate. *Journal of Geophysical Research* 107(C10): 3145.
[132] Longuet-Higgins MS (1952) On the statistical distribution of the heights of sea waves. *Journal of Marine Research* 9: 245–266.
[133] Tayfun MA (1980) Narrow-band nonlinear sea waves. *Journal of Geophysical Research* 85(C3): 1548–1552.
[134] Longuet-Higgins MS (1980) On the distribution of the heights of sea waves: Some effects of nonlinearity and finite bandwidth. *Journal of Geophysical Research* 85: 1519–1523.
[135] Onorato M, Cavaleri L, Fouques S, et al. (2009) Statistical properties of mechanically generated surface gravity waves: A laboratory experiment in a three-dimensional wave basin. *Journal of Fluid Mechanics* 627: 235–257.
[136] Toffoli A, Benoit M, Onorato M, and Bitner-Gregersen EM (2009) The effect of third-order nonlinearity on statistical properties of random directional waves in finite depth. *Nonlinear Processes in Geophysics* 16: 131–139.
[137] Forristall GZ (2005) Understanding rogue waves: Are new physics really necessary? In: *Proceedings of the 14th 'Aha Huliko'a Hawaiian Winter Workshop*, pp. 29–35. Honolulu, HI: University of Hawaii.
[138] Tayfun MA and Fedele F (2007) Wave-height distributions and nonlinear effects. *Ocean Engineering* 34: 1631–1649.
[139] Boccotti P (1981) On the highest waves in a stationary Gaussian process. *Atti Accademia Ligure di Scienze e Lettere* 38: 271–302.
[140] Fedele F and Arena F (2005) Weakly nonlinear statistics of high random waves. *Physics of Fluids* 17(2): 026601, 1–10.
[141] Tayfun MA (2006) Statistics of nonlinear wave crests and groups. *Ocean Engineering* 33(11–12): 1589–1622.
[142] Coles S (2001) *An Introduction to the Statistical Modelling of Extreme Values*. London: Springer-Verlag.
[143] Al-Humoud J, Tayfun MA, and Askar H (2000) Distribution of nonlinear wave crests. *Ocean Engineering* 29: 1929–1943.
[144] Ferreira JA and Guedes Soares C (1999) Modelling the long-term distribution of significant wave height with the Beta and Gamma models. *Ocean Engineering* 26: 713–725.
[145] Mathiesen M, Goda Y, Hawkes P, et al. (1994) Recommended practice for extreme wave analysis. *Journal of Hydraulic Research* 32(6): 803–814.
[146] Guedes Soares C and Scotto MG (2004) Application of the r largest-order statistics for long-term predictions of significant wave height. *Coastal Engineering* 51(5–6): 387–394.
[147] Sobey R and Orloff L (1995) Triple annual maximum series in wave climate analyses. *Coastal Engineering* 26: 135–151.
[148] Van Vledder G, Goda Y, Hawkes P, et al. (1993) Case studies of extreme wave analysis: A comparative analysis. In: Magoon OT and Hemsley JM (eds.) *Ocean Wave Measurement and Analysis*, pp. 978–992. New York: American Society of Civil Engineers.
[149] Guedes Soares C and Scotto MG (2001) Modelling uncertainty of long-term predictions of significant wave height. *Ocean Engineering* 28: 329–342.
[150] Goda Y, Hawkes P, Mansard E, et al. (1993) Intercomparison of extremal wave analysis methods using numerically simulated data. In: Magoon OT and Hemsley JM (eds.) *Ocean Wave Measurement and Analysis*, pp. 963–977. New York: American Society of Civil Engineers.
[151] Elsinghorst C, Groeneboom P, Jonathan P, et al. (1998) Extreme value analysis of North Sea storm severity. *Journal of Offshore Mechanics and Arctic Engineering* 120(3): 177–183.
[152] Ferreira JA and Guedes Soares C (1998) An application of the peaks over threshold method to predict extremes of significant wave height. *Journal of Offshore Mechanics and Arctic Engineering* 120(3): 165–176.
[153] Naess A (1998) Statistical extrapolation of extreme value data based on the peaks over threshold method. *Journal of Offshore Mechanics and Arctic Engineering* 120: 91–96.
[154] Taylor PH and Goh JYK (2000) Extrapolation of long-term storm statistics, the POT method and data transformation. *Proceedings of the 19th International Conference on Offshore Mechanics and Arctic Engineering (OMAE00-6127)*. ASME. New Orleans, 14–17 February 2000.
[155] Guedes Soares C, Ferreira RG, and Scotto MG (2003) On the prediction of extreme values of significant wave heights. *Proceedings of the 22nd International Conference on Offshore Mechanics and Arctic Engineering (OMAE2003-37478)*. Cancun, Mexico, 8–13 June 2003.
[156] Caires S and Sterl A (2005) 100-Year return value estimates for ocean wind speed and significant wave height from the ERA-40 data. *Journal of Climate* 18(7): 1032–1048.
[157] Morton ID, Bowers J, and Mould G (1997) Estimating return period wave heights and wind speeds using a seasonal point process model. *Coastal Engineering* 31: 305–326.
[158] Anderson CW, Carter DJT, and Cotton PD (2001) Wave climate variability and impact on offshore design extremes. *Report for Shell International and the Organization of Oil & Gas Producers*, 90pp. http://info.ogp.org.uk/metocean/JIPweek/att/WCEReport_2sided.pdf (accessed 23 December 2011).
[159] Leadbetter MR, Lindgren G, and Rootzen H (1983) *Extremes and Related Properties of Random Sequences and Processes*. New York: Springer-Verlag.
[160] Tawn JA (1988) An extreme-value theory model for dependent observations. *Journal of Hydrology* 101: 227–250.
[161] Tromans PS and Vanderschuren L (1995) Response based design conditions in the North Sea: Application of a new method. *Proceedings of the 27th Offshore Technology Conference (OTC 7683)*. Houston, TX, 1–4 May 1995.
[162] Stefanakos CN and Athanassoulis GA (2006) Extreme value predictions based on nonstationary time series of wave data. *Environmetrics* 17(1): 25–46.
[163] de Zea Bermudez P and Kotz S (2009) Parameter estimation of the generalized Pareto distribution – Parts I and II. *Journal of Statistical Planning and Inference* doi: 10.1016/j.jspi.2008.11.019 and doi:10.1016/j.jspi.2008.11.020.
[164] Hosking JRM and Wallis JR (1987) Parameter and quantile estimation for the generalized Pareto distribution. *Technometrics* 29: 339–349.
[165] Dupuis DJ and Tsao M (1998) A hybrid estimator for generalized Pareto and extreme-value distributions. *Communications in Statistics – Theory and Methods* 27: 925–941.
[166] Mackay EBL, Challenor PG, and Bahaj AS (2010) A comparison of estimators for the generalised Pareto distribution. *Ocean Engineering* 38(11–12): 1338–1346.
[167] Zhang J (2007) Likelihood moment estimation for the generalised Pareto distribution. *Australian & New Zealand Journal of Statistics* 49(1): 69–77.
[168] Efron B and Tibshirani RJ (1993) *An Introduction to the Bootstrap*. New York: Chapman & Hall.
[169] Gumbel EJ (1958) *Statistics of Extremes*, 375pp. New York: Columbia University Press.
[170] Cunnane C (1978) Unbiased plotting positions – A review. *Journal of Hydrology* 37(3–4): 205–222.
[171] Jonathan P and Ewans KC (2007) The effect of directionality on extreme wave design criteria. *Ocean Engineering* 34: 1977–1994.
[172] Jonathan P and Ewans KC (2008) Modelling the seasonality of extreme waves in the Gulf of Mexico. *Proceedings of the 27th International Conference on Offshore Mechanics and Arctic Engineering (OMAE2008-57131)*. Estoril, Portugal, 15–20 June.
[173] Jonathan P, Ewans K, and Forristall G (2008) Statistical estimation of extreme ocean environments: The requirement for modelling directionality and other covariate effects. *Ocean Engineering* 35: 1211–1225.
[174] Mackay EBL, Challenor PG, and Bahaj AS (2010) On the use of discrete seasonal and directional models for the estimation of extreme wave conditions. *Ocean Engineering* 37: 425–442.
[175] Cardone VJ, Jensen RE, Resio DT, et al. (1996) Evaluation of contemporary ocean wave models in rare extreme events: The "Halloween Storm" of October 1991 and the "Storm of the Century" of March 1993. *Journal of Atmospheric and Oceanic Technology* 13: 198–230.
[176] Jensen RE, Cardone VJ, and Cox AT (2006) Performance of third generation wave models in extreme hurricanes. *Proceedings of the 9th International Workshop on Wave Hindcasting and Forecasting*. Victoria, BC, Canada, 24–29 September.
[177] Brooker DC, Cole GK, and McConochie JD (2004) The influence of hindcast modelling uncertainty on the prediction of high return period wave conditions. *Proceedings of the 23rd International Conference on Offshore Mechanics and Arctic Engineering*. Vancouver, BC, Canada, 20–25 June.
[178] Mackay EBL (2011) Correction for bias in return values of wave heights caused by hindcast uncertainty. *Proceedings of the ASME 30th International Conference on Offshore Mechanics and Arctic Engineering (OMAE2011-49409)*. Rotterdam, The Netherlands, 20–23 June 2011.
[179] Carter DJT and Challenor PG (1990) *Metocean Parameters – Wave Parameters. Part 2: Estimation of Extreme Waves*. UK Department of Energy, OTH89-300. London: HMSO.
[180] Forristall GZ (2008) How should we combine long and short term wave height distributions? *Proceedings of the 27th International Conference on Offshore Mechanics and Arctic Engineering (OMAE2008-58012)*. Estoril, Portugal, 15–20 June.
[181] Battjes JA (1970) Long-term wave height distribution at seven stations around the British Isles. National Institute of Oceanography, Internal Report No. A44, 31pp.

[182] Tucker MJ (1989) Improved 'Battjes' method for predicting the probability of extreme waves. *Applied Ocean Research* 11(4): 212–218.
[183] Krogstad HE (1985) Height and period distributions of extreme waves. *Applied Ocean Research* 7: 158–165.
[184] Arena F and Pavone D (2006) The return period of non-linear high wave crests. *Journal of Geophysical Research* 111: C08004.
[185] Arena F and Pavone D (2009) A generalized approach for long-term modelling of extreme crest-to-trough wave heights. *Ocean Modelling* 26: 217–225.
[186] Boccotti P (2000) *Wave Mechanics for Ocean Engineering*. Oxford: Elsevier Science.
[187] Krogstad HE and Barstow SF (2004) Analysis and applications of second-order models for maximum crest height. *Journal of Offshore Mechanics and Arctic Engineering* 126: 66–71.
[188] Borgman LE (1973) Probabilities for highest wave in hurricane. *Journal of the Waterways, Harbors and Coastal Engineering Division* 99(WW2): 185–207.
[189] Fedele F and Arena F (2010) Long-term statistics and extreme waves of sea storms. *Journal of Physical Oceanography* 40(5): 1106–1117.
[190] Saulnier J-B, Clément AH, Falcão AF de O, *et al.* (2011) Wave groupiness and spectral bandwidth as relevant parameters for the performance assessment of wave energy converters. *Ocean Engineering* 38: 130–147.
[191] Cotton PD and Carter DJT (1994) Cross calibration of TOPEX, ERS-1, and Geosat wave heights. *Journal of Geophysical Research* 99(C12): 25025–25033.

8.04 Development of Wave Devices from Initial Conception to Commercial Demonstration

V Heller, Imperial College London, London, UK

© 2012 Elsevier Ltd. All rights reserved.

8.04.1	A Structured Program to Mitigate Risk – The TRL Approach	80
8.04.2	Funding Opportunities	82
8.04.2.1	Funding for Device Development	82
8.04.2.2	Further Support	83
8.04.3	Physical Model Testing and Similarity	84
8.04.3.1	Introduction	84
8.04.3.2	Similarity between Physical Model and Full-Scale Prototype	85
8.04.3.2.1	Introduction	85
8.04.3.2.2	Mechanical similarity	85
8.04.3.2.3	Froude similarity	86
8.04.3.2.4	Scale effects	86
8.04.3.3	Design and Testing of Physical Scale Models in the Laboratory	88
8.04.3.3.1	Introduction	88
8.04.3.3.2	Test facilities	88
8.04.3.3.3	Wave generation	89
8.04.3.3.4	Absorbing beach	91
8.04.3.3.5	Model design	91
8.04.3.3.6	Measurement equipment	93
8.04.3.3.7	Device testing	95
8.04.4	Sea Trials of Large-Scale Prototypes	96
8.04.4.1	Introduction	96
8.04.4.2	Sea Trials with Scale Models	97
8.04.4.3	Sea Trials with Full-Scale Prototypes	97
8.04.4.3.1	Introduction	97
8.04.4.3.2	Test site	99
8.04.4.3.3	Devices tested at full scale	99
8.04.4.3.4	Device testing and measurements	99
8.04.4.4	Sea Trials with WECs in an Array	101
8.04.4.4.1	Introduction	101
8.04.4.4.2	Test site	102
8.04.4.4.3	Device testing and measurements	102
8.04.5	Frequency versus Time Domain	104
8.04.5.1	Introduction	104
8.04.5.2	Frequency Domain	104
8.04.5.2.1	Introduction	104
8.04.5.2.2	Wave parameters	105
8.04.5.2.3	Fourier analysis	105
8.04.5.2.4	Numerical modeling	107
8.04.5.3	Time Domain	108
8.04.5.3.1	Introduction	108
8.04.5.3.2	Wave parameters	108
8.04.5.3.3	Numerical modeling	109
References		109

Glossary

Array Group of WECs of the same type at one site which share their infrastructure, such as underwater cables.

Capacity factor Ratio of the average power output of a device or array to the device's or array's rated power.

Capture width Ratio of captured power of a device to incident power per meter wave front; the capture width is often made dimensionless with the device diameter.

Energy period For a given spectrum, this corresponds to the period of a regular wave which would have the same significant wave height and energy content as that spectrum.

Fetch length Horizontal distance along open water over which the wind blows and generates waves.

> **Fourier analysis** An analysis separating a periodic function into a sum of simple sinusoidal components, or more technically, a method to transform time domain data to their frequency domain equivalent.
> **Frequency domain** A graph in the frequency domain shows how much of the signal lies within each given frequency band over a range of frequencies.
> **Long-crested waves** Wave field consisting of waves travelling in one direction.
> **Monochromatic waves** A wave train or field consisting of regular waves of one frequency.
> **Mooring** A mechanism which keeps a WEC at a specific position or region.
> **Oscillating water column (OWC)** A common power takeoff principle in wave energy conversion where the waves activate a water surface to rise and fall in an air compression chamber, and this oscillation generates an air current which is used to generate electrical power, typically via a Wells turbine.
> **Panchromatic waves** A wave train or field consisting of irregular waves.
> **Peak period** Wave period determined by the inverse of the frequency at which the variance or wave energy spectrum reaches its maximum.
> **Power matrix** A matrix showing the generated power of a WEC as a function of significant wave height on the ordinate and energy period on the abscissa.
> **Power takeoff (PTO)** A device transforming the power captured by a WEC to a higher form of power, e.g. electrical power.
>
> **Rated power** Maximum power which can be generated by a WEC; it normally equals the maximum electrical output of the generator.
> **Resonance** Tendency of a WEC, or parts of it, to oscillate at a greater amplitude at some so-called resonance frequencies than at other frequencies.
> **Scale effects** They arise due to forces in the fluid, such as surface tension force, which are incorrectly scaled to model scale and therefore affect the results differently than at full scale.
> **Scatter diagram** A plot of the pairs of values (x, y) on a rectangular grid coordinate system, used to assess the relationship between x and y. An example is the power matrix.
> **Short-crested waves** Wave field consisting of waves traveling in different directions.
> **Significant wave height** Average of the highest one-third of the wave heights measured in the time domain. The corresponding value in the frequency domain is defined as a function of the 0th spectral moment. Note that the significant wave heights in the time and frequency domains are not necessarily exactly equal.
> **Technology readiness level (TRL)** They were established by the US space agency NASA to describe the advancement in the development of a technology, herein WECs.
> **Time domain** A signal in a graph in the time domain changes over time.
> **Variance spectrum** It describes how the energy (or variance) of a time series is distributed with frequency.

8.04.1 A Structured Program to Mitigate Risk – The TRL Approach

HMRC [1] proposed a structured program for advancement in the development of wave energy converters (WECs) of buoyant type (second-generation WECs). This program is divided into five main test phases or technology readiness levels (TRLs) as established by the US space agency NASA and widely used by many engineering research establishments. Several documents adapt this TRL approach for WECs including Holmes [2] and IEE [3]. The structure of this chapter is mainly based on this program. **Table 1** gives an overview of the five test phases and these are introduced in more detail below.

Phase 1: Validation model. This includes the initial proof of concept that the design operates as theoretically predicted. Simple idealized models can be used at scale 1:25–100 such that configurations may be quickly and easily changed as required. Initial tests to verify the concept take place in small-amplitude regular waves with a basic model power takeoff (PTO) mechanism. The performance and response are then tested in irregular waves including generic spectra and the device is optimized with the variation of parameters. Mathematical models are developed in parallel and may contribute to the investigation.

Phase 2: Design model. This phase requires a new or modified model at a typical scale of 1:10–25 with an extended measurement array. A larger set of physical parameters will be measured with a more realistic PTO. Tests include short-crested seas, different wave approach directions to validate moorings and behavior of nonaxisymmetric devices, and early survival tests in high-energy seas to investigate extreme motions and loadings, especially in the PTO mechanism. Bench testing of the PTO system can also begin.

Phase 3: Process model. This stage bridges the end of laboratory tests and the beginning of sea trials at a benign outdoor site. The scale is relatively large with 1:3–10 to enable actual components, such as the PTO or mooring system, to be incorporated. Tests can take place either in a large wave basin in the laboratory or at a benign outdoor site. In order to scale the wave conditions and for safety reasons, tests may be possible only in specific seasons of the year at an outdoor site. Extended bench testing of the PTO and generating unit should be considered. Mathematical prediction of the performance should move from frequency into time domain modeling.

Phase 4: Prototype device. By this time, realistic performance data should be available, together with accurate manufacturing and construction costs. In this phase, all operation components must be (scaled) units of the projected final components at a scale of 1:1–2. This phase does not necessarily have to take place in the actual device farm or array site and the grid connection of the

Table 1 Overview of five test phases of WECs

	Phase 1 Validation model (lab.)			Phase 2 Design model (lab.)	Phase 3 Process model	Phase 4 Prototype	Phase 5 Demonstration
	Concept	Performance	Optimization		Sea trials		
Primary scale	1:25–100			1:10–25	1:3–10	1:1–2	Full scale
Tank	2D flume and 3D basin			3D basin	Benign site	Exposed site	Open location
Duration (inc. analysis)	1–3 weeks	1–3 months	1–3 months	6–12 months	6–18 months	12–36 months	1–5 years
Typical no. tests	50–500	250–500	100–250	100–250	50–250	Continous	Statistical sample
Budget (€)	1000–5000	25 000–75 000	25 000–50 000	50 000–250 000	1 000 000–2 500 000	5 000 000–10 000 000	2 500 000–7 500 000
Excitation/ waves	Monochromatic linear waves (10-25 Δf) Panchromatic 5 reference	Panchromatic waves (20 min full scale) +15 classical spectra long crested head seas		Deployment: pilot site sea spectra Long and short crested classical seas Select mean wave approach angle	Extended test period to ensure all seaways included	Full scatter diagram for initial evaluation, continous thereafter	

Source: Data from Holmes B (2009) *Tank Testing of Wave Energy Conversion Systems. Marine Renewable Energy Guides*. Orkney, Scotland: EMEC [2].

device is also not essential, even though it should be considered toward the end of this test phase to test the quality of supply to the electrical grid.

Phase 5: Demonstration device. The full-size WEC is built or relocated, if already used in phase 4, to the projected WEC park if not identical to the location of phase 4. Grid connection and electricity sale must be part of the package at this time. The device may be tested as an isolated device, but a small array configuration should be considered since an isolated unit would probably never be economic.

This chapter aims to give an overview of the development of wave devices from initial conception to commercial demonstration and therefore covers all five test phases. The required funding possibilities for the development of devices are described in Section 8.04.2 with a focus on the United Kingdom. Section 8.04.3 addresses TRLs 1–3, if conducted in the laboratory. Section 8.04.4 covers TRL 3 (if conducted at a benign sea site) and TRLs 4 and 5. Measurement data can be analyzed in the frequency or time domain irrespective of the test phase as discussed in Section (8.04.5).

8.04.2 Funding Opportunities

8.04.2.1 Funding for Device Development

Funding opportunities for research and development (R&D) of WECs are described by Armstrong [4] focusing on Scotland and the United Kingdom and by IEE [3] summarizing the largest ongoing projects at that time funded by the European Commission (EC). The cost and therefore fiscal risk for the R&D of marine (tidal and wave) energy devices increase with each test phase, as shown in **Figure 1**. The figure shows the duration of the investigation, cost, required funding, grant type, and where the support comes from, mainly for the United Kingdom, as a function of the five test phases. The costs are estimates covering all development activities including testing and naval architect services. Funding opportunities from the public sector are available for all five test phases, whereas the strategic investment from the private sector increases more and more from phase 4 onward.

The funding opportunities shown in **Figure 1** are individually addressed below:

- *Research councils.* Research into marine energy is funded by the EPSRC (Engineering and Physical Sciences Research Council) and partners mainly through the SuperGen Marine consortium. The research seeks to increase understanding of the interactions

	Phase 1	Phase 2	Phase 3	Phase 4	Phase 5
Duration (months)	2¼–7[2] 3–9[3]	6–12[2, 3]	6–18[2] 6–36[3]	12–36[2] 24–36[3]	12–60[2] 24–60[3]
Cost (€,000)	51–130[2] 5–125[3]	50–250[2, 3]	1000–2500[2] 500–2500[3]	5000–10 000[2] 5000–15 000[3]	2500–7500[2]
Funding (%)	100–50[3]	100–50[3]	75–50[3]	75–25[3]	0[3]
Grant type	Capital[3]	Capital[3]	Capital[3]	Capital and feed-in tariff[3]	Investment and feed-in tariff[3]
Public sector support	\multicolumn{5}{EPSRC; Carbon Trust (Marine Energy Accelerator, £3.5m); Technology Strategy Board (historically, ×£100K); MRPF (£22m); MRDF (£42m); Technology Strategy Board (£2.5m); Energy Technology Institute (×£10m); European Commission; The Saltire prize (£10m)}
Private sector support				Strategic investors	Strategic investors and project finance

Figure 1 Required funding and sources of funding for R&D of marine (wave and tidal) energy converters as a function of the test phase with particular focus on the United Kingdom. Based on Holmes B (2009) *Tank Testing of Wave Energy Conversion Systems. Marine Renewable Energy Guides.* Orkney, Scotland: EMEC [2]; IEE (2009) State of the art analysis – A cautiously optimistic review of the technical status of wave energy technology. *Report of Waveplam.* Brussels, Belgium: Intelligent Energy Europe [3]; and Armstrong J (2008) Marine energy more than just a drop in the ocean? Report. London, UK: Institution of Mechanical Engineers [4].

between devices and the ocean, from model scale in the laboratory to full size in the open sea. EPSRC is an important source of funding in academia.
- *Carbon Trust.* The Carbon Trust seeks to accelerate the move to a low-carbon economy by working with organizations to reduce carbon emissions and develop commercial low-carbon technologies. It is running a £3.5m Marine Energy Accelerator (and before the Marine Energy Challenge) investing in projects to develop lower cost concept designs, to reduce component costs, and to reduce the cost of installation and operation and maintenance (O&M).
- *Technology Strategy Board (TSB).* The TSB invests in projects and in sharing knowledge. It has historically invested in early-stage marine energy projects with grants of the order of £100K. In January 2011, three marine energy device developers have been granted over £2.5m from the TSB for R&D of their full-scale devices.
- *European Commission.* The EC has been supporting projects in this area since 1992, from the start of the Joule Programmes. Support was, for example, granted to consortiums of EU member states developing FO/P1 (EC FP6), SSG (EC FP6), WaveBob (EC FP7), Wave Dragon (EC FP7), or WaveRoller (EC FP7).
- *Marine Renewables Proving Fund (MRPF).* The MRPF was launched in September 2009 and aims to accelerate the leading and most promising marine devices toward the point where they can qualify for the UK government's existing Marine Renewables Deployment Fund (MRDF) scheme and, ultimately, be deployed at a commercial scale under the standard Renewables Obligation. This new £22m initiative is designed and managed by the Carbon Trust and uses new funding provided by the Department of Energy and Climate Change (DECC). Up to £6m is available to successful applicants to help meet the capital cost of building and deploying wave and tidal stream prototypes. The MRPF provides up to 60% of the eligible project cost, with the rest to be matched by technology developers and their partners (Chapter 8.01).
- *Environmental Transformation Fund (ETF).* The ETF provides funds for low-carbon energy and energy-efficiency technologies. A total of £50m of this fund makes up the MRDF including a £42m wave and tidal energy demonstration scheme set up in 2004. This will fund up to 25% of capital cost to a maximum of £5m per project and also provides revenue support at £100 MWh^{-1} to a maximum of £9m per project. The devices must be grid-connected and demonstrated in representative sea states for 3 months continuously or for 6 months in a 12-month period. Up to now, no device was able to fulfill these requirements, but it is expected that this will be the case in the near future with the help of the MRPF.
- *Energy Technologies Institute (ETI).* In this partnership, both the private (EDF, Shell, BP, E.ON, Rolls-Royce, and Caterpillar) and the public (UK government) sector spend £300m (£600m in total) over the next years to accelerate the deployment of low-carbon energy systems. It includes a marine energy program that is expected to provide about £10m each to a small number of projects.
- *The Saltire Prize.* This prize was announced in April 2008 and offers £10m for an advance in clean energy. The prize is open globally, but the winning team must deliver an advance that is relevant to Scotland and can be deployed within a 2–5 year time frame. Both wave and tidal stream device developers can apply. The application procedure is currently running until January 2015.
- *Wave and Tidal Energy Scheme (WATES).* The WATES supports Scottish devices and was launched in October 2006. It distributed £13.5m funding to nine tidal and wave energy converter developers including Scottish Power Renewables, AWS Ocean Energy, Aquamarine Power, and Wavegen. WATES is excluded from **Figure 1** since currently no further funds are available; however, some devices may still use already granted money.

Funding schemes in the past were sometimes criticized as the "right funding at the wrong time" [3, 4]. For instance, Portuguese authorities announced a support scheme to accelerate wave energy introduction into Portugal. The basis of the scheme was a special guaranteed feed-in tariff for the sale of electricity at 25 €cent kW^{-1}. However, no device developer was ever in the position to take it up during the run time. Similarly, not one machine has been able to apply for the MRDF since its initialization in 2004. However, the UK government reacted in 2009 with the launch of the MRPF to accelerate devices toward the point where they can qualify for the MRDF. Several devices are now being supported under the MRPF scheme. Armstrong [4] also predicted a funding gap of about £40m for the marine energy sector in Scotland for the R&D of full-scale devices (test phase 4). This gap may have been partly addressed with the MRPF and the TSB in the meantime.

8.04.2.2 Further Support

Besides funds for the development of devices shown in **Figure 1**, there is further indirect support from governments and from the EC from which device developers profit. Support is provided to train people, for national and international knowledge exchange, for networking, to conduct generic research, or to establish protocols and guidelines. Such projects resulted in some of the references cited in this chapter (e.g., Payne [5] (SuperGen Marine), Holmes [2] (EMEC), IEE [3] (Waveplam), EquiMar [6] (EquiMar)). EPSRC, for instance, funded the second phase of SuperGen Marine with £7.8m, which was finished in autumn 2011. An important aspect of the SuperGen Marine research program is, besides research, the inclusion of doctorates and training courses. Five UK universities form the consortium together with six affiliates and seven overseas partners.

A key funding institution for WECs is the EC. Four examples of large EC-funded projects that are being just finished or will be finished in the near future are given below:

- *WaveTrain2 (Initial training network for wave energy research professionals)*. This project, coordinated by the Wave Energy Centre in Lisbon, is the holder of a €3.5m grant from the EC FP7 and runs for 3.75 years from October 2008. WaveTrain2 is a graduate and postgraduate training scheme and a support network for the SuperGen programs. A total of 16–20 students take part in the scheme which may be located at any of the 13 partners' establishments or seconded to a selection of 17 associated partners for short, specialist courses. These training projects are the education house for the next generation of wave energy personnel and they produce, for the first time, people tutored in all aspects of ocean energy technology. The principal mechanism for this is the opportunity for the students to learn from experts. In addition, nine research work packages addressing wide aspects of wave energy are incorporated into the program.
- *CORES (Components for ocean renewable energy systems)*. This project is supported with €4m from EC FP7 for 3 years and was concluded in September 2011. The CORES project included 13 partners from 7 EU states under the coordination of Hydraulics and Maritime Research Centre, University College Cork, Ireland. It was a technically based project designed to address the issues and knowledge gaps in specific critical components required for successful deployment of WECs. The activities concentrated particularly around pneumatic devices (oscillating water columns (OWCs)), but it was expected that the data created during the project would be useful to all types of devices.
- *EquiMar (Equitable testing and evaluation of marine energy extraction devices in terms of performance, cost and environmental impact)*. This project was supported with €5.5m from the EC FP7 for 3 years and ended in April 2011. EquiMar was coordinated by Edinburgh University, Scotland, with a total of 24 partners from 11 EU states. The project's aim was to produce impartial guidelines and procedures for ocean energy development together with recommending best practice to follow that will mitigate technical and fiscal risk during the various stages of development of wave and tidal energy devices. It included several device developers representing the industry.
- *Waveplam (Wave energy planning and marketing)*. This project was supported with €1m from the EC FP7 for 3 years from 2007 to 2010. The consortium was coordinated by Ente Vasco de la Energía (EVE) from the Basque Country of Spain and included a total of eight partners from seven EU states. The project focused on nontechnical barriers that may influence the growth of a wave energy industry in the future. Besides collection and collation of cross-border information about the current status of wave energy, one of the main objectives of the project was to establish networking links that will efficiently disseminate the important facts outside of the ocean energy community to a wider audience, including stakeholders, decision makers, investors, and the general public.

Device developers benefit also from test centers. The United Kingdom's national center for the advancement of renewable energies NaREC hosts large-scale facilities for testing WECs. The European Marine Energy Centre (EMEC) on the Orkney Islands, north Scotland, was established with a £15m grant from the Scottish and UK governments and the European Union. It provides at sea berths and infrastructure to grid-connect and test devices in a real ocean environment and it has been used mainly for phase 4 testing up to now. Wave Hub in southwest England provides the infrastructure and subsea connections to plug in devices offshore to gain experience in test phase 5 (**Figure 13**). The Spanish equivalent of Wave Hub is the Biscay Marine Energy Platform (BIMEP) (Section 8.04.4.4). Such projects are often accompanied with a special guaranteed feed-in tariff.

8.04.3 Physical Model Testing and Similarity

8.04.3.1 Introduction

Comprehensive documents addressing physical model testing and model–prototype similarity of WECs include work package 3 (*Concept appraisal and tank testing practices for 1st stage prototype devices*) of EquiMar [6], Holmes [2], sections of Cruz [8–10], Payne [5], and Nielsen [11] (Annex II report of Ocean Energy Systems). This section gives a brief overview of physical scale model testing in the laboratory and similarity theory. The addressed tests cover test phases 1–3 (if taking place in the laboratory) in **Table 1**.

Experimental tank testing is important for the R&D of a WEC since it allows testing in an accessible, controlled, and repeatable environment. The aims of the investigation of a device in physical scale model tests are the following:

- Verification of the concept
- Securing funding for further development
- Validation and calibration of mathematical models
- Quantification of technical performance variables such as capture width
- Evaluation of economics
- Identification and development of understanding of relevant hydrodynamics and other physics processes
- Provision of environmental loading data to allow design(s) to be improved, including moorings and foundations
- Provision of data for optimized performance design
- Generation of detailed information for the PTO engineers
- Qualification of the device's seakeeping ability and general seaworthiness
- Survival
- Environmental impact

Some points, such as the validation and calibration of mathematical models based on linear wave theory, can only be achieved in the laboratory, whereas the investigation of other points would not be economic at full scale since the costs of sea trials are much higher than that of laboratory tests. The disadvantages of physical scale model tests are scale effects addressed in the next section.

8.04.3.2 Similarity between Physical Model and Full-Scale Prototype

8.04.3.2.1 Introduction

Physical model tests always involve scale effects. They arise due to forces, such as friction or surface tension forces, which are more dominant in the model than at full scale. The upscaled model results disagree with the prototype results if significant scale effects are involved. **Figure 2** illustrates scale effects. A jet is falling from an overflow spillway of a dam during a flood in a physical hydraulic model in **Figure 2(a)** and at full scale in **Figure 2(b)**. The air concentration in the jet is not similar between model and prototype due to scale effects. In this case, the surface tension force is not scaled and it is too dominant at model scale, protecting the model jet from air entrainment. Analogous, scale effects may affect relevant quantities in WEC models such as the power captured.

This section describes the required conditions and criteria under which model parameters are similar to prototype parameters and shows how the model results can be upscaled. Scale effects are addressed and it is shown how significant scale effects can be avoided. Detailed reviews about similarity theory and scale effects include Le Méhauté [13], Hughes [14], and Heller [12].

8.04.3.2.2 Mechanical similarity

This section shows under which conditions a model is similar to its full-scale prototype. An important parameter is the scale ratio λ defined as

$$\lambda = \frac{\text{characteristic length in prototype}}{\text{corresponding length in model}}$$

The reciprocal of the scale ratio is the scale 1:λ. The required space, time, and cost to conduct experiments increase with about λ^{-2}, $\lambda^{-1/2}$, and λ^{-3}, respectively [13]. However, with decreasing model size, increasing scale effects are expected and the upscaled model results may deviate from prototype observations. The appropriate selection of λ is therefore an economic and technical optimization and λ may intentionally be selected in a range where scale effects cannot be fully neglected.

A physical scale model is completely similar to its full-scale prototype and involves no scale effects if it satisfies mechanical similarity implying the following three criteria:

Geometric similarity
Kinematic similarity
Dynamic similarity

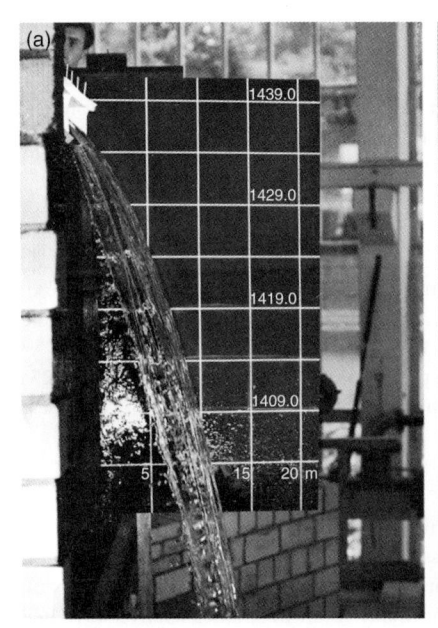

Figure 2 Illustration of scale effects: overflow spillway of Gebidem Dam, Valais, Switzerland, in (a) physical hydraulic model at scale 1:30 and (b) real-world prototype in 1967; air entrainment of free jet differs considerably between model and prototype [12].

The geometric similarity requires similarity in shape, that is, all length dimensions in the model are λ times shorter than in its prototype. The kinematic similarity implies geometric similarity and indicates in addition a similarity of particle motion between model and prototype. It requires constant ratios of time, velocity, acceleration, and discharge in the model and its prototype at all times. The dynamic similarity implies in addition to geometric and kinematic similarities that all ratios of all vectorial forces in the two systems are identical. In fluid dynamics, the most relevant forces are

Inertial force = mass × acceleration
Gravity force = mass × gravitational acceleration
Viscous force = dynamic viscosity × (velocity/distance) × area
Surface tension force = unit surface tension × length
Elastic compression force = Young's modulus × area
Pressure force = unit pressure × area

Dynamic similarity requires constant ratios of all forces, namely, (inertial force)$_P$/(inertial force)$_M$ = (gravity force)$_P$/(gravity force)$_M$ = ... = constant, with P indicating the prototype and M the model. A direct consequence is that (inertial force)$_P$/(gravity force)$_P$ = (inertial force)$_M$/(gravity force)$_M$. The inertial force is normally most relevant in fluid dynamics and is therefore included in all common force ratio combinations:

Froude number = (inertial force/gravity force)$^{1/2}$ = $V/(gL)^{1/2}$
Reynolds number = inertial force/viscous force = LV/v
Weber number = inertial force/surface tension force = $\rho V^2 L/\sigma$
Cauchy number = inertial force/elastic force = $\rho V^2/E$
Euler number = pressure force/inertial force = $p/\rho V^2$

The parameters are characteristic velocity V, characteristic length L, gravitational acceleration g, kinematic viscosity v, fluid density ρ, surface tension σ, Young's modulus E, and pressure p. For L and V, any parameter can be selected as long as they are characteristic of the investigated phenomenon. Possible parameters for L are the water depth, wave height, or diameter of a device and for V the specific wave celerity or the shallow-water wave speed.

If the same fluid for the model with $\lambda \neq 1$ and prototype is employed, only one force ratio can be identical between model and its prototype and mechanical similarity is therefore impossible. The most relevant force ratio, for WECs the Froude number, is selected and, since the values of the remaining force ratios are not identical, it has to be justified that scale effects due to other force ratios are negligible. The larger λ is, the more deviated are these not correctly modeled force ratios and the larger are scale effects. The results from an upscaled model disagree with the observations at full scale. The aim is to conduct the tests in the range where scale effects are insignificant, to try to compensate them or to correct them.

8.04.3.2.3 Froude similarity

The Froude similarity is most often applied in fluid dynamics and the author is not aware of any WEC investigation that was not based on Froude similarity. Froude similarity considers besides inertia the gravity force, which is dominant in most free surface flows, especially if friction effects are negligible or for highly turbulent phenomena such as wave breaking. The Froude similarity requires identical Froude numbers between model and its prototype for each selected experiment. The other force ratios such as the Reynolds number or Weber number are not identical between model and prototype and may therefore result in significant scale effect. The most important scaling ratios to upscale the results of a Froude model to its prototype are shown in **Table 2**. These scaling ratios result from the basic assumption of a Froude model assuming identical Froude number in the model and prototype, namely,

$$\frac{V_M}{(gL_M)^{1/2}} = \frac{V_P}{(gL_P)^{1/2}}$$

Since g is not scaled and the length dimension $L_P = \lambda L_M$ is geometrically scaled, $V_M/(L_M)^{1/2} = V_P/(\lambda L_M)^{1/2}$ and $V_P = \lambda^{1/2} V_M$. The scale ratio $\lambda^{1/2}$ is therefore relevant for upscaling the model velocity V_M. Further scale ratios for other parameters are shown in **Table 2**. As an example, a measured power of 10 W in a scale model of scale 1:λ = 1:25 corresponds to $\lambda^{7/2} \cdot 10 = (25)^{7/2} \cdot 10 = 781\,250$ W at full scale or a capture width of 1 m scales linear with λ and results in a prototype capture width of $\lambda \cdot 1 = 25 \cdot 1 = 25$ m. Further scale ratios for parameters not included in **Table 2** can be found with the unit, such as for torque (N m), which is force (scale ratio λ^3) times length (λ) resulting in a scale ratio λ^4.

8.04.3.2.4 Scale effects

Small WECs following Froude similarity may be affected by significant scale effects due to not identical Weber (surface tension), Reynolds (viscosity), Cauchy (elasticity), or Euler number (pressure or compressibility) between model and prototype. Viscose effects result in very large losses in a model compared to the prototype and the measured power is normally underestimated. Surface tension effects are particularly important for small waves and normally result in smaller relative wave heights compared to the prototype. They are also relevant for small water depths, for example, in overtopping basins. Due to elasticity effects, geometrically correctly scaled materials such as rubber or metal behave too stiff in the model and a material with a lower Young's modulus E

Table 2 Scale ratios for upscaling parameters measured in a Froude model

Parameter	Dimension	Froude scale ratio
Geometric similarity		
Length	L	λ
Area	L^2	λ^2
Volume	L^3	λ^3
Rotation	–	1
Kinematic similarity		
Time	T	$\lambda^{1/2}$
Velocity	LT^{-1}	$\lambda^{1/2}$
Acceleration	LT^{-2}	1
Discharge	L^3T^{-1}	$\lambda^{5/2}$
Dynamic similarity		
Mass	M	λ^3
Force	MLT^{-2}	λ^3
Pressure and stress	$ML^{-1}T^{-2}$	λ
Young's modulus	$ML^{-1}T^{-2}$	λ
Energy and work	ML^2L^{-2}	λ^4
Power	ML^2T^{-3}	$\lambda^{7/2}$

should be applied in the model, in particular for distensible WECs. Compressibility effects are relevant for the air in an OWC, which may behave too stiff and damp the water oscillation compared to its prototype.

Scale effects depend on the relative importance of the involved fluid forces varying from phenomenon to phenomenon and even from parameter to parameter in the same phenomenon (significant scale effects are observed for the air entrainment in **Figure 2** where scale effects for the jet trajectory are negligibly small). Despite these variations, the following points are generally relevant for scale effects:

- Physical hydraulic model tests always involve scale effects if $\lambda \neq 1$ and an identical fluid is applied in the model and prototype since it is impossible to correctly model all force ratios. The relevant question is whether scale effects can be neglected.
- The larger the scale ratio λ, the more deviated the incorrectly modeled force ratios from the prototype ratios and the larger the expected scale effects. However, even though scale effects increase with λ in a specific study, a given value of λ does not indicate whether scale effects can be neglected. The overflow volume in an overtopping device with an overflow height of, say, 0.04 m in small waves will be affected by significant scale effects at scale 1:2, whereas rather small scale effects relative to the motion of an attenuator of 4 m diameter are expected at scale 1:2. Using λ alone to define a limiting criterion to avoid significant scale effects is insufficient.
- The size of scale effects depends on the investigated phenomenon or parameter in a given model study since the relative importance of the involved forces may differ. If one parameter, such as the wave height, is not considerably affected by scale effects, it does not necessarily mean that other parameters, such as the power, are also not affected. Each involved parameter requires its own judgment regarding scale effects.
- Since fluid forces in a model are more dominant than in the full-scale prototype, scale effects normally have a 'damping' effect. Parameters such as the relative wave height, the relative movement of a device, or the dimensionless hydraulic power are normally smaller in the model than in its prototype. A judgment whether the prediction based on the model under- or overestimates the prototype value is therefore often possible.

Some rules of thumb are often applied in physical hydraulic modeling to avoid considerable scale effects. A general list is provided in Heller [12]. The following rules of thumb are relevant for WECs:

- Scale effects increase with decreasing model size and the model should therefore be as large as possible.
- Wave periods in a model should not be smaller than 0.35 s. Waves with smaller periods are considerably affected by surface tension and propagate as capillary and not as gravity waves.
- The water depth should not be smaller than about 0.04–0.05 m to avoid significant scale effects due to surface tension and fluid viscosity. This limitation may be relevant, for example, for overtopping basins.
- Phenomena involving air entrainment require $\lambda \leq 8$ to avoid significant scale effects. Air bubbles do not scale and have a similar size in the model and its prototype (**Figure 2**).
- The investigation of cavitation in a physical model is challenging. Cavitation depends on the local pressure in a fluid relative to atmospheric pressure. The correct modeling of cavitation therefore requires a reduction of the atmospheric pressure, for example, in a cavitation tunnel.
- The downscaling of the PTO suited for a full-scale device to a small-scale physical model is impractical. The power scales with $\lambda^{7/2}$ (**Table 2**) and, say, 1 MW at full scale results in only 12.8 W at scale 1:25 or 1.1 W at scale 1:50. Friction forces (Reynolds number)

are too dominant and the amount of measured power is rather underestimated. As a consequence, friction losses should be kept to a minimum in the model and in particular in the model PTO.

8.04.3.3 Design and Testing of Physical Scale Models in the Laboratory

8.04.3.3.1 Introduction

This section describes suitable test facilities for WEC investigations. It describes typical wave generation systems and the features of the generated waves such as regularity, irregularity, and variance spectrum. Absorbing beaches to reduce reflections in a facility are addressed. Some possibilities of how a model WEC can be designed, in particular model PTOs differing from the full-scale version, are described. A list of measurement equipment suited to measure the hydrodynamics and the body movement of WECs is also presented. Finally, some suggestions for the testing of a device are given.

8.04.3.3.2 Test facilities

WECs at scale 1:100 to 1:10 are typically model tested in the laboratory covering mainly test phases 1 and 2 (**Table 1**). Physical scale model tests of a WEC are mainly conducted in

- Towing tank (2D)
- Wave flume (2D)
- Wave basin (3D)

Towing tanks are long and narrow with a movable carriage that can be driven along the tank as shown in **Figure 3(a)**. They were designed originally for ship model testing whereby a ship hull model was towed along behind or under a dolly or carriage. The dollies or carriages require a long tank length to accelerate, run, and slow down. Many towing tanks were equipped with wavemakers and down-wave energy absorbing beaches making them suitable for WEC tests. The advantages and disadvantages of towing tanks are

+ Long devices can be accommodated.
+ They are relatively easily accessible compared to a wave basin and the carriage or dolly may be used to fix a WEC and/or to accommodate the data acquisition system.
− Reflections from the down-wave beach limit the time gap for conducting an experiment.
− Transversal reflections of radiated waves from the device from the side walls of the tank may affect the results and tests in a towing tank may be regarded as an array layout where the adjacent device is located the width of the tank away.
− Only long-crested (one dominant direction) waves can be generated and any devices sensitivity to main wave approach direction cannot be investigated.
− Standing waves may develop in the width direction of the facility in some frequency ranges, which must be excluded from the test program.
− The ratio of device width to tank width may be large and limit the modeling of a full mooring configuration.

Wave flumes are similar to towing tanks in the sense that the longitudinal dimension is much greater than the width dimension. The length, however, is often shorter than in towing tanks since they are not equipped with a dolly or carriage. They are traditionally used in civil engineering and naval architecture and an example is shown in **Figure 3(b)**. The advantages and disadvantages of wave flumes are generally the same as for towing tanks. Additional points are

Figure 3 Examples of 2D facilities: (a) 60 m long, 3.6 m wide and 1.9 m deep towing tank at Solent University, Southampton, during the testing of Anaconda WEC and (b) 17 m long, 0.4 m wide and 0.7 m deep wave flume at the University of Southampton.

Figure 4 Wave basin at Danish Hydraulic Institute (DHI) (20 × 30 × 3.0 m).

+ Some wave flumes include current flows, which might be important to check mooring forces and hull behavior under a limited number of conditions.
+ Most wave flumes are equipped with glassed side walls and are located at eye level improving the visual observation of a device.

Wave basins are proportionally wider than their length and are equipped with wavemakers along one or sometimes along two adjacent walls. An example is shown in **Figure 4**. Regular and irregular long-crested seaways can be generated, and sometimes short-crested (waves from more than one direction) directional and bimodal seas can also be generated. They were originally designed for the investigation of ships, for offshore problems relevant to the oil and gas industry, or for testing coastal structures. Advanced facilities often have built-in movable floors or deep pools. The advantages and disadvantages of wave basins are

+ Radiated waves present less of a problem compared to tests in 2D facilities.
+ Single and array configurations can be studied.
+ Realistic seaways can be simulated.
+ Some facilities allow for the inclusion of marine currents in combination with waves.
− Standing waves may be a larger problem than in 2D facilities and the corresponding frequency ranges must be excluded from the test program.
− Reflections from the down-wave beach may still be a problem and limit the time gap for conducting an experiment.
− The effort to measure the wave field in wave basins is larger than in 2D facilities.
− The settling time in a wave basin is longer than in 2D facilities.
− The coherent wave fields take some time to reach dynamic equilibrium.
− The annual cost to run a wave basin is about 10 times higher than for a comparable 2D facility.

Nielsen [11] includes a comprehensive list of test facilities in Canada, Denmark, the United Kingdom, Portugal, France, Ireland, and Japan.

8.04.3.3.3 Wave generation

Wave generation systems are relevant for WECs since the choice of a tank and wavemaker depends on the type of research to be conducted. An offshore device (in deep-water waves) generally cannot be investigated in the same facility as an onshore device (in shallow-water waves). The two most common wavemaker paddles are the piston and flap types (**Figure 5**). Both types can be equipped with an active absorption system in order to minimize secondary reflections from the beach, radiations, or reflections from the device itself and to stabilize the generated sea state over time. The settling time in a tank between runs is also reduced with an absorption system.

Piston paddles (**Figure 5(a)**) are vertical and move horizontally. They are better suited to generate shallow-water waves ($L/h > 20$) where the wave length L is much larger than the water depth h. Typical applications in shallow water are the modeling of coastal structures, harbors, and shore-mounted WECs.

Flap paddles (**Figure 5(b)**) are hinged (e.g., at the bottom) and oscillate in a rotational motion. They are better suited to generate deep-water waves ($L/h < 2$) since they cause the water particles to develop orbital velocities quicker than piston paddles. They are typically applied to generate waves for both the investigation of floating structures and the physics of ocean waves. More sophisticated versions of a flap paddle have an additional hinge at mid-depth allowing for the generation of purer sinusoidal wave profiles with less higher harmonics contamination. The waves from a well-controlled paddle need to travel approximately twice the hinge depth of the paddle to become fully developed [9].

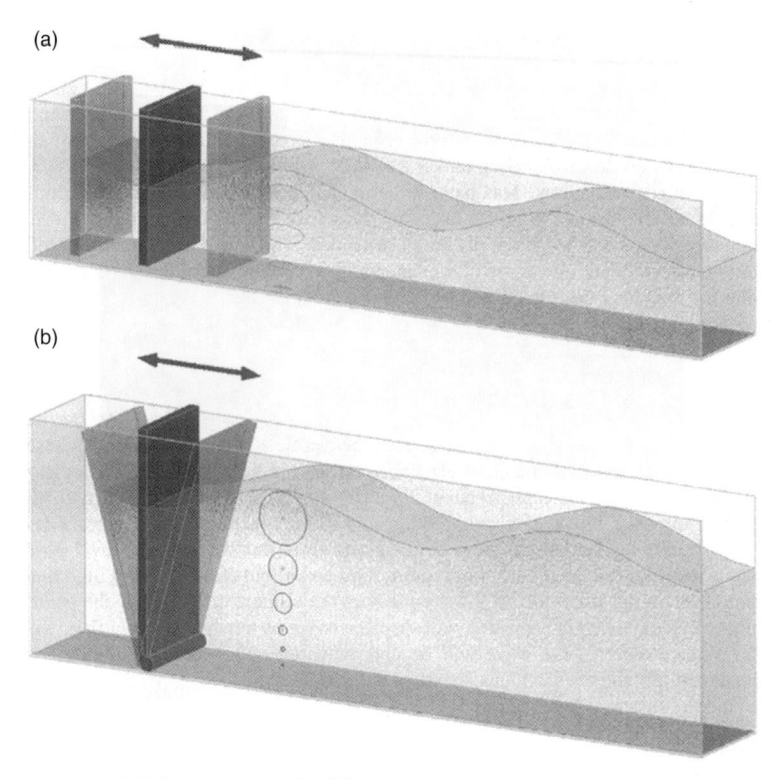

Figure 5 (a) Piston-type wavemaker and (b) flap-type wavemaker [9].

Wavemakers are able to generate regular and/or irregular waves. Regular single-frequency or monochromatic waves are important during the early stage of a WEC development program (test phase 1) to validate and calibrate mathematical models, to observe and monitor device response to regular excitation forces that define the basic operation of a device, and to evaluate higher order effects by comparison of behavior in linear and finite waves. Most numerical models are based on the linear wave theory. A linear wave requires not only a sinusoidal wave profile but in addition it has to be sufficiently small with a relative wave height $H/h < 0.03$ and a wave steepness $H/L < 0.006$ [15]. Consequently, nonlinear or higher order effects can also be investigated in regular sinusoidal waves exceeding those criteria.

Irregular or panchromatic waves allow for the investigation of a WEC in more realistic seaways. The stochastic nature of irregular sea states can be described by variance spectra (sometimes referred to as wave energy spectra), which are a means of expressing the energy content in waves as a function of frequency. **Figure 6(a)** shows a variance spectrum with the spectral density $S(f) = 0.5a/\Delta f$ on the y-axis and the frequency f on the x-axis with wave amplitude a and frequency band width Δf. The spectral density $S(f)$ is related to the wave energy since the energy is directly proportional to a. The waves over a short period of time (about 20 min) can statistically

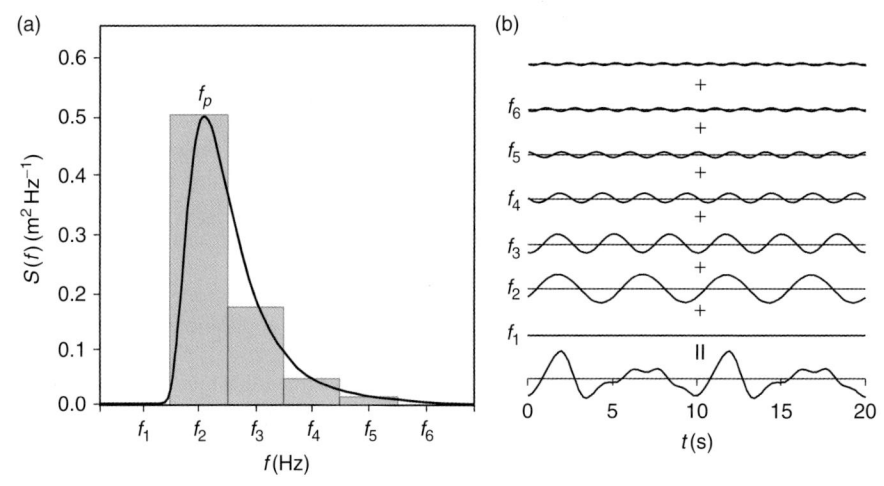

Figure 6 Variance spectrum: spectral density $S(f)$ (m² Hz⁻¹) versus wave frequency f (Hz) (a) and corresponding wave field split in sinusoidal waves of different frequencies (b) reproduced from [11].

be described using a Rayleigh probability distribution function. Spectra, in particular generic ones, follow therefore a probability distribution as shown in **Figure 6(a)**. The spectrum from a sea state can be found by a Fourier or spectral analysis of the water surface elevation assuming that the irregular sea consists of a superposition of regular waves with different amplitudes, periods, and phases (**Figure 6(b)**). The shapes of the spectra in real seas depend on the temporal and spatial fluctuation of both the wind speed and fetch length. The longer the wind duration and fetch length, the larger the generated waves and their energy content. Common generic variance spectra are (Chapter 8.03)

- *Pierson–Moskowitz spectrum.* This spectrum was introduced by Pierson and Moskowitz [16]. It depends on the parameter wind speed only (or peak period $T_P = 1/f_P$) and assumes a fully developed sea, that is, the wind has been blowing over a large ocean area for a sufficiently long time so that the waves reach their full size.
- *Bretschneider spectrum.* This spectrum operates with one or two parameters, namely, the significant wave height (and the zero crossing wave period or similar parameters) for long fetch seas.
- *JONSWAP spectrum.* This spectrum is based on a measurement program in the North Sea under the JOint North Sea Wave Analysis Program (JONSWAP) [17]. It depends on two parameters, namely, the wind speed and fetch length, and is suited to describe seas with limited fetch length (North Sea). This spectrum is similar to a Bretschneider spectrum but includes in addition the peak enhancement factor that describes the energy concentration in the peak region.

Such generic spectra have the advantage that most wavemakers are able to generate one or some of them quickly, accurately, and consistently. They further allow for a comparison with the results of the same device in regular waves or with the results of other devices. They are more generic than a site-specific spectrum and are useful when no or only limited sea state information on a specific site is available. In the later stage of test phase 1 and certainly by phase 2, it is preferable and advantageous if the performance and seaworthiness of the device are tested in the spectrum of a primary deployment location [2].

8.04.3.3.4 Absorbing beach

An energy absorbing beach is normally deployed at the down-wave end of a wave tank or wave basin in order to reduce reflections. An ideal absorbing beach is sloped at about 1:20 and may be covered with an absorbent layer of foam and mesh material and porous absorbing material placed on the berm. Even though beaches do not have to run the full depth of the tank, an ideal beach would often require a too long section of the facility and a compromise between optimum energy absorption and beach length is required. Such a compromise is, for example, surface-piercing parabolic beach reducing reflections to a minimum or the change of the slope from 1:20 to, say, 1:10. Mesh-filled wedges are an alternative in tanks with variable water depths. The efficiency of an absorbing beach depends on the wave period and to a lesser extent on the wave amplitude. An efficient absorbing beach should have reflection coefficients less than 20% by amplitude (reflected relative to incident wave amplitude) at the worst wave period [2]. A review of wave absorbers is given by Ouellet and Datta [18].

8.04.3.3.5 Model design

A model has to satisfy geometric, kinematic, and dynamic similarities to ensure that a scale model is similar to the full-scale device (Section 8.04.3.2). It is often impossible or not reasonable to scale all full-scale features to the model. Examples are the PTO or material properties of a device. This section addresses some specific points about the model design.

8.04.3.3.5(i) Model material

The material density in the model should be identical to the density at full scale. Density has the unit mass/volume, which scales according to **Table 2** with $\lambda^3/\lambda^3 = 1$ (no scaling required). This is due to Froude similarity assuming identical gravitational acceleration between model and full-scale prototype, which also requires identical water density in the model and prototype. The stiffness expressed as Young's modulus should be downscaled, at least if it is relevant for an investigation such as for distensible WECs. The Young's modulus scales linearly with the scale factor λ (**Table 2**), making a distensible device without downscaled Young's modulus too stiff. Unfortunately, there may be no suitable materials available that would represent rubber at full scale in say a 1:25 scale model and significant scale effects, for example, for the body motion, have to be taken into account.

In most laboratory tests, other materials than those used at full scale are employed and components are therefore not failure tested but rather forces are measured, which are upscaled to consider them for the full-scale design. Friction or fluid losses in scale models are normally too dominant and may result in significant scale effects. Friction in the model should therefore be minimized. Alternative materials used in scale models are light alloys, fiberglass, various plastics, acrylics (perspex), or closed-cell plastic foam for buoyancy units. If other materials than those used at full scale are employed, the mass distribution around the scaled device should be correct as expressed by the parameters center of buoyancy, center of gravity, mass moment of inertia, second moment of area, water plane area, metacenter, or metacentric height [2]. Payne [5] describes a method where a set of hollow tubes are included in the buoyancy units, which can be used to put ballast rods in various positions to change the mass distribution of a device. Corrosion is a problem if metals are used in the model. Screws should be made of stainless steel; aluminum components can be protected by anodizing and steel by protective coating, for example, by galvanization.

8.04.3.3.5(ii) Mooring

It is important that the station keeping system is also scaled correctly. The role of the mooring system in the model may be to firmly fix the position of a device, to simulate dynamic mooring with similar compliance and degrees of freedom as in the full-scale device, or, if linearly downscaled, to study interaction with other components of a device.

8.04.3.3.5(iii) Power takeoff

The inclusion of a PTO in the model is important not only to measure power, but also to correctly model the performance such as damping of components of a device or reflection behavior due to the presence of the PTO. Technologies suitable for the PTO of full-scale devices usually do not lend themselves to downscaling (Section 8.04.3.2). Power in a physical model can be defined in various other ways than just electrical power [11]:

- Linear mechanical system: Mechanical power (W) = force (N) × velocity (m s^{-1})
- Hydraulic PTO: Fluid power (W) = flow rate (m^3 s^{-1}) × pressure (N m^{-2})
- OWC system: Air power (W) = flow rate (m^3 s^{-1}) × pressure drop (N m^{-2})
- Overtopping system: Water power (W) = fluid density (kg m^{-3}) × gravitational acceleration (m s^{-2}) × flow rate (m^3 s^{-1}) × head difference (m)
- Rotary mechanical system: Shaft power (W) = shaft torque (N m) × angular velocity (s^{-1})

All parameters used for the definition of power are time dependent. As an alternative, they can be expressed as time-averaged values. The following section describes five approaches to measure power with a model PTO investigated during the testing of the Anaconda WEC. Most of them could similarly be applied in other devices. Anaconda consists essentially of a closed rubber tube filled with water and it is anchored head to the waves in deep-water and oriented parallel to the wave direction. It captures wave power in the form of bulge waves propagating along the tube similar to pressure pulses of the mammalian heart [19]. The PTO is located at the tube stern absorbing the oscillating flow from the bulges. Methods used to investigate the absorbed power are as follows:

1. *Aerodynamic damper (OWC, air power)*. The power of an OWC is in the form of air power. An air turbine can be modeled with an orifice restricting the airflow out of an air chamber and increasing the pressure in the chamber. A calibration results in a relation between pressure drop over the orifice and flow velocity and the flow rate can therefore be expressed as a function of this pressure drop. The pressure drop for an orifice is identical to the pressure measured in the chamber for an orifice open to the atmosphere. For a given calibration relation, air power (flow rate × pressure drop) is then just a function of the pressure in the air chamber. Since some air turbines, for example, the Wells turbine (Chapter 8.05), are nearly linear and regarding numerical simulations, it is desirable that the calibration relation between pressure drop and velocity is linear. This can be achieved by replacing the orifice with layers of felt or with capillary tubes as demonstrated by Chaplin *et al.* [19], resulting in a linear and tunable PTO (**Figures 7**(a) and (b)).

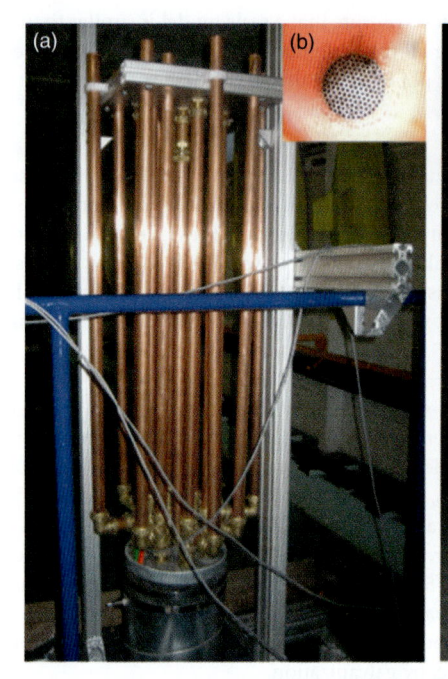

Figure 7 Model PTOs: (a) capillary PTO with 17 copper tubes (b) each filled with about 140 capillary pipes and (c) mechanical damper controlled with an electromagnetic actuator with (d) piston in the gray cylinder; a pressure transducer is fixed in the piston center.

2. *Pressure head difference (water power).* The oscillating flow from the bulges in the Anaconda tube passes a one-way valve to reach a reservoir smoothing the oscillation. This reservoir is connected with an orifice simulating a water turbine to a second reservoir of lower pressure head. The pressure head difference between these two reservoirs generates a constant flow rate through the orifice if the device operates in regular waves. The fluid flow goes back to the rubber tube from the second reservoir with a one-way valve. With the known discharge coefficient (and flow rate) through the orifice as a function of the pressure head difference between the two reservoirs, water power is measured. The water power of an overtopping device may be determined in a similar way.
3. *Mechanical damper (moving piston, mechanical power).* A moving piston can react to oscillating flow similar to an absorbing wavemaker and power is determined with the pressure measured on the piston front (force = pressure × piston area) and known kinematics of the piston (**Figures 7(c)** and **7(d)**). The aim is that the measured dynamic force is used as a feedback signal into a servo control loop for the piston motion to absorb the incoming oscillating flow. Making this servo loop stable can be a challenging task.
4. *Incident, reflected, and transmitted waves.* The absorbed wave power of a WEC is identical to the wave power of the incident waves minus the wave power of both the reflected and transmitted waves if losses due to, for example, rubber hysteresis or fluid turbulence are neglected. This method is mainly applicable in 2D facilities. It is recommended that several wave probes are employed over the facility width since the wave height is often not homogeneous over the width for devices that do not cover the whole facility width.
5. *Radiation theory.* In this rather theoretical approach, the capture width in incident waves is expressed with the far-field radiation characteristics of a WEC performing forced oscillations in still water [20]. In other words, the power can be determined by measuring the radiated waves from a device actuated to move in initially still water like it would move in incident waves during power absorption. This method requires wave measurements at many points. Wave reflections from components of the model itself or the boundaries may even be a problem in a large wave basin [21].

Payne [5] describes further methods for the investigation of power including dynamometers to determine forces between the wave-driven and active body elements, or simple friction brakes on rotating components if only qualitative assessment of the impact of the PTO resistance to the prime mover is required or to simulate its effect on hydrodynamics.

8.04.3.3.6 Measurement equipment

Several important quantities need to be measured in WEC investigations. This section gives an overview of those quantities and the corresponding measurement systems. As was discussed above, power can be defined in various ways. Depending on the definition applied and the specific device under investigation, force (or pressure × area), velocity, flow rate (or velocity × area), pressure, head difference, shaft torque, and/or angular frequency have to be measured. All of the following measurement categories contribute to the validation and calibration of mathematical models:

- *Water surface elevation.* This is important to measure the incident, reflected, and/or radiated waves and to determine the available power for a device or to execute a reflection analysis. The measurement of the free water surface is further relevant for overtopping basins or for free surfaces in OWCs. The velocity of the free surface required to compute power of an OWC can also be deduced from such recordings.
- *Fluid velocity.* This is relevant for the determination of, for example, the air power in an OWC. Flow visualization techniques may reveal large-scale turbulent structures and how streamlined a device is. Cavitation is a further quantity depending on the local fluid velocity.
- *Coherent turbulent structures.* These measurements may help to optimize the design of a device to reduce losses.
- *Flow rate.* This quantity can be relevant for an overtopping device or for the flow through a pipe between two tanks with a head difference.
- *Force.* This parameter is relevant for the determination of power, for example, of mechanical components but also for further parts of a device such as the hull or mooring line. This may further be important for the dimensioning of a structure in cases where a WEC is integrated in a wave breaker.
- *Pressure.* Pressure and force are related and force can be computed as pressure times area under the assumption that the pressure is homogeneous over the area. Cavitation is a further parameter depending on local pressure.
- *Movement analysis (body motion).* This helps to understand the performance of a device and is particularly relevant for flexible or distensible devices. For more theoretical aspects such as the investigation of the radiation problem, the movement of a device may be actuated and it is available from the position sensors of the motion control system.

Table 3 shows these introduced measurement categories and corresponding measurement systems with spatial resolution, their effect on the flow field, and comments.

The level of noise relative to the signal of a sensor can be a serious problem and screened cables should be used. Not all measurement systems in **Table 3** are suited to work underwater without protection such as laser distance sensors, strain gauges including their wires, or camera systems with a higher resolution than common for underwater systems. They can be sheltered with IP68 rated enclosures, where IP68 stands for International Protection Rating with the first digit specifying protection against dust (6 = dust tight) and the second digit protection against liquids (8 = protected against liquids with immersion beyond 1 m). It can be time consuming to make a measurement

Table 3 Measurement systems for WECs: measurement category with measurement systems, spatial resolution, effect on the flow field, and comments

Measurement category	Measurement system	Spatial resolution	Effect on flow field	Comments
Water surface elevation	Capacitance wave gauge	Point measurement	Intrusive	Water has to be mixed prior to calibration
	Resistance wave gauge	Point measurement	Intrusive	
	Acoustic wave gauge	Point measurement	Nonintrusive	Cannot be used to measure breaking waves
	Ultrasound gauge	Point measurement	Nonintrusive	Static pressure is proportional to fluid level above
	Pressure reading	Point measurement	Nonintrusive at measurement point but elsewhere in flow field	
	Drop-depth gauge	Point measurement	Intrusive	For constant or extremely slowly varying water surface levels only
	Camera system	Measurement over an area	Nonintrusive	For optical wave run-up measurement
Fluid velocity	Pitot-Static (or 'pitot') probe	Point measurement	Intrusive	Mainly for constant flows
	Doppler system (laser or acoustic)	Point measurement	Nonintrusive at measurement point but elsewhere in flow field	System may require additional seeding particles; also suited for quantification of turbulence
	Hot wire/film anemometers	Point measurement	Intrusive	Also suited for quantification of turbulence
	Cross-flow/propeller turbine wheel	Point measurement	Intrusive	
	Particle image velocimetry (PIV)	Measurement over an area	Nonintrusive	For velocities and visualization of coherent turbulent structures
	Particle tracking velocimetry (PTV)	Visualization/measurement over an area	Nonintrusive	For visualization of flow and coherent turbulent structures
Coherent turbulent structures	Tracer particles/dye	Visualization of an area	Nonintrusive	Only qualitative information
Flow rate	Electromagnetic meter	Measurement at a cross section	Nonintrusive	E.g., for pipe between two tanks of head differences
	Propeller or orifice meter	Point measurement	Intrusive	E.g., for pipe between two tanks of head differences
Force	Strain gauge	Point measurement	Intrusive	Temperature sensitive
	Force transducer	Point measurement	Intrusive	
Pressure	Pressure transducer	Point measurement (small area)	Nonintrusive if fixed flush to a surface	
Movement analysis (body motion)	Liquid metal strain gauge	Point measurement	Intrusive	Also for strain measurement; liquids are, e.g., mercury or galinstan
	Camera system	Visualization of an area	Nonintrusive	Qualitative information
	Video motion tracking device	Several points	Nonintrusive	Qualitative and quantitative information
	Accelerometer	Point measurement	Practically nonintrusive	Results include body velocity and displacement
	Potentiometer	Point measurement	Intrusive	
	Laser distance sensor	Point measurement	Nonintrusive at measurement point but elsewhere in flow field	
	Electromagnetic actuator		Intrusive	Body motion is actuated with known displacement to investigate, e.g., the radiation problem

Figure 8 Laser distance sensor in an IP68 rated enclosure with a hole for the power supply (top) and a window for the laser (bottom); the closed enclosure is water proven up to a water depth of 1.5 m.

system or sensor waterproof. An example is shown in **Figure 8**. A laser distance sensor is protected with an IP68 rated enclosure with a hole for power supply and a window for the laser. The hole is sealed with an IP68 rated cable gland and LS-X® leak sealer and the window is covered with perplex, fixed with screws from the inside with blind holes, and sealed with both mastic sealer and LS-X®. Strain gauges or wires can be sheltered with Plasti Dip®, a flexible liquid coating that can be used on most materials.

8.04.3.3.7 Device testing

The tests to be undertaken are highly device and site specific, and providing more than general guidance would go beyond this section. Independently of which tests are conducted, the reporting of which tests are carried out in which facility and with which model is important. Since power is the most relevant parameter, programs should be arranged around investigating the device's design variables to optimize power production. The most common way to illustrate the performance of a device is the power matrix (Chapter 8.03). A power matrix of Pelamis is shown in **Figure 9**. This power matrix shows the power as a function of significant wave height H_{m0} (ordinate) and energy period T_e (abscissa).

H_{m0} (m) \ T_e (s)	5.0	5.5	6.0	6.5	7.0	7.5	8.0	8.5	9.0	9.5	10.0	10.5	11.0	11.5	12.0	12.5	13.0
0.5	idle	idle	idle	idle	idle	idle	idle	idle	idle	idle	idle	idle	idle	idle	idle	idle	idle
1.0	idle	22	29	34	37	38	38	37	35	32	29	26	23	21	idle	idle	idle
1.5	32	50	65	76	83	86	86	83	78	72	65	59	53	47	42	37	33
2.0	57	88	115	136	148	153	152	147	138	127	116	104	93	83	74	66	59
2.5	89	138	180	212	231	238	238	230	216	199	181	163	146	130	116	103	92
3.0	129	198	260	305	332	340	332	315	292	266	240	219	210	188	167	149	132
3.5	–	270	354	415	438	440	424	404	377	362	326	292	260	230	215	202	180
4.0	–	–	462	502	540	546	530	499	475	429	384	366	339	301	267	237	213
4.5	–	–	544	635	642	648	628	590	562	528	473	432	382	356	338	300	266
5.0	–	–	–	739	726	731	707	667	670	607	557	521	472	417	369	348	328
5.5	–	–	–	750	750	750	750	750	737	667	658	586	530	496	446	395	355
6.0	–	–	–	–	750	750	750	750	750	750	711	633	619	558	512	470	415
6.5	–	–	–	–	750	750	750	750	750	750	750	743	658	621	579	512	481
7.0	–	–	–	–	–	750	750	750	750	750	750	750	750	676	613	584	525
7.5	–	–	–	–	–	–	750	750	750	750	750	750	750	750	686	622	593
8.0	–	–	–	–	–	–	–	750	750	750	750	750	750	750	750	690	625

Figure 9 Example of numerically deduced power matrix of Pelamis [22].

8.04.3.3.7(i) Tests in regular (monochromatic) waves

Tests in regular or monochromatic waves are mainly conducted to verify the concept of a device, to validate and calibrate mathematical models, and to identify and develop the understanding of relevant hydrodynamics and other physics processes. Points such as quantification of technical performance variables (e.g., capture width) or evaluation of economics may be motivators as well. Not all regular waves are automatically linear and they have to be sufficiently small and flat to satisfy the limitations of linear wave theory (see Section 8.04.3.3.3). The wave power of linear waves per unit length of wave front in deep water is

$$\text{power} = \rho g^2 H^2 T/(32\pi) \text{ (W m}^{-1}) \approx H^2 T \text{ (kW m}^{-1})$$

with wave height H and wave period T. The power (W) actually available for a WEC can be indicated by the power per unit length of wave front (W m^{-1}) multiplied by a characteristic length scale of a device such as the hull width (m). The efficiency of a WEC can be defined with the capture width (m), which is the absorbed power (W) of a device relative to the wave power per unit length of wave front (W m^{-1}). It is common to express the efficiency as a relative capture width (–) which is the capture width (m) divided by a characteristic length scale of a device (m), such as the diameter.

8.04.3.3.7(ii) Tests in irregular (panchromatic) waves

The principal motivators to conduct tests in irregular waves are outlined in Section 8.04.3.1. The main difference compared to tests in regular waves is that the device is now investigated under more realistic conditions. The wave power of irregular waves is

$$\text{power} = \rho g^2 H_s^2 T_z/(64\pi) \text{ (W m}^{-1})$$

with significant wave height H_s and average wave period T_z. Holmes [2] recommends that the duration of an energy capture trial corresponds to 20–30 min at prototype scale. The overall behavior of a structure can be determined with 15–20 of H_s–T_z combinations, for example, with the Bretschneider spectrum, not all combinations in the scatter diagram (**Figure 9**) have to be investigated. Generic spectra such as Bretschneider or JONSWAP are important to study the basic device response to irregular waves, whereas site-specific spectra are useful for understanding device behavior at a proposed site. Nielsen [11] recommends which specific tests should be conducted with a physical scale model of a device whose full-scale version would be located in the North Sea. These tests include the Bretschneider spectrum and also tests with JONSWAP spectrum to investigate the influence of the spectral shape as well as directional spreading.

8.04.3.3.7(iii) Tests in extreme waves

Tests in extreme waves are required before progressing to test phase 3 (**Table 1**) with a medium-scale model in a wave basin. Such tests provide the extreme motions and loads exerted on the hull, PTO, mooring lines (station keeping system), anchors, and foundations for fixed or gravity structures experienced during storm conditions. They should ensure safe station keeping, seaworthiness, survivability, and validation of failure modes of a device. What constitutes extreme conditions is highly site and device specific in terms of what particular combination of conditions produces the worst loading conditions and general guidance cannot be given herein. The most demanding sea state for a specific device can only be achieved by testing across a range of conditions and/or spectral shapes. Measured quantities include the stability and trim, accelerations, displacements and attitude, overtopping volume and frequency, impact loads, and vibration and system dynamics. The conditions under which survival tests are conducted are not well defined. The duration may be a typical storm length of 3 h at full scale and some trials will be conducted for 50- to 100-year storms [2]. Nielsen [11] recommends a duration representing 60 min at full scale and waves occurring once every 10, 20, or 50 years for devices employed in the North Sea. Short-crested seas and directional waves should also be included in the test program.

8.04.4 Sea Trials of Large-Scale Prototypes

8.04.4.1 Introduction

This section addresses test phases 3 (if taking place at a benign sea site) to 5 in **Table 1**. A main difference of sea trials compared to tests in the laboratory is that the ocean environment is not controllable and that, besides the wave climate, tidal variation and currents are likely to have an effect on the performance of a device. The accurate measurement of the (wave) resource with one or several of the methods described in Chapter 8.03 is therefore essential.

Generally speaking, the knowledge and technical literature about sea trials of WECs is much less than about physical model testing in the laboratory. This is particularly the case for WECs in arrays where limited practical experience exists. Nevertheless, documents addressing full-scale prototype testing in the sea include HMRC [1], Nielsen [11], DTI [23], several case studies in Cruz [8, 24–30], and both work packages 4 (*Sea trial testing procedures for ocean energy extraction devices*) and 5 (*Deployment assessment – Performance of multi-megawatt device arrays*) from EquiMar [6]. Furthermore, IEE [3] reviews the current status of the most advanced WECs and addresses European WEC test sites. Not covered herein are environmental and socioeconomic effects of wave energy conversion (see References 31–33) as well as economic aspects of both devices (see Chapter 8.06, References 11, 33, 34) and of wave energy conversion in general (see Reference 4).

Section 8.04.4.2 covers the part of test phase 3 taking place at a benign sea site. Sea trials with full-scale prototypes are addressed in Section 8.04.4.3 and sea trials based on arrays in Section 8.04.4.4.

8.04.4.2 Sea Trials with Scale Models

Test phase 3 suggests testing the device in large-scale facilities and/or at a benign sea site (**Table 1**). Only the latter case will be discussed here, whereas tests in large-scale facilities are covered in Section 8.04.3. Tests in phase 3 provide the final opportunity to quickly, reasonably easily, and relatively inexpensively learn about the inevitable problems still associated with a device, its operation, and deployment techniques. The specific aims of large-scale model tests at benign sea sites are

- Investigation of physical properties not well scaled
- Implication of a realistic/actual PTO and generating system
- Qualification of future environmental factors (marine growth, corrosion, windage, and current drag)
- Validation of the electrical supply quality

The benign sea site is a wave active but partially protected location such as a fresh water lake or sheltered bay offering sufficient water depth and easy land access. Correctly scaled wave conditions relative to the final site are an important consideration of the outdoor location and may restrict safe testing of device to specific seasons of the year. Sites employed to investigate devices in test phase 3 include Nissum Bredning, Denmark, and Galway Bay, Ireland. A selection of devices tested in the sea at reduced scale is shown in **Figure 10**. Sections of the Mediterranean Sea may be suited as a downscaled version of the North Atlantic conditions for the investigation of a 1:2 to 1:4 scale device. The requirements for an appropriate test location are

- Accessibility of a local convenient harbor for light service tasks
- A nearby port for launch and delivery to the model site
- Prearranged licenses and consents for deployment
- Predeployed wave measurement instruments
- Short distance to landfall
- Correct water depth
- Appropriate seabed and bathymetry
- Acceptable wave climate
- Onshore command center backup (electricity, portable or fixed office, security)
- Convenient travel hub
- Basic rectification and engineering maintenance shops
- Modern communication links

The model in this phase includes for the first time all required components, from primary converter to electrical generators and power electronics, albeit at reduced scale. Components such as the PTO or the mooring system are scaled versions of the full-scale prototype. The scale is therefore relatively large with 1:3 to 1:10 (**Table 1**). Test phase 3 also brings together a multidisciplinary team for the first time including device experimentalists, mechanical engineers, electro engineers, and economists. Since the device is still scaled, scale effect may still be relevant for an investigation (Section 8.04.3.2). However, scale effects are smaller than in previous phases and these new tests may help to estimate the amount of scale effects in previous experiments or to validate and/or calibrate the earlier model results which may have been affected by both significant scale effects and model effects such as reflections. The power is still relatively small and say a 1 MW device at full scale results in $1\,000\,000/4^{3.5} \approx 7800\,W$ at scale 1:4. Devices in this phase are normally not grid connected and the relatively small production of electricity is dumped. The model probably consists of the same materials as the prototype but scaled accordingly (**Table 2**). Survival and maximum force conditions may not be achievable in the benign site scenario where full environmental loadings are reduced for safety reasons [1, 2].

8.04.4.3 Sea Trials with Full-Scale Prototypes

8.04.4.3.1 Introduction

In test phase 4, the device is built at scale 1:1–2 and tested in the sea (**Table 1**). This section addresses full-scale prototype testing. The wave energy capture principles of the devices covered in this section are described in Chapter 8.02. The primary objective of these tests is to fully verify the functionality, maintenance, operation, and performance of the device and its ability to survive extreme conditions. This phase will also make the economic feasibility of a specific WEC clearer than investigations in previous test phases. In particular, the objectives of this test phase are [6]

- Demonstration of system integrity and viability of technology
- To seek for aspects (O&M, performance at full scale, economics, etc.) that had not been identified during the previous project phases and to gain experience
- Establish controllability
- Gain operational experience
- Calibration of mathematical model from data from prototype at sea

Figure 10 Selection of WECs tested in phase 3 at benign sea sites: (a) WaveBob at Galway Bay, Ireland, (b) Wavestar at Nissum Bredning, Denmark (courtesy of Wavestar), (c) OWES at Port Kembla, Australia, (d) OE Buoy at Galway Bay, Ireland, (e) Ceto at Fremantle, Australia (courtesy of Carnegie Wave Energy), and (f) Wave Dragon at Nissum Bredning, Denmark (courtesy of Wave Dragon). Remaining pictures reproduced from IEE (2009) State of the art analysis – A cautiously optimistic review of the technical status of wave energy technology. *Report of Waveplam*. Brussels, Belgium: Intelligent Energy Europe [3].

- Early indication of availability of systems considering degradation mechanisms and maintenance routines
- Establish power conversion capabilities

These objectives will be achieved by assembling the complete machine and connecting it to the electrical grid. Important for a device from a technical and economic point of view are factors such as survivability, reliability, maintenance, operability, and cost efficiency. Different developers have different approaches to deal with these issues depending on their device: some WECs have a storm protection mode in order to ensure survivability under extreme conditions where the loads on the structure or PTO would be too large, for example, floaters are raised out of the water from a certain wave height. Other devices dive through the largest waves or extreme waves just wash over the device without damage. The reliability of a WEC may be improved if as much as possible off-the-shelf equipment is used. Redundancy improves further the reliability of a system, such as using subdivided buoyancy tanks rather than employing only one single unit in order that a system is still operable when one tank is damaged. Some planned devices at full scale would have maximum dimensions of several hundred meters and maintenance work can just take place on the device itself without much interruption due to the waves. Other developers bring their devices back to the harbor for maintenance works since it is in their case much cheaper and safer to bring the device to the equipment rather than the equipment to the device. Their mooring is designed such that the device can be disconnected and connected quickly and cheaply across a wide range of wave conditions. Control algorithms may improve the operability and are very valuable since they can improve the performance of a device without any extra capital or maintenance cost. Ways to improve the cost efficiency include the more efficient use of materials or to generate as much power as possible in wide sea conditions. Most devices are tunable where the desirable operation under resonance over wide sea conditions is possible. Cost may also be reduced again by relying on off-the-shelf equipment rather than developing new components and also with new and innovative ways of conducting installation, operation, and maintenance.

The next section addresses the test site for this phase. Eleven devices, which have already been tested at full scale, are presented below and some recommendations about device testing and measurement in the sea are given at the end of Section 8.04.4.3.

8.04.4.3.2 Test site

Tests typically take place at a test center such as the EMEC at the Orkney Islands, Scotland. The location for testing a single device and of the wave energy farm in test phase 5 would be then not identical and the device may be moved afterward. In other cases, such as in the European wave energy pilot plan on the Pico Island, Azores, the device stays fully functional as a single device after the tests and delivers electricity to a small, inhabited island or a remote community such that even the single device could provide an economic electricity supply. Publicity and promotional purposes may be further reasons to remain a single device on station after the completion of the tests. Other developers, with perhaps less mobile devices, select a test site for phase 4 with the intention to extend it to an array arrangement afterward to save cost and time.

Problems encountered during the construction of the WEC on the Pico Island between 1995 and 1999 are described by Sarmento *et al.* [28]. The Pico Island is located about 2000 km away from Lisbon and had only about 15 000 inhabitants with limited infrastructures and qualified manpower. During construction, no direct flights to Lisbon were available and the access to the island was sometimes difficult in winter due to rough weather conditions and in summer because of the limited number of seats in airplanes due to tourism. In addition, storms destroyed parts of the construction and flooded the room with the electrical equipment just a few weeks before the completion of the plant. The authors recommend based on these negative experiences that *in situ* constructions must be avoided whenever possible and that the plant should be as accessible as possible.

To avoid such problems, the test site should satisfy the following general requirements, most of which are similar to the criteria for the outdoor site of phase 3 (Section 8.04.4.2):

- Favorable energy resource
- Known wave resource and environmental data (wind, current climatology, bathymetry, seabed properties) and predeployed wave measurement instruments
- Proximity between shore and national grid
- Access to harbors and shipyards (for O&M and safety reasons)
- Simplified regulations and licensing procedures
- One or more offshore connection points
- Monitoring facilities related to the device itself and the environment
- Small distance between the 50 m contour and the shoreline
- Potential to be extended to test site for small array
- Good accessibility
- Out of the region of major shipping lanes, fishing areas, military training sites, and munitions dumps

8.04.4.3.3 Devices tested at full scale

The WECs shown in **Table 4** were or are being tested at full scale in the sea. The list is not exhaustive and Chapter 8.02 includes further devices. **Table 4** includes besides the device's name the year when tests took place, location, rated power, and the source of information. The rated power equals normally the maximum electrical output of the generator. Some of the devices are still under development and were or are planned to be tested in an array, whereas others were abandoned. The spectrum of device types reaching this test level is large and it seems currently unclear which device(s) will succeed in commercialization. **Figure 11** shows a selection of the devices in **Table 4** and Chapter 8.02 addresses their working principles.

8.04.4.3.4 Device testing and measurements

Work package 4 of EquiMar [6] deals with test phase 4 and most information in this section is from their Deliverable 4.2. The deployment of a full-scale prototype spans a large range of engineering development and introduces heavy offshore operations, device

Table 4 Some full-scale WEC prototypes tested in the sea

Device	Year of tests	Location	Rated power	Source
AWS	2004	Aguçadoura, Portugal	2 MW	IEE [3], Prado [27]
Ceto	2011	Garden Island, Australia	200 kW	Ocean Power Technologies [38]
Direct Drive Linear Generator	2005	Lysekil, Sweden	10 × 10 kW	IEE [3]
EU Pilot Plant	1999	Pico Island, Azores	400 kW	Sarmento *et al.* [36]
LIMPET OWC	2000–07	Islay, Scotland	500 kW	IEE [3]
Mighty Whale	1998	Nansei Town, Japan	120 kW	Clément *et al.* [35]
OWES	2005–06	Port Kembla, Australia	500 kW	IEE [3]
Oyster	2009–11	EMEC, Scotland	300 kW	IEE [3], Aquamarine Power [37]
Pelamis	2004–07	EMEC, Scotland	750 kW	IEE [3], Yemm [30]
	2010–11	EMEC, Scotland	750 kW	IEEE [3], Yemm [30], Pelamis Wave Power [22]
PowerBuoy	2009–10	Hawaii, USA	40 kW	Ocean Power Technologies [38]
PowerBuoy	2011	Invergordon, Scotland	150 kW	Ocean Power Technologies [38]
WavePlane	2008	Hanstholm, Denmark	100 kW	IEE [3]
WaveRoller	2007–08	Peniche, Portugal	2 × 15 kW	IEE [3]

Figure 11 Selection of WECs tested in phase 4 at full scale: (a) AWS at Aguçadoura, Portugal, (b) WavePlane at Hanstholm, Denmark, (c) Oyster at EMEC, Scotland (courtesy of Aquamarine Power), and (d) LIMPET OWC device at Islay, Scotland. Remaining pictures reproduced from IEE (2009) State of the art analysis – A cautiously optimistic review of the technical status of wave energy technology. *Report of Waveplam*. Brussels, Belgium: Intelligent Energy Europe [3].

certification, health and safety considerations, environmental issues, regulatory and permit requirements, and improved economic predictions. Some of these and other issues are covered by *Guidelines on Design and Operation of Wave Energy Converters* [39].

The ocean environment is, in contrast to the laboratory environment, uncontrolled and this has to be compensated for with a careful selection of test site and extended deployment duration. Ideally, the measurement program would require several performance observations to be made in each element of a site's metocean conditions to confidently produce an empirical time-averaged power matrix for a machine (**Figure 9**). This can rarely be achieved in practice since all the possible environmental conditions might not occur during the period of the sea trial, which cannot be arbitrarily long due to high cost. As a consequence, fully completed programs may be the exception rather than the norm. Gaps in the test program are normally filled with a numerical model developed during the laboratory tests and newly calibrated and validated with the available sea trial data. Due to such gaps, the level of confidence, or degree of uncertainty, that dictates the risk assessment for continuing forward should be specified, that is, the average value in the power matrix should be accompanied by a confidence interval or a standard deviation.

Deliverable 4.2 of EquiMar [6] aims to describe a logical and widely applicable method to analyze and present the data obtained from sea trials such as yearly average performance. This deliverable specifies the high-level information required from such sea trials as

- An estimation of the uncertainty of the performance figures
- Overall device power conversion performance at the site of the performed sea trials, with the local sea conditions
- Power production estimates based on the sea trials, but at other sites and possibly at other scales of the device. This will in some cases be possible only through the use of numerical or analytical models of the device as mentioned above

Deliverable 4.2 shows how the data obtained for a device at one specific location can be used to estimate the performance at another location.

The required measurements and measurement sensors in this phase are as varied as the investigated device types. Section 8.04.4.4 includes the required measurements for technologies supported by the MRDF, available for devices in arrays. These required measurements including the wave resource, generated power, and exported/imported power from the electrical grid may be seen as an absolute minimum for test phase 4. In addition, tests at full scale may include many additional measurements such as structural or mooring loads or other parameters required to provide information on the survival and fatigue conditions of the device. The following three examples described in Cruz [8, 27, 36, 40] show how different the employed measurement sensors for various devices can be:

- *AWS (submerged pressure differential, **Figure 11(a)**)*. Measurements in 2004 in Portugal included water pressure on the top of the device (to measure waves), air pressure inside of AWS to identify both the air spring and the motion of the device, and electrical power output at the converter.
- *European Pilot Plant at Pico (OWC, similar to **Figure 11(d)**)*. The monitoring equipment includes sensors to measure the rotational speed of the turbine, air pressure and water free surface elevation in the air chamber, static pressure at both the inner and the outer covers of the air duct immediately upstream and downstream to the stators, dynamic pressure, vibrations and oil temperature at the turbogenerator bearings, temperature, voltage, and current at each of the three electrical circuit phases, lubrication flow, total, active, and reactive power delivered to the grid, and cumulative active energy production.
- *Wave Dragon (offshore overtopping device, **Figure 10(f)**)*. Although the following sensors were used in test phase 3 at Nissum Bredning, Denmark, similar sensors may be relevant for full-scale testing. Over 100 sensors were on board including pressure sensors to measure incoming waves, floating height, and water in the reservoir, strain gauges and force transducers, a wind station, accelerometers and inclinometers to record the position of the device, electrical sensors within the PTO, and web cameras for visual checks of the situation on the platform.

Nielsen [11] recommends for devices in the North Sea to measure in 20 min intervals every 3 h resulting in eight data points over 24 h. He further recommends a sampling frequency of 4 Hz for measurements of the wave conditions. The bin size of the scatter diagram for the wave sensors should be 0.5 m for the significant wave height and 1 s for the mean wave period. The directionality can be presented in bins of 30° as a function of the significant wave height in a second scatter diagram. Such recommendations slightly change from document to document. DTI [23] recommends, for instance, slightly different values for commercial devices in arrays, as mentioned in Section 8.04.4.4.

8.04.4.4 Sea Trials with WECs in an Array

8.04.4.4.1 Introduction

Practical experience and technical literature about WECs in arrays is limited since only one device (the Pelamis WEC) has operated in an array at full scale to date. Most studies investigating effects in arrays at full scale are based on numerical simulations. Documents addressing WECs in arrays are DTI [23] and work package 5 of EquiMar [6]. The general objectives of deployment and performance assessment of multi-megawatt device arrays are described in the latter document as

- Planning and installing a large number of devices in the marine environment in order to extract energy and convey this energy to shore
- Planning effective deployment and maintenance schedules such that
  1. The need for direct intervention is minimized in terms of number of operations and their duration
  2. Where intervention is required the associated difficulty is reduced to an acceptable level
- Identification of the most appropriate configuration and electrical connection of devices
- Optimization of the energy capture of individual devices such that the efficiency of power conversion is maximized from the array
- Standardization of performance parameters from an array. Due to potential device interaction, these will be different from those of an individual device operating in isolation

- Sharing systems (such as electrical connections) between devices such that the costs are reduced compared to an equivalent number of individual devices operating in isolation or a smaller-sized array

A device array in the demonstration phase may typically consist of 3–5 devices, 10 devices at most, and be aligned in a single row perpendicular to the direction of the incoming wave resource. Small commercial wave farms may consist of 10–50, medium ones 50–200, and large ones more than 200 devices. Devices in an array may be affected by wave radiation from the surrounding devices and the absorbed wave energy of a device is not available for another one. In addition, different devices within an array may also be affected differently by the bathymetry or refraction or sheltering due to the local coastline. The resource for a device may therefore possibly vary tens of percents within an array. Wave radiation is not necessarily a negative point. A point absorber in the center of an array can produce more power, due to additional waves generated by the surrounding devices, than on its own at the same location. However, positive interaction effects may be an exception or affect only single devices within an array and an important issue for most types of WECs will be the minimization of negative interaction effects between devices in order to avoid increasing structural loading and/or decreasing power production. Other issues for this phase are the degree of accessibility of the individual devices within an array, the deployment of the devices, and the electrical connections. Common terms such as rated power, availability, capacity factor, conversion efficiency, and capture width can be defined for an array as a whole for absolute and comparative purposes. New terms may also be required such as the spacing number, which is the average spacing between machines divided by the capture width, as suggested by EquiMar [6].

8.04.4.4.2 Test site

The criteria required for the test location of an array are basically the same as for a single full-scale device (Section 8.04.4.3). The available local electrical grid capacity may be of even larger relevance since grid reinforcement would cause additional costs for the developer (Chapter 8.06). Pelamis WEC shown in **Figure 12(a)** is the only device that gained operational experience in an array arrangement in test phase 5, namely, in the Aguçadoura project in Portugal in 2008. However, several devices of other developers are planned or already under construction to be tested in arrays. Two large multidevice test sites in Europe are also approved or suggested:

- *Wave Hub (Chapter 8.01)*. This project in southwest England provides the infrastructure to facilitate the deployment of up to four wave farms with a simplified licensing procedure producing a total connection power of 20 MW. The subsea connections are provided such that the developers can plug in their devices offshore. The project holds a 25-year lease for 8 km² of sea. Currently, the confirmed devices involved are FO, PB150, and Pelamis (**Figure 13**).
- *Biscay Marine Energy Platform (BIMEP)*. This proposed infrastructure for research, demonstration, and operation of WECs has a total capacity of 20 MW, offshore of the Basque Country in Spain. The subsea cables are provided as in Wave Hub. The test site is 4 × 2 km large and the water depth is 50–90 m.

Besides these two multidevice wave farms, several test locations were selected for devices of one or two types such as Mutriku in Spain (turbines, **Figure 12(b)**), Pembrokeshire in Wales (Wave Dragon, **Figure 10(f)**), or Shetland in Scotland (Pelamis, **Figure 12(a)**). A comprehensive list of possible test phase 5 locations in Europe is presented by IEE [3].

8.04.4.4.3 Device testing and measurements

The UK DECC (formerly Department of Trade and Industry (DTI)) has set aside a £42 million share of the MRDF for the Wave and Tidal-stream Energy Demonstration Scheme (Section 8.04.2). Participants of this scheme have to follow a Wave Energy Device Performance Protocol in order that the participating technologies can be assessed in a consistent manner. DTI [23] is a draft of this protocol and its content was agreed in a meeting with invited stakeholders in 2006. The scheme supports technologies that have

Figure 12 Arrays of WECs in test phase 5: (a) three Pelamis WECs in Aguçadoura, Portugal, and (b) construction work for turbine devices at Mutriku, Spain. Pictures reproduced from IEEE (2009) State of the art analysis – a cautiously optimistic review of the technical status of wave energy technology. *Report of Waveplam*. Brussels, Belgium: Intelligent Energy Europe [3].

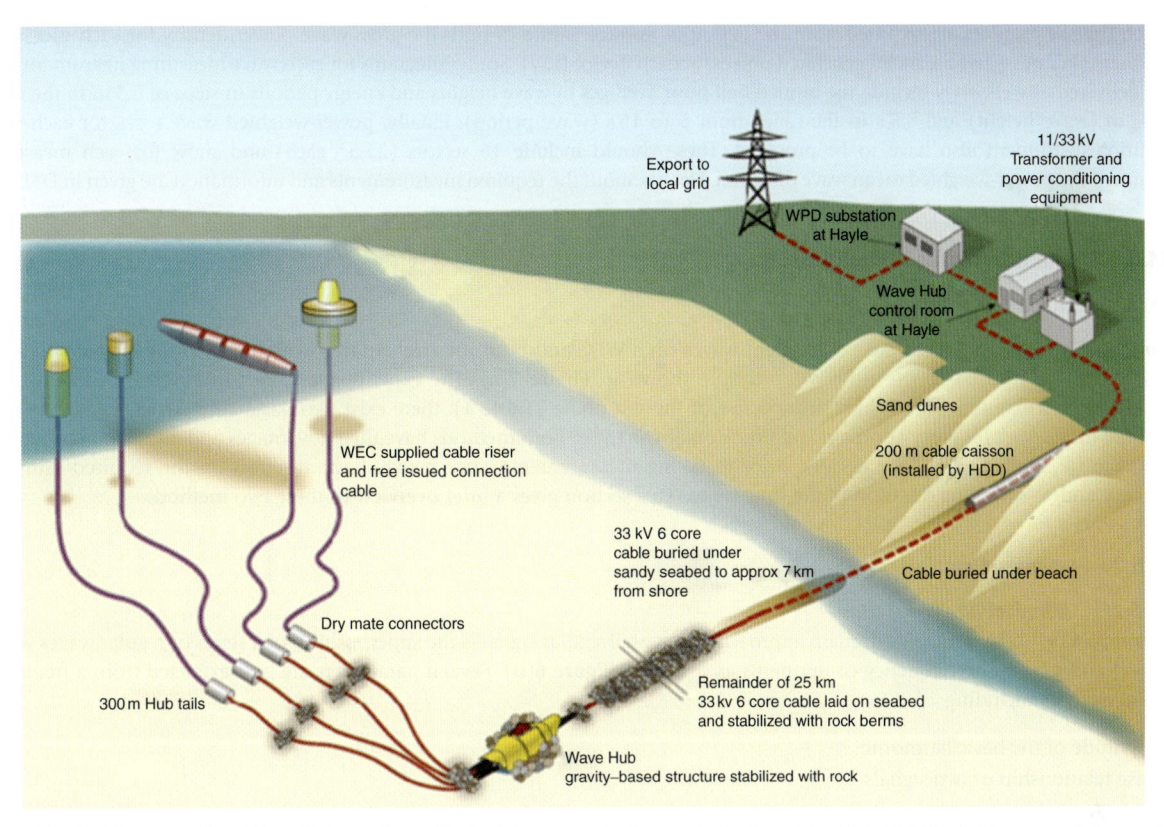

Figure 13 Artist's impression of Wave Hub, southwest England. Reproduced with permission from Wave Hub (2011) http://www.wavehub.co.uk/default.aspx (accessed February 2011) [7].

completed R&D stages and therefore are arranged in an array, are grid connected, and have already been tested for 3 months continuously or for 6 months in a 12-month period. The participating device developers have to deliver the following information, which may be a guide to which measurements and information are required as a minimum for device arrays in test phase 5:

- Project log with records of all significant events (such as changes in the position of the device or measurement sensor, failure of instruments)
- Recordings of the incident waves at the project location with one or more wave measuring instruments archived as half-hour wave records
- Monitoring of the generated electrical power and certain operational status indicators from each project device
- Monitoring of the electrical energy exported to or imported from the network

In addition, project information describing the physical nature of the location (e.g., bathymetry, prevailing wave direction, maximum tidal range), the proposed placement of wave energy devices and wave measuring instruments, the general characteristics of the devices (e.g., number of devices, power matrix, rated power), and the electrical layout of the project have to be specified. Possibilities to quantify the wave resource such as buoy or radar altimetry are described in Chapter 8.03. The most appropriate instrument is perhaps a directional wave-buoy system, probably in combination with a numerical model if the device is located in shallow water and the wave properties change from the measurement to the device location. Measurements down-wave may also be valuable if, for example, the array is extended or the devices are later employed elsewhere in a larger array. The amplitude resolution of the instrument should be 1 cm or better and the sampling frequency should be greater than 1 Hz. The sensor should be placed so that it is not affected by wave radiation from devices, that is, typically at a distance of one to a few hundred meters from the device, but at a maximum distance of 1 km. The averaged values for statistical wave parameters (e.g., wave height, wave period, spectral moments, wave power density) or measured power (e.g., mean, maximum, or minimum power) are based on half-hour intervals. The following headline numbers have to be averaged for all-year and for each month:

- Mean gross wave power density ($kW\,m^{-1}$) for each wave measuring instrument
- Mean net generated power from each device (kW)
- Mean availability of each device (%)
- Mean capacity factor of each device (%)
- Net energy exported from the project to the network (MWh)

Further, time-series plots are required from the half-hour average values of both the gross wave power density for each measuring instrument (kW m^{-1}) and the mean generated power for each device (kW). Scatter diagrams for each wave measuring instrument have to be delivered as well. They include the binned half-hour averages of wave heights and energy periods in steps of 0.5 m in the range 0.5–12 m (wave height) and 0.5 s in the range from 5 to 15 s (wave period). Finally, power-weighted wave roses for each wave measuring instrument also have to be provided. These should include 16 sectors (22.5° each) and show for each measuring instrument the power-weighted mean wave direction. Details about the required measurements and information are given in DTI [23].

8.04.5 Frequency versus Time Domain

8.04.5.1 Introduction

Figure 14 shows measurement data of incident waves on a WEC and both the free surface oscillation and the air pressure head measured in the PTO based on the OWC principle shown in **Figure 7(a)**. The experiments were conducted in a towing tank equipped with a flap-type wavemaker. Irrespective of the test phase (**Table 1**), there exist two basic approaches to analyze such measured time series: frequency domain and time domain analysis. Both methods have their advantages and disadvantages and the method to be applied should be decided prior to taking measurements since it may have an effect on the required sampling frequency and/or sampling duration of the time series. This section gives a brief overview of these two methods.

8.04.5.2 Frequency Domain

8.04.5.2.1 Introduction

The principle behind a frequency domain approach is that an irregular signal is the superposition of a series of regular waves which can be decomposed into frequency components as shown in **Figure 6(b)**. Several parameters are best extracted from a frequency domain analysis including

- Amplitude of the basic harmonic
- Phase relationship of two signals
- Response profile to regular excitation
- Wave direction
- Reflection coefficient
- Variance spectrum

Time series of a WEC investigation may not be perfectly sinusoidal or they may change in magnitude with time due to a suboptimal wave generation or reflections from the beach (**Figure 14**). A frequency–time analysis is applied over say 10 representative cycles resulting in the amplitude of the basic harmonic which is more consistent than the value resulting from one selected oscillation in the time domain.

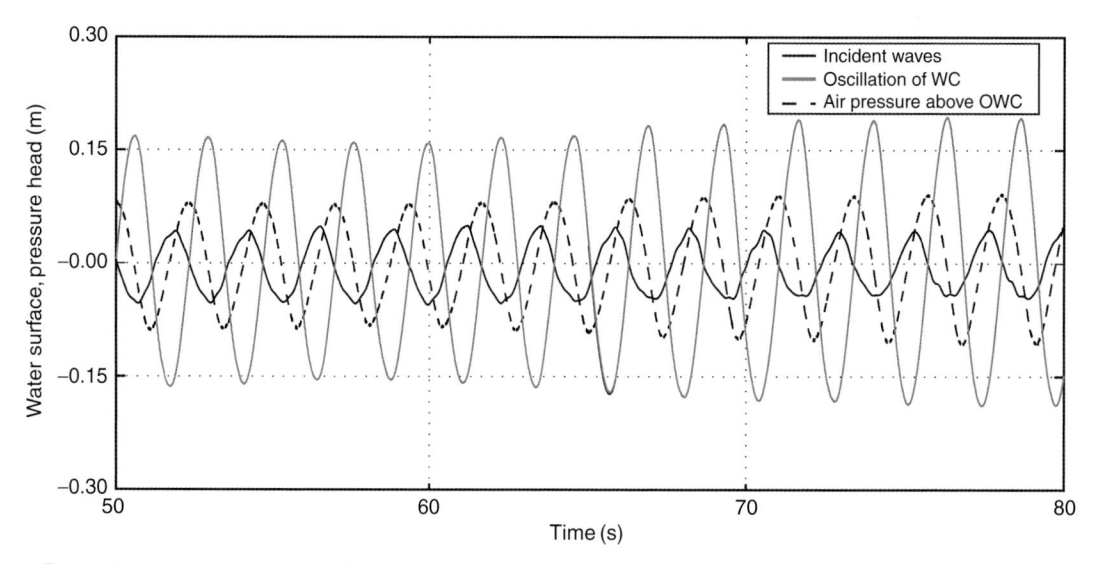

Figure 14 Time series recorded at 200 Hz in a WEC investigation with a PTO based on the oscillating water column (OWC) principle.

8.04.5.2.2 Wave parameters

Some wave parameters are specifically defined in the frequency domain (Chapter 8.03): the significant wave height $H_{m0} = 4(m_0)^{1/2}$ is a function of the 0th spectral moment m_0 (m^2) of the nondirectional variance (or wave energy) spectrum (**Figure 6(a)**). The nth spectral moment is defined with the wave spectral density $S(f)$ and the frequency f as

$$m_n = \int_0^\infty f^n S(f) \mathrm{d}f$$

The 0th spectral moment equals the area under the curve in **Figure 6(a)**. The higher the order of the spectral moment, the greater is the emphasis on the higher frequencies f. A further parameter defined in the frequency domain is the energy period T_e. This period for a given spectrum corresponds to the period of a regular wave which would have the same significant wave height H_{m0} and the same energy content as that spectrum and is therefore defined by

$$\text{power} = \rho g^2 H_{m0}^2 T_e / (64\pi) \; (\text{W m}^{-1})$$

Note that this equation was already introduced in a similar form in Section 8.04.3.3.7 to define the power of irregular waves. The parameter T_e can also be approximated with spectral moments as $T_e \approx m_{-1}/m_0$.

The peak period T_P is also a common parameter in the frequency domain. It is the period for which the nondirectional variance spectrum is maximum corresponding to the inverse of f_P shown in **Figure 6(a)**. The parameter T_P can be calculated from the spectral moments with $T_P = m_{-2} m_1 / m_0^2$.

8.04.5.2.3 Fourier analysis

The base of the frequency domain analysis is Fourier analysis, a method to transform time series (in the time domain) to the frequency domain or more exactly to transform time domain data to their frequency domain equivalent. Fourier analysis is widely used to investigate phenomena involving water waves and a comprehensive overview includes Newland [41]. The background of Fourier analysis is that any piecewise continuous function $F(t)$, such as shown in **Figure 15(a)** or at the bottom of **Figure 6(b)**, can be represented over an interval of time (t to $t + T$) as a sum of sines and cosines, where $F(t)$ is assumed to be periodic in this range. The corresponding analytical definition is

$$F(t) = a_0 + \sum_{n=1}^{\infty} \left(a_n \cos \frac{2\pi n t}{T} + b_n \sin \frac{2\pi n t}{T} \right)$$

The constant Fourier coefficients a_n and b_n are defined as

$$a_0 = \frac{1}{T} \int_{-T/2}^{T/2} F(t) \mathrm{d}t$$

$$a_n = \frac{2}{T} \int_{-T/2}^{T/2} F(t) \cos \frac{2\pi n t}{T} \mathrm{d}t \; \text{for} \; n \geq 1$$

$$b_n = \frac{2}{T} \int_{-T/2}^{T/2} F(t) \sin \frac{2\pi n t}{T} \mathrm{d}t \; \text{for} \; n \geq 1$$

The first coefficient a_0 represents the mean value of the function $F(t)$ (**Figure 15(a)**). **Figure 15(b)** shows graphically the coefficients a_n and b_n as a function of the frequencies of harmonics $\omega_n = 2\pi n/T$.

The experimental measurement of, for example, the incident waves (**Figure 14**) is conducted at a series of regularly spaced times separated by interval Δt, that is, the data x_p are collected as a discrete time series in contrast to the equations above defined for a continuous function. The classical method to conduct a Fourier analysis is to describe the discrete time series with a continuous function (the appropriate correlation function) and to Fourier transform this function. However, a more efficient method is nowadays applied, the discrete Fourier transformation (DFT). The DFT works directly with the discrete time series without

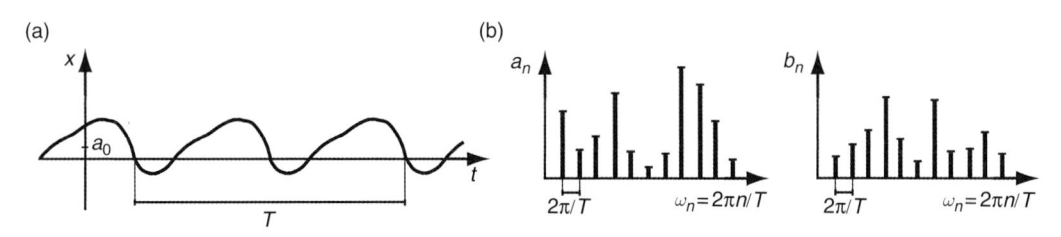

Figure 15 Fourier analysis: (a) arbitrary periodic function of time and (b) graphical representation of Fourier coefficients a_n and b_n. Reproduced from Newland DE (1993) *An Introduction to Random Vibrations, Spectral and Wavelet Analysis*. Essex, UK: Pearson Education Limited [41].

approximating it first with a correlation function. For a discrete time series x_p of r samples ($p = 0, 1, 2,\ldots,r-1$), the constant Fourier coefficients are written in complex form as $X_n = a_n - ib_n$ and can be approximated with the DFT as

$$X_n = \frac{1}{r} \sum_{p=0}^{r-1} x_p e^{-i(2\pi np/r)} \text{ with } n = 0, 1, 2, \ldots, (r-1)$$

Any typical (measured) value x_p of the series is given exactly by the inverse discrete Fourier transform (IDFT) formula

$$x_p = \sum_{n=0}^{r-1} X_n e^{i(2\pi np/r)} \text{ with } p = 0, 1, 2, \ldots, (r-1)$$

Cooley and Tukey [42] introduced the fast Fourier transformation (FFT), a computer algorithm for calculating DFT of a discrete time series x_p of r samples. The FFT is particularly computationally efficient and accurate and can be easily applied in Matlab or other software packages.

An issue important for the measurements is that the sampling frequency selected to sample a continuous time series dictates the frequency range and may have an effect on the quality of the spectrum calculated by the DFT in the following sense [5, 41]:

1. The sampling frequency should be at least twice that of the highest frequency component of the time series since a harmonic function based on the DFT is defined by two points. For a time domain analysis, however, the sampling frequency should be at least 20 points per wave. Under laboratory conditions, memory space is of small concern and a sampling frequency of, for example, 200 Hz is typical (**Figure 14**).
2. *Aliasing*. The DFT is unable to distinguish between components whose frequencies f_1 and f_2 are symmetrical with respect to half of the sampling frequency $f_s/2$ as defined by the criteria $f_1 \leq f_s/2$ and $f_2 = f_s - f_1$. The DFT for instance cannot distinguish between $f_1 = 0.5$ Hz and $f_2 = 3.5$ Hz if the sampling frequency is $f_s = 4$ Hz as shown in **Figure 16**. As a result, the measured amplitudes of the two components are then just equally split between the two frequency components f_1 and f_2 irrespective of whether these are their true values or not. Aliasing can be generalized for any number of frequency components resulting in the repetition of the Fourier coefficients at low ($|\omega| \leq \pi/\Delta t$) to high ($|\omega| > \pi/\Delta t$) frequencies with the angular frequency ω and the sampling interval Δt. This is illustrated in **Figure 17**. The repeated coefficients at high frequencies are called the folding components and they falsely distort frequency components $|\omega| \leq \pi/\Delta t$ due to the equally splitting of the amplitudes (**Figure 17**).

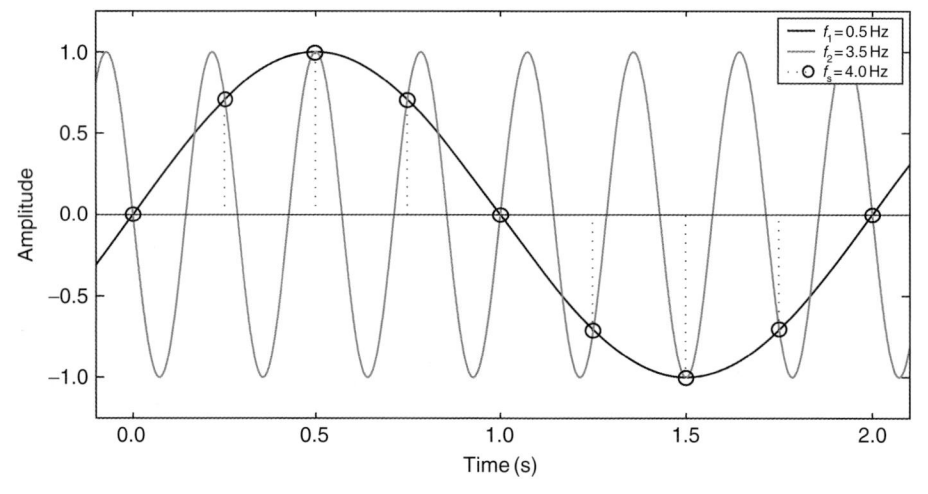

Figure 16 Example of aliasing: points recorded with a sampling frequency $f_s = 4$ Hz cannot reveal which of the two harmonics is measured. Reproduced with permission from Payne GS, Taylor JRM, and Ingram D (2009) Best practice guidelines for tank testing of wave energy converters. University of Edinburgh and *The Journal of Ocean Technology* 4(4): 39–70 [43].

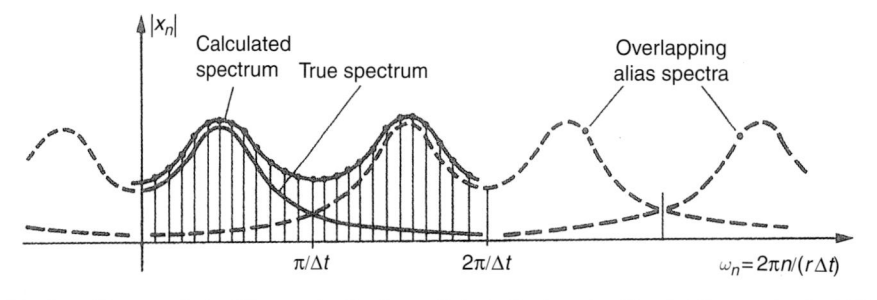

Figure 17 Aliasing distortion of the magnitude of the complex Fourier coefficients X_n when signal bandwidth exceeds $\pi/\Delta t$ [41].

This shortcoming can be avoided: the sampling frequency has to be chosen so that the so-called Nyquist frequency $1/(2\Delta t)$, the maximum frequency that can be detected by the Fourier analysis, is above the frequencies of all the components of the time series and not only of those of interest. This means if ω_1 is the maximum angular frequency component of the selected interval to be Fourier transformed, then the criterion for Δt is

$$\pi/\Delta t > \omega_1$$

This criterion includes the Nyquist frequency if it is rewritten as $1/(2\Delta t) > f_1$ with the maximum frequency component $f_1 = \omega_1/(2\pi)$ replacing ω_1. A practical way to achieve this is to select a high-enough sampling frequency f_s to reduce $\Delta t = 1/f_s$ and/or to use an appropriate low-pass filter before sampling the signal. The time series in **Figure 14** sampled at $\Delta t = 1/200$ Hz can be resolved with a DFT up to a frequency of $f_1 < 100$ Hz without distortion due to aliasing.

3. *Spilling.* The sampling duration T (or more precisely the interval T selected for the DFT) has a direct effect on the frequency resolution of the DFT since the time series is correlated with sinusoids whose frequencies are integer multiples of the inverse of the sampling duration.

$$f_n = \frac{n}{T} \text{ with } n = 0, 1, \ldots, r-1$$

The frequency resolution of the DFT is therefore $1/T$. A time series consisting of a single sinusoid of frequency f_1 is considered as an example. If T is chosen so that f_1 does not correspond to any of the frequencies of the correlation sinusoids $f_1 \neq f_n$ with $n = 0, 1, \ldots, r-1$, then the so-called 'spilling' occurs: the amplitude of the true component is spread over the nearest DFT components as shown in **Figure 18(a)**. The amplitude of the first harmonic, which should be 1, is incorrect. In order to avoid this problem, it is recommended that an appropriate sampling frequency and sampling duration is chosen so that the frequency of each component of the analyzed time series is matched by one of the f_n. An appropriate match is shown in **Figure 18(b)** where the correct amplitude 1 is found. This will not be possible for measurements in the ocean consisting of an infinite number of frequency components. In a wave tank, however, the signal sent to the wavemaker is usually computed by IDFT. It contains therefore a finite number of frequency components, which can be matched to f_n.

The DFT performs generally better if the time series is periodic and if the sampling duration corresponds to an integer multiple of the period (**Figure 15(a)**). The amplitude of the basic harmonic of incident regular waves (**Figure 14**) is an important quantity since it excludes higher order contaminations from the wavemaker. It is determined with a DFT applied, for example, on 10 selected cycles. In that case, the Fourier coefficient a_{10} delivers the required amplitude for the basic harmonic (since the selected interval T consists of 10 oscillations). The component a_0 delivers the mean (offset) of the selected range and a_1 to a_9 and a_{11}, etc., give a small contribution to describe the selected quite regular measurement range. If the sampled signal is not periodic, it is recommended to use a tapered data window to smooth the data at both ends of the sampled time series before carrying out the DFT. A data tapered window is basically a weighing function which gives more importance to the middle of the time series compared to the extremities. This will generally give better results even though this is done at the cost of distorting data [5].

8.04.5.2.4 Numerical modeling

Numerical modeling of WECs can be conducted with computational fluid dynamics (CFD) software or hydrodynamics software where in the latter case the problem includes the equation of motion which can be solved in either the frequency or the time domain

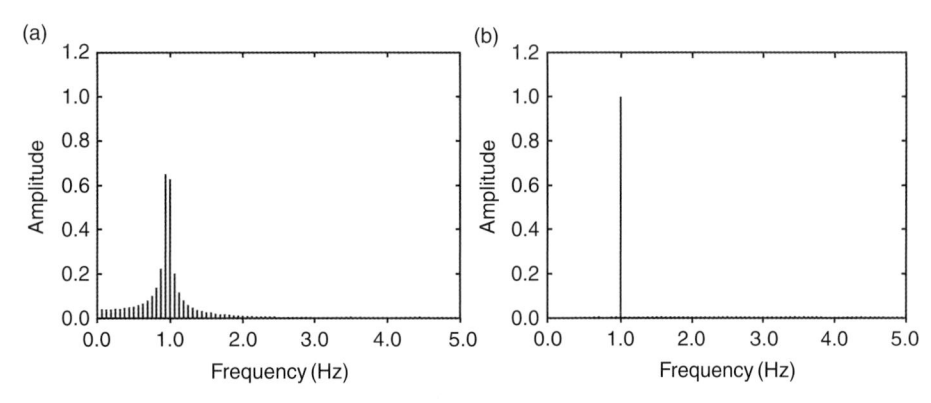

Figure 18 Spilling in discrete Fourier transformation shown with truncated spectra to increase clarity: (a) spectrum with spilling due to inappropriate sampling duration (31/32 Hz signal sampled for 16 s at 32 Hz) and (b) spectrum without spilling (31/32 Hz signal sampled for 32 s at 32 Hz). Reproduced with permission from Payne GS, Taylor JRM, and Ingram D (2009) Best practice guidelines for tank testing of wave energy converters. University of Edinburgh and *The Journal of Ocean Technology* 4(4): 39–70 [43].

[43]. A numerical simulation based on the frequency domain is less complex than that based on the time domain. It is therefore common to start in the frequency domain in test phases 1 and 2 (**Table 1**) and then to move to the time domain for the remaining test phases. Frequency domain solutions are applicable where the wave excitation is either of simple harmonic form or of the superposition of simple harmonic forms. The body motions also have to be of small amplitudes and the boundary conditions have to be linear. Nonlinear effects can be considered in the time domain.

8.04.5.3 Time Domain

8.04.5.3.1 Introduction

Important information can be obtained directly from raw data in the time domain (**Figure 14**) or derived from the combination of two or more signal parameters. This includes [2]

- Quality of signal
- Amplitude
- Phase relationship
- Signal statistics (root mean square, maximum, minimum, mean, standard deviation)
- Response profile to regular excitation
- Instantaneous power
- Resonance proximity

It can immediately be seen in **Figure 14** that the oscillation of the water column and the pressure head have a phase shift of 90°. An FFT, however, may give a more precise value of the phase shift. The power can be calculated with a combination of the two given time series of pressure head and surface velocity where the latter is deduced from the oscillation of the water column (Section 8.04.3.3.5). Further useful information is directly available from the time series if the measured device response is compared to the incident wave creating that response. This includes the magnification or response amplitude operator and the phase relationship. The magnification of the amplitude of the OWC relative to the incident wave amplitude is about 3.5 in **Figure 14**.

Some properties of irregular raw data can also be analyzed in the time domain, whereas other parameters are better analyzed in the frequency domain. Properties available from the time domain include extremes, averages, or variance. Furthermore, the instantaneous power can be extracted, which is an important quantity for the design of a PTO system and the power electronics that will convert the supply to an acceptable quality before feeding it in the grid. Further analysis of irregular data results in information regarding

- The time period for energy above a certain threshold (e.g., average)
- The duration and occurrence of zero energy conversion
- The duration of spikes
- The ratio of average to peak

Time series analysis is further required to aid mooring design [2].

8.04.5.3.2 Wave parameters

Characteristic wave parameters specifically defined by time series are shown in **Figure 19**. These are the zero upcrossing H_u and zero downcrossing wave height H_d and the zero upcrossing T_u or zero downcrossing period T_d. The significant wave height H_s in the time series context is defined as the average of the highest one-third of the wave heights, which can be estimated from a ship without instruments. The significant wave heights H_s (time domain) and H_{m0} (frequency domain) are usually not exactly equal and different subscripts are therefore common.

The time domain analysis is mainly based on the zero crossing method motivated by graphical recordings on paper from when analysis was carried out by hand. Time domain analysis based on this method is still in use even though frequency domain analysis

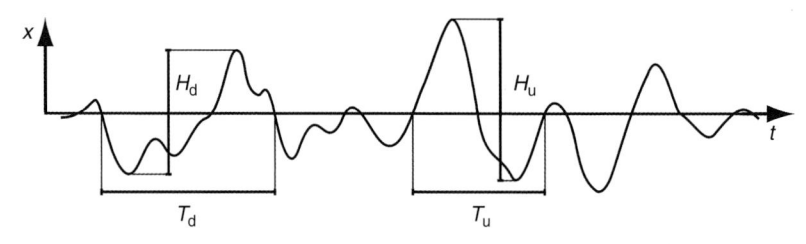

Figure 19 Wave parameters in the time domain.

is now more common. A major drawback of the zero crossing method is that its outcome depends strongly on the sampling frequency. A low sampling frequency may not record high-frequency peaks and therefore underestimate the zero crossing parameters. Measurements sampled at a higher frequency are able to detect these peaks and the zero crossing parameters differ from the parameters based on lower sampling frequencies. The sampling frequency of time series data should therefore be at least 20 points per wave in order that the 'real' crest or trough is not missed.

An advantage of time domain analysis is that it may account better for some of the nonlinearities of the wave field which are lost in a Fourier analysis. One lost nonlinear feature in a frequency domain is the asymmetry of the wave profile.

8.04.5.3.3 Numerical modeling

The simplest method used to obtain the time history of responses is to transform frequency domain results of numerical modeling into the time domain. A numerical time domain solution can apply where nonlinear effects are too large to be ignored and frequency domain techniques no longer produce viable results. Nonlinear effects arise from large-amplitude motions or, perhaps more relevant, from the irregular nature of waves in the sea itself.

References

[1] HMRC (2003) *Ocean Energy: Development & Evaluation Protocol. Part 1: Wave Power*. Cork, Ireland: Hydraulics and Maritime Research Centre (HMRC).
[2] Holmes B (2009) *Tank Testing of Wave Energy Conversion Systems. Marine Renewable Energy Guides*. Orkney, Scotland: EMEC.
[3] IEE (2009) State of the art analysis – A cautiously optimistic review of the technical status of wave energy technology. *Report of Waveplam*. Brussels, Belgium: Intelligent Energy Europe.
[4] Armstrong J (2008) Marine energy more than just a drop in the ocean? Report. London, UK: Institution of Mechanical Engineers.
[5] Payne G (2008) Guidance for the experimental tank testing of wave energy converters. *Report of the SuperGen Marine*. Edinburgh, UK: University of Edinburgh.
[6] EquiMar (2011) Equitable testing and evaluation of marine energy extraction devices in terms of performance, cost and environmental impact. Brussels, Belgium: European Commission.
[7] Wave Hub (2011) http://www.wavehub.co.uk/ (accessed December 2011).
[8] Cruz J (ed.) (2008) *Ocean Wave Energy – Current Status and Future Perspectives*. Berlin, Germany: Springer.
[9] Rea M (2008) Wave tank and wavemaker design. In: Cruz J (ed.) *Ocean Wave Energy – Current Status and Future Perspectives*, pp. 147–159. Berlin, Germany: Springer.
[10] Sarmento A and Thomas G (2008) Guidelines for laboratory testing of WECs. In: Cruz J (ed.) *Ocean Wave Energy – Current Status and Future Perspectives*, pp. 160–169. Berlin, Germany: Springer.
[11] Nielsen K (2003) IEA ocean energy systems. Annex II Report 2003. Denmark: Ramboll.
[12] Heller V (2011) Scale effects in physical hydraulic engineering models. *Journal of Hydraulic Research* 49(3): 293–306.
[13] Le Méhauté B (1976) *An Introduction to Hydrodynamics and Water Waves*. New York: Springer.
[14] Hughes SA (1993) *Physical Models and Laboratory Techniques in Coastal Engineering*. Advanced Series on Ocean Engineering 7. London, UK: World Scientific.
[15] Dean RG and Dalrymple RA (2004) *Water Wave Mechanics for Engineers and Scientists*. Advanced Series on Ocean Engineering 2. Singapore: World Scientific.
[16] Pierson WJ and Moskowitz L (1964) A proposed spectral form for fully developed wind seas based on the similarity theory of S. A. Kitaigorodskii. *Journal of Geophysical Research* 69: 5181–5190.
[17] Hasselmann K, Barnett TP, Bouws E, *et al.* (1973) Measurements of wind-wave growth and swell decay during the JOint North Sea Wave Project (JONSWAP). *Ergänzungsheft zur Deutschen Hydrographischen Zeitschrift Reihe A* 8(12): 95.
[18] Ouellet Y and Datta I (1986) A survey of wave absorbers. *Journal of Hydraulic Research* 24(4): 265–280.
[19] Chaplin JR, Heller V, Farley FJM, *et al.* (2012) Laboratory testing the Anaconda. *Philosophical Transactions of the Royal Society A* 370: 403–424.
[20] Farley FJM (1982) Wave energy conversion by flexible resonant rafts. *Applied Ocean Research* 4(1): 57–63.
[21] Heller V, Chaplin JR, Farley FJM, *et al.* (2010) Physical model tests of the wave energy converter Anaconda. *1st European Conference of IAHR*, Paper MREc: 1–6, 4–6th May, Edinburgh, UK; Madrid, Spain: IAHR.
[22] Pelamis Wave Power (2011) http://www.pelamiswave.com/ (accessed December 2011).
[23] DTI (2007) Preliminary wave energy device performance protocol. London, UK: DTI.
[24] Cruz J, Henderson R, and Yemm R (2008) Pelamis. In: Cruz J (ed.) *Ocean Wave Energy – Current Status and Future Perspectives*, pp. 361–371. Berlin, Germany: Springer.
[25] Heath T (2008) LIMPET. In: Cruz J (ed.) *Ocean Wave Energy – Current Status and Future Perspectives*, pp. 287–294. Berlin, Germany: Springer.
[26] Heath T (2008) Oscillating water column – LIMPET. In: Cruz J (ed.) *Ocean Wave Energy – Current Status and Future Perspectives*, pp. 336–341. Berlin, Germany: Springer.
[27] Prado M (2008) Archimedes wave swing (AWS). In: Cruz J (ed.) *Ocean Wave Energy – Current Status and Future Perspectives*, pp. 297–304 and 350–361 Berlin, Germany: Springer.
[28] Sarmento A, Neumann F, and Brito e Melo A (2008) Oscillating water column – Pico plant. In: Cruz J (ed.) *Ocean Wave Energy – Current Status and Future Perspectives*, pp. 342–350. Berlin, Germany: Springer.
[29] Tedd J, Friis-Madsen E, Kofoed JP, and Knapp W (2008) Wave Dragon. In: Cruz J (ed.) *Ocean Wave Energy – Current Status and Future Perspectives*, pp. 321–335. Berlin, Germany: Springer.
[30] Yemm R (2008) Pelamis. In: Cruz J (ed.) *Ocean Wave Energy – Current Status and Future Perspectives*, pp. 304–321. Berlin, Germany: Springer.
[31] Brooke J (2003) *Wave Energy Conversion*. Elsevier Ocean Engineering Book Series, vol. 6. Amsterdam, The Netherlands: Elsevier.
[32] Huertas-Olivares C and Norris J (2008) Environmental impact assessment. In: Cruz J (ed.) *Ocean Wave Energy – Current Status and Future Perspectives*, pp. 397–423. Berlin, Germany: Springer.
[33] Thorpe TW (1999) *A Brief Review of Wave Energy*. London, UK: DTI.
[34] Carbon Trust (2006) *Future Marine Energy*. London, UK: Carbon Trust.
[35] Clément A, McCullen P, Falcão A, *et al.* (2002) Wave energy in Europe: Current status and perspectives. *Renewable and Sustainable Energy Reviews* 6(5): 405–431.
[36] Sarmento A, Neumann F, and Brito e Melo A (2008) Pico – European pilot plant. In: Cruz J (ed.) *Ocean Wave Energy – Current Status and Future Perspectives*, pp. 294–296. Berlin, Germany: Springer.
[37] Aquamarine Power (2011) http://www.aquamarinepower.com/ (accessed December 2011).
[38] Ocean Power Technologies (2011) http://www.oceanpowertechnologies.com/ (accessed December 2011).
[39] DNV (2005) *Guidelines on Design and Operation of Wave Energy Converters*. London, UK: Carbon Trust.

[40] Tedd J, Kofoed JP, Friis-Madsen E, and Christensen L (2008) Wave Dragon. In: Cruz J (ed.) *Ocean Wave Energy – Current Status and Future Perspectives*, pp. 371–382. Berlin, Germany: Springer.
[41] Newland DE (1993) *An Introduction to Random Vibrations, Spectral and Wavelet Analysis*. Essex, UK: Pearson Education Limited.
[42] Cooley JW and Tukey JW (1965) An algorithm for the machine calculation of complex Fourier series. *Mathematics of Computation* 19: 297–301.
[43] Payne GS, Taylor JRM, and Ingram D (2009) Best practice guidelines for tank testing of wave energy converters. *The Journal of Ocean Technology* 4(4): 38–70.
[44] Carnegie Wave Energy (2011) http://www.carnegiewave.com/ (accessed December 2011).

8.05 Air Turbines

AFO Falcão and LMC Gato, Instituto Superior Técnico, Technical University of Lisbon, Lisbon, Portugal

© 2012 Elsevier Ltd. All rights reserved.

8.05.1	Introduction	111
8.05.2	Basic Equations	112
8.05.3	Two-Dimensional Cascade Flow Analysis of Axial-Flow Turbines	113
8.05.3.1	Wells Turbine	114
8.05.3.1.1	Isolated monoplane rotor	115
8.05.3.1.2	Monoplane rotor with guide vanes	116
8.05.3.1.3	Contra-rotating rotors	117
8.05.3.1.4	Biplane rotor with intermediate guide vanes	118
8.05.3.1.5	Biplane rotor without guide vanes	118
8.05.3.1.6	Biplane turbine with guide vanes	119
8.05.3.1.7	Other variants of the Wells turbine	119
8.05.3.1.8	Nonzero rotor blade thickness	120
8.05.3.2	Self-Rectifying Impulse Turbine	120
8.05.3.3	Wells Turbine versus Impulse Turbine	122
8.05.4	Three-Dimensional Flow Analysis of Axial-Flow Turbines	123
8.05.5	Model Testing of Air Turbines	124
8.05.5.1	Dimensional Analysis	124
8.05.5.2	Test Rigs	125
8.05.6	Wells Turbine Performance	126
8.05.6.1	Advanced Wells Turbine Configurations	128
8.05.6.1.1	Biplane turbine	128
8.05.6.1.2	Contra-rotating turbine	129
8.05.6.1.3	Variable-pitch Wells turbine	129
8.05.7	Performance of Self-Rectifying Axial-Flow Impulse Turbine	131
8.05.8	Other Air Turbines for Bidirectional Flows	132
8.05.8.1	Denniss-Auld Turbine	132
8.05.8.2	Radial-Flow Self-Rectifying Impulse Turbine	136
8.05.8.3	Twin Unidirectional Impulse Turbine Topology	137
8.05.9	Some Air Turbine Prototypes	139
8.05.10	Turbine Integration into OWC Plant	141
8.05.10.1	Hydrodynamics of OWC	141
8.05.10.2	Linear Turbine	142
8.05.10.3	Nonlinear Turbine	145
8.05.10.4	Valve-Controlled Air Flow	146
8.05.10.5	Noise	146
8.05.11	Conclusions	146
References		147

8.05.1 Introduction

The oscillating water column (OWC) is among the first types of wave energy converter to be developed and deployed into the sea, and one of the most successful devices. The OWC device comprises a partly submerged concrete or steel chamber, fixed or floating and open below the water surface, inside which air is trapped above the water free surface. The oscillating motion of the internal free surface produced by the incident waves makes the air flow through a turbine that drives an electrical generator.

More or less conventional unidirectional flow turbines (possibly Francis turbines or axial-flow turbines) can be used for this purpose provided that the wave energy converter is equipped with a rectifying system with non-return valves. This was done in the case of small navigation buoys developed in Japan by pioneer Yoshio Masuda and produced in large numbers since 1965 [1]. The first large-scale wave energy converter to be deployed into the sea was the Kaimei, a large barge (80×12 m) that had 13 open-bottom chambers built into the hull, each having a water plane area of $42-50 \text{ m}^2$. It was deployed off the western coast of Japan in 1978–80 and again in 1985–86 [2, 3]. Eight unidirectional air turbines were tested in 1978–80 with various non-return rectifying valve arrangements; in 1985–86, three unidirectional turbines were tested together with two self-rectifying turbines (a tandem Wells turbine pair and a contra-rotating McCormick turbine).

Figure 1 Dr. Alan A. Wells, inventor of the Wells turbine (1924–2005).

Rectifying valve systems were successfully used in small devices like navigation buoys (in which anyway efficiency is not a major concern). However, they are unpractical in large plants, where flow rates may be of the order of $10^2 \, \text{m}^3 \text{s}^{-1}$ and the required response time is typically less than 1 s. This was confirmed by the experience with Kaimei [2]. Except for Kaimei and small navigation buoys, all (or almost all) OWC prototypes tested so far have been equipped with self-rectifying air turbines.

Most self-rectifying air turbines for wave energy conversion proposed and tested so far are axial-flow machines of two basic types: the Wells turbine and the impulse turbine (other types will be mentioned later in this chapter). The Wells turbine was invented in 1976 by Dr. Alan A. Wells (1924–2005) (at that time at Queen's University of Belfast, UK) [4] (**Figure 1**). The most popular alternative to the Wells turbine seems to be the self-rectifying impulse turbine, patented by I. A. Babintsev in 1975 [5]. Its rotor is basically identical to the rotor of a conventional single-stage steam turbine of axial-flow impulse type (the classical de Laval steam turbine patented in 1889 and developed in the 1890s and early twentieth century by the pioneers of the steam turbine [6]). Since the turbine is required to be self-rectifying, there are two rows of guide vanes, placed symmetrically on both sides of the rotor, instead of a single row (as in the conventional de Laval turbine). These two rows of guide vanes are like the mirror image of each other with respect to a plane through the rotor disc. Several versions of both types of turbines (Wells and impulse) have been proposed and tested, including the use of contra-rotating rotors (the McCormick contra-rotating turbine [7, 8] is based on the impulse turbine concept).

An extensive and detailed review of Wells turbines was published in 1995 by Raghunathan [9]. For the impulse turbine, see Reference 10. More recently, Setoguchi and Takao [11] and Curran and Folley [12] published overviews on self-rectifying air turbines.

8.05.2 Basic Equations

The so-called Euler turbomachinery equation relates the torque T, produced by the flow upon a turbine rotor, to the change in the flux of moment of momentum across the rotor (see, e.g., References 13 and 14)

$$T = \int_{S_1} r_1 V_{t1} \, d\dot{m}_1 - \int_{S_2} r_2 V_{t2} \, d\dot{m}_2 \qquad [1]$$

where r is radial coordinate, V_t is tangential (or circumferential) component of the (absolute) flow velocity $\mathbf{V}$, $\dot{m}$ is mass flow rate, and S_1 and S_2 are surfaces (of revolution) where the fluid enters and leaves the rotor region. In eqn [1], the moment of shear forces on S_1 and S_2, and on the stator inner wall between S_1 and S_2, has been ignored, as usual.

If the one-dimensional approximation is adopted, we have more simply $T = \dot{m}(r_1 V_{t1} - r_2 V_{t2})$, where the values of r and V_t are averaged over the inlet and outlet surfaces S_1 and S_2. For an axial-flow turbine, it is $r_1 = r_2 = r$, and

$$E = \Omega r (V_{t1} - V_{t2}) \qquad [2]$$

Here, $E = \Omega T/\dot{m}$ is energy, per unit mass of fluid, at the rotor shaft and Ω is rotational speed (radians per unit time). We may write

$$E = E_{\text{avai}} - L \qquad [3]$$

where E_{avai} is the available pneumatic energy (per unit mass) and L represents the losses in the turbine and in the ducts (including possibly valves) that connect the turbine to the chamber and to the atmosphere. It is $L = L_{\text{rot}} + L_{\text{GV}} + L_{\text{duct}}$, where the subscripts stand for rotor, guide vanes, and connecting ducts (L_{duct} includes the exit kinetic energy loss).

We express the air pressure in the OWC chamber as $p_a + p_{ch}(t)$, where p_a is atmospheric pressure and $p_{ch}(t)$ is the pressure oscillation. The available energy E_{avai} is the overall isentropic enthalpy drop between the chamber and the atmosphere (for outward flow) or between the atmosphere and the chamber (for inward flow). For a perfect gas, it is

$$E_{avai} = c_p T_{ch} \left[1 - \left(\frac{p_a}{p_a + p_{ch}}\right)^{(\gamma-1)/\gamma}\right] \quad \text{or} \quad E_{avai} = c_p T_a \left[1 - \left(\frac{p_a + p_{ch}}{p_a}\right)^{(\gamma-1)/\gamma}\right] \qquad [4]$$

for $p_{ch} > 0$ or $p_{ch} < 0$, respectively. Here, T_{ch} and T_a are absolute temperatures of air in the chamber and in the atmosphere, $\gamma = c_p/c_v$, and c_p and c_v are the specific heats at constant pressure and volume, respectively. For most purposes in this chapter, it is reasonable to linearize these equations and write approximately

$$E_{avai} = \frac{|p_{ch}|}{\rho} \qquad [5]$$

where ρ is some average value of air density.

The pressure oscillation in the chamber, $p_{ch}(t)$, is related to the incident wave field, to the hydrodynamic characteristics of the submerged parts of the chamber structure, and to the chamber volume above still-water level. It should be emphasized here that it also depends on the characteristic curve (at the instantaneous rotational speed of the turbine) of the pressure head versus turbine flow rate $\dot{m}$ (damping effect). These matters will be addressed in Section 8.05.10.

8.05.3 Two-Dimensional Cascade Flow Analysis of Axial-Flow Turbines

The amplitude of the oscillations in air pressure inside the chamber of a full-sized OWC plant may be nonsmall compared with the atmospheric pressure, especially under the more energetic sea conditions. So, significant compressibility effects (variations in air density) can take place in the flow through the turbine. Here, we adopt a simplified analysis, one of the assumptions being incompressible flow. In addition, the walls of the turbine annular duct are assumed to be coaxial cylindrical surfaces of revolution, long enough so that we may neglect the disturbing end effects upon the flow patterns about the blades. As an additional approximation, we ignore the flow interference between different radii, which means that the radial velocities are neglected. In this case, the flow at each cylindrical stream surface may be represented by the two-dimensional plane flow about a rectilinear cascade of blades (or possibly more than one cascade, if there are several rows of blades). We adopt a system of cylindrical coordinates (r, θ, x) and write $y = r\theta$ in the (x, y) plane of the cascade.

Let us consider the cascade of rotor blades in two-dimensional flow shown in **Figure 2**, corresponding to a cylindrical surface of radius r. The blade chord is c and the circumferential pitch is $t = 2\pi r/Z$, where Z is the number of blades. The blade speed is $U = \Omega r$, where Ω is the angular velocity of the rotor (in radians per unit time). We denote by $\mathbf{W}_1$ and $\mathbf{W}_2$ the relative velocity vectors (averaged along the y-direction in a rotor-fixed frame of reference) of the flow upstream and downstream of the blades, respectively. We define the mean velocity vector $\mathbf{W}_m = (\mathbf{W}_1 + \mathbf{W}_2)/2$ and introduce the velocity angles β_1, β_2, and $\beta_m = \frac{1}{2}\text{arccot}(\cot\beta_1 + \cot\beta_2)$. The aerodynamic force (per unit blade span) is $\mathbf{F}$ and may be decomposed into a drag force $\mathbf{D}$ (along the direction of $\mathbf{W}_m$) and lift force $\mathbf{L}$ (along the direction perpendicular to $\mathbf{W}_m$). As usual in blade cascade theory, we define the lift and drag coefficients

$$c_L = \frac{L}{\frac{1}{2}\rho c W_m^2}, \quad c_D = \frac{D}{\frac{1}{2}\rho c W_m^2} \qquad [6]$$

where ρ is air density. We write $\gamma = \arctan(c_D/c_L)$ (not to be confused with the c_p/c_v ratio in compressible flow).

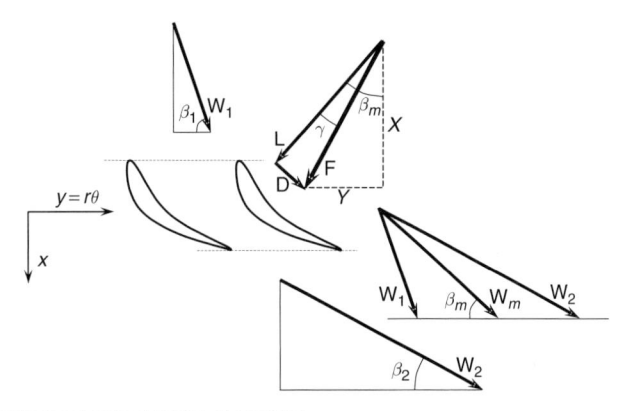

Figure 2 Velocity and force diagram for a cascade of blades of a turbine.

The components of blade force **F** in the axial direction, X, and blade-to-blade direction, Y, are

$$\{X, Y\} = \frac{L}{\cos \gamma} \{\cos(\beta_m - \gamma), \sin(\beta_m - \gamma)\} \qquad [7]$$

From momentum equation, we find

$$X = t\Delta p \qquad [8]$$

$$Y = \rho\, t V_x^2 (\cot \beta_2 - \cot \beta_1) \qquad [9]$$

where Δp is the pressure drop across the blade row and $V_x = W_1 \sin \beta_1 = W_2 \sin \beta_2 = W_m \sin \beta_m$ is the axial component of the flow velocity.

In the case of inviscid fluid, Bernoulli equation gives

$$X = t\Delta p = \frac{\rho t}{2}\left(W_2^2 - W_1^2\right) = \rho t V_x^2 (\cot \beta_2 - \cot \beta_1) \qquad [10]$$

Combining eqns [7], [9], and [10], we find, for an inviscid fluid, $\gamma = 0$ and so $c_D = 0$, $D = 0$, which justifies the definition of D as a drag force.

The work done by the fluid on the rotor blades per unit mass is $E = \Omega r Y (\rho t V_x)^{-1}$, which, taking into account eqn [7], can be written as

$$E = \frac{1}{2} c_L \frac{c}{t} \Omega r V_x \frac{\sin(\beta_m - \gamma)}{\sin^2 \beta_m \cos \gamma} \qquad [11]$$

or, by using eqn [9] for Y instead of eqn [7],

$$E = 2\Omega r V_x (\cot \beta_m - \cot \beta_1) \qquad [12]$$

For given Ωr, V_x, and β_1, eqns [11] and [12] allow β_m and E to be determined if c_L and c_D are known as functions of β_m (or β_1).

By using eqn [7] for X, we find the following expression for the pressure drop across the blade row $\Delta p = X/t$:

$$\Delta p = \frac{1}{2} c_L \frac{c}{t} \rho V_x^2 \frac{\cos(\beta_m - \gamma)}{\sin^2 \beta_m \cos \gamma} \qquad [13]$$

If we define efficiency as $\eta = \rho E/\Delta p$, then, from eqns [11] and [13], we obtain

$$\eta = \frac{\omega r}{V_x} \tan(\beta_m - \gamma) \qquad [14]$$

If these results for a given value of r are to be representative of the global three-dimensional flow through the turbine, r should be suitably chosen between the inner radius $D_i/2$ and the outer radius $D/2$. One criterion is to take $r = [(D_i^2 + D^2)/8]^{1/2}$, so that the circle of radius r divides the annular cross-sectional area into two equal annular areas.

Above, we assumed that there is only one row of rotor blades (single cascade). In what follows, we will also consider more complex assemblies of blades, including guide vanes and/or other rotating rows of blades. In such cases, the wakes shed by the upstream blades will interfere with the downstream blades, if the latter are in motion or not relative to the former. In such cases, we implicitly assume that the axial distance between blade rows (fixed or moving) is large enough for the blade wakes to be smoothed out in the circumferential direction.

8.05.3.1 Wells Turbine

We consider now the special case of the Wells turbine rotor (**Figures 3** and **4**). The rotor blade profile is symmetrical and the blades are set at a stagger angle of 90° (i.e., they are symmetrical with respect to a plane perpendicular to the rotor axis). Early theoretical investigations on the Wells turbine aerodynamics, based on two-dimensional cascade flow model, are reported in References 15–17.

Before dealing with real fluid flow, we derive some remarkable aerodynamic properties of the Wells turbine from well-known analytical results for a cascade of flat plates in incompressible potential flow [14, 18–20]. For that, as an approximation, we assume potential flow and neglect the blade thickness. The cascade interference factor may be defined as $k = c_L/c_{L0}$, where c_{L0} is the lift coefficient of the isolated blade at an angle of attack defined by the mean velocity vector $\mathbf{W}_m$. For a cascade of flat plates at 90° angle of stagger, the following analytical result can be obtained by conformal transformation [14, 18–20]:

$$k = \frac{2t}{\pi c} \tan \frac{\pi c}{2t} \qquad [15]$$

It is well known (see, e.g., Reference 18) that, for an isolated aerofoil of negligible thickness and no curvature, in two-dimensional potential flow, at an angle of incidence β_m, it is $c_{L0} = 2\pi \sin \beta_m$. So we obtain

$$c_L = \frac{4t}{c} \sin \beta_m \tan \frac{\pi c}{2t} \qquad [16]$$

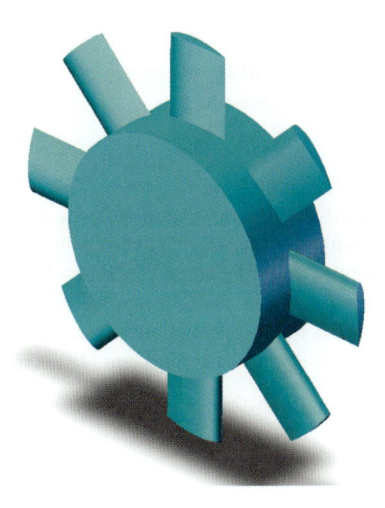

Figure 3 Wells turbine rotor.

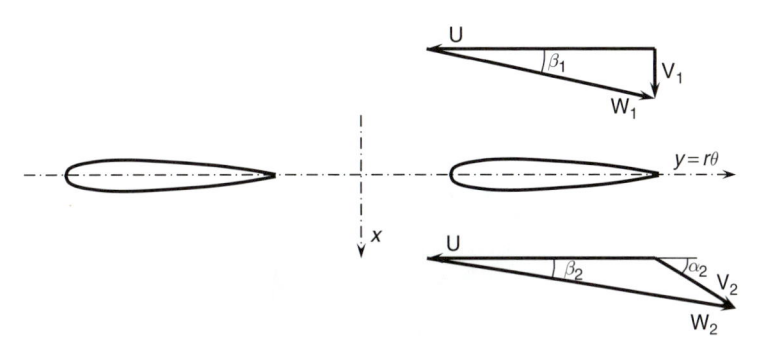

Figure 4 Two-dimensional representation of a monoplane rotor Wells turbine without guide vanes.

From eqns [13] and [16], we easily find

$$\psi = 2\varphi^2 \cot \beta_m \tan \frac{\pi c}{2t} \qquad [17]$$

where $\psi = \Delta p(\rho\Omega^2 r^2)^{-1}$ is a dimensionless coefficient of pressure drop, and $\varphi = V_x\Omega^{-1}r^{-1}$ is a dimensionless flow coefficient.

8.05.3.1.1 Isolated monoplane rotor

We assume now that there are no guide vanes and the incoming flow is purely axial, as represented in **Figure 3**. Then, eqn [12] gives, for the blade work per unit mass,

$$E = \Omega r V_x \cot \alpha_2 \qquad [18]$$

Equations [12], [16], and [18] (with $\gamma = 0$) give

$$\cot \alpha_2 = 2 \tan \frac{\pi c}{2t} \qquad [19]$$

This shows that the (absolute) flow is deflected by an angle $\pi/2 - \alpha_2$ that depends only on the chord-to-pitch ratio c/t (and not on the blade velocity $U = \Omega r$ or the inlet flow velocity V_1). This result, valid for potential flow and blades of negligible thickness, was obtained in Reference 21.

In this case, it is $\cot \beta_1 = \varphi^{-1}$ and $\cot \beta_2 = \varphi^{-1} + \cot \alpha_2$. From eqn [17], we find

$$\psi = 2\varphi\left(1 + \varphi \tan \frac{\pi c}{2t}\right)\tan \frac{\pi c}{2t} \qquad [20]$$

This equation shows that the Wells turbine without guide vanes is approximately a linear turbine (i.e., the pressure drop is approximately proportional to the flow rate at constant rotational speed), assuming that $\varphi \tan(\pi c/2t)$ is much smaller than unity.

8.05.3.1.2 Monoplane rotor with guide vanes

If there are no guide vanes (as in **Figures 3** and **4**), the swirl kinetic energy per unit mass at exit, $E_{kin} = \frac{1}{2}V_x^2 \cot^2 \alpha_2$, is lost. From eqns [18] and [19], the corresponding relative loss may be written as

$$\frac{E_{kin}}{E} = \frac{V_x}{\Omega r}\tan\frac{\pi c}{2t} \qquad [21]$$

that is, for given $V_x/\Omega r$, it increases with the chord-to-pitch ratio (and with the angular deflection of the flow). This loss may be avoided by using guide vanes. Since the turbine is to absorb energy from reversing air flows, its performance should be insensitive to flow direction, and hence there should be two rows of guide vanes, one on each side of the rotor, so that the turbine (rotor and stator) is symmetrical with respect to a plane perpendicular to the rotational axis. This arrangement is shown in **Figure 5**, and in **Figure 6** in plane cascade representation. In this case, the incoming flow to the rotor, deflected by the first row of guide vanes, has a nonzero swirl component (in the y-direction) $V_x \cot \alpha_1$ ($\alpha_1 > \pi/2$), and eqn [18] is replaced by

$$E = \Omega r V_x(\cot \alpha_2 - \cot \alpha_1) \qquad [22]$$

We easily find, from eqns [8], [12], and [15],

$$\cot \alpha_2 = \cot \alpha_1 + 2\tan\frac{\pi c}{2t} \qquad [23]$$

This result (obtained in Reference 22) generalizes eqn [19] and shows that the angle α_2 of the absolute flow velocity at rotor exit depends only on inlet angle α_1 and chord-to-pitch ratio (cascade solidity) c/t. Equation [22] may be rewritten as

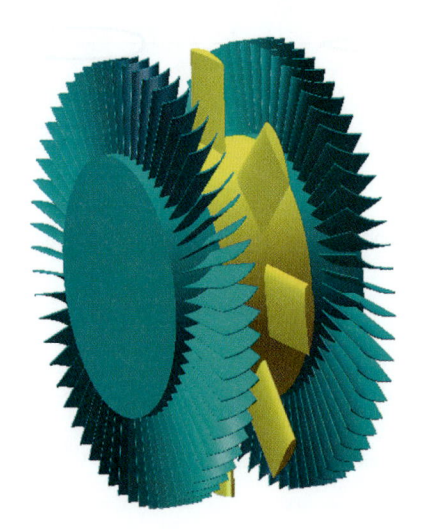

$$E = 2\Omega r V_x \tan\frac{\pi c}{2t} \qquad [24]$$

Figure 5 Wells turbine with double row of guide vanes.

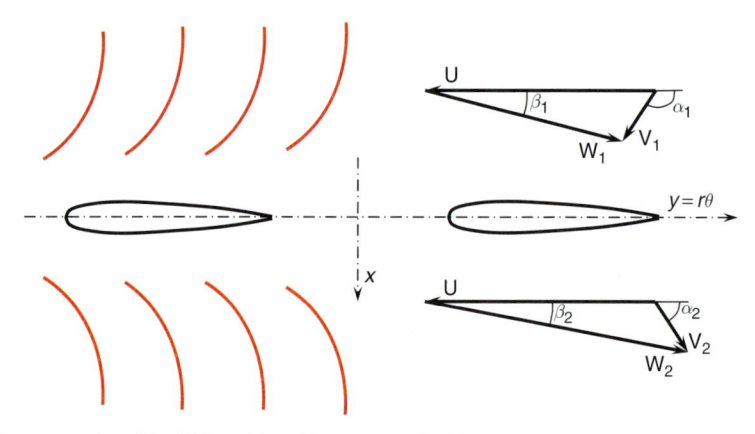

Figure 6 Two-dimensional representation of the Wells turbine with two rows of guide vanes.

which shows that, for fixed rotational speed and flow rate (i.e., given Ωr and V_x), the blade work per unit mass is independent of the direction of the incoming flow (i.e., of α_1), and consequently no change in power output due to the introduction of guide vanes is predicted by two-dimensional potential flow theory.

Each guide vane should have two sharp edges that behave alternately as leading and trailing edges. It is reasonable to adopt, as design conditions, inlet shock-free flow at the leading edges of the blades of both guide vane rows. If potential flow is assumed, this means that the flow velocity is to remain finite at the sharp leading edges. Considering this, together with Kutta condition at the trailing edges, we come to the conclusion that, in ideal design conditions, the flow pattern about one guide vane row is exactly the mirror image, with respect to the y-axis, of the flow about the other guide vane row, and that the flow leaves the turbine without swirl. In particular, this implies that it should be $\alpha_2 = \pi - \alpha_1$ for the angle of the absolute flow velocity. Equation [23] becomes simply

$$\alpha_1 = \frac{\pi}{2}\left(1 + \frac{c}{t}\right) \qquad [25]$$

This equation shows that, in ideal-fluid two-dimensional flow (and rotor blades of negligible thickness), the angle α_1 at which the flow should leave the inlet guide vanes (if shock-free conditions at the outlet guide vanes are to be met) is only a function of the chord-to-pitch ratio of the rotor blades and is independent of blade speed and flow rate. If α_1 satisfies eqn [25], then $\alpha_2 = \pi - \alpha_1$. We note that, under such conditions, the pressure drop across the triple blade row is the same as the pressure drop Δp across the moving blade row.

In the case of guide vanes satisfying condition [25], it is $\cot \beta_m = \varphi^{-1}$ and eqn [20] becomes more simply

$$\psi = 2\varphi \tan \frac{\pi c}{2t} \qquad [26]$$

Equation [26] shows that the Wells turbine is exactly a linear turbine (i.e., the pressure drop is exactly proportional to the flow rate) if the turbine is equipped with a properly designed guide vane system. This is only approximately true for the Wells turbine without guide vanes, as found in Section 8.05.3.1.2 (see eqn [20]). The comparison of eqns [20] and [26] shows that the presence of guide vanes has the effect of decreasing the ratio ψ/φ. This, combined with the fact that, for fixed φ and c/t, the blade work E is independent of the inlet flow angle α_1 (see eqn [24]), shows that the presence of guide vanes results in the same amount of blade work E being done from a smaller pressure difference Δp. It should be recalled that these results are based on two-dimensional potential flow theory for rotor blades of negligible thickness. They were first obtained in Reference 22.

8.05.3.1.3 Contra-rotating rotors

Apart from two rows of guide vanes, one on each side of the rotor, there are other ways of avoiding exit losses due to swirling flow, while keeping the turbine insensitive to reversing flow direction. One of them is the contra-rotating turbine: there are two rows of rotor blades (with identical profile and blade pitch) that move in opposite directions with equal speed, and no guide vanes, as shown in **Figure 7**. At the exit from the first rotor, the angle of the absolute flow α_2 is given by eqn [19]. With respect to the second rotor, it is $\alpha_2^* = \pi - \alpha_2$. Since, from eqn [23], it is

$$\cot \alpha_3^* = \cot \alpha_2^* + 2 \tan \frac{\pi c}{2t} \qquad [27]$$

we immediately conclude that $\alpha_3^* = \pi/2$, that is, the flow at the turbine exit is swirl-free. We easily find that the blade work per unit mass E is equal in both rotors. Proceeding as for the other cases, we obtain, for the dimensionless pressure drop coefficient ψ versus

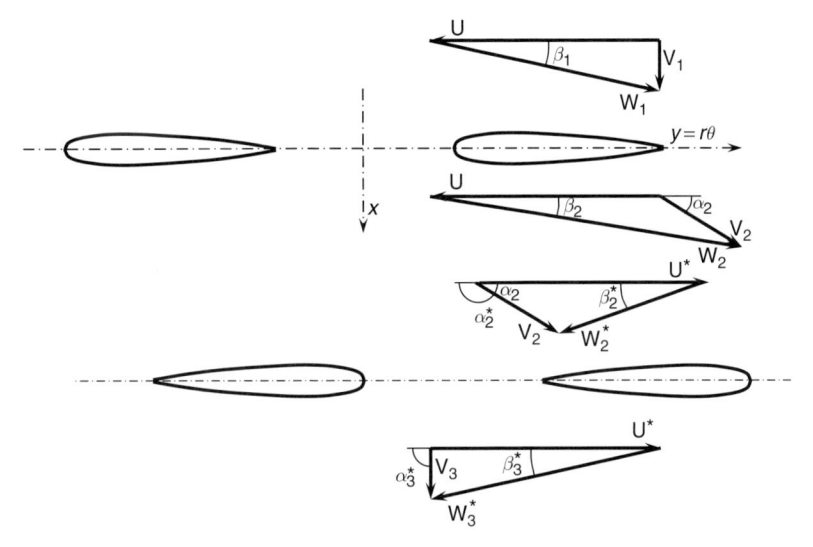

Figure 7 Two-dimensional representation of the Wells turbine with two contra-rotating rotors.

flow rate coefficient φ, $\psi = \psi_1 + \psi_2$, where ψ_1 (for the first rotor) is given by the right-hand side of eqn [20] and ψ_2 (for the second rotor) is

$$\psi_2 = 2\varphi\left(1-\varphi \tan\frac{\pi c}{2t}\right)\tan\frac{\pi c}{2t} \quad [28]$$

For the whole turbine, it is

$$\psi_1 + \psi_2 = 4\varphi \tan\frac{\pi c}{2t} \quad [29]$$

This result shows that the contra-rotating Wells turbine is (exactly) a linear turbine (like the turbine with single rotor and twin guide vane rows). It is also easy to see that, although both rotors do the same amount of work ($E_1 = E_2$), the pressure drop is larger across the first rotor than across the second one ($\psi_1 > \psi_2$). By assuming identical rotors, and comparing eqn [29] (for $\psi_1 + \psi_2$, contra-rotating rotors) with eqn [26] (for ψ, single rotor with guide vanes), we see that $\psi_1 + \psi_2 = 2\psi$. Besides, it is $E_1 + E_2 = E$.

8.05.3.1.4 Biplane rotor with intermediate guide vanes

Another way of achieving zero swirl losses at turbine exit is using two identical rotor blade rows moving in the same direction (a biplane rotor), with a row of guide vanes between them, as shown in **Figure 8** and proposed in Reference 23. The guide vane set is symmetrical with respect to a plane perpendicular to the axis of rotation. If the guide vanes are properly designed, the flow at guide vane inlet should be shock-free (see what was said above on guide vane design for the single rotor with double row of guide vanes) and $\alpha_3 = \pi - \alpha_2$. Theoretically, there should be no pressure variation across the stator vanes. The expressions for the dimensionless pressure drop ψ_1 and ψ_2, across the first and second rotor blade rows, respectively, are identical to those of the contra-rotating turbine (see above). The same is true for the blade work ($E_1 = E_2$). From these points of view, theoretically (in potential flow), the two turbines (if equipped with identical rotor blade rows) perform identically. The contra-rotating turbine has the advantage of dispensing guide vanes (and avoiding the associated aerodynamic losses in real flow). On the other hand, it requires a mechanical arrangement that is more complex and costly than the biplane turbine with intermediate guide vanes.

8.05.3.1.5 Biplane rotor without guide vanes

Equation [20], for an isolated rotor and given flow coefficient φ, shows that the pressure head coefficient ψ increases with the chord-to-pitch ratio c/t. Naturally, this ratio cannot exceed unity. In fact, since radially constant chord is adopted for most Wells turbines, the chord-to-pitch ratio at mid-radius must be substantially smaller than unity. A way to circumvent this limitation, if a large value for ψ is required, is to distribute the rotor blades onto two planes (biplane turbine). The simplest version of the biplane Wells turbine consists of two identical rotor blade rows mounted on the same shaft, with no guide vanes, as shown in **Figure 9**. This

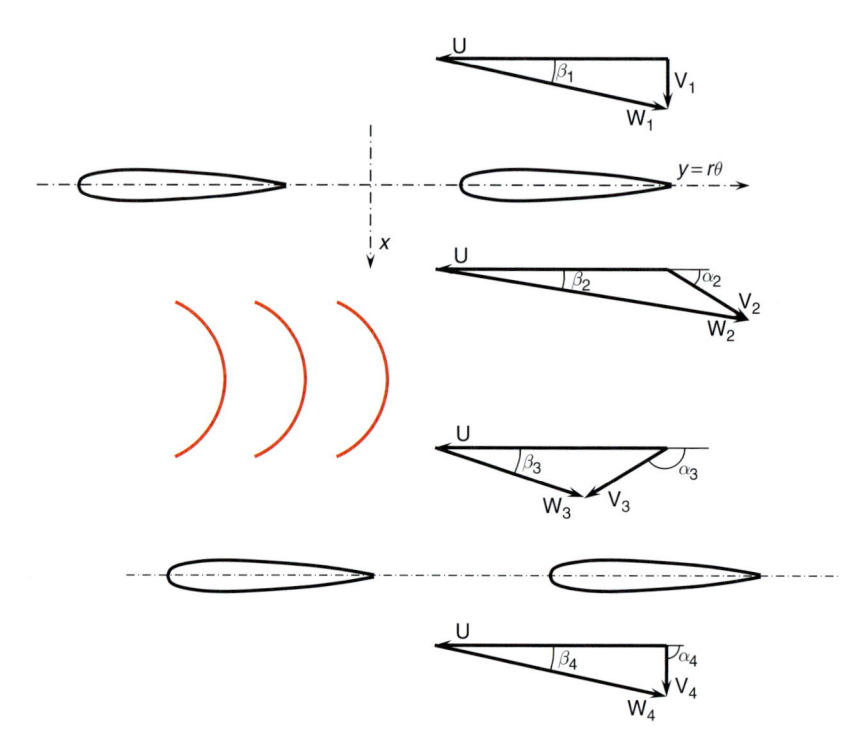

Figure 8 Two-dimensional representation of biplane Wells turbine with intermediate guide vanes.

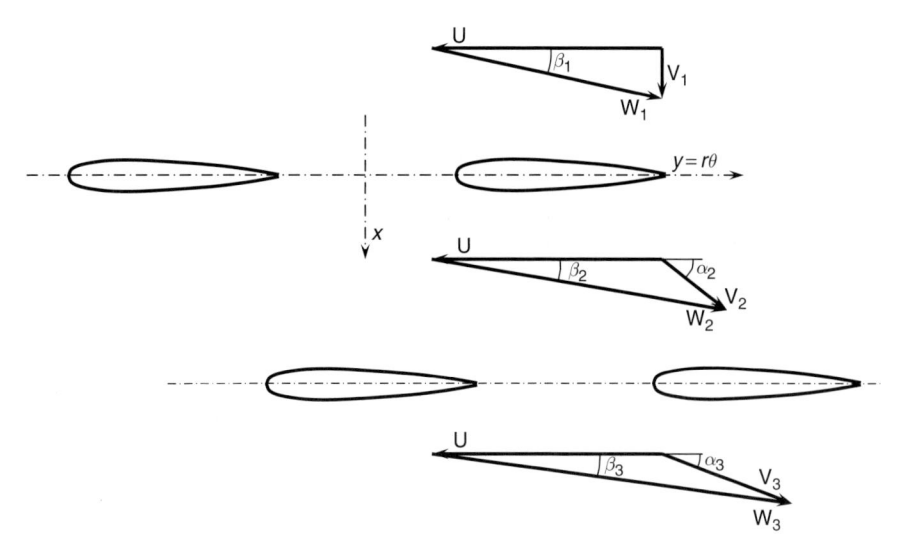

Figure 9 Two-dimensional representation of biplane Wells turbine without guide vanes.

arrangement however does not avoid losses due to exit kinetic energy by swirling flow. Applying the same methodology as above, we find, for the second row of rotor blades,

$$\cot \alpha_3 = 4 \tan \frac{\pi c}{2t} \qquad [30]$$

$$\psi_2 = 2\varphi\left(1+3\varphi\tan\frac{\pi c}{2t}\right)\tan\frac{\pi c}{2t} \qquad [31]$$

The latter equation shows that the second row of rotor blades requires a larger pressure drop than the first one, for the same amount of blade work done $E_1 = E_2$. From eqns [26] and [31], we obtain, for the biplane turbine without guide vanes,

$$\psi_1 + \psi_2 = 4\varphi\left(1+2\varphi\tan\frac{\pi c}{2t}\right)\tan\frac{\pi c}{2t} \qquad [32]$$

which, compared with eqn [29], shows that the biplane without guide vanes, for the same work, requires a larger pressure drop than the contra-rotating turbine.

It is interesting to compare the performance of a monoplane Wells turbine with an even number of rotor blades (chord-to-pitch ratio c/t) with the performance of the biplane turbine that results from splitting the blade set into two planes. Since $\tan(\pi c/2t) > 2 \tan(\pi c/4t)$ ($0 < c/t < 1$), it may easily be found that the work E done by the monoplane is larger than the work $E_1 + E_2$ of the biplane; in the same way, we find, for the pressure drop, $\psi > \psi_1 + \psi_2$. The differences become more marked as c/t gets closer to unity.

8.05.3.1.6 Biplane turbine with guide vanes

The analysis of the biplane Wells turbine with twin guide vane rows (**Figure 10**) can easily be carried out as for the single plane rotor with guide vanes. If the guide vanes are properly designed, it should be $\alpha_1 = \pi - \alpha_3$, $\alpha_2 = \pi/2$, and $\cot \alpha_1 = -2 \tan(\pi c/2t)$. The pressure drop across the whole set of rotor blades and guide vanes is given by the same eqn [29] as for the contra-rotating turbine.

For given cascade solidity c/t, blade speed Ωr, and axial-flow velocity V_x, the contra-rotating Wells turbine and the biplane turbine (with or without guide vanes) produce twice as much energy per unit mass as the single rotor Wells turbine, and may be regarded as more appropriate for the more energetic sea wave climates.

8.05.3.1.7 Other variants of the Wells turbine

In linear (small amplitude) water wave theory, the wave crests and troughs are of similar amplitude and so the predicted air flow velocities through the turbine are of identical magnitudes in both directions. However, this is not true for real sea waves, especially in more energetic sea states. The wave crests tend to be higher and shorter as compared with the wave troughs. This shows that flow conditions through the air turbine may be significantly different, with peak velocities for outward flow in general larger than for inward flow. In order to equalize the peak values of the angle of incidence at the inlet to rotor blades in inward and outward flows (and avoid stalling losses due to excessive incidence), a stagger angle (slightly) different from 90° may be adopted, as proposed in References 24 and 25.

Turbines whose rotor blade setting angle (stagger angle) is adjustable and controllable have been proposed and built. They will be addressed in Section 8.05.6.1.3.

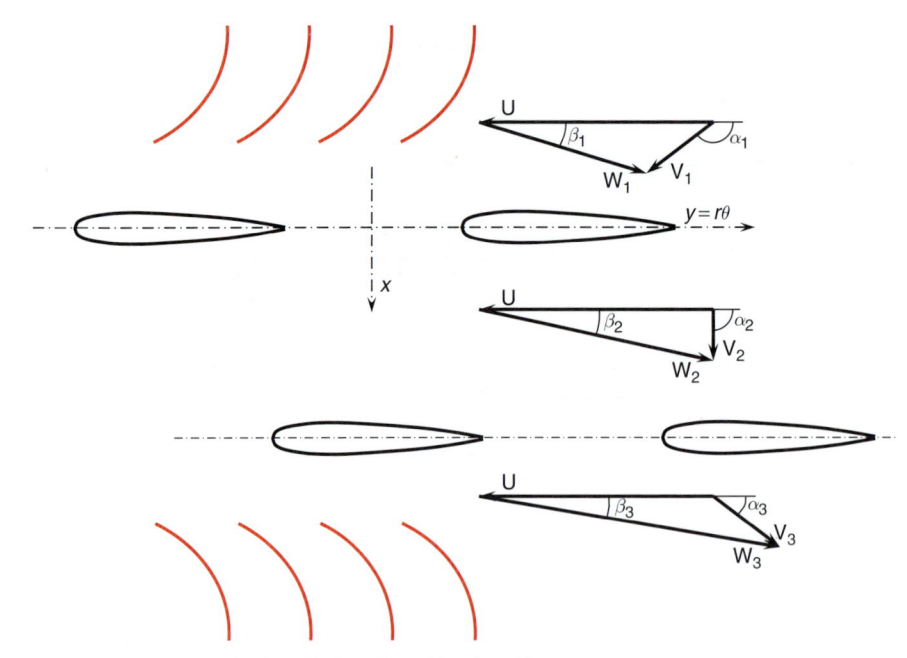

Figure 10 Two-dimensional representation of biplane Wells turbine with twin guide vane rows.

8.05.3.1.8 Nonzero rotor blade thickness

To take advantage of analytical results available for the cascade interference factor k (see eqn [15]), we assumed zero thickness of the rotor blades. In fact, very thin blades (or flat plates) exhibit poor aerodynamic performance as lifting surfaces except possibly at very small angles of incidence. In practice, streamlined blades with relative thickness between 12% and 21% have been used in model testing and prototypes (in most cases with symmetrical profiles of the NACA 00 series). Nonzero thickness is expected to affect the cascade interference factor as well as the lift coefficient of isolated aerofoils. For example, for the classical Joukowsky symmetrical profile of relative thickness d/c, in potential flow at incidence angle α, the lift coefficient becomes $c_{L0} = 2\pi(1 + 0.77\ d/c)\sin\alpha$ (see, e.g., Reference 18). This shows that, even if real fluid effects (viscosity, turbulence, eddy formation) are ignored, some of the results derived above for Wells turbine rotor blades of zero thickness should be taken as approximations. The finite thickness of blades in cascade (potential flow) can be accounted for by numerical methods, like panel methods.

8.05.3.2 Self-Rectifying Impulse Turbine

The most frequently proposed alternative to the Wells turbine is the self-rectifying impulse turbine (**Figure 11**). Unlike in the Wells turbine, in the impulse turbine neighboring blades form channels or ducts. The exit flow angle (in a reference frame fixed to the blade row) is approximately equal to the exit angle of the (moving or fixed) blades (the angular difference corresponding to the effect of slip).

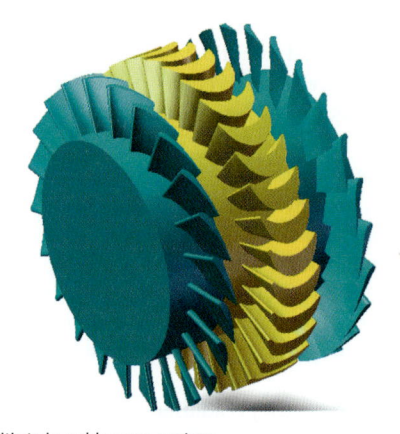

Figure 11 Self-rectifying impulse turbine: rotor with twin guide vane system.

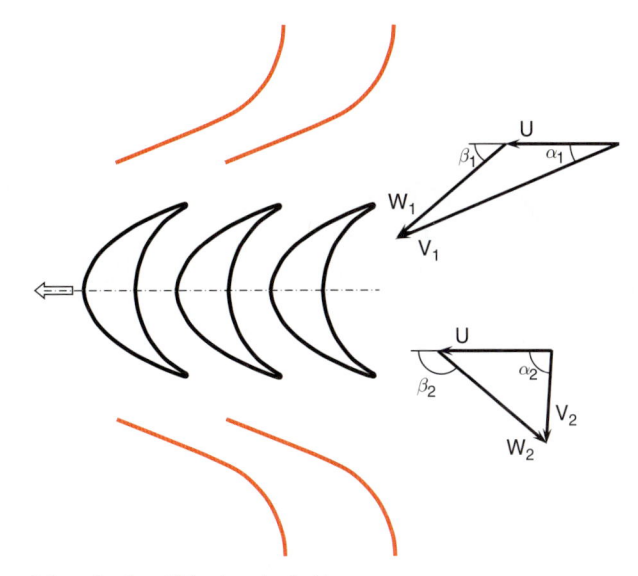

Figure 12 Two-dimensional representation of self-rectifying impulse turbine.

The geometry of the rotor blades is a modified version of the classical steam turbine of impulse type (see, e.g., Reference 26): the symmetry now imposes two sharp edges and equal inlet and outlet blade angles. As for the Wells turbine, we replace the three-dimensional annular row of rotor blades by the corresponding two-dimensional cascade of blades (**Figure 12**) and assume the flow to be incompressible and irrotational. We denote by α and β the angles of the absolute and relative flow velocities. Those angles (at inlet and outlet) are related to each other by

$$\cot \alpha_1 = -\varphi^{-1} + \cot \beta_1 \qquad [33]$$

$$\cot \alpha_2 = -\varphi^{-1} + \cot \beta_2 \qquad [34]$$

where $\varphi = V_x/U$, as before, is a dimensionless flow coefficient. We note that $\alpha_1 > \beta_1$ and $\alpha_2 > \beta_2$.

From potential flow theory of cascade aerodynamics, it is known that (for a given cascade geometry), there is a (single) value, $\hat{\beta}_1$, of the angle β_1 for which it is $\beta_2 = \pi - \beta_1$ (symmetrical inlet and outlet flow angles); theoretically, $\hat{\beta}_1$ depends only on cascade geometry. Since the blades are symmetrical, under such conditions, the relative flow is symmetrical (with respect to the cascade blade-to-blade axis of symmetry) and the (assumedly sharp) leading and trailing edges are stagnation points of the relative flow. Such conditions may be called 'design conditions' on what concerns the rotor blades.

To avoid large losses due to aerodynamic stalling (boundary layer separation) at the rotor blades, the difference $|\beta_1 - \hat{\beta}_1|$ should not be too large. This indicates that the existence of guide vanes upstream of the rotor is essential, as has been recognized since the early times of steam turbines. The exit flow angle from the guide vanes, α_1, depends (in practice) only on the guide vane row geometry; we will assume, for a given turbine, that this angle is fixed and is independent of the flow coefficient φ and also of the conditions downstream. Then, from eqn [33], the 'design' condition $\beta_1 = \hat{\beta}_1$ yields

$$\hat{\varphi} = (\cot \hat{\beta}_1 - \cot \alpha_1)^{-1} \qquad [35]$$

for the 'design' flow coefficient. Equation [35] shows that the existence of a (positive) value for $\hat{\varphi}$ requires that $\alpha_1 > \hat{\beta}_1$.

Let us examine the exit flow from the rotor. For 'design' conditions ($\beta_2 = \pi - \beta_1 = \pi - \hat{\beta}_1$), eqn [34] gives

$$\cot \hat{\alpha}_2 = \cot(\pi - \alpha_1) - 2\hat{\varphi}^{-1} \qquad [36]$$

This clearly means that, under design conditions, the flow leaves the rotor at an angle $\hat{\alpha}_2$ significantly larger than $\pi - \alpha_1$, where α_1 is the exit flow angle from the inlet guide vane row. Now, we note that symmetry considerations require a second guide vane row to exist, which is the mirror image of the first one. The 'ideal' inlet flow angle into this guide vane system (i.e., for stall-free conditions) is equal to $\pi - \alpha_1$. However, for 'design' flow conditions, eqn [36] shows that this cannot occur. An incompatibility situation arises from this: one cannot have simultaneously the right flow incidence (i.e., stall-free conditions) at the rotor blades and at the second guide vane row, a problem that has been known since the beginning to designers of impulse turbines for wave energy applications.

McCormick [7, 8] proposed a contra-rotating self-rectifying impulse turbine, a prototype of which was built and tested in Kaimei in the mid-1980s, as mentioned above. Results from testing can be found in Reference 27. The velocity diagrams in **Figure 13** show that the incidence problem persists in the contra-rotating turbine: in the relative flow at the inlet to the second rotor, and (as in the single rotor turbine) also at the inlet to the second row of guide vanes.

To solve the excessive incidence problem, guide vanes of variable geometry have been proposed by Kim et al. [28] (see also a review in Reference 10). In order to avoid the difficulties of active geometry control, the vanes (or a segment of them) may pivot

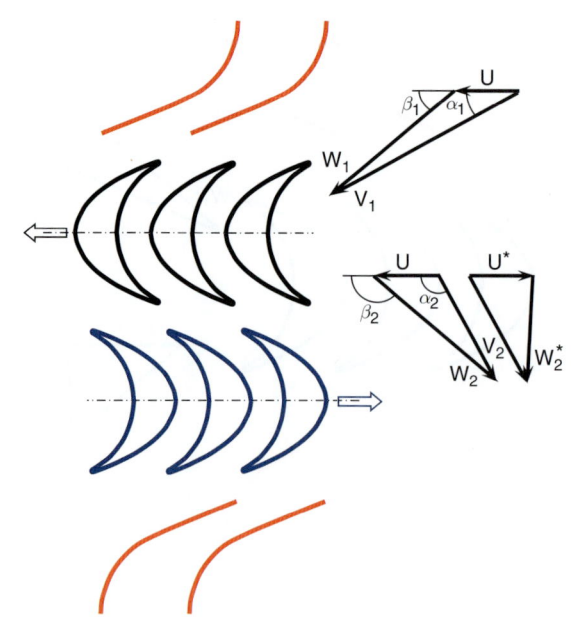

Figure 13 Two-dimensional representation of McCormick's contra-rotating self-rectifying impulse turbine.

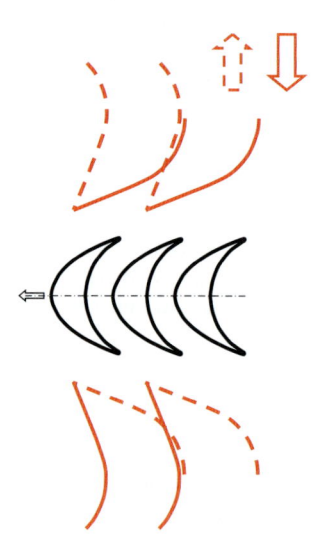

Figure 14 Two-dimensional representation of impulse turbine with self-pitching guide vanes (of mono-vane type) in the two angular positions.

under the action of the aerodynamic moments acting on them, and occupy one of two preset angular positions, depending on whether the air is flowing inward or outward (**Figure 14**). This allows the downstream guide vane row geometry to better match the angle α_2 of the flow leaving the rotor. Although this conception increases the mechanical complexity and introduces additional reliability and maintenance problems, it has been found to improve the aerodynamic performance of the turbine.

In any case, since the flow coefficient φ is strongly time-varying, oscillating irregularly between negative and positive values, it is impossible to avoid aerodynamic stalling at the rotor blades and/or at the downstream guide vanes during a relatively large part of the time.

8.05.3.3 Wells Turbine versus Impulse Turbine

The two-dimensional representation may be used to make comparisons between rotational speed, basic aerodynamic performance, and rotor diameter of the Wells turbine and the impulse turbine.

We start by considering the turbine loading coefficient, defined as $E^* = E(\Omega r)^{-2}$. For the Wells turbine (subscript W) with a single-plane rotor, with or without guide vanes, it is (see eqn [24])

$$E_W^* = 2\frac{V_x}{\Omega r}\tan\left(\frac{\pi c}{2t}\right) \qquad [37]$$

Table 1 Comparison between the Wells turbine and the impulse turbine: parameter ratios for typical turbines and fixed work E and diameter ratio D_i/D

$\dfrac{(\Omega r)_W}{(\Omega r)_{imp}}$	$\dfrac{(V_x^2)_W}{(V_x^2)_{imp}}$	$\dfrac{D_W}{D_{imp}}$	$\dfrac{\Omega_W}{\Omega_{imp}}$
2.28	0.273	1.38	1.65

We note that, in the absence of guide vanes, it is $\varphi = V_x\,(\Omega r)^{-1} = \tan\beta_1$. In real-fluid flow, it is known that aerodynamic stalling (boundary layer separation) will occur (with severe aerodynamic losses) if the angle of incidence β_1 at rotor inlet exceeds a critical value β_{1cr} that depends on blade profile, chord-to-pitch ratio c/t, upstream flow conditions, and Reynolds number. Taking $\beta_1 = \beta_{1cr}$, and assuming as typical $\beta_{1cr} = 11°$ and $c/t = 0.5$, we find, for the loading coefficient, $E_W^* = 0.389$. For the impulse turbine (subscript 'imp'), we take 'design' conditions $\beta_1 = \beta_2 = \hat{\beta}_1$. We easily find, from eqn [2], $E_{imp}^* = 2\hat{\varphi}\cot\hat{\beta}_1$. Assuming, as typical values for the impulse turbine, $\hat{\varphi} = 0.85$ and $\hat{\beta}_1 = 40°$, we find $E_{imp}^* = 2.03$. We conclude that, for fixed work E per unit mass, the blade speed $\Omega r\hat{\varphi}$ of the Wells turbine is typically about $\sqrt{2.03/0.389} = 2.28$ times larger as compared with the impulse turbine.

Now, it is easy to compare the two types of turbines on what concerns other parameters, namely V_x^2 (twice the exit kinetic energy per unit mass), the rotor outer diameter D, and the rotational speed Ω. If we take the same typical values adopted above for β_1, c/t, and $\varphi = V_x\,(\Omega r)^{-1}$, and assume that the work E per unit mass, the turbine flow rate and the inner/outer diameter ratio D_i/D are equal for both turbines, we obtain the results shown in **Table 1**.

Table 1 shows that the rotor blade speed Ωr is much larger in a Wells turbine, which also has a larger diameter and larger rotational speed. This indicates that aerodynamic noise problems are expected to be much more serious in the Wells turbine, which, on the other hand, has a much larger capacity for energy storage by flywheel effect (this is important to smooth out the oscillations in energy flux absorbed from the waves).

The loss related to swirl kinetic energy at the exit from the last row of blades can be avoided (or reduced) by the use of guide vanes or (in the case of the Wells turbine) of contra-rotating rotors. However, the loss of a large part (possibly most) of the kinetic energy (per unit mass) associated with the axial-flow velocity, $V_x^2/2$, can hardly be avoided even if some kind of axisymmetric divergent duct is used as a diffuser. This loss is much greater in the impulse turbine than the Wells turbine, as shown in the second column of **Table 1**. By using the typical values adopted above, we find $V_x^2/(2E) = 0.049$ for the Wells turbine and 0.178 for the impulse turbine. This explains why the use of an axisymmetric diffuser is much more important in an impulse turbine than in a Wells turbine.

It is important to examine how differently real viscous fluid effects affect the aerodynamic performance of the rotor of both turbines. We consider eqn [11] and compare the value of the rotor blade work per unit mass in ideal fluid (potential) flow ($\tilde{E}$) and in real flow (E), assuming that c/t, Ωr, V_x, and β_1 are the same in both cases. We note that the flow angular deflection $\beta_1 - \beta_2$ across the rotor, and so β_2 and β_m, are expected to be affected by real fluid effects. However, we will assume β_m and $\tilde{\beta}_m$ (in potential flow) to be approximately equal. We find

$$\mu = \frac{E}{\tilde{E}} = \frac{c_L}{\tilde{c}_L}\,\frac{\sin(\beta_m - \gamma)}{\sin\beta_m \cos\gamma} \quad [38]$$

We recall that $\gamma = \arctan(c_D/c_L)$, and $\gamma = 0$ in potential flow. Obviously, it is $\mu < 1$, and μ is affected by the ratio $c_L/\tilde{c}_L < 1$ (real fluid effects decrease the lift force component). Equation [38] also shows that μ decreases with increasing γ the more markedly, the smaller β_m is. Typically (close to best efficiency point), the value of β_m for the Wells turbine (about $10°$–$14°$) is much smaller than for the impulse turbine (about $90°$). It is well known that, for fixed angle incidence (in this case, fixed ratio $\varphi = V_x/(\Omega r)$), the ratio c_D/c_L, and hence γ, increases with decreasing Reynolds number. This explains why the aerodynamic efficiency of the Wells turbine is much more sensitive to changes in Reynolds number than the efficiency of the impulse turbine. In particular, it is $E = 0$ if $\gamma = \beta_m$. Mostly because of Reynolds number effects, the Wells turbine is known to perform poorly in small model testing (and small flow velocities), more so than the impulse turbine. A fair comparison between the two turbines should be based on testing results of relatively large models (diameter not smaller than about 0.6 m). Some of the comparisons in the published literature that present the Wells turbine with substantially lower peak efficiency than the impulse turbine are based on testing of models of 0.3 m outer rotor diameter or less and relatively small Reynolds number.

8.05.4 Three-Dimensional Flow Analysis of Axial-Flow Turbines

In addition to flow incompressibility, the preceding Section 8.05.3, on two-dimensional cascade flow, is based on the assumptions that the stream surfaces are cylindrical surfaces of revolution, the radial component of the flow velocity is negligible (and so the axial-flow velocity component is invariant with radial coordinate), and the interference between different radii is insignificant. This may be regarded as (approximately) true if the rotor blade work E per unit mass is constant along the span or, equivalently, if the velocity circulation about the blades does not vary along the radial coordinate (see, e.g., References 14 and 29). Such conditions are not in general satisfied in self-rectifying turbines for OWC applications. In such cases, a fully three-dimensional flow analysis should be performed, or at least corrections to two-dimensional flow results should be introduced.

The simplest method is provided by the actuator disc theory, whose application is particularly appropriate in the case of the isolated Wells turbine rotor, as done in Reference 21. The actuator disc theory was introduced by R. E. Froude in 1889 to model the flow-through marine screw propellers and was later extended to ducted axial-flow turbomachines with cylindrical walls [30] (see also Reference 29). In the general case of blade circulation (and blade work) varying along the blade span, there is vorticity trailing from the blades (as in the case of a screw propeller) that induces radial velocities and makes the stream surfaces to deviate from the circular cylindrical shape. In actuator disc theory, the shed vortex lines are assumed to be circumferentially distributed. In the linear version of the actuator disc theory (as applied to the Wells turbine in Reference 21), the vortex lines are assumed to be convected by a uniform axial flow and form semi-infinite true helical lines of constant pitch. In this case, an analytical solution exists for the actuator disc flow equations in terms of Bessel functions of the radial coordinate and exponential functions of the axial coordinate [30]. The knowledge of the flow field induced, at the actuator disc, by the trailing vorticity provides a correction to the blade cascade flow at each radial station. The actuator disc model can be extended to flows involving more than one blade row [29].

The actuator disc model is a simple version of the quasi-three-dimensional solution technique that combines (1) the two-dimensional blade-to-blade cascade flow at each radial station with (2) the (assumedly) axisymmetric (meridional) through-flow between the hub and the outer casing. The streamline curvature throughflow method is an efficient method of numerically solving this flow problem (see References 14 and 29). It was applied to the Wells turbine in References 31 (isolated rotor) and 22 (rotor with guide vanes).

There are commercial computational fluid dynamics (CFD) codes that solve the fully three-dimensional flow problem in turbomachines; some incorporate turbulence models (mostly $k-\varepsilon$) to solve the Reynolds-averaged Navier–Stokes equations. This was done, for incompressible flow, in References 32–38 for the Wells turbine and in References 39–43 for the impulse turbine.

8.05.5 Model Testing of Air Turbines

Most of what is known about the aerodynamic performance of air turbines for wave energy conversion results from model testing.

Since the time scale for the flow through the turbine is in general much smaller than the typical ocean wave period (about 5–15 s), the reversing flow though the turbine may be represented with a reasonably good accuracy by a succession of constant flow rate situations [44, 45]. This allows the model testing to be carried out under constant flow rate conditions. The tests should cover the range of operational conditions to which the turbine is expected to be subject in real sea. If the self-rectifying turbine is symmetrical and insensitive to flow direction, then a unidirectional flow test rig may be employed.

Significant hysteretic effects are known to characterize the flow through the Wells turbine (and to a less extent the impulse turbine): for a given instantaneous flow rate, the turbine performance depends on whether the flow rate is increasing or decreasing. Such effects are investigated in a test rig capable of producing reversing flow.

8.05.5.1 Dimensional Analysis

To make use of model testing, it is essential to be able to relate the results of the measurements on the small scale model to what would be expected as performance of a machine of different (in general larger) size. This can be done with the aid of the dimensional analysis. We will assume here that the flow is incompressible, that is, the fluid density ρ is constant and uniform.

We consider a family of geometrically similar turbines. The performance of a machine is determined by a set of five variables consisting of its size (possibly its rotor outer diameter D), two control variables (the flow rate Q and the rotational speed Ω), and two fluid variables (the density ρ and the viscosity μ). Any other variable, for example, the torque T, can be written as a function of those five independent variables:

$$T = f(D, Q, \Omega, \rho, \mu) \quad [39]$$

Since there are three basic units (length, mass, and time), the theorem of Buckingham allows us to replace this relationship, involving six dimensional variables, by another relationship involving only 6 − 3 = 3 dimensionless variables [29, 46]:

$$\Pi = f(\Phi, \text{Re}) \quad [40]$$

Here, $\Pi = T\rho^{-1}\Omega^{-2}D^{-5}$ is a torque coefficient, $\Phi = Q\Omega^{-1}D^{-3}$ is a flow coefficient, and $\text{Re} = \rho\Omega D^2\mu^{-1}$ is a Reynolds number. Note that $P_t = \Omega T$ is the turbine power output, and so Π may also be regarded as a dimensionless power coefficient $\Pi = P_t\rho^{-1}\Omega^{-3}D^{-5}$. The effect of varying the Reynolds number is in general much smaller than the flow coefficient effect. Then, in a first approximation, we may write, for the considered family of geometrically similar machines, simply $\Pi = \text{function}(\Phi)$, which is represented by a single curve. Instead of the torque T, we could consider the pressure head p available to the turbine. We would obtain $\Psi = \text{function}(\Phi)$, where $\Psi = p\rho^{-1}\Omega^{-2}D^{-2}$ is a dimensionless pressure coefficient and p is turbine pressure head (difference between stagnation pressure at turbine inlet and outlet). In the same way, we could write, for the aerodynamic efficiency, $\eta = \Pi\Psi^{-1}\Phi^{-1} = \text{function}(\Phi)$. Operating points with equal values of Φ are dynamically similar, which also ensures equal values for Π, Ψ, and η.

In axial-flow turbomachines, it is frequent to define a dimensionless flow coefficient Φ^* as the ratio of the averaged axial-flow velocity to the blade tip speed:

$$\Phi^* = \frac{8Q}{\pi(1-h^2)\Omega D^3} = \frac{8}{\pi(1-h^2)}\Phi \qquad [41]$$

These similarity laws allow the results of tests on a model to be related to the performance of a geometrically similar machine of different size, rotating at a different speed, with a fluid of different density. The effect of varying Reynolds number is usually taken into account as a correction based on more or less empirical laws.

8.05.5.2 Test Rigs

The first tests on the Wells turbine were done in unidirectional flow in the United Kingdom in the late 1970s and early 1980s, at the Central Electricity Generating Board (on a 0.4 m diameter rotor) [16, 47] and at the Queen's University of Belfast, UK (0.2 m diameter rotor) [17, 48]. A larger rig was constructed in 1992 at Instituto Superior Técnico, Lisbon, where Wells (and later also impulse) turbines (rotor diameter 0.6 m) were tested in unidirectional flow (**Figure 15**) [49]. The pressure drop across the turbine is provided by a blowdown variable speed centrifugal fan, with a large plenum chamber located downstream of the test section. The flow rate is measured by means of a calibrated nozzle at the exit from the plenum chamber. A similar test facility was later built at the University of Limerick, Ireland [50] and extensively used.

Most of the R&D on self-rectifying air turbines in Japan was performed at Saga University. The experimental work was done at a test rig capable of producing reversing air flows (**Figure 16**) [51]. The flow is produced by the reciprocating motion of a piston in a

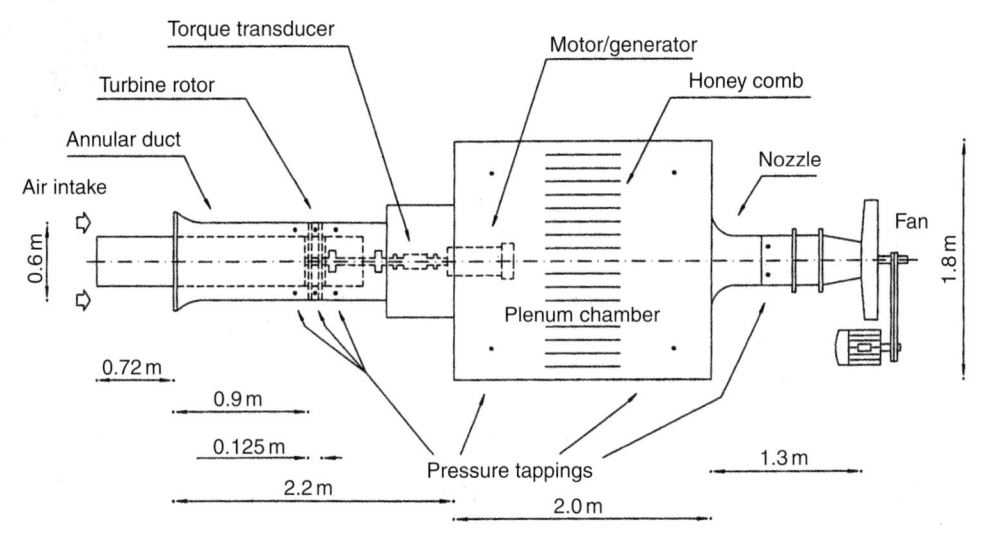

Figure 15 The unidirectional test facility for air turbines at Instituto Superior Técnico, Lisbon.

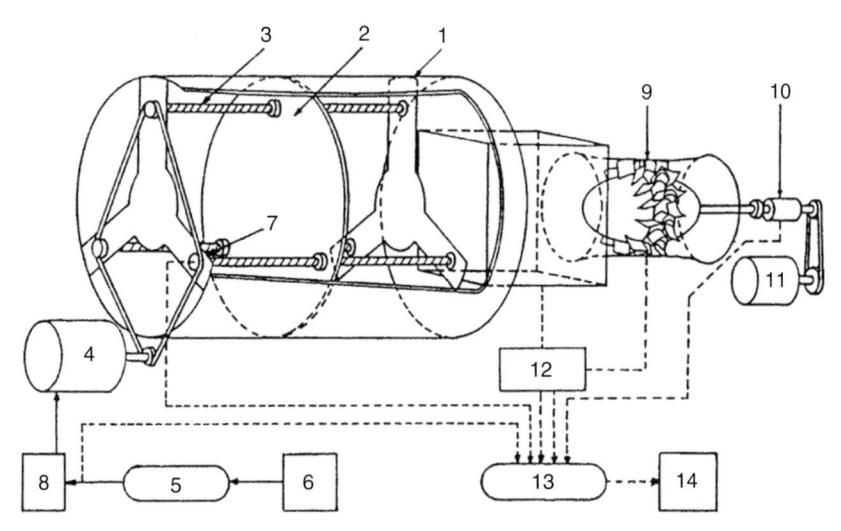

Figure 16 Schematic representation of the reversing air flow test rig for self-rectifying air turbines of Saga University, Japan [51].

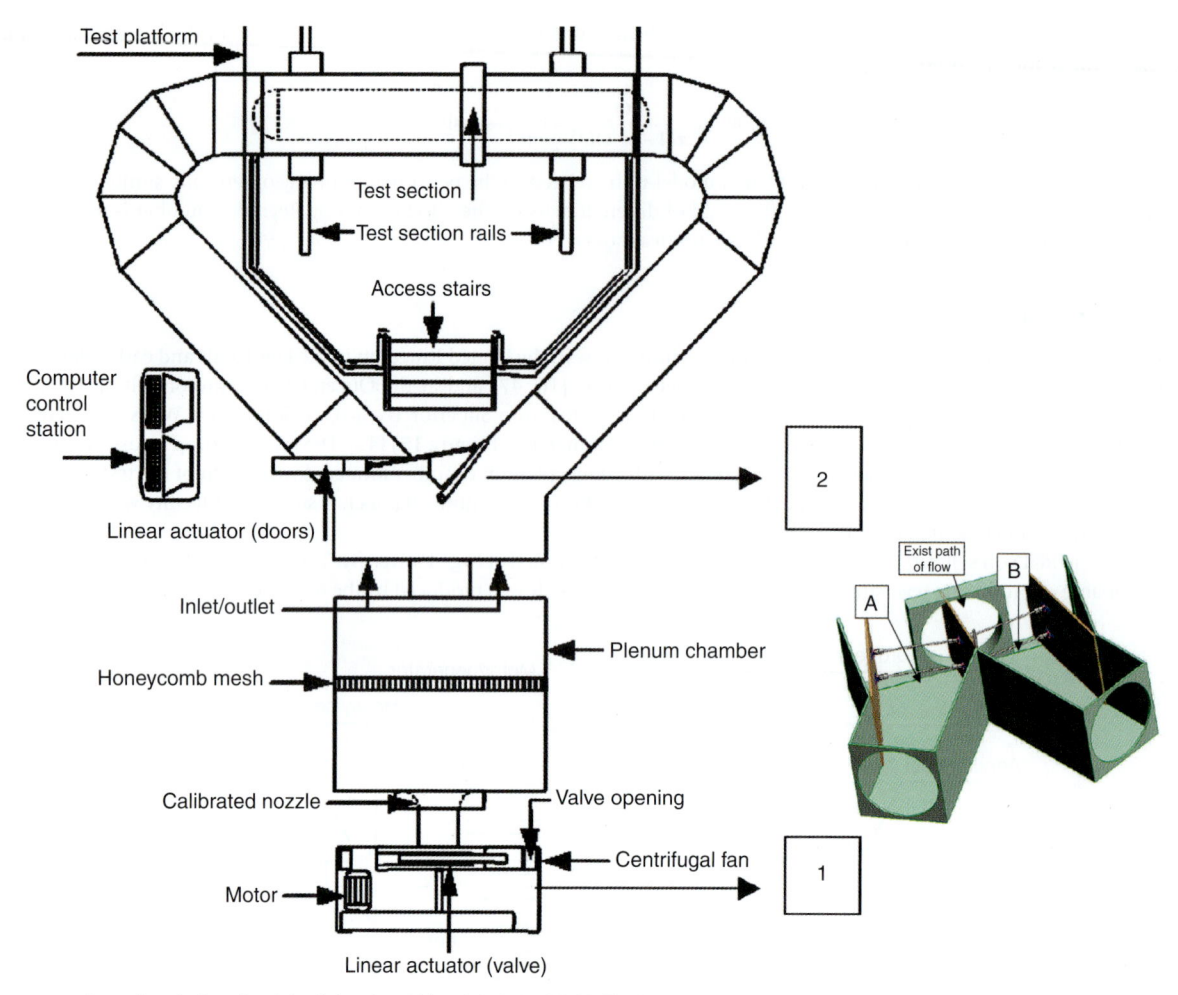

Figure 17 Reversing air flow rig of the University of Limerick, Ireland [52]. The bidirectional flow valve is shown on the right.

large cylinder (1.4 m diameter, 1.7 m long). The piston can be driven back and forth by means of three ball screws acted upon by a DC servomotor. A computer controls the motor to produce any air flow velocity. A settling chamber is located between the cylinder and the 300 mm diameter turbine test section.

An alternative way of producing reversing air flow was adopted at the University of Limerick, Ireland [52], as an modification of their originally unidirectional rig (similar to that shown in **Figure 15**). The modified rig has two automated actuators (1) and (2). The first actuator (1) controls the flow rate, while the second actuator (2) controls the position of a bidirectional valve (**Figure 17**). The direction of the flow through the turbine duct (diameter 0.6 m) depends on the position of the automated bidirectional valve.

The quantities to be measured should include at least air pressure, temperature, air flow rate, pressure drop, turbine rotational speed, and torque. If flow details are to be investigated, velocity distributions should also be measured, by either intrusive methods (traversing by directional probe) or nonintrusive methods (particle image velocimetry).

In real open sea, the pressure drop through the turbine of an OWC plant can exceed 10^4 Pa under very energetic sea conditions, giving rise to nonnegligible air compressibility effects. Such levels of air pressure are not in general attainable in the rigs used so far in model testing of self-rectifying air turbines.

8.05.6 Wells Turbine Performance

We saw, in Section 8.05.5.1, that the turbine performance, in incompressible flow, may be expressed, in dimensionless form, as

$$\eta, \Psi, \Pi \ldots = \text{functions}(\Phi, \text{Re}, \alpha, \beta, \ldots) \quad [42]$$

where η is efficiency; Φ, Ψ, and Π are coefficients of flow, pressure head, and power; Re is Reynolds number; and $\alpha, \beta, \ldots$ are a set of dimensionless geometric parameters (angles, length ratios, number of blade rows, number of blades in each row, etc.) that define the geometry of the machines. The Wells turbine performance has been studied in considerable detail by several research teams and the influence of geometrical parameters has been established by theoretical/numerical modeling as well as by model testing.

Peak efficiencies up to about 0.7 were found to be attainable in model testing of Wells turbines with sufficiently large models and Reynolds numbers. Regardless of the type of Wells turbine (except possibly for variable pitch rotor blades), the curve of efficiency η versus increasing flow rate coefficient Φ is characterized by a (more or less) sharp fall that occurs when the angle of incidence at the rotor blades exceeds the stall-free limit. The aerodynamic losses due to rotor blade stalling in practice severely limit the range of operation of the Wells turbine and constitute its main drawback.

The effect of planar shape of the rotor blades (constant versus varying chord) was studied by actuator disc theory in Reference 21, where several blade shapes were compared for fixed hub-to-tip ratio and solidity: the blade shape was found not to significantly affect the efficiency. An experimental investigation [53] compared constant chord with constant chord-to-radius ratio and found no significant differences in peak efficiency, but the varying chord blades provided a wider range of good efficiency operating conditions. However, (unlike the constant chord rotor) the varying chord bladed rotor was found not to be self-starting. These conclusions were in general confirmed in a more recent experimental study which also compared the turbine with and without guide vanes [49].

In almost every case, constant chord rotor blades have been adopted by technology developers of Wells turbines (possibly for ease of manufacture), and so in what follows we assume the blades to be of constant chord. Especially important, on what concerns the rotor, are the hub-to-tip ratio, the number of blades (or blade aspect ratio), the solidity (total bladed area divided by annular area), and the blade profile.

Raghunathan, in his comprehensive review paper on the Wells turbine [9], compiled the information available up to 1994 on the influence of several geometric parameters and produced recommendations; this included hub-to-tip ratio, rotor solidity, blade aspect ratio, rotor blade profile (especially aerofoil thickness ratio), tip clearance, and blade offset (sweep effect). The same author presented a methodology for Wells turbine design [54].

The rotor solidity σ (total bladed area divided by annular area) is directly related to the chord-to-pitch ratio at each radius. The chosen value for the solidity should be expected to increase with the pressure head available to the turbine in a representative sea state. As explained in Section 8.05.3.1.2 (see eqn [20]), an increase in solidity results in relatively larger losses by exit swirl kinetic energy (and hence a decrease in efficiency). As shown in Section 8.05.3.1.2, the use of guide vanes is especially appropriate for high solidity rotors. An efficiency improvement of up to about 5%, as compared with the vaneless turbine, was measured in the range of high efficiency flow rates (near design conditions) in a 0.593 m diameter turbine with guide vanes and $\sigma = 0.44$ (see **Figure 18** [22]). The figure shows the typical sharp drop in efficiency at a critical value of Φ (which is slightly larger in the vaneless turbine), and also shows that the curves $\Psi(\Phi)$ are approximately straight lines whose slope is reduced by the presence of guide vanes, as predicted by eqns [20] and [26]. Significant gains from the use of guide vanes, up to about 10% in peak efficiency, were also measured in model testing by other authors [49, 55–57]. At high solidity, there could be significant three-dimensional effects near the hub, where the blades are closer to each other and may interact with the hub boundary layer (see Reference 9).

The effect of hub-to-tip ratio h on turbine performance is rather complex. For a given number of blades and blade aspect ratio, there is a lower limit for h, at which the blades touch each other on the hub. The incidence angle of the relative flow on the blades close to the hub is larger than at the tip, and, for given $\bar{V}_x/(\Omega D)$, where $\bar{V}_x$ is average axial-flow velocity in the turbine annulus, increases with decreasing h; thus, it should be expected that a decrease in h should promote an earlier stall and lead to a decrease in aerodynamic efficiency [9]. On the other hand, for given blade tip clearance, the detrimental effect of the tip leakage loss on the

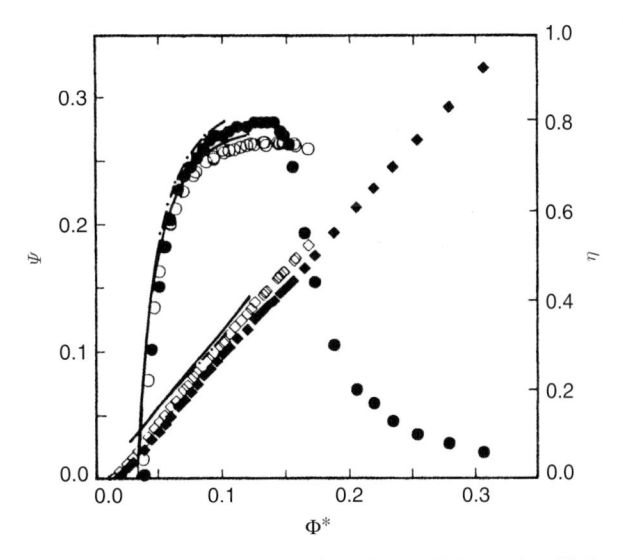

Figure 18 Efficiency η (circles) and pressure head coefficient ψ (diamonds) vs. flow coefficient Φ, for a Wells turbine with $D = 0.593$ m and solidity $\sigma = 0.44$. Experimental results: open symbols, without guide vanes; closed symbols, with guide vanes. From Gato LMC and Falcão AFdeO (1990) Performance of the Wells turbine with double row of guide vanes. *Japan Society of Mechanical Engineers International Journal, Series II* 33: 265–271 [22].

efficiency increases as the hub-to-tip ratio h gets closer to unity. Raghunathan [9] recommends for h a value about 0.6. In the Wells turbines that equip the Pico (Azores) and LIMPET OWC plants, it is $h = 0.59$ and 0.62, respectively [58, 59].

A criterion for choosing h may be the value that maximizes the volume flow rate Q (for given rotor diameter D and rotational speed Ω) prior to rotor blade stall at the hub. For simplicity, we assume that the axial velocity component V_x of the flow approaching the rotor is uniform over the annular cross section, and write

$$Q = \frac{\pi}{4} D^2 (1-h^2) V_x \qquad [43]$$

At the hub, the angle of incidence of the relative flow is $\beta_1 = \arctan 2V_x(\Omega D h)^{-1}$. We denote by an asterisk the critical conditions prior to stalling, and find

$$Q^* = \frac{\pi}{8} \Omega D^3 h (1-h^2) \tan \beta_1^* \qquad [44]$$

The value of h that maximizes Q^* is $h = 3^{-1/2} \cong 0.577$, which is close to the value 0.6 recommended by Raghunathan [9].

For given solidity and hub-to-tip ratio, the blade aspect ratio (AR) (length-to-chord ratio for constant chord blades) is proportional to the number of blades and directly influences the Reynolds number (based on blade chord). Raghunathan [9] recommends $AR \cong 0.5$. This recommended value was approximately met by the 75 kW plant installed on the island of Islay, Scotland (biplane Wells turbine with four blades in each plane, $AR = 0.57$) [60], but was largely exceeded in the Pico 400 kW plant (eight blades, $AR = 1.25$) [58] and the LIMPET 500 kW plant (contra-rotating turbine, seven blades per rotor, $AR = 1.54$) [59]. A smaller number of blades (three per plane) was adopted for the sixteen 18.5 kW biplane Wells turbines developed to equip the OWC breakwater plant at Mutriku (Spain) [61].

The symmetrical aerofoil NACA four-digit series [62] has been adopted by Wells turbine designers as rotor blade profile in almost every case. Numerical optimization of alternative profiles was done in References 63–65, in some cases with validation by model testing [66, 67]. In general, thicker profiles (e.g., NACA0021) tend to delay stalling and enlarge the operational flow range, while increasing the drag. In general, NACA0012–0021 profiles have been adopted by designers.

Air compressibility can affect the flow through the turbine in two ways: first, if the air density (and pressure) is significantly different at turbine inlet and exit, which could occur in a real plant under highly energetic sea conditions, and second, if blade speed is large enough for high subsonic and transonic flow to take place (Mach number effects). The occurrence of shock waves is especially critical (critical Mach number). This should be expected to take place close to blade tip rather than to hub. Transonic flows in Wells turbines were numerically studied in References 68 and 69. Typically, one can say that blade tip speed should not exceed about 150–170 m s^{-1} if aerodynamic losses due to transonic flow and shock waves are to be avoided; this limit should be taken into account in the specification and design of the turbine and generator (especially on what concerns centrifugal stresses).

Wells turbines are particularly affected by hysteresis when subject to unsteady reciprocating flow, as occurs in a real OWC plant. This phenomenon (the instantaneous aerodynamic performance is different depending on whether the flow rate is increasing or decreasing, especially in the stall condition) is not simulated in model testing if quasi-steady flow is assumed in a unidirectional flow rig. Hysteretic effects on Wells turbine performance were studied experimentally with a variety of rotors in sinusoidally time-varying flow rate at the reciprocating test rig facility of the University of Saga (**Figure 16**) [70]. Such effects (namely on torque) were found to be significant and sensitive to rotor geometry, especially solidity and blade thickness; they were also later studied by numerical modeling [34, 71]. Hysteric effects are expected to be smaller on large-scale turbines where the boundary layer on blades is essentially turbulent and relatively thinner [9].

An important issue is the capability of the Wells turbine to self-start from rest, that is, to reach operational rotational speed without the need of an external torque being applied by the electrical machine acting as a motor. That capability is known to depend on the turbine geometry. In general, it can be said that low values of the hub-to-tip ratio h and high values of the rotor solidity σ favor self-starting [54].

8.05.6.1 Advanced Wells Turbine Configurations

In the original configurations of the Wells turbine, the rotor blades were radially set at 90° stagger angle in a single plane, with or without guide vanes [15, 16]. Other versions were later proposed and studied, in some cases reaching the stage of full-sized prototype.

8.05.6.1.1 Biplane turbine

The pressure drop across a Wells turbine rotor (under efficient operational conditions) increases with rotor solidity and is (approximately) proportional to the square of the blade tip speed. This imposes limitations to a monoplane turbine. If the pressure head available for energy conversion is much larger than the maximum possible pressure drop across a single-plane rotor, then a biplane (or a multiplane) Wells turbine (with or without guide vanes) can be used instead, in which the rotor blades are disposed on two planes separated by a gap but fixed to the same shaft (see Sections 8.05.3.1.4 and 8.05.3.1.5). As the original monoplane Wells turbine, the biplane Wells turbine originated also at the Queen's University of Belfast [72] where it was object of investigations whose results are reported in detail in Raghunathan's review paper [9]. It should be mentioned that the 75 kW biplane turbine, which equipped the OWC plant installed in 1991 on the island of Islay, UK, was designed by Raghunathan and his coworkers at the

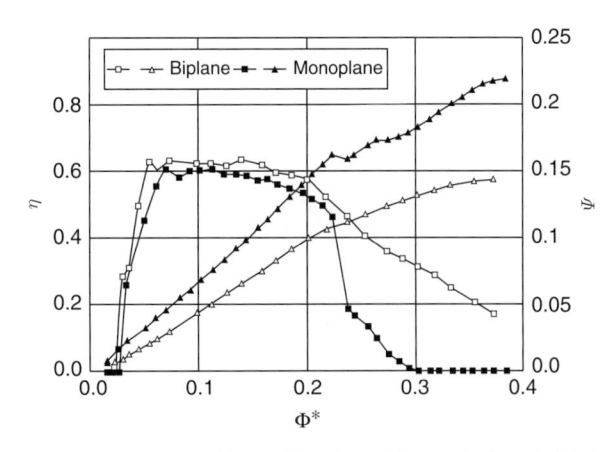

Figure 19 Compared performance of monoplane and biplane Wells turbines (no guide vanes) of equal global solidity: efficiency η (squares) and dimensionless pressure Ψ (triangles) vs. dimensionless flow rate coefficient $\Phi^* = 8\Phi\pi^{-1}(1-h^2)^{-1}$. From Gato LMC and Curran R (1996) Performance of the biplane Wells turbine. *Journal of Offshore Mechanics and Arctic Engineering–Transactions of the American Society of Mechanical Engineers* 118: 210–215 [74].

Queen's University of Belfast. The performance of a biplane rotor is subjected to mutual aerodynamic interference effects between the blades due to the proximity of the planes. It was found that, if the gap between planes is greater than the blade chord length, then the interference between planes can be neglected [73] (see also Reference 74), as was done in the two-dimensional analysis in Sections 8.05.3.1.4 and 8.05.3.1.5. In the 75 kW Islay plant, the gap-to-chord ratio was approximately equal to 1. Since the biplane rotor allows a larger flow deflection than the monoplane, the relative loss by swirl kinetic energy at exit is also larger, which makes the use of guide vanes particularly important. **Figure 19** gives a comparison between the results of model testing a monoplane and a biplane Wells turbine (in both cases without guide vanes), the difference being that the set of eight rotor blades were disposed into one or two planes; total solidity was $\sigma = 0.64$, hub-to-tip ratio $h = 0.68$, and gap-to-chord ratio $G/c = 1.4$, where G is the gap between planes [74]. The curves show slightly better peak efficiency for the biplane. The main distinction is in the stall region where the efficiency of the monoplane drops more sharply. The pressure coefficient of the biplane is about 30% below that of the monoplane, as predicted by the two-dimensional cascade theory (see Section 8.05.3.1.5). In both cases, a significant increase in peak efficiency would be expected by the use of twin sets of guide vanes.

8.05.6.1.2 Contra-rotating turbine

Another way to distribute the rotor blades into two planes, in order to accommodate larger pressure drops, consists in using two contra-rotating rotors, as proposed in 1993 [75]. As explained in Section 8.05.3.1.3, this avoids the exit loss due to swirl kinetic energy without the need of guide vanes. The penalty to be paid is a higher mechanical complexity and the need to duplicate the generators and the power electronics. Two 1 MW contra-rotating Wells turbines equipped the bottom-standing OSPREY prototype, which was destroyed by wave action during installation in 1995. Later, in 2000, a 500 kW machine was installed in the LIMPET shoreline plant, on the island of Islay, UK [59]. The aerodynamics of the contra-rotating turbine is studied in detail in Reference 76; for results of model testing, see References 77 and 78. Since the angle of incidence β_2^* of the flow relative to the downstream row of blades is larger than the angle β_1 relative to the first row for equal contra-rotating speeds (see **Figure 7**), stall is expected to occur first at the second row for increasing flow rate. Because of this, if the stall-free operating range is to be enlarged, the speed of the downstream rotor should be higher than that of the upstream rotor [76, 77], which, in bidirectional flow, would require an appropriate control system. **Figures 20** and **21** show results from model testing [78] of two contra-rotating turbines with $D = 0.590$ m, $h = 0.68$, $G/c = 1.4$, and equal speed for both rotors. In **Figure 20**, the results concern a low solidity turbine ($\sigma = 0.64$, both rotors included); for comparison, the figure also presents results for a monoplane turbine with guide vanes and equal solidity. While there are no clear differences in peak efficiency, the decay in efficiency of the contra-rotating turbine due to stalling is much more gradual. The pressure drop of the monoplane is larger, as predicted by two-dimensional cascade theory (see Section 8.05.3.1). In **Figure 21**, the results are for a high solidity turbine ($\sigma = 1.28$); results are also shown for a biplane turbine of equal solidity without guide vanes. In **Figure 21**, the peak efficiency of the contra-rotating turbine exceeds that of the biplane by about 15%, as a result of the incapacity of the vaneless biplane turbine to recover the large swirl kinetic energy at exit.

8.05.6.1.3 Variable-pitch Wells turbine

A method to avoid or delay the occurrence of blade stalling in a Wells turbine and extend the stall-free operational range consists in introducing a mechanism that allows the blade setting angle to be controlled in such a way that the instantaneous angle of incidence does not exceed the critical limit. Inoue *et al.* [79] proposed a turbine with self-pitch-controlled rotor blades: each blade is set on the hub by a pivot located near its leading edge that enables it to oscillate and occupy two prescribed angular positions $\pm\varepsilon$ depending on the flow direction and the aerodynamic pitching moment on the blade. They found that the turbine is advantageous from the viewpoints of self-starting characteristics and rotor speed reduction in comparison with a fixed-pitch turbine.

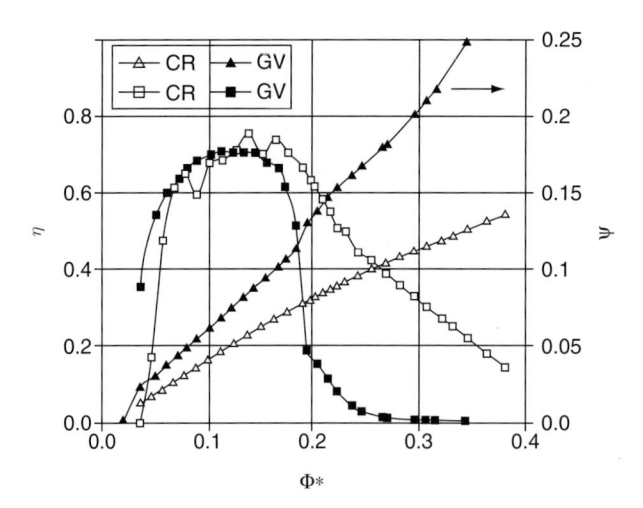

Figure 20 Compared performance of a contra-rotating (CR) turbine and a monoplane turbine with guide vanes (GVs), with equal total solidity $\sigma = 0.64$: efficiency η (squares) and dimensionless pressure Ψ (triangles) vs. dimensionless flow rate coefficient $\Phi^* = 8\Phi\pi^{-1}(1-h^2)^{-1}$. From Curran R and Gato LMC (1997) The energy conversion performance of several types of Wells turbine design. *Proceedings of the Institution of Mechanical Engineers, Part A: Journal of Power and Energy* 211: 133–145 [78].

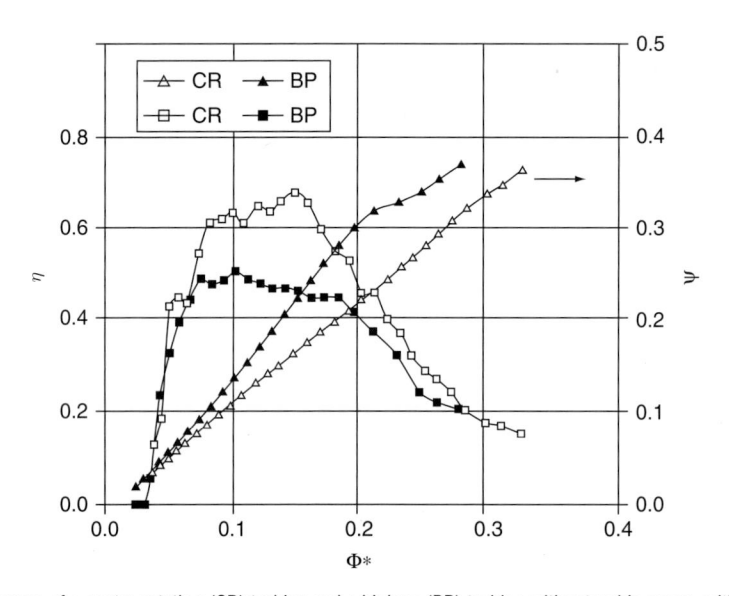

Figure 21 Compared performance of a contra-rotating (CR) turbine and a biplane (BP) turbine without guide vanes, with equal total solidity $\sigma = 1.28$: efficiency η (squares) and dimensionless pressure Ψ (triangles) vs. dimensionless flow rate coefficient $\Phi^* = 8\Phi\pi^{-1}(1-h^2)^{-1}$. From Curran R and Gato LMC (1997) The energy conversion performance of several types of Wells turbine design. *Proceedings of the Institution of Mechanical Engineers, Part A: Journal of Power and Energy* 211: 133–145 [78].

A variable-pitch Wells turbine has an additional degree of freedom compared with the conventional Wells turbine that may be explored in a different way: it allows the instantaneous flow rate to be controlled (within certain limits) independently of the pressure head and the rotational speed. The flow rate may even be reversed (by reversing the sign of the angle of incidence) so that the machine operates as a compressor rather than a turbine. This capability enables the turbomachine to achieve reactive phase control: during part of the wave cycle, the power takeoff system (through the OWC motion) supplies energy to the wave field surrounding the OWC as a way of increasing the total amount of energy absorbed from the waves over the whole cycle [80–83]. Naturally, the main disadvantage of the variable-pitch turbine is its mechanical complexity and inherent reliability issues.

Figure 22 shows results from numerical modeling, and from model testing in unidirectional flow, of a variable-pitch Wells turbine with $D = 0.6$ m, $h = 0.667$, $\sigma = 0.65$, and eight blades [82]. The curves represent the efficiency η_t (turbine mode) and η_c (compressor mode) versus flow rate coefficient Φ^* for several values of the blade setting angle ε (between $-7.5°$ and $20°$). As ε increases, the occurrence of stall is delayed to larger values of Φ^*, as should be expected. Besides, for increasing positive ε, there is an enlarged range of flow rates within which the machine performs as a compressor (curves on the left, corresponding to negative incidence angles); for $\varepsilon = 15°$ and $20°$, the measured peak efficiencies are approximately equal ($\cong 0.7$) in both modes.

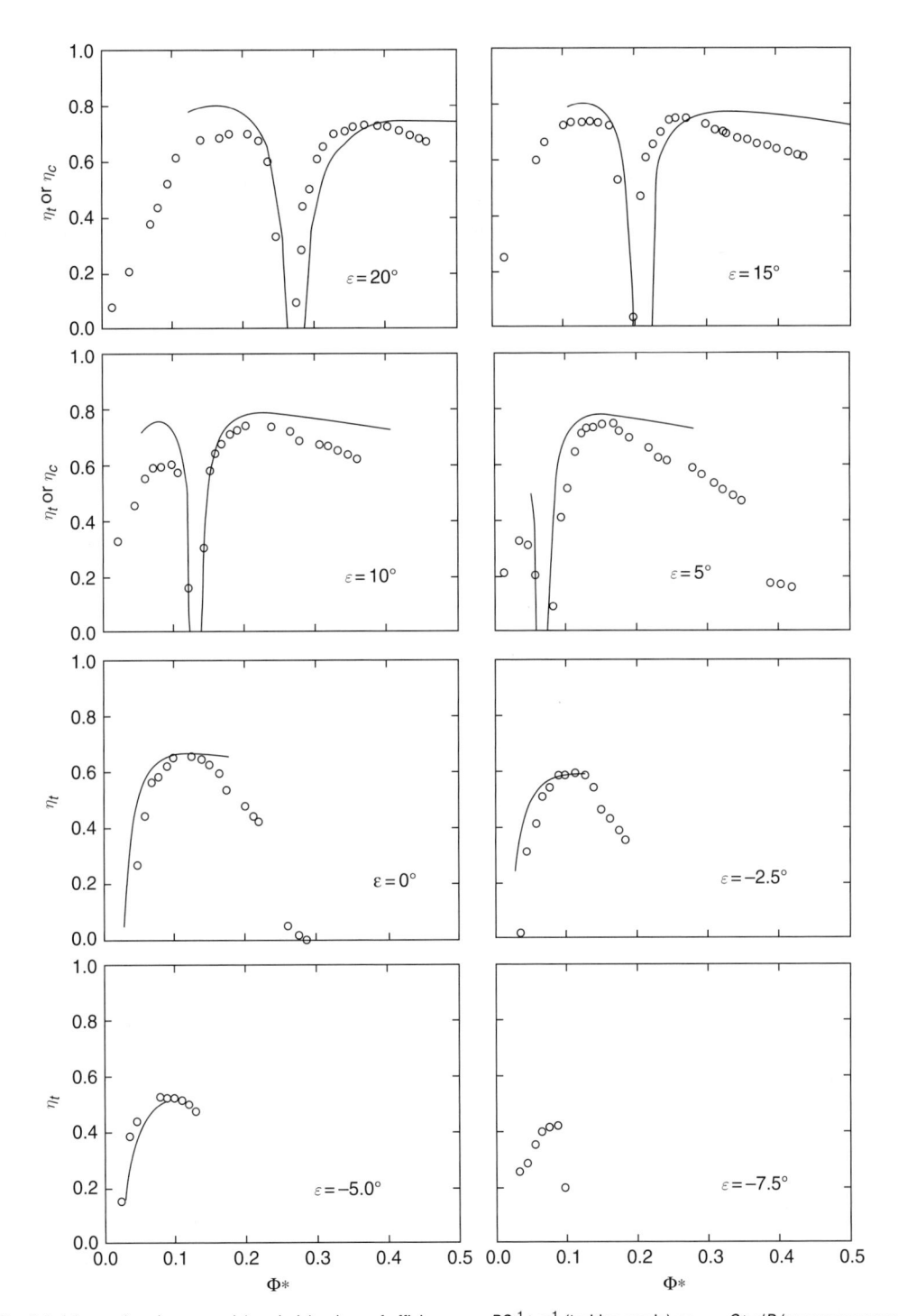

Figure 22 Predicted (curves) and measured (symbols) values of efficiency $\eta_t = PQ^{-1}\Delta p^{-1}$ (turbine mode) or $\eta_c = Q\Delta p/P$ (compressor mode) of a variable-pitch Wells turbine vs. flow rate coefficient Φ^* for several values of blade setting angle ε. The compressor mode curves are on the left for $\varepsilon > 0$. From Gato LMC, Eça LRC, and Falcão AFdeO (1991) Performance of the Wells turbine with variable pitch rotor blades. *Journal of Energy Resources Technology–Transactions of the American Society of Mechanical Engineers* 113: 141–146 [82].

8.05.7 Performance of Self-Rectifying Axial-Flow Impulse Turbine

With the possible exception of the recently developed HydroAir turbine (about whose aerodynamic performance little or nothing has been published), the efficiency of the self-rectifying impulse turbine with fixed guide vanes is severely limited by the losses at the entry to the downstream row of guide vanes (see Section 8.05.3.2). Peak efficiencies measured in model testing do not exceed about 0.5 (as compared with about 0.7 for the Wells turbine). On the other hand, the efficiency curves do not exhibit the sharp drops typical of most Wells turbines. In the Wells turbine, the peak efficiency is attained at a much smaller value of the flow coefficient Φ (or Φ^*) as compared with the impulse turbine. This agrees with the conclusions from the two-dimensional analysis in Section 8.05.3.3 (see **Table 1**), where it was found that, for equal rotor work per unit mass and equal flow rate, the Wells turbine rotor is substantially larger and rotates faster. So, if the efficiency curves of both turbines are to be compared, one should plot η versus the ratio Φ/Φ_η, where Φ_η is the value of Φ at peak efficiency conditions, rather than versus Φ. Also, since the efficiency is much more dependent on Reynolds number in the case of the Wells turbine, the data used in comparisons should be from relatively large models and Reynolds numbers. **Figure 23** presents a plot of the efficiency η versus Φ/Φ_η of a monoplane Wells turbine with guide vanes (experimental data from Reference 78) and also of an impulse turbine with fixed guide vanes (experimental data from Reference 50). The tests were performed in similar test rigs with models of $D \cong 0.6$ m. In the case of the Wells turbine, it was $h = 0.68$ and $\sigma = 0.64$; $h = 0.6$ for the impulse turbine. The values of Φ_η and Φ^*_η for the two turbines are $\Phi_\eta = 0.024$, $\Phi^*_\eta = 0.11$ (Wells turbine) and $\Phi_\eta = 0.25$, $\Phi^*_\eta = 1.0$ (impulse turbine). The curves show that the peak efficiency is significantly larger for the Wells turbine (0.71 compared with 0.48). On the other hand, the impulse turbine does not suffer from the sharp drop in efficiency at larger flow rates (the effect of aerodynamic losses with increasing flow rate is much more gradual). The performance of Wells and impulse turbines in oscillating bidirectional flows is analyzed in Section 8.05.10.

The design of the self-rectifying impulse turbine (more than that of the Wells turbine) could benefit from the development over many years of more conventional turbines, especially impulse steam turbines (see, e.g., References 26 and 84). A detailed review of the self-rectifying impulse turbine can be found in Reference 10, largely based on the extensive work performed at Saga University, Japan.

The rotor blade profile recommended in Reference 10 is formed by a circular arc and an arc of ellipse (major-to-minor axis ratio = 3) (see **Figure 24**), with $\gamma = 60°$ and $b/t = 0.4$.

The performance of the impulse turbine can improve substantially if pivoting guide vanes are used instead of fixed ones. This allows the flow from the rotor to enter the downstream row of guide vanes at a smaller angle of incidence and in this way avoid or reduce the losses due to boundary layer separation. The idea of self-pitching guide vanes was put forward by Kim *et al.* in 1988 [28] (see also Reference 85). The guide vanes are free to rotate between two preset angles determined by mechanical stops. Whenever the airflow changes direction, the guide vanes flip under the action of aerodynamic moments acting on them and take the right orientations. Two guide vane arrangements have been studied: the mono-vane type, in which the whole vane pitches, and the splitter type in which a part of the guide vane is fixed (**Figure 25**).The mono-vane type was found to be superior to the other one [10].

Figures 26 and **27** compare the performance (efficiency η and pressure coefficient Ψ vs. flow coefficient Φ^*) of an impulse turbine with fixed guide vanes and an impulse turbine with self-pitch-controlled guide vanes. The curves are based on results from model testing reported in Reference 11, with a rotor of $D = 0.298$ m and hub-to-tip ratio $h = 0.7$. The movable guide vanes provide higher efficiency, except at large flow rates. The curve of Ψ versus Φ^* shows that the impulse turbine exhibits a marked nonlinear characteristic, in contrast with the quasi-linear behavior of the Wells turbine.

An alternative method of reducing the aerodynamic losses by excessive incidence angle at the entrance to the second row of guide vanes consists in increasing the distance between the guide vane rows and the rotor blades, with the object of reducing the velocity (and hence the kinetic energy) of the flow at the entrance to the second row of guide vanes and in this way reduces the energy losses due to boundary layer separation (stalling) at those vanes. This methodology was proposed in Reference 86: the two rows of guide vanes, one on each side of the rotor, are offset from the rotor blades, radially as well as axially, with annular ducts connecting the guide vane sets with the rotor blade row (**Figure 28**). The radial offset allows, by conservation of angular momentum, the circumferential component of the flow velocity to be reduced at the entrance to the second row of guide vanes. This radial offset, eventually combined with an increase in the gap between the inner and outer walls of the annular ducts (i.e., an increase in blade span of the stator system), also produces a decrease in the meridian component (projected on an axial plane) of the flow velocity. A problem of this configuration is associated with the increased distance the fluid in strongly swirling flow has to travel between the first row of guide vanes and the rotor blades: this is likely to produce significant losses and flow profile distortion due to interaction with the duct wall boundary layers. This type of impulse turbine has been commercialized under the name of HydroAir turbine (**Figure 29**) [87]. No performance data seem to have been published so far.

8.05.8 Other Air Turbines for Bidirectional Flows

8.05.8.1 Denniss-Auld Turbine

The so-called Denniss-Auld turbine, developed in Australia to equip OWC plants [88], is also a self-rectifying axial-flow turbine, which shares some characteristics with the variable-pitch Wells turbine, the main difference being that the setting angle γ of the Denniss-Auld rotor blades (**Figure 30**) may be controlled to vary within a range $\alpha < \gamma < \pi - \alpha$ (where $\alpha \cong 20$–$35°$), whereas in the variable-pitch Wells turbine it is $-\beta < \gamma < \beta$ (where $\beta \cong 25°$). While in the Wells turbine the rotor blade rounded leading edge faces the incoming flow all the time, in the Denniss-Auld turbine both edges of a blade must be identical since (like in the impulse turbine rotor) each edge behaves alternately as a leading edge or as a trailing edge depending on the direction of the reciprocating flow through the turbine. It is to be noted that, whenever the flow changes direction (exhaust or intake), the blades of the Denniss-Auld turbine are required to pivot almost instantaneously between their extreme positions (**Figure 31**), whereas in the Wells turbine, the blades are required to pivot smoothly within a relatively small angular range. Unlike the impulse turbine, no guide vanes are

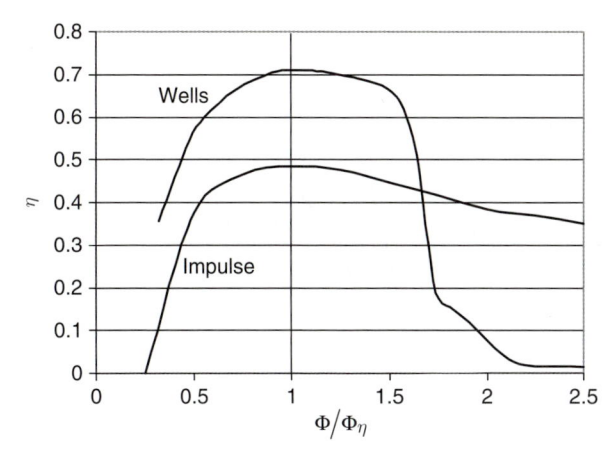

Figure 23 Efficiency vs. flow coefficient ratio Φ/Φ_η for a monoplane Wells turbine with guide vanes and an impulse turbine with fixed guide vanes. Experimental data from Curran R and Gato LMC (1997) The energy conversion performance of several types of Wells turbine design. *Proceedings of the Institute of Mechanical Engineers, Part A: Journal of Power and Energy* 211: 133–145 [78] (Wells turbine) and Thakker A, Frawley P, and Khaleeq HB (2002) An investigation of the effects of Reynolds number on the performance of 0.6m impulse turbine for different hub to tip ratios. In: *Proceedings of the 12th International Offshore Polar Engineering Conference*, pp. 682–686 [50] (impulse turbine).

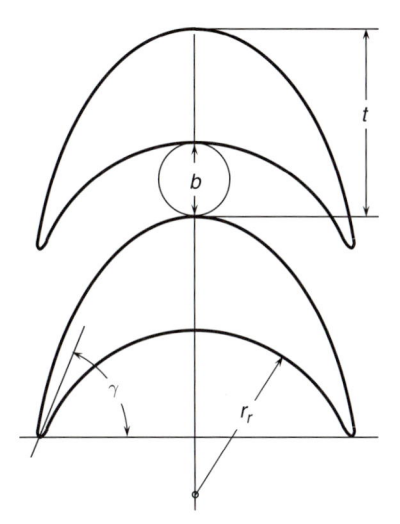

Figure 24 Rotor blade profile of impulse turbine formed by an elliptic arc and a circular arc.

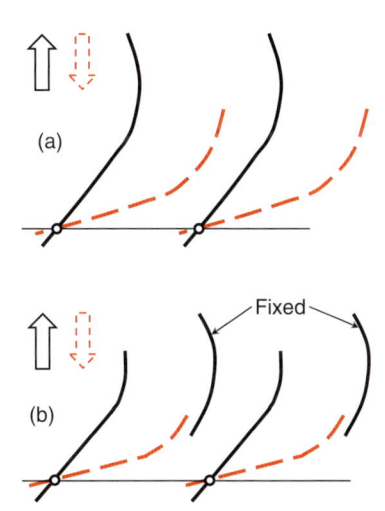

Figure 25 Guide vane geometry: (a) mono-vane type; (b) splitter type. From Setoguchi T, Santhakumar S, Maeda H, *et al.* (2001) A review of impulse turbines for wave energy conversion. *Renewable Energy* 23: 261–292 [10].

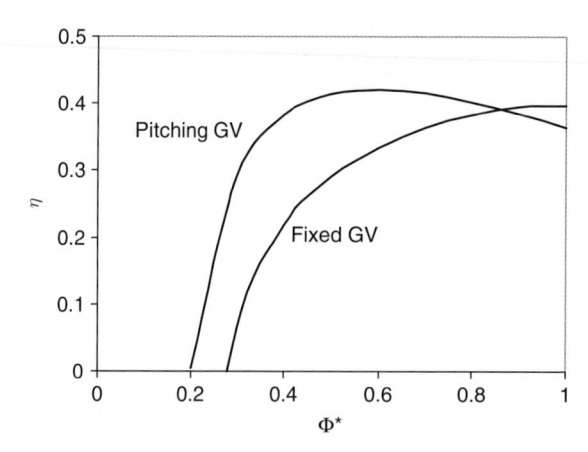

Figure 26 Efficiency η vs. flow coefficient Φ^* of an impulse turbine equipped with self-pitch-controlled guide vanes and with fixed guide vanes. Based on results from model testing reported in Reference 11.

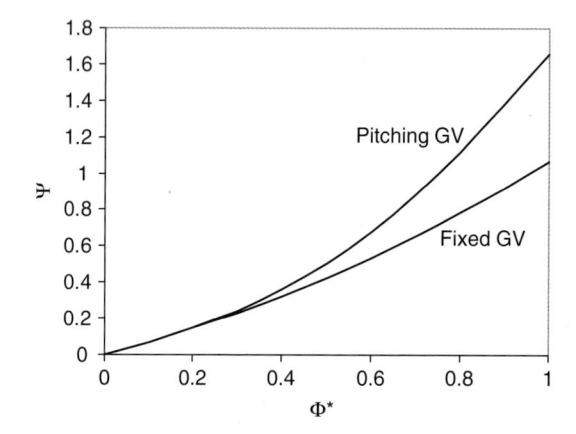

Figure 27 Pressure coefficient Ψ vs. flow coefficient Φ^* of an impulse turbine equipped with self-pitch-controlled guide vanes and with fixed guide vanes. Based on results from model testing reported in Reference 11.

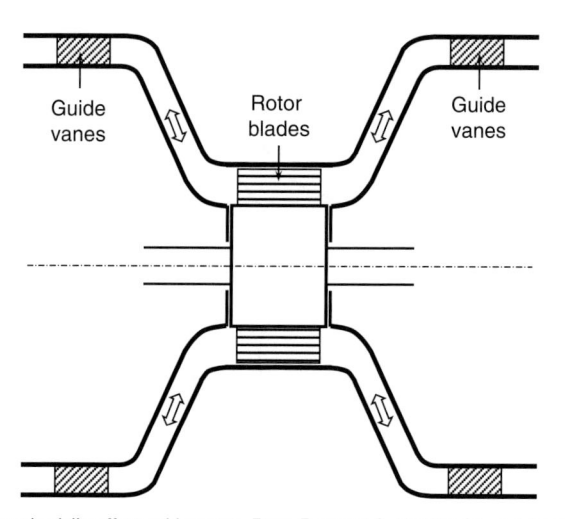

Figure 28 Impulse turbine with radially and axially offset guide vanes. From Freeman C, Herring SJ, and Banks K (2008) Impulse turbine for use in bi-directional flows. WO 2008/012530 A2 [86].

Figure 29 HydroAir turbine. From HydroAir variable radius turbine. http://www.dresser-rand.com/literature/general/2210_HydroAir.pdf (accessed 25 April 2011) [87].

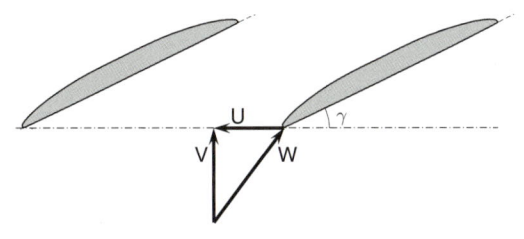

Figure 30 Blades and velocity diagram of the Denniss-Auld turbine.

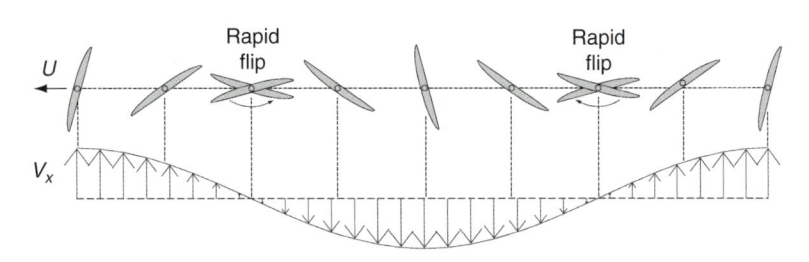

Figure 31 Blade pitching sequence of the Denniss-Auld turbine in oscillating flow (from left to right). From Finnigan T and Auld D (2003) Model testing of a variable-pitch aerodynamic turbine. In: *Proceedings of the 13th International Offshore Polar Engineering Conference*, pp. 357–360. Hononulu, HI, USA [89].

required. In fact, the Denniss-Auld turbine is not equipped with guide vanes, the result being that the exit swirl kinetic energy is not recovered.

Figure 32 shows a plot of the turbine efficiency η versus flow coefficient Φ^* for four values of the setting angle γ (between 20° and 80°), from model testing of a turbine with $D = 0.46$ m, hub-to-tip ratio $h = 0.43$, and eight blades of chord length 0.10 m [89]. The blade profiles were symmetrical about the mid-chord and were based on a NACA65-418 aerofoil, with maximum camber height of 6% and maximum thickness-to-chord ratio of 18%. The peak efficiency (slightly above 0.6) occurs at about $\gamma = 40°$. Under normal operation of an actual Denniss-Auld turbine, the blade angle would be adjusted continuously such that the maximum efficiency is achieved as the flow coefficient changes. **Figure 33** shows the operating efficiency curve corresponding to **Figure 32**. Results from a numerical simulation of the same turbine model can be found in References 90 and 91.

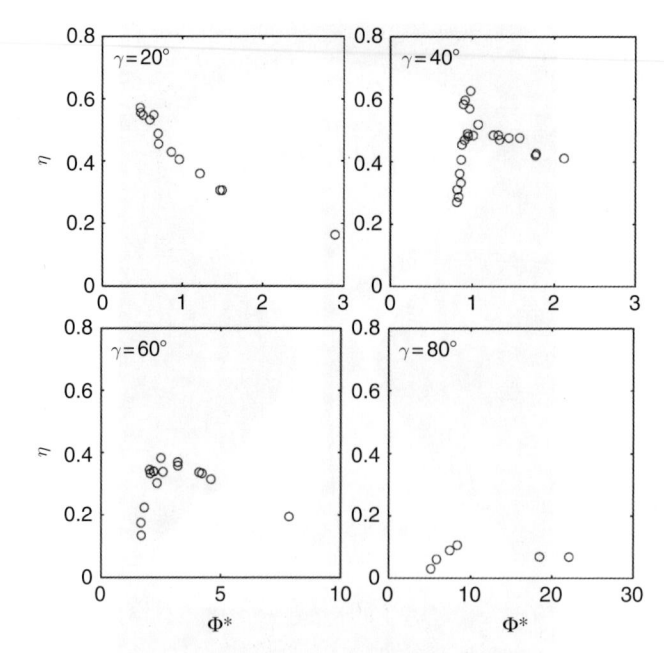

Figure 32 Efficiency η of the Denniss-Auld turbine vs. flow rate coefficient Φ^* for four blade setting angles γ. From model testing Finnigan T and Auld D (2003) Model testing of a variable-pitch aerodynamic turbine. In: *Proceedings of the 13th International Offshore Polar Engineering Conference*, pp. 357–360. Hononulu, HI, USA [89].

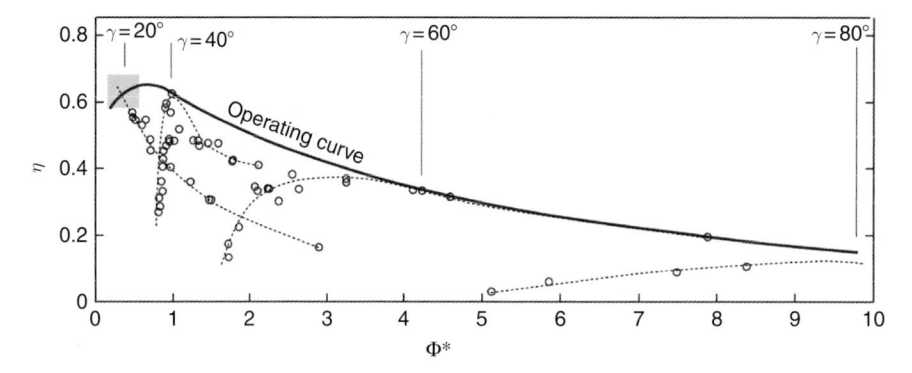

Figure 33 Operating efficiency curve of the Denniss-Auld turbine corresponding to the model test results of **Figure 29** [89].

The 1.6 m diameter turbine used in the sea tests of the bottom-standing OWC plant off Port Kembla, Australia, can be seen in **Figure 34**. The rotor has 21 variable-pitch blades, whose control mechanism appears in the figure.

8.05.8.2 Radial-Flow Self-Rectifying Impulse Turbine

Apart from the more common axial-flow configuration, studies have also been made on radial-flow self-rectifying impulse turbines (**Figure 35**). It should be noted that the turbine is no longer insensitive to the flow direction: the flow through the rotor blades and guide vanes is radially centrifugal or centripetal depending on the wave cycle. The turbine is connected to the OWC chamber by an axial duct, whereas the exit to, or admission from, the atmosphere is radial.

Early model testing on the radial impulse turbine was done in the early 1990s by McCormick *et al.* [92, 93], which was not conclusive. Detailed experiments were later performed by Takao *et al.* [94] on a turbine with rotor diameter 0.509 m, 51 rotor blades, and blade height 43 mm. The measured efficiency is plotted in **Figure 36** versus flow coefficient Φ^* for several values of the setting angle θ_o (angle between the straight part of the guide vane and the circumferential direction) of the outer guide vanes. Here, $\Phi^* = V_r /(\Omega R)$, where R is the mean radius of the rotor (defined at mid-chord point of the blades) and V_r is the mean radial component of the flow velocity at radial coordinate R (in the absence of blades). As expected, the performance is not identical for the exhalation and inhalation flow directions. Takao *et al.* [95] later used the same rig to investigate the effect

Figure 34 Full-sized Denniss-Auld turbine that equipped the bottom-standing OWC tested off Port Kembla, Australia.

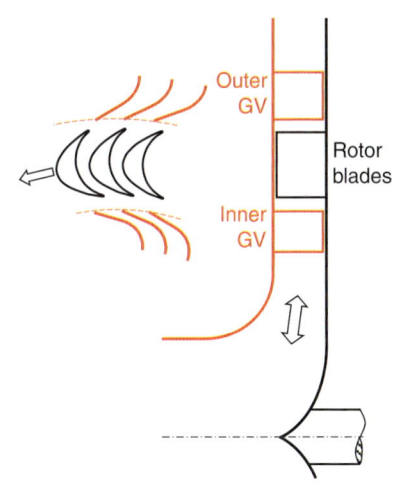

Figure 35 Schematic representation of the radial self-rectifying impulse turbine. The axial duct connects the turbine to the OWC air chamber.

of pitch-controlled (inner and outer) guide vanes and found an increase up to about 15% in the efficiency in comparison with fixed guide vanes.

The radial turbine was investigated by numerical simulation in References 96–99. With the available (experimental and numerical) information, the radial configuration of the impulse turbine appears as an alternative to the axial one, although not necessarily a better choice.

8.05.8.3 Twin Unidirectional Impulse Turbine Topology

Single-stage conventional turbines, like steam and gas turbines, with a row of guide vanes followed by a bladed rotor, are known to attain high efficiencies in unidirectional flow. In such turbines, if the sign of the pressure head is changed (and the rotational speed is kept unaltered), the flow rate (apart from changing sign) becomes much smaller (and the turbine performance becomes very poor). This has led to the idea of associating two identical 'conventional' air turbines (turbines T1 and T2) in parallel to convert the pneumatic energy from an OWC, such that, for a given pressure head situation, the flow sequence guide vanes–rotor blades in turbine T1 is reversed with respect to turbine T2 (see References 100–102). This topology is shown in **Figure 37**. With this arrangement, for a given pressure head (independently of its sign), most of the flow is admitted to one of the turbines (that is

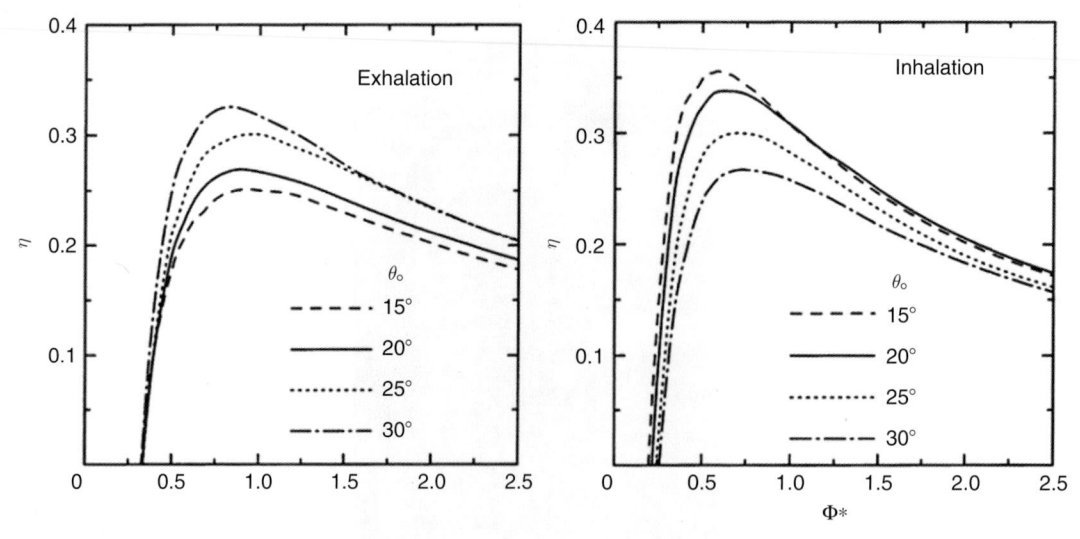

Figure 36 Efficiency η vs. flow coefficient Φ^* for a radial impulse turbine and several values of setting angle of the outer guide vanes [94].

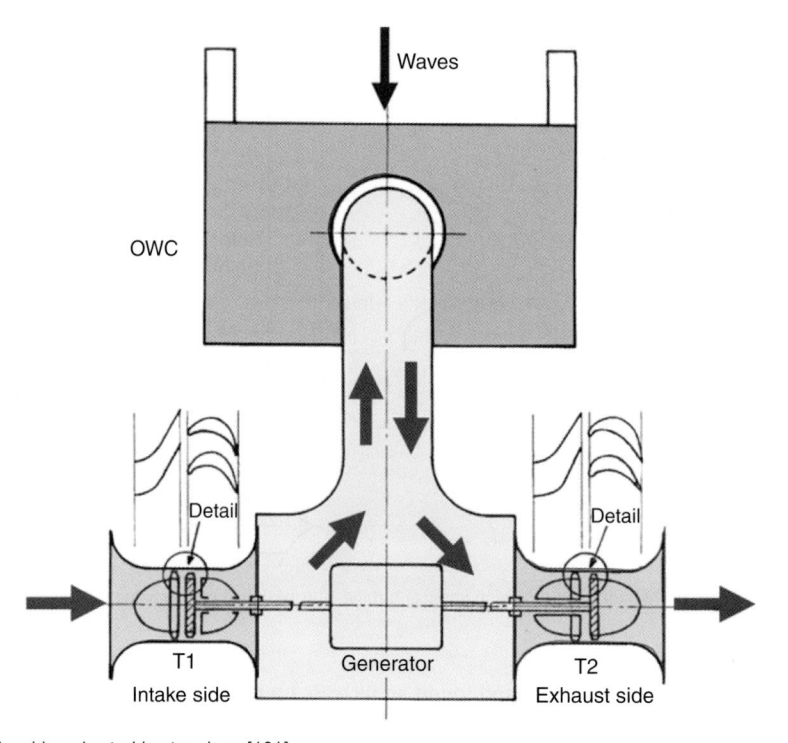

Figure 37 Twin unidirectional impulse turbine topology [101].

driven with good efficiency), while only a small fraction of the flow is admitted to the other turbine (that is in choking mode and operates at very low efficiency). The two turbines can be coupled to a common electrical generator (as in **Figure 37**) or, alternately, each turbine is coupled to its own generator. Since the turbines are not symmetrical, their rotor blades need no longer to be symmetrical with respect to the mid-chord point, as appears to be the case in **Figure 37**. Some positive degree of reaction may be convenient.

Model testing of a unidirectional turbine pair in a rig capable of bidirectional oscillating air flow is reported in Reference 101. The turbine rotor diameter was 165 mm and each turbine was coupled to its own generator. A peak efficiency of 0.6 was measured.

This is a promising new turbine configuration, although the eventual improvement in aerodynamic performance is achieved at the cost of turbine (and possibly generator) duplication.

8.05.9 Some Air Turbine Prototypes

Apart from navigation buoys, several full-sized OWC prototypes have been deployed into the sea; in some cases, large models at scales about one-third to one-fourth have been tested in sheltered waters. The first large prototype was Kaimei, already mentioned in Section 8.05.1, in whose 13 open-bottom chambers different types of turbines were tested (including unidirectional, Wells, and self-rectifying impulse turbines). An OWC plant was installed in 1985 on the shoreline at Toftestallen, near Bergen, Norway. It was equipped with a Wells turbine rated 500 kW, about whose characteristics and performance little seems to have been published. The plant was destroyed by wave action in 1988. Most of the other prototypes were equipped with Wells turbines, some of which are listed in **Table 2**, together with their main characteristics. The largest air turbines built so far were the 2 × 500 kW contra-rotating Wells turbines that equipped the bottom-standing OSPREY prototype (**Figure 38**). They never operated: the plant structure was damaged by the waves during deployment in Scotland in 1995 and was later destroyed.

A pair of 30 kW Wells turbines, coupled to a common horizontal axis electrical generator, equipped the OWC plant integrated in 1989 into a breakwater at Sakata Port, Japan [103] (**Figure 39**). The rotor of a Wells turbine is known to be subject to a large axial load. The arrangement of the Sakata tandem turbines was such that the air flowed through the turbines in opposite directions, which allowed the axial loads on the rotors to cancel each other.

The Mighty Whale was the first large floating OWC since Kaimei. It started operation in 1998 in Japan. The plant had three OWC chambers, each equipped with a pair of monoplane Wells turbines mounted on the same shaft, with opposing air flows [104].

The Pico plant, Azores, Portugal, completed in 1999, is equipped with a 400 kW monoplane Wells turbine with guide vanes (**Figure 40**) [58]. A second 400 kW Wells turbine was built to be side-by-side with the first one, but was never installed: it is a variable-pitch machine whose sophisticated control mechanism was driven by eddy currents (**Figure 41**) [105, 106].

A 2 × 250 kW contra-rotating turbine was installed in the LIMPET plant in 2000 [59, 60]; some years later, one of the rotors was removed and the turbine was left as a monoplane without guide vanes. Results of monitored performance can be found in Reference 60. For a comparison of the turbine performance with theoretical and model test predictions, see Reference 107.

The Indian bottom-standing OWC plant, commissioned in 1991, was operated with several types of air turbines [108]. The first power module was a vertical-axis 2 m diameter monoplane Wells turbine without guide vanes [109]. This was dismantled after 2 years of operation and subsequently replaced by a thrust-opposing twin 1 m diameter pair of Wells turbines with a common 55 kW generator. These were in turn replaced by a 1 m diameter impulse turbine with movable linked guide vanes, followed by an impulse

Table 2 Characteristics of Wells turbines of some OWC prototypes

Plant	Year	Type	D (m)	h	Z	c (m)	σ	P_t (kW)
Sakata, Japan [103]	1989	MP, GV	1.337	0.75	16	0.1625	0.71	30
Vizhijam, India [109]	1991	MP	2.0	0.6	8	0.380	0.611	150
Islay, UK [60]	1991	BP	1.2	0.62	4 + 4	0.4	0.54	75
OSPREY, UK	1995	CR	3.5					2 × 500
Mighty Whale, Japan [104]	1998	MP, GV	1.7	0.706	8			30
Pico, Portugal [58]	1999	MP, GV	2.3	0.598	8	0.375	0.53	400
LIMPET, UK [59]	2000	CR	2.6	0.62	7 + 7	0.329	2 × 0.34	2 × 250
Pico, Portugal [105, 106]	2001	VP	1.7	0.71	15	0.2	0.66	400
Mutriku, Spain [61]	2009	BP	0.75	0.427	5 + 5		0.50	18.5

MP, monoplane; BP, biplane; CR, contra-rotating; GV, with guide vanes; VP, variable-pitch.

Figure 38 The 2 × 500 kW contra-rotating Wells turbine of OSPREY.

Figure 39 Tandem turbine set of the OWC plant of Sakata Port, Japan.

Figure 40 The 400 kW Wells turbine of Pico plant, Portugal: mono-plane with guide vanes.

Figure 41 The 400 kW variable-pitch Wells turbine built for installation at the Pico plant. The control mechanism is driven by eddy currents.

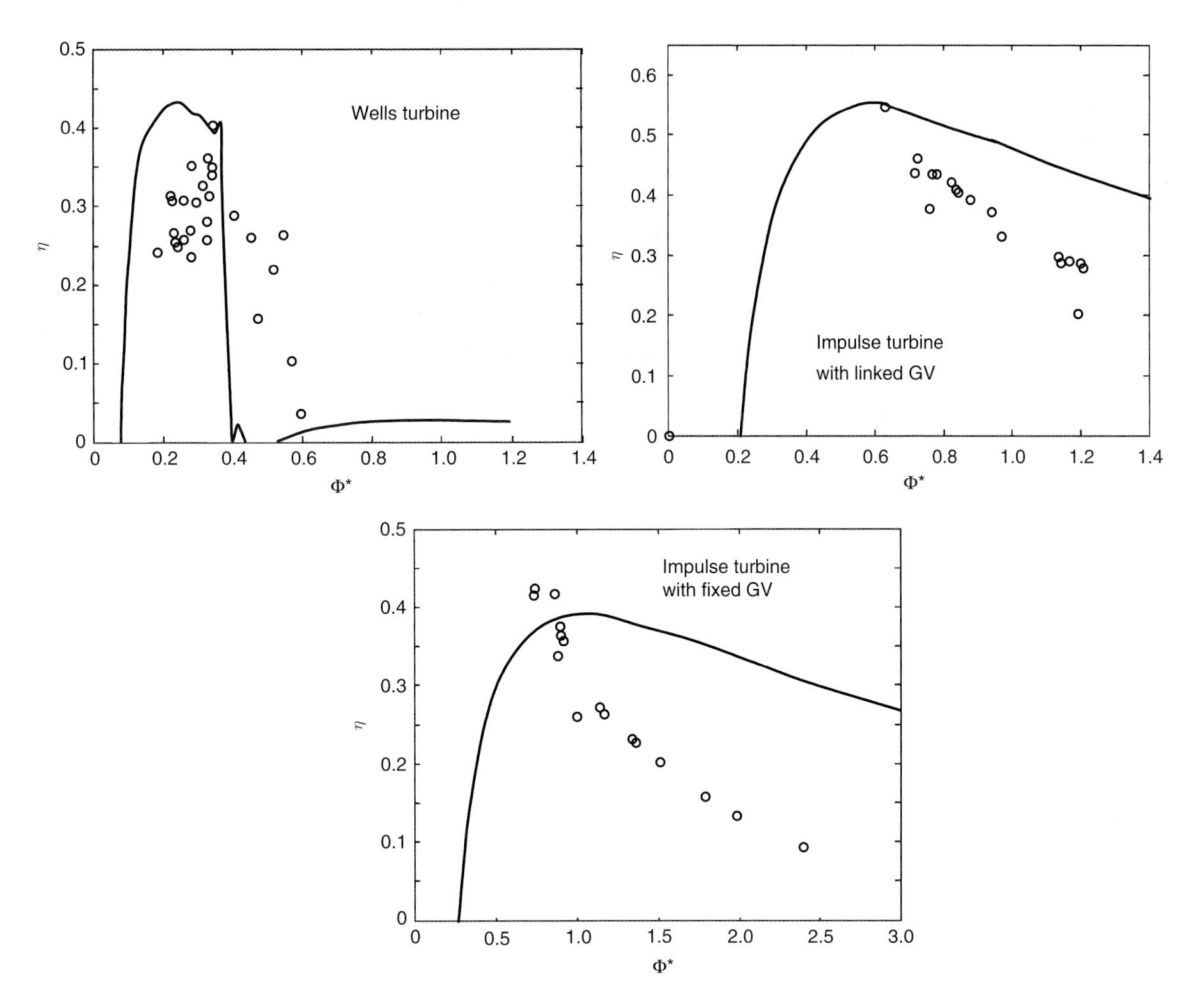

Figure 42 Efficiency of three air turbines that successively equipped the Indian OWC plant: Wells turbine (top left), impulse turbine with linked pitching guide vanes (top right), and impulse turbine with fixed guide vanes (below). Curves: results from model testing in steady flow; symbols: site measurements at cycle peak. From Mala K, Badrinath SN, Chidanand S, et al. (2009) Analysis of power modules in the Indian wave energy plant. In: *Proceedings of Annual IEEE India Conference (INDICON)*, pp. 95–98 [108].

turbine with the same rotor and fixed guide vanes. Results from site measurements of efficiency are shown in **Figure 42** for the twin Wells turbine configuration and for the impulse turbines with movable and fixed guide vanes, together with results from model testing in steady flow [108]. The best efficiency was attained by the impulse turbine with movable guide vanes.

The recently completed Mutriku plant was constructed in northern Spain, integrated into a breakwater, and comprises 16 OWC chambers, each equipped with a 0.75 m diameter vertical axis Wells turbine of monoplane type without guide vanes, rated 18.5 kW [61, 110].

The Denniss-Auld turbine equipped the several OWC prototypes Mk1 (bottom-standing) to Mk3 (floating), developed by the Australian company Oceanlinx (formerly Energetech). The last prototype Mk 3 (one-third scale), briefly tested in 2010, also incorporated a HydroAir impulse turbine.

8.05.10 Turbine Integration into OWC Plant

8.05.10.1 Hydrodynamics of OWC

We briefly present here the hydrodynamics of a fixed-structure single-OWC plant based on linear water wave theory. For more complex situations, namely, multi-OWC plants and floating-structure OWCs, see References 111 and 112.

We consider an OWC subject to an incident wave field, schematically represented in **Figure 43**. The motion of the water free surface inside the chamber, due to the incident wave action, displaces a volume flow rate of air $q(t)$ and produces an oscillating air pressure $p_a + p(t)$ where p_a is the atmospheric pressure. Following Evans [113], we write $q(t) = q_d(t) + q_r(t)$, where q_d is the diffraction flow rate due to the incident waves if the internal pressure is kept constant and equal to p_a, and $q_r(t)$ is the radiation flow rate due to the oscillating air pressure in the absence of incident waves. The mass flow rate of air leaving the chamber through the turbine is $\dot{m} = -d(\rho V)/dt$, where ρ and V are air density and air volume inside the chamber, respectively. We assume that the relative

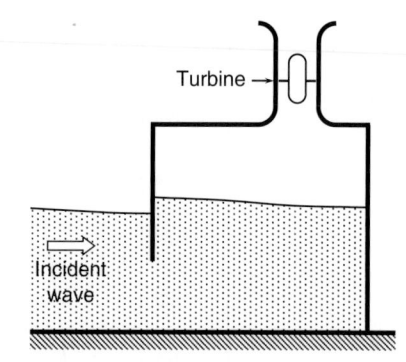

Figure 43 Schematic representation of OWC.

variations in ρ and V are small (which is consistent with the linear water wave theory we are using), and, in addition, that ρ is related to the pressure $p + p_a$ through the linearized isentropic relationship (the adequacy of these assumptions is discussed in detail in Reference 114). Taking into account that $dV/dt = -q$, we easily find

$$\dot{m} = \rho_a q - \frac{V_0}{c_a^2} \frac{dp}{dt} \qquad [45]$$

Here ρ_a and c_a are, respectively, air density and speed of sound in atmospheric conditions and V_0 is the undisturbed value of V.

In order to relate $\dot{m}$ to p, we introduce the turbine characteristic curves. Applying dimensional analysis to incompressible flow turbomachinery (see Section 8.05.5.1) and taking the dimensionless pressure coefficient Ψ (rather than the flow coefficient Φ) as the independent variable, we may write

$$\Pi = f_P(\Psi) \qquad [46a]$$
$$\Phi = f_Q(\Psi) \qquad [46b]$$

where

$$\Psi = \frac{p}{\rho_a \Omega^2 D^2} \qquad [47a]$$

$$\Phi = \frac{\dot{m}}{\rho_a \Omega D^3} \qquad [47b]$$

$$\Pi = \frac{P_t}{\rho_a \Omega^3 D^5} \qquad [47c]$$

Here, Π is dimensionless turbine power output, Ω is rotational speed (radians per unit time), P_t is turbine power output, and D is turbine rotor diameter. Equation [46b] together with eqns [47a] and [47b] relate $\dot{m}$ to p for given turbine and rotational speed Ω.

8.05.10.2 Linear Turbine

It has been found for the Wells turbine (with or without guide vanes) that eqn [46b] is approximately linear (see Sections 8.05.3.1 and 8.05.6), that is, takes the form $\Phi = K\Psi$, K being a proportionality constant depending on turbine geometry but not on Ω, ρ_a, or D. Therefore, we may write approximately, for a Wells turbine of given geometry,

$$\dot{m} = \frac{KDp}{\Omega} \qquad [48]$$

This means that, for a given turbine and constant rotational speed, a linear relationship holds between mass flow rate and pressure fluctuation.

Let us consider a regular incident wave, whose elevation at a given point is $e^{i\omega t}$ (i.e., of unit amplitude). Within the framework of linear water wave theory, the diffraction volume flow rate displaced by the water free surface inside the chamber may be written as $q_d = \Gamma(\omega) e^{i\omega t}$. The complex function $\Gamma(\omega)$ is the frequency response of the linear system (or excitation-volume-flow coefficient) and is assumed known (from theoretical or numerical modeling, or from experiments).

If eqns [45] and [48] are considered as acceptable approximations, then the whole system is linear, and we may write

$$\{p, \dot{m}, q, q_r\} = \{P, \dot{M}, Q, Q_r\} e^{i\omega t} \qquad [49]$$

where P, $\dot{M}$, Q, and Q_r are complex amplitudes. Following Evans [113], we write $Q_r = -(B + iC)P$, where B and C are real, and B is nonnegative. We may call $B + iC$ the radiation admittance, B the radiation conductance, and C the radiation susceptance [112].

These hydrodynamic coefficients are assumed known as functions of the frequency ω for the chamber geometry, from theoretical or numerical modeling or from experiments. From eqns [45] and [47b], it follows that $P = \Gamma\Lambda$, where

$$\Lambda = \left[\left(\frac{KD}{\rho_a \Omega} + B\right) + i\left(\frac{\omega V_0}{\gamma p_a} + C\right)\right]^{-1} \quad [50]$$

and $\gamma = c_p/c_v$ is the specific heat ratio for air. The complex quantity Λ is the frequency response on what concerns pressure (as output) and diffraction flow rate (as input), whereas the product $\Gamma\Lambda$ is the frequency response for the linear system whose input is the incident wave elevation and output is the air pressure.

We assume that the local wave climate may be represented by a set of sea states, each being a stationary stochastic ergodic process. For a given sea state, the probability density function $f(\zeta)$ of the surface elevation ζ at a given observation point will be supposed Gaussian, an assumption widely adopted in ocean engineering applications, and so we write

$$f(\zeta) = \frac{1}{\sqrt{2\pi}\sigma_\zeta} \exp\left(-\frac{\zeta^2}{2\sigma_\zeta^2}\right) \quad [51]$$

where σ_ζ^2 is the variance of ζ and σ_ζ is the standard deviation (or root mean square) of ζ. We assume that the wave climate as described by eqn [51] is not affected by the presence of the plant or, at least, is not significantly influenced by the radiated wave field due to the air pressure oscillation inside the plant's chamber.

Let $S_\zeta(\omega)$ be the density of the incident wave power spectrum (Pierson–Moskowitz or other). Since the air turbine is linear, the air pressure p inside the chamber is a random variable of zero mean whose probability density function is Gaussian with variance (see Reference 115)

$$\sigma_p^2 = \int_{-\infty}^{\infty} S_{q_d}(\omega)|\Lambda(\omega)|^2 d\omega \quad [52]$$

where

$$S_{q_d}(\omega) = \int_0^{2\pi} S_\zeta(\omega,\theta)|\Gamma(\omega,\theta)|^2 d\theta \quad [53]$$

and $S_{q_d}(\omega)$ is a spectral density for the diffraction flow rate q_d that depends on the sea state and on the chamber geometry (but not on the turbine). On the other hand, $\Lambda(\omega)$ depends on the chamber geometry and the turbine (including the turbine rotational speed Ω) but not on the sea state.

We note that, since the system is linear and the free-surface elevation ζ was assumed a Gaussian random process, then both q_d and p are also Gaussian processes.

The instantaneous power output of the turbine is (see eqn [46a])

$$P_t(t) = \rho_a \Omega^3 D^5 f_P\left(\frac{p(t)}{\rho_a \Omega^2 D^2}\right) \quad [54]$$

Taking into account that $p(t)$ has a Gaussian probability density distribution and variance σ_p^2 (given by eqn [52]), we have, for the averaged value of the turbine power output,

$$\bar{P}_t = \frac{\rho_a \Omega^3 D^5}{\sqrt{2\pi}\sigma_p} \int_{-\infty}^{\infty} \exp\left(\frac{-p^2}{2\sigma_p^2}\right) f_P\left(\frac{p}{\rho_a \Omega^2 D^2}\right) dp \quad [55]$$

This can be written in dimensionless form as

$$\bar{\Pi} = \frac{1}{\sqrt{2\pi}\sigma_\Psi} \int_{-\infty}^{\infty} \exp\left(-\frac{\Psi^2}{2\sigma_\Psi^2}\right) f_P(\Psi) d\Psi \quad [56]$$

where $\bar{\Pi}$ is the averaged value of Π (or, equivalently, the dimensionless value of $\bar{P}_t$) and

$$\sigma_\Psi = \frac{\sigma_p}{\rho_a \Omega^2 D^2} \quad [57]$$

If the chamber geometry, the turbine, and its rotational speed are fixed, then eqn [55] (or [56]), together with eqn [52], gives the average power output as a functional of the diffraction flow rate spectral density $S_{q_d}(\omega)$, which characterizes the sea state under consideration.

The instantaneous (pneumatic) power available to the turbine is

$$P_{\text{avai}} = \frac{\dot{m}}{\rho_a} p \quad [58]$$

and the instantaneous turbine efficiency is

$$\eta = \frac{P_t}{P_{avai}} = \frac{\Pi}{\Phi\Psi} \qquad [59]$$

If $\Phi = K\Psi$, where K is constant, then it is $\eta = \Pi K^{-1}\Psi^{-2}$. The averaged available power is given by

$$\bar{P}_{avai} = \int_{-\infty}^{\infty} P_{avai} f(p) dp = \frac{1}{\rho_a \sqrt{2\pi}\sigma_p} \int_{-\infty}^{\infty} \dot{m} \exp\left(-\frac{p^2}{2\sigma_p^2}\right) p\, dp \qquad [60]$$

or, in dimensionless form,

$$\bar{\Pi}_{avai} = \frac{\bar{P}_{avai}}{\rho_a \Omega^3 D^5} = \frac{1}{\sqrt{2\pi}\sigma_p} \int_{-\infty}^{\infty} f_Q(\Psi) \exp\left(-\frac{\Psi^2}{2\sigma_\Psi^2}\right) \Psi d\Psi \qquad [61]$$

The average efficiency of the turbine is defined as $\bar{\eta} = \bar{P}_t/\bar{P}_{avai} = \bar{\Pi}/\bar{\Pi}_{avai}$. If $\Phi = K\Psi$, it is simply (see Reference 115)

$$\bar{\eta} = \frac{\bar{\Pi}}{K\sigma_\Psi^2} \qquad [62]$$

For given turbine geometry, and if the function f_p is known (possibly from model testing), then eqn [56] represents, in dimensionless form, the turbine average power output as a function of the root mean square of the pressure oscillation. The curve represented by this equation is likely to be more useful, in applications with real random waves, than the more conventional curve given by eqn [46a] for the instantaneous power output. The same can be said about the equations for the efficiency. We recall that the results derived above are valid only for linear turbines.

Figure 44 shows typical curves of dimensionless power output and efficiency versus dimensionless pressure head for a Wells turbine: instantaneous power Π and efficiency η versus instantaneous pressure head Ψ, and time-averaged power $\bar{\Pi}$ and efficiency $\bar{\eta}$ versus standard deviation (or root mean square) of pressure oscillation σ_Ψ (in irregular waves). As should be expected, the curves of

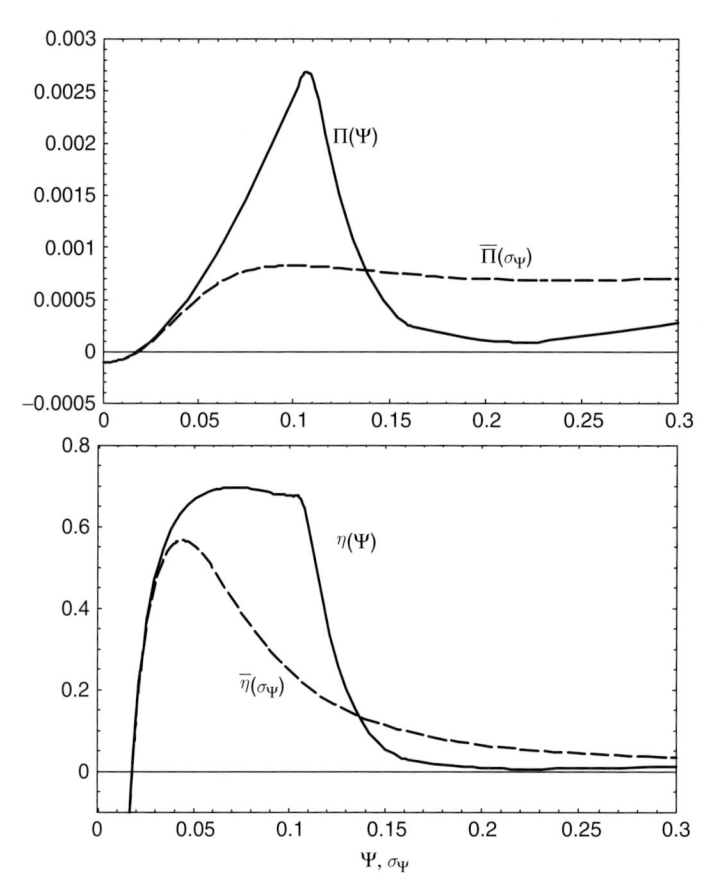

Figure 44 Dimensionless representation of instantaneous and time-averaged values of Wells turbine power output and efficiency vs. pressure head [115].

time-averaged values are smoother and their peaks are lower as compared with the curves for instantaneous values. In particular, the maximum averaged efficiency is about 0.8 times the peak of $\eta(\Psi)$ and occurs for $\sigma_\Psi \cong 0.045$.

This modeling method can be used to optimize the turbine (i.e., choose its geometry and rotational speed) for a given OWC plant located at a site whose wave climate is characterized by a set of representative sea states, each being represented by its spectral density and frequency of occurrence. For simplicity, we consider here a single sea state (for the more realistic situation of a wave climate consisting of several sea states, see Reference 115) and assume that the rotational speed Ω remains constant.

It is assumed that the hydrodynamic coefficients $\Gamma(\omega)$ (excitation-volume-flow coefficient), $B(\omega)$ (radiation conductance), and $C(\omega)$ (radiation susceptance) are known, as well as V_0 (chamber volume above the undisturbed water free surface), and the atmospheric conditions ρ_a (density), and p_a (pressure). The optimization is to be made for a given Wells turbine shape whose function $f_P(\Psi)$ and factor K are known (possibly from aerodynamic model testing). For aerodynamic reasons (especially to avoid shock waves), the rotor blade tip speed $\Omega D/2$ should be bounded, and so we introduce the constraint $\Omega D \leq 2M_{\max} c_a$, where $M_{\max}$ is a Mach number (normally about 0.4–0.5). The pressure standard deviation σ_p for the considered sea state can be calculated from eqns [52] and [53], which in turn allows us to obtain $\bar{P}_t$, for given D and Ω, from eqn [55] (or $\bar{\Pi}$ from eqn [56]). It should be pointed out that the maximization of the produced energy is not necessarily the most appropriate criterion: the maximization of profit (leading to a smaller turbine) could be adopted instead, as done in Reference 116.

The rotational speed control of the turbine is an important issue, since it affects the amount of energy produced and the quality of the electrical energy. The problem to be solved is to find, for a given OWC and a given turbine, the optimal relationship, for each sea state, between the electromagnetic torque of the generator T_e (or the corresponding power $P_e = T_e \Omega$) and the rotational speed Ω. The moment of inertia of the rotating parts is supposed large, so that the variations in Ω are relatively small in a given sea state. We assume that the same applies to P_e, which allows us to write $P_e = \bar{P}_t$, where the bearing friction loss is neglected. Let us consider a given sea state. From the definitions (eqs [56] and [57]), we easily obtain

$$\frac{1}{D^3 \sigma_p} \frac{d\bar{P}_t}{d\Omega} = \frac{3\bar{\Pi}}{\sigma_\Psi} + \left(\frac{\Omega}{\sigma_p} \frac{d\sigma_p}{d\Omega} - 2 \right) \frac{d\bar{\Pi}}{d\sigma_\Psi} \quad [63]$$

The condition for maximum turbine power output implies $d\bar{P}_t/d\Omega = 0$, and so, from eqn [54], it follows that

$$\frac{\sigma_\Psi}{\bar{\Pi}} \frac{d\bar{\Pi}}{d\sigma_\Psi} = \frac{3}{2 - \frac{\Omega}{\sigma_p} \frac{d\sigma_p}{dN}} \quad [64]$$

For a given turbine, the left-hand side of eqn [64] can be regarded as a known function of σ_Ψ which is denoted by $\theta(\sigma_\Psi)$. We recall that, for a given sea state (characterized by its spectral distribution), eqns [52] and [53] give σ_p, and hence the right-hand side of eqn [64] as functions of Ω. It now becomes clear that eqn [64] yields the value of Ω that maximizes the averaged turbine power output $\bar{P}_t$. The optimal control strategy to be implemented in the programmable logic controller (PLC) of the plant consists essentially in setting $P_e = \bar{P}_t$, $\bar{P}_t$ being related to Ω through eqn [64].

If the effect of varying rotational speed upon the hydrodynamic process of wave energy absorption is neglected, then $d\sigma_p/d\Omega = 0$ and eqn [64] reduces to $\theta(\sigma_\Psi) = 3/2$. We denote the solution of this equation by σ_Ψ^* and the corresponding value of $\bar{\Pi}$ by $\bar{\Pi}^*$. We find

$$\bar{P}_t = \rho_a D^5 \Omega^3 \bar{\Pi}^* \quad [65]$$

We note that $\bar{\Pi}^*$ is a characteristic of the turbine that does not depend on rotational speed or on sea state. If the electric power P_e is equated to $\bar{P}_t$, then eqn [65] yields the control strategy for the electrical generator.

If the effect of varying rotational speed upon the wave energy absorption is to be considered (it affects the turbine-produced damping), then the term $(\Omega/\sigma_p)d\sigma_p/d\Omega$ cannot be neglected in eqn [64]. Since the air pressure standard deviation σ_p depends on Ω and also on the spectral distribution that characterizes the sea state under consideration, the relationship (to be implemented in the plant's PLC) between P_e and Ω is expected to become more complicated. However, it was found in Reference 117 that this may be replaced with good approximation by a simple relationship between the average power output $\bar{P}_t$ and the rotational speed Ω, regardless of the wave climate. Naturally, the constraints due to maximum allowable Mach number should be taken into consideration.

This stochastic method was employed in the optimization and specification of the Wells turbine to equip the OWC to be integrated into a breakwater in northern Portugal [118].

8.05.10.3 Nonlinear Turbine

If the turbine's pressure-flow characteristic cannot be considered as linear, which is the case in general of self-rectifying turbines except for Wells turbines, then the whole system is no longer linear. In particular, the air pressure in the chamber is not a simple harmonic function of time even in regular incident waves, and may not be regarded as a Gaussian process. Then a time-domain analysis is to be employed, rather than a frequency analysis, and the resulting integro-differential equation that governs the hydrodynamics of the OWC plant has to be numerically integrated.

The radiation flow rate becomes (see References 112 and 114)

$$q_r(t) = \int_{-\infty}^{t} g_r(t-\tau)p(\tau)d\tau \qquad [66]$$

where

$$g_r(t) = \frac{2}{\pi}\int_{0}^{\infty} B(\omega)\cos \omega t \, d\omega \qquad [67]$$

and $B(\omega)$ is the frequency-dependent radiance conductance as defined in Section 8.05.10.2. The convolution integral in eqn [66] represents the well-known memory effect on the radiation flow rate. Taking into account that $q = q_d + q_r$, eqn [45], together with eqns [46b], [47b], and [66], yields

$$\frac{V_0}{\rho_a c_a^2}\frac{dp}{dt} - \int_{-\infty}^{t} g_r(t-\tau)p(\tau)\,d\tau + \Omega D^3 f_Q\left(\frac{p(t)}{\rho_a \Omega^2 D^2}\right) = q_d(t) \qquad [68]$$

Here, the diffraction flow rate $q_d(t)$ is supposed known from the spectral power density of the sea state under consideration and from the excitation-volume-flow coefficient $\Gamma(\omega)$ of the OWC structure geometry. For fixed Ω and D, the integro-differential equation [66] is to be numerically integrated for $p(t)$, from given initial conditions. The instantaneous turbine power output $P_t(t)$ is then obtained from eqn [47c].

A comparison of the annual averaged performances of Wells and impulse turbines can be found in Reference 119, for several turbine diameters. The simulations, based on the method outlined above, were made for the numerically computed hydrodynamic coefficients of the bottom-standing OWC plant installed on the island of Pico, Azores, Portugal, and for two wave climates (15 and 30 kW m^{-1}) each characterized by 44 sea states. The rotational speed was optimized for each turbine diameter and each sea state. The Wells turbine was found to provide higher annual averaged power output, but, as expected, this requires larger diameter than the impulse turbine.

8.05.10.4 Valve-Controlled Air Flow

It is known that the Wells turbine is characterized by a sharp drop in efficiency and power output whenever the flow rate exceeds the critical stall-free limit. To prevent this from happening, the use of a flow-limiting valve (or set of valves) has been proposed. Two possibilities have been considered: a valve in series with the turbine and a relief valve in parallel. From the hydrodynamic point of view, the effect of partially closing the valve in series is an increase in the power takeoff damping, whereas the effect of opening the relief valves produces a decrease in damping. A detailed analysis in the time domain of the hydrodynamics of an OWC equipped with a valve in series or a relief valve can be found in Reference 114; for an application of the stochastic method, see Reference 115. The details of the control of a relief valve and its effect on the plant performance were examined in Reference 120.

8.05.10.5 Noise

All turbines operating with air or other gas produce noise. This can be a nuisance if the machine is located near an inhabited area and is not properly shielded, as is the case of many wind turbines. Noise can also be a problem with air turbines for wave energy conversion, especially in shoreline or nearshore applications. Produced noise level increases with machine size and especially with flow and rotor blade speed. This means that it may affect particularly Wells turbines, especially in stalled flow conditions. A noise attenuation chamber had to be retrofitted onto the end of the Wells turbine ducting of the LIMPET shoreline plant (Islay island, Scotland) to reduce the transmitted noise [121].

Takao et al. [122] carried a model testing investigation on several self-rectifying air turbines (0.3 m diameter Wells and impulse turbines in the test rig shown in **Figure 16**). They concluded that the Wells turbine produces more noise at exhalation than at inhalation (especially under stalled flow conditions), whereas the difference is much less marked in the case of impulse turbines. In any case, impulse turbines were found to be superior to Wells turbines on what concerns noise characteristics. It was also found that, at best efficiency points, the sound power output is approximately proportional to the product ΩP_t^2, the constant of proportionality being smaller for impulse turbines than for Wells turbines.

8.05.11 Conclusions

Self-rectifying air turbines, especially those of constant geometry, are among the simplest and most reliable types of power takeoff for wave energy conversion (together with hydraulic turbines). Several prototypes have operated and survived under real sea conditions for long periods of time, in some cases exceeding thousands, or even tens of thousands, of hours.

Compared with conventional turbines that operate in unidirectional and more or less steady flow, the time-averaged efficiency of self-rectifying air turbines in bidirectional random flow is relatively modest, hardly exceeding about 50–60% (significantly lower values have been measured in some OWC prototypes). Especially, Wells turbines (due to their large rotor diameter and high rotational speed) can store and release a large amount of kinetic energy by flywheel effect. In this way, they can reduce the power peaks to which the generator and power electronics are subject and provide an important smoothing effect to the electrical energy supplied to the grid. The rotational speed should be controlled to match the level of energy in the waves and ensure that the turbine converts the maximum power. Due to rotational inertia, that control can hardly be made on a timescale smaller than a few wave periods, which makes it difficult to achieve any kind of phase control of the wave energy converter, except if the pitch of the turbine rotor blades can be controlled.

Several types of self-rectifying air turbines have been proposed, studied, and in some cases constructed to equip prototype OWCs. Almost all are axial-flow machines. The Wells turbine concept (with several variants) has been the most frequently chosen for prototypes. Its main drawback lies in the sharp efficiency drop when the flow rate exceeds the stall-free limit. The impulse turbine exhibits a smoother efficiency curve, whose peak, however, hardly exceeds about 50%, unless variable geometry (with its higher mechanical complexity and lesser reliability) is used, which so far has limited its application. Recent conceptions, like the HydroAir turbine and the twin unidirectional impulse turbine topology, need to be tested at large scale.

Air turbines capable of operating with high efficiency over a wide range of random flow conditions, including direction reversal, could possibly require variable geometry and control. This may deter or delay their application in a technological field in which maintenance is difficult and expensive, and reliability is essential.

More than other types of power takeoff, air turbines (especially Wells turbines) produce noise. This may introduce constraints in applications close to inhabited areas.

References

[1] Masuda Y (1986) An experience of wave power generator through tests and improvement. In: Evans DV and Falcão AFdeO (eds.) *Hydrodynamics of Ocean Wave Energy Utilization*, pp. 445–452. Berlin, Germany: Springer.
[2] Masuda Y and McCormick ME (1987) Experiences in pneumatic wave energy conversion in Japan. In: McCormick ME and Kim YC (eds.) *Utilization of Ocean Waves – Wave to Energy Conversion*, pp. 1–33. New York: ASCE.
[3] Hotta H, Miyazaki T, and Ishii SI (1988) On the performance of the wave power device Kaimei: The results on the open sea tests. In: *Proceedings of the 7th International Conference on Offshore Mechanical and Arctic Engineering, New York*, pp. 91–96. New York: American Society of Mechanical Engineers.
[4] Wells AA (1976) Fluid Driven Rotary Transducer. Br. Patent 1,595,700.
[5] Babintsev IA (1975) Apparatus for Converting Sea Wave Energy into Electrical Energy. US Patent 3,922,739 (2 December 1975).
[6] Harris FR (1984) The Parsons centenary – A hundred years of steam turbines. *Proceedings of the Institution of Mechanical Engineers, Part A: Journal of Power and Energy* 198: 183–224.
[7] McCormick ME (1979) Ocean wave energy concepts. In: *Proceedings of MTS-IEEE Oceans 79 Conference*, pp. 553–557. San Diego, CA.
[8] McCormick ME (1981) *Ocean Wave Energy Conversion*. New York: Wiley.
[9] Raghunathan S (1995) The Wells turbine for wave energy conversion. *Progress in Aerospace Sciences* 31: 335–386.
[10] Setoguchi T, Santhakumar S, Maeda H, et al. (2001) A review of impulse turbines for wave energy conversion. *Renewable Energy* 23: 261–292.
[11] Setoguchi T and Takao M (2006) Current status of self rectifying air turbines for wave energy conversion. *Energy Conversion and Management* 47: 2382–2396.
[12] Curran R and Folley M (2008) Air turbine design for OWCs. In: Cruz J (ed.) *Ocean Wave Energy*, pp. 189–219. Berlin, Germany: Springer.
[13] Vavra MH (1960) *Aero-Thermodynamics and Flow in Turbomachines*. New York: Wiley.
[14] Lakshminarayana B (1996) *Fluid Dynamics and Heat Transfer of Turbomachinery*. New York: Wiley.
[15] Sturge DP (1977) Turbine for an oscillating water column wave power system. CEGB Report No. MM/MECH/TA 41. UK: CEGB.
[16] Grant RJ, Johnson CG, and Sturge DP (1981) Performance of a Wells turbine for use in a wave energy system. Future energy concepts. IEE Conference Publication No. 192. London: IEEE.
[17] Raghunathan S, Tan CP, and Wells NAJ (1982) Theory and performance of a Wells turbine. *Journal of Energy* 6: 157–160.
[18] von Kármán T and Burgers JM (1934) General aerodynamic theory – Perfect fluids. In: Durand WF (ed.) *Aerodynamic Theory*, vol. 2. Berlin, Germany: Springer.
[19] Weinig FS (1964) Theory of two-dimensional flow through cascades. In: Hawthorne WR (ed.) *Aerodynamics of Turbines and Compressors*. London, UK: Oxford University Press.
[20] Scholz N (1977) Aerodynamics of cascades. AGARD-AG-220. Neuilly-sur-Seine, France: AGARD.
[21] Gato LMC and Falcão AFdeO (1984) On the theory of the Wells turbine. *Journal of Engineering for Gas Turbines and Power–Transactions of the American Society of Mechanical Engineers* 106: 628–633.
[22] Gato LMC and Falcão AFdeO (1990) Performance of the Wells turbine with double row of guide vanes. *Japan Society of Mechanical Engineers International Journal, Series II* 33: 265–271.
[23] Arlitt R, Banzhaf H-U, Startzmann R, and Biskup F (2009) Air turbine for wave power station. WO 2009/089902 (23 July 2009).
[24] Setoguchi T, Kim TH, Kaneko K, et al. (2002) Air turbine with staggered blades for wave power conversion. In: Chung JS (ed.) *Proceedings of the 12th International Offshore Polar Engineering Conference*, Mountain View, CA, USA, pp. 662–667.
[25] Setoguchi T, Santhakumar S, Takao M, et al. (2003) A modified Wells turbine for wave energy conversion. *Renewable Energy* 28: 79–91.
[26] Dejc ME and Trojanovskij BM (1972) *Untersuchung und Berechnung Axialer Turbinenstufen*. Berlin, Germany: VEB Verlag.
[27] Richards D and Weiskopf FB (1986) Studies with and testing of the McCormick pneumatic wave energy turbine with some comments on PWECS systems. In: McCormick ME and Kim YC (eds.) *Utilization of Ocean Waves – Wave to Energy Conversion*, pp. 80–102. New York: ASCE.
[28] Kim TW, Kaneko K, Setoguchi T, and Inoue M (1988) Aerodynamic performance of an impulse turbine with self-pitch-controlled guide vanes for wave power generator. In: *Proceedings of the 1st KSME–JSME Thermal Fluid Engineering Conference*, vol. 2, pp. 133–137.
[29] Dixon SL and Hall CA (2010) *Fluid Mechanics and Thermodynamics of Turbomachinery*, 6th edn. Amsterdam, The Netherlands: Elsevier.
[30] Hawthorne WR and Horlock JH (1962) Actuator disc theory of the incompressible flow in axial compressors. *Proceedings of the Institution of Mechanical Engineers* 176: 789–814.
[31] Gato LMC and Falcão AFdeO (1988) Aerodynamics of the Wells turbine. *International Journal of Mechanical Sciences* 30: 383–395.
[32] Kim TH, Setoguchi T, Takao M, et al. (2002) Study of turbine with self-pitch-controlled blades for wave energy conversion. *International Journal of Thermal Sciences* 41: 101–107.

[33] Kim TH, Setoguchi T, Kaneko K, and Raghunathan S (2002) Numerical investigation on the effect of blade sweep on the performance of Wells turbine. *Renewable Energy* 25: 235–248.
[34] Setoguchi T, Kinoue Y, Kim TH, et al. (2003) Hysteretic characteristics of Wells turbine for wave power conversion. *Renewable Energy* 28: 2113–2127.
[35] Dhanasekaran TS and Govardhan M (2005) Computational analysis of performance and flow investigation on Wells turbine for wave energy conversion. *Renewable Energy* 30: 2129–2147.
[36] Torresi M, Camporeale SM, Strippoli PD, and Pascazio G (2008) Accurate numerical simulation of a high solidity Wells turbine. *Renewable Energy* 33: 735–747.
[37] Torresi M, Camporeale SM, and Pascazio G (2009) Detailed CFD analysis of the steady flow in a Wells turbine under incipient and deep stall conditions. *Journal of Fluids Engineering–Transactions of the American Society of Mechanical Engineers* 131: 071103.
[38] Taha Z, Sugiyono, and Sawada T (2010) A comparison of computational and experimental results of Wells turbine performance for wave energy conversion. *Applied Ocean Research* 32: 83–90.
[39] Thakker A and Dhanasekaran TS (2003) Computed effects of tip-clearance on performance of impulse turbine for wave energy conversion. *Renewable Energy* 29: 529–547.
[40] Hyun BS, Moon JS, Hong SW, and Lee YY (2004) Practical numerical analysis of impulse turbine for OWC-type wave energy conversion using commercial CFD code. In: Chung JS (ed.) *Proceedings of the 14th International Offshore Polar Engineering Conference*, Mountain View, CA, USA, pp. 253–259.
[41] Thakker A and Dhanasekaran TS (2005) Experimental and computational analysis on guide vane losses of impulse turbine for wave energy conversion. *Renewable Energy* 30: 1359–1372.
[42] Thakker A and Hourigan F (2005) Computational fluid dynamics analysis of a 0.6 m, 0.6 hub-to-tip ratio impulse turbine with fixed guide vanes. *Renewable Energy* 30: 1387–1399.
[43] Thakker A and Hourigan F (2005) A comparison of two meshing schemes for CFD analysis of the impulse turbine for wave energy applications. *Renewable Energy* 30: 1401–1410.
[44] Raghunathan S, Tan CP, and Ombaka OO (1985) Performance of the Wells self-starting air turbine. *Aeronautical Journal* 89: 369–379.
[45] Raghunathan S and Ombaka OO (1985) Effect of frequency of air flow on performance of Wells turbine. *International Journal of Fluid Flow* 8: 127–132.
[46] Csanady GT (1964) *Theory of Turbomachines*. New York: McGraw Hill.
[47] Grant RJ and Johnson CG (1979) Performance tests on a single stage Wells turbine. CEGB Report No. MM/MECH/TF 207. UK: CEGB.
[48] Raghunathan S, Tan CP, and Wells NAJ (1980) Test on 0.2m diameter Wells turbine. The Queen's University of Belfast Report No. WE/80/14R.
[49] Gato LMC, Warfield V, and Thakker A (1996) Performance of high-solidity Wells turbine for an OWC wave power plant. *Journal of Energy Resources Technology–Transactions of the American Society of Mechanical Engineers* 118: 263–268.
[50] Thakker A, Frawley P, and Khaleeq HB (2002) An investigation of the effects of Reynolds number on the performance of 0.6m impulse turbine for different hub to tip ratios. In: Chung JS (ed.) *Proceedings of the 12th International Offshore Polar Engineering Conference*, Mountain View, CA, USA, pp. 682–686.
[51] Maeda H, Santhakumar S, Setoguchi T, et al. (1999) Performance of an impulse turbine with fixed guide vanes for wave power conversion. *Renewable Energy* 17: 533–547.
[52] Thakker A and Abdulhadi R (2008) The performance of Wells turbine under bi-directional airflow. *Renewable Energy* 33: 2467–2474.
[53] Ravindran A, Balabaskaran V, and Swaminathan G (1993) Comparison of performances of constant and varying chord Wells turbine rotors for wave energy applications. In: Elliott G and Caratti G (eds) *Proceedings of European Wave Energy Symposium*, East Kilbride, Scotland, pp. 197–202. Edinburgh, UK.
[54] Raghunathan S (1995) A methodology for the Wells turbine design for wave energy conversion. *Proceedings of the Institution of Mechanical Engineers, Part A: Journal of Power and Energy* 209: 221–232.
[55] Govardhan M and Dhanasekaran TS (2002) Effect of guide vanes on the performance of a self-rectifying air turbine with constant and variable chord rotors. *Renewable Energy* 26: 201–219.
[56] Inoue M, Kaneko K, and Setoguchi T (1985) Studies on Wells turbine for wave power generator. Part 3: Effect of guide vanes. *Bulletin of the Japan Society of Mechanical Engineers* 28: 1986–1991.
[57] Takao M, Setoguchi T, Kim TH, et al. (2000) The performance of Wells turbine with 3D guide vanes. In: Chung JS (ed.) *Proceedings of the 10th International Offshore Polar Engineering Conference*, Mountain View, CA, USA, pp. 381–386. Seattle, WA.
[58] Falcão AFdeO (2000) The shoreline OWC wave power plant at the Azores. In: Ostergaard I and Iversen S (eds) *Proceedings of the 4th European Wave Energy Conference*, Danish Technological Institute, Denmark, pp. 44–48. Aalborg, Denmark.
[59] Heath T, Whittaker TJT, and Boake CB (2000) The design, construction and operation of the LIMPET wave energy converter (Islay, Scotland). In: Ostergaard I and Iversen S (eds) *Proceedings of the 4th European Wave Energy Conference*, Danish Technological Institute, Denmark, pp. 49–55. Aalborg, Denmark.
[60] Raghunathan S, Curran R, and Whittaker TJT (1995) Performance of the Islay Wells air turbine. *Proceedings of the Institution of Mechanical Engineers, Part A: Journal of Power and Energy* 209: 55–62.
[61] Heath TV (2007) The development of a turbo-generation system for application in OWC breakwaters. In: Falcao AFO (ed.) *Proceedings of the 7th European Wave Tidal Energy Conference*. Porto, Portugal.
[62] Abbott IH and von Doenhoff AE (1959) *Theory of Wing Sections*. New York: Dover.
[63] Gato LMC and Henriques JCC (1996) Optimization of symmetrical profiles for the Wells turbine rotor blades. In: *Proceedings of ASME Fluids Engineering Division Summer Meeting*, vol. 3, pp. 623–630. New York: ASME.
[64] Thakker A, O'Dowd M, and Gato LMC (1995) Application of computational fluid dynamics in the study and optimization of Wells turbine blade profiles. In: Elliot G and Diamantaras K (eds) *Proceedings of the 2nd European Wave Power Conference*, Luxembourg, pp. 218–225. Lisbon, Portugal.
[65] Mohamed MH, Janiga G, Pa E, and Thévenin D (2011) Multi-objective optimization of the airfoil shape of Wells turbine used for wave energy conversion. *Energy* 36: 438–446.
[66] Webster M and Gato LMC (2001) The effect of rotor blade shape on the performance of the Wells turbine. *International Journal of Offshore and Polar Engineering* 11: 227–230.
[67] Takao M, Thakker A, Abdulhadi R, and Setoguchi S (2004) Effect of blade profile on the performance of large-scale Wells turbine. In: Chung JS (ed.) *Proceedings of the 14th International Offshore Polar Engineering Conference*, Mountain View, CA, USA, pp. 272–276. Toulon, France.
[68] Henriques JCC and Gato LMC (1998) A study of the compressibility effects in Wells turbine cascade blade flows using an Euler solver. In: Dursthoff W (ed.) *Proceedings of 3rd European Wave Energy Conference*, University of Hannover, Germany, pp. 88–95. Patras, Greece.
[69] Henriques JCC and Gato LMC (2002) Use of a residual distribution Euler solver to study the occurrence of transonic flow in the Wells turbine rotor blades. *Computational Mechanics* 29: 243–253.
[70] Setoguchi T, Takao M, and Kaneko K (1998) Hysteresis on Wells turbine characteristics in reciprocating flow. *International Journal of Rotating Machinery* 4: 17–24.
[71] Kinoue Y, Setoguchi T, Kim TH, et al. (2003) Mechanism of hysteretic characteristics of Wells turbine for wave power conversion. *Journal of Fluids Engineering–Transactions of the American Society of Mechanical Engineers* 125: 302–307.
[72] Raghunathan S and Tan CP (1983) The performance of the biplane Wells turbine. *Journal of Energy* 7: 741–742.
[73] Raghunathan S (1993) The prediction of performance of biplane Wells turbine. In: Chung JS (ed.) *Proceedings of the 3rd International Offshore Polar Engineering Conference*, Mountain View, CA, USA, pp. 167–175. Singapore.
[74] Gato LMC and Curran R (1996) Performance of the biplane Wells turbine. *Journal of Offshore Mechanics and Arctic Engineering–Transactions of the American Society of Mechanical Engineers* 118: 210–215.
[75] Beattie WC and Raghunathan S (1993) A novel contra rotating Wells turbine. In: Elliot G and Caratti G (eds) *Proceedings of European Wave Energy Symposium*, East Kilbride, Scotland, pp. 191–196. Edinburgh, UK.
[76] Raghunathan S and Beattie WC (1996) Aerodynamic performance of contra-rotating Wells turbine for wave energy conversion. *Proceedings of the Institution of Mechanical Engineers, Part A: Journal of Power and Energy* 210: 431–447.
[77] Gato LMC and Curran R (1996) Performance of the contrarotating Wells turbine. *International Journal of Offshore and Polar Engineering* 6: 68–74.
[78] Curran R and Gato LMC (1997) The energy conversion performance of several types of Wells turbine design. *Proceedings of the Institution of Mechanical Engineers, Part A: Journal of Power and Energy* 211: 133–145.

[79] Inoue M, Kaneko K, Setoguchi T, and Hamakawa H (1989) Air turbine with self-pitch-controlled blades for wave power generator. *Japan Society of Mechanical Engineers International Journal, Series II* 32: 19–24.
[80] Gato LMC and Falcão AFdeO (1989) Aerodynamics of the Wells turbine: Control by swinging rotor blades. *International Journal of Mechanical Sciences* 31: 425–434.
[81] Sarmento AJNA, Gato LMC, and Falcão AFdeO (1990) Turbine-controlled wave energy absorption by oscillating water column device. *Ocean Engineering* 17: 481–497.
[82] Gato LMC, Eça LRC, and Falcão AFdeO (1991) Performance of the Wells turbine with variable pitch rotor blades. *Journal of Energy Resources Technology–Transactions of the American Society of Mechanical Engineers* 113: 141–146.
[83] Perdigão J and Sarmento A (2003) Overall-efficiency optimisation in OWC devices. *Applied Ocean Research* 25: 157–166.
[84] Traupel W (2001) Thermische Turbomaschinen. *Erster Band: Thermodynamisch-Strömungstechnische Berechnung*, 4th edn. Berlin, Germany: Springer.
[85] Setoguchi T, Kaneko K, Maeda H, et al. (1993) Impulse turbine with self-pitch-controlled guide vanes for wave power conversion: Performance of mono-vane type. *International Journal of Offshore and Polar Engineering* 3: 73–78.
[86] Freeman C, Herring SJ, and Banks K (2008) Impulse turbine for use in bi-directional flows. WO 2008/012530 A2 (31 January 2008).
[87] Dresser-Rand. HydroAir variable radius turbine. http://www.dresser-rand.com/literature/general/2210_HydroAir.pdf (accessed 25 April 2011).
[88] Curran R, Denniss T, and Boake C (2000) Multidisciplinary design for performance: Ocean wave energy conversion. In: Chung JS (ed.) *Proceedings of the 10th International Offshore Polar Engineering Conference*, vol. 1, Mountain View, CA, USA, pp. 434–441. Seattle, WA, USA.
[89] Finnigan T and Auld D (2003) Model testing of a variable-pitch aerodynamic turbine. In: Chung JS (ed.) *Proceedings of the 13th International Offshore Polar Engineering Conference*, Mountain View, CA, USA, pp. 357–360. Hononulu, HI, USA.
[90] Finnigan T and Alcorn R (2003) Numerical simulation of a variable-pitch turbine with speed control. In: Lewis A and Thomas G (eds) *Proceedings of 5th European Wave Energy Conference*, Cork, Ireland, pp. 213–220. Cork, Ireland.
[91] Cooper P and Gareev A (2007) Numerical analysis of a variable pitch reversible flow air turbine for oscillating water column wave energy systems. In: Falcao AFO (ed.) *Proceedings of the 7th European Wave Tidal Energy Conference*. Porto, Portugal.
[92] McCormick ME, Rehak JG, and Williams BD (1992) An experimental study of a bi-directional radial turbine for pneumatic conversion. In: *Proceedings of Mastering Ocean through Technology*, vol. 2, pp. 866–870.
[93] McCormick ME and Cochran B (1993) A performance study of a bi-directional radial turbine. In: Elliot G and Caratti G (eds.) *Proceedings of European Wave Energy Symposium*, East Kilbride, Scotland, pp. 443–448. Edinburgh, UK.
[94] Takao M, Itakura K, Setoguchi T, et al. (2002) Performance of a radial turbine for wave power conversion. In: Chung JS (ed.) *Proceedings of the 12th International Offshore Polar Engineering Conference*, Mountain View, CA, USA. Kitakyushu, Japan.
[95] Takao M, Fujioka Y, and Setoguchi T (2005) Effect of pitch-controlled guide vanes on the performance of a radial turbine for wave energy conversion. *Ocean Engineering* 32: 2079–2087.
[96] Castro F, El Marjani A, Rodriguez MA, and Parra T (2007) Viscous flow analysis in a radial impulse turbine for OWC wave energy systems. In: Falcao AFO (ed.) *Proceedings of the 7th European Wave Tidal Energy Conference*. Porto, Portugal.
[97] Pereiras B, Castro F, El Marjani A, and Rodriguez MA (2008) Radial impulse turbine for wave energy conversion. A new geometry. In: *Proceedings of the 27th International Conference on Offshore Mechanics and Arctic Engineering*. Paper OMAE2008-57951. Estoril, Portugal.
[98] Pereiras B, Castro F, and Rodriguez AA (2009) Tip clearance effect on the flow pattern of a radial impulse turbine for wave energy conversion. In: Chung JS (ed.) *Proceedings of the 9th International Offshore Polar Engineering Conference*, Mountain View, CA, USA, pp. 290–298. Osaka, Japan.
[99] Pereiras B, Castro F, El Marjani A, and Rodriguez MA (2011) An improved radial impulse turbine for OWC. *Renewable Energy* 36: 1477–1484.
[100] Jayashankar V, Anand S, Geetha T, et al. (2009) A twin unidirectional impulse turbine topology for OWC based wave energy plants. *Renewable Energy* 34: 692–698.
[101] Mala K, Jayara J, Jayashankar V, et al. (2011) A twin unidirectional impulse turbine topology for OWC based wave energy plants – Experimental validation and scaling. *Renewable Energy* 36: 307–314.
[102] Jayashankar V, Mala K, Jayaraj J, et al. (2010) A twin unidirectional turbine topology for wave energy. In: *Proceedings of the 3rd International Conference on Ocean Energy*. Bilbao, Spain.
[103] Suzuki M, Arakawa C, and Takahashi S (2004) Performance of wave power generating system installed in breakwater at Sakata port in Japan. In: Chung JS (ed.) *Proceedings of the 14th International Offshore Polar Engineering Conference*, Mountain View, CA, USA, pp. 202–209. Toulon, France.
[104] Washio Y, Osawa H, Nagata Y, et al. (2000) The offshore floating type wave power device 'Mighty Whale': Open sea tests. In: Chung JS (ed.) *Proceedings of the 10th International Offshore Polar Engineering Conference*, Mountain View, CA, USA, pp. 373–380. Seattle, WA, USA.
[105] Taylor JRM and Caldwell NJ (1998) Design and construction of the variable-pitch air turbine for the Azores wave energy plant. In: Durstohff W (ed.) *Proceedings of the 3rd European Wave Energy Conference*, University of Hannover, Germany, pp. 328–337. Patras, Greece.
[106] Caldwell NJ and Taylor JRM (1998) Eddy-current actuator for a variable pitch air turbine. In: Dursthoff W (ed.) *Proceedings of the 3rd European Wave Energy Conference*, University of Hannover, Germany, pp. 104–110. Patras, Greece.
[107] Folley M, Curran R, and Whittaker T (2006) Comparison of LIMPET contra-rotating Wells turbine with theoretical and model test predictions. *Ocean Engineering* 33: 1056–1069.
[108] Mala K, Badrinath SN, Chidanand S, et al. (2009) Analysis of power modules in the Indian wave energy plant. In: *Proceedings of Annual IEEE India Conference (INDICON)* Gandhinagar, India: IEEE, pp. 95–98.
[109] Raju VS, Ravindran M, and Koola PM (1993) Experiences on a 150 kW wave energy pilot plant. In: Elliot G and Caratti G (eds) *Proceedings of European Wave Energy Symposium*, East Kilbride, Scotland, pp. 277–282. Edinburgh, UK.
[110] Torre-Enciso Y, Ortubia I, López de Aguileta LI, and Marqués J (2009) Mutriku wave power plant: From the thinking out to the reality. In: Leijon M (ed.) *Proceedings of the 8th European Wave Tidal Energy Conference*, pp. 319–329. Uppsala, Sweden.
[111] Falnes J and McIver P (1985) Surface wave interactions with systems of oscillating bodies and pressure distributions. *Applied Ocean Research* 7: 225–234.
[112] Falnes J (2002) *Ocean Waves and Oscillating Systems*. Cambridge, UK: Cambridge University Press.
[113] Evans DV (1982) Wave power absorption by systems of oscillating surface-pressure distributions. *Journal of Fluid Mechanics* 114: 481–499.
[114] Falcão AFdeO and Justino PAP (1999) OWC wave energy devices with air flow control. *Ocean Engineering* 26: 1275–1295.
[115] Falcão AFdeO and Rodrigues RJA (2002) Stochastic modelling of OWC wave power plant performance. *Applied Ocean Research* 24: 59–71.
[116] Falcão AFdeO (2004) Stochastic modelling in wave power-equipment optimization: Maximum energy production versus maximum profit. *Ocean Engineering* 31: 1407–1421.
[117] Falcão AFdeO (2002) Control of an oscillating water column wave power plant for maximum energy production. *Applied Ocean Research* 24: 73–82.
[118] Gato LMC, Justino P, and Falcão AFdeO (2005) Optimisation of power take-off equipment for an oscillating water column wave energy plant. In: Johnstone CM and Johnstone AD (eds) *Proceedings of the 6th European Wave Tidal Energy Conference*. Glasgow, UK.
[119] Scuotto M and Falcão AFdeO (2005) Wells and impulse turbines in an OWC wave power plant: A comparison. In: Johnstone CM and Johnstone AD (eds) *Proceedings of the 6th European Wave Tidal Energy Conference*. Glasgow, UK.
[120] Falcão AFdeO, Vieira LC, Justino PAP, and André JMCS (2003) By-pass air-valve control of an OWC wave power plant. *Journal of Offshore Mechanical and Arctic Engineering–Transactions of the American Society of Mechanical Engineers* 125: 205–210.
[121] Whittaker TJT, Beattie W, Folley M, et al. (2003) Performance of the LIMPET wave power plant – Prediction, measurement and potential. In: Lewis A and Thomas G (eds) *Proceedings of the 5th European Wave Energy Conference*, Cork, Ireland, pp. 97–104. Cork, Ireland.
[122] Takao M, Setoguchi T, Kaneko K, et al. (2002) Noise characteristics of turbines for wave power conversion. *Proceedings of the Institution of Mechanical Engineers, Part A: Journal of Power and Energy* 216: 223–228.

8.06 Economics of Ocean Energy

T Stallard, The University of Manchester, Manchester, UK

© 2012 Elsevier Ltd. All rights reserved.

8.06.1	Introduction	151
8.06.2	Cost Estimates of Wave and Tidal Stream Systems	152
8.06.3	The Capital Investment Decision	153
8.06.3.1	Discounting: Present Value	153
8.06.3.2	Net Present Value	154
8.06.3.3	Discounted COE	154
8.06.3.4	Discount Rates	155
8.06.3.5	Strategy	155
8.06.4	Capital Costs	155
8.06.4.1	Preliminary Works	156
8.06.4.2	Marine Energy Devices	156
8.06.4.3	Civil Engineering Infrastructure	156
8.06.4.3.1	Mooring systems	156
8.06.4.3.2	Bed-connected structures	157
8.06.4.4	Electrical Infrastructure	157
8.06.4.5	Site to Grid Transmission	157
8.06.4.6	Deployment	158
8.06.4.7	Decommissioning	158
8.06.5	Operating Costs	158
8.06.5.1	Periodic Expenditures	159
8.06.5.2	Planned Maintenance	159
8.06.5.3	Unplanned Maintenance	159
8.06.6	Vessels for Offshore Work	160
8.06.6.1	Vessel Type and Unit Cost	160
8.06.6.2	Duration of Offshore Vessel Use	160
8.06.6.2.1	Duration of offshore work	160
8.06.6.2.2	Transit and mobilization time	162
8.06.6.3	Vessel Cost Summary	162
8.06.7	Revenue	162
8.06.7.1	Energy Production	162
8.06.7.1.1	Rated power and capacity factor	162
8.06.7.1.2	Occurrence plot and performance surface	162
8.06.7.1.3	Time-varying performance	163
8.06.7.2	Value of a Unit of Electricity	163
8.06.7.2.1	Market value (UK)	163
8.06.7.2.2	Renewable Obligation Certificates (UK)	164
8.06.7.2.3	Climate change levy (UK)	164
8.06.8	Future Prospects	164
8.06.8.1	Evolution of Costs in the Marine Sector	164
8.06.8.2	Mechanisms for Cost Evolution	166
8.06.8.2.1	Revenue: Increased power output per device	166
8.06.8.2.2	Capital cost: Changes due to scale of deployment	167
8.06.8.2.3	Capital cost: Changes due to elapsed time	167
8.06.8.2.4	Operating cost: Changes	167
8.06.8.3	Summary	168
References		168
Further Reading		169

8.06.1 Introduction

Many studies have been published concerning the economic feasibility of generating electricity from ocean waves and tidal streams. Typically, these studies have been conducted to estimate a single parameter that can be used to compare the economic viability of a farm of either wave or tidal stream devices to alternative electricity generating options such as wind, nuclear, and traditional thermal power stations. The levelized cost per unit of energy is widely reported since it allows straightforward comparison between different technologies (see, e.g., RAEng 2006 [1, 2] and Allan *et al.* 2010). Investors will also consider the payback period, net present value (NPV), and internal rate of return (IRR) of a project among other factors. In this chapter, an overview of recent studies of economic viability of marine energy systems is given (Section 8.06.2), an introduction to the factors that may significantly affect economic viability is given (Sections 8.06.3–8.06.7), and the prospects for future variation of economic viability are briefly discussed (Section 8.06.8).

8.06.2 Cost Estimates of Wave and Tidal Stream Systems

Devices for extracting useful electricity from waves and tides have been in development for approaching 40 years and over this period a wide range of predicted costs have been stated. Thorpe [3] provides a review of the cost of electricity from various wave technologies up to 2000. At that time, the cost of electricity of less than $10\,\text{p}\,\text{kWh}^{-1}$ was forecast for various technologies. However, most of those technologies are no longer in development. Nevertheless, commercial interest in wave and tidal stream systems has increased greatly over the last decade and several devices have been developed to the stage of offshore testing at full scale. Since 2000, many cost estimates have been published with recent estimates, suggesting that the unit cost of electricity from commercial farms is likely to be somewhere in the range $5\text{–}25\,\text{p}\,\text{kWh}^{-1}$. Values for specific capital cost and cost of electricity from various studies over the last decade are given in **Figure 1**. In part, the wide range of predicted costs is due to different assumptions made in the economic assessment. As discussed in the later sections of this chapter, the cost of electricity varies considerably depending on the type of device considered, the site considered, the size of farm considered, and the stage of development of the technology.

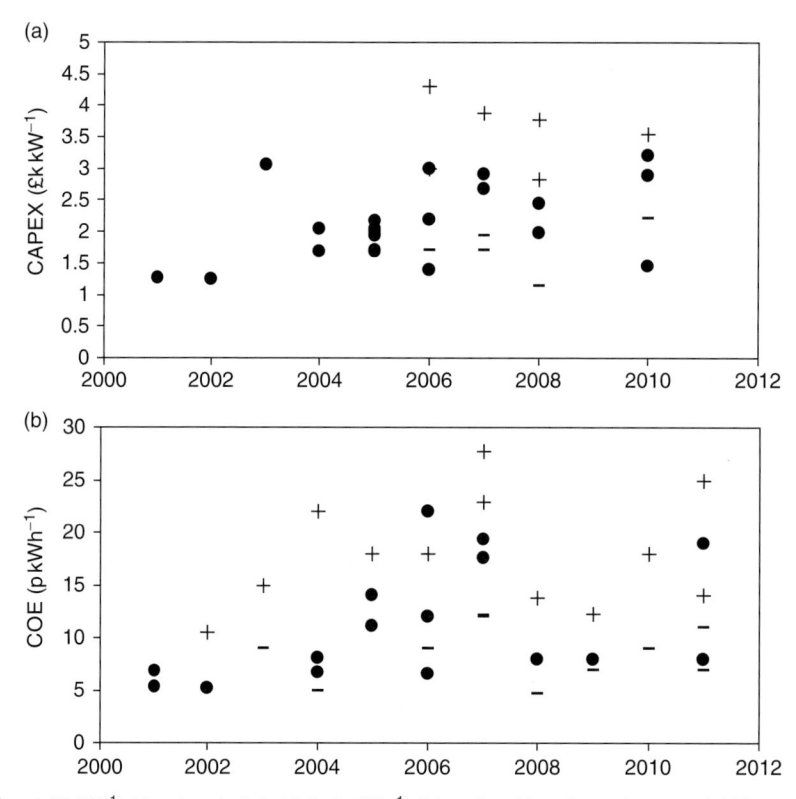

Figure 1 Specific capital cost (£k kW^{-1}) (a) and cost of electricity (p kWh^{-1}) (b) predicted for a farm of wave and tidal stream or marine energy technologies by various authors (2001–11). Installed capacity of the farm, location, and technology differ between studies. Upper (+), central (•), and lower (−) estimates are shown. Data from DTI (2001); Binnie Black & Veatch (2002); Engineering Business (2003); EPRI (2004) Economic assessment methodology for wave power plants. E2I EPRI WP – US – 002 Rev 4 [4]; Enviros (2005); RAEng (2006); EPRI (2006) North America tidal in-stream energy conversion technology feasibility study. EPRI TP-008-NA [5]; The Carbon Trust (2006) Future marine energy. Findings of the marine energy challenge: Cost competitiveness and growth of wave and tidal stream energy [6]; Ernst & Young (2007) Impact of banding the renewables obligation – Costs of electricity production. DTI report URN 07/948 [1]; PIER (2008) Summary of PIER-funded wave energy research. California Energy Commission, PIER Program CEC-500-2007-083, March 2008 [7]; UKERC (2008); Denny *et al.* (2009); UKERC (2010) Marine energy technology roadmap. Energy Technologies Institute and UK Energy Research Centre, October 2008 [8]; and Allan GJ, Bryden I, McGregor PG, *et al.* (2011) Concurrent and legacy economic and environmental impacts from establishing a marine energy sector in Scotland. *Energy Policy* 36: 2734–2753 [9]. Pre-2010 data are adjusted by 3% per annum. Exchange rate is US$1.65 = 1GBP assumed.

Two studies of particular note were conducted by the Carbon Trust [6] and the Energy Policy Research Institute (EPRI) [4]. These studies considered the cost of electricity from small farms of several different devices at several different locations. Farms with a rated capacity of 30 MW were considered by the Carbon Trust and 90 MW by the EPRI. Costs of individual devices were not reported for commercial reasons, but the study suggested that small arrays of the prototype devices considered could generate electricity at a unit cost in the range 21.6–24.9 p kWh^{-1} (Carbon Trust). Capital costs for first farms were estimated to be in the range 1400–3000 £k kW^{-1} for tidal stream systems and 1700–4300 £k kW^{-1} for wave energy devices. The EPRI conducted a detailed assessment of the costs associated with two device types (the Pelamis Wave Power Device and Energetech) at a range of sites. They predicted that a cost of electricity may vary from 9.2 to 11.2 $c kWh^{-1} for the same type of device installed at different locations. As commercial interests have increased, the number of published studies of marine energy device costs has reduced. As a result, the Carbon Trust [6] and EPRI [4] studies have informed many of the more recent technology comparisons conducted by Ernst & Young [1, 2] and Allan *et al.* (2010) among others.

8.06.3 The Capital Investment Decision

The cash flow associated with a marine energy project is typically considered in two phases: a short installation period prior to commissioning during which devices and supporting infrastructure are manufactured and deployed at the selected site and an operating phase during which the farm is periodically maintained so that electricity and hence revenue are generated. Expenditures incurred prior to commissioning are referred to as capital expenditures (CAPEX) and those incurred after commissioning are referred to as operating expenditures (OPEX). A summary of the components of CAPEX and OPEX are given in Sections 8.06.4 and 8.06.5. A simplified cash flow for a marine energy project is shown in **Figure 2**. An operating life of the order of between 15 and 20 years is typically assumed with either decommissioning or farm overhaul occurring at the end of this period.

Clearly, significant CAPEX is required prior to generating any revenue and so investors must have confidence that the net revenue generated will be sufficient to yield a return on their investment. A wide range of approaches can be used to assess economic feasibility of electricity generating technologies. This reflects the even greater range of methods used for economic and financial appraisal of an arbitrary investment (see, e.g., Reference 10). A common measure is payback period, the time it takes for the revenue from a project to match the initial investment. It is very simple and readily understandable and offers a crude measure of investment risk (the faster the investment pays back, the less 'risky'). Its limitation is that it does not account for the timing of costs and revenues, the size of the investment, or the overall return. It is commonly used as a screening method prior to the use of more credible methods. Perhaps the most widely used methods are based on discounting, the principle that a lower value should be placed on future cashflows. Discounted measures include cost of energy (COE), NPV, and IRR and are discussed in the following sections.

8.06.3.1 Discounting: Present Value

Present value methods account for the timing as well as the magnitude of costs and revenues. The basis of these methods is the idea that a lower value – a greater discount – should be placed on cash flows in the future than on those occurring today since there is a risk that future cash flows may not occur. A higher perceived risk attracts a higher discount rate. The discount rate is typically the investor's overall cost of capital or may be adjusted for project-specific risks. Typical discount rate values suggested for marine energy in the United Kingdom are between 8% and 15% [6, 11]. A higher discount rate is normally applied to less developed technologies to represent the greater uncertainty associated with both design and cost estimation. CAPEX, operating expenditures, and revenue are discussed in Sections 8.06.4, 8.06.5, and 8.06.7 respectively.

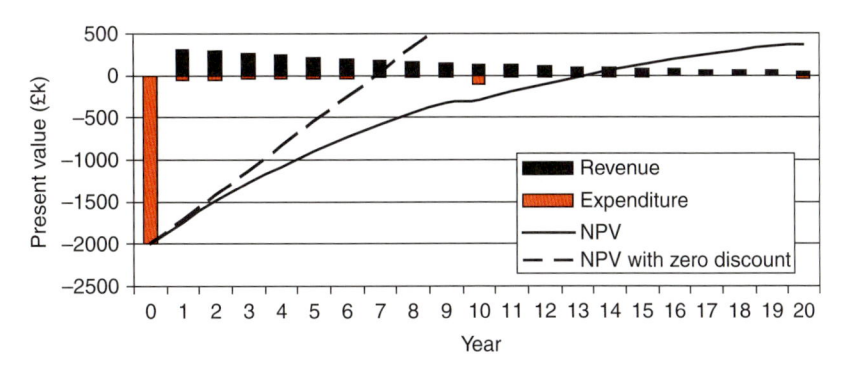

Figure 2 Indicative cash flow for a marine energy project with capital cost of £2000 per MW installed incurred in year 0 only, operating cost 3% of capital cost, refit cost 10% of capital cost in year 10, revenue of 0.1 p kWh^{-1}, and a capacity factor of 0.4. Assuming a discount rate of 10%, the NPV after 20 years is £366k per MW installed. The payback period (e.g., for zero discount rate) is 6.9 years.

8.06.3.2 Net Present Value

The NPV is the sum of all the costs and revenues over the lifetime of the investment discounted to the present day. A project with an NPV greater than zero has a return exceeding the minimum expected rate and would be beneficial to undertake. For a generation project, the NPV can be expressed in € kW^{-1} installed. The NPV is written as the present value of the sum of all quantities X_i incurred in each year i discounted to a base year (typically the year in which the project commences, $i = 0$).

$$\text{NPV} = \sum_{i=1}^{N} \frac{X_i}{(1+r)^i} \quad [1]$$

If the quantity X_i is constant for all increments $i = 1$ to N, eqn [2] reduces to an annuity calculation:

$$\text{NPV} = \frac{(1+r)^N - 1}{r(1+r)^N} X \quad [2]$$

For an energy project, the NPV is the sum of all CAPEX, OPEX, and Revenue over the design life of the project:

$$\text{NPV} = \text{CAPEX} + \sum_{i=1}^{N} \frac{\text{OPEX}_i}{(1+r)^i} + \sum_{i=1}^{N} \frac{\text{REVENUE}_i}{(1+r)^i} \quad [3]$$

where both CAPEX and OPEX are negative. The annual NPV of a nominal project with constant operating cost is shown in **Figure 2**. In this idealized case, both operating cost and revenue are constant during each year of operation. A full cash flow analysis would account for annual, and perhaps seasonal, variation of costs and revenue. At the simplest level, there are four inputs to an NPV calculation: CAPEX, OPEX, Revenue, and discount rate. For a single discount rate model (Section 8.06.3.4), revenue has the greatest effect on the calculated NPV (**Figure 3**).

IRR is related to NPV as it is the discount rate at which the NPV is zero, that is, in which the present value of all expenditures over the lifetime of the project balances the present value of all future revenues. In effect, the IRR measures the cost of capital that the project could support and still break even over the lifetime considered. The project IRR is often compared to a hurdle (minimum) rate that may be the investors cost of capital or a risk-adjusted rate.

8.06.3.3 Discounted COE

The COE or levelized cost aims to capture the lifetime costs of a generator and allocate those costs to the lifetime electrical output with both costs and output discounted to the present value. It is expressed in € kWh^{-1} (or £ kWh^{-1} or $ kWh^{-1}). The approach was developed for regulated monopoly utilities to provide a first estimate of the relative costs of plant. COE is presently widely used by policymakers to indicate the relative merits of different generating technologies as well as in identifying the need for subsidy for developing technologies [12]. Although a useful measure, the COE of high capital cost and low fuel cost technologies such as wave and tidal energy is, as for NPV, very sensitive to variations in discount rates. Furthermore, the revenue side of the investment decision, that is, the influence of electricity prices and associated risks, and the scale of the investment are neglected.

The levelized cost per unit of electricity is equivalent to the present value of all investments made over the project life span divided by the number of units (kWh) of electricity generated over the same interval. An estimate of the cost of electricity is given by (see also Reference 4 and Allan *et al.* 2010):

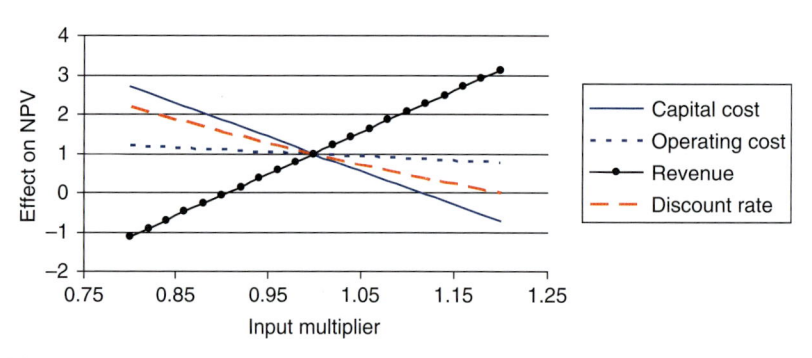

$$\text{COE} = \frac{\text{NPV(CAPEX)} + \text{NPV(OPEX)}}{\text{NPV(Energy)}} \quad [4]$$

Figure 3 Sensitivity of NPV to change of the four main inputs: capital cost, operating cost, revenue, and discount rate. Revenue has greatest influence on project economics.

where CAPEX (£) is the total project investment required prior to commissioning, OPEX (£) is the expenditure required to ensure that the wave power plant operates as designed, and Energy (kWh) is the useful energy generated by the wave farm during a typical year. Note that the COE calculation provides a single value of electricity that represents the average value of each unit of energy produced.

8.06.3.4 Discount Rates

Consideration of risk as well as return is vital in economic appraisal. Discounting methods such as COE, NPV, and IRR attempt to encapsulate risk in a nonspecific way. For example, discount rate is typically the company's weighted average cost of capital that reflects the differing required rates of return for equity (shares) and debt as well as the balance of debt to equity (gearing). Although a discount rate provides an indication of the risk associated with an investment, this does not fully capture the risks affecting specific projects or technologies, particularly for new projects whose risk structure differs from existing activities.

It is common when comparing the COE of different technologies that the same discount rate is applied across the board (i.e., to all cash flows). However, this implicitly suggests that the risk profile of (say) a wave energy converter is the same as that of a gas-fired power station. Common sense suggests this is not true since one has a largely predictable cost stream, whereas the other is exposed to volatile wholesale gas prices. Specification of discount rates on the basis of exposure to specific risk factors has been suggested as a means of properly leveling the playing field [13]. This involves applying different risk-adjusted discount rates to different cost or revenue streams or classes of streams, for example, a higher discount rate would be used for cash flow dependent on fuel prices than for long-term fixed-value contracts. Identification of the risk premium for each risk factor is a significant challenge. However, mirroring practice in financial markets, the use of the capital asset pricing model (CAPM) to translate the required rate of return (i.e., discount rate) to the risk of specific cash flows has also been proposed (see, e.g., Reference 10). A simplified approach is to define a single risk-adjusted discount rate for the project. A difficulty with this approach is that risk is defined in terms of the correlation between a cash flow and the stock market and so limited data are available for emerging sectors such as marine energy. Assessment of risk parameters for sectors that are 'similar' to marine energy [11] suggests that no risk adjustment is required. CAPM applied to individual cash flows may therefore be more appropriate for assessment of marine energy devices.

8.06.3.5 Strategy

Economic assessment of a specific investment against specific metrics such as NPV may ignore the often important strategic benefits of the project. For example, the addition of a particular project to the investor's portfolio that has a different risk profile can offer benefits by spreading risk (e.g., REF). This approach places a higher value on generating options that have predictable and low-variance power output. Further, there may be broader economic benefits to a project such as positive regional benefits (see, e.g., Allan et al. 2008).

8.06.4 Capital Costs

Since marine energy devices do not require fuel to generate electricity, the costs of a renewable energy farm tend to be dominated by capital cost. This is the case for both wave and tidal stream farms although the balance between capital and operating costs and the subdivision of capital costs varies considerably between technology concepts. Furthermore, even for a single technology concept, the subdivision of total capital cost of a farm varies between alternative deployment sites. However, some generalizations can be made. For a specific marine energy project, comprising a farm of many devices installed at a single site, capital costs include manufacture and installation of several major components:

- Preliminary works
- Fabrication and manufacture of marine energy devices and associated infrastructure including:
  - Station-keeping infrastructure
  - Inter-array electrical infrastructure
- Site to grid transmission structure (using appropriate method)
- Deployment of all devices and infrastructure
- Decommissioning
- Expenditures required to provide maintenance and repair schedule (see Sections 8.06.5.2 and 8.06.5.3).

Historically, device developers have focused on reducing the cost to manufacture their preferred concept. Site infrastructure consists of the civil engineering structures required to maintain the wave energy devices in their operating location and electrical connections required to transfer generated electricity from individual devices to the point of transmission.

Table 1 Indicative CAPEX

Item	Need
Contingencies	Damage and repair during construction
Measurement instrumentation	To quantify incident conditions
Management	To maintain stated schedule
Pre-deployment testing	To ensure specifications satisfied
Manufacturing facilities	To produce components at a reduced cost
Special purpose vessels or specific onshore facilities	To reduce costs associated with maintenance vessels

8.06.4.1 Preliminary Works

Many of the preliminary costs will be similar for alternative projects of similar power output at the same site. These include the following:

- Site surveys
- Licenses, consents, notifications, and approvals
- Project management

Several further expenditures may also be included prior to project commissioning. Several examples are listed in **Table 1**.

8.06.4.2 Marine Energy Devices

As discussed in Chapters 1 and 2, a wide variety of device concepts have been proposed. Alternative device concepts comprise many individual components and manufacturing techniques. Indicative cost breakdowns for generic devices are given by the Carbon Trust [6]. Indicative tidal stream device costs were are reported by Binnie Black & Veatch [14]. Representative costs for a Pelamis Wave Power device are reported by EPRI [4, 5]. Broadly speaking, structural costs and the electrical and mechanical equipment comprising the power takeoff system constitute a large part of the capital cost of each device. Reliable and current information on actual device costs is not publicly available due to the commercial interests of device developers. For this reason, device specific costs are not considered further in this chapter. Since large numbers of devices are required for commercial projects, the supporting infrastructure, installation, and maintenance are discussed in the following sections.

8.06.4.3 Civil Engineering Infrastructure

The civil works required for a marine energy project will include all structures required to hold the wave and tidal stream devices on station within the deployment site. Station-keeping systems vary with device type but typically comprise either a mooring system for floating devices or a support structure for bed-mounted devices. For offshore floating converters, moorings are usually separate systems that allow the device to move independently within a limited range and are required to prevent drifting of the device. For bed-mounted devices, the support structure may be integrated into the design of the tidal stream or wave device to resist horizontal loads on the device. The following sections identify factors that affect the capital cost associated with mooring systems and bed-connected support structures for a marine energy project.

8.06.4.3.1 Mooring systems

Since design of foundations and moorings has been a common practice for decades in offshore oil and gas extraction, many standards on mooring design criteria are available and cost accounting procedures of mooring systems have been defined. However, the different scale of oil and gas projects and different safety requirements implies choices that would not be cost-effective at all if applied to marine energy projects. For marine energy mooring systems, the following components are expected to represent a major fraction of capital cost (see, e.g., Johanning *et al.* 2007):

1. Chains and lines that are the largest cost factor
2. Cost of anchors that is dependent on required holding power and weight and this is sensitive to subsurface geotechnical conditions
3. Connectors (shackles, etc.)
4. Buoys and clump weights.

Capital cost of such systems depends on the following factors:

- Complexity of components and overall mooring system: additional cost implication
- Mooring line or chain loading requirements: lower cost for provision of horizontal restoring force
- Anchor requirements: dependent on the required load capacity and direction, weight, and site geotechnical conditions

- Footprint area requirements: in general, a smaller footprint will be associated with a smaller cost
- Provision of redundancy: additional cost implication but increased availability
- Novelty: additional cost implication due to design uncertainty and safety factors
- Number of anchor units installed – cost per unit varies with number of units
- Installation costs for all components of the mooring system based on vessel.

8.06.4.3.2 Bed-connected structures

Most tidal stream device prototypes are supported on rigid structures in the form of monopiles (such as offshore wind), tripod structures, or gravity-based structures. For supporting structures, the major components of capital cost are procurement, fabrication, and installation. Procurement and fabrication costs should be based on steelwork weights obtained from structural design and appropriate unit rates such as raw material costs. Fabrication rates for structures depend on the complexity of the structures involved and the amount of welding required. Cost estimates should therefore be based on a design that is sufficiently detailed to estimate material weights and fabrication complexity. Capital cost of such structures will vary with the following:

- Geotechnical conditions at the deployment site
- Horizontal loading defined by Metocean conditions for the deployment site
- Material weights and complexity
- Installation costs due to the installation vessel required (Section 8.06.6).

8.06.4.4 Electrical Infrastructure

The cost associated with an inter-array cable must account for cable length, cable capacity, installation method, and configuration of the inter-array cabling. Details on the configuration of alternative cabling systems are given by Lopez *et al.* [15]. Alternative configurations are summarized below:

Star collection. Comprising a direct connection between each generator and a transformer. Switchgear, transformers, and a supporting structure or subsea foundation will be included in the cost. Due to the short cable lengths and high cable voltages, losses will be lower. Furthermore, component failure will only isolate one generator and so this approach allows high availability to be maintained.

String collection. Comprising a series connection between multiple generators. This arrangement requires a simple cable 'laying' pattern and shorter cable lengths relative to a star pattern. This is particularly relevant for bed-mounted devices such as many tidal stream turbines or some wave devices. The number of generators per string is limited by the rated power of the cable used. As a result, each repair will result in reduced availability of multiple generators.

Some developers propose the use of hydraulic system to transfer energy between individual marine energy devices and a generator. Costing of farms comprising these devices will include the cost of design, manufacture, and installation of the hydraulic system.

8.06.4.5 Site to Grid Transmission

For commercial scale marine energy power generation schemes, the capital cost of grid connection and construction of fabrication facilities must also be considered. Typically, the most energetic wave regimes are located offshore (typically >20 miles) and so the cost associated with design, manufacture, and installation of the system required to transfer energy from the marine energy farm to a grid connection may represent a large fraction of the total cost of a farm. Several device developers propose the use of a hydraulic pipeline to transfer energy to the shore combined with onshore electricity generation via, for example, low head hydro-turbines. For example; this approach is proposed for the Aquamarine's Oyster system and CETO that are designed for deployment at relatively shallow sites close to a shoreline (www.aquamarinepower.co.uk and www.carnegiecorp.com.au, respectively).

The majority of developers propose electricity generation within individual marine energy devices. For these technologies, costs are associated with deployment of electrical transmission cables and associated infrastructure. These transmission systems are similar to those used for offshore wind farms. However, the greater distances involved may lead to selection of high-voltage DC (HVDC) systems rather than high-voltage AC (HVAC) systems. Several studies of high-voltage electrical interconnections have been published [16, 17, Black & Veatch 2004, 15, 18, 19].

Although direct cost comparison of AC and DC systems is not widely available, at present, installation of 33 kV cables seems to be the cheapest option for distances up to 20 km and power levels up to 200 MW [20]. At greater distances, the appeal of this approach is reduced due to increasing cable-laying costs and electrical losses. The appeal of HVDC cables increases with required power and transmission distance and, in the long term, installation of a direct DC link looks promising for arrays with rated power greater than 200 MW located more than 25 km from shore (Grainger and Jenkins 2003). Other studies suggest that greater transmission distances or rated powers must be considered before HVDC is the lower cost option. EConnect [21] suggests that HVAC transmission is likely to exhibit lower lifetime costs when transmission distance is greater than 60 km or required capacity

Table 2 Cost estimates for electrical transmission system between marine energy site and onshore grid connection point

Cost	System description	Reference
$50 million (total)	8 km 250 MVA (90 MW), California	EPRI [18]
13.5 £ million (total)	20 km cable and 30 MW subsea transformer. Wavehub, Cornwall	Halcrow [19]
210 £ m^{-1}	10 MW transmission cable	Atkins [16]
1620 £ m^{-1}	400 MW transmission cable	
100 £ m^{-1}	Cable procurement	Black & Veatch (2005); Halcrow [19]; EPRI [4]
60 £ m^{-1}	Cable installation	EPRI [4]
225 £ m^{-1}	Cable installation	Garrad Hassan [17]
47.6 + 4.063L for transmission distance L	HVAC (132 or 275 kW) manufacture and installation	Boehme et al. [22]; Section 4.07
162.4 + 0.675L for transmission distance L	HVDC (150 kV) manufacture and installation	Boehme et al. [22]; Section 4.07

All values in currency of year of publication.

greater than 300 MW while Boehme et al. [22] suggest that the costs do not break even until rated powers of 325 MW and transmission distances of 250 km are considered.

The capital cost of both types of electrical transmission system is dependent on distance to shore, electrical power generated in the farm, and the choice of an AC or DC connection. The main costs for either type of electrical transmission system are represented by the foundations, generators, and onshore (grid) connection. These costs increase with increasing distance to shore and water depth. In addition, the cost is sensitive to the composition of the seabed and cable landing facilities [18]. A summary of cost estimates for specific sites and of general cost functions based on unit length are given in **Table 2**. Clearly, estimated costs vary considerably but are not insignificant. For example; the material and installation cost for a single 30 MW transmission cable falls in the range 160–325 £ m^{-1} and so an optimistic estimate for a site located 30 km from the point of grid connection would be around £450 k kW^{-1} (assuming three 30 MW cables based on Halcrow [19]). This represents more than one-third of the specific capital cost estimated for first commercial projects [6]. However, Junginger (2003) suggests that there is significant cost reduction potential for transmission cables and that cable cost reductions of 38% could be observed with each doubling of cumulative installed capacity and cumulative length installed (see Section 8.06.8.1).

For a particular site, the cost of manufacturing and installing a transmission cable from the wave power plant to a grid connector is mainly dependent on cable capacity and so will be similar irrespective of generating technology if the mean output is comparable. For this reason, the cost of transmission is sometimes excluded from cost studies to facilitate comparison between alternative marine technologies.

8.06.4.6 Deployment

It is known from published experiences of offshore wind energy projects that deployment costs are sensitive to both the type and duration of offshore work. To quantify the installation costs associated with a marine energy project, it is necessary to determine both the type of vessel required and the duration of vessel time required. Since vessel costs vary with schedule, site, and technology, a cost per installed capacity or cost per installed device should not be used.

8.06.4.7 Decommissioning

Decommissioning at the end of the project life may take many forms. Options include retrieval to shore for scrapping or disposal at sea (e.g., in the form of an artificial reef). Decommissioning costs would be estimated using a similar process as installation costs in that the cost and duration of offshore work would be estimated. Depending on the disposal strategy, the costs associated with decommissioning may be offset by the scrap value of the device. The multi-decade design life of MECs and the use of discounting are such that the costs of decommissioning tend to be modest when viewed from the outset. For example at a relatively low discount rate of 8%, a decommissioning cost of £1 million incurred after a 20-year operating life would only be valued at £210k at the start of the project. Therefore, these costs generally have little impact on the overall economic assessment.

8.06.5 Operating Costs

In the absence of fuel costs for energy generation, marine energy projects are capital intensive. However, project economics remain sensitive to the operating costs. The following items of operating costs are typically considered:

- Periodic expenditures
- Planned maintenance (servicing)
- Unplanned maintenance (repair).

In many studies, the total operating cost is expressed as a percentage of the total capital cost [23]. Detailed analyses of specific projects consider the reliability of devices and the accessibility of the site to obtain site- and technology-specific costs [18]. The operation and maintenance (O&M) schedule for an offshore renewable energy scheme influences both the period of individual device operation, hence the revenue from electrical output, and the periodic expenditure required to implement the designed schedule. Many studies of operational processes have been produced within the offshore wind industry (Herman 2002 [24]); the greater energy density of waves at the design sites of marine energy schemes increases the importance of efficient O&M planning. AMEC [24] suggests that, for wind turbines at least, maintenance costs should be considered on a per-device basis and this is a logical assumption for offshore devices where the time required to access individual floating structures is not insignificant. Considering that failure is most likely during the winter months when output, and hence revenue, is highest, even a small reduction of availability could incur a significant loss of availability and hence annual revenue.

8.06.5.1 Periodic Expenditures

Costing of a particular project should account for all ongoing costs that are required to provide the availability and device performance that are employed in the revenue calculation (Section 8.06.7). These include (but are not limited to) the following:

- Insurance
- Site lease
- Grid transmission charges
- Management
- Costs associated with environmental monitoring activities
- Taxes and government subsidies relevant to the deployment site.

Insurance and site rentals have received limited attention in the wave energy literature. Dalton *et al.* [23] demonstrated that, for a particular wave energy device and site, the project was only viable for insurance rates of 1%. This compares to insurance rates of 5–10% reported for various projects in the maritime industry. Insurance rates are likely to reduce with increased experience and reliability of marine energy systems but the magnitude remains uncertain. Site lease and grid transmission rates will be specific to the deployment region and the grid operator. In the United Kingdom, the use of the seabed from the shoreline to the 12-mile territorial limit is controlled by the Crown Estate. A constant annual rent is charged on nongenerating sites and a rate proportional to output is typically charged after commissioning (Annex C2) [25]. A lower rate is charged outside territorial waters where most farms are likely to be located but based on a similar system.

8.06.5.2 Planned Maintenance

Planned maintenance and unplanned maintenance (i.e., repair) are typically considered separately. There may be significant overlap between these two categories, but the distinction is important as it allows a more logical appraisal for a variety of maintenance and repair strategies. This approach also provides a direct connection to the availability factor of the project. Planned maintenance costs include all costs involved in servicing the devices in the marine energy project. This includes elements such as consumables, spares, labor, and vessels. There are clearly a number of maintenance schedules available, including service-on-site and return-to-shore options. The approach selected will be based on the time required for service at the site and the environmental conditions.

8.06.5.3 Unplanned Maintenance

The repair strategy for devices is potentially more complex than the maintenance strategy due to the significant uncertainty associated with predicting reliability for early stage technology. The costs associated with repair will be determined using a similar methodology to the planned maintenance costs. Costs are assigned to the access of the device (through vessel rates) and to the repair itself. The frequency of repair visits (or device retrieval operations) is determined by the failure rate of the device. The simplest scenario in terms of repair strategies is that the device is repaired on demand. In this case, a response time element is included in the analysis, this being the mean expected time that will pass before the repair operation can commence. This will be determined based on the environmental conditions at the deployment site (see Section 8.06.6.2) and the availability of suitable vessels. The impact of response time on the availability factor, and therefore on the collected revenue, must be considered.

Repair costs cannot necessarily be entirely separated from planned maintenance since work conducted on failed devices is unlikely to be carried out entirely independently of scheduled servicing. For example, a decision may be made to postpone repair of a device until visited (or retrieved) for scheduled maintenance. This will be the case where a device has been designed with redundant systems or can operate suboptimally until the scheduled maintenance. The mean failure frequency must be estimated based upon an engineering appraisal of the device design. In some cases, failure distributions may be available for individual components, particularly if they are established technology bought 'off the shelf'. Care must be taken, however, if these components are being deployed in an environment significantly different from their usual operating conditions. At present, very little is known about the reliability of alternative marine energy technologies due to the lack of offshore experience. It is perhaps reasonable to assume that more complicated devices will require more regular maintenance. As an indication of the target reliability of commercial wave energy schemes, it is instructive to draw comparison with commercial offshore wind farms. A baseline design for an offshore wind turbine requires between 1.5 and 2.0 maintenance visits during a typical year and a reliable design may only require a single maintenance task per year [24, 26]. Prototype testing and sea trials are ongoing to provide improved understanding of device performance and reliability.

8.06.6 Vessels for Offshore Work

For all marine energy projects, offshore vessels are required for installation and for maintenance and repair. The cost of vessel usage is dependent on both the type of vessel employed and the duration of vessel use. While the type of vessel required is largely governed by the type of foundation selected, the duration of vessel use will be dependent on the type of offshore work required and, to varying extents, on the design environment. The limited experience of offshore testing to date has shown that vessel rates may vary rapidly and that long periods of waiting on weather may be required for some sites.

To estimate the installation costs associated with a marine energy project, it is necessary to estimate the duration of offshore vessel time required. It is known from experiences of offshore wind that these costs are sensitive to the type and duration of offshore work. Vessel rates may vary considerably due to both demand variation and the need to await environmental conditions that are suitable for installation. This is because installation of both wave and tidal stream devices must be conducted when environmental conditions are sufficiently benign to allow safe operation of offshore vessels and handling of material and equipment. Suitable environmental conditions depend on the vessels employed and the task conducted but important parameters include wind speed, significant wave height, and current speed.

8.06.6.1 Vessel Type and Unit Cost

Suitable vessels are required for installation of all components of mooring systems, support structures, electrical infrastructure, and marine energy devices. Most of the offshore floating wave energy converters currently being developed can be towed to the deployment site through the use of vessels generally operating for offshore oil and gas industry. Specific vessels are available for tasks such as pile installation, cable laying, or anchor handling. Most offshore work vessels are operated by supply boat companies and are rented by oil companies either by day or on a longer term basis for specific projects. For the foreseeable future, the marine energy industry is likely to employ the same contracting process although a marine energy-specific vessel market may develop as marine energy farms are deployed at increasingly large scale.

Vessel rates can vary considerably due to location and demand variation. Higher day rates and greater variability of day rate are observed for specific vessels (such as jack-up barges, heavy lift vessels, and large cable laying vessels) since only a handful of these vessels are available globally. Vessel rates are therefore lower for vessels that are widely available. Barrett [27] and Ragliano Salles [28] studied the monthly variation of offshore vessel day rates over a 10- and 5-year period, respectively, for the North Sea fleet. They report mean day rates in the range £5–7.5 k day^{-1} for anchor handling, towing, and supply (AHTS) vessels, approximately £5k for offshore supply vessels (OSVs) and approximately £2.5 k day^{-1} for crew supply vessels. However, rates are observed to vary by more than £10k between successive months depending on local demand. At an early stage of technology development, a long-term average rate may be employed [6]. If this approach is used, a contingency budget may also be included to allow for future variation of costs.

For some marine energy technologies, special purpose vessels are proposed that can undertake installation and maintenance tasks with greater efficiency than standard oil and gas vessels. One or more dedicated vessels may be constructed by a technology developer for use at multiple sites or for a specific project. A representative component of the capital cost of such a vessel must be included in the assessment and an appropriate operating cost employed for the vessel day rate. If the vessel is constructed for use at a specific project, then all design, manufacture, and operating costs should be included in the economic assessment of the project.

8.06.6.2 Duration of Offshore Vessel Use

The duration of time for which vessel costs are allocated is typically based on the following:

- Minimum time required to complete the required offshore work – for example, installation, maintenance, or repair activity
- Time required awaiting suitable environmental conditions at the deployment site to conduct the required offshore work
- Time required for transit of vessel between a suitable port and the deployment site.

While estimates of device reliability, task duration, and travel duration have been included in several wave energy studies [4, 6], the influence of site accessibility has not yet been widely considered for marine energy projects. For offshore wind, turbine accessibility has been a significant source of operating cost uncertainty. This has increased the perceived investment risk and is likely to be even more important for wave and tidal stream sites due to the higher energy densities.

8.06.6.2.1 Duration of offshore work
The 'duration of calm conditions required' to complete the necessary offshore activities is dependent on the proposed installation schedule and maintenance schedule. For projects comprising a small number of devices or located at relatively calm sites, sequential

installation may be possible using a single vessel. For projects comprising large numbers of devices, which may be located at more energetic sites, installation may require simultaneous use of a number of vessels. The installation schedule must take account of the period for which environmental conditions are sufficiently calm for vessels to operate at the deployment site.

The "duration of calm conditions that are available" to conduct the required offshore work depends on the specification of the vessels employed (Section 8.06.6.1) and on several environmental parameters including wind speed (U_w), significant wave height (H_s), and current speed (U_c). For wave energy sites, the most important parameter is likely to be significant wave height with most vessels designed to operate while $H_s < \sim 2$ m ([4], BWEA 2004, and, e.g., vessel supply companies (www.bourbon-offshore.com/en/marine-services/support-offshore)). While the significant wave height is greater than the value required for work, vessels must be paid for but not used, activities can then be completed while conditions allow access (**Figure 4**). For tidal stream sites, conditions suitable for installation and maintenance work are dependent on the joint occurrence of wave conditions and flow speed. Flow speed is a particularly onerous constraint since few vessels operate while $U_c > \sim 0.5$ m s^{-1}. Since commercial scale projects will be deployed at sites where waves and currents are more energetic than both demonstrator projects and many offshore wind projects, projects must be designed to allow maintenance within very short periods of accessible conditions.

A 'waiting on weather' allowance, often of several extra days, must be made for each day of working time to allow for a period of inactivity while the vessel is available but not used. For the purposes of cost-estimating, a statistical analysis of wave conditions may be conducted or a nominal waiting on weather allowance is considered based on comparable sites. For a particular project and site, historical or forecast MetOcean conditions will be analyzed to evaluate alternative deployment schedules. Analysis of time series of metocean conditions at a tidal stream site in France (Saviot 2010; EQUIMAR D7.4.1) has shown that even if vessels can operate in flow speeds of 1.13 m s^{-1}, it is necessary to allow more than 3 days of vessel time for each 12 h period of offshore work. During winter months, this increases to more than 1 week per useable 12 h period (**Figure 5**). These are significant constraints for both installation and maintenance, particularly for large farms comprising tens or hundreds of devices. Access constraints are somewhat less onerous for wave energy sites but even at sites with modest wave power levels; it may be necessary to allocate 2–3 days of vessel time for each day of conditions that are suitable for offshore work (23 kW m^{-1} site shown in **Figure 5**). An indication of the number of days of accessible conditions suitable at wave sites with different average values of annual wave power density (kW m^{-1}) is given in **Figure 6**. For sites with annual power densities greater than 30 kW m^{-1}, there are very periods of accessible conditions during winter months.

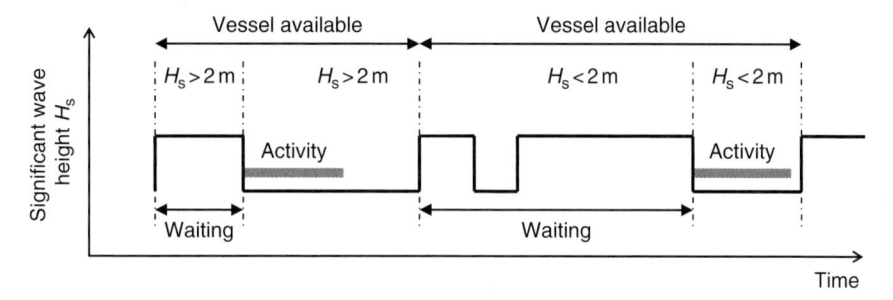

Figure 4 Work completed using single vessel during intervals of accessible conditions defined by significant wave height $H_s < 2$ m.

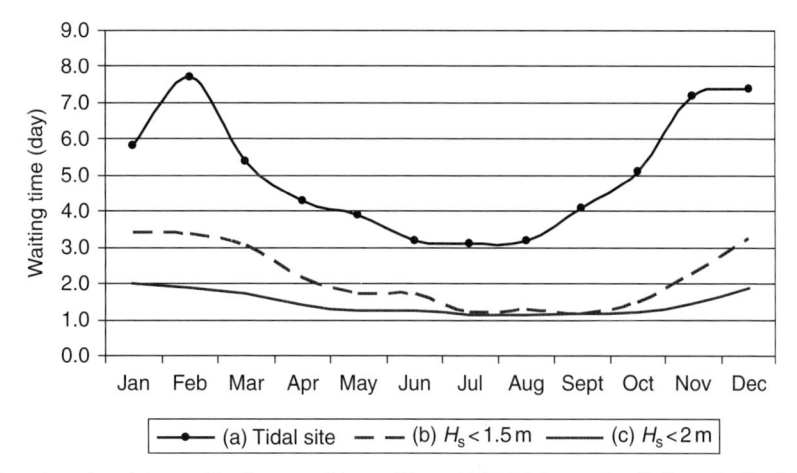

Figure 5 Seasonal variation of number of days waiting for accessible conditions at (a) tidal stream site with flow velocity ~2.5 m s^{-1} during a spring tide and ~1.5 m s^{-1} during a neap tide. Accessible conditions are defined as 12 h duration, current speed $U_c < 1.5$ m s^{-1}, wind speed $U_w < 8$ m s^{-1}, and significant wave height $H_s < 1.5$ m. (b) Wave energy site with annual average significant wave height $H_s = 1.3$ m and average wave power 23 kW m^{-1}. Average duration of accessible conditions and average waiting time for 1 day of accessible conditions shown for $H_s < 1.5$ m only. (c) As (b) but accessible conditions are defined as $H_s < 2.0$ m.

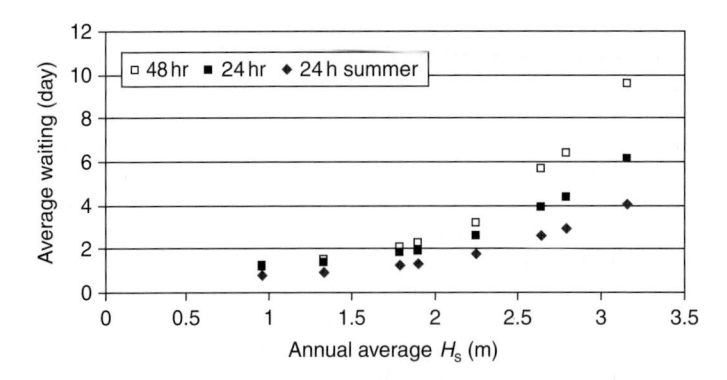

Figure 6 Average number of days waiting required prior to each weather window of 1- or 2-day duration at a range of sites. Eight sites are considered with a different annual average significant wave height. Accessible conditions are defined as $H_s < 2$ m.

8.06.6.2.2 Transit and mobilization time

The time required for vessels to access the site from a suitable port must be included in the total vessel time. This should be based on the distance between port and site and the vessel speed. The time required for vessel mobilization and demobilization should also be included. These are costs associated with relocation of vessels to an appropriate port or site.

8.06.6.3 Vessel Cost Summary

The cost of vessel use is an important component of both installation cost and operating cost. Vessel rates vary significantly so these costs are uncertain and hence high risk. By requirement, the environmental conditions at the sites that are suitable for wave and tidal stream devices are extremely energetic. As a result, conditions at these sites are only suitable for offshore work for relatively short periods. Such access limitations are a particularly important consideration for tidal stream sites where conditions suitable for installation and maintenance work are dependent on the joint occurrence of flow speed and wave conditions. As a consequence, most developers attempt to minimize vessel requirements and some have developed special purpose vessels and techniques to facilitate rapid installation and removal for maintenance.

8.06.7 Revenue

For marine energy projects, revenue is due to the sale of electricity. There are therefore only two considerations: the quantity of energy delivered to the market and the value of that energy.

8.06.7.1 Energy Production

Useful energy, typically in the form of electricity, is the only marketable output from a marine energy farm. Inaccurate prediction of power output can significantly alter economic viability (Section 8.06.3.2). It is therefore important for designers to understand the full range of wave or tidal stream conditions expected at the design site and to understand the power output expected from each device within the farm due to these conditions. Revenue may be calculated via several methods depending on the stage of development of the technology.

8.06.7.1.1 Rated power and capacity factor

The simplest approach to estimate revenue is to consider an average value per unit of electricity and estimate energy production on the basis of the installed capacity of the project.

$$\text{Revenue} = \text{rated power} \times \text{capacity factor} \times T_{yr} \times \text{average revenue} \qquad [5]$$

The capacity factor is defined as the ratio between the average power output of the project and the rated power. Typically, capacity factors are in the range 0.25–0.4, but since they are defined as a function of generator rating artificially high values can be created by a technology that is rated at a lower power than required for the design conditions. Although this approach neglects site-specific conditions, it is widely used for assessing early stage concepts.

8.06.7.1.2 Occurrence plot and performance surface

Perhaps the most widely used approach is based on the performance curve of a typical device, for example, Power(variable), the cumulative duration of Metocean conditions suitable for operation, for example, time(variable), and the mean value of electricity. The duration of conditions time(variable) may be expressed as a probability of occurrence, for example, p(variable), multiplied by the duration of the period of interest. For tidal stream devices, a one-dimensional (1D) performance curve, power(U_C), and 1D occurrence plot, probability(U_C), may be employed. For wave devices, a two-dimensional (2D) performance matrix, for example, power(H_s, T_p) and occurrence matrix probability(H_s, T_p) may be employed. For a wave energy project, revenue would therefore be written as

$$\text{Revenue} = \sum_0^{H_{s,\max}} \sum_0^{T_{p,\max}} \left[\text{power}(H_s, T_p) \times \text{probability}(H_s, T_p)\right] \times \text{availability} \times T_{yr} \times \text{average revenue} \qquad [6]$$

This approach is generally applicable since it accounts for both site and technology dependence of energy production. Further dimensions to the performance curve may be necessary for some technologies to describe sensitivity of power output to additional environmental variables or design parameters.

8.06.7.1.3 Time-varying performance

For medium to large farms, it may be necessary to consider the effect of the time variation of market value of electricity on economic viability. For such projects, energy production can be obtained for each discrete time interval (t) based on known conditions such as significant wave height and peak period and multiplied by the duration of the period (dt).

$$\text{Revenue} = \sum_0^{T_{yr}} \text{power}(H_s(t), T_p(t)) \cdot dt \cdot \text{value}(t) \qquad [7]$$

This approach may be employed for tidal stream projects and either wave or tidal stream projects with large installed capacity.

8.06.7.2 Value of a Unit of Electricity

Revenue is typically determined either by assuming an average value for each unit of electricity or, in some cases, by consideration of the time-varying value of electricity in the operating market. When evaluating COE, the value of each unit is neglected and the calculated COE is simply compared to that from alternative sources. However, when calculating NPV, the value of each unit becomes important. The value of a single unit (kWh) of electricity is dependent on the electricity market in which the project is installed and on the scale of the project. In the United Kingdom, the value per unit is the sum of the market value and, at present, several additional incentives. Many other national electricity systems operate a similar competitive market. **Table 3** summarizes the approximate value of each unit of electricity in the United Kingdom.

8.06.7.2.1 Market value (UK)

In the United Kingdom, the amount paid to an electricity generator for the energy delivered to the national grid is defined by the New Electricity Trading Arrangement (NETA). This arrangement requires generators to submit a contract, in advance of each half-hour generating period for the quantity of electricity they intend to deliver during each half-hour generating period. If the generator has a shortfall in contracted generation, the deficit incurs a penalty charge (i.e., the generator purchases extra electricity from the market at the system buy price (SBP) to compensate for the deficit). Alternatively, if the generator exceeds its contracted generation, it is paid at the system sell price (SSP) (i.e., the market buys the generators surplus to account for shortfalls by other generators). Both the SSP and the SBP vary considerably with demand and operating period and so the accuracy with which power output can be predicted affects the value of the generated electricity. Average values during 2010 are given in **Table 3**.

The actual value which a given operator or farm receives will depend on the scale of the farm. Electricity generated by small-scale farms such as those installed at the early stage of industry development is likely to be valued at toward the lower end of the market. This is because small farms will not influence the market value. Medium-scale projects are likely to arrange long-term power purchase agreements at a slightly lower rate than wholesale market prices in order to mitigate against the risk of market price variation. Large projects – at a similar scale to conventional baseload power stations – will have the potential to affect the market value and so may be able to benefit by bidding for higher values within the market. For such schemes, market price variation should be considered in the revenue calculation. Competitive markets also imply a higher value for electricity sources that are predictable.

Table 3 Indicative values of components of revenue per unit of electricity

Component	Value (p kWh^{-1}) (mean ± standard deviation)	Comment
System sell price (SSP)	3.65 ± 0.9	Average 2010 [29]
System buy price (SBP)	4.80 ± 1.8	Average 2010 [29]
Renewable Obligation Certificates (ROCs)	3.7	Buyout (2009/10)
	4.7	Traded price (2009/10)
CCL contribution	~0.2	Indicative
Total	11.05–14.4	With two ROCs

8.06.7.2.2 Renewable Obligation Certificates (UK)

The Renewables Obligation scheme was introduced in 2002 as a mechanism to support in renewable generating capacity. Initially, each unit of electricity generated by an accredited source receives a single Renewable Obligation Certificate (ROC). Each certificate may subsequently be sold at a buyout price or traded. In 2009, the scheme was amended such that technologies are considered in five different bands, with each band receiving multiples (or fractions) of ROCs per unit of electricity generated depending on their state of development. The intention is to provide a financial incentive for investment in emerging technologies. Both wave and tidal stream technologies are banded as emerging technologies and thus eligible for two ROCs per unit of electricity generated. In 2006–07, the buyout price for a single ROC was 3.32 p kWh^{-1}, but the value has increased annually and is presently 3.72 p Wh^{-1} (2009/10). However, each ROC may yield a greater return because they can be traded. Representative values of traded ROCs are published by the non-fossil purchasing authority (www.nfpa.co.uk).The average value of traded ROCs over the years 2003–10 is approximately 4.7 p kWh^{-1}. Ofgem [30] places the value of ROCs to the electricity supply at the slightly higher value of 5.44 p kWh^{-1} (for 2008/09). The future value of ROCs is strongly dependent on the market uptake of renewables and has been studied by SQW [31].

8.06.7.2.3 Climate change levy (UK)

Some additional income may also be assumed via the climate change levy. All commercial electricity customers are charged an additional 0.43 p kWh^{-1} for electricity from non-renewable sources. Each renewable generator can negotiate for a fraction of this 0.43 p kWh^{-1} to be passed on from the supplier for all electricity that is sold to commercial customers. So, if an exemption value of 0.25 p kWh^{-1} is negotiated and commercial customers represent 75% of the utilities sales, then the generator will receive around 0.2 p kWh^{-1}.

8.06.8 Future Prospects

None of the marine energy devices (wave or tidal stream) presently in development are commercially viable in their present form. At the time of writing, a handful of developers of tidal stream devices (Marine Current Turbines, Tidal Generation Limited, OpenHydro) and wave devices (Pelamis Wave Power, Aquamarine Power) have attracted the interest of commercial electricity suppliers who are supporting the construction and testing of prototypes (SSE, EoN, EdF). However, initial farms will only be possible with the revenue support provided by ROCs [1, 32]. Studies based on prototype designs suggest a central estimate for the unit cost of electricity from a first commercial project to be around 20 p kWh^{-1} for wave energy devices and 15 p kWh^{-1} for tidal stream devices [1, 2, 6]. In contrast, the market value of a unit of electricity is less than 4 p kWh^{-1} (for UK market, see Section 8.06.7.2).

It is recognized that existing designs must be modified and new designs developed so that electricity can be produced at a rate that is competitive with other electricity generation technologies [8]. To understand how electricity generated from wave devices or tidal stream devices may contribute to future supplies, it is important to predict how costs may change as the industry moves from demonstrator schemes to large-scale deployments. This requires consideration of the change of economic viability due to the following:

1. Increased project scale: for example, to understand how the estimated cost of a pre-commercial project (order 1–10 MW installed capacity) relates to a commercial scale project (e.g., an installed capacity of 100 MW or greater).
2. Increased development of the technology that may occur due to a variety of factors including Research and Development and learning from experience of either the technology or the sector.

Experience curves are often used to provide an indication of the future costs of marine energy systems. This approach is briefly described in Section 8.06.8.1. A reduction of the predicted cost of electricity can only be achieved by three processes: (1) reduction of capital cost, (2) reduction of operating cost, and (3) increase of energy production without change of costs. Note that, as discussed in Section 8.06.3.4, discounted measures of economic viability will also reduce with reduction of the perceived risk but these processes are not considered further. The extent by which costs could be reduced or energy production increased is discussed in Section 8.06.8.2.

8.06.8.1 Evolution of Costs in the Marine Sector

In many studies of marine energy economics [4, 6] among many others, it has been assumed that the cost of electricity will fall with the cumulative installed capacity. This approach is based on the assumption that increased experience of designing and using a technology reduces its cost and is referred to as an experience curve. Details of the approach are given in various texts [33, 34] but essentially the approach assumes that, for each doubling of cumulative installed capacity, costs fall to a percentage of those in the reference year by a factor defined as the progress ratio. When the installed capacity is P, the cost can be written as

$$C(P) = C_0 P^{\log_2(\text{PR})} \qquad [8]$$

where PR is the progress rate. An experience curve may also be written in terms of a learning rate (LR = 1 − PR) which defines the percentage cost reduction over each doubling of installed capacity. The experience curve approach is based on observations of the costs of new technologies that have shown that production costs typically reduce with increasing familiarity with the technology (see References 33, 35, and, 36). This can be attributed to a variety of factors including the following:

- Increased efficiency and specialization (learning by experience)
- Innovations caused by R&D (learning by searching)
- Design improvements for operation (learning by interacting)
- Standardization – allowing mass production
- Optimized sizing.

Since there is no historical cost data on which to base marine energy learning curves, the progress rates assumed have typically been based on those observed for a range of other industry sectors, with particular reliance on data drawn from the wind industry. Progress ratios for the installed cost of onshore wind have been reported as 92–94% [37] although variations are observed across states (90–96% for several EU states observed by Neij *et al.* 2003) and with the size of the dataset considered (77–85% globally observed by Junginger *et al.* (2005) and 82–92% by McDonald and Schrattenholzer) [38]. Progress rates for the unit cost of electricity from wind turbines are generally lower than those for capital cost alone. For example, a progress rate of ~88% is observed for €kWh^{-1} in comparison to ~95% for €kW^{-1} installed capacity [37] (www.extool.com). This is because cost of electricity accounts for reductions of both installed cost and operating cost as well as increased performance. In general, progress rates in the range 85–90% have been applied to the COE from marine energy systems [4, 6].

If realized these rates would greatly reduce the cost of electricity from marine energy devices. From a nominal value of 20 p kWh^{-1} at a unit installed capacity, a 10% learning rate suggests that costs would fall to around 6 p kWh^{-1} when 3 GW of capacity has been manufactured and installed (**Figure 7**). These cost reductions will only occur with increased experience so construction of early projects is only possible with additional support (see Section 8.06.7.2). Learning curves have been employed by the Energy Technologies Institute (ETI) and the UK Energy Research Centre (UKERC) to inform the development of a roadmap toward large-scale deployment of marine energy [8]. The roadmap suggests the rate of installation, and increase of performance and reduction of cost that should be achieved at 10-year intervals in order to achieve 10–20 GW cumulative deployment by 2050. Key cost and performance measures are summarized in **Table 4**.

While the experience curve approach is of some use for predicting general trends across the marine energy sector (or any sector), many studies caution the use of this approach, particularly for emerging technologies. A recent example of learning curve limitations is given by the UK offshore wind sector – although costs were expected to fall from 2007 to 2010 [1], they have risen [2]. This cost increase seems to have occurred due to several factors including a doubling of average capital costs and 65% increase in operating costs over a 5-year period. In this case, cost increases appear to be driven by supply chain constraints and (to a lesser extent) real changes of exchange rates ([39], Boccard *et al.* 2009). Principal concerns associated with the application of learning curves are as follows:

- Progress rates are difficult to transfer between industry sectors [33].
- Progress rates estimated from historic data are uncertain. Even when the same set of turbine cost data is employed, the learning rate can vary between 1.8% and 7.9% depending on econometric assumptions [40] so sensitivity ranges are recommended (Neij [37] recommends 2%).
- Progress rates are time-varying and so it extrapolations beyond 2 orders of magnitude from the supporting data may not be valid (IEA 2000).
- Progress rates may not be applicable at early stages of technology development. In a study focused on the investment required for marine energy learning [41], it is noted that experience does not lead to cost reductions until the installed capacity of a single technology type is greater than around 100 MW.

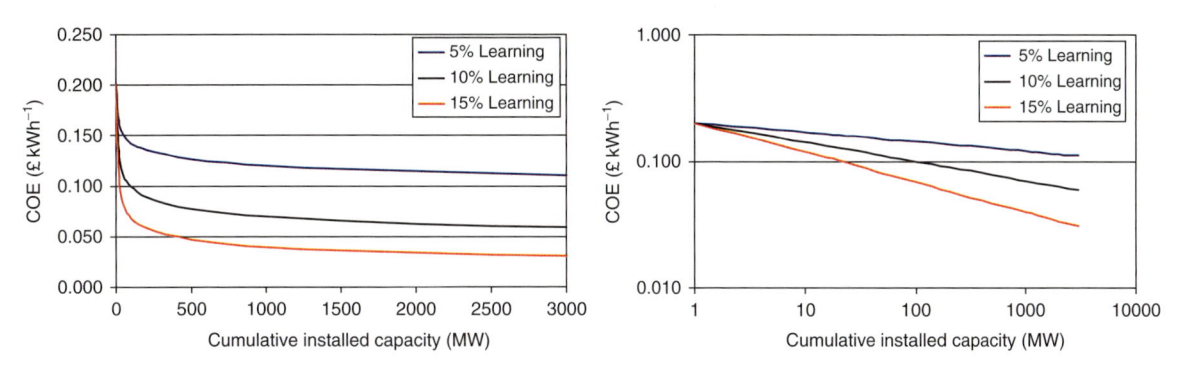

Figure 7 Change of COE with installed capacity for learning rates of 5%, 10%, and 15% (equivalent to progress rates of 95%, 90%, and 85%) from an initial cost C_0 = 0.2 £ MWh^{-1} at installed capacity of 1 MW to a cumulative installed capacity of 3 GW.

Table 4 Cumulative installed capacity and corresponding changes of costs and performance of marine energy systems between 2010 and 2050 proposed by UKERC [8]

Year		2010	2020	2030	2040	2050
Cumulative capacity (GW)	Maximum		2	12	18	20
		0	1.5	9	13.5	15
	Minimum		1	6	9	10
CAPEX (£k kW^{-1})	Maximum	7000	4000	2500		2000
		5500	3250	2250		1750
	Minimum	4000	2500	2000		1500
O&M costs (p kWh^{-1})	Maximum	4	2.5	1.5		1
		2.75	1.75	1		0.65
	Minimum	1.5	1	0.5		0.3
Capacity factor	Maximum	30	0	40		44
		24	33.8	36.5		41
	Minimum	19	0	33		38
COE (p kWh^{-1})	Maximum	40	18	10		8
		28.5	13.5	8.5		6.5
	Minimum	17	9	7		5

Furthermore, even when progress ratios are applied that have been derived for comparable industry sectors, the extent of cost reduction that can be achieved will be limited by the cumulative installed capacity. For example, deployment sites available for wave technologies that operate in nearshore waters of the United Kingdom are limited to 3 GW (capacity factor of 0.3 to produce 7.8 TWh yr^{-1} practical resource estimated by the Carbon Trust [6]) and this effectively limits the cumulative installed capacity over which learning may occur. Differentiation has been made between deployment location on the basis of water depth, particular combinations of site and technology and industry-wide estimates of cost reduction have been employed but to date there has been limited consideration of how the market size for a particular technology may influence cost reduction. Since the ability to compare technologies is important to understand which technology may be most competitive at large scales of deployment, it is useful to consider the processes or mechanisms by which cost reduction could occur.

8.06.8.2 Mechanisms for Cost Evolution

For any electricity generating technology, economic viability (based on a discounted measure such as the levelized cost of electricity or NPV) can only be improved through one of three mechanisms: decrease of either capital or operating costs or increase of revenue. The cost associated with farms of devices is the sum of many individual quantities (components, materials, days of vessel time) and a unit cost associated with each quantity (component cost, material cost, process cost, vessel day rate). To decrease the capital or operating cost, it is necessary to reduce either the quantities required or the unit cost of each quantity. Similarly, revenue is dependent on the quantity of electricity generated and the unit value per quantity. In the following sections, the mechanisms by which unit quantities may reduce, unit costs may reduce, and performance may increase are considered. For wave energy devices and, to a lesser extent, for tidal stream systems, there are several fundamental aspects of design that will influence, and perhaps limit, the extent of cost reduction that could be achieved. These factors are also discussed.

8.06.8.2.1 Revenue: Increased power output per device

As seen in Section 8.06.3.2, a percentage change of revenue has a larger influence on economic viability than the same percentage change of any cost. Increase of power output is therefore an important factor in the reduction of overall costs. This will be achieved by increased reliability but also by improving device design to optimize output for the resource. Furthermore, as device power output increases, the number of devices and hence quantity of associated infrastructure will reduce. For offshore wind, the increasing rated power per turbine has allowed reduction of the number of turbines per farm. However, for both wave and tidal stream systems, there are limits to the power output that may be achieved by individual devices.

Power density limits – that is, the maximum power output that can be achieved from a given wave condition – are well known for certain device configurations. For example; the power output from individual devices that comprise a single wave activated body constrained by a power takeoff system is a function of the incident wave conditions (following point absorber theory), float volume, and allowable response amplitude. Even if a (single) device can be designed to produce maximum output as defined by point absorber theory in all sea states, the average annual output per device remains small (less than 1 MW at sites with annual power density greater than 35 kW m^{-1}; see Table 3 of Reference 42). More accurate predictions of maximum output can of course be made accounting for constraints on a particular device concept, but this is a general limit for single devices. For tidal stream devices, dimensions will be limited by water depth and, as for wind turbines, by structural considerations related to blade and support structure design. Thus, power output will be limited to of the order of 1 MW. Thus, commercial deployments (e.g., 100 MW capacity and above) must comprise very large numbers of individual devices.

8.06.8.2.2 Capital cost: Changes due to scale of deployment

The cost for civil engineering infrastructure (Section 8.06.4.3) and electrical infrastructure (Section 8.06.4.4) depends on the number of devices to be installed, the inter-device spacing, and the vessels required for installation. Although some cost studies have been completed for individual mooring systems, there is limited understanding of how the configuration or installation cost of mooring systems and support structures would vary with installed capacity at a particular site. For large-scale farms, the feasibility of installation is likely to be an important consideration.

For marine energy project cost estimates, a percentage reduction of unit cost has typically been assumed to represent bulk orders [6, 11, 43], and additional costs for construction of mass fabrication facilities have sometimes been considered [16]. The magnitude of the percentage change employed is typically based on 'expert estimates', but the actual values used are not widely reported. Reviews and predictions of cost changes in the offshore wind sector [2, 17, 39] suggest that the following costs may change due to change of deployment scale:

Supply of station-keeping structure. Limited reductions of foundation cost (e.g., €MW^{-1}) are expected due to volume production. For offshore wind, this is expected to yield cost reductions estimated at 15% although this is partly attributed to increased unit size, that is, increased swept area and hence capacity of individual turbines ([17], Boccard *et al.* 2009). A comparison of 1 and 5 MW wind turbines indicates 10% reduction of levelized cost using larger capacity turbines (Kaltschmitt *et al.* 2007, Table 7.3, p. 369 referenced by Boccard 2009). For tidal stream devices, similar mechanisms may occur since increase of swept area increases power output per device. Alternatively, the number of devices on a single support structure may be increased. However, for wave devices, power output per mooring (or per support structure) will only be improved by installation of multiple generating units on the same mooring (or support structure) since power output is not a function of device dimension.

Savings due to volume production should be possible due to standardization [44]. The same mooring connections or foundations are likely to be used for different devices, thus increasing the scale of production of a given component. This is likely to lead to large cost reductions since mass production is a new approach for companies that have traditionally supplied relatively small batch sizes to the oil and gas sector (see, e.g., Reference 17).

Installation of station-keeping structure. Increased project scale is expected to yield substantial savings due to improved utilization of installation vessels and reduction of fixed costs, such as mobilization, per installed MW or per device. Cost reductions of the order of 50% are expected for offshore wind ([17], Table 2.2). Developers with experience of deployed devices estimate installation cost reductions of the order of 5–20% (EQUIMAR 7.1.1). However, impact of installation cost reductions may be moderated by the more demanding nature of deeper, farther offshore sites and by the variation of vessel rates that tend to be a function of vessel supply and demand [39]. A model for wind turbine vessel installation rates proposed by Offshore Design Engineering (ODE) [39] assumes that rates are proportional to planned number of installation operations during the year of deployment, which suggests that costs can increase during the early, rapid deployment of a technology if similar vessels are required for multiple sites.

8.06.8.2.3 Capital cost: Changes due to elapsed time

Change of material procurement costs is likely to be important [44], particularly for structure-supported devices for which, similar to offshore wind, a major fraction of the capital cost will be associated with unit cost of steel. This is therefore particularly important for tidal stream devices that are typically supported on rigid structures rather than on moored floats. Historic trends of market prices are publicly available (e.g., steel price from CRU (www.cruspi.com) and Copper price from Kitco (www.kitcometals.com)). Predicted trends for material prices vary depending on source but may significantly influence predicted project cost. For steel, ODE [39] suggests that a 60% increase of cost per tonne may be observed from 2007 to 2020, whereas Ernst & Young [2] assumes that costs reduce to 2013 and maintain steady at the long-run average from 2014). Similarly, Ernst & Young [2] analyzes historic trends to predict linear growth of labor rate to 2015 and a 5% increase of commodity prices by 2012 assuming a constant exchange rate.

There are significant opportunities for cost reduction due to improved installation methods. This may be caused by reduction of installation, mobilization, and contingency time and by vessel customization; reductions of up to 50% have been observed between early offshore wind farms [17]. Although support structure cost reductions due to accumulated experience and research and development may be large (estimated at 30% by ODE [39] for offshore wind), these cost changes will only be realized if the industry progresses.

8.06.8.2.4 Operating cost: Changes

A parametric estimate of the operating cost for a wave energy scheme would be based on the number and duration of maintenance tasks and would account for the duration of conditions suitable for offshore work and the time required to access the site from a suitable port (Section 8.06.6). As for offshore windfarms [26], maintenance costs for wave devices will be fixed per device and so increasing device output is advantageous for reducing operating cost. As noted above, the rated capacity per generating unit is subject to relatively low physical limits (order of 2 MW) and so the potential for reducing operating cost by increasing the rated capacity and the output of individual devices is limited. Site access limitations also have important implications for both installation strategies and maintenance strategies and become increasingly important for commercial scale projects comprising large numbers of devices. At a site with low average wave power density (kW m^{-1}), accessible conditions will be more persistent but at the expense of a lower average output from individual generators. Both installation and maintenance strategies are therefore likely to change significantly with scale of deployment, particularly for large deployments of similar capacity to offshore wind (order >100 MW).

8.06.8.3 Summary

Capital costs for most new technologies are expected to reduce with accrued experience of design, manufacture, installation, and operation. Reductions of both capital cost and COE are often estimated on the basis of cumulative installed capacity. This approach indicates that substantial cost reductions will occur and has been used to inform deployment plans. However, these are only predictions and several gigawatts of capacity must be installed for wave and tidal stream technologies to be viable without support. Mechanisms by which these cost reductions could occur and by which cost could change with the capacity of a single farm are discussed. For support structures, it is expected that existing concepts will be standardized and new concepts may emerge such that both procurement and installation costs are reduced. For different scales of deployment, costs may change due to only a small number of factors: principally change of procurement costs (the cost per unit) and efficiency of installation processes such that vessel time is reduced. Cost changes due to change of scale of deployment will, to some extent, be caused by experience, but these cost changes require investment and time to occur.

References

[1] Ernst & Young (2007) Impact of banding the renewables obligation – Costs of electricity production. DTI report URN 07/948.
[2] Ernst & Young (2009) Costs of and financial support for offshore wind. DECC URN 09D/534.
[3] Thorpe T (1999) A brief review of wave energy. UK Department of Trade and Industry ETSU-R120.
[4] EPRI (2004) Economic assessment methodology for wave power plants. E2I EPRI WP – US – 002 Rev 4.
[5] EPRI (2006) North America tidal in-stream energy conversion technology feasibility study. EPRI TP-008-NA.
[6] The Carbon Trust (2006) Future marine energy. Findings of the marine energy challenge: Cost competitiveness and growth of wave and tidal stream energy.
[7] PIER (2008) Summary of PIER-funded wave energy research. California Energy Commission, PIER Program CEC-500-2007-083, March 2008.
[8] UKERC (2010) Marine energy technology roadmap. Energy Technologies Institute and UK Energy Research Centre, October 2008.
[9] Allan GJ, Bryden I, McGregor PG, et al. (2011) Concurrent and legacy economic and environmental impacts from establishing a marine energy sector in Scotland. *Energy Policy* 36: 2734–2753.
[10] Brealey RA and Myers SC (2002) *Financing and Risk Management*, 6th edn. New York: McGraw-Hill.
[11] Boud R and Thorpe T (2003) *WAVENET: Results from the work of the European Thematic Network on Wave Energy*.
[12] Gross R, Heptonstall P, and Blyth W (2007) *Investment in Electricity Generation: The Role of Costs, Incentives and Risks*. London, UK: UK Energy Research Centre.
[13] Awerbuch S (2003) Determining the real cost: Why renewable power is more cost-competitive than previously believed. *Renewable Energy World* 6(2): 52–61.
[14] Black & Veatch (2001) The commercial prospects for tidal stream power. ETSU T/06/00209/REP. DTI Sustainable Energy Programme DTI/Pub URN 01/1011.
[15] Lopez, Ricci P, Villate JL, et al. (2010) Preliminary economic assessment and analysis of grid connection schemes for ocean energy arrays. *Proceedings of the 3rd International Conference on Ocean Energy*. 6 October 2010.
[16] Atkins Oil & Gas (1992) A parametric costing model for wave energy technology. ETSU-WV1685.
[17] Garrad Hassan (2003) Offshore wind: Economies of scale, engineering resource and load factor. DTI 3914/BR/01.
[18] EPRI (2005) Offshore wave power feasibility demonstration project – Final summary report. E2I EPRI Global WP009 – US Rev 1.
[19] Halcrow (2005) Wave hub technical feasibility study: Final report. South West of England Regional Development Agency.
[20] Grainger and Jenkins (1998) Offshore wind farm electrical connection options. *Proceedings of the 20th BWEA Wind Energy Conference*, pp. 319–324. September 1998. Professional Engineering Publishing.
[21] EConnect (2005) Study on the development of the offshore grid for connection of the round two wind farms. Reported for Renewables Advisory Board, DTI.
[22] Boehme T, Taylor J, Wallace R, and Bialek J (2006) Matching renewable electricity generation with demand. Academic Study Summary. Scottish Executive & University of Edinburgh.
[23] Dalton G, Alcorn R, and Lewis T (2010) Operational expenditure costs for wave energy projects: O/M, insurance and site rent. *Proceedings of the 3rd International Conference on Ocean Energy (ICOE)*. Bilbao, Spain, 6 October.
[24] AMEC Wind (2001) Monitoring and evaluation of Blyth offshore wind farm. Projected operation and maintenance costs of UK offshore wind farms based on the experience at Blyth. DTI Report W/35/00563/Rep/5 URN04/881.
[25] Crown Estate (2004) *Tender Procedures and Criteria for Round 2 UK Offshore Windfarm Developments*.
[26] van Bussel GJW (1999) The development of an expert system for the determination of availability and O&M costs for offshore wind farms. *Proceedings of European Wind Energy Conference (EWEC)*, pp. 402–405. Nice, France.
[27] Barrett (2005) *The Offshore Supply Boat Sector*. Fortis Securities LLC.
[28] Ragliano Salles B (2003) The offshore and specialised ships markets in 2003. *BRS Annual Review of World Shipping and Shipbuilding Developments in 2003*, ch. 5. Paris, France.
[29] Elexon (2010) *Trading Operations Report November 2010*. Panel Paper 176/02.
[30] Ofgem (2008) *Renewables Obligation: Annual Report 2006–2007, Ofgem* 4 March 2008.
[31] SQW Energy, Redfield Consulting, Cambridge Economic Policy Associates and Econnect (2008) Modelling changes to the renewables obligation. Report commissioned by the Scottish Government, published December 2008.
[32] Allan GJ, Gilmartin M, McGregor P, and Swales K (2011) Levelised costs of wave and tidal energy in the UK: Cost competitiveness and the importance of 'banded' renewables obligation certificates. *Energy Policy* 39: 23–29.
[33] IEA (2006) *Offshore Wind Experiences*. International Energy Agency.
[34] Junginger M, Faaij A, and Turkenburg WC (2004) Global experience curves for wind farms. *Energy Policy* 33: 133–150.
[35] Delionback LM (1975) Guidelines for application of learning/cost improvement curves. NASA Report TM X-64968.
[36] Winskell M, Markusson N, Jeffrey H, et al. (2008) Technology change and energy systems: Learning pathways for future sources of energy, draft report from UKERC research programme on energy technology learning rates and learning effect.
[37] Neij L (2008) Cost development of future technologies for power generation – A study based on experience curves and complementary bottom-up assessments. *Energy Policy* 36: 2200–2211.
[38] McDonald A and Schrattenholzer L (2001) Learning rates for energy technologies. *Energy Policy* 29(4): 255–261.
[39] ODE (2007) Study of the costs of offshore wind generation. *A Report to the Renewables Advisory Board*. DTI URN 07/779.
[40] Soderholm P and Sundqvist T (2007) Empirical challenges in the use of learning curves for assessing the economic prospects of renewable energy technologies. *Renewable Energy* 32(15): 2559–2578.

[41] Jeffrey H (2008) Learning rates in the marine energy sector. *Proceedings of the 2nd International Conference on Ocean Energy*. Brest, Brittany, France, October 2008.
[42] Stallard T, Rothschild R, and Aggidis GA (2008) A comparative approach to the economic modelling of a large-scale wave power scheme. *European Journal of Operational Research* 185(2008): 884–898.
[43] IEA (2005) *Projected Cost of Generating Electricity*. International Energy Agency.
[44] Batten WMJ and Bahaj AS (2007) An assessment of growth scenarios and implications for ocean energy in Europe. *Proceedings of the 7th European Wave and Tidal Energy Conference*. Porto, Portugal.

Further Reading

Boccard N (2010) Economic properties of wind power: A European assessment. *Energy Policy* 38(7): 3232–3244.
The Carbon Trust (2005) Oscillating water column wave energy converter evaluation report. Marine Energy Challenge, ARUP, EON.
ODE (2009) Preliminary design and costing of support structures for an array of wave energy devices. EquiMar-Del7-3-1 REPORT 9181-G-M-0001.
Previsic M, Siddiqui O, and Bedard R (2004) Economic assessment methodology for wave power plants. EPRI Report No. E2I WP – US – 002 – Rev 4.
RAEng (2004) The cost of generating electricity. PB Power report for Royal Academy of Engineering.

INDEX

Notes

Cross-reference terms in *italics* are general cross-references, or refer to subentry terms within the main entry (the main entry is not repeated to save space). Readers are also advised to refer to the end of each article for additional cross-references - not all of these cross-references have been included in the index cross-references.

The index is arranged in set-out style with a maximum of four levels of heading. Major discussion of a subject is indicated by bold page numbers. Page numbers suffixed by *t* and *f* refer to Tables and Figures respectively. *vs.* indicates a comparison.

Where index subentries and sub-subentries pertaining to a subject have the same page number, they have been listed to indicate the comprehensiveness of the text.

2-D *see* two-dimensional
3-D *see* three-dimensional
5 year annual plans: Indian hydropower, **6**: 233, **6**: 234, **6**: 237, **6**: 240
100 mega-watt photovoltaic plants, **1**: 690
250 kW grid-connected fuel cell analysis, **4**: 300
500W to 5kW power generation markets, **4**: 200
1050MW Salto Osorio hydroelectricity project, Brazil, **6**: 114
1890–1940's Spanish hydropower, **6**: 317
1940–1960's Spanish hydropower, **6**: 323
1960–1975's Spanish hydropower, **6**: 327
1970's onwards:
   electricity production, **6**: 1–2, **6**: 2*f*
   Spanish hydropower, **6**: 333
1998–2002 wind turbine financial support, **2**: 710, **2**: 713
2000's wood fuel markets, **5**: 78
2002 to 2006 wind turbine financial support, **2**: 711, **2**: 715
2007 onwards wind turbine financial support, **2**: 711, **2**: 718
2010 photovoltaic global industry overview, **1**: 167
2020 photovoltaic vision, **1**: 183
2020 wind energy price comparisons, **2**: 499
2050 photovoltaic vision, **1**: 185, **1**: 186
6450 MW Madeira hydroelectric project, Brazil, **6**: 104
8125 MW Tucurui hydroelectric project, Brazil, **6**: 101
14000 MW Itaipu hydroelectric project, Brazil, **6**: 96

A

AAEMFC *see* alkaline anion exchange membrane fuel cells
AAR *see* alkali–aggregate reactions
ABB company: wind turbines, **2**: 324, **2**: 325*f*
Abengoa Mojave Solar Project Power Plant, **3**: 631, **3**: 632*f*
Abengoa Solar New Technologies, **3**: 194–195
Aberthaw power plant, **5**: 66
abrasion:
   concrete structure durability, **6**: 390
   high concentration solar collectors, **3**: 171
absorbed solar radiation, **3**: 128, **3**: 259, **3**: 438, **3**: 440*f*
absorbers:
   absorber–cover heat transfer coefficients, **3**: 132, **3**: 133*t*
   agricultural solar thermal systems, **3**: 571
   air flat-plate solar collectors, **3**: 108, **3**: 109*f*
   area receiver analysis, **3**: 174
   coatings, **3**: 104, **3**: 301–312, **3**: 108
   collectors
      high concentration collectors, **3**: 174, **3**: 183, **3**: 185
      low-temperature stationary collectors, **3**: 104, **3**: 108, **3**: 132
      solar water heating systems, **3**: 426
   conduction exchange, **3**: 132
   embedded nanoparticles, **1**: 650
   flat-plate low-temperature stationary collectors, **3**: 104, **3**: 108
   high concentration solar collectors, **3**: 174, **3**: 183, **3**: 185
   industrial solar thermal applications, **3**: 571
   liquid flat-plate low-temperature stationary collectors, **3**: 104
   low-temperature stationary collectors, **3**: 104, **3**: 108, **3**: 132
      flat-plate collectors, **3**: 104, **3**: 108
      liquid flat-plate solar collectors, **3**: 104
   parabolic trough solar collectors, **3**: 183
   photovoltaics
      plasmonics, **1**: 650
      quantum structure nanotechnology, **1**: 526
      thermodynamics, **1**: 316
   quantum structure nanotechnology, **1**: 526
   selective coatings, **3**: **301–312**
   solar dishes, **3**: 185
   solar thermal systems, **3**: **301–312**, **3**: 571
   tests, **3**: 174
   thermodynamics, **1**: 316
absorbing beaches: ocean wave energy, **8**: 91
absorption:
   see also adsorption
   angular variation, **3**: 19
   atmospheric effects, **3**: 36
   chillers, **3**: 612
   coatings, **3**: 301, **3**: **301–312**, **3**: 320
   coefficients, **1**: 401
   energy conversion principles, **1**: 296
   glazings, **3**: 320
   high concentration solar collectors, **3**: 175
   low-temperature stationary collectors, **3**: 126, **3**: 127, **3**: 128
   luminescent solar concentrators, **1**: 589
   parabolic troughs, **3**: 175
   photovoltaic thermodynamics, **1**: 334
   radiation, **3**: 126
   refrigeration, **3**: 464, **3**: 465, **3**: 471, **3**: 472
   selective coatings, **3**: 301, **3**: **301–312**
   solar cell energy conversion principles, **1**: 296
   solar cooling systems, **3**: 461, **3**: 464, **3**: 465, **3**: 471, **3**: 472, **3**: 484
   solar radiation, **3**: 36, **3**: 126, **3**: 128

171

absorption: (*continued*)
   solar resource, **3**: 27
   spectrum, **1**: 589
Abu Dhabi, UAE, **1**: 690, **3**: 547
AC *see* alternating current (AC)
accelerating evolution: photovoltaics, **1**: 20
acceptance issues:
   Three Gorges Project, China, **6**: 208
   wind power, **2**: 396
acceptor atoms, **1**: 293
acceptor molecules, **1**: 440, **1**: 448, **1**: 452
accessibility:
   geothermal energy sustainable development, **7**: 283
   wind energy, **2**: 524
   wind park design, **2**: 186–187, **2**: 189
accessible surface area: lignocellulosic wastes, **5**: 232
access roads: wind power, **2**: 421
accident mitigation/risks:
   hydrogen safety, **4**: 101
   photovoltaic environmental impacts, **1**: 153
Acciona:
   hydropower production, **6**: 315
   wind turbines, **2**: 317, **2**: 320*f*, **2**: 321*t*
accuracy: solar irradiance-photovoltaic power forecasts, **1**: 269, **1**: 281
achieved system efficiencies: luminescent solar concentrators, **1**: 595
acid-base complex membranes, **4**: 189
acid-catalyzed transesterification, **5**: 222
acid fluids: geothermal energy, **7**: 147
acidic gas contaminants, **5**: 173
acid pretreatments, **5**: 235
acid rain, **3**: 4
acoustics:
   see also noise
   Doppler current profilers, **8**: 23
   measurements, **2**: 379
   rotor blades, **2**: 713
   wind energy testing, **2**: 379
acquired immune deficiency syndrome (AIDS), **7**: 289
activated carbon treatments, **5**: 146
active-cavity radiometers, **3**: 27
active control loads: wind turbines, **2**: 251
active electrochromic films, **3**: 344
active materials: organic solar cells, **1**: 450, **1**: 468
active power control, **2**: 582
active solar systems, **3**: **449–480**
   air systems, **3**: 452, **3**: 455, **3**: 474
   array design, **3**: 475
   cooling systems, **3**: **449–480**
      array design, **3**: 475
      heat exchangers, **3**: 477
      module design, **3**: 475
   differential temperature controllers, **3**: 478
   direct circulation systems, **3**: 449, **3**: 451*f*
   domestic hot water heating, **3**: 456
   heat exchangers, **3**: 450, **3**: 452*f*, **3**: 454, **3**: 454*f*, **3**: 477
   heating systems, **3**: **449–480**
   heat storage, **3**: 473
   hot water systems, **3**: 453
   indirect water heating systems, **3**: 450, **3**: 452
   liquid systems, **3**: 474
   modeling thermal systems, **3**: 396
   module design, **3**: 475
   service hot water, **3**: 453
   simulations, **3**: 396
   space cooling systems, **3**: **449–480**
   space heating systems, **3**: **449–480**
      air water heating systems, **3**: 455
      array design, **3**: 475
      domestic hot water, **3**: 456
      heat exchangers, **3**: 450, **3**: 452*f*, **3**: 454, **3**: 454*f*, **3**: 477
      hot water, **3**: 453
      module design, **3**: 475
      service hot water, **3**: 453
      water heating systems, **3**: 453
   thermal storage, **3**: 473
      air systems, **3**: 474
      liquid systems, **3**: 474
      water, **3**: 474
   thermal systems
      daily utilizability, **3**: 406, **3**: 408
      f-chart method, **3**: 396, **3**: 408
      hourly utilizability, **3**: 404, **3**: 407
      modeling, **3**: 396
      simulations, **3**: 396
      utilizability method, **3**: 396, **3**: 404, **3**: 408
   water heating systems, **3**: **449–480**
      air systems, **3**: 452, **3**: 455
      space heating systems, **3**: 453
      thermal storage, **3**: 474
active-stall systems, **2**: 276, **2**: 679
active thermal energy storage, **3**: 247
actuator disk models, **2**: 232
actuators, **2**: 232, **2**: 366
AD *see* anaerobic digestion
Adams, William Grylls, **1**: 34, **1**: 35*f*
adaptive control: solar architecture, **3**: 657–658
additional value extraction:
   biomass and biofuels, **5**: **385–393**
   current status, **5**: 387
   future development, **5**: 389, **5**: 390
   marketplace, **5**: 387, **5**: 389
   plant metabolite exploitation, **5**: **385–393**
adenosine-5′-triphosphate (ATP), **1**: 657, **1**: 657–658
adiabatic pressurized air storage, **3**: 610
adjusting high concentration solar collectors, **3**: 178, **3**: 185, **3**: 195
admittance: chalcopyrite thin films, **1**: 404
admittance transfer, **3**: 364
adsorbents: bioethanol production, **5**: 211
adsorption:
   see also absorption
   chillers, **3**: 613
   refrigeration, **3**: 463
   solar cooling, **3**: 461, **3**: 463, **3**: 486, **3**: 613
   thermal energy storage, **3**: 248, **3**: 250
advanced biofuel processes, **5**: 6, **5**: **155–204**, **5**: 156
advanced configurations: Wells air turbines, **8**: 128
advanced control: passive solar architecture, **3**: 657, **3**: 657*t*
advanced heat storage: solar water heating, **3**: 435, **3**: 436*f*
advanced hydropower technologies, **6**: 40
advanced modeling: wind turbine aerodynamics, **2**: 231
Advanced Plasma Power, **5**: 151
advanced power plants: geothermal energy, **7**: 226, **7**: 228
advanced pretreatments: biomass-to-liquids technology, **5**: 156, **5**: 162*f*, **5**: 163, **5**: 167
advanced thermal storage technologies, **3**: 435, **3**: 436*f*
advection: geothermal energy, **7**: 12, **7**: 13–14
AEM *see* anion exchange membranes
AEMFC *see* anion exchange membrane fuel cells
Aeolus: wind energy, **2**: 1
aeration:
   aerators, **6**: 485, **6**: 497
   Chinese hydraulic research, **6**: 497
   hydropower operating strategies, **6**: 77, **6**: 84
   weirs, **6**: 77
AeroCAN *see* Canadian Sunphotometer Network
aerodynamics:
   actuator disk models, **2**: 232
   advanced modeling, **2**: 231
   blade-element momentum theory, **2**: 225, **2**: 228, **2**: 236
   blades, **2**: 713
   coefficients, **2**: 114, **2**: 671
   computational fluid dynamics, **2**: 232, **2**: 233
   damping, **2**: 259, **8**: 92
   full Navier-Stokes modeling, **2**: 232
   Glauert's optimum rotor method, **2**: 227

loads, **2**: 247
momentum theory, **2**: 226, **2**: 236
Navier-Stokes modeling, **2**: 232
noise, **2**: 238
numerical actuator disk models, **2**: 232
one-dimensional momentum theory, **2**: 226
optimum rotor method, **2**: 227
rotors, **2**: 232, **2**: 233, **2**: 713
vortex models, **2**: 231
wind turbines, **2**: **225–241**
    advanced modeling, **2**: 231
    blade-element momentum theory, **2**: 225, **2**: 228, **2**: 236
    computational fluid dynamics, **2**: 232, **2**: 233
    control systems, **2**: 330, **2**: 331*f*
    Glauert's optimum rotor method, **2**: 227
    momentum theory, **2**: 226, **2**: 236
    noise, **2**: 238
    one-dimensional momentum theory, **2**: 226
    optimum rotor method, **2**: 227
    vortex models, **2**: 231
aeroelastics, **2**: 713, **2**: 714
aerogel glazing, **3**: 336, **3**: 340
   see also thermal insulation...
aeronautics, **2**: 54, **2**: 61
AERONET *see* Aerosol Robotic Network
aeroplanes:
   air traffic, wind power, **2**: 395
   hydrogen, **4**: 290
   wind power, **2**: 395
aerosol optical depth (AOD), **1**: 214, **1**: 231
Aerosol Robotic Network (AERONET), **3**: 60
aerosol transmittance function, **3**: 44
aerospace:
   see also space applications
   hydrogen, **4**: 290
   unmanned air vehicles, **4**: 290
   wind power, **2**: 395
aeroturbine innovation, **2**: 686
aesthetics:
   building-integrated photovoltaic architecture, **1**: 705, **1**: 706
   offshore wind power, **2**: 463
   wind energy, **2**: 182, **2**: 194, **2**: 205, **2**: 463, **2**: 518, **2**: 687
   wind park design, **2**: 182, **2**: 194, **2**: 205
   wind turbines, **2**: 518, **2**: 687
AFC *see* alkaline fuel cells
affordability: geothermal energy, **7**: 283
Africa:
   Republic of Cameroon hydropower, **6**: **129–151**
   solar radiation atlases, **3**: 62
Agencia Nacional De Energia Elétrica (ANEEL), **6**: 93
Agenda 21, **7**: 277
aggregate grading, **6**: 476, **6**: 477*f*
aggregation: hydropower downstream impacts, **6**: 56
agriculture:
   see also crops
   absorbers, **3**: 571
   additional value extraction, **5**: **385–393**
   air heating, **3**: 587
   biochar, **5**: 365, **5**: 379
   bioethanol, **5**: **15–26**, **5**: 218, **5**: 228, **5**: 250
   biomass
     additional value extraction, **5**: **385–393**
     cofiring, **5**: 57
     gasification, **5**: 141
   Brazilian bioethanol development, **5**: **15–26**
   carbon sequestration, **5**: 365, **5**: 379
   characteristics of solar thermal systems, **3**: 568
   collectors, solar thermal systems, **3**: 569
   cooking, **3**: 588
   desalination, **3**: 589
   design of solar thermal systems, **3**: 577
   direct heat drying, **7**: 169, **7**: 173*t*, **7**: 174, **7**: 176*f*, **7**: 180, **7**: 180*f*, **7**: 181, **7**: 182, **7**: 183*f*

direct solar gain, solar thermal systems, **3**: 587
drying, **3**: 579, **7**: 169, **7**: 173*t*, **7**: 174, **7**: 176*f*, **7**: 180, **7**: 180*f*, **7**: 181, **7**: 182, **7**: 183*f*
economics of solar thermal systems, **3**: 569
energy storage, **3**: 569
evacuated tube collectors, **3**: 571, **3**: 587*t*
flat-plate collectors, **3**: 570, **3**: 571, **3**: 587*t*
geothermal energy direct heat drying, **7**: 169, **7**: 173*t*, **7**: 174, **7**: 176*f*, **7**: 180, **7**: 180*f*, **7**: 181, **7**: 182, **7**: 183*f*
greenhouses, **3**: 586
heat systems, **3**: **567–594**, **3**: 587
   design, **3**: 577
   layouts, **3**: 573
hot water, **3**: 577
lignocellulosic wastes, bioethanol, **5**: 218, **5**: 228, **5**: 250
line-axis collectors, **3**: 571, **3**: 587*t*
operational limits of solar thermal systems, **3**: 576
parabolic trough collectors, **3**: 571
photovoltaic/thermal solar collectors, **3**: 292, **3**: 294
real heat system layouts, **3**: 575
residues, biomass cofiring, **5**: 58
solar air heating, **3**: 587
solar cooking, **3**: 588
solar desalination, **3**: 589
solar drying, **3**: 579
solar heat, **3**: **567–594**
solar ponds, **3**: 572, **3**: 587*t*
solar refrigeration, **3**: 592
solar thermal systems, **3**: **567–594**
   absorbers, **3**: 571
   air heating, **3**: 587
   characteristics, **3**: 568
   collectors, **3**: 569
   component layouts, **3**: 573
   cooking, **3**: 588
   desalination, **3**: 589
   design, **3**: 577
   direct solar gain, **3**: 587
   drying, **3**: 579, **7**: 169, **7**: 173*t*, **7**: 174, **7**: 176*f*, **7**: 180, **7**: 180*f*, **7**: 181, **7**: 182, **7**: 183*f*
   economics, **3**: 569
   energy storage, **3**: 569
   evacuated tube collectors, **3**: 571, **3**: 587*t*
   flat-plate collectors, **3**: 570, **3**: 571, **3**: 587*t*
   generic process system layouts, **3**: 573
   greenhouses, **3**: 586
   heating buildings, **3**: 587
   heat system design, **3**: 577
   heat system layouts, **3**: 573
   hot water, **3**: 577
   line-axis collectors, **3**: 571, **3**: 587*t*
   nonconvecting solar ponds, **3**: 572, **3**: 587*t*
   operational limits, **3**: 576
   parabolic trough collectors, **3**: 571
   real heat system layouts, **3**: 575
   refrigeration, **3**: 592
   solar ponds, **3**: 572, **3**: 587*t*
   stationary collectors, **3**: 570, **3**: 571, **3**: 572, **3**: 587*t*
   stills, **3**: 589
   system layouts, **3**: 573
   temperature requirements, **3**: 568, **3**: 569*t*
   thermal energy storage, **3**: 569
   water heating, **3**: 577
stationary collectors, **3**: 570, **3**: 571, **3**: 572, **3**: 587*t*
stills, **3**: 589
thermal energy storage, **3**: 569
ventilation, **3**: 587
water heating, **3**: 577
Aguayo reversible hydropower plant, Spain, **6**: 333, **6**: 334*f*
AI *see* artificial intelligence
AIDS *see* acquired immune deficiency syndrome
aim-point strategies: solar collectors, **3**: 187
air-based solar systems, **3**: 381, **3**: 402

air-breathing stacks, 4: 194, 4: 197, 4: 199
air collectors:
  air-water systems, 3: 286
  flat-plate collectors, 3: 104f, 3: 108, 3: 109f, 3: 114, 3: 115f
  low-temperature stationary collectors, 3: 104f, 3: 108, 3: 109f, 3: 114, 3: 115f
  natural airflow, 3: 274
  photovoltaic/thermal solar collectors, 3: 257, 3: 263, 3: 274, 3: 276, 3: 277, 3: 285
air compressibility, 8: 128
air-conditioning, 3: 250, 3: 460, 6: 144
air-cooling, 4: 199, 7: 224, 7: 225f
aircraft *see* aerospace
air density variation, 2: 146
air-driven condensers, 3: 600, 3: 601f
air entrainment, 6: 387
airflow, 3: 274, 3: 402, 4: 194
airfoils:
  blade-element momentum theory, 2: 231
  drag, 2: 102
  lift, 2: 102
  self-noise, 2: 238
air heating:
  agricultural applications, 3: 587
  flat-plate collectors, 3: 114, 3: 115f
  industrial applications, 3: 587
  solar thermal energy systems, 3: 452, 3: 455, 3: 587
  space heating systems, 3: 455
  water heating systems, 3: 452, 3: 455
air heat recovery, 3: 271, 3: 272
air humidity, 4: 194
air mass (AM), 1: 214, 1: 215–216, 2: 89
air pollution, 2: 504, 3: 6
air quality, 7: 283
air ratio variation, 5: 320–321, 5: 322f
air-sand heat exchangers, 3: 611
air stoichiometry, 4: 184
air storage, 3: 610
air systems:
  see also air collectors; air turbines
  active solar systems, 3: 452, 3: 455, 3: 474
  building-integrated photovoltaic-thermal systems, 3: 381
  f-chart method, 3: 402
  solar thermal energy storage, 3: 215, 3: 227, 3: 228t, 3: 229, 3: 230, 3: 402
  storage capacity corrections, 3: 402
  thermal analysis, 3: 216
  thermal energy storage, 3: 215, 3: 227, 3: 228t, 3: 229, 3: 230, 3: 402, 3: 474
air temperature, 3: 383
air turbines, 8: **111–149**
  bidirectional flows, 8: 132, 8: 141
  biplane rotors, 8: 118, 8: 119, 8: 128
  blades, 8: 113, 8: 128
  cascade flow analysis, 8: 113
  contra-rotating rotors, 8: 117, 8: 129
  dimensional analysis, 8: 124
  equations, 8: 112
  guide vanes, 8: 116, 8: 118, 8: 119, 8: 121–122
  historical overviews, 8: 8
  hydrodynamics, 8: 141
  impulse turbines, 8: 112, 8: 120, 8: 122, 8: 131, 8: 136, 8: 137
  isolated monoplane rotors, 8: 115
  model testing, 8: 124
  monoplane rotors, 8: 115, 8: 116
  noise, 8: 146
  nonzero rotor blade thickness, 8: 120
  ocean energy, 8: **111–149**
  oscillating water columns, 8: 111, 8: 113, 8: 139, 8: 141
  performance, ocean energy, 8: 126, 8: 131
  prototypes, ocean energy, 8: 139
  rotor blades, 8: 113, 8: 128
  self-rectification, 8: 112, 8: 120, 8: 122, 8: 131, 8: 136

test rigs, 8: 125
  unidirectional flow turbines, 8: 111, 8: 137
  valve-controlled air flow, 8: 146
  variable-pitch rotors, 8: 129
air-water solar collectors, 3: 286
Airy diffraction pattern, 1: 768
Airy wave equations, 8: 12
Alagón river hydroproject, Spain, 6: 333–335, 6: 335f
albedo, 1: 214, 1: 233, 3: 644
Al-BSF *see* aluminum back surface field solar cells
alcohol fuels:
  see also alcohols; bioethanol...
  alkaline anion exchange membrane fuel cells, 4: 179
  automotives, 5: 308, 5: 332
    internal combustion engines, 5: 316
    manufacturer's perspective, 5: 313
    physicochemical properties, 5: 317
    safety, 5: 323
    sustainability, 5: 335
  eye contact, 5: 324
  fire safety, 5: 325
  flex-fuel vehicles, 5: 332
  groundwater leakage, 5: 326
  ingestion, 5: 324
  inhalation, 5: 325
  internal combustion engines, 5: 316
  physicochemical properties, 5: 317
  safety, 5: 323
  skin contact, 5: 324
  sustainability, 5: 335
  toxic emissions, 5: 325
  tri flex-fuel vehicles, 5: 332
alcohols:
  see also alcohol fuels; bioethanol...
  biomass-to-liquids technology, 5: 174t, 5: 185, 5: 186, 5: 193
  fermentation, 5: 186, 5: 193, 5: 212, 5: 248
  removal, 5: 212
Aldeadávila hydropower plant, Spain, 6: 324, 6: 336f, 6: 338–339, 6: 340f
algae, 5: 6, 6: 61
Algeria, 3: 634
alkali–aggregate reactions (AAR), 6: 389, 6: 390
alkali amidoboranes, 4: 144
alkaline anion exchange membrane fuel cells (AAEMFC), 4: 178, 4: 179, 4: 180
alkaline earth amidoboranes, 4: 144
alkaline electrolysers, 4: 2, 4: 5f
alkaline fuel cells (AFC), 4: **159–182**, 4: 159
  Allis/Chambers system, 4: 173
  anion exchange membranes, 4: 159, 4: 175
    challenges, 4: 175
    chemistry, 4: 175
    classes, 4: 177
    main classes, 4: 177
  anode catalyst materials, 4: 163
  catalyst materials, 4: 162
    anodes, 4: 163
    cathodes, 4: 162
  cathodes, 4: 160, 4: 162, 4: 163
  challenges, 4: 175
  chemistry, 4: 175
  classes, 4: 177
  design, 4: 170
  electrolyte design, 4: 170
  Elenco fuel cell system, 4: 174
  fundamentals, 4: 160
  gas diffusion electrodes, 4: 165
  General Motors, 4: 173
  general principles, 4: 160
  hydrogen fuel cell technology, 4: 282
  ionomers, 4: 159, 4: 178
  liquid electrolytes, 4: 165
    design, 4: 170

space systems, **4**: 172
stack design, **4**: 170
system achievements, **4**: 172
system design, **4**: 170
terrestrial systems, **4**: 173
main classes, **4**: 177
metal catalysts, **4**: 162, **4**: 163
non-platinum group metal catalysts, **4**: 163
performance, **4**: 163
platinum group metal catalysts, **4**: 162
principles, **4**: 160
proton exchange membrane fuel cells, **4**: 159, **4**: 160, **4**: 161*t*, **4**: 175
quaternary ammonium, **4**: 159, **4**: 175
Siemens fuel cell system, **4**: 174
solid oxide fuel cells, **4**: 243, **4**: 243*t*
space systems, **4**: 172
stack design, liquid electrolytes, **4**: 170
system achievements, **4**: 172
system design, **4**: 170
terrestrial systems, liquid electrolytes, **4**: 173
theory, **4**: **159–182**, **4**: 159
Union Carbide Corporation system, **4**: 173
alkaline membrane direct alcohol fuel cells, **4**: 159
alkaline syngas contaminants, **5**: 176
alkali pretreatments, **5**: 237
alkali-silica reactions (ASR), **6**: 389
allergies, **5**: 40
Allis/Chambers system, **4**: 173
Almendra dam, Spain, **6**: 324, **6**: 336*f*
Almeria, Spain, **3**: 549
Almoguera power plant, **1**: 751, **1**: 751*t*, **1**: 752*f*
Alpine shallow reservoir, **6**: 368
Alsa dam, Spain, **6**: 333, **6**: 334*f*
Alstom, **2**: 323
Alstonvale Home, **3**: 394
alteration: geothermal energy geochemistry, **7**: 103
alternating current (AC):
    rating procedures, **1**: 758, **1**: 759
    resistivity methods, **7**: 61
alternative sulfonated membrane materials, **4**: 188
altimeters, **8**: 23, **8**: 31
altitude angles, **3**: 1, **3**: 11
aluminum:
    aluminum-alloyed back junctions, **1**: 375
    aluminum-gallium-arsenide/gallium-arsenide solar cells, **1**: 497
    aluminum/gallium arsenide solar cells, **1**: 497
    back surface field solar cells, **1**: 355
    casings, **3**: 114, **3**: 114*f*
    geothermal environment power production, **7**: 249
    glazing, **3**: 333
    smelter companies, **6**: 137
    window frames, **3**: 333
AM *see* air mass
Amazon:
    Brazilian sugarcane industry, **5**: 21
    Madeira hydroelectric project, Brazil, **6**: 104
Amazonian dark earths, **5**: 358, **5**: 358*f*, **5**: 359, **5**: 361*f*
ambient air heat pumps, **3**: 502
ambient heat transfer coefficient–glazing, **3**: 131, **3**: 132*t*
ambient temperature: conduction exchange, **3**: 132
Amer 9 biomass cofiring plant, **5**: 65
America *see* United States of America
American Marshall Plan, **2**: 60
American Wind Energy Association (AWEA), **2**: 72
American wind pumps: historical overviews, **2**: 51
amidoboranes, **4**: 144
amine-hydride combinations, **4**: 147*t*, **4**: 149
ammonia:
    borane, **4**: 140, **4**: 142, **4**: 143
    corrosion, **5**: 173, **7**: 246
    production, **4**: 31
    recycled percolation, **5**: 244

water absorption systems, **3**: 471, **3**: 472
amorphous materials: definitions, **1**: 13
amorphous silicon:
    amorphous-silicon–carbon-silicon heterojunctions, **1**: 393
    amorphous silicon–hydrogen thin-films, **1**: 389
    deposition, **1**: 389
    photovoltaics, **1**: 8, **1**: 21, **1**: 144, **1**: 389, **1**: 393
amortization periods, **2**: 472
anaerobic digestion (AD), **4**: 227, **5**: 5
analytical frameworks:
    direct gain models, **3**: 369
    photovoltaics, **1**: 114, **3**: 269
Anasazi: solar energy utilization, **1**: 31, **1**: 32*f*
ancient history: photovoltaics/solar energy utilization, **1**: 31
ancillary hydropower services, **6**: 6, **6**: 53
Andasol 1-3 solar power plant, **3**: 616, **3**: 617*f*
Andreau, J., **2**: 59, **2**: 61*f*
ANEEL *see* Agencia Nacional De Energia Elétrica
anemometry, **2**: 75, **2**: 377
angles:
    see also individual angles
    building-integrated photovoltaics, **1**: 700
Ångström turbidity, **3**: 36, **3**: 44
angular dependence:
    photoluminescence intensity, **1**: 572
    radiation transmittance, **3**: 122–123, **3**: 123*f*, **3**: 124, **3**: 124*f*
angular emission, **1**: 598
anion analysis, **7**: 100
anion exchange membrane fuel cells (AEMFC), **4**: 159, **4**: 161*t*
anion exchange membranes (AEM):
    alkaline fuel cells, **4**: 159, **4**: 175
    challenges, **4**: 175
    chemistry, **4**: 175
    classes, **4**: 177
    ionomer development, **4**: 178
anisotropic radiation, **1**: 323–324, **1**: 327, **3**: 48
Anji County, Zhejiang, **6**: 429
ANN *see* artificial neural networks
annealing organic solar cells, **1**: 459
annihilation statistics, **1**: 543
annual capacity:
    desalination, **2**: 726, **2**: 727*f*
    wind turbines, **2**: 677–679, **2**: 678*f*
annual direct heat utilization, **7**: 172*f*, **7**: 172*t*
annual electricity production calculations, **2**: 196
annual geothermal energy, **7**: 172*f*, **7**: 172*t*
annual Indian hydropower plans, **6**: 233, **6**: 234, **6**: 237, **6**: 240, **6**: 249
annual production: photovoltaic technology, **1**: 5, **1**: 6*f*
annual revision tariffs, **1**: 125
annual solar radiation, **3**: 438, **3**: 439*f*
annual wind climate variations, **2**: 403
annual wind energy production estimates, **2**: 134, **2**: 138
annual wind park expenses, **2**: 211
anodes:
    alkaline fuel cells, **4**: 160, **4**: 163
    catalyst materials, **4**: 163
    definitions, **4**: 241
    hydrogen technology, **4**: 247
    materials, **4**: 190
    molten carbonate fuel cells, **4**: 227, **4**: 229
    proton-exchange membrane fuel cells, **4**: 190
    solid oxide fuel cells, **4**: 247
anoxia, **6**: 62
antennae:
    artificial leaves, **1**: 669
    light-harvesting complexes, **1**: 658, **1**: 661, **1**: 669
antimonide:
    gallium-antimonide solar cells, **1**: 608, **1**: 610, **1**: 614
    gallium-arsenide/gallium-antimonide solar cells, **1**: 608–609
    indium-gallium-antimonide solar cells, **1**: 608, **1**: 610
    indium-gallium-arsenide-antimonide-phosphide solar cells, **1**: 611

antireflective coatings/layers:
   crystalline silicon cells, **1**: 359
   low-temperature stationary collectors, **3**: 104, **3**: 108, **3**: 125
   luminescent down-shifting, **1**: 570
   micro-and nano photovoltaic technologies, **1**: 520
AOD *see* aerosol optical depth
AORA concentrating solar power plant, **3**: 622
apartment housing solar water heating systems, **3**: 443
apertures:
   area ratios, **3**: **149–163**, **3**: 200, **3**: 202
   cover materials, **3**: 570
   solar power satellites, **1**: 768, **1**: 770
Apollo:
   fuel cells, **4**: 26
   Saturn rocket hydrogen technology, **4**: 14
apparent paths: Sun—Earth astronomical relations, **3**: 30, **3**: 30*f*
appeals: wind power, **2**: 398
application-specific solar radiation data conversions, **1**: 226
application temperatures: agricultural solar thermal applications, **3**: 568
appraisals: Indian hydropower, **6**: 234
APU *see* auxiliary power units
Aqaba, Jordan, **3**: 560, **3**: 562*f*, **3**: 563*f*
aquaculture ponds, **7**: 169, **7**: 173*t*, **7**: 174, **7**: 175*f*, **7**: 184, **7**: 185*f*
aquatic ecosystems, **6**: 56, **6**: 62, **6**: 214
aquifers, **3**: 211, **3**: 219, **3**: 521
arbitrage: energy storage, **1**: 200
arboricultural arisings, **5**: 141
archaeology, **2**: 524, **5**: 358
arch dams, **6**: 24, **6**: 492
Archimedes, **1**: 31, **1**: 32*f*, **3**: 86, **6**: 441
architecture:
   building-integrated photovoltaics, **1**: **697–707**
   organic solar cells, **1**: 448, **1**: 463
   passive solar architecture, **3**: **637–665**
   photovoltaic modules, **1**: 703
area constraints:
   product-integrated photovoltaics, **1**: 716
   wind turbines, **2**: 186–187, **2**: 189
area ratios: receivers, **3**: **149–163**, **3**: **165–209**
area receiver analysis, **3**: 173
Areva: Fresnel collectors, **3**: 198
arid area very large-scale photovoltaic systems, **1**: **733–744**
ARIMA *see* autoregressive integrated moving averages
ARM *see* Atmospheric Radiation Measurement
aromaticity: biochar, **5**: 357, **5**: 375
arrays:
   definitions, **8**: 79
   design, **3**: 475
   ocean wave energy seatrials, **8**: 101
   space cooling/heating systems, **3**: 475
   yields, **1**: 775, **1**: 777
arsenide:
   aluminum/gallium arsenide solar cells, **1**: 497
   indium-gallium-arsenide-antimonide-phosphide solar cells, **1**: 611
   indium-gallium-arsenide solar cells, **1**: 610, **1**: 611
   indium-gallium-phosphorous/gallium-arsenide-based 3-junction solar cells, **1**: 497, **1**: 503, **1**: 506
   indium-gallium-phosphorous/gallium-arsenide/germanium-based solar cells, **1**: 497, **1**: 503, **1**: 506
ART *see* Atmospheric Research Team
artificial antennae, **1**: 669
artificial destratification, **6**: 83
artificial geothermal tracers, **7**: 109
artificial intelligence (AI), **1**: 248
artificial leaves, **1**: **657–677**, **1**: 10
   artificial antennae, **1**: 669
   chlorosomes, **1**: 669
   design, **1**: 666, **1**: 667
   donor-acceptor constructs, **1**: 670
   fuel-producing solar cell construction, photosynthesis, **1**: 674
   light-harvesting antenna complexes, **1**: 669
   photosynthesis, **1**: 669, **1**: 674
   photovoltaics, **1**: **657–677**, **1**: 10
   proteins, **1**: 666
   self-assembled artificial antennae, **1**: 669
   self-assembled donor-acceptor constructs, **1**: 672
   solar cell construction, photosynthesis, **1**: 674
artificial neural networks (ANN):
   passive solar architecture, **3**: 644, **3**: 659, **3**: 662*f*
   solar irradiance, **1**: 248
   solar radiation, **3**: 43
   wind speed forecasting, **2**: 88
artistic structural architecture, **1**: 704
arts: product-integrated photovoltaics, **1**: 714
Asahi Dam Reservoir, **6**: 294
ascending power curve segments, **2**: 138
ash environmental impacts, **5**: 49, **5**: 52
ASHRAE model, **3**: 42
Asian wind power, **2**: 666, **2**: 667
asphalt layers, **3**: 648
ASR *see* alkali-silica reactions
assembly processes:
   offshore wind farms, **2**: 456
   wind turbine loads, **2**: 246
assessments:
   concrete structure durability, **6**: 397
   geothermal energy, **7**: **51–94**
   greenhouse gas life cycle assessments, **5**: **109–132**
   ocean wave energy, **8**: 8, **8**: **11–77**
   photovoltaics life-cycles, **1**: 7
   sediment management, **6**: 370
   solar radiation energy conversions, **1**: **213–237**
   sustainable hydropower, **6**: 370
   Three Gorges Project, China, **6**: 208
   wind energy environmental impacts, **2**: 511
assimilating wind energy variable costs, **2**: 489
astronaut environmental control/life support, **4**: 24
astronomical relations: Sun—Earth, solar resource, **3**: 29
asymetrical low-emittance coatings, **3**: 327
asynchronous generators: wind turbines, **2**: 279, **2**: 281, **2**: 339, **2**: 340, **2**: 353, **2**: 354
Atlantic basin: Cameroon, Africa, **6**: 130
Atlantic catchment: Cameroon, Africa, **6**: 131
Atlas-Centaur rocket, **4**: 13
Atlas Model: wind energy, **2**: 86, **2**: 87
atmosphere:
   geothermal energy sustainability, **7**: 283
   solar irradiance forecasting, photovoltaic power, **1**: 246
   solar power satellites, **1**: 771
   solar radiation interference, **3**: 34
   sustainable geothermal energy, **7**: 283
atmospheric carbon dioxide, **5**: 330, **5**: 331
atmospheric filters: solar radiation, **1**: 216
Atmospheric Radiation Measurement (ARM), **3**: 60
Atmospheric Research Team (ART), **3**: 43
atmospheric winds, **2**: 80
attenuation: solar radiation, **3**: 27, **3**: 36
attributional life cycle assessments, **5**: 109, **5**: 112
Auger recombination, **1**: 309, **1**: 315
Ausra/Areva Fresnel collectors, **3**: 198
Austarasel springs, **7**: 130
Australia:
   hydropower, **6**: 75, **6**: 76
   solar radiation atlases, **3**: 62
Austria: solar irradiance-photovoltaic power forecasts, **1**: 273
autoanalyzers: reservoir water quality, **6**: 70
autogenous shrinkage, **6**: 381
automatic voltage regulation, **2**: 586
automotives:
   see also electrical vehicles; hybrid vehicles; road vehicles; urban electrical vehicles; vehicles
   alcohol fuels, **5**: 308, **5**: 332
      internal combustion engines, **5**: 316

physicochemical properties, **5**: 317
safety, **5**: 323
sustainability, **5**: 335
atmospheric carbon dioxide, **5**: 330, **5**: 331
biofuels, **5**: **305–342**
competing fuels, **5**: 308
manufacturer's perspective, **5**: 313
production methods, **5**: 314
biomass limit, **5**: 327
carbon dioxide emissions, **5**: 305, **5**: 308, **5**: 327, **5**: 330, **5**: 331
carbon neutral solutions, **5**: 307
competing fuels, **5**: 308
compression-ignition engines, **5**: 322
concentrating carbon dioxide, **5**: 330
electrification, **5**: 307, **5**: 308
electrofuels, **5**: 328
ethanol safety, **5**: 323
feedstocks, **5**: 305–306, **5**: 314
greenhouse gases, **5**: 305, **5**: 327
hydrogen economy conversion, **5**: 307, **5**: 310
internal combustion engines, **5**: 316
kerosene, **5**: 308, **5**: 316, **5**: 335, **5**: 337
liquid electrofuels, **5**: 331
low-carbon number alcohols, **5**: 319, **5**: 322
manufacturer's perspective, **5**: 313
methanol safety, **5**: 323
physicochemical properties, **5**: 317
safety, **5**: 323
security of feedstock supply, **5**: 305–306
spark-ignition engines, low-carbon number alcohols, **5**: 319
sustainable alcohol fuels, **5**: 335
sustainable organic fuels, **5**: 335
autonomous solar desalination, **3**: 546
autonomous wind energy systems, **2**: **623–655**
autoregressive integrated moving averages (ARIMA), **1**: 248
autosamplers: reservoir water quality, **6**: 70
auxiliary equipment:
hydrogen storage, **4**: 123
stand alone hybrid wind energy systems, **2**: 632
auxiliary heating, **3**: 567
auxiliary heat sources, **3**: 436, **3**: 458
auxiliary power units (APU), **4**: 60, **4**: 200, **4**: 285
availability:
biomass cofiring materials, **5**: 57
geothermal energy, **7**: 282
lithium–water absorption systems, **3**: 469, **3**: 469f
solar radiation, **1**: 227
AVANTIS: wind turbines, **2**: 324
averaging periods: wind speeds, **2**: 80
AWEA *see* American Wind Energy Association
axial-flow air turbines, **8**: 112, **8**: 113, **8**: 123
axial-flow microhydro turbines, **6**: **435–466**
axial momentum theory, **2**: 90
azimuth angles, **3**: 1, **3**: 12
azimuth bearing, **2**: 330

B

back contacts:
cadmium telluride thin films, **1**: 432
chalcopyrite thin films, **1**: 412
crystalline silicon cells, **1**: 368
metallization, **1**: 368
back insulation, **3**: 104, **3**: 113, **3**: 132
back junctions, **1**: 377
back-surface-field (BSF) layers, **1**: 501, **1**: 503
backup power systems:
fuel cell current status, **4**: 34
proton-exchange membrane fuel cells, **4**: 200
backup requirements:
desalination, **2**: 734

wind energy, **2**: 734
variable costs, **2**: 489, **2**: 491, **2**: 492
backward citation analysis, **1**: 62, **1**: 63
Bacon, Francis, **2**: 50
Bacon fuel cells *see* alkaline fuel cells
bacteria:
inoculums, **4**: 273
solar water heating systems, **3**: 437
bacterio chlorophylls, **1**: 657, **1**: 658
bacterio pheophytin, **1**: 657, **1**: 658
bagasse: biomass cofiring, **5**: 59
bag house filters, **5**: 145
Baidi City, **6**: 219, **6**: 219f
Baiheliang inscriptions and carvings, **6**: 217, **6**: 218f
Baixo Iguaçu hydroelectric project, Brazil, **6**: 108
balanced photovoltaic thermodynamic models, **1**: 338
balance equations: lithium–water absorption systems, **3**: 468
balance of plant:
electrical energy storage, **6**: 410
pressure selection, **4**: 198
proton-exchange membrane fuel cells, **4**: 198
wind energy costs, **2**: 474
balance of system:
batteries, **1**: 687
building-integrated photovoltaics, **1**: 702
charge regulators, **1**: 687
inverters, **1**: 685
life cycle inventory, **1**: 147
mounting structures, **1**: 686
photovoltaics, **1**: 685
balancing wind energy costs, **2**: 474, **2**: 484
ballast stabilizers, **2**: 449
Bamendjin dam, **6**: 134, **6**: 136t
bandgaps:
back-surface-field layers, **1**: 501
balance limit efficiency, **1**: 516f, **1**: 516–517
chalcopyrite thin films, **1**: 405f, **1**: 405–406, **1**: 415–416
intermediate band solar cells, **1**: 619
micro-and nano photovoltaic technologies, **1**: 516f, **1**: 516–517
photovoltaics, **1**: 315, **1**: 516f, **1**: 516–517
rare earth elements, down-shifting, **1**: 568f, **1**: 573
selective coatings, **3**: 301
solar energy conversion principles, **1**: 293, **1**: 294, **1**: 297
spectral property radiance, **1**: 318
thermophotovoltaics, **1**: 608, **1**: 609f
band structure: intermediate band solar cells, **1**: 619
bankability: definition, **1**: 13
bank funding: photovoltaics, **1**: 113, **1**: 121, **1**: 128
banking institutes: Indian hydropower, **6**: 229
bank turbines: hydropower, **6**: 26, **6**: 28f
Bao power plant, Spain, **6**: 330, **6**: 331f
Baoying key project, **6**: 401
Barcelona European Council, **2**: 707–708
BARD generators, **2**: 289, **2**: 290f
BARD project, **2**: 448
bark residuals, **5**: 264
Barra Grande hydroelectricity project, Brazil, **6**: 124
barriers:
bioenergy markets, **5**: 81
bioenergy policy development, **5**: 424
chalcopyrite thin films, **1**: 412
hydrogen safety engineering, **4**: 102
Barsch index, **2**: 173, **2**: 173t
base-catalyzed transesterification, **5**: 219
Baseline Solar Radiation Network (BSRN), **3**: 59–60
baseload power plants: definitions, **6**: 1, **6**: 16
basins: hydropower/sediment management, **6**: 365
basin stills, **3**: 589, **3**: 591
basin-wise flow, **6**: 233f, **6**: 233–234
basin-wise storage potentials, **6**: 233f, **6**: 233–234
bathing: geothermal energy, **7**: 169, **7**: 170, **7**: 173t
bathymetric mapping, **6**: 358, **6**: 369, **6**: 371f, **6**: 372f
BATNEEC *see* best available technology not entailing excessive cost

batteries:
    balance of system, **1**: 687
    hybrid energy storage, **4**: 317
    hydrogen technology, **4**: 22, **4**: 285, **4**: 317
    performance evaluation, **4**: 324
    photovoltaics, **1**: 204, **1**: 204f, **1**: 206, **1**: 687, **1**: 722
    product-integrated photovoltaics, **1**: 722
    space applications, **4**: 22
    urban electrical vehicles, **4**: 317
    vehicle performance evaluation, **4**: 324
    wind energy, **2**: 649, **2**: 650
baulk systems, **6**: 88
Bayesian adaptive combination, **2**: 88
Bayesian model averaging, **2**: 89
Beacon Solar, LLC, **3**: 631
beam errors, **3**: 188
beam solar radiation, **1**: 315, **1**: 319, **1**: 325, **1**: 326
BEAT method, **5**: 114–115
Becquerel, Edmund, **1**: 33, **1**: 34f
bed-connected structure capital costs, **8**: 157
Belesar dam, Spain, **6**: 328, **6**: 329f
Belgium, **6**: 400, **6**: 402f, **6**: 431
Bell labs, **1**: 36, **1**: 36f
Belo Monte, **6**: 125
below E_g losses, **1**: 309, **1**: 310
BEM *see* blade-element momentum
Benhssaine, Morocco, **3**: 539f
Benoue river, Cameroon, Africa, **6**: 131
Bernoulli theorem, **6**: 19
best practices:
    Brazilian bioethanol development, **5**: 18
    compressed gas: hydrogen storage, **4**: 116
    promoting solar photovoltaics, **1**: 93
    solar cooling, **3**: 613
Betz limit, **2**: 90, **2**: 114–115, **2**: 115f, **2**: 116f
bidding: construction management, **6**: 208
bidirectional air turbine flows, **8**: 132, **8**: 136, **8**: 141
BIEM vortex model, **2**: 232
bifacial absorbers, **3**: 153, **3**: 154f
BIGCC *see* biomass integrated gasification combined cycles
bikes, **4**: 203, **4**: 285
bilayer organic solar cell architecture, **1**: 448
bilinear passive solar architecture models, **3**: 658–659, **3**: 660f
binary power plants:
    advanced geothermal power plants, **7**: 226
    combined cycle geothermal power plants, **7**: 231
    dual fluid cycles, **7**: 228
    dual pressure cycles, **7**: 227
    evaporator analysis, **7**: 225
    geothermal energy, **7**: 207, **7**: 222, **7**: 231, **7**: 233, **7**: 279
    preheater analysis, **7**: 225
    pressure cycles, **7**: 227
    recuperators, **7**: 226
    systems analysis, **7**: 224, **7**: 225
binary solvent systems, **1**: 461
Bini Warak Project, Cameroon, Africa, **6**: 145, **6**: 145t
bio-alcohols:
    chemical intermediates, **5**: 404
    chemical production, **5**: 404
        hydrogen, **5**: 406
        single-walled carbon nanotubes, **5**: 405
    ethanol fuel cells, **5**: 406
    fuel cells, **5**: 406
    hydrogen, **5**: 406
    single-walled carbon nanotubes, **5**: 405
biochar, **5**: **357–384**, **5**: 357
    agricultural practices, **5**: 365, **5**: 379
    alternative use economics, **5**: 382
    Amazonian dark earths, **5**: 358, **5**: 358f, **5**: 359, **5**: 361f
    archaeology, **5**: 358
    aromaticity, **5**: 357, **5**: 375
    bioenergy, **5**: 379
    bio-oils, **5**: 368, **5**: 379

black carbons, **5**: 357, **5**: 362
Brazilian Amazon, **5**: 358, **5**: 358f, **5**: 359, **5**: 361f
carbon capture and storage, **5**: 360
carbon cycle, **5**: 362, **5**: 363f
carbon-negative energy, **5**: 357, **5**: 360, **5**: 379
carbon sequestration, **5**: 357, **5**: 360, **5**: 379
    agricultural practices, **5**: 365, **5**: 379
    black carbons, **5**: 357, **5**: 362
    carbon cycle, **5**: 362, **5**: 363f
    global carbon cycle, **5**: 362, **5**: 363f
challenges, **5**: 382
charcoal production, **5**: 357, **5**: 366
chemical production, **5**: 406, **5**: 407
chemical properties, **5**: 374
composition, **5**: 372
composting, **5**: 379
coproducts, **5**: 371
dark earths, **5**: 358, **5**: 358f, **5**: 359, **5**: 361f
degradation, **5**: 364
developing countries, **5**: 380
economics, **5**: 382
engineering, **5**: 377
fabricated microwave pyrolysis, **5**: 407
farming impacts, **5**: 379
fast pyrolysis, **5**: 366t, **5**: 368, **5**: 373f, **5**: 379
feedstock pretreatments, **5**: 368
flash pyrolysis, **5**: 366t, **5**: 370, **5**: 379
future progress/development, **5**: 384
gasification, **5**: 366t, **5**: 371, **5**: 373f
global carbon cycle, **5**: 362, **5**: 363f
greenhouse gases, **5**: 379, **5**: 380
half-lives, soils, **5**: 364
handling, **5**: 382
kilns, **5**: 367f, **5**: 367–368, **5**: 369f, **5**: 381–382
nitrogen immobilization, **5**: 383f, **5**: 383–384
physical properties, **5**: 373
pressure, flash pyrolysis, **5**: 370
properties, **5**: 372
pyrolysis, **5**: **357–384**, **5**: 406
remediation practices, **5**: 380
scenarios, **5**: 378
sequestration, **5**: 357, **5**: 360
site remediation, **5**: 380
slow pyrolysis, **5**: 366, **5**: 366t, **5**: 373f
soil fertility, **5**: 358, **5**: 358f, **5**: 362–363, **5**: 365
soil half-lives, **5**: 364
soil organic matter, **5**: 357, **5**: 358, **5**: 365, **5**: 375, **5**: 379–380
sources, **5**: 366
surface chemistry, **5**: 375, **5**: 379–380
surface functionality, **5**: 375
synergies, **5**: 378
syngas, **5**: 366t, **5**: 371
terra preta, **5**: 358, **5**: 358f, **5**: 359, **5**: 360, **5**: 361f
torrefaction, **5**: 366t, **5**: 368, **5**: 373f
traditional charcoal making, **5**: 366
biochemical glycerol production, **5**: 398
biodiesel:
    see also diesel
    additional value extraction, **5**: 388t, **5**: 388–389
    automotives, **5**: 307
    biodiesel-rich phase, **5**: 206, **5**: 209
    chemical production, **5**: 396, **5**: 398
    definitions, **5**: 217
    density separation, **5**: 209
    deployment, **5**: 3
    diesel blends, **5**: 348
    distillation, **5**: 209–210
    economics, **5**: 218
    emission characteristics, **5**: 227
    engine configuration ranges, **5**: 343, **5**: 348
    engine performance, **5**: 226
    environmental factors, **5**: 218
    ethical issues, **5**: 219

extraction, **5**: 208
fermentation, **5**: 2–3
flowsheets, **5**: 206
fossil fuel blends, **5**: 348
frying oil effects, **5**: 219
generic flowsheets, **5**: 206
global market sizes, **5**: 79–80, **5**: 80f
glycerin coproducts, **5**: 396
glycerol, **5**: 396, **5**: 398
glycerol-rich phase, **5**: 206, **5**: 209, **5**: 210
heterogeneous catalysis, **5**: 207, **5**: 223
in situ transesterification, **5**: 208
management, **5**: 218
oil collection, **5**: 219
optimization, **5**: 219
oscillatory baffled reactors, **5**: 206
plug flow reactors, production intensification, **5**: 206
production
    automotives, **5**: 315
    intensification, **5**: 205
    introduction, **5**: 3
quality, **5**: 225
reactions, **5**: 205
reactive extraction, **5**: 208
reactors, **5**: 206
separation, **5**: 206, **5**: 209
social issues, **5**: 219
standards, **5**: 225
stationary engines, **5**: 348
supercritical reactions, **5**: 208
transesterification, **5**: 208, **5**: 219, **5**: 228
ultrasonication, **5**: 224
vegetable oil, **5**: 218, **5**: 228
    challenges, **5**: 219
    economics, **5**: 218
    emission characteristics, **5**: 227
    engine performance, **5**: 226
    environmental factors, **5**: 218
    ethical issues, **5**: 219
    management, **5**: 218
    oil collection, **5**: 219
    optimization, **5**: 219
    quality, **5**: 225
    social issues, **5**: 219
    standards, **5**: 225
    transesterification, **5**: 219, **5**: 228
    ultrasonication, **5**: 224
washing, **5**: 210
waste vegetable oil, **5**: 218, **5**: 228
world production, **5**: 3
biodiesel-rich phase (BRP), **5**: 206, **5**: 209
biodiversity:
    Three Gorges Project, China, **6**: 213
bioelectricity: Brazilian sugarcane industry, **5**: 20
bioenergy:
  barriers, markets, **5**: 81
  biochar, **5**: 379
  biodiesel, **5**: 218
  biomass policy development, **5**: **411–429**
  combined heat and power, **5**: 90
  export subsidies, **5**: 81
  extent of trade, **5**: 79
  feed-in tariffs, **5**: 411, **5**: 423
  feedstocks, woody biomass, **5**: **263–291**
  future direction, **5**: 82
  greenhouse gas reductions, **5**: **411–429**
  import tariffs, **5**: 81
  integrating markets, **5**: 80
  internationalization factors, **5**: 81
  international trade, **5**: **75–85**
  liquid biofuels, **5**: 79
  markets, **5**: **75–85**
    barriers, **5**: 81
    extent of trade, **5**: 79
    future direction, **5**: 82
    integration, **5**: 80
    internationalization factors, **5**: 81
    international trade, **5**: **75–85**
    liquid biofuels, **5**: 79
    policy, **5**: 75
    wood fuels, **5**: 77
  non explicit barriers, **5**: 82
  novel feedstocks, **5**: **263–291**
  policy development, **5**: **411–429**
    airborne emissions, **5**: 424–425
    barrier impacts, **5**: 424
    bioenergy potential, **5**: 413
    command and control instruments, **5**: 411, **5**: 421
    control instruments, **5**: 411, **5**: 421
    economic efficiency, **5**: 424
    economy, **5**: 417, **5**: 424
    energy markets, **5**: 413–414, **5**: 415–416, **5**: 417, **5**: 418, **5**: 424
    environmental policy options, **5**: 419, **5**: 426
    feed-in tariffs, **5**: 411, **5**: 423
    fixed prices, **5**: 411, **5**: 423
    green certificates, **5**: 411, **5**: 422
    greenhouse gas reductions, **5**: **411–429**
    historical overviews, **5**: 426
    holistic approaches, **5**: 427
    impact scales, **5**: 424
    incentive-based instruments, **5**: 422
    investment subsidies, **5**: 411, **5**: 419
    land-use, **5**: 428
    legislation, **5**: 425–426, **5**: 426, **5**: 427
    market failures, **5**: 418
    markets, **5**: 413–414, **5**: 415–416, **5**: 417, **5**: 418, **5**: 424
    multidimensional problems, **5**: 427
    new technology support, **5**: 419
    nonfinancial barrier impacts, **5**: 424
    permits, **5**: 411, **5**: 416–417, **5**: 420f, **5**: 422
    potential concepts, **5**: 413
    quotas, **5**: 411, **5**: 416–417, **5**: 420f, **5**: 422
    supply chains, **5**: 414
    sustainable development, **5**: 416
    technology support, **5**: 419
    tradable permits, **5**: 411, **5**: 416–417, **5**: 420f, **5**: 422
  potential in policy development, **5**: 413
  technology solutions, **5**: **217–261**
  trade, **5**: **75–85**
  trade markets, **5**: **75–85**
  vegetable oil, **5**: 218
  waste materials, **5**: **217–261**
  wood fuel markets, **5**: 77
  woody biomass, **5**: **263–291**
bioethanol, **5**: **15–26**
  adsorbents, **5**: 211
  alcohol removal, **5**: 212
  Brazilian development, **5**: **15–26**
  chemical pretreatments, **5**: 235
  chemical production, **5**: 404
  clean energy matrices, **5**: 20
  consolidated bioprocessing, **5**: 250
  definitions, **5**: 395
  dehydration, **5**: 210
  deployment, **5**: 4
  development, **5**: **15–26**
  distillation, **5**: 210
  environmental responsibility, **5**: 18, **5**: 21
  extractive distillation, **5**: 210
  extrusion, **5**: 241
  fermentation, **5**: 2, **5**: 212, **5**: 248
  future directions, **5**: 24
  global market sizes, **5**: 79–80, **5**: 80f
  greenhouse gas life cycle assessments, **5**: 114–115
  historical overviews, **5**: 15

180 Index

bioethanol (*continued*)
   industry, **5**: 15, **5**: 17
   ionic liquid pretreatments, **5**: 239
   lignocellulosic wastes, **5**: 218, **5**: 228, **5**: 250
     challenges, **5**: 234
     chemical pretreatments, **5**: 235
     consolidated bioprocessing, **5**: 250
     extrusion, **5**: 241
     fermentation, **5**: 248
     ionic liquid pretreatments, **5**: 239
     organosolv, **5**: 238, **5**: 238*t*
     pretreatment, **5**: 234
     saccharification and fermentation, **5**: 248
   membrane separation, **5**: 211, **5**: 214
   organosolv, **5**: 238, **5**: 238*t*
   pervaporation, **5**: 211
   pretreatment, **5**: 234
   production, **5**: 4, **5**: 210, **5**: 315
   saccharification and fermentation, **5**: 248
   social responsibility, **5**: 21
   solvent extraction, **5**: 212
   vapor permeation, **5**: 211
   world production, **5**: 4
biofeedstock additional value extraction, **5**: **385–393**
biofractionation, **5**: 387, **5**: 387*f*
biofuels:
   see also biomass and biofuels; *individual fuels*;
   algae, **5**: 6
   anaerobic digestion, **5**: 5
   automotives, **5**: **305–342**
     competing fuels, **5**: 308
     manufacturer's perspective, **5**: 313
     production methods, **5**: 314
   background, **5**: 1
   biochar, **5**: **357–384**, **5**: 406
   biomass-to-liquids technology, **5**: **155–204**, **5**: 156
   blends with fossil fuels, **5**: 343
   Brazilian development, **5**: **15–26**
   carbon certification, **5**: 104
   case studies, **5**: **15–26**, **5**: **27–53**
   chemical production, **5**: **395–410**
     bio-alcohols, **5**: 404
     biochar, **5**: 406
     bioethanol, **5**: 404
     ethanol, **5**: 404
     fermentation, **5**: 400
     lignins, **5**: 401
     solid biofuels, **5**: 406
   commercial viability expansion, **5**: 7
   competing automotive fuels, **5**: 308
   constraints & limitations, **5**: 4, **5**: **99–108**, **5**: **109–132**
   coproducts, **5**: 110, **5**: 113, **5**: 126
   definitions, **5**: 76, **5**: 109
   deployment, **5**: 3
   development, **5**: 8, **5**: **15–26**
   direct land use change, **5**: 117
   drivers, **5**: 157, **5**: 157*f*, **5**: 187
   dual fuel operation, **5**: 349
   energy balance, **5**: 114
   engine configuration ranges, **5**: **343–356**
   engine historical developments, **5**: 11
   ethics, **5**: **99–108**
     carbon certification, **5**: 104
     CEN standards, transport biofuels, **5**: 105
     indirect land use change, **5**: 107
     International Organization for Standardization, **5**: 105
     International Sustainability & Carbon Certification, **5**: 104
     land use change, **5**: 107
     palm oils, **5**: 104
     production, **5**: **99–108**
     Renewable Energy Directive, **5**: 100, **5**: 103
     Renewable Transport Fuel Obligation, **5**: 100, **5**: 103
     retail sector standards, **5**: 106

     Round Table on Responsible Soy, **5**: 105
     Roundtable on Sustainable Palm Oil, **5**: 104
     soy, **5**: 105
     standards, **5**: **99–108**
     sustainability, **5**: 99, **5**: 103, **5**: 104, **5**: 105
     transport biofuels, CEN standards, **5**: 105
   feedstocks, **5**: 6
     waste materials, **5**: **217–261**
     yield improvement potentials, **5**: **293–303**
   fermentation, **5**: 2, **5**: 400
   fossil fuel blends, **5**: 343
   future prospects, **5**: 8
   future technologies, **5**: 127
   gasoline engines, modification, **5**: 346
   greenhouse gas savings, **5**: **109–132**
   historical perspectives, **5**: **11–14**
     engine developments, **5**: 11
     ethanol, **5**: 11
     vegetable oils, **5**: 12
   indirect land use change, **5**: 107, **5**: 120
   international labor laws, **5**: 106
   International Organization for Standardization, **5**: 105
   International Sustainability & Carbon Certification, **5**: 104
   introduction, **5**: **1–9**
   issues, constraints & limitations, **5**: 4, **5**: **99–108**, **5**: **109–132**
   issues and drivers, **5**: 157, **5**: 157*f*
   labor laws, **5**: 106
   land-use change
     automotives, **5**: 327–328
     ethics, **5**: 107
     greenhouse gas life cycle assessments, **5**: 117, **5**: 120
   land utilization, **5**: 327
   life cycle assessments, **5**: **109–132**
   lignins, **5**: 401
   lignocellulosic wastes, **5**: 218, **5**: 228, **5**: 250
   limitations, **5**: 4, **5**: **99–108**, **5**: **109–132**
   manufacturer's perspective, **5**: 313
   modification
     diesel engines, **5**: 347
     gasoline engines, **5**: 346
     petrol engines, **5**: 346
   net energy balance, **5**: 114
   nitrous oxides, **5**: 113, **5**: 113*t*, **5**: 121
   novel feedstocks, **5**: 6, **5**: **217–261**
   novel uses, **5**: **343–356**
   operation
     diesel engine modification, **5**: 347
     engine modifications, **5**: 346
     petrol engine modification, **5**: 346
   palm oils, **5**: 104
   pathways, biomass-to-liquids technology, **5**: 156, **5**: 157*f*
   photovoltaic/thermal solar collectors, **3**: 295
   power generation case studies, **5**: **27–53**
   processing energy sources, **5**: 123
   production
     automotives, **5**: 314
     ethics, **5**: **99–108**
     intensification, **5**: **205–215**
     introduction, **5**: 3
   Renewable Energy Directive, **5**: 100, **5**: 103
   Renewable Transport Fuel Obligation, **5**: 100, **5**: 103
   retail sector standards, **5**: 106
   Round Table on Responsible Soy, **5**: 105
   Roundtable on Sustainable Palm Oil, **5**: 104
   soil nitrous oxide emissions, **5**: 121
   soy, **5**: 105
   standards, **5**: **99–108**
   stationary engines, **5**: 348
   sustainability, **5**: 99, **5**: 103, **5**: 104, **5**: 105
   technology solutions, **5**: 5, **5**: **217–261**, **5**: 6
   transport use fossil fuel blends, **5**: 343
   vegetable oil, **5**: 218, **5**: 228
   world production, **5**: 3

yield improvement potentials, **5**: 293–303
biogas markets, **5**: 76
bio-inspiration: leaves/solar energy converters, **1**: **657–677**
biological capacity: photovoltaic systems, **1**: 738
biological fuel cells, **4**: **257–280**
  conventional fuel cells, **4**: 258
  electrodes, **4**: 261
  electron transfer methods, **4**: 260
  enzymes, **4**: 259, **4**: 260
    electrodes, **4**: 261
    electron transfer methods, **4**: 260
    immobilization, **4**: 260
    performance, **4**: 264
  immobilization, **4**: 260
  layered structure enzyme electrodes, **4**: 261
  mediators, **4**: 260
  performance, **4**: 264
  polymer matrix enzyme electrodes, **4**: 262
  redox enzymes, **4**: 260
  redox polymers, **4**: 262–263
biological pretreatments: lignocellulosic wastes, **5**: 246
biological processes: concrete structures, **6**: 391
biological production: hydrogen technology, **4**: 51
biomass and biofuels:
  action plans, **5**: 428
  additional value extraction, **5**: **385–393**
    current status, **5**: 387
    future development, **5**: 389, **5**: 390
    marketplace, **5**: 387, **5**: 389
    metabolite exploitation, **5**: **385–393**
    plant metabolites, **5**: **385–393**
  agriculture
    additional value extraction, **5**: **385–393**
    bioethanol, **5**: **15–26**, **5**: 218, **5**: 228, **5**: 250
    Brazilian bioethanol development, **5**: **15–26**
    cofiring, **5**: 57
    gasification, **5**: 141
  algae, **5**: 6
  anaerobic digestion, **5**: 5
  automotives, **5**: **305–342**
    CEN standards, **5**: 105
  background, **5**: 1
  bio-alcohol chemical production, **5**: 404
  biochar, **5**: **357–384**, **5**: 406
  biodiesel, **5**: 218, **5**: 228
  bioethanol
    Brazilian development, **5**: **15–26**
    lignocellulosic wastes, **5**: 218, **5**: 228, **5**: 250
  biomass-to-liquids technology, **5**: 6, **5**: **155–204**, **5**: 156
    advanced pretreatments, **5**: 156, **5**: 162f, **5**: 163, **5**: 167
      Fischer–Tropsch process, **5**: 162f, **5**: 163
    alcohols, **5**: 174t, **5**: 185, **5**: 186, **5**: 193
    alternative fuel options, **5**: 183
    automotives, **5**: 307–308
    biomass conversion, **5**: 162
    BioMCN, **5**: 184, **5**: 189, **5**: 203
    biomethanol plants, **5**: 184, **5**: 189, **5**: 203
    BioSNG, **5**: 156, **5**: 171, **5**: 177, **5**: 183, **5**: 186, **5**: 203
    biosynthetic natural gas, **5**: 156, **5**: 186
    bubbling fluidized bed gasifiers, **5**: 169t, **5**: 171
    capital costs, **5**: 191
    catalysts, **5**: 178, **5**: 185
    centralized biomass collection, **5**: 166
    chemistry, **5**: 178
    Chemrec, **5**: 191
    Choren Industries, Germany, **5**: 190, **5**: 203
    circulating fluidized bed gasifiers, **5**: 169t, **5**: 171
    coal-to-liquids, **5**: 160, **5**: 161–162, **5**: 191, **5**: 197
    commercial plants, **5**: 184, **5**: 188
    comparative land use effectiveness, **5**: 200
    contaminants, **5**: 172
    costs, **5**: 167, **5**: 167f, **5**: 188, **5**: 191, **5**: 194
    decentralized biomass collection, **5**: 166
    development, **5**: 160, **5**: 161f, **5**: 187, **5**: 188, **5**: 189f
    dimethyl ether, **5**: 158, **5**: 184, **5**: 185
    drivers, **5**: 157, **5**: 157f, **5**: 187
    dual fluidized bed gasifiers, **5**: 169t, **5**: 171
    economics, **5**: 167, **5**: 191, **5**: 203
    economies of scale, **5**: 196, **5**: 196f
    Enerkem, **5**: 190
    entrained flow gasifiers, **5**: 169, **5**: 169t
    environmental issues, **5**: 197
    feedstock costs, **5**: 194
    fermentation, **5**: 186, **5**: 193
    Fischer–Tropsch process, **5**: **155–204**, **5**: 156
      advanced pretreatments, **5**: 162f, **5**: 163
      biomass conversion, **5**: 162
      catalysts, **5**: 178
      chemistry, **5**: 178
      gasification, **5**: 168
      historical overviews, **5**: 160
      reactors, **5**: 168, **5**: 180
      syngas cleanup, **5**: 172
      syngas conditioning, **5**: 177
    fluidized bed gasifiers, **5**: 169t, **5**: 170
    fuel options, **5**: 183
    fuel pathways, **5**: 183
    future outlook, **5**: 203
    gasification
      economics, **5**: 191
      Fischer–Tropsch process, **5**: 168
      implementation progress, **5**: 188
      syngas, **5**: 168
    gasoline, **5**: 185
    gas-to-liquids technology, **5**: 159, **5**: 160–161, **5**: 161–162, **5**: 191, **5**: 197
    glycerol, **5**: 189
    greenhouse gases, **5**: 167, **5**: 167f, **5**: 168f, **5**: 197, **5**: 200, **5**: 201
    historical overviews, **5**: 160, **5**: 187
    hydrogen, **5**: 186
    implementation progress, **5**: 188
    Ineos Bio, **5**: 190
    issues and drivers, **5**: 157, **5**: 157f
    land use change, **5**: 197–198, **5**: 199f, **5**: 200
    land use effectiveness, **5**: 197–198, **5**: 199f, **5**: 200
    life cycle assessments, **5**: 156, **5**: 197
    methanation, syngas, **5**: 186
    methanol, **5**: 174t, **5**: 183, **5**: 184, **5**: 185, **5**: 189, **5**: 203
    mixed alcohols, **5**: 174t, **5**: 185
    NSE Biofuels, **5**: 191
    optional fuels, **5**: 183
    plants, **5**: 184, **5**: 188
    plasma gasifiers, **5**: 169t, **5**: 171
    pretreatments, **5**: 156, **5**: 162f, **5**: 163, **5**: 166, **5**: 167
    process development, **5**: 159, **5**: 187
    project development, **5**: 188
    pyrolysis, **5**: 156, **5**: 165
    Range Fuels, **5**: 190
    reactors, **5**: 168, **5**: 180
    syngas, **5**: **155–204**, **5**: 156
      cleanup, **5**: 172
      conditioning, **5**: 177
      contaminants, **5**: 172
      gasification, **5**: 168
      methanation, **5**: 186
    synthetic natural gas, **5**: 156, **5**: 171, **5**: 177, **5**: 183, **5**: 186, **5**: 203
    technology issues, **5**: 188, **5**: 203
    timescales, **5**: 160, **5**: 161f, **5**: 187, **5**: 189f
    torrefaction, **5**: 156, **5**: 164
  boilers, **5**: 32, **5**: 34
  Brazilian bioethanol development, **5**: **15–26**
  bubbling fluidized bed gasifiers, **5**: 137
  bulk density, **5**: 43
  carbonaceous solid residues, **5**: **357–384**
  carbon dioxide, **5**: 91

biomass and biofuels: (*continued*)
  CEN standards, **5**: 105
  characteristics, health and safety, **5**: 42
  chemical production, **5**: **395–410**
    bio-alcohols, **5**: 404
    biochar, **5**: 406
    fermentation, **5**: 400
    glycerin coproduct conversion, **5**: 396
    solid biofuels, **5**: 406
  circulating fluidized bed gasifiers, **5**: 137
  cleaning technologies, **5**: 145
  cofiring, **5**: **55–73**
    Aberthaw power plant, **5**: 66
    agricultural residues, **5**: 58
    agriculture, **5**: 57
    Amer 9 plant, **5**: 65
    available materials, **5**: 57
    bagasse, **5**: 59
    Borssele plant, **5**: 66
    bubbling bed fluidized bed combustion, **5**: 61
    challenges, **5**: 57
    chemical properties, **5**: 70
    circulating bed fluidized bed combustion, **5**: 61
    coal dust exposure, **5**: 69
    combined heat and power, **5**: 67t
    combustion technology, **5**: 61, **5**: 62
    crops, **5**: 57
    cyclone boiler combustion, **5**: 62
    delivery issues, **5**: 70
    Didcot power plant, **5**: 68
    direct cofiring, **5**: 63
    direct gasification, **5**: 62
    Drax, **5**: 68
    dust exposure, **5**: 69
    energy crops, **5**: 57, **5**: 67t
    entrained flow gasifiers, **5**: 63
    E.ON (Kingsnorth), **5**: 68
    exposure risks, **5**: 69
    fires, **5**: 68
    fixed bed gasifiers, **5**: 62
    fluidized bed combustion, **5**: 61
    fluidized bed gasifiers, **5**: 63
    fuel delivery issues, **5**: 70
    gaseous fuels, **5**: 61
    gasification, **5**: 61, **5**: 62
    global overviews, **5**: 64
    global plants, **5**: 64
    global trends, **5**: 56, **5**: 64
    grass, **5**: 59
    grate-fired boiler combustion, **5**: 61
    health and safety, **5**: 68
    husks, **5**: 58
    indirect gasification, **5**: 62
    indirect methods, **5**: 62, **5**: 64
    injection methods, **5**: 63, **5**: 64
    jatropha oils, **5**: 60
    liquids, **5**: 60
    Maasvlakte 1 and 2 plants, **5**: 66
    McNeil generating plant, **5**: 65
    materials, **5**: 57
    milling methods, **5**: 63
    miscanthus, **5**: 57
    Netherlands, **5**: 65
    oil palm residues, **5**: 58
    oils, **5**: 60
    olive residues, **5**: 58
    palm residues, **5**: 58
    parallel methods, **5**: 64
    physical properties, **5**: 70
    plant operations, **5**: 70
    plants, **5**: 64, **5**: 70
    preparation issues, **5**: 70
    processed wood fuels, **5**: 59
    property effects, **5**: 70
    rice husks, **5**: 58
    safety, **5**: 68
    sewage sludge, **5**: 60
    shea residues, **5**: 58
    short-rotation coppice, **5**: 57
    solid materials, **5**: 57, **5**: 58, **5**: 59
    sorghum stalks, **5**: 59
    spontaneous combustion, **5**: 68
    spontaneous fires, **5**: 68
    stoker combustion, **5**: 61
    storage issues, **5**: 70
    straw, **5**: 59
    sugarcane residues, **5**: 59
    supply issues, **5**: 70
    tall oils, **5**: 60
    tallow, **5**: 60
    technical issues, **5**: 57, **5**: 69
    torrefied wood, **5**: 59
    United Kingdom, **5**: 66
    United States, **5**: 64
    waste residues, **5**: 58
    wood-based fuels, **5**: 57, **5**: 59
    wood pellets, **5**: 59
    worldwide trends, **5**: 56, **5**: 64
  combined heat and power generation, **5**: **87–97**
    carbon dioxide, **5**: 91
    combustion, **5**: 88, **5**: 89
    competition, **5**: 92, **5**: 94
    gasification, **5**: 87, **5**: 88, **5**: 89, **5**: 94
    markets, **5**: 91, **5**: 92
    options, **5**: 88
    power generation, **5**: 33, **5**: 39
    scale effects, **5**: 95
    sector competition, **5**: 92
    steam turbines, **5**: 88, **5**: 90, **5**: 94, **5**: 95
    technology properties, **5**: 90
    technology system aspects, **5**: 93
  combustion
    biomass cofiring, **5**: 62
    combined heat and power, **5**: 88, **5**: 89
    dual fuel operation, **5**: 350
    power generation, **5**: 47
  commercial viability expansion, **5**: 7
  competition, **5**: 92, **5**: 94
  configurations, gasifiers, **5**: 136
  constraints & limitations, **5**: 4
    greenhouse gas life cycle assessments, **5**: **109–132**
    production ethics, **5**: **99–108**
  contaminants, **5**: 141, **5**: 142
    biomass gasification, **5**: 141, **5**: 142
    biomass-to-liquids technology, **5**: 172
    feedstocks, **5**: 141
    gasification, **5**: 141, **5**: 142
    syngas, **5**: 172
  conversion
    biomass-to-liquids technology, Fischer–Tropsch process, **5**: 162
    Fischer–Tropsch process, biomass-to-liquids technology, **5**: 162
    gasification, biomass-to-liquids technology, **5**: 168
  crops
    additional value extraction, **5**: **385–393**
    cofiring, **5**: 57
    feedstocks, **5**: 7, **5**: **263–291**
    gasification, **5**: 141
    yield improvement potentials, **5**: **293–303**
  current additional value extraction, **5**: 387
  definitions, **5**: 76, **5**: 217, **5**: 395
  deployment, **5**: 3
  development, **5**: 8, **5**: **15–26**, **5**: 151
  drying, **5**: 163
  dual fluidized bed gasifiers, **5**: 138, **5**: 150

Index

economics, **5**: 29
electricity
   combined heat and power, **5**: **87-97**
   wind energy policy, **2**: 552
emissions
   biomass-to-liquids technology, **5**: 167, **5**: 167f, **5**: 168f, **5**: 197, **5**: 200, **5**: 201
   carbon dioxide, **5**: 29, **5**: 305, **5**: 308, **5**: 327
   limits, **5**: 31, **5**: 33
   power generation, **5**: 31, **5**: 33, **5**: 51
engine configuration ranges, **5**: **343-356**
entrained flow gasifiers, **5**: 136, **5**: 138, **5**: 149
environmental impacts, **5**: 51
extracting additional value, **5**: **385-393**
feedstocks, **5**: 6, **5**: **263-291**, **5**: 7
   biomass-to-liquids technology, **5**: 162, **5**: 162f
   definitions, **5**: 109
   gasifiers, **5**: 139
   woody biomass, **5**: **263-291**
   yield improvement potentials, **5**: **293-303**
fermentation, **5**: 2, **5**: 186, **5**: 193, **5**: 400
financing power generation, **5**: 29
fires, **5**: 41
firing, **5**: 33
fixed bed gasifiers, **5**: 136, **5**: 150
fixed grates, **5**: 33
fluidized bed boilers, **5**: 34
fluidized bed gasifiers, **5**: 136, **5**: 137, **5**: 149
fuel characteristics, **5**: 141
fuel preparation, **5**: 44
fuel processing, **5**: 43
future prospects, **5**: 8
   additional value extraction, **5**: 389, **5**: 390
   gasification, **5**: 151
gas cleaning technologies, **5**: 145
gaseous emissions
   biomass-to-liquids technology, **5**: 167, **5**: 167f, **5**: 168f, **5**: 197, **5**: 200, **5**: 201
   carbon dioxide, **5**: 29, **5**: 305, **5**: 308, **5**: 327
   limits, **5**: 31, **5**: 33
   power generation, **5**: 31, **5**: 33, **5**: 51
gaseous fuels
   cofiring, **5**: 61
   stationary engines, **5**: 351
gasification, **5**: **133-153**
   case studies, **5**: 149
   cleaning technologies, **5**: 145
   combined heat and power, **5**: 87, **5**: 88, **5**: 89, **5**: 94
   contaminants, **5**: 141, **5**: 142
   derivative fuels, **5**: 159, **5**: 159f
   developments, **5**: 151
   examples, **5**: 149
   feedstocks, **5**: 139
   fuel characteristics, **5**: 141
   future development, **5**: 151
   gas cleaning technologies, **5**: 145
   gasifier configurations, **5**: 136
   gasifier feedstocks, **5**: 139
   gasifier oxidants, **5**: 139
   gas processing, **5**: 142
   historical development, **5**: 134
   oxidants, **5**: 139
   power generation, **5**: 37
   syngas quality, **5**: 144, **5**: 144f, **5**: 144t
gas processing, **5**: 142
glycerin coproduct conversion, **5**: 396
grates, **5**: 33
greenhouse gas savings, **5**: **109-132**
handling, **5**: 43, **5**: 142, **5**: 276
health and safety, **5**: 40, **5**: 42, **5**: 68
historical perspectives, **5**: **11-14**
   biomass-to-liquids technology, **5**: 160, **5**: 187
   Fischer-Tropsch process, **5**: 160

gasification, **5**: 134
pyrolysis, **5**: 134
hydropower multibenefit solutions, **6**: 43
integrated gasification combined cycles, **5**: 88, **5**: 90, **5**: 94, **5**: 95
International Organization for Standardization, **5**: 105
introduction, **5**: **1-9**
investment in power generation, **5**: 29
issues, constraints & limitations, **5**: 4
   biofuel production ethics, **5**: **99-108**
   greenhouse gas life cycle assessments, **5**: **109-132**
legislation, **5**: 31
life-cycle analysis, **5**: 29, **5**: **109-132**
lignocellulosic wastes, **5**: 218, **5**: 228, **5**: 250
limitations, **5**: 4
   automotives, **5**: 327
   biofuel production ethics, **5**: **99-108**
   life cycle assessments of greenhouse gases, **5**: **109-132**
markets
   additional value extraction, **5**: 387, **5**: 389
   bioenergy trade, **5**: **75-85**
   combined heat and power, **5**: 91, **5**: 92
   policy, **5**: 75
   trade, **5**: **75-85**
material handling, **5**: 43
metabolite exploitation, **5**: **385-393**
moving grates, **5**: 33
novel feedstocks, **5**: 6, **5**: **217-261**, **5**: **263-291**
novel uses, **5**: **343-356**
oxidants, gasifiers, **5**: 139
oxygen-deficient heating, **5**: **357-384**
photovoltaic/thermal solar collectors, **3**: 295
plant metabolites, **5**: **385-393**
plasma gasifiers, **5**: 139, **5**: 151
policy
   development, **5**: **411-429**
   markets, **5**: 75
   wind energy, **2**: 552
potential power generation fuels, **5**: 37
power generation, **5**: **27-53**
   boilers, **5**: 32, **5**: 34
   bulk density, **5**: 43
   case studies, **5**: **27-53**
   combined heat and power, **5**: 33, **5**: 39
   combustion, **5**: 47
   economics, **5**: 29
   emission limits, **5**: 31, **5**: 33
   environmental impacts, **5**: 51
   finance, **5**: 29
   firing, **5**: 33
   fixed grates, **5**: 33
   fluidized bed boilers, **5**: 34
   fuel preparation, **5**: 44
   fuel processing, **5**: 43
   gaseous emissions, **5**: 31, **5**: 33, **5**: 51
   gasification, **5**: 37
   grates, **5**: 33
   handling, **5**: 43
   health and safety, **5**: 40
   investment, **5**: 29
   legislation, **5**: 31
   life-cycle analysis, **5**: 29
   material handling, **5**: 43
   moving grates, **5**: 33
   potential fuels, **5**: 37
   prices, **5**: 29
   regulation, **5**: 31
   Renewable Obligation, **5**: 32
   storage, **5**: 43
   suspension firing, **5**: 33
   sustainability, **5**: 28
   technology choice availability, **5**: 32
   technology development, **5**: 32
pretreatments, **5**: 156, **5**: 162f, **5**: 163, **5**: 166, **5**: 167

biomass and biofuels: (*continued*)
  prices for power generation, **5**: 29
  production, **5**: 3
    chemical production, **5**: **395–410**
    ethics, **5**: **99–108**
    intensification, **5**: **205–215**
  pyrolysis, **5**: 134, **5**: 135, **5**: 148
    biomass-to-liquids technology, **5**: 156, **5**: 165
  regulation
    COSHH regulations, **5**: 69
    DSEAR, **5**: 43
    power generation, **5**: 31
  Renewable Obligation, **5**: 32
  scale effects, **5**: 95
  sector competition, **5**: 92
  solid biofuels, **5**: 406
  stand-alone power plant trends, **5**: 28
  steam turbines, **5**: 88, **5**: 90, **5**: 94, **5**: 95
  storage
    cofiring, **5**: 70
    combined heat and power, **5**: 89
    power generation, **5**: 43
  supply
    biomass-to-liquids technology, **5**: 187–188
    cofiring, **5**: 70
    security, **5**: 305–306
    woody biomass feedstocks, **5**: 278
  suspension firing, **5**: 33
  sustainability
    additional value extraction, **5**: **385–393**
    biomass-to-liquids technology, **5**: 203
    hydrogen production, **4**: 50
    power generation, **5**: 28
    woody biomass feedstocks, **5**: 281, **5**: 284
  technology aspects
    biomass-to-liquids technology, **5**: **155–204**
    choice availability, **5**: 32
    combined heat and power, **5**: 90, **5**: 93
    development, **5**: 32
    introduction, **5**: 5, **5**: 6
    novel feedstocks, **5**: **263–291**
    properties, **5**: 90
    woody biomass feedstocks, **5**: **263–291**
  thermochemical processing, **5**: **357–384**
  trade, **5**: **75–85**
  transport CEN standards, **5**: 105
  vegetable oils, **5**: 218, **5**: 228
  waste materials, **5**: **217–261**
  wind energy policy, **2**: 552
  woody biomass feedstocks, **5**: **263–291**
  worldwide production, **5**: 3, **5**: 56, **5**: 64
  yield improvement potentials, **5**: **293–303**
biomass integrated gasification combined cycles (BIGCC):
  heat and power, **5**: 88, **5**: 90, **5**: 94, **5**: 95
  hydrogen production, **4**: 50
BioMCN, **5**: 184, **5**: 189, **5**: 203
biomethanol plants, **5**: 184, **5**: 189, **5**: 203
bio-oils, **5**: 348, **5**: 368, **5**: 379
biorefining, **5**: **385–393**, **5**: 395
BioSNG *see* synthetic natural gas
biosynthetic gas, **5**: 128–129, **5**: 129*f*
biotechnology yield improvement potentials, **5**: 301
biotope creation, **6**: 423
biplane rotors, **8**: 118, **8**: 119, **8**: 128
BIPV *see* building-integrated photovoltaics
birds: wind energy impacts, **2**: 182, **2**: 205, **2**: 529, **2**: 687–688
Bird solar radiation model, **3**: 42
Biscay Marine Energy Platform (BIMEP), **8**: 83–84, **8**: 102
bivalent heat pumps, **3**: 501
Bjarnarflag, Iceland, **7**: 111
blackbodies:
  geometrical factors, **1**: 321
  photovoltaic thermodynamics, **1**: 318, **1**: 321, **1**: 322, **1**: 332

  selective coatings, **3**: 303
  solar energy conversion principles, **1**: 293, **1**: 295, **1**: 296
  solar thermal components and applications, **3**: 18
  spectral property radiance, **1**: 318
  Sun, **3**: 79
  thermal radiation thermodynamics, **1**: 318, **1**: 321
  thermodynamics, **1**: 318, **1**: 321, **1**: 322, **1**: 332
  work, **1**: 332
black carbons, **5**: 357, **5**: 362
black liquors, **5**: 264
black paint, **3**: 19, **3**: 108–109, **3**: 109*f*
blade-element momentum (BEM) theory:
  see also blades
  aerodynamic analysis, **2**: 225, **2**: 228, **2**: 236
  airfoil data, **2**: 231
  dynamic inflow, **2**: 230
  dynamic wake, **2**: 230
  heavily loaded rotor corrections, **2**: 230
  inflow, **2**: 230
  loaded rotor corrections, **2**: 230
  rotor optimization, **2**: 236
  tip correction, **2**: 229
  wake, **2**: 230
  wind turbines, **2**: 225, **2**: 228, **2**: 236
  yaw correction, **2**: 230
blades:
  see also blade-element momentum theory
  aerodynamics, **2**: 713
  air turbines, **8**: 113, **8**: 128
  aspect ratio, **8**: 128
  blade numbers, **2**: 61
  construction, **2**: 682
  definition, wind turbines, **2**: 270
  design, **2**: 682
  financial support, **2**: 710
  pitch systems, **2**: 275*f*
  shape, **6**: 455
  technology evolution, **2**: 682, **2**: 710, **2**: 713
  wind turbines, **2**: 682, **2**: 710, **2**: 713
blast furnaces, **2**: 42
blast furnace slag, **6**: 393
blend cells:
  n-type silicon cells, **1**: 379
  organic solar cells, **1**: 440, **1**: 441, **1**: 448, **1**: 448*f*, **1**: 449, **1**: 463
  silicon photovoltaics, **1**: 379, **1**: 393
  thin-films, **1**: 393
Block V specification: photovoltaic standards, **1**: 788
Blythe project, **3**: 631, **3**: 632*f*
Blyth, James, **2**: 53, **2**: 53*f*
Bm fuels, **5**: 343
boats *see* ships
boiler rooms, **3**: 514–515
boilers, **5**: 32, **5**: 34
  biomass cofiring, **5**: 61, **5**: 62
  heat-only boilers, **5**: 94, **5**: 94–95
boiling: geothermal energy geochemistry, **7**: 106
boiling points, **5**: 318*f*, **5**: 318–319, **7**: 16
Bolarque project, Spain, **6**: 320, **6**: 320*f*
Boltzmann losses, **1**: 309, **1**: 311
bonding: hydrogen storage safety, **4**: 125
booster diffuse reflectors, **5**: 281
bore heat exchangers, **7**: 197, **7**: 200, **7**: 203
boreholes, **3**: 211, **3**: 219, **3**: 237, **7**: 18
borohydrides, **4**: 147
boron-diffused back junctions, **1**: 377
boron-diffused front emitters, **1**: 376
Borssele plant: biomass cofiring, **5**: 66
Bosch Rexroth Mobilex GFB pitch motors, **2**: 276*f*
Bosch Solar, **1**: 172
bottom-up manufacturing, **1**: 67
bottom water diversion outlets, **6**: 207
Boudouard reaction, **5**: 135
Boys, C. V., **3**: 92, **3**: 93*f*

brackish water:
    solar desalination, **3**: 529, **3**: 538, **3**: 539t, **3**: 556
        photovoltaic-driven reverse osmosis, **3**: 538, **3**: 539t, **3**: 556, **3**: 558, **3**: 560, **3**: 560t, **3**: 563f
brake specific fuel consumption (BSFC), **5**: 343, **5**: 348, **5**: 349
Brassica breeders, **5**: 300
Brayton engines, **3**: 201
Brazil, **5**: 15–26, **6**: 93–127
    6450MW Madeira hydroelectric project, **6**: 104
    8125MW Tucurui hydroelectric project, **6**: 101
    14000MW Itaipu hydroelectric project, **6**: 96
    alcohol fuel sustainability, **5**: 337
    Amazon biochar, **5**: 358, **5**: 358f, **5**: 359, **5**: 361f
    Barra Grande hydroelectricity project, **6**: 124
    Belo Monte project, **6**: 124
    biochar, **5**: 358, **5**: 358f, **5**: 359, **5**: 361f
    bioethanol development, **5**: 15–26
        clean energy matrices, **5**: 20
        environmental responsibility, **5**: 18, **5**: 21
        future directions, **5**: 24
        historical overviews, **5**: 15
        industry, **5**: 15, **5**: 17
        social responsibility, **5**: 21
    Campos Novos hydroelectricity project, **6**: 123
    clean energy matrices, **5**: 20
    electric sector, **6**: 94
    environmental responsibility, **5**: 18, **5**: 21
    ethanol, **5**: 15
    Foz do Areia hydroelectric project, **6**: 108
    future directions, **5**: 24
    historical overviews, **5**: 15, **6**: 94
    hydropower plants, **6**: 35, **6**: 93–127, **6**: 36t
    Iguaçu River hydroelectric project, **6**: 108
    industry, **5**: 15–26
    Itá hydroelectricity project, **6**: 121
    Itaipu hydroelectric project, **6**: 96
    Jirau hydroelectric project, **6**: 94, **6**: 104f, **6**: 106
    Machadinho hydroelectricity project, **6**: 119
    Madeira hydroelectric project, **6**: 104
    Salto Caxias hydroelectricity project, **6**: 116
    Salto Osorio hydroelectricity project, **6**: 114
    Salto Santiago hydroelectricity project, **6**: 111
    Santo Antonio hydroelectric project, **6**: 104f, **6**: 105
    Segredo hydroelectric project, **6**: 110
    social responsibility, **5**: 21
    sugarcane industry, **5**: 15–26
    sugar production, **5**: 19
    sugar trade, **5**: 19
    Tucurui hydroelectric project, **6**: 101
    Uruguay River hydroelectricity project, **6**: 119
Brazilian Sugarcane Industry Association (UNICA):
    bioethanol development, **5**: 19, **5**: 20, **5**: 22, **5**: 23, **5**: 24
    mission, **5**: 25
    priority issues, **5**: 25
    strategies, **5**: 26
breakthroughs in photovoltaic cost reductions, **1**: 61
breezes: wind speed time variations, **2**: 82
Bretschneider spectrum, **8**: 16, **8**: 16t, **8**: 17f, **8**: 96
bridging power storage technologies, **1**: 206
BrightSource Energy receivers, **3**: 193
British Colombia, Canada, **6**: 153, **6**: 173
British Wind Energy Association (BWEA), **2**: 65, **2**: 71, **2**: 376
broadband solar radiation, **1**: 214, **1**: 217, **1**: 231, **3**: 39
BRP *see* biodiesel-rich phase
Brush, Charles, **2**: 53, **2**: 53f
BSF *see* back-surface-field layers
BSFC *see* brake specific fuel consumption
BSRN *see* Baseline Solar Radiation Network
bubble column reactors, **5**: 181
bubble plumes, **6**: 83
bubbling bed fluidized bed combustion, **5**: 61
bubbling fluidized bed gasifiers, **5**: 137, **5**: 149, **5**: 169t, **5**: 171
budgeting: wind power, **2**: 426

buffer layers, **1**: 412, **1**: 428
Buffon, G. L. L., **3**: 88, **3**: 89f
Bugler model, **3**: 47
building components: building-integrated photovoltaics, **1**: 704
building-integrated photovoltaics (BIPV), **1**: 697–707, **1**: 10, **3**: 380
    angles, design processes, **1**: 700
    artistic structural modules, **1**: 704
    building components, **1**: 704
    definitions, **1**: 698
    design processes, **1**: 700
    distance considerations, **1**: 700
    facade integrated systems, architecture, **1**: 704, **1**: 705
    future markets, **1**: 697
    implementation issues, **1**: 699
    integrated system criteria, **1**: 705
    integration rules, **1**: 701
    long-term operation issues, **1**: 699
    market segmentation, **1**: 191
    module integration, **1**: 706
    module placement, **1**: 702
    operation, **1**: 699
    orientation, **1**: 700
    placement considerations, **1**: 702
    product-integrated photovoltaics, **1**: 710
    reflection, **1**: 701
    roofing louvres, **1**: 705
    roof-integrated systems, **1**: 703, **1**: 705
    shading devices, **1**: 701, **1**: 702, **1**: 704, **1**: 705
    shadow, **1**: 701, **1**: 702
    site layouts, **1**: 699
    solar access, **1**: 699
    solar design, **1**: 702
    step-by-step design, **1**: 702
    trees, **1**: 701
    urban planning, **1**: 697–707
    zoning, **1**: 701
building-integrated photovoltaic-thermal systems:
    air-based systems, **3**: 381
    design, **3**: 394
    design optimization, **3**: 389, **3**: 390
    heat collection functions, **3**: 379
    heating, ventilation, and air-conditioning, **3**: 360–361, **3**: 362, **3**: 391
    heat removal factor, **3**: 388
    integration, **3**: 379
    low-energy homes, **3**: 389
    modeling, **3**: 379
    net-zero energy solar buildings, **3**: 394
    open-loop models, **3**: 381, **3**: 388
    simulations, **3**: 379
    solar technology integration, **3**: 379
    steady-state models, **3**: 381
    transient models, **3**: 381
building-integrated systems: wind energy turbine technology, **2**: 699
building phase: wind power, **2**: 427
building quality: photovoltaics, **1**: 705
buildings:
    coatings, **3**: 313–355
    cooling systems, **3**: 481–494
    glazing, **3**: 313–355
    heating, **3**: 360–361, **3**: 419–447, **3**: 362, **3**: 391, **3**: 587
    passive solar technologies, **3**: 359, **3**: 361
    photovoltaic/thermal solar collectors, **3**: 280, **3**: 282
    solar control, **3**: 289
    solar cooling systems, **3**: 481–494
    solar thermal energy, glazing, **3**: 313–355
    solar thermal energy coatings/glazing, **3**: 313–355
    solar water heating systems, **3**: 419–447
    thermally driven cooling systems, **3**: 481–494
built environment:
    agricultural applications of solar heat, **3**: 587
    heating, **3**: 587

built environment: (*continued*)
   industrial applications of solar heat, 3: 587
   passive solar architecture, 3: **637–665**
   photovoltaic/thermal solar collectors, 3: 280, 3: 282
   ventilation, 3: 587
   windows, 3: 330
bulk converter power loss analysis, 4: 301
bulk density, 5: 43
bulk heterojunctions, 1: 440, 1: 441, 1: 448, 1: 448*f*, 1: 449, 1: 463
bulk intermediate band solar cells, 1: 624
bulk properties: crystalline silicon cells, 1: 368
buoyancy-controlled flows, 4: 90
buoyancy-driven systems, 3: 573*f*, 3: 573–575
buoyancy line stabilizers, 2: 449
buoys: ocean waves, 8: 23
burner hybridization, 3: 607
burning sugarcane, 5: 22
Burntwood River, Manitoba, Canada, 6: 159
buses, 4: 36–37, 4: 63–64, 4: 217, 4: 286
business models: wind power, 2: 429
business-to-business photovoltaic applications, 1: 712
butane burners, 1: 615
1-butanol, 5: 317, 5: 317*t*
Butgenbach dam, Belgium, 6: 400, 6: 402*f*
buttress dams, 6: 30
BWEA *see* British Wind Energy Association
bypass/bypassing:
   reservoirs, 6: 294, 6: 296, 6: 298
   sediment management, 6: 366

C

C&D *see* construction and demolition
cabling, 2: 451
cadmium chloride activation, 1: 431
cadmium solar cell luminescent down-shifting, 1: 568
cadmium sulphide layers, 1: 424, 1: 429
cadmium telluride environmental impacts, 1: 144
cadmium telluride thin-films, 1: **423–438**, 1: 8, 1: 23, 1: 515, 1: 522
   back contacts, 1: 432
   buffer layers, 1: 428
   cadmium chloride activation, 1: 431
   cadmium sulphide layers, 1: 424, 1: 429
   commercial modules, 1: 424
   device designs, 1: 424
   energy-payback times, 1: 436
   environmental impacts, 1: 436
   historical overviews, 1: 423
   industry designs, 1: 424
   initial commercial modules, 1: 424
   junctions, 1: 434
   large-scale deployment considerations, 1: 434
   layer-specific process descriptions, 1: 427
   material properties, 1: 426
   microtechnologies, 1: 515, 1: 517, 1: 522
   mineral availability, 1: 436
   nanotechnologies, 1: 515, 1: 517, 1: 522
   payback times, 1: 436
   photovoltaics, 1: **423–438**, 1: 8, 1: 23
   reliability, 1: 435
   transparent conducting oxide layer(s), 1: 424, 1: 428
CAES *see* compressed air energy storage
calcite scaling, 7: 143
calcium carbonate scaling, 7: 249–250
calculators: product-integrated photovoltaics, 1: 711, 1: 711*f*
calibration:
   numerical ocean wave models, 8: 47
   pyranometers, 1: 223
   pyrheliometers, 1: 220, 1: 223
   radiometers, 1: 221, 3: 67
   satellite altimeters, 8: 37

Californian alcohol fuel sustainability, 5: 337
Californian wind rush, 2: 66
Calluna vulgaris, 5: 390
calm spells: wind energy, 2: 1
calm wind spells, 2: 82, 2: 125
Camarasa dam, Spain, 6: 321
Cameroon, Africa:
   Aluminum smelter company, 6: 137
   Bini Warak Project, 6: 145, 6: 145*t*
   Colomines hydro plant, 6: 145
   current status of hydropower, 6: 148
   dams, 6: 134, 6: 137
   development plans, 6: 135
   funding hydropower, 6: 141, 6: 144, 6: 148, 6: 149
   future hydropower outlooks, 6: 137
   hydropower, 6: **129–151**
   institutional structure reforms, 6: **129–151**
   investments, 6: 144, 6: 148, 6: 149
   laws, 6: 148
   legislation, 6: 148
   Lom Panger storage dam, 6: 137
   Mekin hydropower project, 6: 141
   Memve'Elé hydro plant project, 6: 139
   mid-term development plans, 6: 135
   Ngassona Falls 210 Project, 6: 146
   potentials, 6: 130
   power plants, 6: 131, 6: 135
   reforms, 6: **129–151**
   river systems, 6: 130
   storage dams, 6: 134, 6: 137
Campos Novos hydroelectricity project, Brazil, 6: 123
Canada:
   alcohol fuel sustainability, 5: 337
   British Colombian hydropower, 6: 153, 6: 173
   construction, hydropower, 6: 163
   feed-in-tariffs, 2: 546
   historical hydropower overviews, 6: 153, 6: 156, 6: 161, 6: 173
   hydropower, 6: **153–178**
      construction, 6: 163
      historical overviews, 6: 153, 6: 156, 6: 161, 6: 173
      opportunities, 6: 154
   Manitoba, 6: 153, 6: 156
   market development of photovoltaics, 1: 184
   opportunities in hydropower, 6: 154
   photovoltaic market development, 1: 184
   provincial hydroelectricity generation, 6: **153–178**
   Quebec, 6: 153, 6: 161
   recent hydropower solutions, 6: **153–178**
   sustainability of hydropower, 6: **153–178**
Canadian Solar Inc. (CSI), 1: 171
Canadian solar radiation atlas (CSRA), 3: 62
Canadian Sunphotometer Network (AeroCAN), 3: 61
canal developments, 6: 24
candle filters, 5: 145
Canelles power plant and dam, Spain, 6: 324–325, 6: 326*f*
Canoas River, Brazil, 6: 123
canola, 5: **293–303**
capacitance voltage measurements, 1: 404
capacitor banks, 2: 296
capacitors: wind energy, 2: 650
capacity:
   credit, 2: 491
   desalination, 2: 726, 2: 727*f*, 2: 727–728, 2: 728*t*
   energy storage, 1: 201
   global wind power markets, 2: **657–669**
   hydropower, 6: 362
   offshore wind parks, 2: 688
   wind energy costs, 2: 491
   wind power global markets, 2: **657–669**
capacity factors (CF):
   economics, 4: 45, 4: 53
   electricity grids, 2: 559
   hydrogen economics, 4: 45, 4: 53

ocean energy, **8**: 79, **8**: 162
offshore wind power, **2**: 431
wind turbines, **2**: 1, **2**: 114, **2**: 135, **2**: 153–154, **2**: 677–679, **2**: 678f
research and development, **2**: 671
Capdella power plant, Spain, **6**: 320, **6**: 320f
CAPEX *see* capital expenditure
capital costs:
  biomass-to-liquids technology, **5**: 191
  civil engineering infrastructure, **8**: 156
  decommissioning ocean energy, **8**: 158
  deployment of ocean energy, **8**: 158, **8**: 167
  electrical infrastructures, **8**: 157
  geothermal heat pumps, **7**: 202
  marine energy devices, **8**: 156
  ocean energy, **8**: 152, **8**: 152f, **8**: 153, **8**: 155, **8**: 167
  offshore wind power, **2**: 460
  preliminary ocean energy works, **8**: 156
  site-to-grid transmission, **8**: 157
  solar cooling, **3**: 491
  very large-scale photovoltaic systems, **1**: 737
  wind power design/implementation, **2**: 422, **2**: 424
capital expenditure (CAPEX):
  geothermal energy, **7**: 259, **7**: 260, **7**: 261, **7**: 263
  ocean energy, **8**: 156
capital financing control system, **6**: 209
capital investment, **3**: 231
capital subsidies, **1**: 125
capture widths: ocean energy, **8**: 79
carbohydrates, **1**: 657, **5**: 298
carbon:
  see also carbon capture…; carbon dioxide; carbon monoxide; low-carbon…
  alloy steels, **7**: 247
  carbon-negative energy, **5**: 357, **5**: 360, **5**: 379
  carbon-silicon solar cells, **1**: 393
  Carbon Trust, **8**: 83
  certification, **5**: 104
  cycle, **5**: 362, **5**: 363f
  emissions, **4**: 291, **4**: 296
  financing, **1**: 129
  footprints, **2**: 503
  nanotubes, **1**: 526
  neutral solutions, automotives, **5**: 307
  numbers, **5**: 179, **5**: 179f
  separation, molten carbonate fuel cells, **4**: 238
  sequestration
    agricultural practices, **5**: 365, **5**: 379
    biochar, **5**: 357, **5**: 360, **5**: 379
      agricultural practices, **5**: 365
      black carbons, **5**: 357, **5**: 362
      carbon cycle, **5**: 362, **5**: 363f
      global carbon cycle, **5**: 362, **5**: 363f
    bioenergy policy development, **5**: 412, **5**: 415–416
    carbon cycle, **5**: 362, **5**: 363f
    global carbon cycle, **5**: 362, **5**: 363f
  stock changes, **5**: 119–120
  sustainability reporting, **5**: 103
  taxes, **2**: 485
  trading, **2**: 485
carbonaceous solid residues, **5**: **357–384**
carbonate fuel cells *see* molten carbonate fuel cells
carbonate scaling, **7**: 249–250, **7**: 250
carbonation:
  concrete structure durability, **6**: 386
  environmental conditions, **6**: 386–387
  influential factors, **6**: 386
  prevention, **6**: 387
  working mechanisms, **6**: 386
carbon capture and storage (CCS):
  biochar, **5**: 360
  carbon dioxide emission reduction, **2**: 548
  electrofuels, **5**: 329

hydrogen technology
  economics, **4**: 45, **4**: 46, **4**: 49, **4**: 50, **4**: 64
  fuel cells, **4**: 332, **4**: 333f, **4**: 337
wind energy, carbon dioxide emission reduction, **2**: 548
carbon dioxide:
  see also greenhouse gases
  atmospheric carbon dioxide, **5**: 330, **5**: 331
  automotives, **5**: 305, **5**: 308, **5**: 327, **5**: 330, **5**: 331
    alcohol fuels, **5**: 333
    biomass and biofuels, **5**: 305, **5**: 308, **5**: 327
    electric hybrid vehicles, **5**: 308
    manufacturer's perspective, **5**: 313
  biochar, **5**: 380
  bioenergy policy development, **5**: 412, **5**: 415, **5**: 415t
  biofuels, **5**: 4, **5**: 109
  Brazilian bioethanol development, **5**: 19
  combined heat and power, **5**: 91
  corrosion, **7**: 246
  energy balance, **2**: 22
  engine configuration ranges, **5**: 347
  environmental impacts, **2**: 22, **2**: 504
  flux measurements, **7**: 100
  gas diffusion electrodes, **4**: 169
  geothermal chemistry, **7**: 100, **7**: 120, **7**: 125–126, **7**: 126–127
  geothermal energy cost/investment factors, **7**: 259
  life-cycle analysis, **5**: 29
  lignocellulosic wastes, **5**: 245
  molten carbonate fuel cells, **4**: 228
  policy, wind energy, **2**: 545, **2**: 548
  savings, **2**: 491
  very large-scale photovoltaic systems, **1**: 738, **1**: 738f
  wind energy, **2**: 504
    policy, **2**: 545, **2**: 548
    social benefits/impacts, **2**: 504
    variable costs, **2**: 491
carbon monoxide:
  biomass combustion, **5**: 49, **5**: 51
  engine configuration ranges, **5**: 347, **5**: 348, **5**: 350–351
  environmental impacts, **5**: 49, **5**: 51
  proton-exchange membrane fuel cells, **4**: 187
carbonometers, **5**: 19
Carbon Trust, **8**: 83
car fires, **4**: 79, **4**: 79f
Carnot cycles, **3**: 488, **3**: 497, **3**: 498
Carnot efficiency, **3**: 485–486
Carnot limits, **4**: 250
Carnot losses, **1**: 309, **1**: 311
carotenoid tetraterpenoid organic pigments, **1**: 657, **1**: 658
carp, **6**: 216
carrier-carrier generation/recombination, **1**: 303
carrier concentration, **1**: 298, **1**: 498–500, **1**: 499f
carrier density, **1**: 299
carrier multiplication, **1**: 549
carrier populations, **1**: 298, **1**: 498–500, **1**: 499f
cars, **1**: 714, **1**: 715f, **4**: 287, **5**: **305–342**
  see also automotives; road vehicles; vehicles
CART *see* Controls Advanced Research Turbine
cascade flow analysis, **8**: 113
case studies:
  biomass and biofuel power generation, **5**: **27–53**
  concrete structure durability, **6**: 399
  hydrogen storage, **4**: 128
  power generation, **5**: **27–53**
  wind parks, design, **2**: **169–223**
cash flow analysis, **2**: 424
casings: flat-plate collectors, **3**: 104, **3**: 113
casting: concrete structure durability, **6**: 396
Castro dam, Spain, **6**: 338, **6**: 339f
Catagunya Dam, Australia, **6**: 62, **6**: 81f
catalysts:
  alkaline fuel cell materials, **4**: 162, **4**: 163
  ammonia borane dehydrogenation, **4**: 142
  anode materials, **4**: 163

catalysts: (*continued*)
    biomass-to-liquids technology, **5**: 178, **5**: 185
    cathode materials, **4**: 162
    dehydrogenation, **4**: 142
    Fischer–Tropsch process, **5**: 178
    photovoltaic development, **1**: 33
    physical structure, **4**: 191
    preparation, **4**: 191
    proton-exchange membrane fuel cells, **4**: 190, **4**: 191
    structure, **4**: 191
catch-all efficiency, **6**: 444
categorization:
    see also classification
    photovoltaic/thermal solar collectors, **3**: 256
    wind turbines, **2**: 330, **2**: 331*t*
catenary moored spars (CMS), **2**: 258, **2**: 268
cathodes:
    alkaline fuel cells, **4**: 160, **4**: 162, **4**: 163
    catalyst materials, **4**: 162
    definitions, **4**: 241
    hydrogen technology, **4**: 247
    materials, **4**: 162, **4**: 190
    molten carbonate fuel cells, **4**: 229
    performance, **4**: 163
    proton-exchange membrane fuel cells, **4**: 190
    solid oxide fuel cells, **4**: 247
cation analysis, **7**: 100
cation exchange capacity (CEC), **5**: 357, **5**: 358–359, **5**: 375, **5**: 376
causes:
    cracking, concrete structure durability, **6**: 380
    photovoltaic cost reductions, **1**: 48
    wind energy potential, **2**: 74
    wind energy technical unavailability, **2**: 152
cautious decisions: Three Gorges Project, China, **6**: 200
Cavendish, Henry, **4**: 1, **4**: 2*f*
cavitation:
    Chinese hydraulic research, **6**: 494–495, **6**: 497
    concrete structure durability, **6**: 390, **6**: 391
    Indian hydropower, **6**: 246–247, **6**: 248
    mitigation, **6**: 497
cavity absorbers, **3**: 185
CCS *see* carbon capture and storage
CDF *see* cumulative distribution functions
CDM *see* clean development mechanisms
CEA *see* Central Electricity Authority
Ceara, Brazil, **3**: 556
CEC *see* California Energy Commission; cation exchange capacity
Cedillo power plant and dam, Spain, **6**: 332, **6**: 332*f*
celestial sphere, **3**: 30, **3**: 30*f*
cells:
    see also fuel cells; solar cells
    efficiency
        concentration photovoltaics, **1**: 746, **1**: 747*f*
        dye-sensitized solar cells, **1**: 487
        photovoltaic technology progress, **1**: 20, **1**: 20*f*
    electrical performance, **3**: 261
    electrode materials, **4**: 272
    interconnection, **1**: 503, **1**: 504
    life, alkaline fuel cells, **4**: 160
    materials, multi-junction cells, **1**: 498, **1**: 500, **1**: 503, **1**: 504
    parameters, crystalline silicon cells, **1**: 363, **1**: 369, **1**: 369*t*
    production, photovoltaics, **1**: 162, **1**: 163*f*, **1**: 164
    specifications, photovoltaics, **1**: 798
    stacks, molten carbonate fuel cells, **4**: 229
    technology, photovoltaics, **1**: 746
    voltages, **4**: 197
cellulose conversion, **5**: 400
cellulose crystallinity, **5**: 232
cellulose depolymerization, **5**: 232
cements, **7**: 249
CEN standards, **5**: 105
Central Electricity Authority (CEA), **6**: 227
central heating plant with seasonal storage (CHPSS), **3**: 522, **3**: 525

centralized biomass collection, **5**: 166
centralized energy generation: photovoltaics, **1**: 189
centralized solar thermal systems, **3**: 435
central receiver systems, **3**: 185
central solar heating plants with diurnal storage (CSHPDS), **3**: 527
centrifuge separation, **5**: 209
Centro de Investigaciones Energéticas Medioambientales y Tecnológicas (CIEMAT), Spain, **3**: 549
centrosymmetric photovoltaic upconversion, **1**: 533
CEPO *see* clean energy program office
ceramic matrices, **3**: 301, **3**: 307
cerium oxide, **3**: 346
cermet metal–dielectric composites, **3**: 301, **3**: 307
CERT *see* clean energy research and test-bedding
certification:
    bioenergy policy development, **5**: 411
    condition monitoring systems, **2**: 388
    international standards, **2**: 372
    safety, **2**: 371, **2**: 372, **2**: 383
    standards, **2**: 371, **2**: 383
    wind energy
        condition monitoring systems, **2**: 388
        safety, **2**: 371, **2**: 372, **2**: 383
        standards, **2**: 371, **2**: 383
        turbine standards, **2**: 383
CESA-1 power plant, **3**: 626
cetane numbers, **5**: 322–323, **5**: 343
CF *see* capacity factors
CFC *see* chlorofluorocarbons
CFD *see* computational fluid dynamics
chain of custody greenhouse gas reporting, **5**: 101, **5**: 102*f*
chairmen: IEC TC82, **1**: 800
chalcopyrite thin films, **1**: 399–422, **1**: 8
    absorption coefficients, **1**: 401
    back contacts, **1**: 412
    barrier layers, **1**: 412
    buffer layers, **1**: 412
    copper indium diselenide thin films, **1**: 22
    crystal structure, **1**: 400
    deposition, **1**: 406
    device properties, **1**: 414
    device structure, **1**: 410
    electrical properties, **1**: 403
    front contacts, **1**: 414
    future outlooks, **1**: 417
    glass substrate structures, **1**: 410
    grain boundaries, **1**: 405
    material properties, **1**: 400
    metal substrate structures, **1**: 411
    optical properties, **1**: 401
    photovoltaics, **1**: 399–422, **1**: 8
    polyimide substrate structures, **1**: 412
    sequential deposition, **1**: 406, **1**: 406*f*, **1**: 408
    single-step deposition, **1**: 406, **1**: 406*f*, **1**: 407
    structure, **1**: 400, **1**: 410
    substrate structure, **1**: 410
    surface properties, **1**: 405
chambers: ship locks, **6**: 197, **6**: 223
Chamera Hydroelectric Project, **6**: 244, **6**: 244*f*, **6**: 247
chandeliers, **1**: 714, **1**: 715*f*
Chandreja dam, Spain, **6**: 324, **6**: 325*f*
characteristics:
    agricultural solar thermal applications, **3**: 568
    Chinese hydropower projects, **6**: 485
    design of wind parks, **2**: 211
    dye-sensitized solar cells, **1**: 487
    Fresnel collectors, **3**: 195
    high concentration solar collectors, **3**: 167, **3**: 174, **3**: 185, **3**: 195, **3**: 200
    hydropower, **6**: 16, **6**: 42, **6**: 412, **6**: 413
    industrial solar thermal applications, **3**: 568
    irradiance, photovoltaic power forecasting, **1**: 246
    mesoporous dye-sensitized solar cells, **1**: 487

organic solar cells, **1**: 449
parabolic troughs, **3**: 174
pumped storage hydropower, **6**: 412, **6**: 413
receivers, **3**: 185
reservoirs, hydropower water quality, **6**: 59
solar dishes, **3**: 200
solar distillation, **3**: 98, **3**: 98t
solar irradiance, **1**: 246
solar thermal, agricultural/industrial applications, **3**: 568
wind energy
    integration, **2**: 586
    park design, **2**: 211
    variable costs, **2**: 489
    wind potential, **2**: 74
characterization:
  concentration photovoltaics, **1**: 754
  hydrogen energy chain, **4**: 47
  hydrogen PEM fuel cells, **4**: 307
  photovoltaic financial risk management, **1**: 136
  selective coatings, **3**: 309
  solids, geothermal chemistry, **7**: 97
  volute, **6**: 451
charcoal, **5**: **357–384**, **5**: 357
charge rates: wind energy, **2**: 473
charge regulators, **1**: 687
charge transport:
  purple bacteria, **1**: 661
  semiconductors, **1**: 444, **1**: 445
chemical admixtures, **6**: 394
chemical-based mutagenics, **5**: 301
chemical energy:
  solar energy conversion, **1**: 304
  storage, wind energy, **2**: 650
chemical feedstocks, **5**: 329
chemical geothermometers, **7**: 58, **7**: 59, **7**: 134
chemical hydrides, **4**: 139, **4**: 153
chemical intermediates: bio-alcohols, **5**: 404
chemically resistant top layers, **3**: 327
chemical manufacturing: hydrogen technology, **4**: 31, **4**: 32
chemical methods:
  biomass gasification, **5**: 159, **5**: 159f
  geothermal energy, **7**: 1
  glycerol chemical production, **5**: 398
  hydrogen storage, **4**: **137–157**
  sputtering, **3**: 314
chemical pretreatments, **5**: 235
chemical production:
  bio-alcohols, **5**: 404
    biomass and biofuels, **5**: 404
    hydrogen, **5**: 406
    single-walled carbon nanotubes, **5**: 405
  biochar, **5**: 406, **5**: 407
  biodiesel, **5**: 396, **5**: 398
  bioethanol, **5**: 404
  biomass and biofuels, **5**: **395–410**
    bio-alcohols, **5**: 404
    biochar, **5**: 406
    bioethanol, **5**: 404
    ethanol, **5**: 404
    fermentation, **5**: 400
    lignins, **5**: 401
    solid biofuels, **5**: 406
  ethanol, **5**: 404
  ethyl acetate, **5**: 405
  fabricated microwave pyrolysis, **5**: 407
  fermentation, **5**: 400
  fuel production intermediates, **5**: 400
  glycerin coproducts, **5**: 396
  glycerol, **5**: 396, **5**: 398
  hydrogen, **5**: 406
  lignins, **5**: 401
  lignocellulosic feedstocks, **5**: 400
  polycyclic aromatic hydrocarbons, **5**: 407

  pyrolysis oils, **5**: 406
  single-walled carbon nanotubes, **5**: 405
  solid biofuels, **5**: 406
  sugars, **5**: 400
chemical properties:
  biochar, **5**: 374
  biomass cofiring, **5**: 70
  down-shifting, **1**: 566–567
chemical reactions:
  solar energy thermal energy storage, **3**: 211, **3**: 224
  thermochemical heat, **3**: 224
chemicals:
  biomass gasification, **5**: 159, **5**: 159f
  hydrogen storage, **4**: **137–157**
chemical stability: alkaline fuel cells, **4**: 177
chemical storage: hydrogen, **4**: **137–157**
chemical vapor deposition, **1**: 389, **1**: 390, **3**: 324–325
chemistry:
  alkaline fuel cells, **4**: 175
  anion exchange membranes, **4**: 175
  biomass-to-liquids technology, **5**: 178
  Fischer–Tropsch process, **5**: 178
  molten carbonate fuel cells, **4**: 228
Chemrec, **5**: 191
child mortality rates, **7**: 288
chillers, **3**: 612, **3**: 613
China, **6**: **485–505**, **6**: **179–227**, **6**: **377–403**
  abrasion, **6**: 391
  aerators, **6**: 485, **6**: 497
  cavitation, **6**: 391, **6**: 497
  Chinese Nora, **6**: 31, **6**: 32f
  concrete hydropower structure durability, **6**: **377–403**
  dams, **6**: **485–505**
  desalination, **2**: 735
  discharge facilities, **6**: 485, **6**: 487, **6**: 499
  discharge spraying, **6**: 485, **6**: 499
  energy dissipation, **6**: 485, **6**: 486t, **6**: 487
  field observations, **6**: 502
  flaring pier gates, **6**: 485, **6**: 489
  flow-induced vibration, **6**: 499
  high-arch dams, **6**: 492
  hydraulic research, **6**: 485, **6**: **485–505**
  hydropower
    concrete structure durability, **6**: **377–403**
    historical overviews, **6**: 31, **6**: 32f, **6**: 33
    hydraulic research, **6**: **485–505**
    multibenefit solutions, **6**: 31, **6**: 32f, **6**: 33, **6**: 44
    Three Gorges Project, **6**: **179–227**
  jet flows, **6**: 485, **6**: 492, **6**: 499
  low head hydropower, **6**: **377–403**
  market development of wind power, **2**: 666
  offshore wind power, **2**: 439, **2**: 439f
  orifice spillway tunnels, **6**: 485, **6**: 494
  photovoltaics, **1**: 167
  plunge pools, **6**: 485, **6**: 492
  slit buckets, **6**: 485, **6**: 487, **6**: 490f, **6**: 491f
  solar energy
    history, **3**: 87, **3**: 88f
    utilization, **1**: 31
  spraying, **6**: 485, **6**: 499
  Three Gorges Project, **6**: **179–227**
  Tianhuangping pumped storage, **6**: 429
  vibration, **6**: 499
  vortex shaft spillway tunnels, **6**: 485, **6**: 495
  wind energy
    historical overviews, **2**: 44
    offshore wind power, **2**: 439, **2**: 439f
    power market development, **2**: 666
    turbine manufacturers, **2**: 667, **2**: 669
chloride attack, **6**: 388
chloride concentrations, **7**: 141
chloride enthalpy models, **7**: 138
chloride ion corrosion, **7**: 246

chlorine environmental impacts, 5: 51
chlorofluorocarbons (CFC), 3: 611–612
chlorophyll, 1: 657
chlorophytes, 6: 61
chloroplasts, 1: 657
chlorosomes, 1: 658, 1: 669
Choren Industries, Germany, 5: 190, 5: 203
CHP *see* combined heat and power
CHPSS *see* central heating plant with seasonal storage
chromaticity, 3: 349, 3: 349*f*
chromogenics, 3: 316, 3: 342
    see also electrochromogenics; photochromogenics
Churchill River Diversion Project, 6: 157, 6: 158*f*
Chute-Allard, Quebec, Canada, 6: 162–163, 6: 166*f*
circuits:
    collectors, 3: 431
    equivalent circuits, 1: 535, 1: 550, 1: 717, 1: 718*f*, 4: 327
    gate-drive circuitry, 4: 304
    open circuit potentials, 4: 245
    open-circuit voltage, 1: 340, 1: 416, 4: 184, 4: 197
    solar cells, 1: 294
    solar energy conversion principles, 1: 294
    solar water heating systems, 3: 431
circulating bed fluidized bed combustion, 5: 61
circulating bed fluidized bed reactors, 5: 181
circulating bed fluidized gasifiers, 5: 137, 5: 150, 5: 169*t*, 5: 171
circulation systems:
    see also direct circulation systems
    air water heating systems, 3: 452
    domestic hot water, 3: 426, 3: 428*f*
    solar thermal applications, 3: 573, 3: 574*f*, 3: 575*f*
circulators: photovoltaic thermodynamics, 1: 315
circumsolar radiation, 1: 214
circumsolar ratio (CSR), 3: 168
citation analysis: photovoltaics, 1: 62, 1: 63
citric acid, 5: 399
civil contracting: Horseshoe Bend scheme, 6: 472
civil engineering infrastructure capital costs, 8: 156
civil war, 6: 323
civil works: Three Gorges Project, China, 6: 198
clamping effect, 8: 113
Clapeyron diagrams, 3: 487, 3: 488*f*
classification:
    alkaline fuel cells, 4: 177
    anion exchange membranes, 4: 177
    geothermal chemistry, 7: 101
    geothermal systems, 7: 5
    geothermal wells, 7: 18
    heat pumps, 3: 501
    photovoltaic/thermal solar collectors, 3: 256
    seasonal ground storage, 3: 521
    selective absorber coatings, 3: 304
    small wind turbines, 2: 301, 2: 304*t*
    solar assisted heat pumps, 3: 506
    water geothermal chemistry, 7: 101
    wind turbines, 2: 104, 2: 272, 2: 273*f*, 2: 330, 2: 331*t*
Clausius–Rankine cycles, 3: 602, 3: 603
clean coal, 2: 548
clean development mechanisms (CDM), 7: 290, 7: 291
clean energy matrices, 5: 20
clean energy program office (CEPO), 1: 81
clean energy research program, 1: 81
clean energy research and test-bedding (CERT) program, 1: 81
cleaning:
    biomass gasification, 5: 145
    building-integrated photovoltaics, integration rules, 1: 701
    crystalline silicon cells, 1: 359
    Fresnel collectors, 3: 199
    gasification of biomass, 5: 145
    high concentration solar collectors, 3: 174, 3: 184, 3: 195, 3: 199
    parabolic troughs, 3: 184
    receivers, 3: 174, 3: 184, 3: 195
cleanup: syngas, 5: 172

clean water discharging, 6: 212
clearance environment studies, 6: 234
clear single-glazed windows, 3: 331
clear-sky calculations, 3: 44–45
Cleuson-Dixence hydroelectricity project, Switzerland, 6: 351
climate change:
    geothermal energy sustainability, 7: 272, 7: 283, 7: 290
    Indian hydropower, 6: 230
    levy, 2: 486, 8: 164
    solar thermal system environmental problems, 3: 5
    very large-scale photovoltaic systems, 1: 741
climate data: ocean waves, 8: 31
climate forecast accuracy, 1: 269
climate variability: ocean waves, 8: 51
Clipper Windpower, 2: 322
clogging: wells, 7: 41
closed adsorption systems, 3: 248
closed-circuit recooling systems, 3: 597
closed-loop systems:
    geothermal heat pumps, 7: 190
    two-tank solar heat system layout, 3: 575, 3: 577*f*
cloud cover, 1: 231
cloud layer-sunshine models, 3: 42
cloud motion vectors:
    definitions, 1: 240
    ground-based sky imagers, 1: 251
    imaging, 1: 245, 1: 249, 1: 251
    photovoltaic power forecasting, 1: 245, 1: 249, 1: 251
    satellite images, 1: 249
    sky imagers, 1: 245, 1: 249, 1: 251
    solar irradiance forecasting, 1: 245, 1: 249, 1: 251
cloudy-sky calculations, 3: 45
CMS *see* catenary moored spars
coal:
    biomass cofiring, 5: 57
    carbon capture and storage, 4: 58
    coal-to-liquids, 5: 160, 5: 161–162, 5: 191, 5: 197, 5: 307–308
    dust exposure, 5: 69
    energy balance, 2: 20
    gas, hydrogen technology, 4: 1, 4: 4*f*
    hydropower, Japanese energy issues, 6: 286
    plants, hydrogen production, 4: 50
coalescers: biodiesel, 5: 209
coatings, 3: **301–312**, 3: **313–355**
    see also low-emittance coatings; selective coatings
    absorbers, 3: 104, 3: **301–312**, 3: 108
    absorption, 3: 301, 3: **301–312**, 3: 320
    buildings, 3: **313–355**
    chemically resistant top layers, 3: 327
    doped metal oxides, 3: 316, 3: 325
    emerging technologies, 3: 316
    hydropower, 6: 249–250, 6: 250*f*
    interface layers, 3: 327
    laws, 3: 318
    low-temperature stationary collectors, 3: 104, 3: 108, 3: 125
    mechanically resistant top layers, 3: 327
    metal-based stacks, 3: 316, 3: 325
    metal layers, 3: 316, 3: 325
    modern windows, 3: 316
    optical analysis, 3: 319
    optical properties, 3: 316
    organic solar cells, 1: 473
    passive solar architecture, 3: 646, 3: 648
    radiation refraction, 3: 319
    radiation transmission, 3: 319
    reflection, 3: 320
    refraction, 3: 319
    silver, 3: 325
    single-glazed windows, 3: 331
    solar cooling, 3: 646, 3: 648
    solar irradiation, 3: 316
    solar radiation laws, 3: 318
    thermal properties, 3: 316

thermal radiation laws, **3**: 318
total transmittance, **3**: 317, **3**: 320
transmission, **3**: 319
coconut fiber mats, **6**: 424, **6**: 424f
Coconut Island, **2**: 738
codes:
    compressed gas hydrogen storage, **4**: 116
    hydrogen safety engineering, **4**: 82
coefficient of determination: solar radiation, **3**: 52
coefficient of performance (COP):
    heat pumps, **3**: 496, **3**: 497
    parallel solar assisted heat pumps, **3**: 512–513, **3**: 515–516
    series solar assisted heat pumps, **3**: 510–511
    solar cooling, **3**: 482, **3**: 485–486, **3**: 489
    thermal energy storage, **3**: 226
coefficient of thermal expansion (CTE), **1**: 428
cofferdams, **6**: 201, **6**: 223
    concrete dams, **6**: 201
    earth cofferdams, **6**: 206, **6**: 207
    longitudinal concrete cofferdams, **6**: 206
    rock cofferdams, **6**: 206, **6**: 207
cofiring biomass, **5**: **55–73**
cogeneration:
    combined heat and power, **5**: **87–97**
    concentrating solar power, **3**: 611
    cooling, **3**: 611
    hydrogen technology, **4**: 59
    proton-exchange membrane fuel cells, **4**: 208
Coité-Pedreiras, Ceara, Brazil, **3**: 556
cold recharge porous layer models, **7**: 15
cold stores, **3**: 519
collection:
    geochemical sampling, **7**: 95
    primary forest residues, **5**: 284
collective pitch control systems, **2**: 345
collectors:
    see also evacuated tube collectors; flat collectors; flat-plate collectors; high concentration solar collectors; low concentration ratio collectors; low-temperature stationary collectors
    agricultural applications, **3**: 569
    aperture cover materials, **3**: 570
    circuits, water heating systems, **3**: 431
    configurations, **1**: 231, **1**: 233t
    covers, **3**: 570
    definitions, **3**: 163
    drain-back systems, **3**: 433, **3**: 433f
    efficiency
        solar cooling systems, **3**: 462, **3**: 462f
        solar water heating systems, **3**: 430, **3**: 431f
        stationary collectors, **3**: 138, **3**: 141
    flow rate corrections, **3**: 401
    glass
        heat loss suppression, **3**: 330
        light admittance, **3**: 329
        solar thermal energy, **3**: 329
        weather protection, **3**: 330
    heat loss suppression, glass, **3**: 330
    heat removal factor, **3**: 138
    high concentration solar collectors, **3**: **165–209**
    history, **3**: 85, **3**: 91
    inclination, **3**: 152, **3**: 153f, **3**: 441
    industrial applications, **3**: 569
    integration, water heating systems, **3**: 430, **3**: 432f
    light admittance, **3**: 329
    low concentration ratio systems, **3**: **149–163**
    low-temperature stationary collectors, **3**: **103–147**
    new developments, **3**: 431
    orientation, **3**: 441
    passive solar heating, **3**: 640
    performance determination, **3**: 141
    photovoltaic/thermal systems, **3**: **255–300**
    properties, **3**: 430

shape accuracy, **3**: 167, **3**: 169
solar desalination, **3**: 530, **3**: 544f, **3**: 546f
solar energy, history, **3**: 85, **3**: 91
solar energy history, **3**: 85, **3**: 91
solar thermal agricultural applications, **3**: 569
solar thermal energy, **3**: 329
solar thermal industrial applications, **3**: 569
solar water heating systems, **3**: 420, **3**: 422–423, **3**: 424f, **3**: 426
    circuits, **3**: 431
    inclination, **3**: 441
    integration, **3**: 430, **3**: 432f
    new developments, **3**: 431
    orientation, **3**: 441
    production development, **3**: 422–423, **3**: 424f
    properties, **3**: 430
time constant, **3**: 145, **3**: 146f
top heat loss coefficients, **3**: 134
weather protection, **3**: 330
Colomines hydro plant, Cameroon, Africa, **6**: 145
coloration:
    electrochromogenic devices, **3**: 343
    single-glazed windows, **3**: 331
color composition: building-integrated photovoltaics, **1**: 706
coloured coatings, **3**: 646
coloured cooling materials, **3**: 644
coloured thin-film asphalt layers, **3**: 648
combined cycles:
    see also combined heat and power
    biomass, **5**: 87, **5**: 88
    concentrating solar power, **3**: 605
    geothermal energy, **7**: 231
    power conversion, **3**: 605
    power plants, **7**: 231
    water heating systems, **3**: 444, **3**: 446f
combined heat and power (CHP):
    biomass, **5**: **87–97**
        carbon dioxide, **5**: 91
        cofiring, **5**: 67t
        combustion, **5**: 88, **5**: 89
        competition, **5**: 92, **5**: 94
        gasification, **5**: 87, **5**: 88, **5**: 89, **5**: 94
        integrated gasification combined cycle plants, **5**: 88, **5**: 90, **5**: 94, **5**: 95
        integrated gasification combined cycles, **5**: 88, **5**: 90, **5**: 94, **5**: 95
        markets, **5**: 91, **5**: 92
        options, **5**: 88
        power generation, **5**: 33, **5**: 39
        scale effects, **5**: 95
        sector competition, **5**: 92
        steam turbines, **5**: 88, **5**: 90, **5**: 94, **5**: 95
        technology properties, **5**: 90
        technology system aspects, **5**: 93
    carbon dioxide, **5**: 91
    combustion, **5**: 88, **5**: 89
    competition, **5**: 92, **5**: 94
    direct heat utilization, **7**: 182, **7**: 184f
    durability, **4**: 252
    efficiency, **4**: 250, **4**: 252
    gasification, **5**: 87, **5**: 88, **5**: 89, **5**: 94
    geothermal energy, **7**: 182, **7**: 184f
    heat-to-power ratio, **4**: 253, **4**: 254
    hydrogen technology, **4**: 249
    integrated gasification combined cycles, **5**: 88, **5**: 90, **5**: 94, **5**: 95
    liquid biofuels, **5**: 39
    markets, biomass, **5**: 91, **5**: 92
    molten carbonate fuel cells, **4**: 227
    performance characteristics, **4**: 251
    power generation, **5**: 33, **5**: 39
    scale effects, **5**: 95
    sector competition, **5**: 92

combined heat and power (CHP): (*continued*)
   solar water heating systems, **3**: 444, **3**: 446*f*
   solid oxide fuel cells
     durability, **4**: 252
     efficiency, **4**: 250, **4**: 252
     heat-to-power ratio, **4**: 253, **4**: 254
     hydrogen technology, **4**: 249
     performance characteristics, **4**: 251
   steam turbines, **5**: 88, **5**: 90, **5**: 94, **5**: 95
   technology properties, **5**: 90
   technology system aspects, **5**: 93
   thermophotovoltaics, **1**: 603
combistores, **3**: 454, **3**: 454*f*
   see also combined…
combisystems, **3**: 232
   see also combined…
combustion:
   biomass
     cofiring, **5**: 61
     combined heat and power, **5**: 88, **5**: 89
     power generation, **5**: 47
   combined heat and power, **5**: 88, **5**: 89
   conversion efficiency, **5**: 48
   dual fuel operation, **5**: 350
   flame stability, **5**: 47
   gasification, **5**: 62
   impacts, **5**: 49
   power generation, **5**: 47
   practicalities, **5**: 47
   principles, **5**: 47
   solid residuals, **5**: 51
   vegetable oil, **5**: 351
command and control instruments, **5**: 411, **5**: 421
commercial heat pump classification, **3**: 501
commercial ocean wave energy applications, **8**: 79–110, **8**: 4
commercial photovoltaics:
   banks, **1**: 121
   cadmium telluride thin films, **1**: 424
   concentrating solar power, **3**: 615
   down-shifting, **1**: 580
   grid-connected systems, **1**: 396
   thermal solar collectors, **3**: 295
commercial plants: biomass-to-liquids technology, **5**: 184, **5**: 188
commercial viability biofuel expansion, **5**: 7
comminution:
   Fischer–Tropsch process, **5**: 162
   lignocellulosic wastes, **5**: 240
commissioning:
   concentration photovoltaics, **1**: 753
   dams, **6**: 355–356, **6**: 356*f*
   roller compacted concrete dams, **6**: 480
   voltage balancing, **4**: 305
   wind power plant building, **2**: 428
   world-wide dams, **6**: 355–356, **6**: 356*f*
Commission for Sustainable Development (CSD), **7**: 277
communication:
   IEC standards, **2**: 375
   wind energy, **2**: 624, **2**: 740, **2**: 741, **2**: 742
community acceptance: wind park design, **2**: 202
community development: photovoltaics, **1**: **733–744**
community participation: photovoltaics, **1**: 120
compacted density, **6**: 477, **6**: 478*f*
compact heat pump classification, **3**: 501
compact membrane distillation, **3**: 532*f*, **3**: 544, **3**: 544*f*
comparisons:
   biofuel saving effectiveness, **5**: 200
   conventional electrical power–wind energy integration, **2**: 592
   energy technologies, **1**: 155
   geothermal energy, **7**: 261, **7**: 262*t*
   land use effectiveness, **5**: 200
   photovoltaic environmental impacts, **1**: 155
   solar cooling, **3**: 490
   wind energy costs, **2**: 477, **2**: 481

competition:
   automotive biofuels, **5**: 308
   combined heat and power biomass, **5**: 92, **5**: 94
   photovoltaic future visions, **1**: 181, **1**: 187
complementary electric generator units, **2**: 632
complex absorber systems, **1**: 526
complex hydrides, **4**: 147, **4**: 153
complex polymer hydrolysis: microbial fuel cells, **4**: 273
components:
   agricultural solar thermal applications, **3**: 573
   certificates, wind energy standards, **2**: 388
   concentration photovoltaics, **1**: 749
   domestic hot water, **3**: 420, **3**: 426, **3**: 428*f*
   dye-sensitized solar cells, **1**: 490
   failure, wind turbines, **2**: 152, **2**: 153
   Fresnel collectors, **3**: 195
   fuel cell specifications, **4**: 325
   heat pumps, **7**: 192
   high concentration solar collectors, **3**: **165–209**
   hydrogen technology, **4**: 246
   industrial solar thermal systems, **3**: 573
   layouts, **3**: 573
   modeling solar thermal systems, **3**: **357–417**
   ocean renewable energy systems, **8**: 84
   parabolic troughs, **3**: 175
   parallel solar assisted heat pumps, **3**: 514–515, **3**: 515*f*
   photovoltaic performance, **1**: 19
   power electronic fuel cell specifications, **4**: 325
   receivers, **3**: 186
   selective coatings, **3**: **301–312**
   simplified generic axial-flow microhydro turbines, **6**: 443
   simulating solar thermal systems, **3**: **357–417**
   solar dishes, **3**: 200
   solar thermal systems
     introduction, **3**: **1–25**
     layouts, **3**: 573
     modeling, **3**: **357–417**
     selective coatings, **3**: **301–312**
     simulations, **3**: **357–417**
     thermal energy storage, **3**: **211–253**
     water heating systems, **3**: 420, **3**: 426, **3**: 428*f*
   solid oxide fuel cells, **4**: 246
   thermal energy storage, **3**: **211–253**
   water heating systems, **3**: 420, **3**: 426, **3**: 428*f*
   wind turbine energy yields, **2**: 152, **2**: 153
composites:
   compressed gas vessels, **4**: 116
   hubs, **2**: 714
   photovoltaics, **1**: 523
   rotor blades, **2**: 713
   selective coatings, **3**: 301, **3**: 307
   wood window frames, **3**: 333
composition: biochar, **5**: 372
composting biochar, **5**: 379
compound parabolic collectors (CPC):
   agricultural applications, **3**: 587*t*
   evacuated tube collectors, **3**: 118, **3**: 119*f*, **3**: 159
   industrial applications, **3**: 587*t*
   integrated collector storage, **3**: 159
   low concentration ratio solar collectors, **3**: 150, **3**: 151, **3**: 153, **3**: 154, **3**: 159, **3**: 163
   maximum concentration ratios, **3**: 151
   optical analysis, **3**: 154
   solar desalination, **3**: 534
   thermal analysis, **3**: 154
compressed air energy storage (CAES), **1**: 210, **2**: 649, **2**: 650, **4**: **111–135**
compressed gas: hydrogen storage:
   best practices, **4**: 116
   case studies, **4**: 128
   codes, **4**: 116
   composite vessels, **4**: 116
   containment vessels, **4**: **111–135**

design principles, **4**: 112, **4**: 128
design theory, **4**: 112, **4**: 128
HyPOD® enclosure, **4**: 134
materials, **4**: 112, **4**: 116, **4**: 129
physical methods, **4**: 137
pressure vessels, **4**: **111–135**
Pure Project case study, **4**: 131
safety, **4**: 124
standards, **4**: 116
steel vessels, **4**: 112
vessels, **4**: **111–135**
compressibility: air turbines, **8**: 128
compression-ignition engines, **5**: 322
compression-photovoltaic systems, **3**: 489
compressive strength, **6**: 476, **6**: 477, **6**: 478*f*
compressors: hydrogen technology, **4**: 2, **4**: 8*f*
computational fluid dynamics (CFD), **2**: 232, **2**: 233, **2**: 234
computer modeling:
   see also individual programs; software ;
   geochemistry reaction paths/speciation, **7**: 128
   geothermal energy physics, **7**: 35
   reservoir water quality, **6**: 53
concave mirrors, **3**: 88, **3**: 89*f*
concentrated fall projects, **6**: 22
concentrating carbon dioxide, **5**: 330
concentrating collectors: low concentration ratios, **3**: **149–163**, **3**: 163
concentrating solar power (CSP):
   see also concentration/concentrators; concentration photovoltaics
   absorption chillers, **3**: 612
   adsorption chillers, **3**: 613
   air-driven condensers, **3**: 600, **3**: 601*f*
   Andasol 1-3 power plant, **3**: 616, **3**: 617*f*
   AORA power plant, **3**: 622
   CESA-1 power plant, **3**: 626
   closed-circuit recooling systems, **3**: 597
   cogeneration, **3**: 611
   combined cycles, **3**: 605
   commercial solar thermal power plants, **3**: 615
   concentration effect, **3**: 596
   cooling, cogeneration, **3**: 611
   costs, **1**: 506, **3**: 266, **3**: 629
   CSIRO power plant, **3**: 628
   Desertec, **3**: 631, **3**: 632*f*
   Direct Solar Stream power plant, **3**: 626
   dishes, **3**: 199, **3**: 605, **3**: 622
   draft cooling systems, **3**: 598, **3**: 600
   economics, **3**: 629
   efficiency, **3**: 596
   emissions, **3**: 630
   energy balance, **3**: 597
   environmental aspects, **3**: 630
   EURELIOS power plant, **3**: 628
   Europe, **3**: 631
   examples, **3**: 615
   fauna, **3**: 630
   flora, **3**: 630
   future potential, **3**: 631
   future research, **3**: 634
   GAST study, **3**: 629
   gas turbines, **3**: 604
   Gemasolar solar thermal power plant, **3**: 623
   grid-connected systems, **3**: 597
   high concentration solar collectors, **3**: **165–209**
   hybrid cooling towers, **3**: 599
   integrated solar combined cycles, **3**: 606
   island systems, **3**: 597
   Kimberlina solar thermal power plant, **3**: 623
   life-cycle assessments, **3**: 630
   low concentration ratio systems, **3**: **149–163**
   mass balance, **3**: 597
   MENA countries, **3**: 634
   natural draft cooling towers, **3**: 598, **3**: 600

   Nevada Solar One power plant, **3**: 620, **3**: 621*f*
   operational hours, **3**: 605
   PE 1 power plant, **3**: 622, **3**: 623*f*
   PHOEBUS study, **3**: 629
   Planta Solar 10&20 (PS10&20), **3**: 617
   power conversion systems, **3**: 600
   power plant examples, **3**: 615
   principles, **3**: 596
   recooling, **3**: 597
   research, **3**: 624, **3**: 634
   SEGS power plant, **3**: 615, **3**: 616*f*
   Sierra SunTower Generating Station, **3**: 620, **3**: 621*f*
   small solar power system, **3**: 627
   solar cooling, **3**: 611
   solar dishes, **3**: 605, **3**: 622
   Solar Energy Development Center, **3**: 628
   Solar One power plant, **3**: 624
   Solar Research Facility Unit power plant, **3**: 628
   solar thermal systems, **3**: **595–636**
   Solar Two power plant, **3**: 625
   Spain, **3**: 192
   SPP-5 power plant, **3**: 629
   Stirling dishes, **3**: 605, **3**: 622
   STJ power plant, **3**: 619, **3**: 627
   storage, **3**: 609
   Sunshine power plant, **3**: 629
   Themis power plant, **3**: 627
   thermally driven cooling, **3**: 611–612, **3**: 612
   United States, **3**: 631
   wet cooling systems, **3**: 597
concentration/concentrators:
   see also concentrating solar power; concentration photovoltaics
   collectors
      evacuated tube collectors, **3**: 158
      high concentration ratio systems, **3**: **165–209**
      low concentration ratio systems, **3**: **149–163**
      solar radiation resources assessments, **1**: 232
      solar water heating systems, **3**: 420, **3**: 426
   concentration effect, **3**: 596
   concentration ratios, **3**: **149–163**, **3**: 200, **3**: 202
   effect, **3**: 596
   evacuated tube collectors, **3**: 158
   high concentration solar collectors, **3**: **165–209**
   history, solar energy, **3**: 95
   low concentration ratio systems, **3**: **149–163**
   luminescence photovoltaics, **1**: **587–601**, **1**: 9
   organic solar cells, **1**: 459
   photovoltaics, **1**: **587–601**, **1**: 9, **1**: 325
   power production, **3**: 95
   ratios, **3**: **149–163**, **3**: **165–209**
   solar energy, history, **3**: 95
   thermodynamics, **1**: 325
concentration photovoltaics (CPV), **1**: **745–765**
   see also concentrating solar power; concentration/concentrators
   alternating current rating procedures, **1**: 758, **1**: 759
   cell technology, **1**: 746
   characterization, **1**: 754
   commissioning, **1**: 753
   components, **1**: 749
   constructing power plants, **1**: 753
   costs, **1**: 506, **3**: 266
   demonstration power plants, **1**: 750
   design qualification, **1**: 797
   direct current rating procedures, **1**: 755, **1**: 759
   engineering, power plants, **1**: 753
   future outlooks, **1**: 763
   global industry overview, **1**: 163, **1**: 168–169
   historical overviews, **1**: 749
   IEC standards, **1**: 749, **1**: 797
   InGaP/GaAs/Ge 3-junction solar cells, **1**: 506
   introduction, **1**: 10
   ISFOC demonstration power plants, **1**: 750
   modules, **1**: 748

concentration photovoltaics (CPV) (*continued*)
    multiple junction solar cell costs, **1**: 506
    operation and maintenance, **1**: 762
    optics, **1**: 747
    performance, **1**: 760
    power plants, **1**: 750, **1**: 753
    power rating standards, **1**: 798
    production, **1**: 760, **1**: 762
    ratings, **1**: 754
    regulatory frameworks, **1**: 751
    Royal Decrees, **1**: 751
    standardization, **1**: 749
    standards, **1**: 797, **1**: 798
    standard test conditions, **1**: 755
    technology progress, **1**: 17, **1**: 24
    test conditions, **1**: 755
    thermal management, **1**: 747, **1**: 756, **1**: 756*f*
    thermal solar collectors
        applications, **3**: 291
        categorization, **3**: 257
        design, **3**: 267–268, **3**: 291
        general considerations, **3**: 265, **3**: 267
    tracking, **1**: 748, **1**: 799, **3**: 267
    tracking systems, **1**: 748
concentration ratio, **3**: 163
Concentrix – El Villar power plant, **1**: 751, **1**: 751*t*, **1**: 752*f*, **1**: 752*t*
conception: ocean wave energy, **8**: **79–110**
concrete:
    see also concrete dams; concrete hydropower structure durability
    casting, **6**: 396
    contraction, **6**: 387, **6**: 388
    expansion, **6**: 387, **6**: 388
    kilns, **5**: 368
    solar thermal energy storage, **3**: 212, **3**: 242
    spiral case structures, **6**: 191, **6**: 221
concrete dams:
    see also concrete hydropower structure durability; roller compacted concrete dams
    cofferdams, **6**: 201
    essential features, **6**: 28, **6**: 29
    gravity dams, **6**: 184
    Horseshoe Bend hydroelectric scheme, **6**: 467, **6**: 469, **6**: 472, **6**: 473
concrete hydropower structure durability, **6**: **377–403**
    abrasion, **6**: 390
    alkali–aggregate reaction, **6**: 389
    alkali-silica reactions, **6**: 389
    assessments, **6**: 397
    background, **6**: 378
    Baoying key project, **6**: 401
    Belgium, **6**: 400, **6**: 402*f*
    biological processes, **6**: 391
    Butgenbach dam, Belgium, **6**: 400, **6**: 402*f*
    carbonation, **6**: 386
    case histories, **6**: 399
    casting, **6**: 396
    cavitation, **6**: 390
    chemical admixtures, **6**: 394
    China, **6**: **377–403**
    chloride attack, **6**: 388
    concrete casting, **6**: 396
    concrete contraction, **6**: 387
    concrete expansion, **6**: 387
    construction, **6**: 391, **6**: 396
    contraction, **6**: 387
    corrosion, **6**: 386
    cracking, **6**: 380, **6**: 398
    crack width control, **6**: 382
    curing, **6**: 396
    damage, **6**: 386
    design concepts, **6**: **377–403**
    early cracking, **6**: 380
    expansion, **6**: 387

    expert systems, **6**: 392
    Fengman complex, **6**: 399, **6**: 401*f*
    fire damage, **6**: 391
    freezing, **6**: 387
    future research, **6**: 392
    geomembranes, **6**: 394
    Haikou key project, **6**: 399
    high-performance concretes, **6**: 395
    hydropower design concepts, **6**: **377–403**
    inadequate performance, **6**: 379
    inspections, **6**: 397
    instrumental inspections, **6**: 397
    low head hydropower, **6**: **377–403**
    maintenance, **6**: 393
    materials selection, **6**: 393
    membranes, **6**: 394
    mineral admixtures, **6**: 393
    mix design, **6**: 395
    monolith size control, **6**: 382
    performance, **6**: 379
    performance-based design, **6**: 392
    polymer fibers, **6**: 394
    quality evaluations, **6**: 396
    quality factors, **6**: 387
    rehabilitation, **6**: 397
    reinforcement corrosion, **6**: 386
    reinforcement placement, **6**: 396
    research, **6**: 392
    scouring, **6**: 390
    seepage scouring, **6**: 390
    self-compacting concrete, **6**: 394
    self-healing concrete, **6**: 394
    service life, **6**: 392, **6**: 397
    Shi Lianghe key project, **6**: 399, **6**: 400*f*
    structural design, **6**: 391, **6**: 395
    sulfate attack, **6**: 388
    thawing, **6**: 387
    visual inspections, **6**: 397
condensation corrosion, **7**: 247
condensors, **7**: 214
conditioning:
    hydrogen PEM fuel cells, **4**: 311
    syngas, **5**: 177
condition monitoring:
    offshore wind parks, **2**: 714
    power electronics, **2**: 364
    wind energy certification, **2**: 388
    wind power design and implementation, **2**: 428
    wind turbine power electronics, **2**: 364
conduction/conductivity:
    ambient temperature, **3**: 132
    exchange, **3**: 132
    geothermal energy exploration techniques, **7**: 85
    geothermal heat pumps, **7**: 198
    intermediate bands, **1**: 619
    organic semiconductor physics, **1**: 444
    porous rock, **7**: 79
    proton-exchange membranes, **4**: 185
    rock matrix, **7**: 78
    solar dish losses, **3**: 200–201
conduit systems:
    Japanese hydropower history, **6**: 267
    Three Gorges Project, China, **6**: 190, **6**: 193, **6**: 195*f*, **6**: 197
Confederado farms, **5**: 359–360
conferences:
    Conference on the Human Environment in Stockholm, **7**: 277
    geothermal energy, **7**: 273, **7**: 276
confidence intervals, **1**: 270, **1**: 281, **1**: 289
configurations:
    biomass gasifiers, **5**: 136
    hydropower, **6**: 21, **6**: 22
    molten carbonate fuel cells, **4**: 228
    solar assisted heat pumps, **3**: 506

wind powered telecommunication stations, **2**: 742
wind power farm layouts, **2**: 399, **2**: 415f, **2**: 416f
conflicting interests: wind power, **2**: 395, **2**: 403
Congo basin, **6**: 130
conical diffusers, **6**: 456
connection/connectors:
    hydrogen storage, **4**: 120
    wind park electricity networks, **2**: 209
consent issues, **6**: 467, **6**: 469, **6**: 470
consequentional life cycle assessments, **5**: 109, **5**: 112
conservation: hydropower impact management, **6**: 58, **6**: 73
conservative constituents: geothermal energy, **7**: 108, **7**: 109, **7**: 141
consolidated bioprocessing, **5**: 250
constant loads: wind turbine turbulence, **2**: 256, **2**: 257f
constant operating conditions: wind energy desalination, **2**: 734
construction:
    Canadian hydropower, **6**: 163
    concentration photovoltaic power plants, **1**: 753
    concrete hydropower structure durability, **6**: 391, **6**: 396
    development constraints, **6**: 49–91
    Fresnel collectors, **3**: 197
    heliostats, **3**: 190
    high concentration solar collectors, **3**: 178, **3**: 190, **3**: 197, **3**: 203
    Horseshoe Bend hydroelectric scheme, **6**: **467–483**
    hydropower, **6**: 49–91, **6**: 163
    impact management, **6**: 49–91
    milestones, **6**: 201
    noise, **2**: 526
    offshore wind power, **2**: 436, **2**: 437t
    Okinawa, Japan seawater pumped storage hydropower, **6**: 422, **6**: 423
    parabolic troughs, **3**: 178
    power plants, **1**: 753
    quality control, **6**: 208
    Quebec, Canada, hydropower, **6**: 163
    solar dishes, **3**: 203
    staged construction, **6**: 201
    supervision, **6**: 208
    technology, **6**: 200, **6**: 223
    Three Gorges Project, China, **6**: 200, **6**: 223
    water diversion, **6**: 205
    wind park environmental impacts, **2**: 512t, **2**: 512–513
    wind power design and implementation, **2**: 427
construction and demolition (C&D), **5**: 286
consultation considerations, **6**: 234, **6**: 236, **6**: 236f
consumers:
    hydrogen vehicle costs, **4**: 62
    photovoltaics
        finance/grants, **1**: 121, **1**: 125
        product-integration, **1**: 711
        signal transmission, **1**: 196
        thin-film silicon technology, **1**: 396
consumption:
    planet energy balance, **2**: **11–39**
    primary energy, **2**: 12, **6**: 33, **6**: 34f, **6**: 34t
contact firing crystalline silicon cells, **1**: 360
contact metallization, **1**: 366, **1**: 368
contact screen printing, **1**: 360
containment vessels:
    compressed gas: hydrogen storage, **4**: **111–135**
    geochemical sampling, **7**: 95
contaminants/contamination:
    biomass gasification, **5**: 141, **5**: 142
    biomass-to-liquids technology, syngas, **5**: 172
    feedstocks, **5**: 141
    gasification, **5**: 141, **5**: 142
    gas processing, **5**: 142
    hydrogen storage safety, **4**: 127
    soils, biochar, **5**: 383
    syngas, **5**: 172
contemporary wind turbine energy yields, **2**: **113–168**
contingency energy reserves, **1**: 200
continuous process kilns, **5**: 368, **5**: 369f

continuous spectrum approximation, **1**: 317
contraction: concrete structure durability, **6**: 387, **6**: 388
contracts:
    Horseshoe Bend hydroelectric scheme, **6**: 472
    Three Gorges Project, China, **6**: 208
    wind power plant building, **2**: 427
contra-rotating McCormick air turbines, **8**: 111, **8**: 121, **8**: 122f
contra-rotating rotors, **8**: 117, **8**: 129
control:
    see also control systems
    bioenergy policy development, **5**: 411, **5**: 421
    concrete structure durability, **6**: 382
    corrosion, **7**: 253
    cracking, **6**: 382
    Fresnel collectors, **3**: 196
    geological hazards, **6**: 216
    geothermal power production, **7**: 253, **7**: 255
    high concentration solar collectors, **3**: 168, **3**: 177, **3**: 187, **3**: 196, **3**: 205
    instruments, bioenergy policy development, **5**: 411, **5**: 421
    parabolic troughs, **3**: 177
    receivers, **3**: 187
    reservoir water quality, **6**: 69
    scaling geothermal power production, **7**: 255
    solar dishes, **3**: 205
    tunnel outlets, **6**: 473
    valves, **6**: 473
    variables, passive solar architecture, **3**: 655
controlled condition rotor blade experiments, **2**: 713
controlled parameters: passive solar architecture, **3**: 655
controlled renewables: hydrogen fuel cell technology, **4**: **295–329**
controlling structure mapping, **7**: 55
Controls Advanced Research Turbine (CART), **2**: 332, **2**: 333f, **2**: 335f
Control of Substances Hazardous to Health (COSHH), **5**: 69
control systems:
    actuators, **2**: 366
    electrical systems, **2**: 272
    generators, **2**: 330, **2**: 352, **2**: 358
    grid connections, **2**: 330, **2**: 331f, **2**: 358, **2**: 362
    hardware, **2**: 366
    loads, **2**: 251
    mechanical modeling, **2**: 334
    modeling, **2**: 333
    passive solar architecture, **3**: 654
    pitch, **2**: 330, **2**: 331f, **2**: 345, **2**: 358
    sensors, **2**: 366
    wind power plant IEC standards, **2**: 375
    wind turbines, **2**: **329–370**
        actuators, **2**: 366
        electrical systems, **2**: 272
        generators, **2**: 330, **2**: 352, **2**: 358
        grid connections, **2**: 330, **2**: 331f, **2**: 358, **2**: 362
        hardware, **2**: 366
        loads, **2**: 251
        mechanical modeling, **2**: 334
        modeling, **2**: 333
        pitch, **2**: 330, **2**: 331f, **2**: 345, **2**: 358
        sensors, **2**: 366
        time evolution, **2**: 98
        yaw, **2**: 330, **2**: 331f, **2**: 360
convection:
    absorber–cover heat transfer coefficients, **3**: 132, **3**: 133t
    geothermal system classification, **7**: 5
    glazing–ambient heat transfer coefficients, **3**: 131, **3**: 132t
conventional biological fuel cells, **4**: 258
conventional control: passive solar architecture, **3**: 656
conventional evacuated glazing, **3**: 338
conventional fuels: life cycle assessments, **5**: 114, **5**: 114t
conventional heating systems: geothermal heat pumps, **7**: 202
conventional power systems:
    offshore wind power, **2**: 431
    wind energy integration, **2**: 571, **2**: 592

conversion efficiency:
   biomass to biofuels, **5**: 76, **5**: 76f
   combined heat and power, **5**: 90, **5**: 90t
   combustion, **5**: 48
   downconversion, **1**: **549–561**
   hydropower, **6**: 24
   InGaP/GaAs/Ge 3-junction solar cells, **1**: 503, **1**: 505, **1**: 505f, **1**: 506, **1**: 506f
   multi-junction cells, **1**: 497, **1**: 498f, **1**: 503
   photovoltaics
      downconversion, **1**: **549–561**
      InGaP/GaAs/Ge 3-junction solar cells, **1**: 503, **1**: 505, **1**: 505f, **1**: 506, **1**: 506f
      multi-junction cells, **1**: 497, **1**: 498f, **1**: 503
      solar energy, **1**: **293–313**
      thermodynamics, **1**: 328
      upconversion, **1**: **533–548**
   solar energy, **1**: **293–313**
   thermodynamics, **1**: 328
   upconversion, **1**: **533–548**
   wave energy historical overviews, **8**: 7–9
conversion factors, **3**: 80, **3**: 430
converters:
   wind turbine modeling, **2**: 336
   wind turbine power electronics, **2**: 332, **2**: 332f, **2**: 340
Coober Pedy, Australia, **3**: 100, **3**: 100f
cooking:
   see also solar cooking
   agricultural applications, **3**: 588
   biochar, **5**: 358
   industrial applications, **3**: 588
cooling, **3**: **449–480**, **3**: **481–494**
   see also space cooling
   active solar systems, **3**: **449–480**
      array design, **3**: 475
      heat exchangers, **3**: 477
      module design, **3**: 475
   array design, **3**: 475
   binary power plants, **7**: 224, **7**: 224f, **7**: 225f
   biomass gasification, **5**: 147
   cogeneration, **3**: 611
   coloured materials, **3**: 644
   concentrating solar power, **3**: 611
   desiccant systems, **3**: 461, **3**: 464, **3**: 482, **3**: 483
   differential temperature controllers, **3**: 478
   dry-steam power plants, **7**: 209–210, **7**: 211f, **7**: 215
   effectiveness, **3**: 483
   geothermal heat pumps, **7**: 193
   greenhouses, **3**: 586
   heat exchangers, **3**: 477
   heat storage, **3**: 473
   history, **3**: 94
   hydrogen space instruments, **4**: 24
   loads, **3**: 378
   materials, passive solar architecture, **3**: 644, **3**: 646, **3**: 648
   module design, **3**: 475
   passive solar architecture, **3**: 642, **3**: 644, **3**: 646, **3**: 648
   proton-exchange membrane fuel cells, **4**: 199
   solar energy history, **3**: 94
   space instruments, **4**: 24
   storage tanks, **3**: 473
   thermal storage, **3**: 473
   towers, **7**: 224, **7**: 224f, **7**: 225f
   urban buildings, **3**: 642, **3**: 644
   wells, **7**: 41, **7**: 42
cool materials: passive solar architecture, **3**: 637
Coo-Trois Ponts, Belgium, **6**: 431, **6**: 432, **6**: 433
COP *see* coefficient of performance
copolymer macromolecules, **1**: 440
copper alloys: geothermal environments, **7**: 249
copper indium diselenide thin films, **1**: 22, **1**: **399–422**
copper (indium, gallium) selenide$_2$ thin films, **1**: 22, **1**: **399–422**

copper (indium, gallium) (selenide, sulfur)$_2$ thin films, **1**: 22, **1**: 515, **1**: 517, **1**: 522
coppice crops, **5**: 263, **5**: 264
coproduction/coproducts:
   allocation, **5**: 109, **5**: 110, **5**: 113, **5**: 126
   biochar, **5**: **357–384**
   greenhouse gas life cycle assessments, **5**: 109, **5**: 110, **5**: 113, **5**: 126
   hydrogen economics, **4**: 58, **4**: 67, **4**: 70, **4**: 72
corn grinding, **2**: 42, **2**: 45
correction factors: alternating current rating, **1**: 758
corrosion:
   ammonia, **7**: 246
   biomass combustion, **5**: 50
   carbon dioxide, **7**: 246
   chloride ions, **7**: 246
   concrete structure durability, **6**: 386
   control, **7**: 253
   cracking, **7**: 243
   definitions, **7**: 240
   embrittlement, **7**: 243
   fatigue, **7**: 244
   films, **7**: 240, **7**: 241
   fluid velocity, **7**: 246
   gas diffusion electrodes, **4**: 169
   geothermal energy geochemistry, **7**: 143, **7**: 146, **7**: 151
   geothermal power production, **7**: **239–257**
   high-temperature geothermal fields, **7**: 240, **7**: 240t
   hydrogen-induced cracking, **7**: 243
   hydrogen ions, **7**: 246
   hydrogen sulfide, **7**: 246
   oxygen, **7**: 246
   rates
      pH levels, **7**: 245
      solid deposition, **7**: 245
      suspended solids, **7**: 245
      temperature, **7**: 245
   scaling control, **7**: 253
   sulfates, **7**: 247
   sulfide stress cracking, **7**: 244
   wells, **7**: 41
   wind turbine energy yields, **2**: 152, **2**: 153
COSHH *see* Control of Substances Hazardous to Health
costs:
   backward citation analysis, **1**: 62, **1**: 63
   biomass combined heat and power, **5**: 90, **5**: 90t, **5**: 94, **5**: 95
   biomass-to-liquids technology, **5**: 167, **5**: 167f, **5**: 188, **5**: 191, **5**: 194
   bottom-up photovoltaic manufacturing, **1**: 67
   combined heat and power, **5**: 90, **5**: 90t, **5**: 94, **5**: 95
   comparisons
      solar cooling, **3**: 491
      wind energy, electricity generation, **2**: 477, **2**: 481
   concentrating solar power, **1**: 506, **3**: 266, **3**: 629
   concentration photovoltaic systems, **1**: 506, **3**: 266
   cooling, **3**: 491, **3**: 492
   delivery infrastructure, **4**: 52
   desalination, **2**: 736
   design, wind parks, **2**: 169, **2**: 170, **2**: 177, **2**: 210
   developing countries, photovoltaics, **1**: 116
   distance from shore, offshore wind, **2**: 481
   economies of scale, **1**: 50
   electrical networks, wind energy integration, **2**: 612
   electricity generation
      geothermal energy, **7**: **259–270**
      ocean wave energy, **8**: 5
      photovoltaic future visions, **1**: 195
      wind energy, **2**: **469–501**
   enzymes, **5**: 248
   estimates, ocean energy, **8**: 152
   evolution, ocean energy, **8**: 166
   feedstocks, **5**: 194
   forecasting photovoltaic technology, **1**: 47, **1**: 54, **1**: 195

geothermal energy, **7**: **259–270**
    electricity production, **7**: **259–270**
    heat pumps, **7**: 202
    sustainability, **7**: 281
high concentration solar collectors, **3**: 206
hot water cost-effectiveness, **3**: 492
hydrogen technology
    consumer costs, **4**: 62
    delivery infrastructure, **4**: 52
    gasification, **4**: 50, **4**: 50t
    refueling stations, **4**: 54
    steam methane reforming, **4**: 49t, **4**: 49–50
hydropower, **6**: 6, **6**: 21, **6**: 24, **6**: 40, **6**: 45
levelized energy costs, **2**: 424, **8**: 153, **8**: 154
marine sector, **8**: 164
Memve'Elé hydro plant project, Cameroon, Africa, **6**: 139
minimization, wind park design, **2**: 169, **2**: 170, **2**: 177
multi-junction cells, **1**: 506
ocean wave energy, **8**: 152, **8**: 156, **8**: 158, **8**: 164, **8**: 166, **8**: 167
    economics, **8**: 153, **8**: 154
    electrical power generation, **8**: 5
    marine sector, **8**: 164
    mechanisms, **8**: 166
offshore wind, **2**: 459
    distance from shore, **2**: 481
    operation and maintenance, **2**: 480
    shore distance considerations, **2**: 481
    technical evaluation, **2**: 478, **2**: 480
    water depth, **2**: 481
onshore wind, **2**: 475, **2**: 477
operation and maintenance, **2**: 480
performance, wind energy, **2**: 474, **2**: 475
photovoltaics, **1**: 5, **1**: 7
    cost reductions, **1**: **47–72**
    developing countries, **1**: 116
    forecasting, **1**: 47, **1**: 54, **1**: 195, **1**: 196
    micro-and nanotechnologies, **1**: 517
    research and development, **1**: 49, **1**: 54, **1**: 68
    very large-scale systems, **1**: 736, **1**: 739
pollution, wind energy, **2**: 485
product-integrated photovoltaics, **1**: 725
proton-exchange membrane fuel cells, **4**: 187
quality, photovoltaic technology, **1**: 53
reductions, **1**: **47–72**
    breakthroughs, **1**: 61
    causes, **1**: 48
    demand, **1**: 52
    drivers, **1**: 49, **1**: 52
    expert opinion, **1**: 62, **1**: 65, **1**: 67
    future demand expectations, **1**: 50
    future directions, **1**: 50, **1**: 69
    intertechnology spillovers, **1**: 51
    learning from experience, **1**: 51, **1**: 54
    materials, **1**: 51
    niche photovoltaic markets, **1**: 49
    non-incremental changes, **1**: 61, **1**: 67
    patent analysis, **1**: 62, **1**: 65
    photovoltaics, **1**: **47–72**
        backward citation analysis, **1**: 62, **1**: 63
        bottom-up manufacturing, **1**: 67
        breakthroughs, **1**: 61
        causes, **1**: 48
        demand, **1**: 52
        drivers, **1**: 49, **1**: 52
        economies of scale, **1**: 50
        expert opinion, **1**: 62, **1**: 65, **1**: 67
        future demand expectations, **1**: 50
        future directions, **1**: 50, **1**: 69
        intertechnology spillovers, **1**: 51
        learning from experience, **1**: 51, **1**: 54
        materials, **1**: 51
        niche markets, **1**: 49
        non-incremental changes, **1**: 61, **1**: 67

        patent analysis, **1**: 62, **1**: 65
        product attribute changes, **1**: 53
        quality, **1**: 53
        research and development, **1**: 49, **1**: 54, **1**: 68
        supply and demand drivers, **1**: 52
    product attribute changes, **1**: 53
    supply and demand drivers, **1**: 52
refueling stations, **4**: 54
research and development, photovoltaics, **1**: 49, **1**: 54, **1**: 68
shore distance considerations, **2**: 481
short-rotation forestry, **5**: 277
small onshore wind turbines, **2**: 477
solar cooling, **3**: 491, **3**: 492
solar hot water cost-effectiveness, **3**: 492
solar power satellites, **1**: 772
technical evaluation, wind energy, **2**: **469–501**
thermal energy storage, **3**: 230
thin-film silicon photovoltaic technology, **1**: 389
tidal stream systems, **8**: 152
time evolution, wind turbines, **2**: 702
transport distance, **5**: 167, **5**: 167f
vehicles
    hydrogen
        consumer costs, **4**: 62
        delivery infrastructure, **4**: 52
        refueling stations, **4**: 54
very large-scale photovoltaic systems, **1**: 736, **1**: 739
water depth, offshore wind, **2**: 481
wave stream systems, **8**: 152
wind energy
    balancing, **2**: 474, **2**: 484
    desalination, **2**: 736
    electricity generation, **2**: **469–501**, **2**: 612
    inputs, **2**: 471
    integration, **2**: 612
    performance, **2**: 474, **2**: 475
    pollution, **2**: 485
    technical evaluation, **2**: **469–501**
    turbine technology, **2**: 702, **2**: 709
wind parks, **2**: 169, **2**: 170, **2**: 177, **2**: 210
wind power design and implementation, **2**: 420
wind turbines, **2**: 477, **2**: 702, **2**: 709
    aerodynamic analysis, **2**: 236–237
    onshore wind, **2**: 477
    technology, **2**: 702, **2**: 709
    wind park design, **2**: 186–187, **2**: 189
cottonwoods, **5**: 264, **5**: 268
Council Directive 97/11/EC [10], **2**: 510
counter electrodes, **1**: 486, **1**: 492
countermeasures:
    construction management, **6**: 209
    debris control, **6**: 81
country-specific subsidies, **3**: 206
coupled pitch—generator control systems, **2**: 358
coupling:
    high concentration solar collectors, receivers, **3**: 187
    mini-grid hybrid photovoltaic power, **1**: 192
    receivers, **3**: 187
La Cour, Poul, **2**: 54, **2**: 54f
covariates: peaks-over-threshold method, **8**: 65
coverage effects: photovoltaic plasmonics, **1**: 647
covered ground heating, **7**: 169
covers:
    collectors, **3**: 570
    flat-plate collectors, **3**: 104, **3**: 111
    heat transfer coefficient–absorbers, **3**: 132, **3**: 133t
    low-temperature stationary collectors, **3**: 104, **3**: 111, **3**: 122–123, **3**: 123f, **3**: 132
CPC *see* compound parabolic collectors
CPCR2 models: solar radiation modeling, **3**: 42
CPV *see* concentration photovoltaics
cracking:
    autogenous shrinkage, **6**: 381

cracking: (*continued*)
    causes, **6**: 380
    concrete structure durability, **6**: 380, **6**: 398
    control, **6**: 382
    corrosion, **7**: 243
    definitions, **6**: 380
    drying shrinkage, **6**: 381
    foundation friction, **6**: 382
    foundation uneven settlement, **6**: 381
    friction, **6**: 382
    geothermal power production, **7**: 243
    joints, **6**: 382
    reinforcement, **6**: 382
    repairs, **6**: 398
    shrinkage, **6**: 381
    state-of-art joints, **6**: 382
    stress corrosion, **7**: 243
    thermal stress, **6**: 380
    uneven settlement, **6**: 381
    width control, **6**: 382
crest heights, **8**: 52, **8**: 70
crest-to-trough heights, **8**: 52
Cretian wind park design, **2**: 202, **2**: 204*f*, **2**: 216
crevice corrosion, **7**: 242
CrI *see* crystallinity indices
critical parameters: luminescent down-shifting, **1**: 569
crops:
    see also agriculture
    additional value extraction, **5**: **385–393**
    biochar, **5**: **357–384**
    biomass cofiring, **5**: 57
    biomass gasification, **5**: 141
    feedstocks, **5**: 7, **5**: **263–291**
    management, yield improvement, **5**: 299
    woody biomass feedstocks, **5**: **263–291**
    yield improvement potentials, **5**: **293–303**
cross-flow turbines, **6**: 26, **6**: 28*f*
cross-polarization, **5**: 376, **5**: 377*f*
cross-sections:
    dams, **6**: 180, **6**: 184, **6**: 185*f*
    gallium-antimonide solar cells, **1**: 609, **1**: 609*f*
    roller compacted concrete dams, **6**: 474, **6**: 481*f*
cross-spectral matrices, **8**: 25
Crown Estate, **8**: 5
crown glass, **3**: 315
crude glycerol, **5**: 396
crude oil, **2**: 544*t*, **5**: 79–80, **5**: 80*f*
cryogenic storage, **4**: 137
crystalline silicon, **1**: **353–387**
    Abu Dhabi desert area, **1**: 691
    aluminum-alloyed back junctions, **1**: 375
    back contact metallization, **1**: 368
    back junctions, **1**: 377
    boron-diffused back junctions, **1**: 377
    boron-diffused front emitters, **1**: 376
    bulk properties, **1**: 368
    cell parameters, **1**: 363, **1**: 369, **1**: 369*t*
    contact metallization, **1**: 366, **1**: 368
    current status, **1**: 355
    dielectric surface passivation, **1**: 364
    efficiency, **1**: **353–387**
    emitter wrap-through cells, **1**: 374
    front contact metallization, **1**: 366
    future technologies, photovoltaics, **1**: **353–387**
    high-efficiency cell structures, **1**: 371, **1**: 375
    historical development, **1**: 354
    improvement strategies, **1**: 364
    markets, **1**: 353
    material parameters, **1**: 363, **1**: 369, **1**: 369*t*
    maximum achievable efficiencies, **1**: 354
    metallization, **1**: 366
    metal-wrap-through cells, **1**: 372, **1**: 373
    parameter influence, **1**: 363
    passivated emitter and rear cell devices, **1**: 371, **1**: 373
    passivation, **1**: 364, **1**: 371
    photovoltaics, **1**: 8
        Abu Dhabi desert area, **1**: 691
        cell parameters, **1**: 363, **1**: 369, **1**: 369*t*
        current status, **1**: 355
        dielectric surface passivation, **1**: 364
        disruptive technologies, **1**: 21
        evolutionary technologies, **1**: 20
        future technologies, **1**: **353–387**
        global industry overview, **1**: 163
        high-efficiency cell structures, **1**: 371, **1**: 375
        improvement strategies, **1**: 364
        markets, **1**: 353
        material environmental impacts, **1**: 144
        material parameters, **1**: 363, **1**: 369, **1**: 369*t*
        metallization, **1**: 366
        parameter influence, **1**: 363
        passivation, **1**: 364, **1**: 371
        state-of-the-art technology, **1**: **353–387**
        surface passivation, **1**: 364
        technology progress, **1**: 20, **1**: 21, **1**: 25
    physical structure, **1**: 355
    production process, **1**: 358
    state-of-the-art technology, **1**: **353–387**
    structure, **1**: 355
    surface passivation, **1**: 364
    technology progress, **1**: 20, **1**: 21, **1**: 25
crystallinity indices (CrI), **5**: 232, **5**: 248
crystal structure: chalcopyrite thin films, **1**: 400
CSD *see* Commission for Sustainable Development
CSHPDS *see* central solar heating plants with diurnal storage
CSI *see* Canadian Solar Inc.
CSIRO power plant: concentrating solar power, **3**: 628
CSP *see* concentrating solar power
CSR *see* circumsolar ratio
CSRA *see* Canadian solar radiation atlas
CTE *see* coefficient of thermal expansion
cubic power curve models, **2**: 130
cultural heritage, **2**: 524
cultural relic protection, **6**: 217
cumulative distribution: wind speed, **2**: 85
cumulative distribution functions (CDF), **3**: 23, **8**: 57
cup anemometers, **2**: 75
cupola dams, **6**: 31
curing: concrete structures, **6**: 396
current:
    see also current-voltage analysis
    multi-junction cells, **1**: 501
    solar energy conversion principles, **1**: 305, **1**: 309
    wind farm offshore projects, **2**: 454
    wind turbine loads, **2**: 253
current status:
    biomass additional value extraction, **5**: 387
    Cameroon, Africa hydropower, **6**: 148
    crystalline silicon cells, **1**: 355
    developing country photovoltaics, **1**: 114
    direct heat utilization, **7**: 169, **7**: 172*t*, **7**: 173*t*
    dye-sensitized solar cells, **1**: 482
    electricity generation costs, **2**: 477
    electricity prices, **1**: 181
    forecasting tools, wind energy, **2**: 616
    fuel cells, hydrogen technology, **4**: **13–43**
    geothermal energy
        direct heat utilization, **7**: 169, **7**: 172*t*, **7**: 173*t*
        Iceland, **7**: 286
        sustainable development, **7**: 286
    grid-connected photovoltaics, **1**: 114
    hydrogen technology fuel cells, **4**: **13–43**
        space applications, **4**: 13
    hydropower
        Cameroon, Africa, **6**: 148
        India, **6**: 227

Japan, 6: 274
Iceland, geothermal energy, 7: 286
Indian hydropower, 6: 227
installed costs, onshore wind, 2: 479
Japanese hydropower, 6: 274
mesoporous dye-sensitized solar cells, 1: 482
off-grid photovoltaics, 1: 114
onshore wind, 2: 476, 2: 477, 2: 479
photovoltaics
    competiveness, 1: 181
    crystalline silicon cells, 1: 355
    developing countries, 1: 114
    grid-connected systems, 1: 114
    markets, 1: 180
    module prices, 1: 181
    off-grid technologies, 1: 114
    policy support, 1: 182
    prices, 1: 181
    technology development, 1: 41, 1: 43, 1: 181
plant costs, onshore wind, 2: 476
space applications, 4: 13
space propulsion, 4: 13
state of art electrical power generation, 8: **1–6**
state of art ocean wave energy, 8: **1–6**
sustainable geothermal energy development, 7: 286
technology development, photovoltaics, 1: 41, 1: 43, 1: 181
thin-film photovoltaics, 1: 42–43
wind energy
    electricity generation costs, 2: 477
    introduction, 2: **1–10**
    turbine technology, 2: 675
wind turbine loads, 2: 253
woody biomass annual increment, 5: 263
current-voltage analysis:
see also current
    chalcopyrite thin films, 1: 414, 1: 416
    concentration photovoltaics, 1: 755, 1: 756, 1: 757f
    crystalline silicon cells, 1: 362
    downconversion, 1: 552–553
    dye-sensitized solar cells, 1: 487
    organic solar cells, 1: 449
    photovoltaics
        concentration photovoltaics, 1: 755, 1: 756, 1: 757f
        modules, 1: 680f, 1: 680–681, 1: 681–682
        performance determination, 1: 790
        product-integration, 1: 717, 1: 719f
        thermal solar collectors, 3: 262
    solar cells in circuits, 1: 294
curtains: hydropower, 6: 84
cusp-type collectors, 3: 159
cut-in wind speed, 2: 114, 2: 114–115, 2: 125, 2: 126f, 2: 127, 2: 128f, 2: 129, 2: 134–135, 2: 138
cut-out wind speed, 2: 114, 2: 115–116, 2: 126, 2: 127, 2: 128f, 2: 134–135, 2: 138
cyanobacteria, 6: 61
cyclones, 5: 62, 5: 145
cylinders: hydrogen technology, 4: 2, 4: 7f, 4: 117
cylindrical absorbers, 3: 154, 3: 155f
cylindrical reflector collectors, 3: 587t

D

DAFC *see* direct alcohol fuel cells
daily diffuse fraction, 3: 40
daily solar irradiation, 1: 691, 1: 691f
daily utilizability, 3: 406, 3: 408
damage: concrete structures, 6: 386
damped composite rotor blades, 2: 713
dams:
    see also concrete dams; *individual dams*; roller compacted concrete dams;
    arch dams, 6: 24, 6: 492

Brazilian hydroelectricity, 6: **93–127**
break analysis, 6: 219, 6: 220
buttress dams, 6: 30
Cameroon, Africa, 6: 134, 6: 137
cavitation mitigation, 6: 497
Chinese hydropower projects, 6: **485–505**
cofferdams, 6: 201, 6: 223
concrete construction, 6: 224
cross-sectional size, 6: 180, 6: 184, 6: 185f
cupola dams, 6: 31
development, 6: 267
earth cofferdams, 6: 206, 6: 207
economic growth, 6: 270
embankment dams, 6: 28
failures, 6: 219
fish life, 6: 58, 6: 73
foundation treatments, Three Gorges Project, China, 6: 184
gravity dams, 6: 29–30, 6: 184
high-arch dams, 6: 492
Horseshoe Bend hydroelectric scheme, 6: 467, 6: 469, 6: 472, 6: 473
hydrology, 6: 135, 6: 136t, 6: 473
hydropower/hydroelectricity
    Brazil, 6: **93–127**
    Cameroon, Africa, 6: 134, 6: 137
    downstream flow regime impacts, 6: 56
    environmental issues, 6: 9, 6: 52, 6: 54f
    essential features, 6: 16, 6: 28
    historical overviews, 6: 33
    impact management, 6: 52, 6: 54f, 6: 56, 6: 58, 6: 73
    Japan, 6: 265, 6: 288, 6: 294
    in operation, 6: 4, 6: 5t
    plants, 6: 346, 6: 347, 6: 350
    sediment management, 6: **355–376**
    social issues, 6: 9
    Switzerland, 6: 346, 6: 347
    under construction, 6: 4, 6: 6t
Japan, 6: 265, 6: 288, 6: 294
longitudinal concrete cofferdams, 6: 206
long-term sediment management, 6: **355–376**
Mekin hydropower project, Cameroon, Africa, 6: 131
rapid economic growth, 6: 270
rock cofferdams, 6: 206, 6: 207
rockfill dams, 6: 29, 6: 200
sediment management, 6: **355–376**
stable economic growth, 6: 270
sustainable hydropower, 6: **355–376**
Switzerland, 6: 346
Three Gorges Project, China, 6: 184, 6: 200, 6: 219
toe power plants, 6: 188
types, 6: 28
water levels, 6: 135, 6: 136t
Dangerous Substances and Explosive Atmosphere Regulations (DSEAR), 5: 43
Daniel-Johnson Dam, 6: 161, 6: 164f, 6: 167t
dark earths, 5: 358, 5: 358f, 5: 359, 5: 361f
Darrieus wind turbines:
    historical overviews, 2: 55, 2: 55f
    rotor classification, 2: 107
    technology evolution, 2: 673, 2: 674f, 2: 693–694, 2: 694
Dashidaira Dam: Japan, 6: 288
data analysis:
    geothermal energy, 7: 263
    photovoltaic standards, 1: 792
    reservoir water quality, 6: 70
    solar irradiance-photovoltaic power forecasts, 1: 267
    solar radiation/meteorological data, 1: 230, 1: 231
    solar radiation resources assessments, 1: 227, 1: 228
    wind turbine technology evolution, finance, 2: 719
databases:
    solar radiation resources assessments, 1: 229
    wind turbine selection, 2: 158
data conversions: application-specific solar radiation data conversions, 1: 226

data mining forecasting, 2: 615
data record gaps: solar radiation/meteorological data, 1: 230
data set properties: solar radiation resources assessments, 1: 227
dating geothermal fluids origins, 7: 110
day lengths, 3: 12
DC *see* direct current
DC Chemical *see* OCI Company Ltd.
DDT *see* deflagration-to-detonation transition
dead-state radiation, 1: 330
debris control, 6: 77, 6: 79, 6: 81, 6: 82
debris sluicing structures, 6: 188
decarbonization, 4: 65, 4: 66, 4: 69
de Caux, Solomon, 3: 88, 3: 88f
decentralized biomass collection, 5: 166
decentralized energy generation, 1: 189, 1: 191, 2: 496
decentralized solar water heating systems, 3: 435
decentralized storage, 1: 191
decision making: Three Gorges Project, China, 6: 200
declination angles, 3: 1, 3: 10, 3: 30, 3: 30f
decommissioning:
 noise, 2: 526
 ocean energy costs, 8: 158
 wind power design and implementation, 2: 429
dedicated wind energy storage, 2: 495
deep-level impurities, 1: 624
deep level transient spectroscopy (DLTS), 1: 505, 1: 506f
deep outlets, 6: 187
deep stilling basis spillways, 6: 77
deepwater:
 cofferdam construction, 6: 223
 offshore floating technology, 2: 449
 wind turbines, 2: 720
deflagration, 4: 77, 4: 78, 4: 78f, 4: 81, 4: 82, 4: 99, 4: 103, 4: 104
deflagration-to-detonation transition (DDT), 4: 81, 4: 82, 4: 99, 4: 103
deflectometry, 3: 170
deforestation, 5: 381–382
degradation:
 biochar, 5: 364
 hydropower downstream impacts, 6: 56
 Three Gorges Project, China, 6: 212
dehumidification, 3: 501, 3: 542
dehydration, 5: 210
dehydrogenation, 4: 142, 4: 143
delayed ignition, 4: 97
delivery formats: solid biofuels, 5: 39
delivery infrastructure: hydrogen technology costs, 4: 52
delivery issues: biomass cofiring, 5: 70
delivery times: wind turbines, 2: 186–187, 2: 189
Delta IV rocket, 4: 17
demand:
 photovoltaic cost reductions, 1: 52
 Tokyo Electric Power Co., Inc:, 6: 282
 wind energy variable costs, 2: 471, 2: 488
demand management: wind energy, 2: 471, 2: 556
demand-side management (DSM):
 hydrogen technology, 4: 331, 4: 332
 photovoltaic future visions, 1: 191
 wind energy policy, 2: 556
demonstration projects:
 concentration photovoltaics, 1: 750
 ocean wave energy, 8: 79–110
 Three Gorges Project, China, 6: 200
Denmark:
 offshore wind power, 2: 437, 2: 438
  historical overviews, 2: 433
  market development, 2: 667
  support structures, 2: 451, 2: 451f
 wind power market development, 2: 665
 wind turbines, 2: 60, 2: 668–669
Denniss-Auld air turbine, 8: 132, 8: 141
dense battery hybrid energy storage, 4: 317

density:
 air density variation, 2: 146
 biochar, 5: 373–374
 biodiesel separation, 5: 209
 bulk density, 5: 43
 carrier density, 1: 299
 compacted density, 6: 477, 6: 478f
 dislocation density, 1: 500f, 1: 500–501
 electron states, 1: 298, 1: 299, 1: 300f
 energy density, 4: 81
 flux property density, 1: 331, 1: 331t
 particle density, 5: 373–374
 photon state density, 1: 306
 power density, 4: 184
deploy-and plug ocean zone, 8: 4–5, 8: 5f
deployment:
 barriers to electrical energy storage, 6: 406
 biodiesel, 5: 3
 bioethanol, 5: 4
 incentive support mechanisms, 1: 3
 ocean energy costs, 8: 158, 8: 167
 policy support mechanisms, 1: 3
 solar water heating systems, 3: 420, 3: 420f, 3: 422
 support mechanisms, 1: 3
 very large-scale photovoltaic systems, 1: 734
depolymerization, 5: 232, 5: 401
deposition:
 amorphous silicon, 1: 389
 chalcopyrite thin films, 1: 406
 chemical vapor deposition, 1: 389, 1: 390, 3: 324–325
 geothermal energy, 7: 143
 glazings, 3: 324
 glow discharge technique, 1: 389, 1: 390
 hydropower, 6: 361, 6: 362
 low-emittance coatings, 3: 324
 organic solar cells, 1: 470
 physical vapor deposition, 3: 324
 plasma-enhanced chemical vapor deposition, 1: 389, 1: 390
 reservoir surveys, 6: 361
 sediment management, 6: 361, 6: 362
 solid deposition, 7: 245
 thin-film silicon photovoltaics, 1: 389
depreciation: wind power, 2: 422
depth considerations:
 geothermal energy shallow systems, 7: 189, 7: 189f, 7: 190f
 heat flow, 7: 87
 offshore wind costs, 2: 481
 reservoir surveys, 6: 361
derating wind turbines, 2: 735
derivative amidoboranes, 4: 144
derivative fuels: biomass gasification, 5: 159, 5: 159f
Derwent River, Australia, 6: 62, 6: 81f
desalination, 2: **725–747**, 3: **529–565**
 see also solar desalination
 backup requirements, 2: 734
 costs, 2: 736
 definitions, 2: 725, 3: 529, 3: 567
 design issues, 2: 733
 economics, 2: 736
 energy requirements, 2: 729
 future trends, 2: 740
 Greece, 2: 735, 2: 739
 history, 3: 85, 3: 97
 hybrid energy systems, 2: 735, 2: 740
 integrated systems, 2: 732
 Libya, 2: 739
 membranes, 2: 726, 2: 727f, 2: 728, 2: 733
 Morocco, 2: 739, 3: 539f, 3: 540f
 operational issues, 2: 734, 2: 735
 photovoltaic/thermal solar collectors, 3: 295
 plants, 2: 726
 processes, 2: 726
 project implementation, 2: 735

reverse osmosis, **2**: 726, **2**: 727f, **2**: 728, **2**: 732, **2**: 734, **2**: 738
solar cooling, **3**: 614
solar energy, **3**: 85, **3**: **529–565**, **3**: 97
solar thermal systems, **3**: 529, **3**: 530, **3**: 547, **3**: 589
Spain, **2**: 739
storage, **2**: 733, **2**: 734
technical difficulties, **2**: 734
technological developments, **2**: 740
turbines, **2**: 733, **2**: 735
unit switching, **2**: 734
very large-scale photovoltaic, **1**: 733
water demand, **2**: 726, **2**: 732
wind energy, **2**: **725–747**
Desertec, **1**: 739, **3**: 631, **3**: 632f
desert region very large-scale photovoltaic systems, **1**: **733–744**
desiccant cooling systems, **3**: 461, **3**: 464, **3**: 482, **3**: 483
design:
   agricultural solar thermal applications, **3**: 577
   alkaline fuel cells, **4**: 170
   annual electricity production calculations, **2**: 196
   area constraints, photovoltaics, **1**: 716
   artificial leaves, **1**: 666, **1**: 667
   building-integrated photovoltaics, **1**: 700, **3**: 389, **3**: 394
   case studies, wind parks, **2**: **169–223**
   cell stacks, **4**: 229
   characteristic case studies, wind parks, **2**: 211
   compressed gas: hydrogen storage, **4**: 112, **4**: 128
   concentration photovoltaics, **1**: 797, **3**: 267–268, **3**: 291
   concrete structure durability, **6**: **377–403**
   costs, wind parks, **2**: 169, **2**: 170, 177, **2**: 210
   desalination, **2**: 733
   domestic hot water, **3**: 438
   economic analysis, wind parks, **2**: 169, **2**: 170, **2**: 177, **2**: 210
   electricity production calculations, wind parks, **2**: 196
   electricity production maximization, wind parks, **2**: 169, **2**: 169–170, **2**: 171
   flat-type photovoltaic/thermal solar collectors, **3**: 263
   gas diffusion electrodes, **4**: 166
   gasifiers, **5**: 136
   geothermal heat pumps, **7**: 197
   Horseshoe Bend hydroelectric scheme, **6**: 467, **6**: 469, **6**: 473, **6**: 482
   hybrid photovoltaic/thermal solar collectors, **3**: 277
   hybrid solar–diesel systems, **1**: 688
   hydraulic structures, **6**: 221
   hydropower
      long-term sediment management, **6**: **355–376**
      pumped storage hydropower, **6**: **405–434**
      sediment management, **6**: **355–376**
      simplified generic axial-flow microhydro turbines, **6**: **435–466**
   industrial solar thermal applications, **3**: 577
   infrastructure, hydrogen technology, **4**: 53
   installation wind park site selection, **2**: 171
   large sized noninterconnected wind power systems, **2**: 211, **2**: 216
   liquid electrolytes, alkaline fuel cells, **4**: 170
   lithium–water absorption systems, **3**: 470
   loads, wind turbines, **2**: 246
   long-term sediment management, **6**: **355–376**
   low-energy home building-integrated photovoltaics, **3**: 389
   maintenance, concrete structure durability, **6**: 395
   manufacturing, product-integrated photovoltaics, **1**: 728
   mechanical-dynamic loads, **2**: 246
   meteorological conditions, solar water heating systems, **3**: 438
   microbial fuel cells, **4**: 271
   micro-siting wind parks, **2**: 188–189, **2**: 190
   modified photovoltaic/thermal solar collectors, **3**: 276
   modules, photovoltaics, **1**: 679, **1**: 680
   molten carbonate fuel cells, **4**: 229
   net-zero energy solar buildings, **3**: 394
   noninterconnected wind power systems, **2**: 211, **2**: 212, **2**: 216
   ocean wave energy, **8**: 80, **8**: 81t, **8**: 88
   offshore wind power
      wind farms, **2**: 452
      wind parks, **2**: 190, **2**: 211, **2**: 220
      wind turbines, **2**: 440
   onshore wind parks, **2**: 211, **2**: 218
   panels, photovoltaics, **1**: 679, **1**: 680
   passive solar architecture, **3**: 639
   passive solar technologies, **3**: 359
   photovoltaics, **1**: **679–695**
      artificial leaves, **1**: 666
      building-integrated photovoltaics, **1**: 700, **3**: 389, **3**: 394
      hybrid systems, **3**: 277
      modules, **1**: 679, **1**: 680
      panels, **1**: 679, **1**: 680
      product-integration, **1**: 716, **1**: 723, **1**: 728
      system performance, **1**: 679–680, **1**: 692
      thermal solar collectors, **3**: 263, **3**: 267–268, **3**: 276, **3**: 277
   power penetration, wind parks, **2**: 183, **2**: 199, **2**: 206, **2**: 208, **2**: 212, **2**: 214, **2**: 216
   power plants, molten carbonate fuel cells, **4**: 229
   product-integrated photovoltaics, **1**: 716, **1**: 723, **1**: 728
   pumped storage hydropower, **6**: **405–434**
   qualification, concentration photovoltaic standards, **1**: 797
   Roscoe Wind Park, Texas, **2**: 218
   sediment management, **6**: **355–376**
   set-up costs, wind parks, **2**: 169, **2**: 170, **2**: 177, **2**: 210
   simplified generic axial-flow microhydro turbines, **6**: **435–466**
   simulation tools, solar water heating systems, **3**: 438, **3**: 441f
   single-effect lithium–water absorption systems, **3**: 470
   site selection, wind parks, **2**: 171
   small sized noninterconnected wind power systems, **2**: 211, **2**: 212
   social approval/attitude, wind parks, **2**: 202
   solar energy, thermal energy storage, **3**: 213
   solar thermal applications, **3**: 577
   solar water heating systems, **3**: 438
      meteorological conditions, **3**: 438
      simulation tools, **3**: 438, **3**: 441f
   stand alone hybrid wind energy systems, **2**: 649, **2**: 651
   standards, wind turbines, **2**: 373
   storage plants, pumped storage hydropower, **6**: **405–434**
   storage systems, stand alone hybrid wind energy systems, **2**: 649
   sustainable hydropower, **6**: **355–376**
   system performance, photovoltaics, **1**: 679–680, **1**: 692
   tanks, hydrogen storage, **4**: 128
   Thanet Wind Park, United Kingdom, **2**: 220
   thermal energy storage, **3**: 213
   time minimization, wind parks, **2**: 169, **2**: 170, **2**: 181
   turbine standards, **2**: 373
   urban planning, **1**: 700
   water pumping systems, wind energy, **2**: 728
   weak systems, wind parks, **2**: 183, **2**: 206
   wind energy
      desalination, **2**: 733
      offshore wind power, **2**: 440, **2**: 452
      power projects, **2**: **391–391**
      stand alone hybrid systems, **2**: 649, **2**: 651
      turbine loads, **2**: 246
      turbine mechanical-dynamic loads, **2**: 246
      turbine standards, **2**: 373
      water pumping systems, **2**: 728
   wind parks
      annual electricity production calculations, **2**: 196
      case studies, **2**: **169–223**
      characteristic case studies, **2**: 211
      cost minimization, **2**: 169, **2**: 170, **2**: 177
      costs, **2**: 169, **2**: 170, **2**: 177, **2**: 210
      economic analysis, **2**: 169, **2**: 170, **2**: 177, **2**: 210
      electricity production calculations, **2**: 196
      electricity production maximization, **2**: 169–170, **2**: 171
      installation site selection, **2**: 171
      large sized noninterconnected power systems, **2**: 211, **2**: 216
      micro-siting, **2**: 188–189, **2**: 190
      noninterconnected power systems, **2**: 211, **2**: 212, **2**: 216

design: (*continued*)
    offshore wind energy projects, **2**: 190, **2**: 211, **2**: 220
    onshore wind energy projects, **2**: 211, **2**: 218
    power penetration, **2**: 183, **2**: 199, **2**: 206, **2**: 208, **2**: 212, **2**: 214, **2**: 216
    set-up costs, **2**: 169, **2**: 170, **2**: 177, **2**: 210
    site selection, **2**: 171
    small sized noninterconnected power systems, **2**: 211, **2**: 212
    social approval/attitude, **2**: 202
    time minimization, **2**: 169, **2**: 170, **2**: 181
    weak systems, **2**: 183, **2**: 206
    wind power penetration, **2**: 183, **2**: 199, **2**: 206, **2**: 208, **2**: 212, **2**: 214, **2**: 216
  wind turbines, **2**: 246, **2**: 373, **2**: 440
desilting basins, **6**: 246–247, **6**: 247*f*
DESIRE project, **2**: 718
destratification, **6**: 83
detailed balanced models, **1**: 308, **1**: 338
detailed numerical modeling, **7**: 35
detection methods: hydrogen safety engineering, **4**: 103
detectors: solar radiation, **1**: 219
Det Norske Veritas-OS-J101 standard, **2**: 376
detonation: hydrogen safety, **4**: 77, **4**: 81–82, **4**: 99, **4**: 103, **4**: 104
Deutsche Forschungsanstalt für Luft und Raumfahrt (DLR), Germany, **3**: 549
developers: Fischer–Tropsch process, **5**: 177, **5**: 177*t*
developing country photovoltaics, **1**: **111–141**
  annual revision tariffs, **1**: 125
  bank funding, **1**: 113, **1**: 121, **1**: 128
  biochar, **5**: 380
  capital subsidies, **1**: 125
  carbon financing, **1**: 129
  community participation, **1**: 120
  consumer grants, **1**: 125
  costs, **1**: 116
  current status, **1**: 114
  development assistance, **1**: 113
  economics, **1**: 113, **1**: 120
  feed-in tariffs, **1**: 130–131, **1**: 134
  finance, **1**: 113, **1**: 120, **1**: 125, **1**: 130
  financial risk management, **1**: 135
  fiscal incentives, photovoltaics, **1**: 128
  funding, **1**: 113, **1**: 120, **1**: 125
  global energy transfer feed-in tariffs, **1**: 128, **1**: 135
  grants, **1**: 125
  guarantees, **1**: 125
  import duty reductions, **1**: 128
  incentives for off-grid photovoltaics, **1**: **111–141**
  international funds, **1**: 113
  leasing, **1**: 126
  loans, **1**: 128
  local participation, **1**: 119
  low interest loans, **1**: 128
  market development finance, **1**: 123
  Millennium Development Goals, **1**: 111
  off-grid technologies, **1**: **111–141**
  organization, **1**: 119
  ownership, **1**: 119
  poverty alleviation, **1**: 124
  private operators, **1**: 120
  private ownership, **1**: 120
  public finance pools, **1**: 128
  public sector finance, **1**: 124, **1**: 128
  regulation, **1**: 127
  renewable energy premium tariff, **1**: 130
  renewable portfolio standards, **1**: 127
  risk management, **1**: 135
  rural electrification, **1**: **111–141**
  rural energy service companies, **1**: 120, **1**: 126, **1**: 132
  small power producer regulation, **1**: 127
  soft loans, photovoltaics, **1**: 128
  solar water heating systems, **3**: 422, **3**: 422*f*
  subsidies, photovoltaics, **1**: 125
  support mechanisms, **1**: **111–141**
  tariff incentives, **1**: 124
  tariff setting, **1**: 124
  tender systems, **1**: 128
  value added tax reductions, **1**: 128
developing country wind energy, **2**: 11
development:
  bioenergy policy development, **5**: **411–429**
  biomass and biofuels, **5**: 8, **5**: **15–26**, **5**: 151
    biomass-to-liquids technology, **5**: 160, **5**: 161*f*, **5**: 187, **5**: 188, **5**: 189*f*
    gasification, **5**: 151
    introduction, **5**: 8
  Cameroon, Africa, **6**: 135
  catalysts, photovoltaics, **1**: 33
  construction impact management, hydropower, **6**: **49–91**
  dams, **6**: 267
  developing country assistance, **1**: 113
  direct heat utilization, **7**: 170
  environmental impact management, hydropower, **6**: **49–91**
  gasification, **5**: 151
  geothermal energy, **7**: 170, **7**: **271–295**
  global wind power markets, **2**: **657–669**
  Goldisthal pumped storage plant, Germany, **6**: 426
  historical photovoltaics, **1**: 33
  hydroelectricity/hydropower, **6**: 4
    benefits, **6**: **15–47**, **6**: 284
    Cameroon, Africa, **6**: 135
    China, **6**: **485–505**
    construction impact management, **6**: **49–91**
    environmental impact management, **6**: **49–91**
    essential features, **6**: 22
    Horseshoe Bend, Teviot River, New Zealand, **6**: **467–483**
    hydraulic research, **6**: **485–505**
    India, **6**: **227–252**
    Japanese current status, **6**: 274
    multibenefit solutions, **6**: **15–47**
    operation impact management, **6**: **49–91**
    research, China, **6**: **485–505**
    Spain, **6**: **309–341**
  hydrogen technology policies, **4**: 67
  Indian hydropower, **6**: **227–252**
  InGaP/GaAs/Ge 3-junction solar cells, **1**: 503
  microbial fuel cells, **4**: 265
  multibenefit solutions, hydropower, **6**: **15–47**
  National Solar Radiation Data Base, **1**: 229
  offshore wind power drivers, **2**: 434
  operation impact management, hydropower, **6**: **49–91**
  photovoltaics, **1**: **5–11**
    catalysts, **1**: 33
    developing country assistance, **1**: 113
    global industry overview, **1**: 164
    historical developments, **1**: 33
    thermal solar collectors, **3**: 258
  policies, hydrogen technology, **4**: 67
  pumped storage hydropower, **6**: 284, **6**: **405–434**, **6**: 286
  Spanish hydropower, **6**: **309–341**
  sustainable geothermal energy, **7**: **271–295**
  wind farms
    financial support, **2**: 711
    turbine technology, **2**: 711, **2**: 714
  wind power global markets, **2**: **657–669**
  wood fuel markets, **5**: 77
deviation significance: photovoltaic costs, **1**: 58
device designs: cadmium telluride thin films, **1**: 424
device development:
  dye-sensitized solar cells, **1**: 490
  ocean wave energy conversion
    commercial demonstration, **8**: **79–110**
    electrical power generation, **8**: 4
    initial conception, **8**: **79–110**
    technology development assessments, **8**: 3, **8**: 3*f*
    testing, **8**: 95

device layouts: photochromogenics, **3**: 346–348, **3**: 348f
device operation: photochromogenics, **3**: 346–348, **3**: 348f
device properties: chalcopyrite thin films, **1**: 414
device structure: chalcopyrite thin films, **1**: 410
Dewar, James, **4**: 1, **4**: 3f
DeWind generators, **2**: 270, **2**: 287f
DFC *see* direct fuel cells
DFT *see* discrete Fourier transformations
DHW *see* domestic hot water
diagnostics: peaks-over-threshold method, **8**: 61
Didcot power plant, **5**: 68
Dieke diagrams, **1**: 568f, **1**: 573
dielectric medium:
   dielectric/metal/dielectric multilayers, **3**: 325
   layer passivation, **1**: 364
   material properties, photovoltaics, **1**: 646
   metal particle matrices, **3**: 302–303, **3**: 307
   plasmonic photovoltaics, **1**: 646
   surface passivation, **1**: 364
diesel:
   see also biodiesel
   blends, **5**: 344, **5**: 348
   diesel-biodiesel blends, **5**: 348
   engine configuration ranges, **5**: 344, **5**: 348
   engine operation modification, **5**: 347
   ethanol-diesel blends, **5**: 344
   hybrid photovoltaic systems, **1**: 687
   safety, **5**: 323
   stand alone hybrid wind energy, **2**: 623–624, **2**: 636, **2**: 639f
differential temperature controllers (DTC), **3**: 478
differential thermal analysis, **7**: 99
diffraction:
   electron back scatter diffraction, **1**: 405, **1**: 405f
   solar power satellites, **1**: 768
   wind turbines, loads, **2**: 250
   X-ray diffraction, **7**: 98
diffuse horizontal irradiance: predictions, definitions, **1**: 240
diffusion:
   see also gas diffusion electrodes
   booster diffuse reflectors, **3**: 281
   boron-diffused back junctions, **1**: 377
   boron-diffused front emitters, **1**: 376
   conical diffusers, **6**: 456
   daily diffuse fraction, **3**: 40
   diffuse hemispherical radiation, **1**: 214, **1**: 216, **1**: 219, **1**: 224, **1**: 227
   diffuser-augmented wind energy systems, **2**: 687
   diffuse reflectors, **3**: 151f, **3**: 151–152, **3**: 159, **3**: 159f, **3**: 281, **3**: 285f
   diffuse solar radiation thermodynamics, **1**: 315
   flat-plate diffuse reflector collectors, **3**: 151f, **3**: 151–152, **3**: 159, **3**: 159f
   gas diffusion layers, **4**: 192
   geothermal energy physics, **7**: 10
   heat diffusion equation, **7**: 13
   impurity diffusion, **1**: 428, **1**: 502
   minority-carrier diffusion lengths, **1**: 498–500, **1**: 499f
   phosphorus diffusion, **1**: 359
   pressure diffusion, **7**: 10
   proton-exchange membrane fuel cells, **4**: 187
   sawtooth diffuse reflectors, **3**: 151–152, **3**: 152f
   simplified generic axial-flow microhydro turbines, **6**: 456, **6**: 460
digestibility: lignocellulosic wastes, **5**: 232
digital controllers: passive solar architecture, **3**: 655
diluted thermal radiation, **1**: 322
dilution limits: alcohol fuels, **5**: 320
dimensional analysis: air turbines, **8**: 124
dimensional flame length correlation, **4**: 91
dimensioning site investigations, **7**: 195, **7**: 198
dimensionless flame length correlation, **4**: 92
dimethyl carbonate, **5**: 396
dimethyl ether (DME), **5**: 158, **5**: 183f, **5**: 183–184, **5**: 185

diodes, **1**: 552–553, **3**: 262
dioxin environmental impacts, **5**: 51
dips: voltage variation, **2**: 594
direct alcohol fuel cells (DAFC), **4**: 282
direct beam irradiance, **1**: 214, **1**: 216, **1**: 224, **1**: 226
   see also direct normal irradiation
direct biomass cofiring, **5**: 63
direct circulation systems, **3**: 449, **3**: 451f
direct current (DC):
   rating procedures, **1**: 755, **1**: 759
   resistivity methods, **7**: 61, **7**: 63
direct-drive gearbox systems, **2**: 680
direct drive technology: wind turbine control systems and power electronics, **2**: 370
direct-drive variable-speed indirect-grid coupling generators, **2**: 289
direct dry-steam power plants, **7**: 209
direct expansion solar-assisted heat pump (DX SAHP), **3**: 507
direct four-electron pathways, **4**: 162
direct fuel cells (DFC), **4**: 231, **4**: 232, **4**: 238
   molten carbonate fuel cells, **4**: 227
direct gain systems, **3**: 360–361, **3**: 361, **3**: 369, **3**: 390
direct gasification, **5**: 62
direct-grid coupling generators, **2**: 286, **2**: 287
direct heat utilization, **7**: **169–186**
   agricultural drying, **7**: 169, **7**: 173t, **7**: 174, **7**: 176f, **7**: 180, **7**: 180f, **7**: 181, **7**: 182, **7**: 183f
   aquaculture ponds, **7**: 169, **7**: 173t, **7**: 174, **7**: 175f, **7**: 184, **7**: 185f
   bathing, **7**: 169, **7**: 170, **7**: 173t
   case histories, **7**: 180
   combined heat and power, **7**: 182, **7**: 184f
   current status, **7**: 169, **7**: 172t, **7**: 173t
   development, **7**: 170
   district heating, **7**: 169, **7**: 171, **7**: 174f, **7**: 180, **7**: 181f, **7**: 182, **7**: 184, **7**: 184f
   district heating systems, **7**: 169, **7**: 171
   downhole pumps, **7**: 176, **7**: 177f
   drying, **7**: 169, **7**: 173t, **7**: 174, **7**: 176f, **7**: 180, **7**: 180f, **7**: 181, **7**: 182, **7**: 183f
   environmental considerations, **7**: 179
   equipment selection, **7**: 175
   examples, **7**: 180
   geothermal energy, **7**: **169–186**
   global distribution, **7**: 170, **7**: 172t, **7**: 173t
   greenhouses, **7**: 169, **7**: 170, **7**: 172t, **7**: 173t, **7**: 174, **7**: 175f, **7**: 181
   heat exchangers, **7**: 178, **7**: 178f, **7**: 179f
   industrial applications, **7**: 169, **7**: 173t, **7**: 174, **7**: 176f, **7**: 180, **7**: 180f, **7**: 181, **7**: 182, **7**: 183f
   onion dehydration, **7**: 182, **7**: 183f
   piping, **7**: 177, **7**: 178f
   pools, **7**: 169, **7**: 170, **7**: 173t
   pumps, **7**: 176, **7**: 177f
   Reykjavik, Iceland, district heating, **7**: 180, **7**: 181f
   space heating, **7**: 169, **7**: 171, **7**: 173t, **7**: 174f, **7**: 180, **7**: 181f, **7**: 182, **7**: 184, **7**: 184f
   spa heating, **7**: 169, **7**: 170, **7**: 173t
   swimming pools, **7**: 169, **7**: 170, **7**: 173t
   timber drying, **7**: 181, **7**: 183f
   tomato drying, **7**: 180, **7**: 180f
direct heavy metal emissions, **1**: 151
direction: wind, **2**: 74, **2**: 76
directional properties: ocean waves, **8**: 15, **8**: 18, **8**: 25
directives:
   Council Directive 97/11/EC [10], **2**: 510
   Industrial Emissions Directive, **5**: 31
   Large Combustion Plant Directive, **5**: 31
   Renewable Energy Directive, **5**: 100, **5**: 103
   Waste Incineration Directive, **5**: 31
direct land use change, **5**: 117, **5**: 197–198, **5**: 199f
direct liquid fuel cells (DLFC), **4**: 205, **4**: 208
direct methanol fuel cells (DMFC):
   proton-exchange membrane fuel cells, **4**: 185, **4**: 188, **4**: 190, **4**: 196–197, **4**: 200, **4**: 202, **4**: 205

direct methanol fuel cells (DMFC): (*continued*)
   transport applications, **4**: 282
direct normal irradiation (DNI):
   concentration photovoltaics, **1**: 753, **1**: 755
   predictions, definitions, **1**: 240
   resources assessments, **1**: 214, **1**: 216, **1**: 220, **1**: 224, **1**: 226, **1**: 227, **3**: 27
direct numerical simulation (DNS), **2**: 232–233
direct polarization, **5**: 376, **5**: 378*f*
direct-return array piping, **3**: 475–476, **3**: 476*f*
direct sizing: axial-flow microhydro turbines, **6**: 463
direct solar assisted heat pumps, **3**: 507
direct solar gain, **3**: 587
Direct Solar Insolation Code (DISC), **1**: 226
direct solar radiation, **1**: 315, **1**: 319, **1**: 325, **1**: 326
Direct Solar Stream (DISS) power plant, **3**: 626
direct time series methods: solar irradiance, **1**: 248
direct-use:
   geothermal energy sustainability, **7**: 279
   lignins, **5**: 401
DIRINT, **1**: 226
dirty economics, **1**: 772
disassembly: lignins, **5**: 401
DISC *see* Direct Solar Insolation Code
discharge:
   Chinese hydraulic research, **6**: 485, **6**: 487, **6**: 499
   electrical energy storage, **6**: 409*t*, **6**: 409–410
   geothermal wells, **7**: 20–21
   Three Gorges Project, China, **6**: 186, **6**: 188, **6**: 212
discounted cost of ocean energy, **8**: 153, **8**: 154, **8**: 155
discoveries:
   hydrogen, **4**: 1, **4**: 2*f*
   photovoltaics, **1**: 5
discrete Fourier series, **3**: 379
discrete Fourier transformations (DFT), **8**: 105–106
discretization: direct gain passive solar technologies, **3**: 361
diseases:
   Legionnaires' disease, **3**: 437
   Millennium Development Goals, **7**: 289
   water-related diseases, **3**: 437, **6**: 63
dished end steel vessels, **4**: 115
dishes *see* solar dishes
disinfection: water heating, **3**: 437
dislocation density, **1**: 500*f*, **1**: 500–501
disparities: geothermal energy, **7**: 283
dispatchability: hydrogen fuel cells, **4**: 332, **4**: 333*f*
dispersion:
   energy-dispersive X-ray spectroscopy, **7**: 99
   ocean waves, **8**: 13
   polymer-dispersed liquid crystal switching devices, **3**: 351
displaced workers, **5**: 22
disposal yard restoration/revegetation, **6**: 423
disruptive photovoltaic technologies, **1**: 13, **1**: 15–16, **1**: 21
DISS *see* Direct Solar Stream power plant
dissipation:
   Chinese hydropower projects, **6**: 485, **6**: 486*t*, **6**: 487
   Three Gorges Project, China, **6**: 186
distance factors:
   building-integrated photovoltaics, **1**: 700
   offshore wind, **2**: 456, **2**: 481
Distant Offshore Wind Farms with No Visual Impact in Deepwater (DOWNWIND) project, **2**: 718
distillation:
   see also membrane distillation
   biodiesel, **5**: 209–210
   bioethanol, **5**: 210
   desalination, **2**: 726
   history, **3**: 85, **3**: 97
   solar desalination, **3**: 529, **3**: 541, **3**: 543
   solar energy history, **3**: 85, **3**: 97
distributed generation:
   electrical energy storage, **6**: 408
   molten carbonate fuel cells, **4**: 227
   stand alone hybrid wind energy systems, **2**: 626
distribution:
   see also global distribution
   alkali–aggregate reaction, **6**: 389
   Cameroon, Africa, hydropower, **6: 129–151**
   conventional power energy storage, **1**: 201
   cumulative distribution, **2**: 85, **3**: 23, **8**: 57
   direct heat utilization, **7**: 170, **7**: 172*t*, **7**: 173*t*
   electrical energy storage, **6**: 408
   electrical networks, wind energy, **2**: 602
   electricity generation, **6**: 2, **6**: 3, **6**: 3*f*
   extreme sea state estimations, **8**: 52, **8**: 54, **8**: 65
   Fermi-Dirac distribution, **1**: 299
   future photovoltaic power, **1**: 197
   generalized Pareto distribution, **8**: 55, **8**: 57
   hydropower
     multibenefit solutions, **6**: 43
     world examples, **6**: 43, **6**: 44, **6**: 258
     worldwide, **6**: 33, **6: 129–151**, **6**: 43, **6**: 44, **6**: 258
   ocean waves, **8**: 18, **8**: 52, **8**: 54, **8**: 61, **8**: 65
   Pareto distributions, **8**: 55, **8**: 57
   photovoltaics
     future visions, **1**: 197
     geographical, **1**: 14, **1**: 14*f*
     technology progress, **1**: 14, **1**: 14*f*
   Rayleigh distribution, **2**: 118
   solar water heating, **3**: 423
   Weibull wind potential evaluation, **2**: 184, **2**: 186*f*, **2**: 197, **2**: 197*f*, **2**: 198, **2**: 198*t*
   Weibull wind speed distribution, **2**: 84, **2**: 117, **2**: 120, **2**: 124, **2**: 144
   wind energy electrical networks, **2**: 602
   wind energy geographics, **2**: 591
   wind frequency, **2**: 82, **2**: 404
   worldwide hydropower, **6**: 33, **6: 129–151**, **6**: 43, **6**: 44, **6**: 258
   worldwide solar water heating, **3**: 423
district heating:
   biomass combined heat and power, **5**: 88, **5**: 89, **5**: 90*t*, **5**: 91, **5**: 93, **5**: 95, **5**: 96
   geothermal direct heat utilization, **7**: 169, **7**: 171, **7**: 174*f*, **7**: 180, **7**: 181*f*, **7**: 182, **7**: 184, **7**: 184*f*
disturbances: turbine electrical networks, **2**: 593
ditch construction, **6**: 423
diurnal breezes, **2**: 82
diverse parabolic troughs, **3**: 177, **3**: 185
diverse solar dishes, **3**: 177, **3**: 185, **3**: 205
diversification: geothermal energy, **7**: 281
diversion schemes:
   Horseshoe Bend hydroelectric scheme, **6**: 474
   Three Gorges Project, China, **6**: 205, **6**: 206, **6**: 207
divided fall projects, **6**: 22*f*, **6**: 23
Dixence hydroelectricity project, Switzerland, **6**: 350
Dja Faunal Natural Reserve, Cameroon, Africa, **6**: 141
Dja River, Cameroon, Africa, **6**: 141
DLFC *see* direct liquid fuel cells
DLR *see* Deutsche Forschungsanstalt für Luft und Raumfahrt
DLTS *see* deep level transient spectroscopy
DMFC *see* direct methanol fuel cells
DML *see* dimethyl ether
DNI *see* direct normal irradiation
DNS *see* direct numerical simulation
Dobson Unit: solar resource, **3**: 27
documentation:
   hydrogen storage, **4**: 130
   wind power, **2**: 425
domestic heat pump classification, **3**: 501
domestic hot water (DHW), **3: 419–447**
   active solar systems, **3**: 456
   apartment housing, **3**: 443
   circulation, **3**: 426, **3**: 428*f*
   components, **3**: 420, **3**: 426, **3**: 428*f*
   concepts, solar water heating systems, **3**: 426
   design principles, **3**: 438

dual solar assisted heat pumps, 3: 515
  forced circulation, 3: 426
  households, 3: 442
  multi-family housing, 3: 443
  natural circulation, 3: 426, 3: 428f
  parallel solar assisted heat pumps, 3: 511
  single-family housing, 3: 442
  solar space heating, 3: 456
  solar water heating systems, 3: 419–447
  technologies, 3: 425
donor atoms, 1: 293
donor materials:
  artificial leaves, 1: 670
  organic solar cells, 1: 440, 1: 448, 1: 451, 1: 457
Don Quixote's windmills, 2: 48, 2: 48f
doping:
  metal oxide low-emittance coatings, 3: 316, 3: 325
  solar energy conversion principles, 1: 293, 1: 300
Doppler anemometers, 2: 76
double fed induction generators, 2: 284, 2: 339, 2: 353, 2: 370
double-flash power plants, 7: 207, 7: 217, 7: 217f, 7: 219, 7: 220
double glazing, 3: 124, 3: 124t, 3: 314
double-line ship lock, 6: 223
double-sided flat-plate collectors, 3: 152–153, 3: 153f
double silver layer low-emittance coatings, 3: 327
downconversion, 1: 549–561
  carrier multiplication, 1: 549
  efficiency, 1: 549–561
  equivalent circuits, 1: 550
  multi-exciton generation, 1: 549, 1: 557
  multiple exciton generation, 1: 549, 1: 554
  photovoltaics, 1: 549–561, 1: 9, 1: 549
  practical applications, 1: 554
  quantum cutting, 1: 549, 1: 555
  singlet fission, 1: 549, 1: 559
  single threshold solar cells, 1: 549–561
  space separated quantum cutting, 1: 555
downdraft fixed bed gasifiers, 5: 136
downhole pumps, 7: 176, 7: 177f
down-shifting, 1: 563–585
  commercial applications, 1: 580
  incident light, 1: 563–585
  lanthanides, 1: 566, 1: 573
  luminescence, 1: 563–585
  organic dyes, 1: 578
  patents, 1: 580
  photovoltaics, 1: 563–585, 1: 9, 1: 519
  quantum dots, 1: 566–567, 1: 575
  quantum size effects, 1: 576
  rare earths, 1: 566, 1: 573
  simulation methods, 1: 571
  spectral response modeling, 1: 571
downstream flow, 6: 56, 6: 237
downstream scouring, 6: 212
downstream surge, 6: 370, 6: 375f
DOWNWIND see Distant Offshore Wind Farms with No Visual Impact in Deepwater
downwind rotor configurations, 2: 255
DPSIR see Driver, Pressure, State, Impact, Response
draft cooling systems, 3: 598, 3: 600
draft tube efficiency, 6: 444, 6: 456
drag: wind turbines, 2: 102
drainage basins, 6: 343, 6: 345f
drain-back collectors, 3: 433, 3: 433f, 3: 476, 3: 477f
drain-down direct circulation systems, 3: 450, 3: 451f
drain-down indirect water heating systems, 3: 451, 3: 452f
Drax: biomass cofiring, 5: 68
dredging, 6: 366
drilling:
  geothermal wells, 7: 21
  molten rocks, 7: 57
  Theistareykir, NE Iceland, 7: 158

Driver, Pressure, State, Impact, Response (DPSIR) analytical framework, 6: 355–376
drivers:
  biomass-to-liquids technology, 5: 157, 5: 157f, 5: 187
  hydropower sediment management, 6: 357, 6: 365
  photovoltaic cost reductions, 1: 49, 1: 52
  wind power global markets, 2: 657–669
drives:
  high concentration solar collectors, 3: 177, 3: 196
  hydrogen vehicles, 4: 63
drying:
  see also solar drying
  agricultural applications, 3: 579, 7: 169, 7: 173t, 7: 174, 7: 176f, 7: 180, 7: 180f, 7: 181, 7: 182, 7: 183f
  biomass-to-liquids technology, 5: 163
  concrete structure durability, 6: 381
  geothermal direct heat utilization, 7: 169, 7: 173t, 7: 174, 7: 176f, 7: 180, 7: 180f, 7: 181, 7: 182, 7: 183f
  hydrogen fuel cells, 4: 2, 4: 6f
  industrial applications, 3: 579
  solar thermal systems, 3: 579, 7: 169, 7: 173t, 7: 174, 7: 176f, 7: 180, 7: 180f, 7: 181, 7: 182, 7: 183f
dry-steam power plants:
  condensers, 7: 214
  cooling towers, 7: 209–210, 7: 211f, 7: 215
  generators, 7: 209, 7: 211f, 7: 214
  geothermal energy, 7: 207, 7: 209, 7: 279
  moisture removal, 7: 211
  pumps, 7: 216
  systems analysis, 7: 211
  turbines, 7: 209, 7: 211f, 7: 212
  water-cooling towers, 7: 209–210, 7: 211f, 7: 215
dry tower multiport intake towers, 6: 88
DSEAR see Dangerous Substances and Explosive Atmosphere Regulations
DSM see demand-side management
DTC see differential temperature controllers
dual admission turbines, 7: 208
dual fluid cycles, 7: 228
dual fluidized bed gasifiers, 5: 138, 5: 150, 5: 169t, 5: 171
dual fuel operation:
  biofuels, 5: 349
  combustion, 5: 350
  engine configuration ranges, 5: 349
  fuels, 5: 350
  gaseous biofuels, 5: 351
  operational experience, 5: 350
  stationary engines, 5: 350
dual photovoltaic/thermal solar collectors, 3: 286
dual pressure cycles, 7: 227
dual source solar assisted heat pumps, 3: 516
dual-way five-step ship locks, 6: 193
duct system solar assisted heat pumps, 3: 520
Duero System, 6: 336
Duhring charts, 3: 466, 3: 468f
durability:
  combined heat and power systems, 4: 252
  concrete hydropower structure, 6: 377–403
  gas diffusion electrodes, 4: 169
  solid oxide fuel cells, 4: 252
dust exposure, 5: 41, 5: 69
Dutch windmills, 2: 47
DX SAHP see direct expansion solar-assisted heat pump
dyes:
  dye-sensitized solar cells, 1: 491
  luminescent solar concentrators, 1: 593
dye-sensitized solar cells, 1: 481–496, 1: 9
  cell efficiency, 1: 487
  characteristics, 1: 487
  component development, 1: 490
  counter electrodes, 1: 486, 1: 492
  current status, 1: 482
  current-voltage measurements, 1: 487

dye-sensitized solar cells (*continued*)
   device development, **1**: 490
   dyes, **1**: 491
   efficiency, **1**: 487, **1**: 488
   electrodes, **1**: 490
   electrolytes, **1**: 492
   electron injection, **1**: 485
   electron loss reactions, **1**: 486
   electron-transfer, kinetic models, **1**: 484
   excited state decay, **1**: 485
   external quantum efficiencies, **1**: 488
   future directions, **1**: 494
   incident photon-to-current conversion efficiency, **1**: 488
   internal quantum efficiencies, **1**: 488
   kinetic models, **1**: 484
   material component development, **1**: 490
   mesoporous oxide working electrodes, **1**: 490
   module development, **1**: 492
   molecular structure, **1**: 482, **1**: 483f, **1**: 487, **1**: 487f
   operating principles, **1**: 482
   oxide working electrodes, **1**: 490
   quantum efficiencies, **1**: 488
   redox mediator transport, **1**: 486
   structure, **1**: 482, **1**: 483f, **1**: 487, **1**: 487f
   technology progress, **1**: 26
   toolbox concept, **1**: 489
dynamic analysis:
   wind energy speed, **2**: 87
   wind turbine mechanical-dynamic loads, **2**: 244
dynamic inflow, **2**: 230
dynamic modeling: geothermal energy, **7**: 31
dynamic programming: passive solar architecture, **3**: 655
dynamic security: wind park design penetration, **2**: 208
dynamic similarity: ocean wave energy, **8**: 85
dynamic voltage balancing, **4**: 303
dynamic wake, **2**: 230
Dynamotive, Canada: pyrolysis, **5**: 148

E

early cracking, **6**: 380
early solar energy history, **3**: 86
early wind energy history, **2**: 49
Earth:
   atmosphere, **3**: 34, **3**: 54
   Earth Summit, **7**: 273–274, **7**: 274
   heat transport, **7**: 84
   net solar radiation, **3**: 54
   solar radiation, **3**: 34, **3**: 54
   Sun, **1**: 215
earth cofferdams, **6**: 206, **6**: 207
earthfill embankment dams, **6**: 29
earthquakes, **6**: 217, **7**: 285
East African desalination, **2**: 735
Eastmain-1, Quebec, Canada, **6**: 162–163, **6**: 166f, **6**: 167
Eastmain–Sarcelle–Rupert Diversion Project, Quebec, Canada, **6**: 167
east-west tracking: moving surface incidence angles, **3**: 14, **3**: 16, **3**: 17
EBPT *see* energy payback time
EBSD *see* electron back scatter diffraction
ebullating bed slurry reactors, **5**: 181
EC *see* European Commission
ecliptic planes: solar resource, **3**: 27
ECMWF *see* European Centre for Medium-Range Weather Forecasts
ecology:
   bioenergy policy development, **5**: 417
   hydropower discharge, **6**: 56
   Japanese hydropower, **6**: 298, **6**: 299, **6**: 305
   Three Gorges Project, China, **6**: 213
   very large-scale photovoltaic systems, **1**: 738
economic indexes, **2**: 211

economics:
   agricultural solar applications, **3**: 569
   biochar, **5**: 382
   biodiesel, **5**: 218
   bioenergy policy development, **5**: 417, **5**: 424
   biomass combined heat and power, **5**: 90, **5**: 90t, **5**: 94, **5**: 95
   biomass power generation, **5**: 29
   biomass-to-liquids technology, **5**: 167, **5**: 191, **5**: 203
   capacity factor, **4**: 45, **4**: 53
   combined heat and power, **5**: 90, **5**: 90t, **5**: 94, **5**: 95
   concentrating solar power, **3**: 629
   dams, **6**: 270
   desalination, **2**: 736
   developing country photovoltaics, **1**: 113, **1**: 120
   economic indexes, **2**: 211
   electricity generation, **2**: **469–501**, **2**: 555, **6**: 6
   embedded generation benefits, wind energy, **2**: 484, **2**: 486
   end-use hydrogen technology, **4**: 58
   energy chains, hydrogen technology, **4**: 47
   fuel cells, **4**: **45–75**, **4**: 45
   geothermal energy, **7**: 1–2, **7**: **259–270**, **7**: 274, **7**: 280, **7**: 286
   global wind energy markets, **2**: 542
   high concentration solar collectors, **3**: 206
   hydrogen technology, **4**: **45–75**
      automotives, **5**: 312
      capacity factor, **4**: 45, **4**: 53
      end-use applications, **4**: 58
      end-use technologies, **4**: 58
      energy chains, **4**: 47
      fuel cells, **4**: **45–75**, **4**: 45
      infrastructure, **4**: 52
      production, **4**: 48
      storage, **4**: 55
   hydropower, **6**: 6
      essential features, **6**: 21, **6**: 24
      India, **6**: 229, **6**: 251
      Iran, **6**: 253, **6**: 258
      multibenefit solutions, **6**: 21, **6**: 24, **6**: 40, **6**: 45
      sustainability, **6**: 50
   Indian hydropower, **6**: 229, **6**: 251
   industrial solar applications, **3**: 569
   infrastructure, hydrogen technology, **4**: 52
   Mekin hydropower project, Cameroon, Africa, **6**: 144, **6**: 145
   ocean energy, **8**: **151–169**, **8**: 3, **8**: 3f
   offshore wind, **2**: 459, **2**: 478, **2**: 480
   onshore wind, **2**: 475
   photovoltaics, **1**: 5, **1**: 7, **1**: 113, **1**: 120, **1**: 725, **3**: 269
   power generation, biomass and biofuels, **5**: 29
   pretreatments, **5**: 167
   primary forest residues, **5**: 284
   product-integrated photovoltaics, **1**: 725
   production, hydrogen technology, **4**: 48
   pumped-storage power plants, **6**: 287
   sediment management, **6**: 370
   solar desalination, **3**: 564
   solar power satellites, **1**: 772
   solar thermal systems, **3**: 6, **3**: 569
      agricultural applications, **3**: 569
      energy storage, **3**: 228
      industrial applications, **3**: 569
      renewable energy technology, **3**: 6
      water heating systems, **3**: 436, **3**: 438f
   storage, hydrogen technology, **4**: 55
   sustainable geothermal energy, **7**: 274, **7**: 280, **7**: 286
   technical evaluation, wind energy, **2**: **469–501**
   thermal energy storage, **3**: 227, **3**: 228
   Three Gorges Project, China, **6**: 211
   vegetable oil, **5**: 218
   very large-scale photovoltaics, **1**: 733, **1**: 734t, **1**: 736, **1**: 739
   wind energy, **2**: 542, **2**: 555
      desalination, **2**: 736
      documentation, **2**: 426
      electricity generation, **2**: **469–501**, **2**: 555

electricity production, **2**: 555
embedded generation benefits, **2**: 484, **2**: 486
offshore wind, **2**: 459, **2**: 478, **2**: 480
onshore wind, **2**: 475
planet energy balance, **2**: **11–39**
policy, **2**: 542
power design and implementation, **2**: 420, **2**: 422, **2**: 423, **2**: 426
technical evaluation, **2**: **469–501**
wind park design, **2**: 169, **2**: 170, **2**: 177, **2**: 210
wind turbine evolution, **2**: 100
wind power, **2**: 420, **2**: **469–501**, **2**: 422, **2**: 423, **2**: 426
economies of scale:
   biomass-to-liquids technology, **5**: 196, **5**: 196f
   photovoltaic cost reductions, **1**: 50
   wind energy electricity network costs, **2**: 488
ecosystems *see* ecology
EcoTerra home: design, **3**: 394
Edea plant, **6**: 131, **6**: 133f, **6**: 133t, **6**: 134, **6**: 134t
edge insulation, **3**: 104, **3**: 113, **3**: 132
edge isolation, **1**: 362
EDLC *see* electric double-layer capacitors
education:
   hydrogen storage safety, **4**: 125
   Millennium Development Goals, **7**: 288
   proton-exchange membrane fuel cells, **4**: 202
EEA *see* European Environment Agency
EF *see* entrained flow; exciton fission
effective photovoltaic support mechanisms, **1**: 78
effective thermal capacity, **3**: 145
efficiency:
   see also conversion efficiency; electrical efficiency; quantum efficiency
   air turbines, **8**: 127, **8**: 127f
   cells
      concentration photovoltaics, **1**: 746, **1**: 747f
      dye-sensitized solar cells, **1**: 487
      photovoltaic technology progress, **1**: 20, **1**: 20f
   collectors
      solar cooling systems, **3**: 462, **3**: 462f
      solar water heating systems, **3**: 430, **3**: 431f
      stationary collectors, **3**: 138, **3**: 141
   combined heat and power systems, **4**: 250, **4**: 252
   concentrating solar power, **3**: 596, **3**: 602
   crystalline silicon cells, **1**: **353–387**
   diffuse reflectors, **3**: 281
   donor molecules, **1**: 457
   downconversion, **1**: **549–561**
   down-shifting
      organic dyes, **1**: 579
      quantum dots, **1**: 576
      rare earth elements, **1**: 574
      spectral response modeling, **1**: 571
   dye-sensitized solar cells, **1**: 487, **1**: 488
   flow rate coefficients, **8**: 127, **8**: 127f
   Fresnel collectors, **3**: 196
   fuel cells, **4**: 335
   high concentration solar collectors, **3**: 168, **3**: 178, **3**: 187, **3**: 196, **3**: 202
   hydrogen technology, **4**: 250, **4**: 252, **4**: 335
   hydropower, **6**: 10, **6**: 20
   low-temperature stationary collectors, **3**: 138, **3**: 141
   luminescent solar concentrators, **1**: 588, **1**: 589, **1**: 595, **1**: 596
   multi-junction cells, **1**: **497–514**
   open-loop models, **3**: 384
   organic dye-based down-shifting, **1**: 579
   organic solar cells, **1**: 440, **1**: 440t, **1**: 450, **1**: 457
   parabolic troughs, high concentration solar collectors, **3**: 178
   photovoltaics, **3**: 259, **3**: 261
      diffuse reflectors, **3**: 281
      downconversion, **1**: **549–561**
      micro-and nanotechnologies, **1**: 515
      modules, **1**: 684
      multi-junction cells, **1**: **497–514**
      organic solar cells, **1**: 440, **1**: 440t, **1**: 450, **1**: 457
      technology progress, **1**: 19, **1**: 19f
      thermal solar collectors, **3**: 259, **3**: 261, **3**: 278
      upconversion, **1**: **533–548**
   quantum dots, **1**: 576, **1**: 631, **1**: 632
   rare earth elements, **1**: 574
   ratios, geothermal power plants, **7**: 207, **7**: 208, **7**: 235
   receivers, **3**: 187
   simplified generic axial-flow microhydro turbines, **6**: 443, **6**: 444
   solar cooling, **3**: **481–494**
   solar dishes, **3**: 200, **3**: 202
   solar energy conversion principles, **1**: 294
   solid oxide fuel cells, **4**: 250, **4**: 252
   spectral response modeling, **1**: 571
   tests, photovoltaic/thermal solar collectors, **3**: 278
   upconversion, **1**: **533–548**
   wind energy, **2**: 743
effluent water monitoring, **7**: 111
egg-beater windmills, **2**: 672
E_g losses, **1**: 309, **1**: 310
EGS *see* enhanced geothermal systems
Egypt: solar energy utilization, **1**: 31, **3**: 634
EIA *see* environmental impact assessments
Einstein, Albert: photovoltaics, historical developments, **1**: 34, **1**: 35f
ejector cooling systems, **3**: 489
elapsed time capital costs, **8**: 167
electrical characteristics: wind energy testing, **2**: 380
electrical components:
   photovoltaic/thermal solar collectors, **3**: 271
   wind turbine modeling, **2**: 336
electrical conductors, **3**: 343–344, **3**: 344
electrical conversion: absorbed solar radiation, **3**: 259
electrical efficiency:
   biomass combined heat and power, **5**: 90, **5**: 90t
   open-loop models, **3**: 384
   photovoltaic/thermal solar collectors, **3**: 283f, **3**: 284f
electrical grounding, **4**: 125
electrical infrastructures: ocean energy capital costs, **8**: 157
electrical insulators: hydrogen safety engineering, **4**: 81
electrical performance: photovoltaic/thermal solar collectors, **3**: 261
electrical priority operation (EPO), **3**: 261
electrical properties: chalcopyrite thin films, **1**: 403
electrical resistivity, **7**: 61
electrical space heating, **2**: 497
electrical systems:
   grid-connected wind turbines, **2**: **269–269**
   hydropower multibenefit solutions, **6**: 40
   small wind turbines, **2**: 301
   wind turbines, **2**: **269–269**
      control, **2**: 272
      generators, **2**: 279, **2**: 281
      industry, **2**: 306
      manufacturers, **2**: 306
      power control, **2**: 272
electrical vehicles:
   battery hybrid energy storage, **4**: 317
   biomass and biofuels, **5**: 307, **5**: 308
   carbon dioxide emissions, **5**: 308
   dense battery hybrid energy storage, **4**: 317
   energy requirements, **4**: 318
   fuel cells, **4**: 317, **4**: 333
   hybrid energy storage, **4**: 317
   hydrogen fuel cells, **4**: 317, **4**: 333
   PEM fuel cells, **4**: 317
   power requirements, **4**: 318
   wind energy, **2**: 496
electrical water heating, **2**: 497
electrical works: Mekin hydropower project, Cameroon, Africa, **6**: 143
electric double-layer capacitors (EDLC), **1**: 204, **1**: 204f, **1**: 205

electricity:
   see also electrical...; grid...; hydroelectricity; photovoltaics; solar photovoltaic electricity
   balancing strategies, 2: 718
   biomass
      combined heat and power, 5: 87–97
      wind energy policy, 2: 552
   Brazilian sugarcane industry, 5: 20
   Cameroon, Africa, 6: 132
   capacity, 2: 14
   combined heat and power, biomass, 5: 87–97
   cooling, concentrating solar power, 3: 611–612
   demand, 3: 421, 3: 421f, 6: 161
   demand management, wind energy policy, 2: 556
   demand side, wind energy policy, 2: 556
   economic growth, Japanese hydropower history, 6: 270
   fuel cells, hydrogen technology, 4: 331–340
   future visions, photovoltaics, 1: 189
   generation
      active power control, 2: 582
      cogeneration, 4: 214
      commercial ocean wave energy, 8: 4
      costs
         current status, 2: 477
         onshore wind, 2: 477
         photovoltaic future visions, 1: 195
         technical evaluation, 2: 469–501
         wind energy, 2: 469–501, 2: 612
      current state of art ocean wave energy, 8: 1–6
      device development, 8: 4
      distribution, 6: 2, 6: 3, 6: 3f
      economics, 2: 469–501, 2: 555, 6: 6
      fuel cell current status, 4: 33
      future prospects, 8: 5
      historical overviews, 2: 52, 2: 54
      loads, 2: 579
      mechanisms, microbial fuel cells, 4: 265
      ocean wave energy, 8: 1–6
         commercial farms, 8: 4
         current state of art, 8: 1–6
         device development, 8: 4
         future prospects, 8: 5
         prototypes, 8: 4
         technology development assessments, 8: 3
         wave farm development, 8: 4
      operating states, 2: 581
      operational objectives, 2: 581
      planet energy balance, 2: 14
      planning, 2: 596
      prototypes, 8: 4
      simplified generic axial-flow microhydro turbines, 6: 444
      stationary power, 4: 208
      technology development assessments, 8: 3
      voltage control, 2: 585
      wave currents, 8: 1–6
      wave farm development, 8: 4
      wind energy
         costs, 2: 469–501, 2: 612
         economics, 2: 469–501, 2: 555
         historical overviews, 2: 52, 2: 54
         integration, 2: 571
         planning, 2: 596
      worldwide evolution, 2: 15
   geothermal energy, 7: 1
   hybrid systems, stand alone, wind energy, 2: 623–655
   hydrogen technology
      fuel cells, 4: 331–340
      policy development, 4: 69
      stationary power, 4: 334
   Iran, 6: 253–264
   long-distance transmission, 6: 266
   markets
      economics, 2: 542
      wind energy policy, 2: 542, 2: 546
   networks
      backup reserves, 2: 489
      connection, 2: 209
      costs, 2: 612
      demand fluctuations, 2: 488
      distribution networks, 2: 602
      disturbances, 2: 593
      economies of scale, 2: 488
      frequency variations, 2: 593
      future trends, 2: 617
      harmonics, 2: 595
      integrating wind energy, 2: 569–622
      interaction disturbances, 2: 593
      microgrids, 2: 571, 2: 592–593, 2: 600, 2: 607
      operation, 2: 581, 2: 596
      operational reserve, 2: 488
      phase voltage imbalance, 2: 594
      planning, 2: 596
      plant margins, 2: 489
      reserve costs, 2: 489
      transmission networks, 2: 602
      variability costs, 2: 488
      voltage flicker, 2: 594
      voltage variations, 2: 594
      wind energy
         costs, 2: 612
         distribution networks, 2: 602
         integration, 2: 569–622
         microgrids, 2: 571, 2: 592–593, 2: 600, 2: 607
         operation, 2: 581, 2: 596
         planning, 2: 596
         repercussions, 2: 596
         requirements, 2: 613
         transmission networks, 2: 602
         variability costs, 2: 488
         wind park connection, 2: 209
      wind turbines
         disturbances, 2: 593
         frequency variations, 2: 593
         harmonics, 2: 595
         interaction disturbances, 2: 593
         phase voltage imbalance, 2: 594
         planning, 2: 596
         voltage flicker, 2: 594
         voltage variations, 2: 594
   policy
      hydrogen technology, 4: 69
      wind energy, 2: 542, 2: 546, 2: 552, 2: 555
   postwar reorganization, 6: 269
   prices, current status, 1: 181
   production
      1970 onwards, 6: 1–2, 6: 2f
      calculations, wind park design, 2: 196
      costs, 7: 259–270
      economics, wind energy, 2: 555
      geothermal energy, 7: 259–270
      hydropower multibenefit solutions, 6: 15–47
      investment factors, 7: 259–270
      maximization, wind park design, 2: 169, 2: 169–170, 2: 171
      offshore wind power, 2: 431–468
      wind energy economics, 2: 555
      wind park design, 2: 169, 2: 169–170, 2: 171, 2: 196
      wind turbine electrical systems, 2: 279
   rapid economic growth, 6: 270
   shortages, 6: 269
   stand alone hybrid wind energy systems, 2: 623–655
   stationary power, hydrogen technology, 4: 334
   storage
      applications, 6: 407
      benefits, 6: 406
      concept, 6: 406
      deployment barriers, 6: 406

discharge times, **6**: 409t, **6**: 409–410
distributed generation, **6**: 408
distribution stabilization, **6**: 408
end use applications, **6**: 410
general issues, **6**: 406
load management, **6**: 408
location, **6**: 407
solar thermal energy storage, **3**: 225t
spinning reserve, **6**: 408
system location, **6**: 407
transmission stabilization, **6**: 408
transmission upgrades deferral, **6**: 408
voltage regulation, **6**: 408
transmission, **6**: 266
transportation, **6**: 132
unit values, **8**: 163
wholesale markets, **2**: 557
wind energy
balance, **2**: 3, **2**: 4f
hybrid systems, stand alone, **2**: **623–655**
policy, **2**: 542, **2**: 546, **2**: 552, **2**: 555
biomass, **2**: 552
stand alone hybrid systems, **2**: **623–655**
variability, **2**: 588
electric sector: historical overviews, **6**: 94
electrification:
automotives, **5**: 307, **5**: 308
ICE hybridization, **5**: 308
photovoltaics in rural areas, **1**: 114
electrochemistry, **4**: 10
electrochromogenics:
devices
active films, **3**: 344
coloration mechanisms, **3**: 343
glazing, **3**: 314, **3**: 316, **3**: 336, **3**: 338, **3**: 342, **3**: 343
materials, **3**: 344, **3**: 346, **3**: 347t
operating principles, **3**: 343
performance, **3**: 346
properties, **3**: 346, **3**: 347t
solar thermal energy, **3**: 314, **3**: 316, **3**: 336, **3**: 338, **3**: 342, **3**: 343
structure, **3**: 343, **3**: 343f, **3**: 343–344
transparent conductive films, **3**: 343–344, **3**: 344
materials
glazing, **3**: 314, **3**: 316, **3**: 336, **3**: 338, **3**: 342, **3**: 343
ion storage, **3**: 345
magnesium fluoride, **3**: 346
molybdenum oxide, **3**: 345
protective layers, **3**: 345
Prussian blue, **3**: 345
solar thermal energy, **3**: 314, **3**: 316, **3**: 336, **3**: 338, **3**: 342, **3**: 343
tungsten oxide, **3**: 344
vanadium pentoxide, **3**: 345
windows
emerging technologies, **3**: 336
evacuated glazing, **3**: 338
solar thermal energy, **3**: 314, **3**: 316, **3**: 336, **3**: 338, **3**: 342, **3**: 343
electrodes:
see also gas diffusion electrodes
biological fuel cells, **4**: 261
design, **4**: 166
durability, **4**: 169
dye-sensitized solar cells, **1**: 490
enzymes, **4**: 261
fabrication, **4**: 166, **4**: 168
materials, **1**: 456
modeling, **4**: 167
organic solar cells, **1**: 456, **1**: 466
proton-exchange membrane fuel cells, **4**: 190
electrodialysis, **3**: 529, **3**: 536, **3**: 537, **3**: 538f, **3**: 540f, **3**: 541f, **3**: 547

electrodialysis reversal, **3**: 529
electrofuels: automotives, **5**: 328, **5**: 335
electrolysis, **4**: 45, **4**: 48, **4**: 273
electrolytes:
alkaline fuel cells, **4**: 170
definitions, **4**: 241
dye-sensitized solar cells, **1**: 492
hydrogen technology, **4**: 246
molten carbonate fuel cells, **4**: 227, **4**: 230
proton-exchange membrane fuel cells, **4**: 185
resistivity, **7**: 78
solid oxide fuel cells, **4**: 246
electrolyzers, **4**: 2, **4**: 5f, **4**: 103
electromagnetism:
communication interference, **2**: 524
induction generators, **2**: 279, **2**: 281
interference, **2**: 182, **2**: 524
resistivity methods, **7**: 61, **7**: 62, **7**: 65
wind turbine control systems, **2**: 330, **2**: 331f
electromechanics, **6**: 143
electron back scatter diffraction (EBSD), **1**: 405, **1**: 405f
electron beam gun evaporation, **3**: 324
electronic conversions: product-integrated photovoltaics, **1**: 724
electronics:
fuel cells, **4**: 36, **4**: **295–329**
hydrogen technology fuel cells, **4**: 36, **4**: **295–329**
wind energy stand alone hybrid systems, **2**: 632
wind turbine power electronics, **2**: **269–269**, **2**: **329–370**
electrons:
energy levels see bandgaps
excitation, **1**: 363
injection, **1**: 485
loss reactions, **1**: 486
microscopy, **7**: 98
pathways, **4**: 162
ratios, **1**: 363
state density, **1**: 298, **1**: 299, **1**: 300f
state occupation, **1**: 299
transfer, **1**: 484, **1**: 664, **4**: 260
volts, **1**: 214
electrostatic precipitation, **5**: 145
Elenco fuel cell system, **4**: 174
elevation changes: geothermal energy hazards, **7**: 58
eligibility: photovoltaic promotion schemes, **1**: 94
Elkem AS, **1**: 175
El Villar power plant, **1**: 751, **1**: 751t, **1**: 752f, **1**: 752t
EMA see Energy Market Authority
embankment dams, **6**: 28
embedded generation benefits: wind energy, **2**: 484, **2**: 486
embedded nanoparticles, **1**: 650
embedded spiral case structures, **6**: 191, **6**: 221
embodied energy: definition, **2**: 671
embrittlement, **4**: 117, **4**: 129, **7**: 243
EMEC see European Marine Energy Centre
emerging technologies: coatings/glazings, **3**: 316, **3**: 336, **3**: 339, **3**: 342
Emerson, William, **2**: 50
Emirate of Abu Dhabi, **3**: 634
emissions:
see also gaseous emissions; greenhouse gases
alcohol fuel safety, **5**: 325
biomass-to-liquids technology, **5**: 167, **5**: 167f, **5**: 168f, **5**: 197, **5**: 200, **5**: 201
carbon, **4**: 291, **4**: 296
concentrating solar power, **3**: 630
direct heat utilization, **7**: 179
geothermal direct heat utilization, **7**: 179
limits, **5**: 31, **5**: 33
losses, **1**: 309, **1**: 311
toxicity, **5**: 325
vegetable oil biodiesel, **5**: 227
emissivity: selective coatings, **3**: 301

emittance:
    absorber coatings, 3: 110, 3: 110f, 3: 111t
    passive solar urban architecture, 3: 644
    selective coatings, 3: 301
emitters:
    n-type silicon cells, photovoltaics, 1: 380
    passivation, 1: 371
    photovoltaics, *n*-type silicon cells, 1: 380
    thermophotovoltaic energy conversion, 1: 603, 1: 604, 1: 615
    wrap-through cells, 1: 374
empirical distribution methods, 2: 120, 8: 61
empirical solar radiation models, 1: 214
employment:
    Brazilian bioethanol development, 5: 22, 5: 23
    displaced workers, 5: 22
    wind power social benefits/impacts, 2: 507, 2: 508
    wind turbine time evolution, 2: 704, 2: 706f
empowerment of women: Millennium Development Goals, 7: 276
EN 14214 standard specification, 5: 225
encapsulation: organic solar cells, 1: 465
enclosed thermal radiation work, 1: 328
enclosures: flat-plate collectors, 3: 104, 3: 113
Endesa, 6: 315
endoreversible models, 1: 335, 1: 337
endotoxins, 5: 69
end-use applications:
    electrical energy storage, 6: 410
    hydrogen technology
        economics, 4: 58
        transport, 4: 61, 4: 62, 4: 63
Eneas, Aubrey G., 3: 92, 3: 92f
Enercon: wind turbines, 2: 275f, 2: 290, 2: 309, 2: 309f, 2: 310f
energy: definitions, 6: 1, 6: 16
energy balance:
    biofuels, 5: 114
    biomass-to-liquids technology, 5: 163–164, 5: 164f, 5: 165, 5: 165f
    carbon dioxide emissions, 2: 22
    coal, 2: 20
    concentrating solar power, 3: 597
    environmental impacts, 2: 22
    equations
        air heat recovery, 3: 272
        flat-type photovoltaic/thermal collectors, 3: 270, 3: 272
        lithium–water absorption systems, 3: 468
        water-cooled photovoltaic/thermal solar collectors, 3: 270
    flat-plate low-temperature stationary collectors, 3: 129
    fossil fuel status, 2: 17, 2: 21
    global wind energy markets, 2: **11–39**
    low-temperature stationary collectors, 3: 129
    natural gas, 2: 20
    oil data, 2: 17
    product-integrated photovoltaics, 1: 723
    pyrolysis, 5: 165, 5: 165f
    solar cooking, 3: 589
    wind energy global markets, 2: **11–39**
energy chains: hydrogen economics, 4: 47
energy conservation equation, 3: 303
energy consumption: historical trends, 6: 1, 6: 2f
energy content:
    biochar, 5: 374–375
    geothermal energy, 7: 9, 7: 16
energy conversion:
    absorption, 1: 296
    carbon emissions, hydrogen technology, fuel cells, 4: 296
    far-field thermophotovoltaics, 1: 613
    Fischer–Tropsch process, 5: 168f
    geothermal energy power plants, 7: **207–237**, 7: 207
    low carbon emissions, hydrogen technology, fuel cells, 4: 296
    micron-gap thermophotovoltaics, 1: 613
    performance monitoring, photovoltaics, 1: 775, 1: 776
    photovoltaics, 1: **293–313**, 1: 8, 1: 9
        performance monitoring, 1: 775, 1: 776
        thermal solar collectors, 3: 259

radioisotope thermophotovoltaics, 1: 613
resources assessments, 1: **213–237**
solar energy, photovoltaics, 1: **293–313**, 1: 8
solar radiation, 1: **213–237**
thermal radiation, 1: 328
thermophotovoltaics, 1: **603–618**, 1: 9, 1: 603
energy costs: wind power design and implementation, 2: 424
energy crops:
    biomass cofiring, 5: 57, 5: 67t
    woody biomass feedstocks, 5: **263–291**
energy density, 4: 81
energy-dispersive X-ray spectroscopy, 7: 99
energy dissipation: Chinese hydropower projects, 6: 186, 6: 485, 6: 486t, 6: 487
energy evaluation: glazing/window thermal properties, 3: 321
energy fluxes: diluted thermal radiation, 1: 322–323
energy fuel mix: wind energy, 2: 11
energy grade lines, 6: 18, 6: 19f
Energy Market Authority (EMA), Singapore, 1: 80
energy markets:
    bioenergy policy development, 5: 413–414, 5: 415, 5: 415–416, 5: 417, 5: 418, 5: 424
    wind energy policy, 2: 542
energy mix:
    hydrogen fuel cells, 4: **331–340**
    wind energy, 2: 11
energy pattern factor method, 2: 122
energy payback ratios, 6: 6, 6: 8f
energy-payback times (EPBT), 1: 147, 1: 436, 1: 737, 1: 738f, 2: 1
energy performance: photovoltaic standards, 1: 795
energy periods: ocean energy, 8: 79
energy piles: geothermal heat pumps, 7: 191
energy potential: very large-scale photovoltaic systems, 1: 734
energy predictions: photovoltaic performance monitoring, 1: 778
energy prices: wind energy, 2: 470, 2: 471, 2: 472, 2: 478
energy production:
    ocean energy, 8: 162
    wind turbine energy yields, 2: 115, 2: 132
energy productivity: geothermal wells, 7: 19
energy rating: photovoltaic standards, 1: 795
energy recovery: desalination, definitions, 3: 529
energy-related environmental problems: solar thermal systems, 3: 3
energy requirements:
    desalination, 2: 729
    urban electric vehicles, 4: 318
energy rose: wind power, 2: 399, 2: 411
energy savings: solar thermal energy storage, 3: 227
energy seasonal storage: solar assisted heat pumps, 3: 519
energy security:
    geothermal energy, 7: **271–295**, 7: 272
    hydrogen fuel cells, 4: 332, 4: 333f
    very large-scale photovoltaic systems, 1: 733, 1: 734t
    wind energy policy, 2: **541–568**
energy sources: river waters, 6: 268
energy storage:
    agricultural solar applications, 3: 569
    grid impacts, 1: 199, 1: 201
    hydrogen, 4: 22, 4: 221
    industrial solar applications, 3: 569
    management, photovoltaics, 1: 208
    photochemical thermodynamics, 1: 664
    photosynthesis design, photochemical thermodynamics, 1: 664
    photovoltaics, 1: **199–212**
        grid impacts, 1: 199, 1: 201
        management, 1: 208
    proton-exchange membrane fuel cells, 4: 221
    seasonal, 3: 519
    solar assisted heat pumps, 3: 519
    solar thermal systems
        agricultural applications, 3: 569
        components, 3: **211–253**
        industrial applications, 3: 569
    space applications, 4: 22

stand alone hybrid wind energy systems, **2**: 647
wind energy
  mitigating variable costs and effects, **2**: 495
  stand alone hybrid systems, **2**: 647
  wind power penetration, **1**: 201
  wind power repercussions, **2**: 599
Energy Technologies Institute (ETI): ocean wave energy funding, device development, **8**: 83
energy technology:
  photovoltaics
    environmental impacts, **1**: 155
    rural areas, **1**: 115
  rural areas, photovoltaics, **1**: 115
energy transfer: rare earth elements, **1**: 574
energy yields:
  air density variation, **2**: 146
  annual wind energy production estimates, **2**: 134, **2**: 138
  contemporary wind turbines, **2**: **113–168**
  energy production estimation, **2**: 115, **2**: 132
  hub heights, wind turbines, **2**: 144
  instantaneous power output, **2**: 132
  mean power coefficients, **2**: 135, **2**: 136
  power coefficients, **2**: 115, **2**: 116f, **2**: 135, **2**: 136
  power curves, **2**: 127, **2**: 138
  power output parameters, **2**: 140, **2**: 151
  power production estimation, **2**: 115, **2**: 132
  selection techniques, **2**: 158
  technical availability impacts, **2**: 151
  theoretical distributions, **2**: 140
  turbines, **2**: **113–168**
  wake effect impacts, **2**: 149
  wind potential evaluation, **2**: 117
  wind speed distribution, **2**: 117, **2**: 120, **2**: 124, **2**: 144
  wind turbines, **2**: **113–168**
Enerkem: biomass-to-liquids technology, **5**: 190
Enfield-Andreau machines, **2**: 59, **2**: 61f
En fuels, **5**: 343
engineering:
  see also hydrogen safety engineering
  biochar, **5**: 377
  civil engineering infrastructure costs, **8**: 156
  concentration photovoltaics, **1**: 753
  geothermal heat pumps, **7**: 197
engines, **5**: 343–356
  biodiesel novel uses, **5**: 343, **5**: 348
  biodiesel performance, **5**: 226
  biofuel historical perspectives, **5**: 11
  biofuel operation modifications, **5**: 346
  configuration ranges, **5**: 343–356
  diesel-biodiesel blends, **5**: 348
  dual fuel operation, **5**: 349
  historical overviews, **3**: 85, **3**: 91, **5**: 11
  novel uses, **5**: 343–356
  solar energy, history, **3**: 85, **3**: 91
  vegetable oil performance, **5**: 226
enhanced geothermal systems (EGS), **7**: 5, **7**: 22
  power plants, **7**: 207, **7**: 233
ENSYN, Canada, **5**: 148
enthalpy:
  geochemistry, **7**: 138, **7**: 141
  geothermometry, **7**: 138
  solid oxide fuel cells, **4**: 243–244
  thermal radiation thermodynamics, **1**: 328–329
entrained flow (EF) gasifiers:
  biomass, **5**: 136, **5**: 138, **5**: 149
  cofiring, **5**: 63
  reactor types, **5**: 169, **5**: 169t
entrained liquid carryover, **7**: 247
entropy:
  diluted thermal radiation, **1**: 322–323
  ocean wave measurements, **8**: 27
  solid oxide fuel cells, **4**: 243–244
  thermal radiation thermodynamics, **1**: 317, **1**: 318, **1**: 328–329

environment:
  see also climate...; environmental impact...
  acid rain, **3**: 4
  air pollution, **2**: 504
  astronaut missions, **4**: 24
  benefits, wind energy/wind power, **2**: **503–539**
  best practices, Brazilian bioethanol, **5**: 18
  biodiesel, vegetable oil, **5**: 218
  bioenergy policy development, **5**: 419, **5**: 426
  bioethanol development, **5**: 18, **5**: 21
  biomass-to-liquids technology, **5**: 197
  Brazilian bioethanol development, **5**: 18, **5**: 21
  carbonation, **6**: 386–387
  carbon dioxide emissions, **2**: 504
  characteristics
    solar thermal systems, **3**: 7
    sun path diagrams, **3**: 17
  concentrating solar power, **3**: 630
  conservation, Japanese ecosystem mitigation, **6**: 303
  direct heat utilization, **7**: 179
  Eastmain–Sarcelle–Rupert Diversion Project, Quebec, Canada, **6**: 173
  geothermal energy
    cost and investment factors, **7**: 259
    direct heat utilization, **7**: 179
    heat pumps, **7**: 203
    Millennium Development Goals, **7**: 289
  global climate change, **3**: 5
  greenhouse effect, solar thermal systems, **3**: 5
  heavy metal impacts, **1**: 151, **5**: 52
  hydropower, **6**: 9, **6**: 9f
    development and progress, **6**: 9
    India, **6**: 234
    multibenefit solutions, **6**: 41
    sediment management, **6**: 355–376
  Indian hydropower, **6**: 234
  La Romaine Complex, Quebec, Canada, **6**: 165
  laws, high concentration solar collectors, **3**: 206
  loads, wind turbines, **2**: 246–247, **2**: 262
  Millennium Development Goals, **7**: 289
  offshore wind power, **2**: 463
  ozone layer depletion, **3**: 4
  photovoltaics, **1**: 7
    Abu Dhabi desert area, **1**: 694
    reliability testing, **1**: 794
    thermal solar collectors, **3**: 269
  pollutants, **2**: 504
  primary forest residues, **5**: 284
  product-integrated photovoltaics, **1**: 725
  Revelstoke Complex, British Colombia, Canada, **6**: 177
  sediment management, **6**: 355–376
  social benefits/impacts
    air pollution, **2**: 504
    carbon dioxide emissions, **2**: 504
    future trends, **2**: 536
    pollutants, **2**: 504
    water consumption, **2**: 505
    wind energy/wind power, **2**: **503–539**
  solar thermal systems, **3**: 5
    components and applications, **3**: 3
    renewable energy technology, **3**: 5
  Three Gorges Project, China, **6**: 213
  vegetable oil, **5**: 218
  water consumption, **2**: 505
  wind energy/wind power
    benefits/impacts, **2**: **503–539**
    offshore wind power, **2**: 463
    turbines
      loads, **2**: 246–247, **2**: 262
      reduction, **2**: 687
      wind park design, **2**: 186–187
  Wuskwatim Generating Station Project, Manitoba, Canada, **6**: 160

environmental impact assessments (EIA): wind energy/wind power, 2: 397, 2: 426, 2: 511
environmental impacts:
  benefits, wind energy/wind power, 2: **503–539**
  biomass power generation, 5: 51
  cadmium telluride thin films, 1: 436
  carbon dioxide emission energy balance, 2: 22
  development constraints, hydropower, 6: 49–91
  energy balance, carbon dioxide emissions, 2: 22
  energy payback times, photovoltaics, 1: 147
  fauna, 2: 522, 2: 528
  fish-life, 6: 58, 6: 63, 6: 73, 6: 76
  flora, 2: 522
  geothermal energy sustainability, 7: 276, 7: 278, 7: 283, 7: 287, 7: 289
  greenhouse gas emissions, 1: 148
  greenhouse gas life cycle assessments, 5: **109–132**
  heavy metal emissions, photovoltaics, 1: 151
  hydropower
    development constraints, 6: 49–91
    fish-life, 6: 58, 6: 63, 6: 73, 6: 76
    operation, 6: 49–91
    reservoir water quality, 6: 58
    water quality, 6: 53, 6: 58
  life cycles
    inventory, 1: 146
    photovoltaics, 1: **143–159**
    risk analysis, 1: 153
  Mekin hydropower project, Cameroon, Africa, 6: 144
  Memve'Elé hydro plant project, Cameroon, Africa, 6: 141
  mitigating wind power, 2: 530
  ocean wave energy, 8: 3, 8: 3f
  offshore wind power, 2: 463, 2: 525
  Okinawa, Japan seawater pumped storage hydropower, 6: 421, 6: 422, 6: 422t
  photovoltaics, 1: **143–159**
    cadmium telluride thin films, 1: 436
    energy payback times, 1: 147
    greenhouse gas emissions, 1: 148
    heavy metal emissions, 1: 151
    life cycles, 1: **143–159**
      inventory, 1: 146
      risk analysis, 1: 153
    pollutants, 1: 150
    risk analysis, 1: 153
  pollutants, 1: 150
  power generation, biomass and biofuels, 5: 51
  reduction, wind turbines, 2: 687
  reservoir water quality, hydropower, 6: 58
  risk analysis, photovoltaics, 1: 153
  social benefits/impacts, wind energy/wind power, 2: **503–539**
  sustainable geothermal energy, 7: 276, 7: 278, 7: 283, 7: 287, 7: 289
  turbine technology, 2: 687
  very large-scale photovoltaics, 1: 733, 1: 734t, 1: 737, 1: 741
  water quality, 6: 53, 6: 58
  wildlife, 2: 522, 2: 528, 2: 529
  wind energy/wind power, 2: 397, 2: **503–539**, 2: 426
    assessments, 2: 511
    benefits/impacts, 2: **503–539**
    birds, 2: 182, 2: 205, 2: 529, 2: 687–688
    fauna, 2: 522, 2: 528
    flora, 2: 522
    mitigation, 2: 530
    offshore wind power, 2: 463
    social benefits/impacts, 2: **503–539**
    wildlife, 2: 522, 2: 528, 2: 529
    wind farms, 2: 510, 2: 530
    wind parks, 2: 186–187, 2: 512t, 2: 512–513, 2: 513t, 2: 514t
    wind power, 2: **503–539**
    wind turbines, 2: 687
      loads, 2: 246–247, 2: 262
      reduction, 2: 687
    wind park design, 2: 186–187
Environmental Transformation Fund (ETF), 8: 83
enzymatic fuel cells, 4: 259, 4: 264
enzymatic hydrolysis, 5: 232
enzymatic pretreatments, 5: 246
enzymatic transesterification, 5: 223
enzymes:
  biodiesel, 5: 396
  biological fuel cells, 4: 259, 4: 260
    electrodes, 4: 261
    electron transfer methods, 4: 260
    immobilization, 4: 260
  costs, 5: 248
  electrodes, 4: 261
  electron transfer methods, 4: 260
  immobilization, 4: 260
  lignocellulosic wastes, 5: 248, 5: 249
  saccharification and fermentation, 5: 248, 5: 249
E.ON España, 6: 315
E.ON (Kingsnorth), 5: 68
EPBT *see* energy-payback times
EPER *see* European Pollution Emission Register
EPO *see* electrical priority operation
equation of time (ET): solar energy, 3: 8
Equilibrium demonstration program, 3: 394
EquiMar, 8: 84
equinox: solar resource, 3: 27
equipment:
  direct heat utilization, 7: 175
  geothermal energy, 7: 175
  hydropower essential features, 6: 17
  manufacture, Three Gorges Project, China, 6: 225
  offshore wind power, 2: 452
  power measurement, ocean wave energy, 8: 93
  ship lift, 6: 199
  transportation, wind turbines, 2: 177
  wind farms, 2: 452
equity: geothermal energy, 7: 282
equivalence problem: resistivity methods, 7: 63
equivalence ratios, 4: 77
equivalent cells, 1: 755, 1: 757
equivalent circuits:
  downconversion, 1: 550
  fuel cell power electronics, 4: 327
  power electronics, 4: 327
  product-integrated photovoltaics, 1: 717, 1: 718f
  upconversion, 1: 535
equivalent triangular storm (ETS), 8: 70, 8: 71
erbium oxide emitters, 1: 606, 1: 606f, 1: 607, 1: 607f
erecting wind turbines, 2: 180
Ericsson engines, 3: 90, 3: 91f
erosion:
  see also corrosion
  geothermal energy exploration techniques, 7: 89
  Indian hydropower, 6: 246–247, 6: 248
errors:
  Fresnel collectors, 3: 197
  high concentration solar collectors, 3: 178, 3: 197, 3: 203
  numerical ocean wave models, 8: 46, 8: 47
  parabolic troughs, 3: 178
  qualitative descriptions, 8: 47
  solar dishes, 3: 203
  solar radiometry, 3: 67
  wind power planning tools, 2: 412
Ertan Arch Dam, 6: 492
Ertan project, 6: 492, 6: 501, 6: 501f
eruptions: volcanic events, 7: 56
escape cone losses, 1: 596
Esla development, Spain: hydropower, 6: 336–337
eSolar concentrating solar power, 3: 193, 3: 633
eSolar heliostat field, 3: 620, 3: 621f
eSolar receivers, 3: 193
ESRA *see* European solar radiation atlas

estimation:
  buoy data, **8**: 24
  ocean wave measurements, **8**: 24
  power production, **2**: 403
  wind power production, **2**: 403
  wind turbine energy yields, **2**: 131, **2**: 153
Estinnes, Belgium pilot demonstration, **2**: 719
ET *see* equation of time
ETA *see* extremely thin absorbers
ETC *see* evacuated tube collectors
Étendue, **1**: 325
ETF *see* Environmental Transformation Fund
ethanol:
  see also bioethanol
  automotives, **5**: 307
    manufacturer's perspective, **5**: 313
    safety, **5**: 323
    sustainability, **5**: 337
  biomass-to-liquids technology, **5**: 185, **5**: 193
  Brazilian sugarcane, **5**: 15
  chemical production, **5**: 404
  compression-ignition engines, **5**: 322
  dehydration, **5**: 210
  electrofuels, **5**: 328
  ethanol-diesel blends, **5**: 344
  fuel cells, **5**: 406
  historical perspectives, **5**: 11
  lignocellulosic wastes, **5**: 233
  physicochemical properties, **5**: 317, **5**: 317*t*
  production intensification, **5**: 210
  safety, **5**: 323
  spark-ignition engines, **5**: 319
  sugarcane, **5**: 15
ethics, **5**: 99–108
  biodiesel vegetable oil, **5**: 219
  biofuels
    carbon certification, **5**: 104
    indirect land use change, **5**: 107
    International Sustainability & Carbon Certification, **5**: 104
    land use change, **5**: 107
    palm oils, **5**: 104
    production, **5**: 99–108
    Renewable Energy Directive, **5**: 100, **5**: 103
    Renewable Transport Fuel Obligation, **5**: 100, **5**: 103
    soy, **5**: 105
    standards, **5**: 99–108
    sustainability, **5**: 99, **5**: 103, **5**: 104, **5**: 105
  indirect land use change, **5**: 107
  international labor laws, **5**: 106
  International Organization for Standardization, **5**: 105
  International Sustainability & Carbon Certification, **5**: 104
  labor laws, **5**: 106
  land use change, **5**: 107
  palm oils, biofuels
  production of biofuels, **5**: 99–108
  Renewable Energy Directive, **5**: 100, **5**: 103
  Renewable Transport Fuel Obligation, **5**: 100, **5**: 103
  retail sector standards, **5**: 106
  Round Table on Responsible Soy, **5**: 105
  Roundtable on Sustainable Palm Oil, **5**: 104
  soy, biofuels, **5**: 105
  standards, **5**: 99–108
  sustainability, **5**: 99, **5**: 103, **5**: 104, **5**: 105
  vegetable oil, **5**: 219
ethyl acetate: biofuels, **5**: 405
ethyl alcohol *see* ethanol
ETI *see* Energy Technologies Institute
E-Ton Solar Tech Co: Ltd:, **1**: 172
ETR *see* extraterrestrial solar radiation
ETS *see* equivalent triangular storm
Etten-Leur project, **1**: 698, **1**: 698*f*
EU *see* European Union
EUA *see* European Union Allowances

eucalyptus, **5**: 264, **5**: 267*t*, **5**: 277
Eume dam, Spain: hydropower, **6**: 326, **6**: 327*f*
EU-MENA *see* Europe, the Middle East, and North Africa
EURELIOS power plant, **3**: 628
EuroDish, **3**: 203
Europe, **6**: 343–354
  concentrating solar power, future potential, **3**: 631
  high concentration solar collector markets, **3**: 192
  hydropower, Switzerland, **6**: 343–354
  mainstream power sources, **1**: 183
  market development, **2**: 662
  offshore wind parks, **2**: 688–689, **2**: 690
  photovoltaics, **1**: 167
  supergrids, **2**: 496
  Switzerland, hydropower, **6**: 343–354
  wave energy, **8**: 7
  wind energy, historical overviews, **2**: 44
  windmills, **2**: 44
  wind power market development, **2**: 662
  wind turbine finance, **2**: 710
  wind turbine manufacturers, **2**: 668
European Centre for Medium-Range Weather Forecasts (ECMWF), **1**: 245, **1**: 252, **1**: 254, **1**: 280
European Commission (EC):
  Joint Research Centre, **1**: 788
  photovoltaic Framework Programme, **1**: 161
  photovoltaic standards, **1**: 788
  wave energy conversion, **8**: 7
European Environment Agency (EEA), **5**: 283, **6**: 357
European Marine Energy Centre (EMEC), **8**: 83–84
European Pollution Emission Register (EPER), **5**: 31
European solar radiation atlas (ESRA), **3**: 42, **3**: 61
European Standard EN 50308, **2**: 376
European Union Allowances (EUA), **5**: 411, **5**: 416–417, **5**: 420*f*, **5**: 422
European Union (EU):
  biomass-to-liquids technology, **5**: 158
  feed-in tariffs, **1**: 91
  photovoltaics, **1**: 90, **1**: 93, **1**: 103
  promotion schemes, **1**: 90, **1**: 93, **1**: 103
  support mechanisms, **1**: 90, **1**: 93, **1**: 103
  wind park design, **2**: 202, **2**: 202*f*, **2**: 203*f*
European Wave Energy Atlas, **8**: 8
European Wind Energy Association (EWEA), **2**: 65, **2**: 71
European Wind Integration Study (EWIS), **2**: 715
Europe, the Middle East, and North Africa (EU-MENA), **1**: 739
EuroTrough, **3**: 179
eutrophication:
  algae, **6**: 61
  anoxia, **6**: 62
  aquatic plants, **6**: 62
  fish yields, **6**: 63
  hydropower, water quality, **6**: 61, **6**: 72
  hypereutrophy, **6**: 62
  nitrate concentrations, **6**: 63
  nutrient recycling, **6**: 63
  species changes, **6**: 62
  trophic status assessments, **6**: 63
  water quality, **6**: 61, **6**: 72
  water-related diseases, **6**: 63
evacuated glazing:
  conventional glazing, **3**: 338
  electrochromic windows, **3**: 338
  heat transfer, **3**: 336
  operating principles, **3**: 336
  solar thermal energy, **3**: 314, **3**: 336
  state of the art, **3**: 337
  technology problems, **3**: 336
evacuated tube collectors (ETC):
  agricultural applications, **3**: 571, **3**: 587*t*
  compound parabolic collectors, **3**: 118, **3**: 119*f*, **3**: 159
  compound parabolic reflectors, **3**: 118, **3**: 119*f*
  heat pipes, **3**: 116, **3**: 117*f*, **3**: 118, **3**: 118*f*

evacuated tube collectors (ETC): (*continued*)
    history, **3:** 85, **3:** 96, **3:** 100, **3:** 101*f*
    incident angle modifiers, **3:** 143–144, **3:** 144*f*
    industrial applications, **3:** 571, **3:** 587*t*
    low concentration ratio solar collectors, **3:** 158, **3:** 163
    low-temperature stationary collectors, **3:** 116
    solar agricultural applications, **3:** 571, **3:** 587*t*
    solar desalination, **3:** 534
    solar energy history, **3:** 85, **3:** 96, **3:** 100, **3:** 101*f*
    solar industrial applications, **3:** 571, **3:** 587*t*
    U-tubes, **3:** 117*f*, **3:** 117–118, **3:** 118*f*, **3:** 119*f*
evaluation:
    economics of wind energy, **2: 469–501**
    hybrid solar–diesel systems, **1:** 690
    photovoltaic power forecasting, **1:** 265, **1:** 271, **1:** 285
    seasonal ground storage, **3:** 521
    solar irradiance forecasting, **1:** 265, **1:** 271, **1:** 285
    solar radiation, **3:** 49
    solar resource, **3:** 49
    stand alone hybrid wind energy systems, **2:** 651
    very large-scale photovoltaic systems, **1:** 734
    wind energy
        economics, **2: 469–501**
        stand alone hybrid systems, **2:** 651
        technical considerations, **2: 469–501**
evaporation:
    binary geothermal power plants, **7:** 225
    glazings, **3:** 324
    passive solar cooling, **3:** 642, **3:** 642*f*
    proton-exchange membrane fuel cells, **4:** 194
    selective coatings, **3:** 301
EWEA *see* European Wind Energy Association
EWIS *see* European Wind Integration Study
excited state decay, **1:** 485
exciton energy transfer, **1:** 664
exciton fission (EF), **1:** 549
exciton generation, **1:** 525, **1:** 657
exergy:
    biomass combined heat and power, **5:** 87, **5:** 94
    geothermal power plants, **7:** 207
    latent heat, **3:** 222
    lithium–water absorption systems, **3:** 469
    solar radiation, **1:** 316, **1:** 328
    thermal energy storage, **3:** 222, **3:** 230, **3:** 230*f*
exfoliation, **7:** 245
exhausted air, **3:** 502–503
Exmork/Energy Systems, **6:** 440
exogenous biomass combined heat and power, **5:** 87
exothermic water gas shift reaction, **5:** 136
expansion: concrete structure durability, **6:** 387, **6:** 388
expenses: wind parks, **2:** 211
experience curves: photovoltaic cost forecasting, **1:** 54, **1:** 57
experimental studies:
    collector time constant, **3:** 145, **3:** 146*f*
    fuel cell power electronics, **4:** 303
    wind energy historical overviews, **2:** 49
expert systems:
    concrete structure durability, **6:** 392
    photovoltaic costs, **1:** 62, **1:** 65, **1:** 67
exploiting hydropower potential, **6:** 10, **6:** 11
exploration techniques, **7: 51–94**
    chemical geothermometers, **7:** 58, **7:** 59, **7:** 134
    electrical resistivity, **7:** 61
    electromagnetic resistivity methods, **7:** 61, **7:** 62, **7:** 65
    geochemistry, **7:** 58
    geohazards, **7:** 56
    geological explorations, **7:** 52
    geological hazard assessments, **7:** 56
    geothermal energy, **7: 51–94**
    geothermometers, **7:** 58
    hazard assessments, **7:** 56
    heat flow, **7:** 84, **7:** 86, **7:** 87
    importance, **7:** 52

    magnetotelluric measurements, **7:** 52, **7:** 61, **7:** 63, **7:** 69
    mineral equilibria, **7:** 60
    multiple mineral equilibria, **7:** 60
    ratio-based geothermometers, **7:** 59
    resistivity methods, **7:** 61
    rock resistivity, **7:** 78
    temperature, **7:** 58
    thermal methods, **7:** 83
    thermometers, **7:** 58
    transient electromagnetic resistivity methods, **7:** 61, **7:** 62, **7:** 65, **7:** 68
    univariant geothermometers, **7:** 59
explosions, **5:** 41, **5:** 42
export subsidies, **5:** 81
exposure risks: biomass cofiring, **5:** 69
exterior painting: hydrogen storage, **4:** 130
external costs:
    climate change levy, **2:** 486
    embedded generation benefits, **2:** 484, **2:** 486
    market solutions, wind energy, **2:** 485
    support mechanisms, **2:** 486
    technical evaluation, **2:** 483, **2:** 484
    wind energy
        climate change levy, **2:** 486
        embedded generation benefits, **2:** 484, **2:** 486
        market solutions, **2:** 485
        support mechanisms, **2:** 486
        technical evaluation, **2:** 483, **2:** 484
external heat exchangers, **3:** 450, **3:** 452*f*
external humidification, **4:** 195
externality: bioenergy policy development, **5:** 411
external quantum efficiency:
    dye-sensitized solar cells, **1:** 488
    luminescent down-shifting, **1:** 564, **1:** 568, **1:** 568*f*
    organic solar cells, **1:** 450
    upconversion, **1:** 540
extinction loss, **1:** 214
extraction:
    additional value from biomass, **5: 385–393**
    biodiesel production intensification, **5:** 208
extractive distillation, **5:** 210
extra humidification systems, **4:** 194
extra short-term wind energy reserves, **2:** 490
extraterrestrial solar radiation (ETR), **1:** 214, **1:** 215, **1:** 216, **1:** 226
extremely thin absorbers (ETA), **1:** 523
extreme sea states, **8:** 52, **8:** 70
    crest heights, **8:** 52, **8:** 70
    device tests, **8:** 96
    long-term distributions, **8:** 54, **8:** 65
    peaks-over-threshold method, **8:** 54
    short-term distribution, **8:** 52, **8:** 65
extreme temperatures, **2:** 413
extreme wind speeds, **2:** 413
extrusion: bioethanol, **5:** 241
eye contact safety, **5:** 324

F

fabricated microwave pyrolysis, **5:** 407
fabrication:
    chalcopyrite thin films, **1:** 416–417
    gas diffusion electrodes, **4:** 166, **4:** 168
    membrane electrode assembly, **4:** 178
    metal nanoparticles, **1:** 651
    nanoparticles, **1:** 651
    silicon thin films, **1:** 395
    single-junction solar cells, **1:** 497–498
facade integrated systems, **1:** 704, **1:** 705
facets: receivers, **3:** 187
fail criteria: photovoltaics, reliability, **1:** 793
failures:
    bioenergy policy development, **5:** 418

dams, 6: 219
photovoltaics, reliability testing, 1: 793
wind turbines, 2: 152, 2: 153
Fair-trade: biofuel production, 5: 106
fan-assisted natural draft cooling towers, 3: 600
fan beater mills, 5: 46
far-field thermophotovoltaics, 1: 613
farming impacts, 5: 379
see also agriculture
fashion items, 5: 392, 5: 392f
fast Fourier transformation (FFT), 8: 105–106
fast pyrolysis, 5: 366t, 5: 368, 5: 373f, 5: 379
fatigue:
    corrosion, 7: 244
    rotor blades, 2: 713
fault accommodation: wind turbines, 2: 364
fault conditions: wind turbines, 2: 246–247
fault mapping, 7: 56
fault movements, 7: 57
fault-ride-through: definitions, wind turbines, 2: 370
fauna, 2: 522, 2: 528, 3: 630, 6: 422
FC *see* fuel cells
f-chart method:
    active solar thermal systems, 3: 396, 3: 408
    air-based solar thermal systems, 3: 402
    airflow rate corrections, 3: 402
    air systems, solar thermal systems, 3: 402
    collector flow rate corrections, 3: 401
    heat exchanger size corrections, 3: 401, 3: 410
    liquid-based solar thermal systems, 3: 400
    load heat exchanger size corrections, 3: 401
    pebble-bed storage capacity corrections, 3: 402
    solar thermal systems, 3: 411
        air systems, 3: 402
        heat exchanger size corrections, 3: 401, 3: 410
        liquid systems, 3: 400
        service water heating, 3: 403
        storage capacity corrections, 3: 401, 3: 402, 3: 410
        water heating, 3: 403
        water systems, 3: 400
    storage capacity corrections, 3: 401, 3: 402, 3: 410
    water heating, 3: 403
    water systems, solar thermal systems, 3: 400
FDC *see* flow duration curves
feasibility studies:
    wind park design, 2: 170
    wind power, 2: 394
Federation of Registered Rural Workers in the State of São Paulo (FERAESP), 5: 22
feed-in-tariffs (FIT), 1: **73–109**
    bioenergy policy development, 5: 411, 5: 423
    calculation methodology, 1: 94
    Canada, 2: 546
    common features, 1: 93
    degression, 1: 99
    developing countries, 1: 130–131, 1: 134
    differentiation, 1: 98, 1: 99
    European Union, 1: 91
    financing mechanisms, 1: 97
    Germany, 1: 91
    high concentration solar collectors, 3: 206
    inflation indexation, 1: 101
    market integration design, photovoltaics, 1: 102
    payment duration, 1: 97
    photovoltaics
        common features, 1: 93
        current policy support, 1: 182
        developing countries, 1: 130–131, 1: 134
        European Union, 1: 91
        Germany, 1: 91
        global industry overview, 1: 161
        inflation indexation, 1: 101
        market integration design, 1: 102
        progress reports, 1: 98
        tariff calculation methodology, 1: 94
        tariff degression, 1: 99
        tariff payment duration, 1: 97
        United States, 1: 88
    plant size, 1: 98
    plant type, 1: 99
    progress reports, 1: 98
    promotion schemes, 1: **73–109**
    United States, 1: 88
    very large-scale photovoltaic, 1: 739
    wind energy, 2: 1
    wind energy policy, 2: 546
    wind turbines, 2: 671, 2: 703–704, 2: 705f
feedstocks, 5: 7, 5: **217–261**, 5: **263–291**, 5: **385–393**
    additional value extraction, 5: **385–393**
    algae, 5: 6
    automotives, 5: 305–306, 5: 314
    biochar torrefaction, 5: 368
    biomass and biofuels
        additional value extraction, 5: **385–393**
        gasifiers, 5: 139
        introduction, 5: 6
        waste materials, 5: **217–261**
        woody biomass, 5: **263–291**
        yield improvement potentials, 5: **293–303**
    contaminants, 5: 141
    coppice crops, 5: 263, 5: 264
    costs, 5: 194
    crops, 5: 7, 5: **263–291**
    extracting additional value feedstocks, 5: **385–393**
    Fischer–Tropsch process, 5: 162, 5: 162f
    forestland-derived resources, 5: 263, 5: 282
    forest residues, 5: 263, 5: 283
    gasifiers, 5: 139
    handling, 5: 142, 5: 276
    hardwoods, 5: 263, 5: 264, 5: 268
    hydrogen technology, 4: 331, 4: 332, 4: 337
    loblolly pine, 5: 264, 5: 274
    pines, 5: 264, 5: 274, 5: 277
    preparation, 5: 162, 5: 162f
    pretreatments, 5: 162, 5: 162f, 5: 368
    primary forest residues, 5: 263, 5: 283
    reception, 5: 142
    residue processing, 5: 286
    short-rotation woody crops, 5: 263, 5: 264
    single-stem woody crops, 5: 263, 5: 264, 5: 268, 5: 274, 5: 276
    softwoods, 5: 274
    supply security, 5: 305–306
    urban residues, 5: 263, 5: 264, 5: 286
    waste materials, 5: **217–261**
    wood processing residues, 5: 286
    woody biomass, 5: **263–291**, 5: 263
    yield improvement potentials, 5: **293–303**
Fengman complex, 6: 399, 6: 401f
FERAESP *see* Federation of Registered Rural Workers in the State of São Paulo
fermentation:
    alcohols, 5: 186, 5: 193, 5: 212, 5: 248
    bioethanol, 5: 2, 5: 212, 5: 248
    biomass and biofuels, 5: 2, 5: 186, 5: 193, 5: 400
        chemical production, 5: 400
    biomass-to-liquids technology, 5: 186, 5: 193
    chemical production, 5: 400
    definitions, 5: 395
    fuel production intermediates, 5: 400
    lignocellulosic feedstocks, 5: 248, 5: 400
Fermi-Dirac distribution, 1: 299
Fermi levels, 1: 293, 1: 315, 1: 620
ferrous alloys, 7: 247
fertile soils, 5: 358, 5: 358f
fetch lengths: ocean energy, 8: 79
FFT *see* fast Fourier transformation

fiberglass, 3: 114, 3: 114f, 3: 334
field laboratories: geothermal chemistry, 7: 100
field observations:
   Chinese hydraulic research, 6: 502
   roller compacted concrete dams, 6: 476
field-of-view: solar resource, 3: 27
Filkenstein–Schafer (FS) statistical method, 3: 23
filling materials: joints, 6: 383
film mixtures: electrochromogenic glazing, 3: 319–320
filters: thermophotovoltaics, 1: 604, 1: 607, 1: 610
final yields: photovoltaics, 1: 775, 1: 777
finance, 2: 469–501
   biomass and biofuel power generation, 5: 29
   developing country photovoltaics, 1: 113, 1: 120, 1: 125, 1: 130
   energy generation, Iran, 6: 253
   feed-in tariffs, 1: 97
   future photovoltaics, 1: 197
   hydropower, 6: 6, 6: 141, 6: 144, 6: 148, 6: 149, 6: 229
      India, 6: 229
      Iran, 6: 253, 6: 258
   incentive support mechanisms, 1: 1, 1: 2t
   Indian hydropower, 6: 229
   offshore wind, 2: 478, 2: 480
   onshore wind, 2: 475
   photovoltaics, 1: 7
      Abu Dhabi desert area, 1: 693
      developing countries, 1: 113, 1: 120, 1: 125, 1: 130
      feed-in tariffs, 1: 97
      future visions, 1: 197
      promotion schemes, 1: 97
      rural areas, 1: 113, 1: 120, 1: 125, 1: 130
   power generation, 5: 29
   promotion schemes, 1: 97
   risk management
      characterization, 1: 136
      developing country photovoltaics, 1: 135
      fossil-fuels, 1: 136
      photovoltaics, 1: 135, 1: 136, 1: 137
      return expectations, 1: 137
   rural area photovoltaics, 1: 113, 1: 120, 1: 125, 1: 130
   technical wind energy evaluations, 2: 469–501
   Three Gorges Project, China, 6: 209
   turbine technology, 2: 708, 2: 710, 2: 713, 2: 715, 2: 718
   wind energy, 2: 469–501, 2: 708, 2: 710, 2: 713, 2: 715, 2: 718
      power design and implementation, 2: 420, 2: 425, 2: 426
      technical evaluation, 2: 469–501
      turbine technology, 2: 708, 2: 710, 2: 713, 2: 715, 2: 718
   wood fuel markets, 5: 78
fin-and-tube absorbers, 3: 118f
fingerprints, 2: 411
finite difference, 3: 369, 3: 370f
fire, 4: 77–109, 4: 77
   alcohol fuel safety, 5: 325
   biomass cofiring, 5: 68
   concrete structure durability, 6: 391
   fighting, 6: 144
   health and safety, 5: 41, 5: 325
   hydrogen safety engineering, 4: 77–109, 4: 77
   primary forest residues, 5: 283
   resistance ratings, 4: 77
   safety, 4: 77–109, 4: 77, 5: 41, 5: 325
firing: biomass power generation, 5: 55–73
FIRMWIND, 2: 715
first generation biofuels: definitions, 5: 218
First Solar LLC, 1: 169
first-stage construction works: Three Gorges Project, China, 6: 201, 6: 206
fiscal incentives: developing country photovoltaics, 1: 128
Fischer–Tropsch (FT) diesel see syngas
Fischer–Tropsch (FT) process, 5: 155–204, 5: 156
   advanced pretreatments, 5: 162f, 5: 163
   biomass conversion, 5: 162
   biomass-to-liquids technology, 5: 155–204, 5: 156
   catalysts, 5: 178
   chemistry, 5: 178
   developers, 5: 177, 5: 177t
   flow diagrams, 5: 177, 5: 177f
   gasification, 5: 168
   historical overviews, 5: 160
   products, 5: 179
   reactors, 5: 168, 5: 180
   syngas cleanup, 5: 172
   syngas conditioning, 5: 177
fish:
   hydropower environmental impact management, 6: 58, 6: 63, 6: 73, 6: 76
   Mekin hydropower project, Cameroon, Africa, 6: 144
   migration, 6: 58, 6: 73
   offshore wind power, 2: 528
   reservoir water quality, 6: 63
   Three Gorges Project, China, 6: 216
   wind energy environmental impacts, 2: 528
FIT see feed-in-tariff
fittings: hydrogen storage, 4: 120
five-step ship locks, 6: 193, 6: 223
five year annual plans: Indian hydropower, 6: 233, 6: 234, 6: 237, 6: 240
fixed bed gasifiers, 5: 62, 5: 136, 5: 150
fixed bottom structures, 2: 431
fixed grates, 5: 33
fixed platform instruments, 8: 23
fixed prices, 1: 84, 5: 411, 5: 423
fixed-speed direct-grid coupling generators, 2: 286
fixed speed power systems, 2: 295
fixed-speed squirrel-cage induction generators, 2: 282
fixed tubular bed reactors, 5: 181
flame lengths, 4: 91, 4: 92
flame stability, 5: 29, 5: 47
Flaming Gorge Dam, Utah, 6: 90
flammability ranges, 4: 77, 4: 81, 4: 86
flammable limits, 4: 77, 4: 81, 4: 86, 4: 94, 4: 104
flare: biomass gasification, 5: 147
flaring pier gates, 6: 485, 6: 489
flashing:
   facilities, 6: 288
   geothermal energy, 7: 146
flash pyrolysis, 5: 366t, 5: 370, 5: 379
flash-steam geothermal power plants, 7: 207, 7: 216, 7: 217, 7: 231, 7: 279
flat absorbers, 3: 153, 3: 154, 3: 154f, 3: 155f
flat collectors:
   see also flat-plate collectors
   air heat recovery, 3: 271
   design principles, 3: 263
   energy balance equations, 3: 270, 3: 272
   heat recovery, 3: 270, 3: 271
   liquid heat recovery, 3: 270
   performance, 3: 270
   photovoltaic/thermal solar collectors, 3: 256–257, 3: 263
   thermal losses, 3: 271
flat-plate collectors, 3: 103–147, 3: 151
   absorbers, 3: 104, 3: 108
   agricultural applications, 3: 570, 3: 571, 3: 587t
   back insulation, 3: 104, 3: 113
   casings, 3: 104, 3: 113
   covers, 3: 104, 3: 111
   diffuse reflectors, 3: 151, 3: 151f, 3: 151–152, 3: 159, 3: 159f
   edge insulation, 3: 104, 3: 113
   enclosures, 3: 104, 3: 113
   glazing, 3: 104, 3: 111
   history, 3: 85, 3: 92, 3: 93, 3: 93f
   incident angle modifiers, 3: 143, 3: 144f
   industrial applications, 3: 570, 3: 571, 3: 587t
   insulation, 3: 104, 3: 111, 3: 113
   low concentration ratio solar collectors, 3: 150, 3: 151, 3: 152
   low-temperature stationary collectors, 3: 103–147

resources assessments, **1**: 218, **1**: 232
selective surfaces, **3**: 93
solar agricultural applications, **3**: 570, **3**: 571, **3**: 587t
solar energy history, **3**: 85, **3**: 92, **3**: 93, **3**: 93f
solar industrial applications, **3**: 570, **3**: 571, **3**: 587t
solar radiation resources assessments, **1**: 218, **1**: 232
solar water heating systems, **3**: 420, **3**: 426, **3**: 429
space heating, solar energy history, **3**: 95
steady-state energy balance, **3**: 129
thermal analysis, **3**: 129
flex-fuel vehicles, **5**: 17, **5**: 332
flexible substrate processing, **1**: 395
flicker:
   voltage variation, **2**: 594
   wind energy, **2**: 182, **2**: 522
flip buckets, **6**: 485, **6**: 489, **6**: 492, **6**: 492f, **6**: 492–493
float glass, **3**: 314, **3**: 315, **3**: 327, **3**: 328
floating debris, **6**: 77, **6**: 188
floating foundations: wind park design, **2**: 179, **2**: 181f
floating offshore wind power technology, **2**: 431, **2**: 449
floating offtakes, **6**: 87
flooding:
   deep outlet flood discharging, **6**: 187
   discharging, **6**: 187
   gas diffusion electrodes, **4**: 169
   geothermal energy hazard assessments, **7**: 58
   sediment reservoir bypass, **6**: 294
   Three Gorges Project, China, **6**: 183, **6**: 220
   turbid water reservoir bypass, **6**: 294
flora, **2**: 522, **3**: 630, **6**: 422
flow:
   batteries, **1**: 208
   debris control, **6**: 81
   diagrams
      dry-steam power plants, **7**: 209, **7**: 210f
      Fischer–Tropsch process, **5**: 177, **5**: 177f
      membrane distillation, **3**: 545f, **3**: 545–546
   Eastmain–Sarcelle–Rupert Diversion Project, Quebec, Canada, **6**: 169
   geochemistry, **7**: 108, **7**: 141
   geothermal fluids, geochemistry, **7**: 108
   hydraulic research, China, **6**: 499
   hydropower downstream impacts, **6**: 56
   hydropower sediment management, **6**: 369, **6**: 373f, **6**: 374f
   induced vibration, **6**: 499
   lithium–water absorption systems, **3**: 469, **3**: 469f
   rates
      coefficients, **8**: 127, **8**: 127f
      ocean wave energy, **8**: 93, **8**: 127, **8**: 127f
   sediment management, **6**: 369, **6**: 373f, **6**: 374f
   velocity fields, **6**: 369, **6**: 373f, **6**: 374f
flow duration curves (FDC), **6**: 437, **6**: 437f
flowering: yield improvement potentials, **5**: 297
flowsheets: biodiesel production, **5**: 206
fluid analysis: geochemistry, **7**: 100
fluid composition effects: geochemistry, **7**: 106
fluid flow:
   energy balance, **3**: 138, **3**: 140f
   geothermal energy, **7**: 10, **7**: 88
   heat flow, **7**: 88
fluid inclusion: geochemistry, **7**: 105
fluidized bed boilers, **5**: 34
fluidized bed combustion, **5**: 61
fluidized bed gasifiers:
   biomass, **5**: 136, **5**: 137, **5**: 149
   biomass cofiring, **5**: 63
   biomass-to-liquids technology, **5**: 169t, **5**: 170
fluidized bed processes, **1**: 173
fluidized bed reactors, **5**: 181
fluid properties: geothermal energy, **7**: 240
fluid sampling: geochemistry, **7**: 95
fluid saturation, **7**: 78
fluid velocity, **7**: 246, **8**: 93

fluorinated polymers, **4**: 188
flushing:
   reservoir sediments, **6**: 288, **6**: 366, **6**: 369, **6**: 371f, **6**: 372f
   Three Gorges Project, China, **6**: 188
fluvial data: sediment management, **6**: 361
flux property density, **1**: 331, **1**: 331t
fly ash, **6**: 393
flywheels, **1**: 204, **1**: 204f, **1**: 205, **2**: 650
folded tandem architecture, **1**: 464
food: Brazilian bioethanol, **5**: 22
forced advection, **7**: 12, **7**: 13–14
forced circulation, **3**: 426, **3**: 573, **3**: 574f, **3**: 575f
force majeure problems, **2**: 152, **2**: 153
forecasting:
   costs, photovoltaics, **1**: 47, **1**: 54
   current implemented tools, **2**: 616
   finance, wind turbines, **2**: 710, **2**: 719
   irradiance, **1: 239–292**
   photovoltaics
      costs, **1**: 47, **1**: 54, **1**: 195, **1**: 196
      solar irradiance, **1: 239–292**
   solar irradiance, **1: 239–292**
   statistical methods, **1**: 248, **1**: 265, **2**: 615
   technology evolution, wind turbines, **2**: 710, **2**: 714
   wind energy, **2**: 31, **2**: 494, **2**: 616, **2**: 710, **2**: 714, **2**: 719
      electrical network integration, **2**: 616
      variability costs and effects, **2**: 494
      wind power time evolution, **2**: 31
      wind turbine finance, **2**: 710, **2**: 719
      wind turbine technology evolution, **2**: 710, **2**: 714
   wind speed, **2**: 88
foreign direct investment, **7**: 259
forestry/forests:
   forestland-derived resources, **5**: 263, **5**: 282
   forest residues, **5**: 263, **5**: 283
   gasification, **5**: 141
   geothermal energy, **7**: 284
   wind power planning, **2**: 413
   woody biomass, **5**: 263
Forestry Stewardship Council (FSC), **5**: 106
forklifts, **4**: 37, **4**: 284
Fortnum/Vapo, Finland, **5**: 148
FORTRAN, **3**: 396, **3**: 411
forward commitment procurement: hydrogen technology, **4**: 45, **4**: 68–69, **4**: 71–72
fossil fuels:
   blends
      stationary engines, **5**: 348
      transport use, **5**: 343
   combined power conversion cycles, **3**: 607
   energy balance, **2**: 17, **2**: 21
   financial risk management, **1**: 136
   geothermal energy, **7**: 229, **7**: 272
   geothermal hybrid power plants, **7**: 229
   global energy markets, **2**: 542
   photovoltaic financial risk management, **1**: 136
   planet energy balance, **2**: 17, **2**: 21
   savings, **2**: 507
   social benefits/impacts, wind power, **2**: 507
   substitution, **2**: 507
   time depletion, **2**: 22
   wind energy, **2**: 11
   wind energy policy, **2**: 542, **2**: 548, **2**: 552
   wind power social benefits/impacts, **2**: 507
foundations:
   dams, **6**: 184
   friction, **6**: 382
   grouting, **6**: 477, **6**: 480f, **6**: 482
   offshore wind power, **2**: 431
   uneven settlement, **6**: 381
   wind power design, **2**: 178, **2**: 421
Fourier analysis:
   ocean wave energy, **8**: 25, **8**: 80, **8**: 105

Fourier analysis: (*continued*)
  series decomposition, **8**: 25
Fourier transform infrared spectroscopy (FTIR), **5**: 375–376, **5**: 376*f*
Foz do Areia hydroelectric project, Brazil, **6**: 108
fracture models, **7**: 14
frames: glazing/windows, **3**: 333, **3**: 334
framework programs, **2**: 671
France:
  desalination, **2**: 735
  enhanced geothermal systems, **7**: 233, **7**: 234*f*
  space propulsion, **4**: 22
  wind power market development, **2**: 664
  wind turbines, **2**: 60
Francis turbines, **6**: 25, **6**: 28*f*
free advection: geothermal energy, physics, **7**: 12
free energy, **1**: 315, **1**: 328–329
free thermal radiation, **1**: 330
freeze protection, **3**: 450, **3**: 451, **3**: 451*f*, **3**: 452*f*
freezing: concrete structure durability, **6**: 387
Freiburg, Germany, **5**: 149
frequency distribution:
  wind power, **2**: 404
  wind speed time variations, **2**: 82
frequency domain:
  ocean wave energy, **8**: 80, **8**: 104
  passive solar technologies, **3**: 362, **3**: 375
frequency fluctuations: wind turbines, **2**: 207
frequency spectrum: ocean waves, **8**: 15
frequency variations: wind turbine electrical networks, **2**: 593
freshwater solar desalination, **3**: 529–565
Fresnel collectors:
  agricultural applications, **3**: 571–572, **3**: 572*f*, **3**: 587*t*
  Ausra/Areva, **3**: 198
  characteristics, **3**: 195
  cleaning, **3**: 199
  components, **3**: 195
  construction, **3**: 197
  control, **3**: 196
  drives, **3**: 196
  efficiency, **3**: 196
  error sources, **3**: 197
  heat transfer fluids, **3**: 196
  high concentration solar collectors, **3**: 195
  industrial applications, **3**: 571–572, **3**: 572*f*, **3**: 587*t*
  maintenance, **3**: 199
  manufacturers, **3**: 197
  materials, **3**: 196
  Mirroxx, **3**: 199
  models, **3**: 197
  NOVATEC Biosol, **3**: 198
  operation and maintenance, **3**: 199
  part's replacements, **3**: 199
  performance, **3**: 196
  research, **3**: 199
  size, **3**: 196
  solar control of buildings, **3**: 289
  Solarmundo, **3**: 198
  Solar Power Group, **3**: 197
  structure, **3**: 195
  system-specific performance determination, **3**: 196
  tracking systems, **3**: 196
  types, **3**: 196
Fresnel lenses, **3**: 289
Fresnel technology: solar desalination, **3**: 530–531, **3**: 531*f*
friction:
  cracking, **6**: 382
  photovoltaics, **3**: 275
  wind power planning, **2**: 409
front contacts:
  chalcopyrite thin films, **1**: 414
  crystalline silicon cells, **1**: 366
front-located nanoparticles: plasmonics, **1**: 648
Froude numbers, **6**: 369, **6**: 374*f*

Froude similarity, **8**: 86
frying oil effects, **5**: 219
FS *see* Filkenstein–Schafer statistical method
FSC *see* Forestry Stewardship Council
FT *see* Fischer–Tropsch
FTIR *see* Fourier transform infrared spectroscopy
fuel cells (FC):
  see also alkaline fuel cells; biological fuel cells; electrical vehicles; molten carbonate fuel cells; proton-exchange membrane fuel cells
  Apollo, **4**: 26
  back-up power supplies, **4**: 34
  batteries, **4**: 324
  bio-alcohols, **5**: 406
  bulk converter power loss analysis, **4**: 301
  component specifications, **4**: 325
  controlled renewables, **4**: 295–329
  current hydrogen technology, **4**: 13–43
  definitions, **4**: 227
  dynamic voltage balancing, **4**: 303
  economics, **4**: 45–75, **4**: 45
  efficiency, **4**: 335
  electricity
    hydrogen technology, **4**: 331–340
    current status, **4**: 33
  electrochemistry, **4**: 10
  electronics, **4**: 36, **4**: 295–329
  equivalent circuits, **4**: 327
  experimental studies, **4**: 303
  forklift vehicles, **4**: 284
  future hydrogen technology, **4**: 331–340
  gate-drive circuitry, **4**: 304
  Gemini spacecraft, **4**: 26
  H-bridge operation, **4**: 305
  holistic hydrogen technology, **4**: 331, **4**: 335
  hydrogen technology
    chemicals, storage, **4**: 137–157
    compressed gas, storage, **4**: 111–135
    controlled renewables, **4**: 295–329
    current status, **4**: 13–43
    economics, **4**: 45–75, **4**: 45
    efficiency, **4**: 335
    electricity, **4**: 331–340
    electric vehicles, **4**: 333
    electrochemistry, **4**: 10
    electronics, **4**: 295–329
    end-use technologies, **4**: 58
    forklift vehicles, **4**: 284
    future perspectives, **4**: 331–340
    holistic considerations, **4**: 331, **4**: 335
    infrastructure, **4**: 283, **4**: 333, **4**: 337, **4**: 339
    introduction, **4**: 1–11
    inverter safe operating areas, **4**: 297
    liquids, storage, **4**: 137–157
    low carbon energy conversion, **4**: 296
    power electronics, **4**: 295–329
    power inverter safe operating areas, **4**: 297
    production, transport applications, **4**: 283
    safety engineering, **4**: 77–109
    solid oxide fuel cells, **4**: 241–257
    stationary power, **4**: 334
    storage
      chemicals, **4**: 137–157
      compressed gas, **4**: 111–135
      liquids, **4**: 137–157
    terrestrial applications, **4**: 296
    traditional inverter safe operating areas, **4**: 297
    transitions, **4**: 331–340
    transport, **4**: 333, **4**: 281–293
    vehicles, **4**: 284, **4**: 333
    volume, **4**: 2
  hydropower multibenefit solutions, **6**: 43
  infrastructure, **4**: 283, **4**: 333, **4**: 337, **4**: 339

inherent safer designs, 4: 101
inverter power loss analysis, 4: 300
inverter safe operating areas, 4: 297
laboratory test environments, 4: 303
low carbon energy conversion, 4: 296
microbial fuel cells, 4: **257–280**
military current status, 4: 40
modeling power electronics, 4: 320, 4: 325
multiswitch voltage inverters, 4: 299, 4: 303
operating point power loss analysis, 4: 302
operation, 4: 322
performance evaluation, 4: 324
portable electronic systems, current status, 4: 36
power electronics, 4: **295–329**
    bulk converter power loss analysis, 4: 301
    component specifications, 4: 325
    dynamic voltage balancing, 4: 303
    equivalent circuits, 4: 327
    experimental studies, 4: 303
    gate-drive circuitry, 4: 304
    H-bridge operation, 4: 305
    inverter power loss analysis, 4: 300
    laboratory test environments, 4: 303
    model data, 4: 325
    modeling, 4: 320, 4: 325
    multiswitch voltage inverters, 4: 299, 4: 303
    operating point power loss analysis, 4: 302
    power loss analysis, 4: 300, 4: 301, 4: 302
    static voltage balancing, 4: 303
    switch voltage balance implementation, 4: 304
    transportation, 4: 320
    two-switch voltage inverters, 4: 303
    voltage balancing, 4: 303, 4: 304, 4: 305
    voltage inverters, 4: **295–329**
    voltage regulation systems, 4: 299
power generation current status, 4: 33
power inverter safe operating areas, 4: 297
power loss analysis, 4: 300, 4: 301, 4: 302
power supply current status, 4: 34
pure battery electric mode, 4: 325
safety engineering, 4: **77–109**
space applications, 4: 26
    Apollo, 4: 26
    Gemini spacecraft, 4: 26
space shuttle, 4: 29
static voltage balancing, 4: 303
stationary power, hydrogen technology, 4: 334
switch voltage balance implementation, 4: 304
terrestrial hydrogen applications, 4: 296
traditional inverter safe operating areas, 4: 297
transitions in hydrogen technology, 4: **331–340**
transport, hydrogen technology, 4: 333, 4: **281–293**
transportation power electronics, 4: 320
two-switch voltage inverters, 4: 303
vehicles
    battery performance evaluation, 4: 324
    current status, 4: 36
    hydrogen technology, 4: 284, 4: 333
    operation, 4: 322
voltage balancing, 4: 303, 4: 304, 4: 305
voltage inverters, 4: **295–329**
voltage regulation, 4: 299
volume in hydrogen technology, 4: 2
fuels:
see also biofuels; *individual fuels*;
biomass-to-liquids technology, 5: 44, 5: 162f, 5: 183
blending, 5: 17
characteristics, gasification, 5: 141
costs, geothermal energy sustainability, 7: 281
delivery, biomass cofiring, 5: 70
dual fuel operation, 5: 350
Fischer–Tropsch process, 5: 162f
food, 5: 22

preparation
    biomass and biofuels, 5: 44
    fan beater mills, 5: 46
    hammer mills, 5: 44
    mills, 5: 44
    power generation, 5: 44
    spindle mills, 5: 45
    tube-ball mills, 5: 45
    vertical spindle mills, 5: 45
prices, wind energy future outlook, 2: 498
processing, 5: 43
production
    artificial leaves, 1: 674
    fermentation, 5: 400
    photosynthesis, 1: 674
properties, 5: 350
solar energy collectors, 1: 217
solar energy conversion, 1: **213–237**
solar energy potential, 1: **213–237**
supply diversity, 3: 6
treatment thinning, 5: 263, 5: 285
usage, 5: 17
woody biomass feedstocks, 5: **263–291**, 5: 263
fugacity: definitions, 4: 241
Fuhrländer AG, 2: 323
full demonstration: Three Gorges Project, China, 6: 200
fullerenes, 1: 440
fulling: wind energy, 2: 45
full Navier-Stokes modeling, 2: 232
full-power converters, 2: 298
full-scale ocean wave energy prototypes, 8: 85
full tracking, 3: 14
function testing wind turbines, 2: 381
fundamental causes of wind, 2: 74
funding:
    Cameroon, Africa, hydropower, 6: 141, 6: 144, 6: 148, 6: 149
    developing country photovoltaics, 1: 113, 1: 120, 1: 125
    hydropower, 6: 6, 6: 141, 6: 144, 6: 148, 6: 149, 6: 229
        Cameroon, Africa, 6: 141, 6: 144, 6: 148, 6: 149
    Mekin hydropower project, Cameroon, Africa, 6: 144
    Memve'Elé hydro plant project, Cameroon, Africa, 6: 141
    ocean wave energy, 8: 82
    photovoltaics, 1: 113, 1: 120, 1: 125
    research and development, 2: 708, 2: 713, 2: 715
    wind energy
        research and development, 2: 708
        turbine technology, 2: 708, 2: 710, 2: 713, 2: 715, 2: 718
        wind park design economics, 2: 210
fungal pretreatments, 5: 246, 5: 246t
furans, 5: 51
furling wind speed, 2: 115–116, 2: 126, 2: 127, 2: 128f, 2: 134–135, 2: 138
furnaces, 3: 87
furnace slag, 6: 393
future directions:
    additional value extraction, 5: 389, 5: 390
    biochar, 5: 384
    bioenergy markets/trade, 5: 82
    bioethanol development, 5: 24
    biomass and biofuels
        additional value extraction, 5: 389, 5: 390
        biomass-to-liquids technology, 5: 203
        gasification, 5: 151
        greenhouse gas life cycle assessments, 5: 127
        introduction, 5: 8
    Brazilian bioethanol development, 5: 24
    building-integrated photovoltaics, 1: 697
    Cameroon, Africa, hydropower, 6: 137
    centralized energy generation, 1: 189
    chalcopyrite thin films, 1: 417
    concentrating solar power, 1: 763, 3: 631
    concentration photovoltaics, 1: 763
    costs, photovoltaics, 1: **47–72**, 1: 195, 1: 196

future directions: (*continued*)
    crystalline silicon cells, **1: 353–387**
    decentralized energy generation, 1: 189, 1: 191
    decentralized storage, 1: 191
    demand expectations, photovoltaics, 1: 50
    desalination, 2: 740
    DSM concept, 1: 191
    dye-sensitized solar cells, 1: 494
    electrical network–wind energy integration, 2: 617
    electrical power generation, 8: 5
    electricity system changes, 1: 189
    environmental–social benefits/impacts, wind power, 2: 536
    financing photovoltaics, 1: 197
    fuel cells, hydrogen technology, **4: 331–340**
    fuel prices, wind energy, 2: 498
    gasification, 5: 151
    generation systems, photovoltaics, 1: 15, 1: 25
    geothermal energy, 7: 2
    global installed capacity, 1: 185
    grid development, 1: 187, 1: 188, 1: 190, 1: 192, 1: 197
    grid infrastructure adaptations, 1: 188, 1: 197
    grid management, 1: 188
    hydrogen technology
        fuel cells, **4: 331–340**
        safety engineering, **4: 77–109**, 4: 104
    hydropower
        Cameroon, Africa, 6: 137
        India, 6: 227
        Japan, 6: 280
        projects, 6: 1, 6: 11, 6: 12
        Spain, 6: 339
    Indian hydropower, 6: 227
    infrastructure adaptations, photovoltaics, 1: 188, 1: 197
    innovative photovoltaic markets, 1: 188
    integrating wind energy, 2: 617
    investments, photovoltaics, 1: 196
    Japanese hydropower, 6: 280
    luminescent solar concentrators, 1: 596
    markets, photovoltaics, 1: 183, 1: 184, 1: 188, 1: 191, 1: 697
    microtechnology, photovoltaics, 1: 528
    module prices, 1: 193
    molten carbonate fuel cells, 4: 238
    multi-junction cells, 1: 509
    nanotechnology, photovoltaics, 1: 528
    ocean wave energy, 8: 5, 8: 164
    off-grid application photovoltaics, 1: 192
    offshore wind power, 2: 464
    on-grid application photovoltaics, 1: 192
    organic solar cells, 1: 473
    passive solar architecture, 3: 663
    peak loads, photovoltaics, 1: 190
    photovoltaics, **1: 179–198**
        centralized energy generation, 1: 189
        chalcopyrite thin films, 1: 417
        competiveness, 1: 181, 1: 187
        costs, **1: 47–72**, 1: 195, 1: 196
        crystalline silicon cells, **1: 353–387**
        decentralized energy generation, 1: 189, 1: 191
        decentralized storage, 1: 191
        demand expectations, 1: 50
        DSM concept, 1: 191
        electricity system changes, 1: 189
        financing, 1: 197
        global industry overview, 1: 175
        global installed capacity, 1: 185
        grid development, 1: 187, 1: 188, 1: 190, 1: 192, 1: 197
        grid infrastructure adaptations, 1: 188, 1: 197
        grid management, 1: 188
        infrastructure adaptations, 1: 188, 1: 197
        innovative market designs, 1: 188
        investments, 1: 196
        markets, 1: 183, 1: 184, 1: 188, 1: 191, 1: 697
            designs, 1: 188
        development, 1: 183, 1: 188
        segmentation, 1: 191
    microtechnology, 1: 528
    module prices, 1: 193
    multi-junction cells, 1: 509
    nanotechnology, 1: 528
    off-grid application share, 1: 192
    on-grid application share, 1: 192
    organic solar cells, 1: 473
    peak loads, 1: 190
    plasmonics, 1: 654
    policy recommendations, 1: 188, 1: 196
    power distribution systems, 1: 197
    project investments, 1: 196
    promotion schemes, 1: 82, 1: 89, 1: 103
    recommendations, 1: 188, 1: 196
    regulatory frameworks, 1: 196
    research and development, 1: 196, 1: 197, 3: 634
    signal transmission, 1: 196
    silicon cells, **1: 353–387**
    smart grids, 1: 190
    storage, 1: 191
    sunbelt countries investments, 1: 197
    super smart grids, 1: 190
    support regulatory frameworks, 1: 196
    system prices, 1: 193
    technological trends, 1: 192
    technology investments, 1: 196
    transmission systems, 1: 197
    upconversion, 1: 546
    variability management, 1: 189
plasmonic photovoltaics, 1: 654
policy recommendations, photovoltaics, 1: 188, 1: 196
power distribution systems, 1: 197
price trends, wind energy, 2: 471
product-integrated photovoltaics, 1: 730
project investments, photovoltaics, 1: 196
promotion schemes, photovoltaics, 1: 82, 1: 89, 1: 103
recommendations, photovoltaics, 1: 188, 1: 196
regulatory frameworks, photovoltaics, 1: 196
research
    concentrating solar power, 3: 634
    concrete structure durability, 6: 392
    photovoltaics, 1: 196, 1: 197, 3: 634
signal transmission, 1: 196
silicon cell photovoltaics, **1: 353–387**
Singapore photovoltaics, 1: 82
smart grids, 1: 190
solar power satellites, 1: 771
solar radiation resources assessments, 1: 234
solar water heating systems, **3: 419–447**
Spanish hydropower, 6: 339
storage, photovoltaics, 1: 191
sunbelt countries photovoltaic investments, 1: 197
super smart grids, photovoltaics, 1: 190
support regulatory frameworks, photovoltaics, 1: 196
system prices, photovoltaics, 1: 193
technological trends, photovoltaics, 1: 192
technology investments, photovoltaics, 1: 196
thermophotovoltaic energy conversion, 1: 616
transmission systems, photovoltaics, 1: 197
United States photovoltaics, 1: 89, 1: 184
upconversion, 1: 546
variability management, photovoltaics, 1: 189
very large-scale photovoltaic systems, 1: 741
wind energy, **2: 1–10**, 2: 35
    desalination, 2: 740
    environmental–social benefits/impacts, 2: 536
    fuel prices, 2: 498
    integration, 2: 617
    price trends, 2: 471
    wind turbine electrical systems, 2: 303
fuzzy logic, 3: 659, 3: 661f, 3: 662

G

Gabriel y Galán dam, Spain, **6**: 333–335, **6**: 335*f*
gain scheduling, **2**: 348, **2**: 348*f*
Gaitanejo dam, Spain, **6**: 322, **6**: 323*f*
gallium:
    aluminum-gallium-arsenide/gallium-arsenide multi-junction cells, **1**: 497
    indium-gallium-antimonide solar cells, **1**: 608, **1**: 610
    indium-gallium-arsenide solar cells, **1**: 608, **1**: 610, **1**: 611, **1**: 614
gallium-antimonide solar cells, **1**: 608, **1**: 610, **1**: 614
gallium-arsenide:
    aluminum-gallium-arsenide/gallium-arsenide multi-junction cells, **1**: 497
    gallium-antimonide solar cells, **1**: 608–609
    indium-gallium-arsenide solar cells, **1**: 608, **1**: 610, **1**: 614
    InGaP/GaAs/Ge 3-junction solar cells, **1**: 497, **1**: 503, **1**: 506
    luminescent down-shifting, **1**: 568
    multi-junction cells, **1**: 497
    single-junction solar cells, **1**: 497–498, **1**: 498–500, **1**: 499*f*
galvanic corrosion, **7**: 242
galvanized steel enclosures, **3**: 114, **3**: 114*f*
Gamesa: wind turbine electrical systems, **2**: 310, **2**: 311*t*, **2**: 312*f*, **2**: 313*f*
gamma spectra: ocean waves, **8**: 16, **8**: 16*t*, **8**: 17*f*
garage-like enclosure hydrogen safety, **4**: 95
gas analysis: geothermal chemistry, **7**: 100
gas cleaning, **5**: 145, **5**: 162*f*
gas diffusion electrodes, **4**: 165
    carbon dioxide, **4**: 169
    corrosion, **4**: 169
    design, **4**: 166
    durability, **4**: 169
    electrode modeling, **4**: 167
    fabrication, **4**: 166, **4**: 168
    flooding, **4**: 169
    materials, **4**: 166
    modeling, **4**: 167
    operation mechanisms, **4**: 167
    weeping, **4**: 169
gas diffusion layers, **4**: 192
gas engines: combined power conversion cycles, **3**: 607
gaseous biofuels, **5**: 61, **5**: 351
gaseous emissions:
    biomass and biofuels, **5**: 31, **5**: 33, **5**: 51
    carbon dioxide, **5**: 29, **5**: 305, **5**: 308, **5**: 327
    combustion, **5**: 51
    environmental impacts, **5**: 51
gases:
    see also compressed gas
    collection/sampling, **7**: 95
    contamination monitoring, **4**: 127
    origins, geochemistry, **7**: 117–118
gas flume hazard assessments, **7**: 57
gasification, **5**: 133–153
    arboricultural arisings, **5**: 141
    basic technology, **5**: 135
    biochar, **5**: 366*t*, **5**: 371, **5**: 373*f*
    biomass, **5**: 133–153
        basic technology, **5**: 135
        case studies, **5**: 149
        cleaning technologies, **5**: 145
        cofiring, **5**: 61, **5**: 62
        combined heat and power, **5**: 87, **5**: 88, **5**: 89, **5**: 94
        contaminants, **5**: 141, **5**: 142
        conversion, **5**: 168
        developments, **5**: 151
        examples, **5**: 149
        fuel characteristics, **5**: 141
        future development, **5**: 151
        gas cleaning technologies, **5**: 145
        gas processing, **5**: 142
        historical development, **5**: 134
        power generation, **5**: 37

        syngas quality, **5**: 144, **5**: 144*f*, **5**: 144*t*
    biomass-to-liquids technology, **5**: 156, **5**: 159, **5**: 159*f*, **5**: 162, **5**: 162*f*, **5**: 163*t*
        economics, **5**: 191
        Fischer–Tropsch process, **5**: 168
        implementation progress, **5**: 188
        syngas, **5**: 168
    case studies, **5**: 149
    cleaning technologies, **5**: 145
    combined heat and power, **5**: 87, **5**: 88, **5**: 89, **5**: 94
    combustion technology, **5**: 62
    contaminants, biomass, **5**: 141, **5**: 142
    developments, **5**: 151
    economics, **5**: 191
    examples, **5**: 149
    Fischer–Tropsch process, **5**: 168
    forestry arisings, **5**: 141
    fuel characteristics, **5**: 141
    future development, **5**: 151
    gas cleaning technologies, **5**: 145
    gas processing, **5**: 142
    historical development, **5**: 134
    hydrogen technology, **4**: 50
    mixed wood, **5**: 140
    operation scales, **5**: 172, **5**: 172*f*
    power generation, **5**: 37
    pyrolysis, biomass, **5**: 135
    reactor types, **5**: 169
    sawmill coproducts, **5**: 141
    scales of operation, **5**: 172, **5**: 172*f*
    solid fuel recovery, **5**: 140, **5**: 142*t*
    syngas, **5**: 168
    virgin biomass feedstocks, **5**: 141, **5**: 142*t*
    waste biomass feedstocks, **5**: 140, **5**: 142*t*
        mixed wood, **5**: 140
        solid fuel recovery, **5**: 140, **5**: 142*t*
    wood, **5**: 140, **5**: 141, **5**: 142*t*
    woodchip, **5**: 141
gasifiers:
    biochar, **5**: 358
    biomass, **5**: 136, **5**: 139
    configurations, **5**: 136
    design, **5**: 136
    feedstock supplies, **5**: 139
    oxidants, **5**: 139
Gas Natural SDG, **6**: 315
gasochromogenics, **3**: 316, **3**: 350
gasoline:
    alcohol fuels, **5**: 321, **5**: 322
    biofuel operation, **5**: 346
    biomass-to-liquids technology, **5**: 185
    displacement, **5**: 333
    engine modifications, **5**: 346
    fire safety, **4**: 79, **4**: 79*f*
    physicochemical properties, **5**: 317, **5**: 317*t*
    safety, **5**: 323
    synthesis, **5**: 158, **5**: 183*f*, **5**: 185
gas processing:
    biomass gasification, **5**: 142
    contaminants, **5**: 142
    gasification, **5**: 142
    impurities, **5**: 142
gas sampling, **7**: 95
gas supersaturation, **6**: 73, **6**: 75
gas thermometers, **7**: 140
gas-to-liquids (GTL):
    automotives, **5**: 307–308
    biomass-to-liquids technology, **5**: 159, **5**: 160–161, **5**: 161–162, **5**: 191, **5**: 197
GAST study, **3**: 629
gas turbines, **2**: 574, **3**: 604, **3**: 608–609
gate-drive circuitry, **4**: 304
GCL-Poly Energy Holdings Limited, **1**: 174

gearboxes:
    direct-drive systems, 2: 680
    IEC standards, 2: 375
    medium speed generators, 2: 293
    wind turbines, 2: 680
gearless machines, 2: 680
Gedser machine, 2: 60, 2: 63f
GE energy, 2: 313, 2: 313f, 2: 314f, 2: 315t
Gemasolar solar thermal power plant, 3: 623
Gemini spacecraft, 4: 26
gender equality, 7: 276
generalized Pareto distribution, 8: 55, 8: 57
generalized Planck equation, 1: 305
General Motors, 4: 173
general principles: alkaline fuel cells, 4: 160
generation:
    see also cogeneration; electricity...; multi-exciton generation; power...
    carrier-carrier generation, 1: 303
    costs
        very large-scale photovoltaic systems, 1: 736
        wind energy, 2: **469–501**
            prices, 2: 477, 2: 481
    hydropower source economics, 6: 40
    power prices, 2: 477, 2: 481, 5: 29
    power system structures, 2: 571
    reserve capacity, wind power, 2: 598
    solar energy conversion principles, 1: 293, 1: 301
generators:
    Canadian hydropower, 6: **153–178**
    control systems, 2: 330, 2: 352, 2: 358
    Coo-Trois Ponts , Belgium, 6: 432
    dry-steam power plants, 7: 209, 7: 211f, 7: 214
    electrical systems, wind turbines, 2: 279, 2: 281
    hydropower, Canada, 6: **153–178**
    modeling wind turbines, 2: 336
    simplified generic axial-flow microhydro turbines, 6: 444
    small wind turbine electrical systems, 2: 301
    wind turbines
        control systems, 2: 330, 2: 352, 2: 358
        electrical systems, 2: 279, 2: 281
        modeling, 2: 336
        stand alone hybrid systems, 2: 631
generic axial-flow microhydro turbines, 6: **435–466**
generic flowsheets: biodiesel production, 5: 206
generic process system layouts, 3: 573
genetic algorithms, 2: 652, 2: 653t, 3: 655, 3: 659
genetics: yield improvement potentials, 5: 299, 5: 300
geocentric systems, 3: 30, 3: 30f, 3: 31, 3: 31f
geochemistry, 7: **95–168**
    alteration, 7: 103
    carbon dioxide emissions, 7: 100, 7: 120
    classification, water, 7: 101
    computer programs, 7: 128
    exploration techniques, 7: 58
    flow, 7: 108, 7: 141
    fluid analysis, 7: 100
    fluid sampling, 7: 95
    gas sampling, 7: 95
    geothermal energy, 7: **95–168**
    geothermal fluid flow/origins, 7: 108
    liquid sampling, 7: 95
    origins of geothermal fluids, 7: 108
    production of geothermal energy, 7: 141
    reaction path calculations, 7: 128
    sampling, 7: 95, 7: 97
    speciation, 7: 128
    temperature, 7: 103, 7: 141
    Theistareykir, NE Iceland, 7: 155
    thermometry, 7: 58, 7: 59, 7: 134
    vapor phase sampling, 7: 95
    water classification, 7: 101
geographical information systems (GIS), 1: 226, 2: 407

geographics:
    hydropower, Iran, 6: 257
    photovoltaic distribution, 1: 14, 1: 14f
    wind farms, 2: 591
    wind park design, 2: 186–187, 2: 195
    wind power variability, 2: 591
geohazards, 6: 216, 7: 56
geological explorations, 7: 52
    controlling structure mapping, 7: 55
    direct current resistivity methods, 7: 61, 7: 63
    exploration techniques, 7: 52
    fault mapping, 7: 56
    geothermal energy, 7: 52
    hydrology, 7: 54
    mapping, 7: 53, 7: 54
    rifts, geothermal energy, 7: 55
    structure mapping, 7: 55
    subsurface mapping, 7: 55
    surface mapping, 7: 54
    time considerations, 7: 55
    topography, 7: 54
geological hazards, 6: 216, 7: 56
geological maps: geothermal energy explorations, 7: 53
geological setting: Horseshoe Bend hydroelectric scheme, 6: 473
geology:
    Indian hydropower, 6: 235, 6: 240, 6: 242
    Three Gorges Project, China, 6: 181
geomembranes: maintenance, 6: 394
geometrical factors:
    blackbodies, 1: 321
    isotropic radiation, 1: 319
    nonisotropic radiation, 1: 321
    photovoltaics, thermodynamics, 1: 319
    solar energy conversion principles, 1: 306
    thermal radiation, 1: 319
    thermodynamics, 1: 319
geometric similarity: ocean waves, 8: 85
geometry:
    axial-flow microhydro turbines, 6: 454
    high concentration solar collectors, 3: 169, 3: 186, 3: 201
    microbial fuel cells, 4: 271
    photovoltaic/thermal solar collectors, 3: 273
    receiver aperture, 3: 186
    solar dishes, 3: 201
geopressured systems, 7: 5
geosynchronous orbits, 1: 772
geothermal baskets, 5: 191
geothermal chemistry, 7: 100, 7: 101, 7: 120
    see also geochemistry
Geothermal Education Office diagrams, 7: 169, 7: 171f
geothermal energy, 7: **1–2**
    advanced power plants, 7: 226, 7: 228
    agricultural drying, 7: 169, 7: 173t, 7: 174, 7: 176f, 7: 180, 7: 180f, 7: 181, 7: 182, 7: 183f
    alteration, 7: 103
    aquaculture ponds, 7: 169, 7: 173t, 7: 174, 7: 175f, 7: 184, 7: 185f
    assessment techniques, 7: **51–94**
    atmosphere, 7: 283
    bathing, 7: 169, 7: 170, 7: 173t
    binary power plants, 7: 207, 7: 222, 7: 231, 7: 233, 7: 279
    boreholes, 7: 18
    capital expenditure, 7: 259, 7: 260, 7: 261, 7: 263
    case histories, 7: 180
    chemical geothermometers, 7: 58, 7: 59, 7: 134
    chemical methodologies, 7: 1
    clean development mechanisms, 7: 290, 7: 291
    climate change, sustainability, 7: 272, 7: 283, 7: 290
    combined cycle power plants, 7: 231
    company comparisons, 7: 261, 7: 262t
    computer modeling, 7: 35
    conferences, 7: 273
    controlling structure mapping, 7: 55
    costs, 7: **259–270**, 7: 259

current status
   direct heat utilization, 7: 169, 7: 172t, 7: 173t
   Iceland, 7: 286
   sustainable development, 7: 286
detailed numerical modeling, 7: 35
diffusion physics, 7: 10
direct current resistivity methods, 7: 61, 7: 63
direct dry-steam power plants, 7: 209
direct heat utilization, 7: **169–186**
   agricultural drying, 7: 169, 7: 173t, 7: 174, 7: 176f, 7: 180, 7: 180f, 7: 181, 7: 182, 7: 183f
   aquaculture ponds, 7: 169, 7: 173t, 7: 174, 7: 175f, 7: 184, 7: 185f
   bathing, 7: 169, 7: 170, 7: 173t
   case histories, 7: 180
   current status, 7: 169, 7: 172t, 7: 173t
   development, 7: 170
   district heating, 7: 169, 7: 171, 7: 174f, 7: 180, 7: 181f, 7: 182, 7: 184, 7: 184f
   downhole pumps, 7: 176, 7: 177f
   drying, 7: 169, 7: 173t, 7: 174, 7: 176f, 7: 180, 7: 180f, 7: 181, 7: 182, 7: 183f
   environmental considerations, 7: 179
   equipment selection, 7: 175
   examples, 7: 180
   global distribution, 7: 170, 7: 172t, 7: 173t
   greenhouses, 7: 169, 7: 170, 7: 172t, 7: 173t, 7: 174, 7: 175f, 7: 181
   heat exchangers, 7: 178, 7: 178f, 7: 179f
   industrial applications, 7: 169, 7: 173t, 7: 174, 7: 176f, 7: 180, 7: 180f, 7: 181, 7: 182, 7: 183f
   industrial drying, 7: 169, 7: 173t, 7: 174, 7: 176f, 7: 180, 7: 180f, 7: 181, 7: 182, 7: 183f
   piping, 7: 177, 7: 178f
   pools, 7: 169, 7: 170, 7: 173t
   pumps, 7: 176, 7: 177f
   space heating, 7: 169, 7: 171, 7: 173t, 7: 174f, 7: 180, 7: 181f, 7: 182, 7: 184, 7: 184f
   spa heating, 7: 169, 7: 170, 7: 173t
   swimming pools, 7: 169, 7: 170, 7: 173t
   tomato drying, Greece, 7: 180, 7: 180f
direct-use applications, 7: 279
district heating, 7: 169, 7: 171, 7: 174f, 7: 180, 7: 181f, 7: 182, 7: 184, 7: 184f
double-flash power plants, 7: 207, 7: 217, 7: 217f, 7: 219, 7: 220
downhole pumps, 7: 176, 7: 177f
drying, 7: 169, 7: 173t, 7: 174, 7: 176f, 7: 180, 7: 180f, 7: 181, 7: 182, 7: 183f
dry-steam power plants, 7: 207, 7: 209
economics, 7: **259–270**
   overview/introduction, 7: 1–2
   sustainable development, 7: 274, 7: 280, 7: 286
education, 7: 288
electrical resistivity, 7: 61
electricity
   overview/introduction, 7: 1
   production costs, 7: **259–270**
   production investment factors, 7: **259–270**
electromagnetic resistivity methods, 7: 61, 7: 62, 7: 65
elevation changes, 7: 58
energy security, 7: **271–295**
environmental impacts, 7: 179, 7: 276, 7: 278, 7: 283, 7: 287, 7: 289
equity, 7: 282
exploration techniques, 7: **51–94**
   chemical geothermometers, 7: 58, 7: 59, 7: 134
   electrical resistivity, 7: 61
   electromagnetic resistivity methods, 7: 61, 7: 62, 7: 65
   geochemistry, 7: 58
   geohazards, 7: 56
   geological explorations, 7: 52
   geological hazard assessments, 7: 56
   geothermometers, 7: 58, 7: 59, 7: 134

   hazard assessments, 7: 56
   heat flow, 7: 84, 7: 86, 7: 87
   importance, 7: 52
   magnetotelluric measurements, 7: 52, 7: 61, 7: 63, 7: 69
   mineral equilibria, 7: 60
   multiple mineral equilibria, 7: 60
   ratio-based geothermometers, 7: 59
   resistivity methods, 7: 61
   rock resistivity, 7: 78
   temperature, 7: 58
   thermal methods, 7: 83
   thermometers, 7: 58, 7: 59, 7: 134
   transient electromagnetic resistivity methods, 7: 61, 7: 62, 7: 65, 7: 68
   univariant geothermometers, 7: 59
fault mapping, 7: 56
fault movements, 7: 57
flash-steam power plants, 7: 207, 7: 216
flooding hazard assessments, 7: 58
flow geochemistry, 7: 108, 7: 141
fluid analysis, 7: 100
fluid flow, 7: 10, 7: 88
fluid properties, 7: 240
fluid sampling, 7: 95
fossil fuels, 7: 229, 7: 272
future outlooks, 7: 2
gas flumes, 7: 57
gas sampling, 7: 95
geochemistry, 7: **95–168**
   alteration, 7: 103
   exploration techniques, 7: 58
   flow, 7: 108, 7: 141
   fluid analysis, 7: 100
   fluid sampling, 7: 95
   gas sampling, 7: 95
   liquid sampling, 7: 95
   production, 7: 141
   reaction path calculations, 7: 128
   sampling, 7: 95, 7: 97
   speciation, 7: 128
   temperature, 7: 103, 7: 141
   Theistareykir, NE Iceland, 7: 155
   thermometry, 7: 58, 7: 59, 7: 134
   vapor phase sampling, 7: 95
geohazards, 7: 56
geological explorations, 7: 52
   controlling structure mapping, 7: 55
   direct current resistivity methods, 7: 61, 7: 63
   exploration techniques, 7: 52
   fault mapping, 7: 56
   hydrology, 7: 54
   mapping, 7: 53, 7: 54
   rifts, 7: 55
   structure mapping, 7: 55
   subsurface mapping, 7: 55
   surface mapping, 7: 54
   time considerations, 7: 55
   topography, 7: 54
geological hazards, 7: 56
geothermal heat pumps, 7: **187–206**
geothermometers, 7: 58, 7: 59, 7: 134
global distribution, 7: 170, 7: 172t, 7: 173t
global partnerships, 7: 290
goals in sustainable development, 7: 272, 7: 274, 7: 277, 7: 287
greenhouse gases, 7: 272, 7: 283, 7: 290
greenhouses, 7: 169, 7: 170, 7: 172t, 7: 173t, 7: 174, 7: 175f, 7: 181
hazard assessments, 7: 56
   elevation changes, 7: 58
   fault movements, 7: 57
   flooding, 7: 58
   gas flumes, 7: 57
   molten rock drilling, 7: 57

geothermal energy (*continued*)
    sliding, 7: 58
    volcanic events, 7: 56
  health, 7: 287
  heat exchangers, 7: 178, 7: 178f, 7: 179f
  heat flow, 7: 84, 7: 86, 7: 87
  heat pumps, 7: **187–206**
    resources, 7: 187
    sustainable development, 7: 279
  heat transfer, 7: 12
  historical overviews, 7: 276, 7: 286
  hunger eradication, 7: 288
  hybrid power plants, 7: 207, 7: 229
  hydrology, 7: 54
  Iceland, 7: 286
  importance of exploration techniques, 7: 52
  indicators, 7: 277, 7: 278
  indirect-use applications, 7: 279
  industrial direct heat utilization, 7: 169, 7: 173t, 7: 174, 7: 176f, 7: 180, 7: 180f, 7: 181, 7: 182, 7: 183f
  industrial drying, 7: 169, 7: 173t, 7: 174, 7: 176f, 7: 180, 7: 180f, 7: 181, 7: 182, 7: 183f
  industrial macroeconomic factors, 7: 259, 7: 263
  industrial microeconomic analysis, 7: 260
  international investment, 7: **259–270**
  investment factors, 7: 2, 7: **259–270**, 7: 259
  joint inversion, 7: 71
  Kalina binary cycles, 7: 207, 7: 228, 7: 233
  Kyoto Protocol, 7: 290, 7: 291
  liquid sampling, 7: 95
  lumped parameter modeling, 7: 31
  macroeconomic factors, 7: 259, 7: 263
  magnetotelluric measurements, 7: 52, 7: 61, 7: 63, 7: 69
  mapping, 7: 53, 7: 54
  microeconomic analysis, 7: 260
  Millennium Development Goals, 7: 272, 7: 274, 7: 287
  mineral equilibria, 7: 60
  modeling, 7: 29, 7: 30, 7: 31
  molten rock drilling, 7: 57
  multinational firms, 7: 259, 7: 259–260, 7: 260, 7: 261, 7: 263, 7: 265
  multiple mineral equilibria, 7: 60
  numerical modeling, 7: 35
  performance assessments, 7: 235
  permeability, 7: 16–18
  physical methodologies, 7: 1
  physics, 7: **3–50**
  piping, 7: 177, 7: 178f
  policy, 2: 554
  pools, 7: 169, 7: 170, 7: 173t
  poverty eradication, 7: 288
  power plants, 7: **207–237**
    definitions, 7: 240
    overview/introduction, 7: 1
    performance assessments, 7: 235
  power production
    corrosion, 7: **239–257**
    corrosion films, 7: 241
    cracking, 7: 243
    crevice corrosion, 7: 242
    erosion corrosion, 7: 245
    exfoliation, 7: 245
    fatigue, 7: 244
    galvanic corrosion, 7: 242
    hydrogen embrittlement, 7: 243
    hydrogen-induced cracking, 7: 243
    hydropower multibenefit solutions, 6: 43
    intergranular corrosion, 7: 242
    material selection, 7: **239–257**
    pitting corrosion, 7: 241
    scaling, 7: **239–257**
    stress corrosion cracking, 7: 243
    sulfide stress cracking, 7: 244
    uniform corrosion, 7: 241
  pressure, 7: 8, 7: 10, 7: 19, 7: 46f
  pressure diffusion physics, 7: 10
  primary education, 7: 288
  processes, 7: 8
  production
    costs, 7: **259–270**
    geochemistry, 7: 141
    potentials, 7: 22
    sustainability, 7: 272, 7: 280
  properties, 7: 8
  pumps, 7: 176, 7: 177f
  ratio-based geothermometers, 7: 59
  reaction path calculations, 7: 128
  regression results, 7: 265, 7: 266t, 7: 267t, 7: 268t, 7: 269t
  reinjection, 7: 39
  relative permeability, 7: 16–18
  renewability, 7: 43
  resistivity methods, 7: 61, 7: 71
    Schlumberger soundings, 7: 64, 7: 68
    shift effect, 7: 71
  resources
    heat pumps, 7: 187
    management, 7: 36
    physics, 7: **3–50**
  rifts, 7: 55
  rock resistivity, 7: 78
  sampling, 7: 95, 7: 97
  scale effects/scaling, wells, 7: 41, 7: 42, 7: 252, 7: 253
  Schlumberger soundings, 7: 64, 7: 68
  shallow geothermal heat pumps, 7: **187–206**
  shift effect, 7: 71
  single-flash power plants, 7: 207, 7: 217, 7: 217f, 7: 218, 7: 231
  sliding, 7: 58
  social issues, 7: 275, 7: 282, 7: 287
  space cooling, 7: 1–2
  space heating, 7: 1–2, 7: 169, 7: 171, 7: 173t, 7: 174f, 7: 180, 7: 181f, 7: 182, 7: 184, 7: 184f
  spa heating, 7: 169, 7: 170, 7: 173t
  speciation, 7: 128
  static modeling, 7: 30
  steam power plants, 7: 207, 7: 209
  structure mapping, 7: 55
  subsurface mapping, 7: 55
  surface mapping, 7: 54
  surface rock, 7: 1
  sustainable development, 7: **271–295**
    atmosphere, 7: 283
    clean development mechanisms, 7: 290, 7: 291
    climate change, 7: 272, 7: 283, 7: 290
    conferences, 7: 273
    current status, 7: 286
    definitions, 7: 277
    direct-use applications, 7: 279
    economics, 7: 274, 7: 280, 7: 286
    environmental impacts, 7: 276, 7: 278, 7: 283, 7: 287, 7: 289
    equity, 7: 282
    global partnerships, 7: 290
    goals, 7: 272, 7: 274, 7: 277, 7: 287
    greenhouse gases, 7: 272, 7: 283, 7: 290
    health, 7: 287
    heat pumps, 7: 279
    historical overviews, 7: 276, 7: 286
    Iceland, 7: 286
    indicators, 7: 277, 7: 278
    indirect-use applications, 7: 279
    investment, 7: 261, 7: 262f
    Kyoto Protocol, 7: 290, 7: 291
    Millennium Development Goals, 7: 272, 7: 274, 7: 287
    physics, 7: 43
    production, 7: 272, 7: 280
    social issues, 7: 275, 7: 282, 7: 287
    water impacts, 7: 285

swimming pools, 7: 169, 7: 170, 7: 173t
systems
   building-integrated photovoltaic-thermal systems, 3: 391
   classification, 7: 5
   definitions, 7: 4
   monitoring, 7: 24
   physics, 7: **3–50**
   processes, 7: 8
   properties, 7: 8
   water-air heat pumps, 3: 391
temperature, 7: 58, 7: 103, 7: 141
Theistareykir, NE Iceland, 7: 155
thermal methods, exploration techniques, 7: 83
thermometry, 7: 58, 7: 59, 7: 134
time considerations, 7: 55
tomato drying, Greece, 7: 180, 7: 180f
topography, 7: 54
Torfajökull high-temperature fields, Iceland, 7: 60
transient electromagnetic resistivity methods, 7: 61, 7: 62, 7: 65, 7: 68
two-phase regions/systems, 7: 15
univariant geothermometers, 7: 59
universal primary education, 7: 288
usage, sustainable development, 7: 280
utilization response, 7: 22
vapor phase sampling, 7: 95
volcanic events, 7: 56
volumetric assessments, 7: 30
water heat pumps, 3: 391, 3: 505
water impacts, 7: 285
wells
   physics, 7: 18
   scale effects/scaling, 7: 41, 7: 42, 7: 252, 7: 253
wind energy policy, 2: 554
geothermal environments:
   material performance, 7: 247
   scaling power production, 7: 249
geothermal fields: definitions, 7: 4
geothermal fluids:
   chemical composition, 7: 126
   definitions, 7: 240
   flow, 7: 108
   mixing, 7: 130
   origins, 7: 108
geothermal ground sources: heat pumps, 3: 503–504
geothermal heat pumps (GHP), 7: **187–206**
   bore heat exchangers, 7: 197, 7: 200, 7: 203
   capital costs, 7: 202
   closed-loop systems, 7: 190
   conductivity, 7: 198
   conventional heating systems, 7: 202
   cooling, 7: 193
   costs, 7: 202
   design, 7: 197
   dimensioning site investigations, 7: 195, 7: 198
   energy piles, 7: 191
   engineering design, 7: 197
   environmental issues, 7: 203
   geothermal baskets, 7: 191
   groundwater systems, 7: 201
   heat flow values, shallow systems, 7: 196
   heating, 7: 193
   heat source media, 3: 505
   installation, 7: 199
   licensing, 7: 203
   local heat flow values, 7: 196
   maintenance, 7: 202
   on-site ground thermal conductivity, 7: 195
   open-loop systems, 7: 190
   operation and maintenance, 7: 202
   planning, 7: 199
   production sustainability, 7: 203
   shallow systems, 7: **187–206**
   site investigations, 7: 195, 7: 198
   sustainable production, 7: 203
   thermal conductivity, 7: 198
   thermal response tests, 7: 195, 7: 196
   types, 7: 190
geothermal reservoirs, 7: 5
geothermometry, 7: 58, 7: 59, 7: 134
germanium:
   indium-gallium-phosphorous/gallium-arsenide/germanium-based 3-junction solar cells, 1: 497, 1: 503, 1: 504, 1: 506
   substrate lattice matching, 1: 503, 1: 504
   tandem stack coatings, 3: 306
   thermophotovoltaic energy conversion, 1: 611
Germany:
   bioenergy policy development, 5: 426
   enhanced geothermal systems, 7: 233
   feed-in tariffs, 1: 91
   Goldisthal pumped storage plant, 6: 406
   high concentration solar collector markets, 3: 192, 3: 193
   market development, wind power, 2: 662
   offshore wind power
      activity, 2: 436–437, 2: 439f, 2: 439–440
      market development, 2: 667
      tripile support structures, 2: 449
   photovoltaics
      industry overview, 1: 165, 1: 166, 1: 168, 1: 170, 1: 171, 1: 172
      promotion schemes, 1: 90, 1: 93, 1: 103
      support mechanisms, 1: 90, 1: 93, 1: 103
   solar irradiance-photovoltaic power forecasts, 1: 273, 1: 277
   wind energy
      historical overviews, 2: 65, 2: 68f
      wind power market development, 2: 662
      wind turbine manufacturers, 2: 669
GET FiT *see* global energy transfer feed-in tariffs
getters: solar collectors, 3: 177
geysers, 7: 209
GHP *see* geothermal heat pumps
Gibbs free energy, 1: 315, 4: 241, 4: 243–244, 4: 250
Giddens propeller turbines, 6: 441–442
gigawatt hours (GWh), 6: 1, 6: 16
giga-watt photovoltaic markets, 1: 15, 1: 19
GIN *see* grout intensity number
Gintech Energy Corporation, 1: 171
GIS *see* Geographical Information Systems; geographical information systems
glaciers, 6: 232, 6: 232f
glass:
   see also glazing
   capillary transparent insulation, 3: 341
   chalcopyrite thin films, 1: 410
   glazings, 3: 315, 3: 321, 3: 327
      manufacture, 3: 315, 3: 328
   heat loss suppression, 3: 330
   light admittance, 3: 329
   manufacture
      float glass, 3: 328
      glazings, 3: 315, 3: 328
      historical development, 3: 315
   plate processing, 1: 395
   solar collectors, 3: 329, 3: 330
   solar thermal energy, 3: 329
      glazings, 3: 315, 3: 321, 3: 327
   superstrate cadmium telluride thin films, 1: 428
   weather protection, 3: 330
glass fibres, 3: 114, 3: 114f, 3: 334
Glauert's optimum rotor method, 2: 227
glazing, 3: **313–355**
   see also evacuated glazing; glass
   absorption, 3: 320
   aluminum window frames, 3: 333
   ambient heat transfer coefficients, 3: 131, 3: 132t
   buildings, 3: **313–355**
   chemical vapor deposition, 3: 324–325

glazing (*continued*)
    chromogenic materials, **3:** 316, **3:** 342
    composite wood products, **3:** 333
    deposition, **3:** 324
    electrochromogenic devices/materials, **3:** 314, **3:** 316, **3:** 336, **3:** 338, **3:** 342, **3:** 343
    electron beam gun evaporation, **3:** 324
    emerging technologies, **3:** 316, **3:** 336, **3:** 339, **3:** 342
    energy evaluation, **3:** 321
    evaporation, **3:** 324
    fiberglass window frames, **3:** 334
    flat-plate collectors, **3:** 104, **3:** 111
    float glass, **3:** 314, **3:** 315, **3:** 327
    frames, **3:** 333, **3:** 334
    gasochromogenics, **3:** 316, **3:** 350
    glazing–ambient heat transfer coefficients, **3:** 131, **3:** 132*t*
    glazing–sky radiation exchange, **3:** 130
    heat transfer coefficients, **3:** 131, **3:** 132*t*, **3:** 321, **3:** 322, **3:** 330, **3:** 330*t*, **3:** 332, **3:** 332*f*, **3:** 334, **3:** 334*t*
    hybrid materials, **3:** 334
    laws, **3:** 318
    liquid crystal switching devices, **3:** 351
    low-emittance coatings
        deposition, **3:** 324
        solar control, **3:** 323
        solar thermal energy, **3:** 314, **3:** 316, **3:** 323
        thermal insulation, **3:** 323
    low-temperature stationary collectors, **3:** 104, **3:** 111, **3:** 124, **3:** 124*t*, **3:** 130, **3:** 131, **3:** 132
    manufacture
        glass, **3:** 315, **3:** 328
        toughened glass, **3:** 329
    metal hydride switchable mirrors, **3:** 350
    metal oxide layers, **3:** 316, **3:** 325, **3:** 344, **3:** 345, **3:** 346
    micro-blind switching devices, **3:** 351
    optical analysis, **3:** 319
    optical properties, **3:** 316
    passive solar technologies, **3:** 359
    photochromogenics, **3:** 316, **3:** 346
    physical vapor deposition, **3:** 324
    plastics, window frames, **3:** 334
    polymer-dispersed liquid crystal switching devices, **3:** 351
    radiation exchange, **3:** 130
    radiation refraction, **3:** 319
    radiation transmission, **3:** 319
    reflection, **3:** 320, **3:** 331
    refraction, **3:** 21, **3:** 319
    sealants, **3:** 335
    sky radiation exchange, **3:** 130
    solar control, **3:** 323
    solar irradiation, **3:** 316
    solar radiation, **3:** 21, **3:** 318
    solar thermal energy, **3: 313–355**
    spacers, **3:** 335
    sputtering, **3:** 324
    suspended particle switching devices, **3:** 351
    switchable mirrors, **3:** 350
    thermal evaporation, **3:** 324
    thermal insulation, **3:** 323
    thermal properties, **3:** 316
        energy evaluation, **3:** 321
        frames, **3:** 334
        heat transfer coefficients, **3:** 321, **3:** 322, **3:** 330, **3:** 330*t*, **3:** 332, **3:** 332*f*, **3:** 334, **3:** 334*t*
        solar thermal energy, **3:** 316
        window frames, **3:** 334
    thermal radiation, **3:** 318
    thermogenics, **3:** 316, **3:** 350
    thermoplastics, **3:** 334
    total transmittance, **3:** 317, **3:** 320
    toughened glass, **3:** 328, **3:** 329
    vapor deposition, **3:** 324, **3:** 324–325
    vinyl window frames, **3:** 334
    windows
        emerging technologies, **3:** 316, **3:** 336, **3:** 339, **3:** 342
        frames, **3:** 333
            composite wood products, **3:** 333
            fiberglass, **3:** 334
            hybrid materials, **3:** 334
            plastics, **3:** 334
            thermal properties, **3:** 334
            thermoplastics, **3:** 334
            vinyls, **3:** 334
            wood, **3:** 333
            wood composites, **3:** 333
        sealants, **3:** 335
        solar thermal energy, **3:** 315, **3:** 321, **3:** 327
        spacers, **3:** 335
    wood composite window frames, **3:** 333
    wood window frames, **3:** 333
Glen Canyon Dam, Arizona, **6:** 90
global annual solar radiation, **3:** 438, **3:** 439*f*
global biomass cofiring overviews, **5:** 56, **5:** 64
global carbon cycle, **5:** 362, **5:** 363*f*
global climate change, **3:** 5
global distribution: direct heat utilization, **7:** 170, **7:** 172*t*, **7:** 173*t*
global energy forecast scenarios, **6:** 1
global energy transfer feed-in tariffs (GET FiT), **1:** 128, **1:** 135
global geothermal energy partnerships, **7:** 290
global geothermal energy utilization, **7:** 187, **7:** 188*f*
global hemispherical radiation, **1:** 214, **1:** 224, **1:** 227
global horizontal irradiance: predictions, definitions, **1:** 240
global horizontal radiation, **1:** 226
global installed capacity, **1:** 74, **1:** 74*f*, **1:** 75*f*, **1:** 185
globally sourced biomass, **5:** 38
global markets:
    bioenergy and biomass, **5: 75–85**
    energy balance, **2: 11–39**
    photovoltaics, **1:** 16, **1:** 74
    wind energy
        energy balance, **2: 11–39**
        policy, **2:** 542
        wind power development, **2: 657–669**
        wind power industry, **2: 657–669**
global offshore wind power projects, **2: 431–468**
global oilseed rape production, **5:** 294*f*, **5:** 294*t*, **5:** 294–295, **5:** 295*f*, **5:** 296*t*
global photovoltaic industry, **1: 161–177**
global warming abatement, **3:** 6
global wind potential, **2:** 331*f*
glow discharge deposition technique, **1:** 389, **1:** 390
glycerine, **5:** 184, **5:** 189, **5:** 396
glycerol:
    biochemical methods, **5:** 398
    biodiesel, **5:** 396, **5:** 398
    biomass-to-liquids technology, **5:** 189
    chemical production, **5:** 396, **5:** 398
    citric acid, chemical production, **5:** 399
    current uses, **5:** 397
    literature reviews, **5:** 398
    methanol, **5:** 189
    propylene glycol, **5:** 399
    purification, **5:** 396
glycerol-rich phase (GRP), **5:** 206, **5:** 209, **5:** 210
glycosyl residues, **5:** 232
goals: geothermal energy sustainable development, **7:** 272, **7:** 274, **7:** 277, **7:** 287
golden eagles, **6:** 299, **6:** 305
Goldisthal pumped storage plant, Germany, **6:** 406, **6:** 426, **6:** 427
Goldwind: wind turbines, **2:** 322
Gongboxia Project, **6:** 495, **6:** 496, **6:** 497*f*
good practice: hydropower, **6:** 12
Gore Select® materials, **4:** 187
government incentives, **1:** 2, **1:** 2*t*
grain:
    additional value extraction, **5:** 386, **5:** 386*f*, **5:** 387–388, **5:** 389

boundaries, **1**: 405
mills, **6**: 31, **6**: 32f
Gran Canaria Island, **2**: 738–739, **3**: 558
Grandas de Salime power plant and dam, Spain, **6**: 324, **6**: 326f
Grande-Dixence hydroelectricity project, Switzerland, **6**: 350
grants:
    developing country photovoltaics, **1**: 125
    support mechanisms, **1**: 1, **1**: 2t
granular aerogels, **3**: 340
granulated blast furnace slag, **6**: 393
graphical analysis:
    photovoltaic power/irradiance forecasts, **1**: 265
    Weibull wind speed distribution, **2**: 120
grass: biomass cofiring, **5**: 59
grate-fired boiler combustion, **5**: 61
grates: power generation, **5**: 33
Grätzel cells, **1**: 9, **1**: 26, **1**: 440
gravitational loads, **2**: 251
gravity dams, **6**: 29–30, **6**: 184
gravity foundations, **2**: 441, **2**: 443f, **2**: 445
gravure coating, **1**: 472
gray bodies *see* semiconductors
Greece:
    desalination, **2**: 735, **2**: 739
    solar energy utilization, **1**: 31
    wind park design, **2**: 212
green certificates, **5**: 411, **5**: 422
green chemistry, **5**: 395
greenhouse effect, **3**: 5, **3**: 322
greenhouse gases, **2**: 541–568, **5**: 109–132, **5**: 411–429
    automotives, **5**: 305, **5**: 327
    biochar, **5**: 379, **5**: 380
    bioenergy policy development, **5**: **411–429**
    biofuels, **5**: 4–5, **5**: **109–132**
    biomass-to-liquids technology, **5**: 167, **5**: 167f, **5**: 168f, **5**: 197, **5**: 200, **5**: 201
    Brazilian bioethanol development, **5**: 19
    carbon dioxide emissions, **2**: 22
    comparative saving effectiveness, **5**: 200
    coproducts, **5**: 110, **5**: 113, **5**: 126
    definitions, **5**: 109
    desalination, **2**: 727–728, **2**: 728t
    direct land use change, **5**: 117
    environmental impacts, **1**: 148
    future biofuel technologies, **5**: 127
    geothermal chemistry, **7**: 120
    geothermal energy sustainability, **7**: 272, **7**: 283, **7**: 290
    hydrogen technology, **4**: 332
    hydropower, **6**: 9, **6**: 9f, **6**: 41
    indirect land use change, **5**: 120
    land use change, **5**: 117, **5**: 120
    life cycles, **1**: 148, **5**: **109–132**
    nitrous oxides, **5**: 113, **5**: 113t, **5**: 121
    photovoltaics, **1**: 148
    processing energy sources, **5**: 123
    saving effectiveness, **5**: 200
    soil nitrous oxide emissions, **5**: 121
    solar cooling, **3**: 611–612
    Three Gorges Project, China, **6**: 221
    transport distance, **5**: 167, **5**: 167f, **5**: 168f
    wind energy policy, **2**: **541–568**
greenhouses:
    agricultural applications, **3**: 586
    cooling, **3**: 586
    definitions, **3**: 567
    geothermal direct heat utilization, **7**: 169, **7**: 170, **7**: 172t, **7**: 173t, **7**: 174, **7**: 175f, **7**: 181
    heating, **3**: 586
    industrial applications, **3**: 586
    microclimates, **3**: 586
    passive solar heating, **3**: 640–641, **3**: 641f
    photovoltaic/thermal solar collectors, **3**: 294–295
    solar thermal energy, **3**: 230, **3**: 231, **3**: 586

green power programs, **1**: 86
Green Protocol, **5**: 22
green spaces, **3**: 651
grids:
    architecture, **2**: 717
    capacity, **3**: 206
    compatibility, wind turbines, **2**: 418
    concentrating solar power, **3**: 597
    control systems, **2**: 330, **2**: 331f, **2**: 358, **2**: 362
    current photovoltaic status, **1**: 114
    decarbonization, **4**: 66, **4**: 69
    dependent generators, **4**: 202
    electricity, wind energy policy, **2**: 556, **2**: 559
    energy storage
        photovoltaics, **1**: 199, **1**: 201
        wind power penetration, **1**: 201
    flexibility, photovoltaic storage, **1**: 199
    fuel cell power electronic analysis, **4**: 300
    future photovoltaics, **1**: 187, **1**: 188, **1**: 190, **1**: 192, **1**: 197
    high concentration solar collectors, **3**: 206
    hybrid solar–diesel systems, **1**: 687
    hydrogen technology, **4**: 66, **4**: 69
    infrastructure adaptations, **1**: 188, **1**: 197
    integrating photovoltaics, **1**: 241
    management, photovoltaics, **1**: 188
    molten carbonate fuel cells, **4**: 233
    operation requirements, wind turbines, **2**: 271
    photovoltaics
        components, **1**: 679
        current status, **1**: 114
        design, **1**: 679
        energy storage, **1**: 199, **1**: 201
        future visions, **1**: 187, **1**: 188, **1**: 190, **1**: 192, **1**: 197
        hybrid solar–diesel systems, **1**: 687
        infrastructure adaptations, **1**: 188, **1**: 197
        integration, **1**: 241
        management, **1**: 188
        performance monitoring, **1**: 775
        reliability, **1**: 199
        storage, **1**: 199, **1**: 201
        thin-film silicon, **1**: 396
    proton-exchange membrane fuel cells, **4**: 202
    reliability, photovoltaics, **1**: 199
    storage
        photovoltaics, **1**: 199, **1**: 201
        wind power penetration, **1**: 201
    technical unavailability, wind turbines, **2**: 152
    thin-film silicon photovoltaic technology, **1**: 396
    wind energy
        mitigating variable costs and effects, **2**: 496
        policy, **2**: 556, **2**: 559
        power design and implementation, **2**: 395, **2**: 421
        power penetration, **1**: 201
    wind turbines
        compatibility, **2**: 418
        control systems, **2**: 330, **2**: 331f, **2**: 358, **2**: 362, **2**: 370
        electrical systems, **2**: **269–269**
        technical unavailability, **2**: 152
        technology evolution, **2**: 717
Griggs-Putnam index, **2**: 173, **2**: 173t
grinding: wind energy, **2**: 42, **2**: 45
Grosse Windkraft Anlage (GROWIAN) wind turbine, **2**: 65, **2**: 68f
ground-based sky imagers, **1**: 251
ground cooling, **3**: 460, **3**: 642, **3**: 642f
ground granulated blast furnace slag, **6**: 393
ground heat sources, **3**: 503–504, **3**: 517
grounding: hydrogen storage safety, **4**: 125
ground storage:
    heat transfer, **3**: 524
    mass transfer, **3**: 524
    solar assisted heat pumps, **3**: 520, **3**: 521
ground thermal conductivity, **7**: 195

groundwater:
    alcohol fuel safety, **5**: 326
    geothermal heat pumps, **7**: 201
    heat pumps, **3**: 505, **3**: 523
group III-V material multi-junction cells, **1**: 9
group speed: regular ocean waves, **8**: 13
grouted connections: offshore wind power, **2**: 442–445, **2**: 445f
grout enrichment, **6**: 476, **6**: 476f, **6**: 477
grout intensity number (GIN), **6**: 477, **6**: 480f, **6**: 482
GROWIAN *see* Grosse Windkraft Anlage wind turbine
growth:
    automotive biomass and biofuels, **5**: 306f, **5**: 306–307
    photovoltaics
        concentration photovoltaics, **1**: 763, **1**: 764, **1**: 764f
        technology progress, **1**: **13–30**
        thin-film silicon, **1**: 389
    wind turbine installed capacity, **2**: 94
GRP *see* glycerol-rich phase
G. sulfurreducens: microbial fuel cells, **4**: 273
GTL *see* gas-to-liquids
guarantees: photovoltaics, **1**: 125
Gueymard model, **3**: 47
guidelines:
    hydrogen safety engineering, **4**: 84, **4**: 84t
    hydropower, **6**: 12
guide vanes:
    air turbines, **8**: 116, **8**: 118, **8**: 119, **8**: 121–122
    axial-flow microhydro turbines, **6**: 464, **6**: 464–465
Guijo de Granadilla dam, Spain, **6**: 333–335, **6**: 335f
Güssing, Austria, **5**: 150
gust determination, **2**: 81, **2**: 126
g-values, **3**: 323

H

Haikou key project, **6**: 399
half-lives: biochar/soils, **5**: 364
hammer mills, **5**: 44
hammers: windmills, **2**: 51, **2**: 51f
handling:
    biochar, **5**: 382
    biomass and biofuels, **5**: 43, **5**: 142, **5**: 276
    feedstocks, **5**: 142, **5**: 276
    roller compacted concrete dams, **6**: 475
    single-stem woody crops, **5**: 276
Hanwha SolarOne, **1**: 172
Harboore, Denmark, **5**: 150
hardware: wind turbine power electronics, **2**: 366
hardwoods, **5**: 264
harmonics: wind turbines, **2**: 207, **2**: 295, **2**: 595
harmonizing support schemes, **1**: 4
harvesting single-stem woody crops, **5**: 276
Hay solar radiation model, **3**: 47
Hay–Willmott solar radiation model, **3**: 47
hazards:
    geothermal energy
        elevation changes, **7**: 58
        exploration techniques, **7**: 56
        fault movements, **7**: 57
        flooding, **7**: 58
        gas flumes, **7**: 57
        geological hazards, **6**: 216, **7**: 56
        molten rock drilling, **7**: 57
        sliding, **7**: 58
        volcanic events, **7**: 56
    hydrogen safety engineering, **4**: 77, **4**: 81, **4**: 105
H-bridge operation, **4**: 305
HC Energía, **6**: 315
HD *see* humidification–dehumidification
HDR systems, **7**: 5
heads: hydropower, **6**: 19
head sites: axial-flow microhydro turbines, **6**: 445

health:
    see also safety
    biomass characteristics, **5**: 42
    biomass cofiring, **5**: 68
    biomass power generation, **5**: 40
    explosions, **5**: 41, **5**: 42
    fires, **5**: 41
    Millennium Development Goals, **7**: 287
    personnel issues, **5**: 40
    photovoltaic lifecycles, **1**: **143–159**
    power generation, **5**: 40
    process safety, **5**: 41
    wind energy, **2**: 525
Healthy Forest Restoration Act (HFRA), **5**: 283
heat:
    see also combined heat and power
    balance diagrams, **7**: 207
    biomass, **5**: **87–97**
    building-integrated photovoltaic-thermal systems, **3**: 379, **3**: 388
    capacity, **3**: 145
    collection functions, **3**: 379
    conduction, geothermal energy, physics, **7**: 12
    diffusion equation, **7**: 13
    energy storage
        see also thermal energy storage
    engines, **3**: 495
    exchangers
        active solar systems, **3**: 450, **3**: 452f, **3**: 454, **3**: 454f, **3**: 477
        cooling systems, **3**: 477
        geothermal direct heat utilization, **7**: 178, **7**: 178f, **7**: 179f
        heat source media, **3**: 503–504
        indirect water heating systems, **3**: 450, **3**: 452f
        size corrections, **3**: 401, **3**: 410
        solar assisted heat pumps, **3**: 517
        solar cooling systems, **3**: 477
        solar space heating systems, **3**: 450, **3**: 452f, **3**: 454, **3**: 454f, **3**: 477
        space heating systems, **3**: 450, **3**: 452f, **3**: 454, **3**: 454f, **3**: 477
        water heating systems, **3**: 454, **3**: 454f
        water storage, **3**: 216
    flow
        depth, **7**: 87
        geothermal energy exploration techniques, **7**: 84, **7**: 86, **7**: 87
        geothermal heat pumps, **7**: 196
        geothermal system physics, **7**: 28
        measurements, **7**: 84
        theory, **7**: 84
    gains, **3**: 460–461
    heat-only boilers, **5**: 94, **5**: 94–95
    heat-to-power ratio, **4**: 253, **4**: 254
    islands, **3**: 644
    loads, **4**: 251
    loss
        coefficients, **3**: 430
        low-temperature stationary collectors, **3**: 133, **3**: 134
        suppression, **3**: 330
        Theistareykir, NE Iceland, **7**: 157–158
    low-temperature stationary collectors, **3**: 138
    management
        proton-exchange membrane fuel cells, **4**: 187
        solar water heating systems, **3**: 440
    pipes
        definitions, **3**: 163
        evacuated tube collectors, low-temperature stationary collectors, **3**: 116, **3**: 117f, **3**: 118, **3**: 118f
        history, solar energy, **3**: 85, **3**: 97
        solar energy, history, **3**: 85, **3**: 97
    and power generation *see* combined heat and power
    pumps
        see also solar assisted heat pumps
        classification, **3**: 501
        components, **7**: 192
        fundamentals, **3**: 495

geothermal energy
  building-integrated photovoltaic-thermal systems, **3**: 391
    resources, **7**: 187
      shallow systems, **7**: **187–206**
      sustainable development, **7**: 279
  heat source media, **3**: 501–502, **3**: 502
  operation principles, **3**: 495
  processes, **7**: 192
  renewable heat sources, **3**: 502
  resources, **7**: 187
    shallow systems, **7**: **187–206**
  solar space heating, **3**: 459
  sustainable development, **7**: 279
  thermodynamic cycles, **3**: 497
  vapor compression cycles, **3**: 497
  water heating systems, **3**: 459
recovery, **3**: 270, **3**: 271, **3**: 606, **3**: 607f
removal factor, **3**: 138, **3**: 388
sinks, **3**: 502, **7**: 187, **7**: 188f
solid oxide fuel cells, hydrogen technology, **4**: 251
sources
  heat pumps, **3**: 501–502, **3**: 502
  solar water heating systems, **3**: 436
  thermophotovoltaics, **1**: 604, **1**: 605
storage, **3**: 434, **3**: 473, **3**: 524
  see also thermal energy storage
  active solar systems, **3**: 473
  cooling systems, **3**: 473
  definitions, **3**: 567
  solar heating systems, **3**: 473
  solar space cooling systems, **3**: 473
  solar thermal systems, **3**: 473
  solar water heating systems, **3**: 434
  space cooling systems, **3**: 473
  space heating systems, **3**: 473
system design/layouts, **3**: 573, **3**: 577
transfer
  building-integrated photovoltaic-thermal systems, **3**: 383, **3**: 384
  coefficients
    building-integrated photovoltaic-thermal systems, **3**: 384
    direct gain passive solar technologies, **3**: 361
    glazing thermal properties, **3**: 321, **3**: 322, **3**: 330, **3**: 330t, **3**: 332, **3**: 332f, **3**: 334, **3**: 334t
    low-temperature stationary collectors, **3**: 130, **3**: 131, **3**: 132
    photovoltaic/thermal solar collectors, **3**: 275
  cold recharge porous layer models, **7**: 15
  evacuated glazing, **3**: 336
  flat-plate collectors, **3**: 103
  fluids
    Fresnel collectors, **3**: 196
    high concentration solar collectors, **3**: 176, **3**: 186, **3**: 196
    parabolic troughs, **3**: 176
    receivers, **3**: 186
  fracture models, **7**: 14
  geothermal energy physics, **7**: 12
  ground storage, pumps, **3**: 524
  horizontal fracture models, **7**: 14
  porous layer models, **7**: 14, **7**: 15
  solar assisted heat pumps, ground storage, **3**: 524
transport
  geothermal energy exploration techniques, **7**: 84
  high concentration solar collectors, **3**: 173
  urban building passive solar architecture, **3**: 644
of vaporization, **5**: 318f, **5**: 318–319, **5**: 320–321
heaters: hydrogen technology, **4**: 2, **4**: 6f
heather, **5**: 390
heating:
  see also air heating; space heating; water...
  active solar systems, **3**: **449–480**
  biochar, **5**: 358
  biomass combined heat and power, **5**: 88, **5**: 89, **5**: 90t, **5**: 91, **5**: 93, **5**: 95, **5**: 96
  buildings, **3**: 360–361, **3**: **419–447**, **3**: 362, **3**: 391, **3**: 587

central plants with storage, **3**: 522, **3**: 525, **3**: 527
geothermal direct heat utilization, **7**: 169, **7**: 171, **7**: 174f, **7**: 180, **7**: 181f, **7**: 182, **7**: 184, **7**: 184f
geothermal heat pumps, shallow systems, **7**: 193
greenhouses, solar thermal systems, **3**: 586
history, solar energy, **3**: 94, **3**: 97
hot water systems, **3**: **419–447**, **3**: **449–480**
loads, **3**: 378
passive solar architecture, **3**: 639
solar energy history, **3**: 94, **3**: 97
solar space heating systems, **3**: **449–480**
solar water heating systems, **3**: **419–447**, **3**: **449–480**
spas, **7**: 169, **7**: 170, **7**: 173t
heating, ventilation, and air-conditioning (HVAC) systems, **3**: 360–361, **3**: 362, **3**: 391
heat-only boilers (HOB), **5**: 94, **5**: 94–95
heat-to-power ratio, **4**: 253, **4**: 254
heavily loaded rotor corrections, **2**: 230
heavy metal environmental impacts, **1**: 151, **5**: 52
height parameters:
  extreme sea state estimations, **8**: 52, **8**: 54, **8**: 70
  irregular ocean waves, **8**: 14
  satellite altimeters, **8**: 37
heliocentric systems, **3**: 29f, **3**: 29–30
heliostats:
  agricultural applications, **3**: 587t
  construction, **3**: 190
  drives, **3**: 187
  high concentration solar collectors, **3**: 187, **3**: 188, **3**: 190
  industrial applications, **3**: 587t
  loss mechanisms, **3**: 188
  receivers, **3**: 187, **3**: 188, **3**: 190
  solar energy history, **3**: 95, **3**: 95f
HelioTrough, **3**: 181
Helmholtz free energy, **1**: 328–329
hemicellulose acetylation, **5**: 232
hemicellulose sheathing, **5**: 232
hemispherical radiation, **1**: 214, **1**: 216–217, **1**: 224, **1**: 226
Hemlock Semiconductor Corporation, **1**: 174
hemp, **5**: 386, **5**: 387, **5**: 387f
Hero of Alexandria, **2**: 44
heteroface structure bottom cells, **1**: 503, **1**: 504
heterogeneous catalysts, **5**: 207, **5**: 223
heterojunctions:
  n-type silicon cells, **1**: 379
  organic solar cells, **1**: 440, **1**: 441, **1**: 448, **1**: 448f, **1**: 449, **1**: 463
  silicon photovoltaics, **1**: 393
  thin-film silicon photovoltaic technology, **1**: 393
HFRA see Healthy Forest Restoration Act
HF radar or X-band marine radar, **8**: 23
HHV see higher heating values
high altitude wind turbines, **2**: 720
high-arch dams, **6**: 492
high concentration solar collectors, **3**: **165–209**
  abrasion tests, **3**: 171
  absorbers, **3**: 174, **3**: 183, **3**: 185
  absorption, **3**: 175
  adjustment, **3**: 178, **3**: 185, **3**: 195
  aim-point strategies, **3**: 187
  area receiver analysis, **3**: 173, **3**: 174
  beam errors, **3**: 188
  Brayton engines, **3**: 201
  central receiver systems, **3**: 185
  characteristics, **3**: 167, **3**: 174, **3**: 185, **3**: 195, **3**: 200
  cleaning, **3**: 174, **3**: 184, **3**: 195, **3**: 199
  components, **3**: **165–209**
  construction, **3**: 178, **3**: 190, **3**: 197, **3**: 203
  control, **3**: 168, **3**: 177, **3**: 187, **3**: 196, **3**: 205
  costs, **3**: 206
  country-specific subsidies, **3**: 206
  coupling receivers, **3**: 187
  deflectometry, **3**: 170
  dishes, **3**: 199

high concentration solar collectors (*continued*)
   diverse parabolic troughs, **3**: 177, **3**: 185
   diverse solar dishes, **3**: 205
   drives, **3**: 177, **3**: 196
   economics, **3**: 206
   efficiency, **3**: 168, **3**: 178, **3**: 187, **3**: 196, **3**: 202
   environmental laws, **3**: 206
   error sources, **3**: 178, **3**: 197, **3**: 203
   EuroDish, **3**: 203
   EuroTrough, **3**: 179
   facets, receivers, **3**: 187
   feed-in-tariffs, **3**: 206
   Fresnel collectors, **3**: 195
   general considerations, **3**: 167
   geometry, **3**: 169, **3**: 186, **3**: 201
   getters, **3**: 177
   grid capacity, **3**: 206
   heat transfer fluids, **3**: 176, **3**: 186, **3**: 196
   heat transport tests, **3**: 173
   heliostats, **3**: 187, **3**: 188, **3**: 190
   HelioTrough, **3**: 181
   hydrogen absorption, **3**: 173
   infrared radiation, **3**: 172, **3**: 174
   in-situ assembly, **3**: 178
   installation, **3**: 178
   kinematics, **3**: 187
   laser scanning, **3**: 171
   linear Fresnel collectors, **3**: 195
   linear receiver analysis, **3**: 172
   line-focusing, **3**: 195
   LS-1, LS-2 and LS-3 parabolic trough collectors, **3**: 178
   luminance, **3**: 173
   Luz parabolic trough collectors, **3**: 178
   maintenance, **3**: 174, **3**: 184, **3**: 195, **3**: 199, **3**: 205
   manufacturers, **3**: 192, **3**: 197, **3**: 203
   markets, **3**: 192
   mass flow measurements, **3**: 173, **3**: 174
   materials, **3**: 176, **3**: 196, **3**: 201
   mirrors, receivers, **3**: 187
   models, **3**: 178, **3**: 197, **3**: 203
   moving bars, **3**: 174
   net systems, technology selection criteria, **3**: 206
   operation and maintenance, **3**: 174, **3**: 184, **3**: 195, **3**: 199, **3**: 205
   optical analysis, **3**: 169, **3**: 187
   optics, **3**: 169, **3**: 187, **3**: 189
   parabolic troughs, **3**: 174
   ParaScan, **3**: 172
   performance, system-specific determination, **3**: 168, **3**: 178, **3**: 187, **3**: 196, **3**: 202
   photogrammetry, **3**: 169
   point-focusing, **3**: 199
   pressure tests, **3**: 173
   PT-1 parabolic trough collectors, **3**: 182
   receivers, **3**: 172, **3**: 173, **3**: 185, **3**: 199
   reflection, **3**: 167, **3**: 169, **3**: 175
     reflectivity measurements, **3**: 170
     reflector analysis, **3**: 167, **3**: 169
     reflector shape accuracy, **3**: 167
   research, **3**: 183, **3**: 199, **3**: 204
   Schott Solar absorbers, **3**: 183
   secondary concentrators, **3**: 189
   secondary optics, **3**: 189
   SenerTrough, **3**: 183
   shape accuracy, **3**: 167, **3**: 169
   Siemens absorbers, **3**: 184
   size, **3**: 176, **3**: 196
   SkyTrough, **3**: 182
   solar dishes, **3**: 199
   SolarGenix collectors, **3**: 180
   Solar Power Group, **3**: 197
   specular reflectivity, **3**: 167
   Stirling devices, **3**: 201, **3**: 203
   structure, **3**: 169, **3**: 174, **3**: 185, **3**: 195, **3**: 200
   subsidies, **3**: 206
   sunshape, **3**: 168
   surface characteristics, **3**: 201
   system-specific performance determination, **3**: 168, **3**: 178, **3**: 187, **3**: 196, **3**: 202
   technology selection criteria, **3**: 205
   thermal analysis, **3**: 169, **3**: 173, **3**: 174, **3**: 187
   thermocouples, **3**: 173, **3**: 174
   thermography, **3**: 173
   tower construction, receivers, **3**: 187
   tower reflectors, **3**: 187, **3**: 189
   tracking accuracy, **3**: 169, **3**: 188
   tracking systems, **3**: 177, **3**: 196
   transmission, **3**: 175
   types, **3**: 176
   Ultimate Trough collectors, **3**: 181
   vacuum hydrogen absorption, **3**: 173
   working gases, **3**: 202
high-cost hydropower developments, **6**: 24
high-efficiency photovoltaic devices, **1**: **497–514**
   crystalline silicon cells, **1**: 371, **1**: 375
   multi-junction cells, **1**: **497–514**
   n-type silicon cells, **1**: 375
   p-type silicon cells, **1**: 371
   technology progress, **1**: 24
high energy dense battery hybrid energy storage, **4**: 317
higher heating values (HIV):
   biochar, **5**: 374–375
   hydrogen economics, **4**: 45
higher hydrocarbon geochemistry, **7**: 122
high-flow collector circuits, **3**: 432
high-penetration levels: wind energy, **2**: 492
high-performance concretes, **6**: 395
high-performance flat-plate collectors, **3**: 429
high-pressure electrolyzers, **4**: 103
high-pressure hydrogen, **4**: 137
high-pressure processing: Iranian hydropower, **6**: 258, **6**: 259, **6**: 259*f*, **6**: 260*f*, **6**: 264*t*
high-speed flow: Chinese hydraulic research, **6**: 498
high-temperature fields:
   corrosion, **7**: 240, **7**: 240*t*
   resistivity, **7**: 81
high-temperature heat methods, **4**: 51
high-temperature proton conductors, **4**: 189
high temperature resistance, **3**: 327
high-temperature selective coatings, **3**: **301–312**
high-temperature solar power plants, **3**: 239
high-temperature storage, **3**: 522, **3**: 523
high-voltage direct currents (HVDC), **6**: 157
high-voltage organic solar cells, **1**: 464
hills: wind power, **2**: 409
Himalaya, **6**: **227–252**
   downstream flow, **6**: 237
   economics, **6**: 229, **6**: 251
   hydropower, **6**: **227–252**
   project planning/implimentation, **6**: 240
   rehabilitation, **6**: 239
   reservoirs, **6**: 237
   resettlements, **6**: 239
   run-off-river plants, **6**: 237, **6**: 240, **6**: 242
   sediment transport, **6**: 244
   socioeconomics, **6**: 229, **6**: 251
   storage, **6**: 242
hindcast ocean wave data uncertainties, **8**: 66
Hindenburg disaster, **4**: 78, **4**: 78*f*
HIPRWIND project, **2**: 720
hire purchase: photovoltaics, **1**: 126
HISP *see* Hogsara Island Demonstration Project
historical overviews:
   American wind pumps, **2**: 51
   bioenergy policy development, **5**: 426
   bioethanol development, **5**: 15
   biomass and biofuels, **5**: **11–14**
     biomass-to-liquids technology, **5**: 160, **5**: 187

engine developments, 5: 11
ethanol, 5: 11
Fischer–Tropsch process, 5: 160
gasification, 5: 134
pyrolysis, 5: 134
vegetable oils, 5: 12
blade numbers, 2: 61
Brazilian bioethanol development, 5: 15, 6: 94
British Colombia, Canada, hydropower, 6: 173
British Wind Energy Association, 2: 65, 2: 71
cadmium telluride thin films, 1: 423
California wind rush, 2: 66
Canadian hydropower, 6: 153, 6: 156, 6: 161, 6: 173
collectors, 3: 85, 3: 91
concentrating systems, 3: 95
concentration photovoltaics, 1: 749
cooling, solar energy, 3: 94
costs, onshore wind performance, 2: 475
crystalline silicon cells, 1: 354
desalination, 3: 85, 3: 97
distillation, 3: 85, 3: 97
early times
   solar energy, 3: 86
   wind energy, 2: 49
electrical wind power, 2: 52, 2: 54
electric sector, Brazil, 6: 94
energy consumption, 6: 1, 6: 2f
engines, 3: 85, 3: 91, 5: 11
ethanol, 5: 11
European wind energy, 2: 44, 2: 65, 2: 71
evacuated-tube solar collectors, 3: 85, 3: 96, 3: 100, 3: 101f
experiment, wind energy, 2: 49
Fischer–Tropsch process, 5: 160
flat-plate solar collectors, 3: 85, 3: 92, 3: 93, 3: 93f
gasification, 5: 134
Gedser machine, 2: 60, 2: 63f
geothermal energy, 7: 276, 7: 286
glass manufacture, 3: 315
heating, solar energy, 3: 94, 3: 97
heat pipes, 3: 85, 3: 97
horizontal axis machines, 2: 45
Horseshoe Bend hydroelectric scheme, 6: 468
Hütter, Ulrich, 2: 61, 2: 63, 2: 64f
hydropower
   British Colombia, Canada, 6: 173
   Canada, 6: 153, 6: 156, 6: 161, 6: 173
   environmental impact management, 6: 50
   Japan, 6: 265, 6: 283
   multibenefit solutions, 6: 31
   Spain, 6: 309, 6: 315
   Tokyo Electric Power Co., Inc:, 6: 283
Icelandic geothermal energy, 7: 286
International Energy Agency, 2: 71
Japanese hydropower, 6: 265, 6: 283
large wind energy machines, 2: 54
Manitoba, Canada, hydropower, 6: 156
meteorological wind data, wind power production, 2: 406
Middle Ages, solar energy, 3: 87
multibenefit hydropower solutions, 6: 31
ocean wave energy, 8: 7–9
offshore wind power, 2: 432
oilseed rape, production, 5: 293
oilseed rape production, 5: 293
onshore wind
   costs, 2: 475
   price trends, 2: 478
organizations, wind energy, 2: 71
passive solar architecture, 3: 638
Persian vertical axis designs, 2: 44
photovoltaics
   cadmium telluride thin films, 1: 423
   costs, 1: 47–72
   development, 1: 31–45
   research and development, 1: 31–45

   standards, 1: 787
   technology progress, 1: 13
   thermal solar collectors, 3: 258
post mills, 2: 46
postwar programs, 2: 58
price trends, onshore wind, 2: 478
product-integrated photovoltaics, 1: 711
proton-exchange membrane fuel cells, 4: 184–185
pumped storage hydropower, 6: 412
pumps, wind energy, 2: 51
pyrolysis, 5: 134
Quebec, Canada, hydropower, 6: 161
research and development, photovoltaics, 1: 31–45
sails, 2: 41, 2: 42f, 2: 43f, 2: 44
scientific meetings/conventions, 3: 96
selective surfaces, solar energy, 3: 85, 3: 93
Smith-Putnam Machine, 2: 56
solar energy, 3: 85–102
   collectors, 3: 85, 3: 91
   concentrating systems, 1: 749, 3: 95
   cooling, 3: 94
   desalination, 3: 85, 3: 97
   distillation, 3: 85, 3: 97
   early times, 3: 86
   engines, 3: 85, 3: 91
   evacuated-tube solar collectors, 3: 85, 3: 96, 3: 100, 3: 101f
   flat-plate solar collectors, 3: 85, 3: 92, 3: 93, 3: 93f
   heating, 3: 94, 3: 97
   heat pipes, 3: 85, 3: 97
   Middle Ages, 3: 87
   power satellites, 1: 767
   scientific meetings/conventions, 3: 96
   selective surfaces, 3: 85, 3: 93
   solar collectors, 3: 85, 3: 91
   solar distillation, 3: 85, 3: 97
   solar-driven desalination, 3: 85, 3: 100
   solar engines, 3: 85, 3: 91
   space cooling, 3: 94
   space heating and cooling, 3: 94
   Sun, 3: 86
   twentieth century, 3: 91
space cooling/heating, 3: 94
Spanish hydropower, 6: 309, 6: 315
stand alone wind energy hybrid systems, 2: 624
standards
   photovoltaics, 1: 787
   wind turbines, 2: 371
Sun, 3: 86
sustainable geothermal energy, 7: 276, 7: 286
technological wind energy developments, 2: 48
theory, wind energy, 2: 49
three bladed wind energy systems, 2: 61
tidal energy, 8: 7–9
Tokyo Electric Power Co., Inc:, 6: 283
tower mills, wind energy, 2: 46
transparent insulation, 3: 339
turbines, wind energy, 2: 54, 2: 55, 2: 55f, 2: 56, 2: 71, 2: 624
twentieth century solar energy, 3: 91
two bladed wind energy systems, 2: 61, 2: 64
vegetable oils, 5: 12
vertical axis designs, 2: 44, 2: 71
wave energy, conversion, 8: 7–9
wind energy, 2: 41–72
   American wind pumps, 2: 51
   blade numbers, 2: 61
   British Wind Energy Association, 2: 65, 2: 71
   California wind rush, 2: 66
   early science, 2: 49
   early times, 2: 49
   electrical power, 2: 52, 2: 54
   Europe, 2: 44, 2: 65, 2: 71
   experiment, 2: 49

historical overviews: (*continued*)
    Gedser machine, **2**: 60, **2**: 63*f*
    horizontal axis machines, **2**: 45
    Hütter, Ulrich, **2**: 61, **2**: 63, **2**: 64*f*
    International Energy Agency, **2**: 71
    large machines, **2**: 54
    meteorological wind data, **2**: 406
    organizations, **2**: 71
    Persian vertical axis designs, **2**: 44
    post mills, **2**: 46
    postwar programs, **2**: 58
    pumps, **2**: 51
    sails, **2**: 41, **2**: 42*f*, **2**: 43*f*, **2**: 44
    Smith-Putnam Machine, **2**: 56
    stand alone hybrid systems, **2**: 624
    standardization, **2**: 371
    technological developments, **2**: 48
    theory, **2**: 49
    three bladed systems, **2**: 61
    tower mills, **2**: 46
    turbines, **2**: 54, **2**: 55, **2**: 55*f*, **2**: 56, **2**: 71, **2**: 371
    two bladed systems, **2**: 61, **2**: 64
    vertical axis designs, **2**: 44, **2**: 71
    windmills, **2**: **41–72**
    wind pumps, **2**: 51
    wind turbines, **2**: 54, **2**: 55, **2**: 55*f*, **2**: 56, **2**: 71
    windows, **3**: 315
    wind pumps, wind energy, **2**: 51
Hitachi Metals Ltd., Japan, **5**: 151
HIV *see* human immunodeficiency virus; higher heating values
HOB *see* heat-only boilers
Hodgson's hawk eagles, **6**: 299, **6**: 305
HOGA *see* Hybrid Optimization by Genetic Algorithms
Hogsara Island Demonstration Project (HISP), **2**: 718
holistic considerations:
    bioenergy policy development, **5**: 427
    hydrogen technology fuel cells, **4**: 331, **4**: 335
Hollands and Crha solar radiation model, **3**: 40
HOMER *see* Hybrid Optimization Model for Electric Renewables
homogeneous catalytic dehydrogenation, **4**: 142
honeycomb covers, **3**: 112*f*, **3**: 112–113
Hongrin Léman Plus hydroelectricity project, Switzerland, **6**: 354
horizontal axis wind turbines (HAWT), **2**: 45, **2**: 104, **2**: 270, **2**: 440
horizontal cyclone separators, **7**: 218, **7**: 219*f*
horizontal fracture models, **7**: 14
horizontal irradiance: predictions, definitions, **1**: 240
horizontal surface solar radiation, **3**: 39
Horseshoe Bend hydroelectric scheme, **6**: **467–483**
    civil contracting, **6**: 472
    consents, **6**: 467, **6**: 469, **6**: 470
    construction, **6**: **467–483**
    contract frameworks, **6**: 472
    control valves, **6**: 473
    dams, **6**: 467, **6**: 469, **6**: 472, **6**: 473
    design, **6**: 467, **6**: 469, **6**: 473, **6**: 482
    geological setting, **6**: 473
    historical overviews, **6**: 468
    hydrological setting, **6**: 473
    land tenure, **6**: 470
    layouts, **6**: 468, **6**: 474
    location, **6**: 468
    project development, **6**: 470
    project management, **6**: 472
    resource consents, **6**: 467, **6**: 469, **6**: 470
    risk management, **6**: **467–483**
    roller compacted concrete dams, **6**: 467, **6**: 469, **6**: 472, **6**: 473, **6**: 482
    scheme layouts, **6**: 468, **6**: 474
    site layouts, **6**: 474
    specifications, **6**: 468
    tenure issues, **6**: 470, **6**: 482
    tunnel outlets, **6**: 473

hot-carriers, **1**: 26, **1**: 525, **1**: 526
hot flashes, **1**: 26
hot water:
    active solar systems, **3**: 453
    agricultural applications, **3**: 577
    heating, **3**: **419–447**, **3**: **449–480**
    industrial applications, **3**: 577
    integrating solar cooling, **3**: 492
    solar agricultural applications, **3**: 577
    solar heat, **3**: **419–447**, **3**: **449–480**
    solar industrial applications, **3**: 577
    space heating systems, **3**: 453
    tanks, **3**: 434
hot-wire anemometers, **2**: 76
hour angle, **3**: 1, **3**: 11
hourly utilizability, **3**: 404, **3**: 407
households: domestic hot water, **3**: 442
housing:
    hydrogen fuel cells, **4**: 337
    solar water heating systems, **3**: **419–447**
Howdens, **2**: 71
H-rotor vertical axis wind turbines, **2**: 694
hubs:
    definition, **2**: 270
    heights, **2**: 144, **2**: 676
    hub-to-tip ratios, **8**: 127–128, **8**: 128
    wind turbine technology evolution, **2**: 714
human activity impacts: wind turbines, **2**: 186–187
human development: geothermal energy, **7**: 275, **7**: 275*f*
human factors: product-integrated photovoltaics, **1**: 727
human immunodeficiency virus (HIV), **7**: 289
human interpretation considerations: numerical weather predictions, **1**: 260
humidification, **3**: 542, **4**: 187, **4**: 194
humidification–dehumidification (HD) process, **3**: 542
hundred mega-watt photovoltaic plants, **1**: 690
hunger eradication, **7**: 288
husks: biomass cofiring, **5**: 58
Hütter, Ulrich, **2**: 61, **2**: 63, **2**: 64*f*
HVAC *see* heating, ventilation, and air-conditioning
HVDC *see* high-voltage direct currents
Hybrid2 software, **2**: 652, **2**: 653*t*
hybrid concentrating solar power, **3**: 605
hybrid cooling towers, **3**: 599
hybrid glazing materials, **3**: 334
Hybrid Optimization by Genetic Algorithms (HOGA), **2**: 652, **2**: 653*t*
Hybrid Optimization Model for Electric Renewables (HOMER) software, **2**: 652, **2**: 653*t*
hybrid power plants:
    coupling mini-grids, **1**: 192
    fossil-geothermal plants, **7**: 229
    geothermal energy, **7**: 207, **7**: 229
    solar-geothermal plants, **7**: 230
hybrid systems:
    desalination, **2**: 735, **2**: 740
    heat pump classification, **3**: 501
    photovoltaic/thermal solar collectors, **3**: 256–257, **3**: 257–258, **3**: 277
    solar–diesel systems, **1**: 687
    stand alone wind energy systems, **2**: 1, **2**: **623–655**, **2**: 623
    water pumping systems, **2**: 744, **2**: 744*f*
    wind energy, **2**: **623–655**, **2**: 735, **2**: 740, **2**: 744, **2**: 744*f*
hybrid vehicles:
    energy storage, **4**: 317
    hydrogen PEM fuel cells, **4**: 317
    internal combustion engines, **5**: 308
    power conversion, concentrating solar power, **3**: 605
    proton-exchange membrane fuel cells, **4**: 215
    urban electrical vehicles, **4**: 317
hybrid window frames, **3**: 334
hydraulics:
    complex structures, Three Gorges Project, China, **6**: 183

hydropower, **6**: **485–505**
  floating debris control, **6**: 77
  gas supersaturation, **6**: 73, **6**: 75
  operation impact management, **6**: 73
ocean wave energy, **8**: 84
pump-turbines, **6**: 413
research, **6**: **485–505**
  aerators, **6**: 485, **6**: 497
  cavitation mitigation, **6**: 497
  China, **6**: **485–505**
  discharge facilities, **6**: 485, **6**: 487, **6**: 499
  discharge spraying, **6**: 485, **6**: 499
  energy dissipation, **6**: 485, **6**: 486t, **6**: 487
  field observations, China, **6**: 502
  flaring pier gates, **6**: 485, **6**: 489
  flow-induced vibration, China, **6**: 499
  high-arch dams, **6**: 492
  hydropower, **6**: **485–505**
  jet flow collision, **6**: 485, **6**: 492
  jet flows, **6**: 485, **6**: 492, **6**: 499
  orifice spillway tunnels, **6**: 485, **6**: 494
  plunge pools, **6**: 485, **6**: 492
  slit buckets, **6**: 485, **6**: 487, **6**: 490f, **6**: 491f
  spraying, **6**: 485, **6**: 499
  vibration, **6**: 499
  vortex shaft spillway tunnels, **6**: 485, **6**: 495
retention times, **4**: 269
Rupert River, Quebec, Canada, **6**: 172
solar water heating systems, **3**: 440, **3**: 442f
structures
  Rupert River, Quebec, Canada, **6**: 172
  Three Gorges Project, China, **6**: 183, **6**: 187, **6**: 198, **6**: 221, **6**: 226
Three Gorges Project, China, **6**: 183, **6**: 187, **6**: 198, **6**: 221, **6**: 226
turbines, ocean wave energy, **8**: 8–9
wind energy policy, **2**: 553
Hydraulienne siphon turbines, **6**: 27
hydrides: hydrogen storage, **4**: 139, **4**: 147, **4**: 153
hydro-aero-servo-elastic simulations, **2**: 246
hydrocarbons:
  carbon numbers, **5**: 179, **5**: 179f
  engine configuration ranges, **5**: 348, **5**: 350–351
  gasification, **4**: 50
  geochemistry, **7**: 122
hydrochloric acid, **5**: 51
hydrodynamics:
  air turbines, **8**: 141
  damping, **2**: 259
  loads, **2**: 249
  oscillating water columns, **8**: 141
  reservoirs, **6**: 59
  wind turbine electrical systems, **2**: 287, **2**: 288f
hydroelectricity:
  see also hydropower
  ancillary services, **6**: 6
  Barra Grande hydroelectricity project, Brazil, **6**: 124
  Belo Monte project, Brazil, **6**: 125
  Brazil, **6**: **93–127**
  Cameroon, Africa, **6**: **129–151**
  Campos Novos hydroelectricity project, Brazil, **6**: 123
  Canadian recent solutions, **6**: **153–178**
  Cleuson-Dixence hydroelectricity project, Switzerland, **6**: 351
  costs, **6**: 6
  dams
    environmental issues, **6**: 9
    in operation, **6**: 4, **6**: 5t
    social issues, **6**: 9
  development, **6**: 4
    India, **6**: **227–252**
    Japanese current status, **6**: 274
  Dixence hydroelectricity project, Switzerland, **6**: 350
  economics, **6**: 6
  environmental issues, **6**: 9, **6**: 9f
  evolution, **6**: 4
  finance, **6**: 6
  Foz do Areia hydroelectric project, Brazil, **6**: 108
  Grande-Dixence hydroelectricity project, Switzerland, **6**: 350
  greenhouse gas emissions, **6**: 9, **6**: 9f
  Hongrin Léman Plus hydroelectricity project, Switzerland, **6**: 354
  Horseshoe Bend, Teviot River, Zealand, **6**: **467–483**
  Iguaçu hydroelectric project, Brazil, **6**: 108
  India, **6**: **227–252**
  institutional structure reforms, **6**: **129–151**
  introduction, **6**: **1–14**
  Iran, **6**: **253–264**
  Itá hydroelectricity project, Brazil, **6**: 121
  Itaipu project, Brazil, **6**: 96
  Jirau hydroelectric project, Brazil, **6**: 94, **6**: 104f, **6**: 106
  key features, **6**: 6
  Linthal 2015 hydroelectricity project, Switzerland, **6**: 353
  Machadinho hydroelectricity project, Brazil, **6**: 119
  Madeira project, Brazil, **6**: 104
  multibenefit solutions, **6**: **15–47**
  Nant de Dranse hydroelectricity project, Switzerland, **6**: 352
  new developments, Switzerland, **6**: 349, **6**: 352
  New Zealand, Horseshoe Bend, Teviot River, **6**: **467–483**
  progress, **6**: 4
  pumped-storage plants, development and progress, **6**: 7
  recent solutions, Canada, **6**: **153–178**
  Salto Caxias hydroelectricity project, Brazil, **6**: 116
  Salto Osorio hydroelectricity project, Brazil, **6**: 114
  Salto Santiago hydroelectric project, Brazil, **6**: 111
  Santo Antonio hydroelectric project, Brazil, **6**: 94, **6**: 104f, **6**: 105
  Segredo hydroelectric project, Brazil, **6**: 110
  social issues, **6**: 9
  Spain, **6**: **309–341**
  storage plants, **6**: 7
  Switzerland, **6**: **343–354**
  Tucurui project, Brazil, **6**: 101
  turbine generation units, **6**: 191, **6**: 192t, **6**: 193t, **6**: 194t
  wind energy integration, **2**: 571, **2**: 573
hydrogen:
  see also hydrogen safety engineering
  absorption, **3**: 173
  aircraft, **4**: 290
  alkali amidoboranes, **4**: 144
  alkaline anion exchange membrane fuel cells, **4**: 178
  alkaline earth amidoboranes, **4**: 144
  amidoboranes, **4**: 144
  amine-hydride combinations, **4**: 147t, **4**: 149
  ammonia borane, storage, **4**: 140
  ammonia production, **4**: 31
  anodes, **4**: 247
  Apollo Saturn rocket, **4**: 14
  application economics, **4**: 58
  astronaut environmental control, **4**: 24
  astronaut life support, space applications, **4**: 24
  Atlas-Centaur rocket, **4**: 13
  auxiliary power supplies, **4**: 60
  batteries, **4**: 22, **4**: 285, **4**: 317
  bikes, **4**: 285
  bio-alcohols, **5**: 406
  biological fuel cells, **4**: **257–280**
  biological production economics, **4**: 51
  biomass-to-liquids technology, **5**: 186
  borohydrides, **4**: 147
  buses, **4**: 63–64, **4**: 286
  capacity factor, **4**: 45, **4**: 53
  carbon capture and storage, **4**: 45, **4**: 46, **4**: 49, **4**: 50, **4**: 64
  cathodes, **4**: 247
  chemical hydrides, **4**: 139, **4**: 153
  chemical manufacturing status, **4**: 31, **4**: 32
  chemical production, bio-alcohols, **5**: 406
  chemical storage, **4**: **137–157**
  combined heat and power systems, **4**: 249
  complex hydrides, **4**: 147, **4**: 153

hydrogen: (continued)
   components, solid oxide fuel cells, 4: 246
   compressed gas storage, 4: 111–135
   consumer costs, 4: 62
   controlled renewables, 4: 295–329
   cooling technologies, 4: 24
   coproduction economics, 4: 58, 4: 67, 4: 70, 4: 72
   costs
      consumer costs, 4: 62
      delivery infrastructure, 4: 52
      gasification, 4: 50, 4: 50t
      refueling stations, 4: 54
      steam methane reforming, 4: 49t, 4: 49–50
   current status
      fuel cells, 4: 13–43
      space applications, 4: 13
      space propulsion, 4: 13
   cylinders, 4: 2, 4: 7f, 4: 117
   decarbonization, 4: 65, 4: 66, 4: 69
   delivery infrastructure costs, 4: 52
   Delta IV rocket, 4: 17
   development policies, 4: 67
   drive trains, 4: 63
   economics, 4: 45–75, 4: 45
      applications, 4: 58
      automotives, 5: 312
      capacity factor, 4: 45, 4: 53
      end-use applications, 4: 58
      end-use technologies, 4: 58
      energy chains, 4: 47
      infrastructure, 4: 52
      production, 4: 48
      storage, 4: 55
   economy conversion, automotives, 5: 307, 5: 310
   efficiency, fuel cells, 4: 250, 4: 252, 4: 335
   electricity
      fuel cells, 4: 331–340
      grid decarbonization, 4: 66, 4: 69
      policy development, 4: 69
      stationary power, 4: 334
   electrochemistry, 4: 10
   electrolysis, 4: 45, 4: 48
   electrolytes, 4: 246
   electronics, fuel cells, 4: 295–329
   embrittlement, 7: 243
   end-use applications, 4: 58, 4: 61, 4: 62, 4: 63
   energy chains, 4: 47
   forklift vehicles, 4: 284
   forward commitment procurement, 4: 45, 4: 68–69, 4: 71–72
   fuel cells, 4: 331–340, 4: 337
      biological fuel cells, 4: 257–280
      compressed gas, storage, 4: 111–135
      controlled renewables, 4: 295–329
      current status, 4: 13–43
      economics, 4: 45–75, 4: 45
      efficiency, 4: 335
      electricity, 4: 331–340
      electric vehicles, 4: 333
      electrochemistry, 4: 10
      electronics, 4: 295–329
      end-use technologies, 4: 58
      forklift vehicles, 4: 284
      future perspectives, 4: 331–340
      holistic considerations, 4: 331, 4: 335
      infrastructure, 4: 283, 4: 333, 4: 337, 4: 339
      introduction, 4: 1–11
      inverter safe operating areas, 4: 297
      low carbon energy conversion, 4: 296
      microbial fuel cells, 4: 257–280
      power electronics, 4: 295–329
      power inverter safe operating areas, 4: 297
      safety engineering, 4: 77–109
      solid oxide fuel cells, 4: 241–257
      stationary power, 4: 334
      storage, compressed gas, 4: 111–135
      sustainability, 4: 331–340
      terrestrial applications, 4: 296
      traditional inverter safe operating areas, 4: 297
      transitions, 4: 331–340
      transport, 4: 333, 4: 281–293
      vehicles, 4: 284, 4: 333
      volume, 4: 2
   future fuel cell perspectives, 4: 331–340
   gasification, 4: 50, 4: 50t
   high-temperature heat water splitting, 4: 51
   holistic considerations, 4: 331, 4: 335
   hydrides, 4: 139, 4: 147, 4: 153
   hydropower multibenefit solutions, 6: 43
   impulse magnetoplasma rockets, 4: 19
   induced cracking, 7: 243
   infrastructure
      economics, 4: 52
      fuel cells, 4: 283, 4: 333, 4: 337, 4: 339
   instrument cooling technologies, 4: 24
   interconnects, 4: 248
   internal combustion engines, 4: 58, 4: 281–293
   inverter safe operating areas, 4: 297
   ions, corrosion, 7: 246
   legislation, 4: 291
   liquids, storage, 4: 137–157
   low-carbon energy, 4: 63, 4: 65
   low-carbon energy conversion, 4: 296
   low-carbon energy resources, 4: 65
   low-carbon vehicle drive trains, 4: 63
   magnetoplasma rockets, 4: 19
   market opportunities, vehicles, 4: 63
   metal hydrides, 4: 139
   microbial fuel cells, 4: 257–280
   Nernst equation, 4: 244, 4: 245
   niche end-use applications, 4: 60
   oil refineries, 4: 31
   passenger transport, 4: 61, 4: 63–64, 4: 286
   PEM fuel cells
      battery hybrid energy storage, 4: 317
      conditioning, 4: 311
      dense battery hybrid energy storage, 4: 317
      high energy dense battery hybrid energy storage, 4: 317
      hybrid energy storage, 4: 317
      lead-acid batteries, 4: 323
      road vehicle applications, 4: 307
      test characterization, 4: 307
      urban electrical vehicles, 4: 317
      vehicle traction batteries, 4: 322, 4: 327
   performance, storage, 4: 55
   physical storage, 4: 137
   Planck spacecraft, 4: 25
   plasma, thin-film silicon photovoltaics, 1: 389
   policy development, 4: 67, 4: 68, 4: 69
   power electronics, fuel cells, 4: 295–329
   power inverter safe operating areas, 4: 297
   pressure vessels, 4: 111–135
   production
      direct fuel cells, 4: 238
      economics, 4: 48
      fuel cell technology, 4: 238, 4: 283
      molten carbonate fuel cells, 4: 228, 4: 238
   proton-exchange membrane fuel cells, 4: 185, 4: 221
   prototype vehicles, 4: 62
   reactions, alkaline fuel cells, 4: 160
   refueling station costs, 4: 54
   research policies, 4: 70
   scientific instrument cooling technologies, 4: 24
   scientific research policies, 4: 70
   shipping, end-use applications, 4: 64, 4: 289
   solid oxide fuel cells, 4: 241–257
      anodes, 4: 247

cathodes, 4: 247
combined heat and power systems, 4: 249
components, 4: 246
efficiency, 4: 250, 4: 252
electrolytes, 4: 246
example systems, 4: 249
interconnects, 4: 248
materials, 4: **241–257**
Nernst equation, 4: 244, 4: 245
operation principles, 4: 246
theory, 4: **241–257**
thermodynamics, 4: 243, 4: 245
space applications
  astronaut environmental control, 4: 24
  astronaut life support, 4: 24
  battery power, 4: 22
  current status, 4: 13
  energy storage, 4: 22
  instrument cooling technologies, 4: 24
  propulsion current status, 4: 13
  scientific instrument cooling technologies, 4: 24
  space shuttle, 4: 17
specific impulse magnetoplasma rockets, 4: 19
stand alone wind energy hybrid systems, 2: 645, 2: 650
stationary power
  electricity, 4: 334
  end-use applications, 4: 59
  fuel cells, 4: 334
steam methane reforming, 4: 49, 4: 49t, 4: 49–50
storage, 4: **111–135**, 4: **137–157**
  alkali amidoboranes, 4: 144
  alkaline earth amidoboranes, 4: 144
  amidoboranes, 4: 144
  amine-hydride combinations, 4: 147t, 4: 149
  ammonia borane, 4: 140
  applications, 4: 57
  automotives, 5: 312
  borohydrides, 4: 147
  chemical hydrides, 4: 139, 4: 153
  chemicals, 4: **137–157**
  complex hydrides, 4: 147, 4: 153
  compressed gas, 4: **111–135**
  economics, 4: 55
  fuel cell technology, 4: 285
  hydrides, 4: 139, 4: 147, 4: 153
  liquids, 4: **137–157**
  metal hydrides, 4: 139
  pending issues, 4: 153
  performance, 4: 55
  proton-exchange membrane fuel cells, 4: 221
  safety, 4: 125
  space applications, 4: 22
  vehicle performance, 4: 55
sulfide corrosion, 7: 246
sustainability, fuel cells, 4: **331–340**
terrestrial application fuel cells, 4: 296
theory, solid oxide fuel cells, 4: **241–257**
thermodynamics, 4: 243, 4: 245
thin-film silicon photovoltaics, 1: 389
traditional inverter safe operating areas, 4: 297
transitions, fuel cells, 4: **331–340**
transport
  decarbonization, 4: 65
  end-use applications, 4: 61, 4: 62, 4: 63
  fuel cells, 4: 333, 4: **281–293**
  policy development, 4: 68
unmanned air vehicles, 4: 290
variable specific impulse magnetoplasma rockets, 4: 19
vehicles
  costs
    consumer costs, 4: 62
    delivery infrastructure, 4: 52
    refueling stations, 4: 54
  drive trains, 4: 63
  fuel cells, 4: 284, 4: 287, 4: 333
  market opportunities, 4: 63
  prototypes, 4: 62
  storage performance, 4: 55
volume, fuel cells, 4: 2
water electrolysis, 4: 45, 4: 48
water splitting, 4: 51
whole-energy-system context, 4: 65
wide-field infrared survey explorer, 4: 24
wind energy stand alone hybrid systems, 2: 645, 2: 650
hydrogen safety engineering (HSE), 4: **77–109**
  accident mitigation strategies, 4: 101
  barrier effectiveness, 4: 102
  buoyancy-controlled flows, 4: 90
  codes, 4: 82
  compressed gas: hydrogen storage guidelines, 4: 132, 4: 135
  deflagration, 4: 77, 4: 78, 4: 78f, 4: 81, 4: 82, 4: 99, 4: 103, 4: 104
  deflagration-to-detonation transition, 4: 81, 4: 82, 4: 99, 4: 103
  delayed ignition, 4: 97
  detection methods, 4: 103
  detonation, 4: 77, 4: 81, 4: 81–82, 4: 99, 4: 103, 4: 104
  dimensional flame length correlation, 4: 91
  dimensionless flame length correlation, 4: 92
  electrolyzers, 4: 103
  fires, 4: **77–109**, 4: 77
  flame lengths, 4: 91, 4: 92
  flammable limits, 4: 77, 4: 81, 4: 86, 4: 94, 4: 104
  fuel cells, 4: **77–109**
  future development, 4: 104
  future progress, 4: **77–109**, 4: 77
  garage-like enclosures, 4: 95
  guidelines, 4: 84, 4: 84t
  hazards, 4: 77, 4: 81, 4: 105
  high-pressure electrolyzers, 4: 103
  ignition, 4: 81, 4: 97
  ignition phenomena, 4: 81, 4: 97, 4: 104
  inherent safer designs, 4: 101
  jet fires, 4: 79, 4: 79f, 4: 91, 4: 95
  jet flame tip location, 4: 94
  jet releases, 4: 86, 4: 90
  momentum-controlled jet releases, 4: 86, 4: 90
  nonpremixed jets, delayed ignition, 4: 97
  pressure effects, 4: 95
  regulations, 4: 82
  release consequence mitigation, 4: 102
  release phenomena, 4: 86, 4: 95, 4: 102, 4: 104
  risks, 4: 78, 4: 82, 4: 105
  sensors, 4: 103
  separation distances, 4: 78, 4: 94, 4: 102
  standards, 4: 82, 4: 101
  state-of-the-art technology, 4: **77–109**, 4: 77
  storage, 4: 105, 4: 132, 4: 135
  underexpanded jets, 4: 78, 4: 86, 4: 86f, 4: 89
  unignited releases, 4: 86, 4: 95
  unscheduled releases, 4: 95
hydrogen sulfide corrosion, 7: 246
hydrological cycles, 6: 17
hydrology:
  dams, 6: 135, 6: 136t, 6: 473
  geothermal energy geological explorations, 7: 54
  Horseshoe Bend hydroelectric scheme, 6: 473
  Indian hydropower, 6: 230
  roller compacted concrete dams, 6: 473
  Spanish hydropower, 6: 311
hydrolysis: bioethanol development, 5: 24
hydromechanical works, 6: 143, 6: 144
hydrometeorology, 6: 180
hydrophone sensors, 6: 494, 6: 494f
hydropower:
  see also hydroelectricity
  1890–1940 Spain, 6: 317
  1940–1960 Spain, 6: 323

hydropower (continued)
   1960–1975 Spain, 6: 327
   1970 onwards Spain, 6: 333
   advanced technology economics, 6: 40
   aeration, 6: 77, 6: 84
   Africa, 6: **129–151**
   aggregation, 6: 56
   arrangements, 6: 21, 6: 22
   artificial destratification, 6: 83
   axial-flow microhydro turbines, 6: **435–466**
   banking institutes, 6: 229
   bank turbines, 6: 26, 6: 28f
   bathymetric mapping, 6: 358, 6: 369, 6: 371f, 6: 372f
   Bernoulli theorem, 6: 19
   Bini Warak Project, Cameroon, Africa, 6: 145, 6: 145t
   biomass multibenefit solutions, 6: 43
   Brazil, 6: 35, 6: **93–127**, 6: 36t
   British Colombia, Canada, 6: 153, 6: 173
   bubble plumes, 6: 83
   Burntwood River, Manitoba, Canada, 6: 159
   Cameroon, Africa
      current status, 6: 148
      dams, 6: 134, 6: 137
      development plans, 6: 135
      funding, 6: 141, 6: 144, 6: 148, 6: 149
      future outlooks, 6: 137
      institutional structure reforms, 6: **129–151**
      investments, 6: 144, 6: 148, 6: 149
      laws, 6: 148
      legislation, 6: 148
      mid-term development plans, 6: 135
      potentials, 6: 130
      power plants, 6: 131, 6: 135
      reforms, 6: **129–151**
      river systems, 6: 130
      storage dams, 6: 134, 6: 137
      world-wide schemes, 6: **129–151**
   Canada, 6: **153–178**
      construction, 6: 163
      generating units, 6: **153–178**
      historical overviews, 6: 153, 6: 156, 6: 161, 6: 173
      opportunities, 6: 154
      sustainability, 6: **153–178**
   characteristics, 6: 16, 6: 42, 6: 412, 6: 413
   China
      historical overviews, 6: 33
      hydraulic research, 6: **485–505**
      Three Gorges Project, 6: **179–227**
   civil war, 6: 323
   climate change, 6: 230
   Colomines hydro plant, Cameroon, Africa, 6: 145
   companies, Spain, 6: 315
   concentrated fall projects, 6: 22
   concrete dams, 6: 28, 6: 29
   concrete structure durability, 6: **377–403**
   configurations, 6: 21, 6: 22
   construction
      Canada, 6: 163
      environmental impact management, 6: 50
      impact management, 6: **49–91**
   costs, 6: 6, 6: 21, 6: 24, 6: 40, 6: 45
   cross-flow turbines, 6: 26, 6: 28f
   current status
      Cameroon, Africa, 6: 148
      Japan, 6: 274
   curtains, 6: 84
   dams
      Cameroon, Africa, 6: 134, 6: 137
      essential features, 6: 16, 6: 28
      historical overviews, 6: 33
      impact management, 6: 52, 6: 54f, 6: 56, 6: 58, 6: 73
      sediment management, 6: **355–376**
      Switzerland, 6: 346
      types, 6: 28
   debris control, 6: 77
   definitions, 6: 1, 6: 16
   degradation, 6: 56
   design
      concrete structure durability, 6: **377–403**
      long-term sediment management, 6: **355–376**
      sediment management, 6: **355–376**
      simplified generic axial-flow microhydro turbines, 6: **435–466**
   destratification, 6: 83
   development, 6: **15–47**, 6: **485–505**, 6: **49–91**
      Cameroon, Africa, 6: 135
      Chinese hydraulic research, 6: **485–505**
      construction impact management, 6: **49–91**
      environmental impact management, 6: **49–91**
      Horseshoe Bend, Teviot River, New Zealand, 6: **467–483**
      hydraulic research, China, 6: **485–505**
      India, 6: **227–252**
      Japanese current status, 6: 274
      Japanese hydropower history, 6: 271, 6: 273
      multibenefit solutions, 6: **15–47**
      operation impact management, 6: **49–91**
      pumped-storage power plants, 6: 273, 6: 277, 6: 281
      research, China, 6: **485–505**
      river systems, 6: 271
      Spain, 6: **309–341**
      types, 6: 22
   development benefits, 6: **15–47**, 6: 284
   distribution, 6: 43, 6: 44, 6: 258
   divided fall projects, 6: 22f, 6: 23
   downstream flow, 6: 56, 6: 237
   dredging, 6: 366
   Driver, Pressure, State, Impact, Response analytical framework, 6: **355–376**
   driving forces, 6: 357, 6: 365
   Duero System, Spain, 6: 336
   Eastmain–Sarcelle–Rupert Diversion Project, Quebec, Canada, 6: 167
   ecological discharge, 6: 56
   economics
      essential features, 6: 21, 6: 24
      India, 6: 229, 6: 251
      multibenefit solutions, 6: 21, 6: 24, 6: 40, 6: 45
   ecosystem measures, 6: 56, 6: 298
   efficiency, 6: 10, 6: 20
   embankment dams, 6: 28
   energy, work, 6: 17
   energy grade lines, 6: 18, 6: 19f
   energy issues, Japan, 6: 280
   environment
      development constraints, 6: **49–91**
      fish-life, 6: 58, 6: 63, 6: 73, 6: 76
      India, 6: 234
      multibenefit solutions, 6: 41
      reservoir water quality, 6: 58
      sediment management, 6: **355–376**
      water quality, 6: 53, 6: 58
   equipment issues, 6: 17
   essential features, 6: 16
   eutrophication, 6: 61, 6: 72
   exploitation, 6: 10, 6: 11
   finance, 6: 141, 6: 144, 6: 148, 6: 149, 6: 229
   fish-life, 6: 58, 6: 63, 6: 73, 6: 76
   fish migration, 6: 58, 6: 73
   floating debris control, 6: 77
   flow regimes, 6: 56
   flushing, 6: 366, 6: 369, 6: 371f, 6: 372f
   Francis turbines, 6: 25, 6: 28f
   fuel cells, multibenefit solutions, 6: 43
   funding, 6: 6, 6: 141, 6: 144, 6: 148, 6: 149, 6: 229
   future directions
      Cameroon, Africa, 6: 137
      India, 6: 227

Index

introduction, 6: 1, 6: 11, 6: 12
   Japan, 6: 280
   Spain, 6: 339
gas supersaturation, 6: 73, 6: 75
generating units, 6: **153–178**
generation source economics, 6: 40
generic axial-flow microhydro turbines, 6: **435–466**
geographic issues, Iran, 6: 257
geothermal power multibenefit solutions, 6: 43
global energy forecast scenarios, 6: 1
good practice, 6: 12
greenhouse gas emissions, 6: 41
guidelines, 6: 12
heads, 6: 19
high-cost developments, 6: 24
high-pressure processing, 6: 258, 6: 259, 6: 259f, 6: 260f, 6: 264t
Himalaya, 6: **227–252**
historical overviews, 6: 32, 6: 156, 6: 161, 6: 173
   Canada, 6: 153, 6: 156, 6: 161, 6: 173
   environmental impact management, 6: 50
   Japan, 6: 265, 6: 283
   multibenefit solutions, 6: 31
   Spain, 6: 309, 6: 315
Horseshoe Bend, Teviot River, New Zealand, 6: **467–483**
hydraulic processes
   debris control, 6: 77
   floating debris control, 6: 77
   gas supersaturation, impact management, 6: 73
   impact management, 6: 73
hydraulic research, China, 6: **485–505**
Hydraulienne siphon turbines, 6: 27
hydrogen, multibenefit solutions, 6: 43
hydrological cycles, 6: 17
hydrology
   India, 6: 230
   Spain, 6: 311
hypolimnetic aeration and oxygenation, 6: 84
impact management
   environment, 6: **49–91**
   hydraulic process, 6: 73
   mitigations measures, 6: 87
   operating strategies, 6: 83
   screening, 6: 88, 6: 234
   sedimentation, 6: 363, 6: 367
   sediments, 6: 57, 6: 74, 6: 363, 6: 367
   water quality, 6: 53, 6: 58
India, 6: **227–252**
   banking institutes, 6: 229
   climate change, 6: 230
   development, 6: **227–252**
   downstream flow, 6: 237
   economics, 6: 229, 6: 251
   environment studies, 6: 234
   finance, 6: 229
   future planning, 6: 227
   hydrology, 6: 230
   peninsular rivers, 6: 228, 6: 231, 6: 244
   planning, 6: 227
   present status, 6: 227
   project implementation, 6: 240
   project planning, 6: 240
   rehabilitation, 6: 236, 6: 239
   reservoirs, 6: 237
   resettlements, 6: 236, 6: 239, 6: 243f
   run-off-river plants, 6: 237, 6: 240, 6: 242
   sediment transport, 6: 244
   socioeconomic development, 6: 251
   storage, 6: 233f, 6: 233–234, 6: 242
   World banks, 6: 229
institutional structure reforms, 6: **129–151**
integrated water resources management, 6: 12
international cooperation, 6: 12
introduction, 6: **1–14**

investments, 6: 144, 6: 148, 6: 149
Iran, 6: **253–264**
   considerations, 6: 256
   high-pressure processing, 6: 258, 6: 259, 6: 259f, 6: 260f, 6: 264t
   limitations, 6: 256
   potentiality, 6: 258
   pumped-storage plants, 6: 259, 6: 263f
   requirements, 6: 256
   run-off-river plants, 6: 259, 6: 261f, 6: 262f
   spatial distribution, 6: 258
   storage plants, 6: 259, 6: 260f, 6: 263f
James Bay region, Quebec, Canada, 6: 161
Japan, 6: **265–307**
   current status, 6: 274
   ecosystem measures, 6: 298
   energy issues, 6: 280
   future challenges, 6: 280
   historical overviews, 6: 37, 6: 265, 6: 283
   Kansai Electric Power Co:, 6: 288, 6: 294
   Oku-yoshino Power Plant, 6: 288, 6: 294
   pumped-storage power plants, 6: 273, 6: 277, 6: 294
   successful efforts, 6: 281
   Tokyo Electric Power Co., Inc:, 6: 281
Kansai Electric Power Co:, 6: 288, 6: 294
Kaplan turbines, 6: 25, 6: 26f
La Romaine Complex, Quebec, Canada, 6: 163, 6: 169f, 6: 169t
laws, 6: 148
layouts, 6: 21, 6: 22
legislation, 6: 148
loads, 6: 20
Lom Panger storage dam, Cameroon, Africa, 6: 137
long-term sediment management, 6: **355–376**
low-cost developments, 6: 24
management
   construction impacts, 6: **49–91**
   environmental impacts, 6: **49–91**
   operation impacts, 6: **49–91**
Manitoba, Canada, 6: 153, 6: 156
measurement techniques, 6: 358, 6: 360
mechanical stirrers, operating strategies, 6: 83
Mekin project, Cameroon, Africa, 6: 141
Memve'Elé hydro plant project, Cameroon, Africa, 6: 139
mid-term development plans, 6: 135
minimum flow, 6: 56
mitigations measures, 6: 87
modeling sediment management, 6: 361, 6: 367
multibenefit solutions, 6: **15–47**
multipurpose settings, 6: 38
negative issues, 6: 41
New Zealand, 6: **467–483**
Ngassona Falls 210 Project, Cameroon, Africa, 6: 146
nitrogen, 6: 66
numerical modeling, 6: 361, 6: 367
nutrient dynamics, 6: 66
Oku-yoshino Power Plant, 6: 288, 6: 294
Omega siphon turbines, 6: 27
Ontario, Canada, 6: 153, 6: 155t, 6: 156, 6: 159f
operating strategies, 6: 83
operation, 6: **49–91**
   environmental impact management, 6: 52
   hydraulic processes, 6: 73, 6: 75
opportunities, Canada, 6: 154
organizational issues, 6: 258
oxygen, 6: 64
oxygenation, 6: 61, 6: 84
peak load energy, 6: 40
Pelton turbines, 6: 25
peninsular rivers, 6: 228, 6: 231, 6: 244
phosphorus, 6: 66
plant layouts, 6: 21, 6: 22
plant life, economics, 6: 40
pollution, 6: 52t, 6: 59

hydropower: (*continued*)
    population protection measures, 6: 87
    potential head, historical overviews, 6: 31, 6: 33*f*
    potentials, 6: 130
    powerhouses, 6: 17
    power plants, 6: 131, 6: 135, 6: 313
    present status in India, 6: 227
    pressure, 6: 357, 6: 365
    primary energy
        consumption, 6: 33, 6: 34*f*, 6: 34*t*
        Japanese current status, 6: 274
    production companies, Spain, 6: 315
    project implementation, India, 6: 240
    project planning, India, 6: 240
    pumped-storage, **6: 405–434**
        Iran, 6: 259, 6: 263*f*
        Japan, 6: 273, 6: 277, 6: 294
    pumped-storage power plants, Japanese successful efforts, 6: 281
    Quebec, Canada, 6: 153, 6: 161
    reforms, Cameroon, Africa, **6: 129–151**
    rehabilitation, 6: 236, 6: 239
    reservoirs
        filling management, 6: 84
        India, 6: 237
        long-term sediment management, **6: 355–376**
        sedimentation, 6: 53
        sediment management, **6: 355–376**
        water quality, 6: 53, 6: 58
    resettlements, 6: 210, 6: 236, 6: 239, 6: 243*f*
    resource, definition, 6: 1, 6: 16
    responses, sediment management, 6: 365
    Revelstoke Complex, British Colombia, Canada, 6: 175
    river networks, Spain, 6: 311
    river systems, 6: 130
    run-off-river plants
        India, 6: 237, 6: 240, 6: 242
        Iran, 6: 259, 6: 261*f*, 6: 262*f*
    safety, 6: 10
    scheme evolution, 6: 315
    screening, 6: 88, 6: 234
    sedimentation impacts, 6: 363, 6: 367
        turbines, 6: 57
        upstream impacts, 6: 53
    sediment management, **6: 355–376**
        bathymetric mapping, 6: 358, 6: 369, 6: 371*f*, 6: 372*f*
        dams, **6: 355–376**
        design, **6: 355–376**
        dredging, 6: 366
        driving forces, 6: 357, 6: 365
        environment, **6: 355–376**
        flushing, 6: 366, 6: 369, 6: 371*f*, 6: 372*f*
        hydraulic processes impact management, 6: 74
        impacts, 6: 57, 6: 74, 6: 363, 6: 367
        measurement techniques, 6: 358, 6: 360
        modeling, 6: 361, 6: 367
        numerical modeling, 6: 361, 6: 367
        pressures, 6: 357, 6: 365
        reservoirs, **6: 355–376**
        responses, 6: 365
        state considerations, 6: 362, 6: 366
        stresses, 6: 357, 6: 365
        transport, 6: 244
    simplified generic axial-flow microhydro turbines, design concepts, **6: 435–466**
    social issues, 6: 38, 6: 210, 6: 236, 6: 251
    solar energy multibenefit solutions, 6: 43
    Spain, **6: 309–341**
        1890–1940, 6: 317
        1940–1960, 6: 323
        1960–1975, 6: 327
        1970's onwards, 6: 333
        civil war, 6: 323
        development, **6: 309–341**
        Duero System, 6: 336
        future directions, 6: 339
        historical development, 6: 309, 6: 315
        hydrology, 6: 311
        power plants, 6: 313
        river networks, 6: 311
        scheme evolution, 6: 315
        strategic importance, 6: 310
        twentieth century, 6: 315
    spatial distribution, 6: 258
    stand alone wind energy hybrid systems, 2: 643, 2: 649–650
    state considerations, sediment management, 6: 362, 6: 366
    storage
        Cameroon, Africa, 6: 134, 6: 137
        India, 6: 233*f*, 6: 233–234, 6: 242
        Iran, 6: 259, 6: 260*f*, 6: 263*f*
    stresses, 6: 357, 6: 365
    supersaturation, 6: 73, 6: 75
    surge, 6: 56, 6: 370, 6: 375*f*
    sustainability
        Canada, **6: 153–178**
        environmental impact management, 6: 50
        guidelines, 6: 12
    Switzerland, **6: 343–354**
    tailrace, 6: 17, 6: 223
    technical issues, 6: 257
    Teviot River, Central Otago, New Zealand, **6: 467–483**
    Three Gorges Project, China, **6: 179–227**
    Tokyo Electric Power Co., Inc:, 6: 281
    turbines, 6: 24, 6: 57
        axial-flow microhydro turbines, **6: 435–466**
        bank turbines, 6: 26, 6: 28*f*
        cross-flow turbines, 6: 26, 6: 28*f*
        Francis turbines, 6: 25, 6: 28*f*
        generic axial-flow microhydro turbines, **6: 435–466**
        Hydraulienne siphon turbines, 6: 27
        Kaplan turbines, 6: 25, 6: 26*f*
        Omega siphon turbines, 6: 27
        Pelton turbines, 6: 25
        sedimentation impacts, 6: 57
        simplified generic axial-flow microhydro turbines, **6: 435–466**
        water turbine types, 6: 24
    twentieth century Spain, 6: 315
    United States of America, 6: 36, 6: 37*f*, 6: 37*t*
    unsteady flows, 6: 74, 6: 86
    upstream impacts, 6: 53
    velocity head, 6: 31
    wastes, multibenefit solutions, 6: 41, 6: 41*t*
    water characteristics, 6: 57
    water conveyance structures, 6: 16
    water quality
        environmental impact management, 6: 53, 6: 58
        eutrophication, 6: 61, 6: 72
        impact management, 6: 53, 6: 58
        oxygenation, 6: 61
        reservoirs, 6: 53, 6: 58
        upstream impacts, 6: 53
    water turbine types, 6: 24
    wind energy stand alone hybrid systems, 2: 643, 2: 649–650
    wind power multibenefit solutions, 6: 43
    work, 6: 17
    World banks, 6: 229
    world examples, historical overviews, 6: 33
    worldwide distribution, 6: 43
    world-wide schemes
        Brazil, 6: 35, **6: 93–127**, 6: 36*t*
        Cameroon, Africa, **6: 129–151**
        Canada, **6: 153–178**
        China, 6: 33, **6: 485–505**, **6: 179–227**
        Himalaya, **6: 227–252**
        India, **6: 227–252**
        Iran, **6: 253–264**
        Japan, **6: 265–307**

New Zealand, **6**: **467–483**
  pumped storage developments, **6**: 412–413, **6**: 414t
  Spain, **6**: **309–341**
  Switzerland, **6**: **343–354**
  Three Gorges Project, China, **6**: **179–227**
  Wuskwatim Generating Station Project, Manitoba, Canada, **6**: 159
hydrothermal pretreatments, **5**: 242
hydrothermal systems, **7**: 3
hygienic aspects: solar water heating systems, **3**: 437
hypereutrophy, **6**: 62
HyPOD® enclosure, **4**: 134
hypolimnetic aeration and oxygenation, **6**: 84
HySafe, **4**: 80
hysteresis: air turbines, **8**: 128

I

IAEA *see* International Atomic Energy Agency
Iberdrola: hydropower production, **6**: 315, **6**: 336
IBSC *see* intermediate band solar cells
ICE *see* internal combustion engines
ice forces standardization, **2**: 718
Iceland:
  current status, **7**: 286
  economics, **7**: 286
  effluent water monitoring, **7**: 111
  environmental impacts, **7**: 287
  geothermal energy
    current status, **7**: 286
    economics, **7**: 286
    environmental impacts, **7**: 287
    historical overviews, **7**: 286
    social issues, **7**: 287
    sustainable development, **7**: 286
  historical overviews, **7**: 286
  social issues, **7**: 287
  sustainable development, **7**: 286
ice loads, **2**: 253
ICPC *see* integrated compound parabolic collectors
ICS *see* integrated collector storage
IEA *see* International Energy Agency
IEA-OES *see* International Energy Agency, Implementing Agreement on Ocean Energy Systems
IEA-PVPS *see* International Energy Agency Photovoltaic Power Systems Programme
IEC *see* International Electrotechnical Commission
IED *see* Industrial Emissions Directive
IENICA project (2000), **5**: 389
IGCC *see* integrated gasification combined cycles
ignition phenomena, **4**: 81, **4**: 97, **4**: 104
Iguaçu River hydroelectric project, **6**: 108
III–V group compound multi-junction cells, **1**: **497–514**
illumination effects, **3**: 261
imaging:
  cloud motion vectors, **1**: 245, **1**: 249, **1**: 251
  low concentration ratio solar collectors, **3**: 150
imbalance: voltage variation, **2**: 594
immersed heat exchange, **3**: 454, **3**: 454f
immobilization: enzymes, **4**: 260
impact: definitions, wind power, **2**: 503
impact ionization, **1**: 316, **1**: 339
impact management:
  hydropower environments, **6**: **49–91**
    hydraulic process, **6**: 73
    mitigations measures, **6**: 87
    operating strategies, **6**: 83
    sedimentation, **6**: 57, **6**: 74, **6**: 363, **6**: 367
    water quality, **6**: 53, **6**: 58
impact scales: bioenergy policy development, **5**: 424
implanted emitters, **1**: 380
implementation issues:
  biomass-to-liquids technology, **5**: 188

building-integrated photovoltaics, **1**: 699
  pitch control, **2**: 275
  wind power projects, **2**: **391–391**
Implementing Agreement on Ocean Energy Systems wave energy conversion, **8**: 7
import dependency: geothermal energy, **7**: 281
import duty reductions, **1**: 128
import tariffs: bioenergy trade barriers, **5**: 81
improvement scores, **1**: 269
impulse air turbines, **8**: 112, **8**: 120, **8**: 122, **8**: 131, **8**: 136, **8**: 137
impulse magnetoplasma rockets, **4**: 19
impurities:
  diffusion, **1**: 428, **1**: 502
  gas processing, **5**: 142
  generation, **1**: 303
  intermediate band photovoltaics, **1**: 624
  recombination, **1**: 303
incentives:
  bioenergy policy development, **5**: 422
  developing country off-grid photovoltaics, **1**: **111–141**
  harmonizing support schemes, **1**: 4
  investment opportunities, **1**: 3
  support schemes, **1**: **1–4**
incidence angles:
  low-temperature stationary collectors, **3**: 143
  solar energy environmental characteristics, **3**: 1, **3**: 12, **3**: 13
  solar radiation, **1**: 214, **1**: 215, **3**: 21
incident light down-shifting, **1**: **563–585**
incident ocean waves, **8**: 93
incident photon-to-current conversion efficiency (IPCE), **1**: 488, **1**: 550
incident solar radiation, **1**: 216–217, **5**: 297–298
incident spectra, **1**: 569
inclination: collectors, **3**: 152, **3**: 153f, **3**: 441
inclined flat-plate collectors, **3**: 152, **3**: 153f
income generators: biochar, **5**: 357, **5**: 381
incremental hydrogen technology methods, **4**: 54
independent power producers (IPP), **1**: 131
index of agreement, **3**: 52
India, **6**: **227–252**
  banking institutes, **6**: 229
  climate change, **6**: 230
  downstream flow, **6**: 237
  economics, **6**: 229, **6**: 251
  environment studies, **6**: 234
  finance, **6**: 229
  future planning, **6**: 227
  hydroelectricity, **6**: **227–252**
  hydrology, **6**: 230
  hydropower, **6**: **227–252**
    banking institutes, **6**: 229
    climate change, **6**: 230
    development, **6**: **227–252**
    downstream flow, **6**: 237
    economics, **6**: 229, **6**: 251
    environment studies, **6**: 234
    finance, **6**: 229
    future planning, **6**: 227
    hydrology, **6**: 230
    peninsular rivers, **6**: 228, **6**: 231, **6**: 244
    planning, **6**: 227
    present status, **6**: 227
    project implementation, **6**: 240
    project planning, **6**: 240
    rehabilitation, **6**: 236, **6**: 239
    reservoirs, **6**: 237
    resettlements, **6**: 236, **6**: 239, **6**: 243f
    run-off-river plants, **6**: 237, **6**: 240, **6**: 242
    sediment transport, **6**: 244
    socioeconomic development, **6**: 251
    storage, **6**: 233f, **6**: 233–234, **6**: 242
    World banks, **6**: 229
  North Eastern Region, **6**: 252

India (*continued*)
    peninsular rivers, **6**: 228, **6**: 231, **6**: 244
    photovoltaics, **1**: 167
    planning, **6**: 227
    project implementation, hydropower, **6**: 240
    project planning, **6**: 240
    rehabilitation, **6**: 236, **6**: 239
    reservoirs, **6**: 237
    resettlements, **6**: 236, **6**: 239, **6**: 243*f*
    run-off-river plants, **6**: 237, **6**: 240, **6**: 242
    sediment transport, **6**: 244
    socioeconomic development, **6**: 251
    solar radiation atlases, **3**: 39
    storing hydropower, **6**: 233*f*, **6**: 233–234, **6**: 242
    water resources, **6**: 230, **6**: 230*t*
    World banks, **6**: 229
indicators: geothermal energy, **7**: 277, **7**: 278
Indira Sagar hydroelectric project, **6**: 244, **6**: 245*f*
indirect biomass cofiring, **5**: 62, **5**: 64
indirect gain: passive solar technologies, **3**: 361
indirect gasification, **5**: 62
indirect-grid coupling generators, **2**: 289
indirect heavy metal emissions, **1**: 151
indirect land use change:
    biofuels, **5**: 107, **5**: 120
    biomass-to-liquids technology, **5**: 197–198, **5**: 199*f*
    ethics, **5**: 107
    greenhouse gases, **5**: 120
indirect monitoring: geothermal systems, ph, **7**: 26
indirect-use geothermal energy, **7**: 279
indirect water heating systems, **3**: 450, **3**: 452
indium-arsenide/gallium-arsenide quantum dots, **1**: 633
indium-gallium-antimonide solar cells, **1**: 608, **1**: 610
indium-gallium-arsenide-antimonide-phosphide solar cells, **1**: 611
indium-gallium-arsenide solar cells, **1**: 610, **1**: 611
indium-gallium-phosphorous/gallium-arsenide-based solar cells, **1**: 506
    development, **1**: 503
    heteroface structure bottom cells, **1**: 503, **1**: 504
    lattice matching, **1**: 503, **1**: 504
    radiation resistance, **1**: 505
    space applications, **1**: 506
    terrestrial applications, **1**: 506
indium-phosphide solar cells, **1**: 610
individual pitch control systems, **2**: 348
indoor irradiance, **1**: 721
indoor stoves, **1**: 614
induced seismicity, **7**: 285
induction: wind energy electrical power, **2**: 52
induction generators:
    wind turbines
        control systems, **2**: 353, **2**: 354
        definitions, **2**: 270
        electrical systems, **2**: 279, **2**: 281
        modeling, **2**: 339, **2**: 340
industrial applications:
    see also industry
    absorbers, **3**: 571
    air heating, **3**: 587
    collectors, **3**: 569
    design, solar thermal systems, **3**: 577
    direct heat utilization, **7**: 169, **7**: 173*t*, **7**: 174, **7**: 176*f*, **7**: 180, **7**: 180*f*, **7**: 181, **7**: 182, **7**: 183*f*
    direct solar gain, **3**: 587
    drying, **7**: 169, **7**: 173*t*, **7**: 174, **7**: 176*f*, **7**: 180, **7**: 180*f*, **7**: 181, **7**: 182, **7**: 183*f*
    evacuated tube collectors, **3**: 571, **3**: 587*t*
    flat-plate collectors, **3**: 570, **3**: 571, **3**: 587*t*
    geothermal energy, direct heat utilization, **7**: 169, **7**: 173*t*, **7**: 174, **7**: 176*f*, **7**: 180, **7**: 180*f*, **7**: 181, **7**: 182, **7**: 183*f*
    greenhouses, **3**: 586
    heating buildings, **3**: 587
    heat system design, **3**: 577
    heat system layouts, **3**: 573
    hot water, **3**: 577
    line-axis collectors, **3**: 571, **3**: 587*t*
    parabolic trough collectors, **3**: 571
    real heat system layouts, **3**: 575
    solar cooking, **3**: 588
    solar desalination, **3**: 589
    solar drying, **3**: 579
    solar heat, **3**: **567–594**
    solar ponds, **3**: 572, **3**: 587*t*
    solar refrigeration, **3**: 592
    solar thermal systems, **3**: **567–594**
        absorbers, **3**: 571
        air heating, **3**: 587
        characteristics, **3**: 568
        collectors, **3**: 569
        component layouts, **3**: 573
        cooking, **3**: 588
        desalination, **3**: 589
        design, **3**: 577
        direct solar gain, **3**: 587
        drying, **3**: 579
        economics, **3**: 569
        energy storage, **3**: 569
        evacuated tube collectors, **3**: 571, **3**: 587*t*
        flat-plate collectors, **3**: 570, **3**: 571, **3**: 587*t*
        generic process system layouts, **3**: 573
        greenhouses, **3**: 586
        heating buildings, **3**: 587
        heat system design, **3**: 577
        heat system layouts, **3**: 573
        hot water, **3**: 577
        line-axis collectors, **3**: 571, **3**: 587*t*
        operational limits, **3**: 576
        parabolic trough collectors, **3**: 571
        real heat system layouts, **3**: 575
        refrigeration, **3**: 592
        solar ponds, **3**: 572, **3**: 587*t*
        stationary collectors, **3**: 570, **3**: 571, **3**: 572, **3**: 587*t*
        stills, **3**: 589
        system layouts, **3**: 573
        temperature requirements, **3**: 568, **3**: 569*t*
        thermal energy storage, **3**: 569
        ventilation, **3**: 587
        water heating, **3**: 577
    stationary collectors, **3**: 570, **3**: 571, **3**: 572, **3**: 587*t*
    stills, **3**: 589
    thermal energy storage, **3**: 569
    ventilation, **3**: 587
    water heating, **3**: 577
Industrial Emissions Directive (IED), **5**: 31
industrial revolution: solar energy utilization, **1**: 31–32
industry:
    see also industrial applications
    bioethanol development, **5**: 15, **5**: 17
    Brazil, **5**: 15, **5**: **15–26**, **5**: 17
        bioethanol development, **5**: 15, **5**: 17
        sugarcane, **5**: **15–26**
    cadmium telluride thin films, **1**: 424
    cost reductions in photovoltaic technology, **1**: 52
    crystalline silicon cells, **1**: 355, **1**: 358
    economics of solar thermal systems, **3**: 569
    electrical systems, wind turbines, **2**: 306
    generic process solar system layouts, **3**: 573
    global overview, photovoltaics, **1**: **161–177**
    heat pump classification, **3**: 501
    macroeconomic factors, geothermal energy, **7**: 259, **7**: 263
    microeconomic analysis, geothermal energy, **7**: 260
    operational limits, solar thermal systems, **3**: 576
    photovoltaics
        cadmium telluride thin films, **1**: 424
        cost reductions, **1**: 52
        development, **1**: 7

global overview, **1: 161–177**
introduction, **1**: 7
technology progress, **1**: 16
thermal solar collectors, **3**: 292
solar system layouts, **3**: 573
sugarcane, Brazil, **5: 15–26**
temperature requirements, solar thermal systems, **3**: 568, **3**: 569t
turbine technology, wind energy, **2: 671–724**
wind energy, turbine technology, **2: 671–724**
wind power, **2: 657–669**
wind turbines, **2**: 306, **2: 671–724**
Ineos Bio, **5**: 190
inertial loads, **2**: 251
Infinia Solar System (ISS), **3**: 204
inflation indexation, **1**: 101
inflow:
    blade-element momentum theory, **2**: 230
    debris control, **6**: 82
    noise, **2**: 238
    reservoir water quality, **6**: 70
infrared radiation, **1**: 596, **3**: 172, **3**: 174
infrastructure:
    costs
        geothermal energy, **7**: 259
        offshore wind power, **2**: 461
    design, hydrogen technology, **4**: 53
    economics, hydrogen technology, **4**: 52
    geothermal energy cost and investment factors, **7**: 259
    hydrogen
        design, **4**: 53
        economics, **4**: 52
        fuel cells, **4**: 283, **4**: 333, **4**: 337, **4**: 339
    photovoltaic visions, **1**: 188, **1**: 197
ingestion: alcohol fuel safety, **5**: 324
Ingeteam, **2**: 325, **2**: 327f
inhabitant opinion: wind park design, **2**: 171, **2**: 173
inhalation: alcohol fuel safety, **5**: 325
inherent safer hydrogen engineering, **4**: 101
inhibitors: saccharification and fermentation, **5**: 248
initial commercial cadmium telluride thin films, **1**: 424
initial conception: ocean wave energy device development, **8: 79–110**
initiatives: very large-scale photovoltaic, **1**: 739
injection biomass cofiring, **5**: 63, **5**: 64
inkjet printing, **1**: 471
inland fish farming, **6**: 144
inlet air temperature, **3**: 383
inlet hydrogen pressure, **4**: 314
inlet swirl, **6**: 460
inlet volute limits, **6**: 452, **6**: 463
innovation:
    building-integrated photovoltaics, **1**: 706
    future photovoltaics, **1**: 188
    wind turbine technology, **2: 671–724**
inoculums, **4**: 273
inorganic luminescent solar concentrators, **1**: 594
inorganic materials: definitions, **1**: 13
inorganic semiconductor physics:
    charge transport, **1**: 444, **1**: 445
    organic solar cells, **1**: 442
    working principles, **1**: 445
inorganic solar cells, **1**: 442
input data errors: ocean wave numerical models, **8**: 46
in-situ assembly: high concentration solar collectors, **3**: 178
in situ transesterification, **5**: 208
insolation, **3**: 163
inspections:
    concrete structure durability, **6**: 397
    hydrogen storage, **4**: 130
installation:
    geothermal heat pumps, **7**: 199
    high concentration solar collectors, **3**: 178
    offshore wind power, **2**: 452

wind park site selection, **2**: 171
wind turbines, **2**: 177
installed capacity:
    Cameroon, Africa electricity, **6**: 132, **6**: 134t
    direct heat utilization, **7**: 172f, **7**: 172t
    geothermal direct heat utilization, **7**: 172f, **7**: 172t
    Iranian high-pressure processing, **6**: 261, **6**: 264f
    photovoltaics, **1**: 17, **1**: 18f
    wind turbines, **2**: 94
installed costs:
    onshore wind, **2**: 479
    wind speed performance evaluations, **2**: 475
installed photovoltaic system operation, **1**: 8
instantaneous efficiency: low-temperature stationary collectors, **3**: 142, **3**: 142f, **3**: 143f
instantaneous power output: wind turbines, **2**: 132
instantaneous wind speeds, **2**: 81
institutional structure reforms: Cameroon, Africa, **6: 129–151**
instrumentation:
    buoy measurements, **8**: 24
    concrete structure durability, **6**: 397
    cooling technologies, **4**: 24
    ocean waves, **8**: 24, **8**: 34
    satellite altimeters, **8**: 34
    solar radiation, **3**: 64
    space cooling technologies, **4**: 24
insulation:
    see also transparent insulation
    flat-plate low-temperature stationary collectors, **3**: 104, **3**: 111, **3**: 113
    hydrogen safety engineering, **4**: 81
intake:
    axial-flow microhydro turbines, **6**: 437, **6**: 443
    towers, hydropower impact management, **6**: 88
    types, Three Gorges Project, China, **6**: 221
integrated collector storage (ICS) systems, **3**: 159, **3**: 163
integrated compound parabolic collectors (ICPC), **3**: 159
integrated gasification combined cycles (IGCC), **4**: 50, **4**: 331, **4**: 332
Integrated Pollution Prevention and Control (IPPC) Directive, **5**: 31
integrated solar combined cycles, **3**: 606
integrated time domain analysis, **2**: 244, **2**: 254
integrated water resources management: hydropower, **6**: 12
integrated wind energy resource planning, **2**: 485
Integrated Wind Turbine Design (UPWIND), **2**: 717
integration:
    bioenergy markets, **5**: 80
    building-integrated photovoltaics, **1**: 701, **1**: 705
    building-integrated photovoltaic-thermal systems, **3**: 379
    collectors, **3**: 430, **3**: 432f
    costs, wind energy, **2**: 612
    desalination, **2**: 732
    electrical networks-wind energy, **2: 569–622**
    future wind energy trends, **2**: 617
    local wind park networks, **2**: 206
    power systems, wind energy, **2**: 591
    solar technologies, **3**: 379, **3**: 430, **3**: 432f
    solar water heating systems, **3**: 430, **3**: 432f
    thermal energy storage, **3**: 214
    turbine technology, **2**: 711, **2**: 714
    wind energy
        conventional electrical power system overviews, **2**: 571
        costs, **2**: 612
        desalination, **2**: 732
        electrical networks, **2: 569–622**
        financial support, **2**: 711
        future trends, **2**: 617
        microgrid systems, **2**: 571, **2**: 592–593, **2**: 600, **2**: 607
        power systems, **2**: 591
        wind park local networks, **2**: 206
        wind turbine technology, **2**: 711, **2**: 714
intelligent control techniques, **3**: 637, **3**: 657t, **3**: 659
interaction disturbances: electrical networks-wind turbines, **2**: 593

interannual ocean wave variability, 8: 51
intercell connections, 1: 502
interconnections:
    building-integrated photovoltaics, 1: 702
    definitions, 4: 241
    hydrogen technology, 4: 248
    solid oxide fuel cells, 4: 248
interest rates, 2: 472, 2: 473
interfacial layers:
    low-emittance coatings, 3: 327
    organic solar cells, 1: 467
interfacial organic solar cells, 1: 453
interfacing proteins, 1: 666
interference:
    Earth's atmosphere, 3: 34
    electromagnetic communication systems, 2: 524
    organic solar cells, 1: 463
    solar radiation, 3: 34
    stacks, selective coatings, 3: 306
    wind turbines, 2: 524
Intergovernmental Panel on Climate Change (IPCC), 5: 415, 5: 415t
intergranular corrosion, 7: 242
intermediate band solar cells (IBSC), 1: 619–639, 1: 9
    band structure, 1: 619
    deep-level impurities, 1: 624
    impurity-based approaches, 1: 624
    InAs/GaAs quantum dots, 1: 633
    non-Stranski–Krastanov quantum dots, 1: 635
    photovoltaics, 1: 619–639, 1: 9
    quantum dots, 1: 623, 1: 628
    quantum structure nanotechnology, 1: 527
    structure, 1: 619
    theoretical models, 1: 619
intermediate water technology, 2: 446
intermittent energy sources, 2: 554
intermolecular conduction, 1: 444
internal combustion engines (ICE):
    alcohol fuels, 5: 316
    automotives, 5: 316
    biofuels, 5: 308
    hybridization, 5: 308
    hydrogen economy conversion, biofuels, 5: 310
    hydrogen end-use technologies, 4: 58
    hydrogen transport applications, 4: 281–293
internal embrittlement, 4: 117
internal energy: thermal radiation thermodynamics, 1: 328–329
internal quantum efficiency, 1: 450, 1: 488, 1: 564, 1: 570
internal rate of return (IRR), 2: 424, 2: 472
internal standards: wind energy, 2: 372
International Atomic Energy Agency (IAEA), 7: 276, 7: 277, 7: 278
international connections: wind energy storage systems, 2: 496
international cooperation: hydropower, 6: 12
International Electrotechnical Commission (IEC), 1: 787–803
    60891 series, 1: 792
    60904 series, 1: 791
    61400 series, 2: 330, 2: 331t, 2: 372, 2: 373, 2: 374
    61853 series, 1: 796
    62108 series, 1: 797
    62670 series, 1: 798
    concentration photovoltaics, 1: 749, 1: 797
    design-related standards, 2: 372, 2: 374
    photovoltaic standards, 1: 787–803
    technical committee 82 , 1: 787–803
    type approval testing, photovoltaic reliability, 1: 793
    wind classes, 2: 418
    wind energy, 2: 372, 2: 373, 2: 374, 2: 418
International Energy Agency (IEA):
    wave energy, 8: 7
    wind energy, 2: 71
International Energy Agency, Implementing Agreement on Ocean Energy Systems (IEA-OES), 8: 7
International Energy Agency Photovoltaic Power Systems Programme (IEA-PVPS), 1: 733, 1: 734, 1: 741

international funds: developing country photovoltaics, 1: 113
international geothermal energy investment, 7: 259–270
internationalization factors: bioenergy markets, 5: 81
international labor laws, 5: 106
International Labour Organization, 5: 106
International Organization for Standardization (ISO), 2: 373, 4: 83, 5: 105
international recognition: very large-scale photovoltaics, 1: 733, 1: 734t
international regulations: hydrogen safety, 4: 83, 4: 83t
international standards:
    photovoltaics, 1: 793
    wind energy, 2: 372
International Sustainability & Carbon Certification (ISCC), 5: 104
international trade:
    bioenergy markets, 5: 75–85
    wood fuel, 5: 77
interpretation considerations: numerical weather prediction models, 1: 260
intertechnology spillovers: photovoltaic costs, 1: 51
intramolecular conduction, 1: 444
intrinsic loss mechanisms, 1: 294, 1: 309
intrinsic selective coatings, 3: 304
intrusion prevention net installations, 6: 422
intrusions: volcanic events, 7: 56
inundated practicality index, 6: 210
inverse heat transfer coefficient (R-value), 3: 322
inverse tandem stacks, 3: 305
inverted flat-plate collectors, 3: 152, 3: 153f
inverted metamorphic multijunction cells, 1: 24, 1: 25f
inverters, 1: 6
    balance of system, 1: 685
    hydrogen technology, 4: 297
    power loss analysis, 4: 300
    safe operating areas, 4: 297
    small wind turbines, 2: 301
investment, 7: 259–270
    annual net profits, 2: 211
    annual revenue calculations, 2: 210
    biomass and biofuels, 5: 29
    Cameroon, Africa, hydropower, 6: 144, 6: 148, 6: 149
    costs, offshore wind power, 2: 461–462
    electricity production, geothermal energy, 7: 259–270
    future photovoltaics, 1: 196
    geothermal energy, 7: 259–270
        electricity production, 7: 259–270
        overview/introduction, 7: 2
    hydropower, 6: 144, 6: 148, 6: 149
    incentive support mechanisms, 1: 3
    investor certainty, 1: 3
    Mekin hydropower project, Cameroon, Africa, 6: 144
    offshore wind power, 2: 461–462
    photovoltaics
        future visions, 1: 196
        global industry overview, 1: 162
        promotion schemes, 1: 74, 1: 75–76, 1: 78, 1: 106
        technology progress, 1: 15, 1: 15f
    policy support mechanisms, 1: 3
    power generation, 5: 29
    promoting photovoltaics, 1: 74, 1: 75–76, 1: 78, 1: 106
    solar power satellites, 1: 772
    subsidies, bioenergy policy development, 5: 411, 5: 419
    support mechanisms, 1: 3
    Three Gorges Project, China, 6: 210, 6: 211
    wind park design, 2: 210, 2: 211
    wind power, economics, 2: 421
    wind turbines, 2: 421
invisibility: building-integrated photovoltaics, 1: 706
ionic conductivity, 4: 176–177
ionic liquid membranes, 4: 189
ionic liquid pretreatments, 5: 239
ionization: photovoltaic thermodynamics, 1: 316, 1: 339
ionomers: alkaline fuel cells, 4: 159, 4: 178

ion storage, 3: 345
IPCC *see* Intergovernmental Panel on Climate Change
IPCE *see* incident photon-to-current conversion efficiency
IPP *see* independent power producers
IPPC *see* Integrated Pollution Prevention and Control
Iqbal's parameterization models, 3: 42
Iranian hydropower, 6: 253–264
   energy flows, 6: 253
   energy generation, 6: 253
   high-pressure processing, 6: 258, 6: 259, 6: 259f, 6: 260f, 6: 264t
   large hydropower projects, 6: 258
   pumped-storage plants, 6: 259, 6: 263f
   run-off-river plants, 6: 259, 6: 261f, 6: 262f
   storage plants, 6: 259, 6: 260f, 6: 263f
IRR *see* internal rate of return
irradiance, 1: 239–292
   characteristics, 1: 246
   photovoltaic power forecasts, 1: 239–292, 1: 240
   product-integrated photovoltaics, 1: 720, 1: 724
   solar cell performance, 1: 681, 1: 720
irradiation: bioethanol, 5: 241
irregular ocean waves, 8: 13, 8: 14, 8: 15, 8: 96
irregular wind wave theory, 2: 266
ISCC *see* International Sustainability & Carbon Certification
isentropic efficiency ratio, 7: 207, 7: 208
ISFOC demonstration power plants, 1: 750
island systems: concentrating solar power, 3: 597
ISO *see* International Organization for Standardization
isolated electrical grids, 2: **623–655**
isolated monoplane rotors, 8: 115
isolated power system security, 2: 715
isotopes: geothermal chemistry, 7: 100–101
isotropic radiation, 1: 319, 3: 47, 3: 48
ISS *see* Infinia Solar System
Itá hydroelectricity project, Brazil, 6: 121
Itaipu hydroelectric project, Brazil, 6: 96
Italy:
   bioenergy policy development, 5: 426
   wind power, 2: 664
Ivanpah Solar Electric Generating System, 3: 632, 3: 633f

J

Jablonski diagrams, 1: 542
jacket foundations, 2: 179, 2: 180f, 2: 443f, 2: 447
Jain and Ratto model, 3: 41
James Bay region, Quebec, Canada, 6: 161
Jándula Dam, Spain, 6: 322, 6: 322f
Japan, 6: **265–307**
   ecosystem measures, 6: 298
   energy issues, 6: 280
   future challenges, 6: 280
   historical overviews, 6: 265, 6: 283
   hydropower, 6: **265–307**
     current status, 6: 274
     development, 6: 274
     ecosystem measures, 6: 298
     energy issues, 6: 280
     future challenges, 6: 280
     historical overviews, 6: 37, 6: 265, 6: 283
     Kansai Electric Power Co:, 6: 288, 6: 294
     Oku-yoshino Power Plant, 6: 288, 6: 294
     pumped-storage power plants, 6: 273, 6: 277, 6: 294
     successful efforts, 6: 281
     Tokyo Electric Power Co., Inc:, 6: 281
   Kansai Electric Power Co:, 6: 288, 6: 294
   ocean wave energy, 8: 7
   Oku-yoshino Power Plant, 6: 288, 6: 294
   photovoltaics, 1: 166, 1: 167, 1: 170, 1: 171, 1: 172, 1: 184
   pumped-storage power plants, 6: 273, 6: 277, 6: 294
   seawater pumped storage hydropower, 6: 418
   solar radiation atlas, 3: 62
   space propulsion, 4: 20–21
   Tokyo Electric Power Co., Inc:, 6: 281
   wave energy conversion, 8: 7
jatropha oils, 5: 60
jet fires, 4: 79, 4: 79f, 4: 91, 4: 95
jet flame tip location, 4: 94
jet flows, 6: 485, 6: 492, 6: 499
jet releases, 4: 86
JingAo Solar Co: Ltd, 1: 170
Jirau hydroelectric project, Brazil, 6: 94, 6: 104f, 6: 106
JM de Oriol Dam, Spain, 6: 328, 6: 330f
job opportunities: wind power, 2: 507, 2: 508
Johannesburg declaration, 7: 278
joint inversion, 7: 71
JOint North SeaWave Project (JONSWAP), 8: 16, 8: 16t, 8: 17f, 8: 91, 8: 96
Joint Research Centre (JRC), 1: 788
joints:
   condition, 6: 384
   cracking, 6: 382
   hydrogen storage, 4: 120
   repairs, 6: 397
JONSWAP *see* JOint North SeaWave Project (JONSWAP)
José M: de Oriol power plant, Spain, 6: 332, 6: 332f
JRC *see* Joint Research Centre
Juul, Johannes, 2: 60

K

Kadei river, Cameroon, Africa, 6: 145
Kalina binary cycles, 7: 207, 7: 228, 7: 233
KAM *see* Kraftanlagen München
Kansai Electric Power Co: (KEPCO):
   flood conditions, 6: 294
   Japanese hydropower, 6: 288, 6: 294
   reservoir bypassing, 6: 294
   reservoir sediment flushing, 6: 288
   sediment reservoir bypass, 6: 294
   turbid water reservoir bypass, 6: 294
Kaplan turbines, 6: 25, 6: 26f
Karpathos Island, 2: 212
Kasos Island, 2: 212
Kasten solar radiation model, 3: 42
KEPCO *see* Kansai Electric Power Co.
kerosene, 5: 308, 5: 316, 5: 335, 5: 337
Kettle Generating Station, 6: 157, 6: 157f
kilns, 5: 367, 5: 367f, 5: 367–368, 5: 368, 5: 369f, 5: 381–382
kilowatt grid-connected fuel cells, 4: 300
kilowatt hours: definitions, 3: 529
Kimberlina solar thermal power plant, 3: 623
Kimolos Island, Greece, 3: 100, 3: 100f
kinematics:
   high concentration solar collectors, 3: 187
   hydropower specific speed, 6: 25
   ocean wave energy, 8: 85
kinetics:
   dye-sensitized solar cells, 1: 484
   electron-transfer, 1: 484
King River Power Development, 6: 76
Kingsnorth plant, 5: 68
Kircher: solar energy history, 3: 88, 3: 88f
Kirchhoff's law, 3: 303–304
Kite Gen design, 2: 686
Klucher solar radiation model, 3: 47
Krafla, Iceland, 7: 111
Kraftanlagen München (KAM), 3: 193
Kraft pulping, 5: 264
Kribi thermal plan, 6: 139
Kurobe Basin, 6: 290
Kurobe River, 6: 290
Kyocera Corporation, 1: 171
Kyoto Protocol, 7: 290, 7: 291

L

laboratory test/trials, 4: 303, 6: 475, 8: 88
labor laws, 5: 106
labor practices, 5: 22, 5: 23
La Cohilla dam, Spain, 6: 326, 6: 327f
Lagdo plant: Cameroon, Africa, 6: 132, 6: 133f, 6: 133t, 6: 134, 6: 134t
Lagerwey's generators, 2: 293, 2: 293f
La Grande River, Quebec, Canada, 6: 161
Lagrange invariant, 1: 316, 1: 325
Lagrangian: solar radiation concentration, 1: 325
Lahti, Finland, 5: 150
Lake Chad tributaries, 6: 130, 6: 131
Lake Mývatn, Iceland, 7: 111
Lake numbers, 6: 68, 6: 70
lake stability, 6: 68
Lake Winnipeg Regulation, 6: 157
Lambertian surfaces, 1: 316
laminar burning velocity, 4: 77
Lampedusa Island, Italy, 3: 553
La Muela pumping plant, Spain, 6: 333, 6: 335f
La Nava power plant, 1: 750, 1: 751t
land morphology: wind park design, 2: 174
landscape turbulence, 2: 78
land-sea breezes, 2: 82
landslides, 6: 86f
land-use:
    bioenergy policy development, 5: 428
    biofuels
        automotives, 5: 327, 5: 327–328
        ethics, 5: 107
        greenhouse gas life cycle assessments, 5: 117, 5: 120
    biomass-to-liquids technology, 5: 197–198, 5: 199f, 5: 200
    direct heat utilization, 7: 179–180
    ethics, 5: 107
    geothermal energy, 7: 179–180, 7: 284
    greenhouse gases, 5: 117, 5: 120
    Horseshoe Bend hydroelectric scheme, 6: 470
    leasing power, 2: 397, 2: 422
    life cycle assessments, 5: 117, 5: 120
    restoration considerations, 3: 6
    solar thermal systems, 3: 6
    tenure arrangements, 6: 470
    wind energy, 2: 174, 2: 182, 2: 395, 2: 688
    wind park design, 2: 174
    wind power, 2: 395
lanthanides, 1: 566, 1: 573
Large Combustion Plant Directive (LCPD), 5: 31
large eddy simulations (LES), 2: 232–233
large-scale deployment: cadmium telluride thin films, 1: 434
large-scale hydropower plants:
    Brazil, 6: 93–127
    exploitation, 6: 11
    Iran, 6: 258
    Switzerland, 6: 345
large-scale noninterconnected power systems, 2: 211, 2: 216
large-scale production: organic solar cells, 1: 472
large-scale prototypes: ocean wave energy sea trials, 8: 96
large-scale wind energy machines, 2: 54
La Romaine Complex, Quebec, Canada, 6: 163, 6: 169f, 6: 169t
laser beaming, 1: 770
laser distance sensors, 8: 93–95, 8: 95f
laser Doppler anemometers, 2: 76
laser scanning, 3: 171
Las Portas dam, Spain, 6: 328, 6: 329f
latent heat:
    definitions, 3: 221
    exergy analysis, 3: 222
    solar assisted heat pumps, 3: 517–518
    solar thermal energy storage, 3: 211, 3: 221, 3: 222, 3: 225t, 3: 227, 3: 228t, 3: 229, 3: 230, 3: 230f, 3: 231, 3: 243, 3: 247
lattice constants, 1: 608, 1: 609f
lattice matching, 1: 500, 1: 503, 1: 504
lattice relaxation multiple-phonon emission, 1: 626
laws:
    Cameroon, Africa, hydropower, 6: 148
    coatings, 3: 318
    glazings, 3: 318
    high concentration solar collectors, 3: 206
    Kirchhoff's law, 3: 303–304
    labor laws, 5: 106
    log law, wind speed profiles, 2: 79
    Planck's law, 3: 33
    solar radiation, 3: 318
    Stefan–Boltzmann law, 3: 20, 3: 34, 3: 303
    thermal radiation, 3: 318
    Wien's displacement law, 1: 605, 1: 605f, 3: 33
Lawson-Tancred's machine, 2: 62, 2: 65f
layers:
    see also individual layer entries
    dielectric surface passivation, 1: 365
    enzyme electrodes, 4: 261
    organic solar cells, 1: 470
    superstrate cadmium telluride devices, 1: 427
layouts:
    building-integrated photovoltaics, 1: 699
    components, 3: 573
    conduit systems, 6: 190
    heat system design, 3: 573, 3: 577
    Horseshoe Bend hydroelectric scheme, 6: 468, 6: 474
    hydropower, 6: 21, 6: 22
    Mekin hydropower project, Cameroon, Africa, 6: 142
    Memve'Élé hydro plant project, Cameroon, Africa, 6: 140
    photochromogenic devices, 3: 346–348, 3: 348f
    powerhouses, 6: 188, 6: 193, 6: 195f
    real heat systems, 3: 575
    roller compacted concrete dams, 6: 474
    ship locks, 6: 196
    site layouts, 1: 699, 6: 474
    solar thermal system components, 3: 573
    solar thermal systems, 3: 573
    Three Gorges Project, China, 6: 188, 6: 193, 6: 195f, 6: 196
    underground power plants, Three Gorges Project, China, 6: 193, 6: 195f
    wind farms, 2: 399
    wind power micro-siting, 2: 399, 2: 415f, 2: 416f
LCA *see* life-cycle assessments/analysis
LDK Solar Co: Ltd:, 1: 174
lead–acid batteries, 1: 206, 4: 323
LEAF *see* Linking Environment and Farming
learning curves: photovoltaic cost forecasting, 1: 47, 1: 54
learning from experience: photovoltaic cost reductions, 1: 51, 1: 54
learning methods: solar irradiance-photovoltaics, 1: 248
leasing:
    developing country photovoltaics, 1: 126
    wind power, 2: 397, 2: 422
leaves, 1: 657–677, 1: 10
    see also artificial leaves
    natural photosynthesis design, 1: 657, 1: 663
    photosynthesis design, 1: **657–677**
LED *see* light-emitting diodes
Legionnaires' disease, 3: 437
legislation:
    bioenergy policy development, 5: 425–426, 5: 426, 5: 427
    biofuel sustainability, 5: 337–338
    biomass and biofuel power generation, 5: 31
    Cameroon, Africa, hydropower, 6: 148
    hydrogen, transport applications, 4: 291
    hydropower, Cameroon, Africa, 6: 148
    power generation, 5: 31
    wind park design, 2: 170–171, 2: 182–183
lenses, 3: 88, 3: 88f, 3: 88–90, 3: 89f
LES *see* large eddy simulations
levelized energy costs (LEC), 2: 424, 8: 153, 8: 154

levunic acid: sugars, **5**: 401
LH$_2$/LOX *see* liquid hydrogen/oxygen
liberalized electricity markets, **2**: 715
Libya, **2**: 739
licenses/licensing:
   geothermal heat pumps, **7**: 203
   wind parks, **2**: 170–171, **2**: 182
life-cycle assessments/analysis (LCA):
   see also life-cycles
   bioenergy policy development, **5**: 412
   biomass and biofuels
      biomass-to-liquids technology, **5**: 156, **5**: 197
         greenhouse gas savings, **5**: **109–132**
         power generation, **5**: 29
   concentrating solar power, **3**: 630
   coproducts, **5**: 110, **5**: 113, **5**: 126
   definitions, **5**: 109
   direct land use change, **5**: 117
   future biofuel technologies, **5**: 127
   greenhouse gases
      biofuels, **5**: **109–132**
         coproducts, **5**: 110, **5**: 113, **5**: 126
         direct land use change, **5**: 117
         future biofuel technologies, **5**: 127
         indirect land use change, **5**: 120
         land use change, **5**: 117, **5**: 120
         nitrous oxides, **5**: 113, **5**: 113*t*, **5**: 121
         processing energy sources, **5**: 123
         soil nitrous oxide emissions, **5**: 121
   indirect land use, **5**: 120
   land use change, **5**: 117, **5**: 120
   nitrous oxides, **5**: 113, **5**: 113*t*, **5**: 121
   photovoltaics, **1**: 7, **3**: 258, **3**: 630
   power generation, **5**: 29
   processing energy sources, **5**: 123
   soil nitrous oxide emissions, **5**: 121
   very large-scale photovoltaic systems, **1**: 737
life-cycles:
   see also life-cycle assessments/analysis
   costs, **2**: 431, **2**: 462, **3**: 491
   energy payback times, **1**: 147
   environmental impacts, **1**: **143–159**
   greenhouse gas emissions, **1**: 148
   health effects, **1**: **143–159**
   heavy metal emissions, **1**: 151
   hydropower, economics, **6**: 40
   inventory, **1**: 146
   photovoltaics, **1**: **143–159**
   pollutants, **1**: 150
   risk analysis, **1**: 153
   wind energy, **2**: 1
life raft stills, **3**: 98, **3**: 99*f*
life support: astronaut missions, **4**: 24
lifetimes:
   building-integrated photovoltaics, **1**: 702
   organic solar cell stability, **1**: 469
   photovoltaic reliability testing, **1**: 795
lift: wind turbines, **2**: 102
lift-off processing, **1**: 522
light admittance, **3**: 329
light adsorption reflectance, **3**: 318
light-emitting diodes (LED), **1**: 552–553
light-harvesting antenna complexes (LHC), **1**: 658, **1**: 661, **1**: 669
lighting products: photovoltaics, **1**: 712, **1**: 713*f*, **1**: 721, **1**: 725–726
light management: photovoltaic plasmonics, **1**: **641–656**
lightning protection, **2**: 272, **2**: 287*f*, **2**: 298, **2**: 375
light reduction, **5**: 298
light reflectance, **3**: 318
light sources: photovoltaics, **1**: 790
light traction, **4**: 203
light-transmission integration, **3**: 380
light transmittance, **3**: 318
light trapping, **1**: 9, **1**: 393, **3**: 118, **3**: 119*f*

lignins:
   barrier, **5**: 232
   biofuels, **5**: 401
   chemical production, **5**: 401
   depolymerization, **5**: 401
   direct use, **5**: 401
   disassembly, **5**: 401
   uses, **5**: 404
lignocellulosic wastes/feedstocks:
   accessible surface area, **5**: 232
   ammonia recycled percolation, **5**: 244
   bioethanol, **5**: 218, **5**: 228, **5**: 250
      challenges, **5**: 234
      chemical pretreatments, **5**: 235
      consolidated bioprocessing, **5**: 250
      extrusion, **5**: 241
      fermentation, **5**: 248
      ionic liquid pretreatments, **5**: 239
      organosolv, **5**: 238, **5**: 238*t*
      pretreatment, **5**: 234
      saccharification and fermentation, **5**: 248
   biological pretreatments, **5**: 246
   carbon dioxide, **5**: 245
   cellulose crystallinity, **5**: 232
   cellulose depolymerization, **5**: 232
   challenges, **5**: 234
   chemical pretreatments, **5**: 235
   chemical production, **5**: 400
   consolidated bioprocessing, **5**: 250
   crystallinity indices, **5**: 232
   depolymerization, **5**: 232
   digestibility, **5**: 232
   enzymatic hydrolysis, **5**: 232
   enzymatic pretreatments, **5**: 246
   enzymes, **5**: 248, **5**: 249
   ethanol, **5**: 233
   extrusion, **5**: 241
   fermentation, **5**: 248, **5**: 400
   fungal pretreatments, **5**: 246, **5**: 246*t*
   hemicellulose acetylation, **5**: 232
   hemicellulose sheathing, **5**: 232
   ionic liquid pretreatments, **5**: 239
   lignin barrier, **5**: 232
   organosolv, **5**: 238, **5**: 238*t*
   physicochemical pretreatments, **5**: 242, **5**: 247*t*
   pore volumes, **5**: 232
   pretreatment, **5**: 234
   pretreatments, **5**: 218
   recalcitrance, **5**: 231
   saccharification and fermentation, **5**: 248, **5**: 249
   sources, **5**: 231
   supercritical fluid technology, **5**: 245
   surface area, **5**: 232
   wet oxidation, **5**: 245
Lillgrund wind farm, **2**: 415*f*, **2**: 416*f*
lime pretreatments, **5**: 238, **5**: 238*t*
limit state: mechanical-dynamic loads, **2**: 268
Lindal diagrams, **7**: 169, **7**: 170*f*
linear air turbines, **8**: 142
linear concentration photovoltaic/thermal solar collectors, **3**: 268
linear Fresnel collectors, **3**: 195
linear power curves: wind turbine energy yields, **2**: 130
linear receiver analysis, **3**: 172
line-axis collectors, **3**: 571, **3**: 587*t*
line-focusing, **3**: 195
Linke turbidity, **3**: 38
Linking Environment and Farming (LEAF), **5**: 106
Linthal 2015 hydroelectricity project, Switzerland, **6**: 353
liquid-based solar thermal systems, **3**: 400
liquid biofuels:
   bioenergy markets, **5**: 79
   power generation, **5**: 39
liquid crystal switching devices, **3**: 351

liquid desiccants, **3**: 483
liquid electrofuels, **5**: 331
liquid electrolytes:
    alkaline fuel cells, **4**: 165
    design, **4**: 170
    space systems, **4**: 172
    stack design, **4**: 170
    system achievements, **4**: 172
    system design, **4**: 170
liquid flat-plate solar collectors:
    absorbers, **3**: 104
    collector efficiency factors, **3**: 139*t*
    low-temperature stationary collectors, **3**: 104, **3**: 104*f*, **3**: 114, **3**: 115*f*
    organic absorbers, **3**: 107, **3**: 107*f*, **3**: 108*f*
    roll-bond absorbers, **3**: 106, **3**: 107*f*
    stamped absorbers, **3**: 104, **3**: 105*f*
    tube absorbers, **3**: 104, **3**: 105*f*, **3**: 107*f*
liquid heat recovery, **3**: 270
liquid hot water treatments, **5**: 242
liquid hydrogen/oxygen (LH$_2$/LOX), **4**: 13
liquid membranes, **4**: 189
liquid oxygen (LOX), **4**: 13
liquid phase epitaxy, **1**: 497–498
liquids:
    active solar systems, **3**: 474
    biomass cofiring, **5**: 60
    collection, geochemical sampling, **7**: 95
    f-chart method, solar thermal systems, **3**: 400
    hydrogen storage, **4**: **137–157**
    solar thermal energy storage, **3**: 216, **3**: 219, **3**: 227, **3**: 228*t*, **3**: 232, **3**: 239
    solar thermal systems, **3**: 400
    storage, hydrogen, **4**: **137–157**
    thermal storage, **3**: 474
liquid sampling: geochemistry, **7**: 95
lithium-bromide–water absorption systems, **3**: 465, **3**: 471*t*, **3**: 472
lithium–ion batteries, **1**: 207
lithium–water absorption systems, **3**: 465, **3**: 466, **3**: 470, **3**: 471*t*, **3**: 472
Little Red Tractor mark, **5**: 106
Liu and Jordan solar radiation model, **3**: 41
Llauset dam, Spain, **6**: 333, **6**: 334*f*
loaded rotor corrections, **2**: 230
load following: conventional power systems, **1**: 200–201
loads:
    see also mechanical-dynamic loads
    design analysis, **2**: 246
    dynamic analyses, **2**: 244
    electrical energy storage management, **6**: 408
    electrical power–wind energy integration, **2**: 579
    energy storage management, **6**: 408
    energy storage regulation, **1**: 200
    environmental conditions, **2**: 246–247, **2**: 262
    heat exchanger size corrections, **3**: 401
    hydropower, **6**: 20
    management, **6**: 408
    microbial fuel cells, **4**: 269
    offshore wind farms, **2**: 454
    offshore wind turbines, **2**: 247, **2**: 258
    onshore wind turbines, **2**: 254
    power production, **2**: 246, **2**: 254
    regulation, energy storage, **1**: 200
    turbulence, **2**: 256, **2**: 257*f*, **2**: 259
    wave theory, **2**: 265
    wind farms, **2**: 454
    wind turbines, **2**: **243–268**
        design analysis, **2**: 246
        dynamic analyses, **2**: 244
        environmental conditions, **2**: 246–247, **2**: 262
        offshore wind turbines, **2**: 247, **2**: 258
        onshore wind turbines, **2**: 254
        power production, **2**: 246, **2**: 254
        turbulence, **2**: 256, **2**: 257*f*, **2**: 259
        wave theory, **2**: 265
        wind theory, **2**: 263
loans:
    photovoltaics, **1**: 128
    Three Gorges Project, China, **6**: 209
loblolly pine, **5**: 264, **5**: 274
local acceptance: wind power, **2**: 396
local authorities: hydrogen storage safety, **4**: 125
local heat flow values, **7**: 196
localized surface plasmons (LSP), **1**: 643
local networks: wind park integration, **2**: 206
local participation: developing country photovoltaics, **1**: 119
local solar time, **3**: 1
location:
    electrical energy storage, **6**: 407
    high concentration solar collectors, **3**: 205
    Horseshoe Bend hydroelectric scheme, **6**: 468
    metal nanoparticles, **1**: 648
    sea trials, **8**: 99, **8**: 102
    Three Gorges Project, China, **6**: 180, **6**: 181*f*, **6**: 210
    Wuskwatim Generating Station Project, Manitoba, Canada, **6**: 159
logging residues, **5**: 263, **5**: 264
logistics: biomass-to-liquids technology, **5**: 203
log law: wind speed profiles, **2**: 79
Lom Panger storage dam, Cameroon, Africa, **6**: 137
long-crested waves, **8**: 80
long-distance transmission, **6**: 266
longitude correction, **3**: 8
longitudinal concrete cofferdams, **6**: 206
long-term correlation: wind data, **2**: 407
long-term distributions: extreme sea state estimations, **8**: 54, **8**: 65
long-term operation: building-integrated photovoltaics, **1**: 699
long-term sediment management, **6**: **355–376**
long-term wind climate, **2**: 403
long-term wind potential evaluation, **2**: 124
losses:
    loss of load hours, **2**: 623
    loss of load probability, **2**: 623
    loss of power supply probability, **2**: 623
    mechanisms
        hydrogen fuel cells, **4**: 320
        incident light down-shifting, **1**: 563, **1**: 566
        photovoltaics, **1**: 516–517, **1**: 563, **1**: 566
        solar energy conversion principles, **1**: 294, **1**: 309
    mesoporous dye-sensitized solar cells, **1**: 486
    wind energy, **2**: 114, **2**: 412
low alloy steels, **7**: 247
low-carbon bioethanol development, **5**: 19
low-carbon energy:
    conversion, **4**: 296
    hydrogen technology, **4**: 63, **4**: 65
    transport decarbonization, **4**: 65
low-carbon number alcohols, **5**: 319, **5**: 322
low-carbon vehicle drive trains, **4**: 63
low concentration ratio solar collectors, **3**: **149–163**
    compound parabolic collectors, **3**: 150, **3**: 151, **3**: 153, **3**: 159
    concentrating evacuated tube collectors, **3**: 158
    diffuse reflectors, **3**: 151
    evacuated tube collectors, **3**: 158
    flat plate collectors, **3**: 150, **3**: 151, **3**: 152
    integrated collector storage systems, **3**: 159
    maximum concentration ratios, **3**: 150
    nonimaging systems, **3**: **149–163**
    optical analysis, **3**: 154
    reverse flat plate collectors, **3**: 150, **3**: 152
    thermal analysis, **3**: 154
low-cost hydropower developments, **6**: 24
low-cost potentials: multi-junction cells, **1**: 506
low-emittance coatings:
    asymetrical coatings development, **3**: 327
    chemically resistant top layers, **3**: 327

deposition, 3: 324
dielectric/metal/dielectric multilayers, 3: 325
doped metal oxides, 3: 316, 3: 325
double silver layers, 3: 327
evacuated glazing, 3: 336
glazings, 3: 314, 3: 316, 3: 323, 3: 324
high temperature resistance, 3: 327
interface layers, solar thermal energy, 3: 327
mechanically resistant top layers, 3: 327
metal-based stacks, 3: 316, 3: 325
metal-dielectric stacks, 3: 316, 3: 325
metal layers, 3: 316, 3: 325
silver, 3: 325
single-glazed windows, 3: 331
solar control, 3: 323
solar thermal energy, 3: 314, 3: 316, 3: 323
thermal insulation, 3: 323
low-energy homes, 3: 389
lower heating values, 4: 46, 5: 318f, 5: 318–319
Lower Pieman Power Scheme, 6: 75
low-flow collector circuits, 3: 432–433
low head hydropower, 6: **377–403**
low interest loans, 1: 128
low-loss tunnel junctions, 1: 502
low-power portable applications, 4: 202
low-temperature activity: geothermal systems, 7: 7
low-temperature stationary collectors, 3: **103–147**
   absorbed solar energy, 3: 128
   absorbers, 3: 104, 3: 108, 3: 132
   absorption, 3: 126, 3: 127, 3: 128
   air flat-plate solar collectors, 3: 104f, 3: 108, 3: 109f, 3: 114,
      3: 115f
   antireflective coatings, 3: 104, 3: 108, 3: 125
   back insulation, flat-plate solar collectors, 3: 104, 3: 113
   casings, flat-plate collectors, 3: 104, 3: 113
   coatings, 3: 104, 3: 108, 3: 125
   collector efficiency factors, 3: 138, 3: 141
   collector-heat removal factor, 3: 138
   collector performance determination, 3: 141
   collector top heat loss coefficients, 3: 134
   conduction exchange, 3: 132
   covers, 3: 104, 3: 111, 3: 122–123, 3: 123f, 3: 132
   edge insulation, 3: 104, 3: 113
   effective thermal capacity, 3: 145
   efficiency factors, 3: 138, 3: 141
   enclosures, 3: 104, 3: 113
   energy balance, 3: 129
   evacuated tube collectors, 3: 116
   flat-plate collectors, 3: **103–147**
     absorbers, 3: 104, 3: 108
     back insulation, 3: 104, 3: 113
     casings, 3: 104, 3: 113
     covers, 3: 104, 3: 111
     edge insulation, 3: 104, 3: 113
     enclosures, 3: 104, 3: 113
     glazing, 3: 104, 3: 111
     insulation, 3: 104, 3: 111, 3: 113
   glazing, 3: 104, 3: 111, 3: 124, 3: 124t, 3: 130, 3: 131, 3: 132
   heat capacity, 3: 145
   heat loss, 3: 133, 3: 134
   heat removal factor, 3: 138
   heat transfer coefficients, 3: 130, 3: 131, 3: 132
   incident angle modifiers, 3: 143
   instantaneous efficiency, 3: 142, 3: 142f, 3: 143f
   insulation, 3: 104, 3: 111, 3: 113
   liquid flat-plate solar collectors, 3: 104, 3: 104f, 3: 114, 3: 115f
   optical analysis, 3: 120
   overall thermal loss determination, 3: 133
   performance determination, 3: 141
   radiation absorption, 3: 126
   radiation reflection, 3: 120
   radiation transmission, 3: 120
   reflection, 3: 120

   single glass-type evacuated tube collectors, 3: 116
   solar collector top heat loss coefficients, 3: 134
   solar radiation absorption, 3: 126
   steady-state energy balance, 3: 129
   thermal analysis, 3: 129
   thermal capacity, 3: 145
   thermal loss determination, 3: 133
   top heat loss coefficients, 3: 134
   transmittance–absorptance product, 3: 127, 3: 128f
   twin glass-type evacuated tube collectors, 3: 117f, 3: 117–118,
      3: 118f, 3: 119f
   vacuum tube collectors, 3: 116
low-temperature stores: solar assisted heat pumps, 3: 521–522
LOX *see* liquid oxygen
LPCD *see* Large Combustion Plant Directive
LS-1, LS-2 and LS-3 parabolic trough collectors, 3: 178
LSP *see* localized surface plasmons
luminance: high concentration solar collectors, 3: 173
luminescent down-shifting, 1: **563–585**
   antireflective coatings, 1: 570
   cadmium solar cells, 1: 568
   critical parameters, 1: 569
   gallium arsenide solar cells, 1: 568
   incident light down-shifting, 1: 564, 1: 567
   incident spectra, 1: 569
   materials, 1: 564, 1: 567
   organic solar cells, 1: 569
   silicon based solar cells, 1: 567
   surface recombination, photovoltaics, 1: 570
luminescent solar concentrators, 1: **587–601**, 1: 9
   achieved system efficiencies, 1: 595
   angular emission, 1: 598
   dyes, 1: 593
   efficiency, 1: 588, 1: 589, 1: 595, 1: 596
   escape cone losses, 1: 596
   future development, 1: 596
   infrared spectral range extensions, 1: 596
   inorganic materials, 1: 594
   materials, 1: 593
   organic dyes, 1: 593
   ray tracing, 1: 592
   spectral range extensions, 1: 596
   system designs, 1: 594
   system efficiency, 1: 588–589, 1: 595
   theory, 1: 588
   thermodynamic efficiency limits, 1: 589
   thermodynamics, 1: 589, 1: 590
luminous adsorbtion, 3: 318
luminous reflectance, 3: 318
luminous transmittance, 3: 318
lumped parameter geothermal modeling, 7: 31
Luz parabolic trough collectors, 3: 178

M

Maasvlakte 1 and 2 plants, 5: 66
MABE *see* mean absolute bias error
MAC *see* McMaster model
Macagnan's solar radiation model, 3: 41
McCormick air turbines, 8: 111, 8: 121, 8: 122f
Machadinho hydroelectricity project, Brazil, 6: 119
mach disks, 4: 78, 4: 86
machine maintenance: power electronics, 2: 364
McMaster (MAC) model, 3: 42
McNeil generating plant, 5: 65
macroeconomics: geothermal energy, 7: 259, 7: 263
Madeira hydroelectric project, Brazil, 6: 104
Madesta's concept, 2: 302–303, 2: 304f, 2: 305f
Magenn Air Rotor System (MARS), 2: 685–686
Maglev: wind energy, 2: 686
magnesium fluoride, 3: 346
magnetic synchronous generators, 2: 337, 2: 356

magnetoplasma rockets, 4: 19
magnetotelluric (MT) measurements, 7: 52, 7: 61, 7: 63, 7: 69
Magnus effect, 2: 54
MAI *see* mean annual increment
main classes: alkaline fuel cells, 4: 177
mainstream power sources: photovoltaics, 1: 183
maintenance:
   see also operation and maintenance
   concrete structure durability, 6: 393
   design, 6: 395
   Fresnel collectors, 3: 199
   geothermal heat pumps, 7: 202
   high concentration solar collectors, 3: 174, 3: 184, 3: 195, 3: 199, 3: 205
   offshore wind power, 2: 452
   operating costs, 8: 159
   parabolic troughs, 3: 184
   power electronics, 2: 364
   receivers, 3: 195
   solar dishes, 3: 205
   technical unavailability, 2: 152
   wind farms, 2: 452
   wind power design and implementation, 2: 428
   wind turbines, 2: 246, 2: 364
malaria: Millennium Development Goals, geothermal energy, 7: 289
management:
   biodiesel, vegetable oil, 5: 218
   construction impacts, hydropower, 6: 49–91
   electricity grids, 2: 561, 2: 562
   energy storage, photovoltaics, 1: 208
   environmental impacts, hydropower, 6: 49–91
   geothermal energy, 7: 282
   hydropower, 6: 49–91
   operational impacts, 6: 49–91
   photovoltaics
      energy storage, 1: 208
      storage options, 1: 208
   turbine technology, 2: 711, 2: 714
   vegetable oil, biodiesel, 5: 218
   wind energy policy, 2: 561, 2: 562
   wind farms, 2: 711, 2: 714
mandatory fuel blending, 5: 17
Mandhoo Island, 1: 687
Manicouagan river basins, Quebec, Canada, 6: 161, 6: 164f, 6: 167t
Manitoba, Canada, 6: 153, 6: 156
man-made effects: geothermal energy exploration techniques, 7: 88
mantle heat exchangers, 3: 450, 3: 452f
manufacture:
   equipment, Three Gorges Project, China, 6: 225
   glazings, 3: 315, 3: 328, 3: 329
   product-integrated photovoltaics, 1: 728
   toughened glass, 3: 329
   wind turbine evolution, 2: 677, 2: 678f
manufacturers:
   automotive biofuels, 5: 313
   electrical systems, wind turbines, 2: 306
   Fresnel collectors, 3: 197
   high concentration solar collectors, 3: 192, 3: 197, 3: 203
   polysilicon, 1: 173
   proton-exchange membrane fuel cells, 4: 189, 4: 219t
   solar dishes, high concentration solar collectors, 3: 203
   vehicles, 4: 189, 4: 219t, 5: 313
   wind turbines, 2: 306, 2: 667
Maopingxi Dam, 6: 200
Mape dam, 6: 134, 6: 136t
mapping/maps:
   financial support, 2: 710
   geological explorations, 7: 53, 7: 54
   ocean waves, 8: 41
   satellite altimeters, 8: 41
   wind resource planning tools, 2: 394, 2: 396, 2: 414

wind turbines
   financial support, 2: 710
   technology evolution, 2: 710, 2: 714
marginal effects: combined heat and power, 5: 88, 5: 91, 5: 92
MARINA PLATFORM, 2: 719
marine animals, 4: 528
marine currents, 8: 1
marine energy device capital costs, 8: 156
marine industry: proton-exchange membrane fuel cells, 4: 218
Marine Renewables Proving Fund (MRPF), 8: 83
marine sector: ocean energy cost evolution, 8: 164
market development:
   see also markets
   Asian wind power, 2: 666
   Chinese wind power, 2: 666
   concentration photovoltaics, 1: 764
   developing country photovoltaics, 1: 123
   European wind power, 2: 662
   finance, developing country photovoltaics, 1: 123
   future visions, photovoltaics, 1: 183, 1: 188
   German wind power, 2: 662
   North American wind power, 2: 665
   offshore wind power, 2: 666
   photovoltaics
      developing countries, 1: 123
      future visions, 1: 183, 1: 188
      promotion schemes, 1: 74
   solar water heating systems, 3: 420, 3: 420f, 3: 422–423, 3: 424f
   Spanish wind power, 2: 663
   United States
      photovoltaics, 1: 184
      wind power, 2: 665
   wind power
      Asia, 2: 666
      China, 2: 666
      Europe, 2: 662
      Germany, 2: 662
      North America, 2: 665
      Spain, 2: 663
      United States, 2: 665
markets:
   see also market development
   additional value extraction, 5: 387, 5: 389
   barriers to bioenergy, 5: 81
   bioenergy, 5: 75–85
      barriers, 5: 81
      extent of trade, 5: 79
      future direction, 5: 82
      internationalization factors, 5: 81
      international trade, 5: 75–85
      liquid biofuels, 5: 79
      policy development, 5: 413–414, 5: 415–416, 5: 417, 5: 418, 5: 424
      wood fuels, 5: 77
   biomass and biofuels, 5: 75–85
      additional value extraction, 5: 387, 5: 389
      bioenergy trade, 5: 75–85
      combined heat and power, 5: 91, 5: 92
   combined heat and power, 5: 91, 5: 92
   crystalline silicon cells, 1: 353
   current photovoltaic status, 1: 180
   deployment, solar water heating systems, 3: 420, 3: 420f, 3: 422
   designs
      photovoltaic future visions, 1: 188
      photovoltaic promotion schemes, 1: 102
   external costs, wind energy, 2: 485
   failures, bioenergy policy development, 5: 418
   future directions
      bioenergy, 5: 82
      photovoltaics, 1: 183, 1: 184, 1: 188, 1: 191, 1: 697
   growth, thin-film silicon, 1: 389
   high concentration solar collectors, 3: 192
   hydrogen technology, vehicles, 4: 63

integration, bioenergy, **5**: 80
integration design, photovoltaics, **1**: 102
internationalization factors, **5**: 81
liquid biofuels, **5**: 79
niches, hydrogen economics, **4**: 46
ocean energy revenue, **8**: 163
photovoltaics
   crystalline silicon cells, **1**: 353
   future directions, **1**: 183, **1**: 184, **1**: 188, **1**: 191, **1**: 697
   global industry overview, **1**: **161–177**
   technology progress, **1**: 16
   thermophotovoltaics, **1**: 616
   thin-film silicon, **1**: 389
policy, bioenergy and biomass, **5**: 75
proton-exchange membrane fuel cells, **4**: 200
receivers, **3**: 192
segmentation, **1**: 191, **4**: 200
solar cooling, **3**: 614
solar desalination, **3**: 564
solar water heating systems, **3**: 422
thermophotovoltaics, **1**: 616
thin-film silicon photovoltaic technology, **1**: 389
United Kingdom ocean energy revenue, **8**: 163
vehicles, hydrogen technology, **4**: 63
wind energy, external costs, **2**: 485
wind power, **2**: **657–669**
wind turbines, electrical systems, **2**: 303
wood fuels, bioenergy, **5**: 77
MARS *see* Magenn Air Rotor System
mass absorbers, **3**: 304
mass balance, **3**: 468, **3**: 597, **5**: 165, **5**: 165*f*
mass content: geothermal energy physics, **7**: 16
mass flow, **2**: 89, **3**: 173, **3**: 174
mass transfer, **3**: 524
mass walls, **3**: 640, **3**: 641*f*
Masuda, Yoshio, **8**: 7, **8**: 8*f*
materials:
   anodes, **4**: 190
   biomass and biofuels, power generation, **5**: 43
   biomass cofiring, **5**: 57
   building-integrated photovoltaics, **1**: 706
   cathodes, **4**: 162, **4**: 190
   component development, dye-sensitized solar cells, **1**: 490
   composite compressed gas vessels, **4**: 116, **4**: 129
   composition, building-integrated photovoltaics, **1**: 706
   compressed gas: hydrogen storage, **4**: 112, **4**: 116, **4**: 129
   concrete structure durability, **6**: 393
   cost reductions, photovoltaics, **1**: 51
   crystalline silicon cells, photovoltaics, **1**: 363, **1**: 369, **1**: 369*t*
   dye-sensitized solar cells, **1**: 490
   electrochromogenic devices, **3**: 344, **3**: 346, **3**: 347*t*
   extraction, photovoltaic life cycles, **1**: 144, **1**: 145, **1**: 145*f*
   failure, wind turbine energy yields, **2**: 152, **2**: 153
   Fresnel collectors, **3**: 196
   gas diffusion electrodes, **4**: 166
   geothermal environments, **7**: 247
   geothermal power production, **7**: **239–257**
   handling, biomass power generation, **5**: 43
   high concentration solar collectors, **3**: 176, **3**: 196, **3**: 201
   hydrogen technology, **4**: **241–257**
   lattice matching, **1**: 500
   life cycles, **1**: 144, **1**: 145, **1**: 145*f*
   luminescent solar concentrators, **1**: 593
   membranes, **4**: 185
   microbial fuel cells, **4**: 268
   multi-junction cells, **1**: 498, **1**: 500
   ocean wave energy, **8**: 91
   organic solar cells, **1**: 450
   parabolic troughs, **3**: 176
   passive solar architecture, **3**: 644, **3**: 646, **3**: 648
   performance, geothermal environments, **7**: 247
   photovoltaics
      cost reductions, **1**: 51

      crystalline silicon cells, **1**: 363, **1**: 369, **1**: 369*t*
      life cycles, **1**: 144, **1**: 145, **1**: 145*f*
      organic solar cells, **1**: 450
   power generation, biomass and biofuels, **5**: 43
   properties
      cadmium telluride thin films, **1**: 426
      chalcopyrite thin films, **1**: 400
      electrochromogenic devices, **3**: 346, **3**: 347*t*
      organic solar cell efficiency, **1**: 461
      plasmonic photovoltaics, **1**: 646
   proton-exchange membrane fuel cells, **4**: 185, **4**: 190
   rotor blades, **2**: 713
   selection
      concrete structure durability, **6**: 393
      geothermal power production, **7**: **239–257**
      multi-junction cells, **1**: 498
   solar cell thermophotovoltaics, **1**: 608
   solar cooling, **3**: 644, **3**: 646, **3**: 648
   solar dishes, **3**: 201
   solid oxide fuel cells, **4**: **241–257**
   steel vessels, **4**: 112, **4**: 129
   superstrate cadmium telluride thin films, **1**: 427
   thermophotovoltaics, solar cells, **1**: 608
   transparent insulation, **3**: 340
   wind turbine energy yields, **2**: 152, **2**: 153
maternal health, **7**: 289
mathematical models:
   irregular waves, **8**: 13
   ocean waves, **8**: 12
   regular waves, **8**: 12
   solar drying, **3**: 582
   wave energy, **8**: 12
   wind speed, **2**: 83
matrices: definitions, **4**: 227
maximum achievable efficiencies, **1**: 354
maximum concentration, **1**: 340
maximum concentration ratios, **3**: 150
maximum current annual increment, **5**: 263
maximum efficiency:
   photovoltaic thermodynamics, **1**: 340
   solid oxide fuel cells, **4**: 250, **4**: 250*t*
maximum entropy methods, **8**: 27
maximum likelihood:
   ocean wave measurements, **8**: 27
   wind speed distribution, **2**: 121
maximum mean annual increment, **5**: 263
maximum power coefficient variation, **2**: 277, **2**: 278*f*
Maxwell solar radiation model, **3**: 41
Maxwell Technologies, **2**: 327
Mbakaou dam: Cameroon, Africa, **6**: 134, **6**: 136*t*
MBE *see* mean bias error
MCFC *see* molten-carbonate fuel cells
MCS *see* Microgeneration Certification Scheme
MDG *see* Millennium Development Goals
MDMO-PPV:PCBM *see* poly[2-methoxy-5-(3′,7′-dimethyloctyloxy)-1,4-phenylene vinylene]:phenyl-C$_{61}$-butyric-acid-methyl ester
MEA *see* membrane electrode assembly
mean absolute bias error (MABE), **3**: 51
mean annual capacity factors, **2**: 677–679, **2**: 678*f*
mean annual increment (MAI), **5**: 263
mean bias error (MBE), **1**: 240, **3**: 51
mean drift, **2**: 250
mean occupation numbers, **1**: 328
mean power coefficients, **2**: 114, **2**: 135, **2**: 136
mean wind loads, **2**: 262
measurements:
   geothermal energy exploration techniques, **7**: 84
   heat flow, **7**: 84
   hydropower, **6**: 358, **6**: 360
   instrumentation, **3**: 64
   ocean wave energy, **8**: 23, **8**: 99, **8**: 102
   performance monitoring, **1**: 783

measurements: (*continued*)
  photovoltaics
    performance determination, **1**: 790, **1**: 791
    performance monitoring, **1**: 783
    power forecasts, **1**: 271
    standards, **1**: 790, **1**: 791
  quality testing, wind energy, **2**: 382
  sediment management, **6**: 358, **6**: 360
  solar irradiance-photovoltaic power forecasts, **1**: 271
  solar radiation, **1**: 219, **1**: 227, **3**: 64
  standards, photovoltaics, **1**: 790, **1**: 791
  testing, wind energy, **2**: 376
  wind energy
    potential, **2**: 75
    testing, **2**: 376, **2**: 382
    wind turbine finance, **2**: 719
  wind speed, **2**: 398
mechanical comminution, **5**: 240
mechanical components: wind turbines, **2**: 333
mechanical damper: ocean wave energy, **8**: 93
mechanical design: pump-turbines, **6**: 416
mechanical draft cooling systems, **3**: 598
mechanical-dynamic loads:
  design analysis, **2**: 246
  dynamic analyses, **2**: 244
  integrated time domain analysis, **2**: 244, **2**: 254
  offshore wind turbines, **2**: 247, **2**: 258
  time domain analysis, wind turbines, **2**: 244, **2**: 254
  wave theory, **2**: 265
  wind theory, **2**: 263
  wind turbines, **2**: **243–268**
mechanical efficiency: axial-flow microhydro turbines, **6**: 444
mechanical interfaces: ocean wave energy, **8**: 8
mechanical load measurements, **2**: 378
mechanically driven heat pumps, **3**: 501
mechanically resistant top layer coatings, **3**: 327
mechanical modeling: wind turbine control, **2**: 334
mechanical power: axial-flow microhydro turbines, **6**: 444
mechanical similarity: ocean wave energy, **8**: 85
mechanical solar cooling systems, **3**: 462
mechanical stirrers, **6**: 83
MED *see* multieffect distillation
mediatorless microbial fuel cells, **4**: 267
mediators:
  biological fuel cells, **4**: 260
  microbial fuel cells, **4**: 265
medium-sized wind turbine technology, **2**: 713
medium speed generators, **2**: 293
medium-temperature stores, **3**: 522
MEG *see* multi-exciton generation
megawatts (MW):
  definitions, **6**: 1, **6**: 16
  photovoltaics, **1**: 690, **1**: **733–744**
  wind turbines, **2**: 713
Mekin hydropower project, Cameroon, Africa, **6**: 141
membrane distillation:
  compact systems, **3**: 532*f*, **3**: 544, **3**: 544*f*
  flow diagrams, **3**: 545*f*, **3**: 545–546
  solar desalination, **3**: 543
membrane electrode assembly (MEA) fabrication, **4**: 178
membranes:
  concrete structure durability, **6**: 394
  desalination, **2**: 726, **2**: 727*f*, **2**: 728, **2**: 733, **3**: 529
  materials, **4**: 185
  microbial fuel cells, **4**: 272
  photosynthesis design, **1**: 661
  proton-exchange membrane fuel cells, **4**: 185
  separation, **5**: 211, **5**: 214
  wind energy desalination, **2**: 726, **2**: 727*f*, **2**: 728, **2**: 733
MEMC Electronic Materials Inc., **1**: 174
Meme River, **6**: 146
Memorandum of Understanding (MoU), **5**: 24
Memve'Elé hydro plant project, Cameroon, Africa, **6**: 139

MENA *see* Middle East, and North Africa regions
Mengibar power station and dam, Spain, **6**: 322, **6**: 323*f*
Mensforth, Tom, **2**: 58–59, **2**: 59*f*, **2**: 60*f*
Mequinenza power plant and dam, Spain, **6**: 326, **6**: 327*f*
Mercier, Quebec, Canada, **6**: 161, **6**: 165*f*
MES-DEA PEM fuel cells, **4**: 308, **4**: 310, **4**: 311
mesoporous oxide films, **1**: 485
mesoporous oxide working electrodes, **1**: 490
mesoporous solar cells *see* dye-sensitized solar cells
mesoscale models: solar irradiance photovoltaic power, **1**: 256
metabolite exploitation, **5**: **385–393**
metal-based stacks, **3**: 316, **3**: 325
metal catalysts: alkaline fuel cells, **4**: 162, **4**: 163
metal-dielectrics:
  composites, selective coatings, **3**: 301, **3**: 307
  layer interference stacks, selective coatings, **3**: 306
  matrices, selective coatings, **3**: 302–303, **3**: 307
  selective coatings
    composites, **3**: 301, **3**: 307
    layer interference stacks, **3**: 306
    matrices, **3**: 302–303, **3**: 307
    stacks, **3**: 301, **3**: 302–303, **3**: 306, **3**: 307
  stacks, selective coatings, **3**: 301, **3**: 302–303, **3**: 306, **3**: 307
metal hydrides, **4**: 139
  switchable mirrors, **3**: 350
metal kilns, **5**: 368
metal layer low-emittance coatings, **3**: 316, **3**: 325
metallic materials: geothermal power production, **7**: 247, **7**: 248
metallization: crystalline silicon cells, **1**: 366
metal nanoparticles, **1**: **641–656**
  fabrication, **1**: 651
  location effects, **1**: 648
  position effects, **1**: 648
metal oxidation, **4**: 33
metal oxide layer glazing, **3**: 316, **3**: 325, **3**: 344, **3**: 345, **3**: 346
metal particles:
  ceramic matrices, **3**: 301, **3**: 307
  dielectric matrices, **3**: 302–303, **3**: 307
  selective coatings, **3**: 301, **3**: 302–303, **3**: 307
metal-reducing bacteria, **4**: 273
metal roll sheets, **3**: 110, **3**: 111*f*
metal substrate chalcopyrite thin films, **1**: 411
metal-wrap-through cells, **1**: 372, **1**: 373
metamorphic materials, **1**: 13
meteorological radiation model (MRM), **3**: 43
meteorological/statistical model (METSTAT), **1**: 230, **3**: 42
meteorological year, **3**: 22
meteorology:
  forecast accuracy, **1**: 269
  solar irradiance-photovoltaic power forecasts, **1**: 269
  solar radiation data, **1**: 230
  solar water heating systems, **3**: 438
  wind data, **2**: 406
  wind energy potential, **2**: 74
methanation, **5**: 136, **5**: 186
methane:
  bioenergy policy development, **5**: 415, **5**: 415*t*
  emission, **7**: 120
  life cycle assessments, **5**: 113, **5**: 113*t*
  reformation, **5**: 147
methanogen suppression, **4**: 273
methanol:
  automotive safety, **5**: 323
  biomass-to-liquids technology, **5**: 174*t*, **5**: 183, **5**: 184, **5**: 185, **5**: 189, **5**: 203
  compression-ignition engines, **5**: 322
  electrofuels, **5**: 328
  glycerol, **5**: 189
  hydrogen technology, **4**: 32
  physicochemical properties, **5**: 317, **5**: 317*t*
  plants, **5**: 184, **5**: 189, **5**: 203
  safety, **5**: 323
  spark-ignition engines, **5**: 319

sustainability, 5: 335
methanol-to-gasoline (MTG) process, 5: 158, 5: 183f
METSTAT *see* meteorological/statistical model
microbial fuel cells (MFC), 4: **257–280**
   concepts, 4: 265
   design, 4: 271
   development, 4: 265
   electricity generation mechanisms, 4: 265
   electrolysis, 4: 273
   hydraulic retention times, 4: 269
   inoculums, 4: 273
   loading rates, 4: 269
   material aspects, 4: 268
   mediatorless systems, 4: 267
   mediators, 4: 265
   operating conditions, 4: 268
   operation principles, 4: 266
   organic loading rates, 4: 269
   organic matter removal, 4: 267
   pH, 4: 269
   retention times, 4: 269
   temperatures, 4: 268
   working principles, 4: 266
micro-blind switching devices, 3: 351
Microcab Industries Ltd, 4: 287
microchannel reactors, 5: 182
microclimates, 2: 523, 2: 530, 3: 586
micro combined heat and power systems, 4: 251
microcredits, 1: 121
microcrystalline materials: definitions, photovoltaics, 1: 13
microcrystalline silicon, 1: 8, 1: 389–390, 1: 391
microeconomic analysis: geothermal energy, 7: 260
Microgeneration Certification Scheme (MCS), 2: 373
microgravity monitoring, 7: 27
microgrids, 2: 571, 2: 592–593, 2: 600, 2: 607
   benefits, 2: 611
   modeling, 2: 611
   problems, 2: 612
microhydropower turbines, 6: **435–466**
micron-gap thermophotovoltaics (MTPV), 1: 613
microprobes: solids characterization, 7: 99
microscopy: solids characterization, 7: 98
micro-silicon thin films, 1: 21
micro-siting: wind power, 2: 188–189, 2: 190, 2: 397, 2: 398, 2: 431, 2: 455–456
microtechnology: photovoltaics, 1: **515–531**, 1: 8, 1: 9
microwave beaming, 1: 768, 1: 769
microwave-enhanced transesterification, 5: 225
microwave pyrolysis, 5: 407
microwires, 1: 524
Middle Ages: solar energy history, 3: 87
Middle East, and North Africa regions (MENA), 1: 739, 3: 634
Midnight Sun®, 1: 614
mid-pane values, 3: 330, 3: 330t
mid-term development plans: hydropower, Cameroon, Africa, 6: 135
Mie scattering, 3: 28, 3: 36, 3: 44
Mighty Whale, 8: 139
migration issues: passive solar architecture, 3: 637–638
milestone development: photovoltaics, 1: 196
military:
   fuel cell current status, 4: 40
   wind power, 2: 395
Millennium Development Goals (MDG), 7: 289
   AIDS, 7: 289
   child mortality rates, 7: 288
   developing country photovoltaics, 1: 111
   empower women, 7: 276
   environmental sustainability, 7: 289
   gender equality, 7: 276
   geothermal energy, 7: 272, 7: 274, 7: 287, 7: 289
   global partnerships, 7: 290
   health, 7: 287
   human immunodeficiency virus, 7: 289
   malaria, 7: 289
   maternal health, 7: 289
   mortality rates, 7: 288
   photovoltaics, 1: 111
   sustainable development, 7: 272, 7: 274, 7: 287
   women empowerment, 7: 276
Millennium Summit, 7: 274
milling:
   biomass cofiring, 5: 63
   lignocellulosic wastes, 5: 240
   wind energy, 2: 41, 2: 42
mill residues: woody biomass, 5: 263
mills: fuel preparation, 5: 44
Milos Island, Greece, 2: 739
mineral admixtures, 6: 393
mineral availability: cadmium telluride thin films, 1: 436
mineral equilibria, 7: 60
mini-grids: renewable energy premium tariff, 1: 131
minimum flow: hydropower, 6: 56
minority-carrier diffusion lengths, 1: 498–500, 1: 499f
minority-carrier lifetimes, 1: 498–500, 1: 499f
mirrors:
   burning, 1: 31, 1: 32f
   high concentration solar collectors, 3: 187
   receivers, 3: 187
   solar energy, 3: 86, 3: 90, 3: 91f, 3: 92
Mirroxx, 3: 199
Miscanthus, 5: 57, 5: 389, 5: 389t
mispointing effects, 8: 36
missing data: solar radiation/meteorological data, 1: 230
mission: Brazilian Sugarcane Industry Association, 5: 25
MIT: solar energy history, 3: 94, 3: 94f
mitigation:
   baulk systems, 6: 88
   dry tower multiport intake towers, 6: 88
   ecosystem measures, 6: 299, 6: 305
   environmental impacts, wind power, 2: 530
   Flaming Gorge Dam, Utah, 6: 90
   floating offtakes, 6: 87
   Glen Canyon Dam, Arizona, 6: 90
   hydropower impact management, 6: 87
   intake towers, 6: 88
   multilevel offtake towers, 6: 87
   multiport intake towers, 6: 88
   ocean wave energy risk, 8: 80
   offtake towers, 6: 87
   reservoir bypassing, 6: 296, 6: 298
   screen options, 6: 88
   sediment flushing, 6: 291, 6: 292
   sediment reservoir bypassing, 6: 296, 6: 298
   Shasta temperature control device, 6: 90
   structural options, 6: 87
   temperature control devices, 6: 90
   turbid water reservoir bypassing, 6: 296, 6: 298
   wind energy, 2: 398
      environmental impacts, 2: 530
      variability costs, 2: 494
Mitsubishi Materials Corporation, 1: 168
mix design:
   concrete structure durability, 6: 395
   roller compacted concrete dams, 6: 475
mixed alcohols: biomass-to-liquids technology, 5: 174t, 5: 185
mixed-reactant fuel cells (MRFC), 4: 205, 4: 208
mixed wood feedstocks, 5: 140
mixing ratios, 1: 459
MM5 mesoscale models, 1: 243
Mobile Self-Installing Platform (MSIP), 2: 179, 2: 180f
mobilization times: ocean energy economics, 8: 162
model-free directional ocean wave parameters, 8: 26
model output statistics (MOS), 1: 240

models/modeling:
  active solar systems, 3: 396
  air turbines, 8: 124
  building-integrated photovoltaic-thermal systems, 3: 379
  coefficient of determination, 3: 52
  components, solar thermal systems, 3: **357–417**
  control systems, wind turbines, 2: 333
  converters, wind turbines, 2: 336
  direct gain systems, 3: 360–361, 3: 361
  electrical components, wind turbines, 2: 336
  experience curves, photovoltaics, 1: 54
  Fresnel collectors, 3: 197
  fuel cell power electronics, 4: 320, 4: 325
  gas diffusion electrodes, 4: 167
  generators, wind turbines, 2: 336
  geothermal energy
    macroeconomic factors, 7: 263
    physics, 7: 29, 7: 30, 7: 31
  high concentration solar collectors, 3: 178, 3: 197, 3: 203
  hydropower, 6: 361, 6: 367
  index of agreement, 3: 52
  macroeconomic factors, 7: 263
  mean absolute bias error, 3: 51
  mean bias error, 3: 51
  mechanical components, wind turbines, 2: 333
  microgrids, 2: 611
  net solar radiation, 3: 54
  non-incremental changes, photovoltaics, 1: 67
  ocean energy, air turbines, 8: 124
  ocean wave numerical models, 8: 46
  ocean waves, 8: 23
  parabolic troughs, 3: 178
  passive solar technologies, 3: 359
  peaks-over-threshold method, 8: 61
  photovoltaic costs, 1: 54
  photovoltaic power, 1: 243
  photovoltaic-thermal systems, 3: 379
  power curves, wind turbine energy yields, 2: 129
  power electronics, 4: 320, 4: 325
  reservoir water quality, 6: 70
  root mean square error, 3: 50
  sediment management, 6: 361, 6: 367
  solar broadband radiation, 3: 39
    horizontal surfaces, 3: 39
  solar dishes, 3: 203
  solar irradiance, photovoltaic power, 1: 243
  solar radiation
    coefficient of determination, 3: 52
    evaluation models, 3: 49
    index of agreement, 3: 52
    mean absolute bias error, 3: 51
    mean bias error, 3: 51
    resources assessments, 1: 214, 1: 227
    root mean square error, 3: 50
    spectral models, 3: 54
    standard deviation, 3: 50
    t-tests, 3: 51
  solar resource, 3: 39, 3: 49
  solar thermal systems, 3: **357–417**
  standard deviation, 3: 50
  t-tests, 3: 51
  wind turbines
    control systems, 2: 333
    converters, 2: 336
    electrical components, 2: 336
    finance, 2: 719
    generators, 2: 336
    mechanical components, 2: 333
    wind park design, 2: 186
modern history: photovoltaics, 1: 37
modern window coatings, 3: 316
modes of operation: solar assisted heat pumps, 3: 495, 3: 510, 3: 513, 3: 515, 3: 517, 3: 519

modification:
  biofuel operation, 5: 346, 5: 347
  diesel engines, 5: 347
  gasoline engines, 5: 346
  petrol engines, 5: 346
modified linear wave theory, 2: 266
modified log law, 2: 79
modified membranes, 4: 188
modified photovoltaic/thermal solar collectors, 3: 276
modules, 1: **5–11**
  active solar systems, 3: 475
  building-integrated photovoltaics, 1: 702, 1: 706
  chalcopyrite thin film photovoltaics, 1: 416–417
  concentration photovoltaics, 1: 748
  cooling systems, 3: 475
  dye-sensitized solar cells, 1: 492
  efficiency, photovoltaics, 1: 684
  energy predictions, photovoltaics, 1: 778
  fabrication, 1: 395, 1: 416–417
  life cycle inventory, 1: 146
  performance monitoring, 1: 777, 1: 778, 1: 781
  photovoltaics, 1: **5–11**
    design, 1: 679, 1: 680
    efficiency, 1: 684
    energy predictions, 1: 778
    global industry overview, 1: 162, 1: 163*f*
    life cycle inventory, 1: 146
    performance monitoring, 1: 777, 1: 781
    power forecasting, 1: 260
    prices, 1: 181, 1: 193
  simplified generic axial-flow microhydro turbines, 6: 463
  solar irradiance, 1: 260
  solar space heating, 3: 475
  space cooling systems, 3: 475
  space heating, 3: 475
  thin-film silicon photovoltaic technology, 1: 395
moisture removal, 7: 211
mold: health and safety, 5: 29
molecular photophysics, 1: 542
molecular structure: dye-sensitized solar cells, 1: 482, 1: 483*f*, 1: 487, 1: 487*f*
Molinar power plant, Spain, 6: 318–319, 6: 319*f*
molten-carbonate fuel cells (MCFC), 4: **227–239**, 4: 227
  carbon dioxide, 4: 228
  carbon separation, 4: 238
  cell stacks, 4: 229
  chemistry, 4: 228
  configurations, 4: 228
  design, 4: 229
  direct fuel cells, 4: 231, 4: 232
  future applications, 4: 238
  grid support, 4: 233
  hydrogen fuel cell technology, 4: 282
  hydrogen production, 4: 228, 4: 238
  power plants, 4: 229, 4: 231, 4: 232
  self-generation applications, 4: 233
  solid oxide fuel cells, 4: 243, 4: 243*t*, 4: 246
  system configurations, 4: 228
  theory, 4: **227–239**
molten rock drilling, 7: 57
molten salts, 3: 239, 3: 600, 3: 602*f*
molybdenum oxide, 3: 345
moment method: wind speed, 2: 122
momentum-controlled jet releases, 4: 86, 4: 90
momentum theory, 2: 226, 2: 236
Mongolian solar radiation atlas (MSRA), 3: 62
monitoring:
  see also condition monitoring
  effluent water monitoring, 7: 111
  gas contamination, 4: 127
  geothermal energy systems, 7: 24
  photovoltaic performance, 1: **775–786**
  power electronics, 2: 364

reservoir water quality, 6: 69
technical availability, wind energy, 2: 155
Theistareykir, NE Iceland, 7: 157–158
wind power
   design and implementation, 2: 428
   IEC standards, 2: 375
   turbine power electronics, 2: 364
monochromatic optical efficiency, 1: 539
monochromatic waves, 8: 80, 8: 96
monocrystalline silicon, 1: 144, 1: 355
monogap solar cells, 1: 334
monolithic silica aerogels, 3: 341
monolith size control, 6: 382
monopile foundations, 2: 441
monoplane rotors, 8: 115, 8: 116
monovalent heat pumps, 3: 501
moored buoys, 8: 23
moorings:
   capital costs, 8: 156
   ocean wave energy, 8: 80, 8: 92
   wind turbine loads, 2: 252
Morison formula, 2: 250
Morocco:
   concentrating solar power, 3: 634
   desalination, 2: 739, 3: 539f, 3: 540f
morphology:
   organic solar cell efficiency, 1: 457
   reservoirs, 6: 59
   selective coatings, 3: 301
mortality rates, 7: 288
MOS *see* model output statistics
Motech Solar, 1: 170
motion vector fields, 1: 245, 1: 249, 1: 251
motor homes, 4: 285
   see also vehicles
MoU *see* Memorandum of Understanding
Mouchot, August, 3: 90, 3: 91f
mound kilns, 5: 367, 5: 367f
mountability: building-integrated photovoltaics, 1: 701
mounting structures: photovoltaic balance of system, 1: 686
movement analysis: ocean wave energy, 8: 93
moving bars, 3: 174
moving grates, 5: 33
moving line stabilizers, 2: 449
moving surface incidence angles:
   east-west tracking, 3: 14, 3: 16, 3: 17
   full tracking, 3: 14
   north-south axis polar/east-west tracking, 3: 14
   north-south axis tilted/tilt daily adjustments, 3: 14
   north-south tracking, 3: 13
   solar energy environmental characteristics, 3: 12, 3: 13
   tracking mechanisms, 3: 13
MRFC *see* mixed-reactant fuel cells
MRM *see* meteorological radiation model
MRPF *see* Marine Renewables Proving Fund
Msaim, Morocco, 3: 540f
MSF *see* multistage flash
MSIP *see* Mobile Self-Installing Platform
MSRA *see* Mongolian solar radiation atlas
MSW *see* municipal solid wastes
MT *see* magnetotelluric
MTG *see* methanol-to-gasoline
MTPV *see* micron-gap thermophotovoltaics
multibar trickle bed reactors, 5: 181
multibenefits of hydropower electricity production, 6: **15–47**
multicrystalline silicon, 1: 144, 1: 355
multidimensional problems: bioenergy policy development, 5: 427
multieffect distillation (MED), 3: 531, 3: 533, 3: 533f, 3: 534, 3: 534t, 3: 535, 3: 535f, 3: 536f, 3: 547, 3: 549
multieffect evaporation, 3: 589, 3: 590f
multi-exciton generation (MEG):
   carbon nanotubes, 1: 526
   downconversion, 1: 549, 1: 557

nanostructures, 1: 557
photovoltaics
   downconversion, 1: 549, 1: 557
   quantum structure nanotechnology, 1: 525
   technology progress, 1: 26
quantum dots, 1: 525, 1: 526
semiconductor nanostructures, 1: 557
multi-family housing, 3: 443
multi-junction cells, 1: 24, 1: **497–514**, 1: **619–639**
   back-surface-field layers, 1: 501
   bandgap back-surface-field layers, 1: 501
   cell materials, 1: 500, 1: 503, 1: 504
   cell material selection, 1: 498
   concentration photovoltaics, 1: 506, 1: 746, 1: 746f
   costs, 1: 506
   future directions, 1: 509
   high efficiency realization, 1: **497–514**
   intermediate band solar cells, 1: **619–639**
   lattice matching, 1: 500, 1: 503, 1: 504
   low-cost potentials, 1: 506
   materials, 1: 498, 1: 500
   organic cells, 1: 463
   photovoltaics, 1: **497–514**, 1: **619–639**
   quality, 1: 498
   recent results, 1: 509
   solar spectrum, 1: 746, 1: 746f
   substrates, 1: 500, 1: 503, 1: 504
   thin-film silicon technology, 1: 389, 1: 392
   wide bandgap back-surface-field layers, 1: 501
multi-layer models: reservoir water quality, 6: 71, 6: 72
multi-layer stacks: selective coatings, 3: 306
multilevel offtake towers, 6: 87
multinational firms: geothermal energy, 7: 259, 7: 259–260, 7: 260, 7: 261, 7: 263, 7: 265
multiple-glazed windows, 3: 314, 3: 332, 3: 333
multiple mineral equilibria, 7: 60
multiple-phonon emission, 1: 626
multiple tank storage, 3: 217, 3: 218f
multiport intake towers, 6: 88
multipurpose settings: hydropower development, 6: 38
multi-scale data assimilation, 2: 719
multistage chalcopyrite thin film deposition, 1: 407
multistage flash (MSF):
   evaporation, 3: 589, 3: 590f
   solar desalination, 3: 531, 3: 532, 3: 532f, 3: 534, 3: 534t
multiswitch voltage inverters, 4: 299, 4: 303
Muneer model, 3: 47–48
municipal solid wastes (MSW), 5: 89, 5: 90, 5: 90t, 5: 286
mycotoxins, 5: 69

N

nacelle:
   definition, 2: 270
   mass, 2: 676
Nafion, 4: 184, 4: 186, 4: 186f
Nam Theum 2 aeration weir, 6: 77
nanocrystalline materials, 1: 13
nanoparticles:
   fabrication, 1: 651
   plasmonics for photovoltaics, 1: 641
   thin-film photovoltaics, 1: 515, 1: 517, 1: 522
nanoscale metals, 1: **641–656**
nanostructures, 1: **641–656**
   aerogel glazings, 3: 317, 3: 319
   multiple exciton generation, 1: 557
   nanoarchitectures, 1: 523
   nanocomposite photovoltaics, 1: 523
   nano-silicon thin film photovoltaics, 1: 21
   nanowires, 1: 524
   organic solar cells, 1: 464
   photovoltaics, quantum structures, 1: 525

nanostructures (*continued*)
   plasmonic photovoltaics, **1: 641–656**
   quantum structures, **1**: 525
   thin-film photovoltaics, **1**: 515, **1**: 517, **1**: 522
nanotechnology:
   photovoltaics, **1: 515–531**
     future outlooks, **1**: 528
     introduction, **1**: 9
     technology progress, **1**: 21, **1**: 26
Nant de Dranse hydroelectricity project, Switzerland, **6**: 352
narrow band semiconductors, **1**: 340
NASA: solar power satellites, historical overviews, **1**: 767
Nathpa Jhakri Hydroelectric Project, **6**: 243, **6**: 243*f*, **6**: 244*f*, **6**: 247, **6**: 247*f*
National Commitment: labor practices, **5**: 23
National Fire Plan, **5**: 283
national grid extensions, **1**: 192
National Institute of Public Health and Environment (RIVM), **6**: 357
National Renewable Energy Plan, **1**: 92
National Solar Radiation Data Base (NSRDB), **1**: 229
natural airflow, **3**: 274
natural circulation, **3**: 426, **3**: 428*f*, **3**: 454, **3**: 454*f*
natural condition: Three Gorges Project, China, **6**: 180
natural draft cooling towers, **3**: 598, **3**: 600
natural environmental conservation: Japanese hydropower, **6**: 303
natural gas, **2**: 20, **2**: 549
natural integration: building-integrated photovoltaics, **1**: 706
natural phenomena impacts: direct heat utilization, **7**: 180
natural photosynthesis design, **1**: 657, **1**: 658, **1**: 663
Navier-Stokes modeling, **2**: 232
navigation:
   Three Gorges Project, China, **6**: 183, **6**: 193, **6**: 205, **6**: 207, **6**: 221
   Yangtze River, China, **6**: 183, **6**: 193
near-optimal low-energy home design, **3**: 389
neighbor issues: wind power, **2**: 395, **2**: 397
NEL electrolysers, **4**: 2, **4**: 4*t*
Nelson River development, **6**: 156
Nemiscau-1 dam, Quebec, Canada, **6**: 170
Neo Solar Power Corporation, **1**: 171
NER *see* North Eastern Region
Nernst equation, **4**: 244, **4**: 245
net energy balance, **5**: 114
Netherlands:
   biomass cofiring, **5**: 65
   offshore wind power, **2**: 433, **2**: 438–439
net metering, **1**: 74, **1**: 75–76, **1**: 77, **1**: 86
net present value, **2**: 471, **8**: 154
net profits: wind parks, **2**: 211
net solar radiation, **3**: 28, **3**: 54
net systems: high concentration solar collectors, **3**: 206
Network of Excellence (NoE), **4**: 80
network integration:
   solar radiation stations, **3**: 58
   wind park design, **2**: 206
network spatial expansions: hydropower, **6**: 287
net-zero energy solar buildings, **3**: 394
NEUBrew *see* NOAA-EPA Brewer Spectrophotometer UV and Ozone Network
neural networks:
   Bayesian adaptive combination, **2**: 88
   passive solar architecture, **3**: 657–658, **3**: 659, **3**: 662
   sediment management, **6**: 361–362
   wind energy, **2**: 1, **2**: 88
neutral atmospheric stability, **2**: 78
Neuwirth solar-heated brewery, Austria, **3**: 575, **3**: 576*f*
Nevada Solar One power plant, **3**: 620, **3**: 621*f*
new developments:
   collectors, **3**: 431
   hydroelectricity, Switzerland, **6**: 349, **6**: 352
   solar water heating systems, **3**: 431
NEWGEN 3MW project, **2**: 717
new technology support: bioenergy policy development, **5**: 419

New Zealand's hydropower, **6: 467–483**
Ngassona Falls 210 Project, Cameroon, Africa, **6**: 146
niche end-use applications: hydrogen technology, **4**: 60
niche markets: photovoltaic cost reductions, **1**: 49
Nicholson, William, **4**: 1, **4**: 3*f*
nickel alloys, **7**: 248
nickel hydrogen batteries, **4**: 22
nickel oxide, **3**: 346
nicotinamide adenine dinucleotide phosphate (NADPH), **1**: 657, **1**: 657–658
Niger basin, **6**: 130
NIGHTWIND project, **2**: 717
nitrate concentrations, **6**: 63
nitrogen:
   immobilization, **5**: 383*f*, **5**: 383–384
   reservoir water quality, **6**: 66
   water quality, **6**: 66
nitrogen oxides:
   engine configuration ranges, **5**: 347, **5**: 348–349, **5**: 350–351
   environmental impacts, **5**: 51
nitrous oxides:
   bioenergy policy development, **5**: 415, **5**: 415*t*
   life cycle assessments, **5**: 113, **5**: 113*t*, **5**: 121
NMR *see* nuclear magnetic spectroscopy
NOAA-EPA Brewer Spectrophotometer UV and Ozone Network (NEUBrew), **3**: 61
noble gases, **7**: 109
NoE *see* Network of Excellence
Noguera Pallaresa, Spain, **6**: 321, **6**: 321*f*
noise:
   see also acoustics; signal noise
   aerodynamic analysis, **2**: 238
   air turbines, **8**: 146
   direct heat utilization, **7**: 179
   geothermal energy, **7**: 179, **7**: 285
   offshore wind power, **2**: 463, **2**: 525, **2**: 526
   qualitative considerations, wind turbines, **2**: 513
   quantitative considerations, wind turbines, **2**: 513
   testing, wind energy, **2**: 379
   valve-controlled air flow, **8**: 146
   wind energy, **2**: 513, **2**: 525, **2**: 526
     testing, **2**: 379
     wind park design, **2**: 182, **2**: 194, **2**: 205
   wind turbines, **2**: 513
     aerodynamic analysis, **2**: 238
     environmental impact reduction, **2**: 687
     qualitative considerations, **2**: 513
     quantitative considerations, **2**: 513
nominal power: wind turbines, **2**: 186–187, **2**: 188, **2**: 418
nonbank financing institutions, **1**: 121
noncatalytic transesterification, **5**: 224
non concentrating collectors, **3**: 420, **3**: 426
nonconvecting solar ponds, **3**: 572, **3**: 587*t*
non explicit barriers: bioenergy trade, **5**: 82
nonferrous alloys/metals, **7**: 248
nonfinancial barrier impacts: bioenergy policy, **5**: 424
nonimaging low concentration ratio collectors, **3: 149–163**
non-incremental changes: photovoltaic cost reductions, **1**: 61, **1**: 67
noninterconnected power systems, **2**: 211, **2**: 212, **2**: 216
nonisotropic radiation, **1**: 321
nonlinear air turbines, **8**: 145
nonlinear loading: wind turbines, **2**: 245
nonmetallic materials: geothermal environments, **7**: 249
non-platinum group metal catalysts, **4**: 163
nonpremixed jets: hydrogen safety, **4**: 97
nonradiative transitions: rare earth elements, **1**: 574
non stationary collectors, **3**: 571–572, **3**: 572*f*, **3**: 587*t*
non-Stranski–Krastanov quantum dots, **1**: 635
nonzero rotor blade thickness, **8**: 120
Nordex, **2**: 317
normalization: solar irradiance-photovoltaic power forecasts, **1**: 267
NORSEWIND *see* Northern Seas Wind Index Database
North Africa: very large-scale photovoltaic, **1**: 739

North America, **2**: 665, **8**: 7
North Eastern Region (NER): Indian hydropower, **6**: 252
Northern Seas Wind Index Database (NORSEWIND), **2**: 719
north-south axis tracking, **3**: 13
   polar/east-west tracking, **3**: 14
   tilted/tilt daily adjustments, **3**: 14
Norway, **1**: 171, **8**: 7
NOVATEC Biosol, **3**: 198
novel concepts:
   building-integrated photovoltaics, **1**: 706
   engine configuration ranges, **5**: 343–356
novel feedstocks:
   biomass and biofuels, **5**: 6, **5**: 217–261, **5**: 263–291
   crops, **5**: 7
   waste materials, **5**: 217–261
   woody biomass, **5**: 7, **5**: 263–291
novel uses: biomass and biofuels, **5**: 343–356
nozzles: steel vessels, **4**: 115
NSE Biofuels, **5**: 191
NSRDB *see* National Solar Radiation Data Base
n-type semiconductors, **1**: 293
n-type silicon cells:
   aluminum-alloyed back junctions, **1**: 375
   boron-diffused back junctions, **1**: 377
   boron-diffused front emitters, **1**: 376
   emitters, **1**: 380
   heterojunctions, **1**: 379
   high-efficiency cell structures, **1**: 375
   implanted emitters, **1**: 380
   photovoltaics, **1**: 375
   polysilicon emitters, **1**: 380
nuclear energy:
   hydropower, **6**: 280
   planet energy balance, **2**: 11, **2**: 13f, **2**: 15, **2**: 16–17, **2**: 22
   wind energy integration, **2**: 594
   wind energy policy, **2**: 548
nuclear magnetic spectroscopy (NMR), **5**: 376, **5**: 377f, **5**: 378f
nuclear weapons, **3**: 6
nuisance issues: biomass and biofuel power generation, **5**: 41
numerical actuator disk models, **2**: 232
numerical modeling:
   calibration, **8**: 47
   errors in ocean wave models, **8**: 46, **8**: 47
   frequency domain, **8**: 107
   geothermal energy, **7**: 35
   hydropower, **6**: 361, **6**: 367
   ocean waves
     calibration, **8**: 47
     errors, **8**: 46, **8**: 47
     resource assessments, **8**: 23, **8**: 45
     wave energy converters, **8**: 49, **8**: 50
   sediment management, **6**: 361, **6**: 367
   solar thermal systems, **3**: 358, **3**: 368, **3**: 374, **3**: 379, **3**: 383, **3**: 411
   time domain, **8**: 109
   wave energy converters, **8**: 49, **8**: 50
   weather prediction, **1**: 240, **1**: 240–241, **1**: 245, **1**: 248, **1**: 252, **1**: 257, **1**: 271, **1**: 273, **1**: 275
nut allergies, **5**: 40
nutrient dynamics, **6**: 66
nutrient leaching, **5**: 379
nutrient recycling, **5**: 357, **6**: 63

O

O&M *see* operation and maintenance
objectives:
   Cameroon, Africa, hydropower, **6**: 135
   dual-way five-step ship locks, **6**: 193
   hydropower, Cameroon, Africa, **6**: 135
   Maopingxi Dam, **6**: 200
   ship lift, **6**: 198
   Three Gorges Project, China, **6**: 182
   underground power plants, **6**: 191
OBR *see* oscillatory baffled reactors
obstacles issues: wind power, **2**: 190, **2**: 409
occupation:
   electron states, **1**: 299
   photon state occupation, **1**: 307
occurrence plots: ocean energy revenue, **8**: 162
ocean wave energy, **8**: **11–77**, **8**: **79–110**, **8**: **111–149**, **8**: **151–169**, **8**: **1–6**
   absorbing beaches, **8**: 91
   air turbines, **8**: **111–149**
     cascade flow analysis, **8**: 113
     impulse turbines, **8**: 112, **8**: 120, **8**: 122, **8**: 131, **8**: 136, **8**: 137
     model testing, **8**: 124
     self-rectification, **8**: 112, **8**: 120, **8**: 122, **8**: 131, **8**: 136
   airy wave equations, **8**: 12
   altimeters, **8**: 23, **8**: 31
   assessment techniques, **8**: 8, **8**: **11–77**
   axial-flow air turbines, **8**: 112, **8**: 113, **8**: 123
     three-dimensional flow analysis, **8**: 123
   bidirectional flow air turbines, **8**: 132
   Bretschneider spectrum, **8**: 16, **8**: 16t, **8**: 17f, **8**: 96
   buoys, **8**: 23
   calibration, **8**: 47
   capital costs, **8**: 152, **8**: 152f, **8**: 153, **8**: 155, **8**: 167
   cascade flow analysis, **8**: 113
   climate data, **8**: 31
   climatic variability, **8**: 51
   commercial demonstration, **8**: **79–110**
   commercial farms, **8**: 4
   conception, **8**: **79–110**
   costs, **8**: 152, **8**: 156, **8**: 158, **8**: 164, **8**: 166, **8**: 167
   crest heights, **8**: 52, **8**: 70
   current state of art, **8**: **1–6**
   demonstration, **8**: **79–110**
   Denniss-Auld air turbine, bidirectional flows, **8**: 132
   design models, conception to demonstration, **8**: 88
   device development, **8**: **79–110**, **8**: 4
   device measurements, **8**: 99, **8**: 102
   device testing, **8**: 95
   directional distribution, **8**: 18, **8**: 65
   directional properties, **8**: 15, **8**: 18, **8**: 25
   economics, **8**: **151–169**, **8**: 3, **8**: 3f
   electrical power generation, **8**: **1–6**
     commercial farms, **8**: 4
     current state of art, **8**: **1–6**
     device development, **8**: 4
     future prospects, **8**: 5
     prototypes, **8**: 4
     technology development assessments, **8**: 3
     wave farm development, **8**: 4
   energy production revenue, **8**: 162
   environmental impacts, **8**: 3, **8**: 3f
   equivalent triangular storm method, **8**: 70, **8**: 71
   errors in numerical models, **8**: 46, **8**: 47
   extreme sea state estimations, **8**: 52
     crest heights, **8**: 52, **8**: 70
     height parameters, **8**: 52, **8**: 70
     long-term distributions, **8**: 54, **8**: 65
     peaks-over-threshold method, **8**: 54
     short-term distribution, **8**: 52, **8**: 65
   flow rates, **8**: 93, **8**: 127, **8**: 127f
   frequency domain, **8**: 104
   frequency spectrum, **8**: 15
   full-scale prototypes, **8**: 85
   funding, **8**: 82
   future prospects, **8**: 5, **8**: 164
   height parameters, **8**: 37, **8**: 52, **8**: 70
   hindcast wave data uncertainties, **8**: 66
   historical overviews, **8**: **7–9**
   impulse turbines, **8**: 112, **8**: 120, **8**: 122, **8**: 131, **8**: 136, **8**: 137
   initial conception, **8**: **79–110**

ocean wave energy (*continued*)
  interannual variability, **8**: 51
  laboratory tests, **8**: 88
  large-scale prototypes, **8**: 96
  long-term distributions, **8**: 54, **8**: 65
  mapping, **8**: 41
  marine sector cost evolution, **8**: 164
  materials, **8**: 91
  mathematical descriptions, **8**: 12
  measurements, **8**: 23, **8**: 99, **8**: 102
  mechanical interfaces, **8**: 8
  mechanism cost evolution, **8**: 166
  modeling, **8**: 23, **8**: 45, **8**: 46, **8**: 47, **8**: 49, **8**: 50, **8**: 124
  moored buoys, measurements, **8**: 23
  mooring, **8**: 92
  numerical models, **8**: 23, **8**: 45, **8**: 46, **8**: 47, **8**: 49, **8**: 50
  offshore work vessels, **8**: 160
  operating costs, **8**: 156, **8**: 158, **8**: 167
  peaks-over-threshold method, **8**: 54
  performance assessments, **8**: 30
  physical model testing, **8**: 84, **8**: 88
  power equipment, **8**: 8
  power estimations, **8**: 20
  power measurements, **8**: 92, **8**: 94t
  power takeoff, **8**: **79–110**
  predictability, **8**: 50
  prototypes, **8**: **79–110**, **8**: 4
  radial-flow self-rectifying impulse air turbines, **8**: 136
  resource assessments, **8**: **11–77**
  revenue, **8**: 162, **8**: 166
  risk mitigation, **8**: 80
  sampling variability, **8**: 28, **8**: 37, **8**: 51
  satellite altimeters, **8**: 41
  scale effects, **8**: 85
  scale models, sea trials, **8**: 97
  seasonal variability, **8**: 51
  sea surface elevation, **8**: 19
  sea trials, **8**: 80, **8**: 81t, **8**: 96, **8**: 97
  self-rectification, **8**: 112, **8**: 120, **8**: 122, **8**: 131, **8**: 136
  short-term distribution, **8**: 52, **8**: 65
  similarity, **8**: 84
  spectral wave models, **8**: 45
  standard shapes, **8**: 15, **8**: 18, **8**: 19
  state of art, **8**: **1–6**
  surface elevation, **8**: 19
  synoptic variability, **8**: 51
  technology development assessments, **8**: 3
  technology readiness levels, **8**: 3, **8**: 80
  temporal averages, buoy measurements, **8**: 28
  test phases, **8**: 84, **8**: 88, **8**: 96
  three-dimensional flow analysis, **8**: 123
  tidal currents, **8**: **1–6**
  tidal stream systems, cost estimates, **8**: 152
  time domain, **8**: 104, **8**: 108
  turbines, **8**: 8, **8**: **111–149**, **8**: 8–9
  twin unidirectional impulse air turbines, **8**: 137
  unidirectional impulse air turbines, **8**: 137
  variability, **8**: 28, **8**: 37, **8**: 50
  wave climate data, **8**: 31
  wave currents, **8**: **1–6**
  wave energy converters
    climatic variability, **8**: 51
    interannual variability, **8**: 51
    numerical models, **8**: 49, **8**: 50
    performance assessments, **8**: 30
    power estimations, **8**: 20
    predictability, **8**: 50
    sampling variability, **8**: 51
    seasonal variability, **8**: 51
    synoptic variability, **8**: 51
    variability, **8**: 50
  wave farm development, **8**: 4
  wave generation tests, **8**: 89
  wave stream systems, **8**: 152
  Wells air turbines, **8**: 111, **8**: 112, **8**: 112f, **8**: 114, **8**: 122, **8**: 125, **8**: 126, **8**: 139
Ochi spectra, **8**: 16, **8**: 16t, **8**: 17f
OCI Company Ltd:, **1**: 174
OCV *see* open-circuit voltage; open current voltage
odor issues, **5**: 41
OECD *see* Organisation for Economic Co-operation and Development
off-grid technologies:
  application share, **1**: 192
  current status, **1**: 114
  developing country photovoltaics, **1**: **111–141**
  on-grid generation systems, **1**: 130
  photovoltaics, **1**: **111–141**, **1**: 7, **1**: 192
off-heat usage, **3**: 615
office buildings, **3**: 237
Office of Saline Water, **3**: 99
Off-Shore Renewable Energy Conversion Platforms – Coordination Action (ORECCA), **2**: 718
offshore substations, **2**: 450
offshore wind power, **2**: **431–468**
  aesthetics, **2**: 463
  birds, **2**: 529
  cabling, **2**: 451
  construction noise, **2**: 526
  costs, **2**: 459
    distance from shore, **2**: 481
    operation and maintenance, **2**: 480
    shore distance considerations, **2**: 481
    technical evaluation, **2**: 478, **2**: 480
    water depth, **2**: 481
  decommissioning noise, **2**: 526
  design
    wind farms, **2**: 452
    wind parks, **2**: 190, **2**: 211, **2**: 220
    wind turbines, **2**: 440
  distance factors, **2**: 456, **2**: 481
  distance from shore, **2**: 481
  economics, **2**: 459, **2**: 478, **2**: 480
  environmental impacts, **2**: 525
  environmental issues, **2**: 463
  equipment selection requirements, **2**: 452
  financial issues, **2**: 478, **2**: 480
  fish, **2**: 528
  floating technology, **2**: 449
  foundations, **2**: 178, **2**: 179f
  future outlooks, **2**: 464
  historical overviews, **2**: 432
  installation, **2**: 452
  maintenance, **2**: 452
  marine animals, **2**: 528
  market development, **2**: 666
  microclimate, **2**: 530
  noise impacts, **2**: 463, **2**: 525, **2**: 526
  operational noise, **2**: 526
  operation and maintenance, **2**: 458, **2**: 480
  prediction, **2**: 717
  projects, **2**: **431–468**
  public attitude analysis, **2**: 535
  shallow water technology, **2**: 441
  shore distance considerations, **2**: 481
  social issues, **2**: 463, **2**: 535
  status, **2**: 432
  substations, **2**: 450
  supplementary equipment, **2**: 450
  support structures
    cabling, **2**: 451
    floating technology, **2**: 449
    shallow water technology, **2**: 441
    supplementary equipment, **2**: 450
    transitional water technology, **2**: 446
    underwater cabling, **2**: 451

technical evaluation, **2**: 478, **2**: 480
Thanet Wind Park, United Kingdom, **2**: 220
transitional water technology, **2**: 446
transportation, wind farms, **2**: 456
turbines, **2**: **431–468**, **2**: 688, **2**: 713
underwater cabling, **2**: 451
visual impacts, **2**: 463, **2**: 527
water depth, **2**: 481
wildlife impacts, **2**: 463
wind farms
  activity, **2**: 434
  assembly processes, **2**: 456
  basic features, **2**: 440
  design, **2**: 452
  electrical power transmission, **2**: 603
  equipment selection requirements, **2**: 452
  installation, **2**: 452
  maintenance, **2**: 452
wind parks
  capacity, **2**: 688
  condition monitoring, **2**: 714
  definitions, **2**: 503
  design, **2**: 190, **2**: 211, **2**: 220
  development, **2**: 714
  forecasting resources, **2**: 714
  turbine technology, **2**: 688, **2**: 713
wind turbines
  aerodynamic damping, **2**: 259
  catenary moored spars, loads, **2**: 258
  design, **2**: 440
  Det Norske Veritas-OS-J101 standard, **2**: 376
  hydrodynamic damping, **2**: 259
  IEC standards, **2**: 375
  loads, **2**: 247, **2**: 258
  mechanical-dynamic loads, **2**: 247, **2**: 258
  servo-induced negative damping, **2**: 260
  support structures, **2**: 376
  technology evolution, **2**: 688
  tension leg spars, loads, **2**: 258
  turbulence, **2**: 259
  wave-induced loads, **2**: 258
  wind-induced loads, **2**: 258
  wind park design, **2**: 190
offshore work vessels, **8**: 160
offtakes: hydropower impact management, **6**: 87
Ohtori Power Stations, **6**: 298
oil analysis: wind turbine power electronics, **2**: 365
oil collection, **5**: 219
oil data: energy balance, **2**: 17
oil palm residues, **5**: 58
oil refineries, **4**: 31
oil requirements: desalination, **2**: 727–728, **2**: 728*t*
oil reserves:
  automotives, **5**: 305–306, **5**: 306*f*
  wind energy, **2**: 61
oils: biomass cofiring, **5**: 60
oilseed rape, **5**: **293–303**
Okinawa, Japan Seawater Pumped Storage Power Plant, **6**: 418
Okutadami Power Stations, **6**: 298
Oku-yoshino Power Plant, **6**: 288, **6**: 294
olive residues, **5**: 58
OLS *see* ordinary least squares
Omega siphon turbines, **6**: 27
omnicolor solar convertors, **1**: 345, **1**: 349
omnidirectional spectra estimations, **8**: 24
onboard vehicle requirements: hydrogen technology, **4**: 55
one-dimensional models: reservoir water quality, **6**: 70, **6**: 71
one-dimensional momentum theory, **2**: 226
one-hand business finance model, **1**: 122
on-grid generation systems, **1**: 130, **1**: 192
onion dehydration, **7**: 182, **7**: 183*f*
online control systems: passive solar architecture, **3**: 657, **3**: 657*t*
onshore substations, **2**: 451

onshore wind:
  costs, **2**: 475, **2**: 477
  current status, **2**: 476, **2**: 477, **2**: 479
  design, wind parks, **2**: 211, **2**: 218
  economics, **2**: 475
  electricity generation costs, **2**: 477
  energy prices, **2**: 478
  financial issues, **2**: 475
  forecasting resources, **2**: 714
  historical costs, **2**: 475
  historical price trends, **2**: 478
  installed costs, current status, **2**: 479
  performance trends, **2**: 475
  plant costs, **2**: 476
  price trends, **2**: 478
  Roscoe Wind Park, Texas, **2**: 218
  small wind turbines, **2**: 477
  technical evaluation, **2**: 475
  wind farms, **2**: 714
  wind park design, **2**: 211, **2**: 218
  wind turbines, **2**: 254
    costs, **2**: 477
    downwind rotor configurations, **2**: 255
    loads, **2**: 254
    rotor configurations, **2**: 255
    small-scale systems, **2**: 477
    thrust loads, **2**: 254
    tower shadow, **2**: 255, **2**: 256*f*, **2**: 257*f*
    upwind rotor configurations, **2**: 255
    wind-induced loads, **2**: 254
on-site ground thermal conductivity, **7**: 195
onsite measurement data: estimating wind power production, **2**: 406
Ontario, Canada:
  feed-in tariffs, **2**: 546
  hydropower, **6**: 153, **6**: 155*t*, **6**: 156, **6**: 159*f*
ON–OFF control: passive solar architecture, **3**: 655, **3**: 656
opaque electrodes, **1**: 456
OPEC *see* Organization of Petroleum Exporting Countries
open adsorption systems, **3**: 250
open circuit potentials, **4**: 245
open-circuit voltages (OCV), **1**: 340, **1**: 416, **4**: 184, **4**: 197
open-current voltages (OCV), **1**: 293, **4**: 245
open diversion channels, **6**: 206
open flumes: design concepts, **6**: 449
openings: steel vessels, **4**: 115
open-loop geothermal heat pumps, **7**: 190
open-loop models:
  building-integrated photovoltaic-thermal systems, **3**: 388
  heat removal factor, **3**: 388
  photovoltaic-thermal systems, **3**: 381
  steady-state models, **3**: 381
  thermal efficiency, **3**: 388
  transient models, **3**: 381
operating conditions: microbial fuel cells, **4**: 268
operating expenses (OPEX):
  geothermal energy, **7**: 259
  maintenance, **8**: 159
  ocean energy, **8**: 156, **8**: 158, **8**: 167
  periodic expenditures, **8**: 159
  planned maintenance, **8**: 159
  unplanned maintenance, **8**: 159
  wind energy performance issues, **2**: 474
operating pH: microbial fuel cells, **4**: 269
operating point power loss analysis, **4**: 302
operating principles:
  dye-sensitized solar cells, **1**: 482
  electrochromogenic devices, **3**: 343
  evacuated glazing, **3**: 336
  proton-exchange membrane fuel cells, **4**: 184, **4**: 184*f*
operating states: electrical power–wind energy integration, **2**: 581
operating temperatures:
  microbial fuel cells, **4**: 268
  proton-exchange membrane fuel cells, **4**: 199

operation:
   building-integrated photovoltaics, urban planning, 1: 699
   desalination, 2: 734, 2: 735
   electrical networks, 2: 581, 2: 596
   fuel cells, vehicle applications, 4: 322
   gas diffusion electrodes, 4: 167
   gasification, 5: 172, 5: 172f
   heat pumps, 3: 495
   hydrogen technology, 4: 246
   hydropower, impact management, 6: 49–91
   microbial fuel cells, 4: 266
   parallel solar assisted heat pumps, 3: 513
   passive solar architecture, 3: 639
   photochromogenic devices, 3: 346–348, 3: 348f
   reservoirs, 6: 75, 6: 214
   road vehicle fuel cells, 4: 322
   security, wind turbines, 2: 715
   solar assisted heat pumps, 3: 495, 3: 510, 3: 513, 3: 515, 3: 517, 3: 519
   solid oxide fuel cells, 4: 246
   wind energy
      electrical networks, 2: 581, 2: 596
      power design and implementation, 2: 428
      wind park impacts, 2: 512–513, 2: 513t
      wind turbine security, 2: 715
operational experience: dual fuel operation, 5: 350
operational hours: concentrating solar power, 3: 605
operational limits: solar thermal systems, 3: 576
operational noise: offshore wind power, 2: 526
operational objectives: electrical power–wind energy integration, 2: 581
operational parameters: photovoltaic/thermal solar collectors, air heat recovery, 3: 273
operational reserve: electricity networks, 2: 488
operation and maintenance (O&M):
   see also maintenance
   concentration photovoltaics, 1: 762
   costs, 2: 480
   Fresnel collectors, 3: 199
   geothermal heat pumps, shallow systems, 7: 202
   high concentration solar collectors, 3: 174, 3: 184, 3: 195, 3: 199, 3: 205
   offshore wind power, 2: 458, 2: 480
   parabolic troughs, 3: 184
   receivers, 3: 195
   solar dishes, 3: 205
   wind farms, 2: 458
   wind power design and implementation, 2: 422, 2: 423
OPEX see operating expenses
opinion considerations: wind park design, 2: 171, 2: 173
opposing interests: wind power, 2: 395, 2: 403
optical air mass, 3: 35, 3: 80t
optical analysis:
   coatings, 3: 319
   compound parabolic collectors, 3: 154
   glazings, 3: 319
   high concentration solar collectors, 3: 169, 3: 187
   low concentration ratio solar collectors, 3: 154
   low-temperature stationary collectors, 3: 120
optical efficiency, 1: 539
optical losses, 3: 187
optical microscopy, 7: 98
optical properties:
   chalcopyrite thin films, 1: 401
   coatings, 3: 316
   definitions, 3: 317
   glazings, 3: 316
   mid-pane values, 3: 330, 3: 330t
   organic dye-based down-shifting, 1: 578
   selective coatings, 3: 303
   transparent insulation, 3: 339
   window glazing coatings, 3: 330, 3: 330t
optics:
   concentration photovoltaics, 1: 747
   high concentration solar collectors, 3: 169, 3: 187, 3: 189
   receivers, 3: 187, 3: 189
optimization:
   biodiesel vegetable oil, 5: 219
   ocean wave energy, 8: 80, 8: 81t
   stand alone hybrid wind energy systems, 2: 632
   vegetable oil biodiesel, 5: 219
   wind energy stand alone systems, 2: 632
   wind power micro-siting, 2: 397, 2: 401
optimum rotor method, 2: 227
optimum voltages, 1: 342
optional fuels: biomass-to-liquids technology, 5: 183
optoelectronic properties: microcrystalline silicon, 1: 392
ORC see organic Rankine cycles
ordinary least squares (OLS), 7: 259, 7: 265, 7: 266t
ORECCA see Off-Shore Renewable Energy Conversion Platforms – Coordination Action
organic absorbers, 3: 107, 3: 107f, 3: 108f
organic dye-based down-shifting, 1: 578, 1: 579
organic dyes, 1: 593
organic loading rates, 4: 269
organic materials, 1: 13, 1: 559
organic matter removal, 4: 267
organic media storage, 3: 609
organic molecules, 1: 439–480, 1: 440, 1: 541, 1: 546
   organic solar cells, 1: 439–480, 1: 440
   upconversion, 1: 541, 1: 546
organic Rankine cycles (ORC), 3: 603, 5: 88, 5: 89, 7: 222
organic salts, 5: 239
organic semiconductor physics, 1: 442, 1: 444, 1: 445
organic solar cells (ORS), 1: 439–480
   acceptor materials, 1: 452
   acceptor molecules, 1: 440, 1: 448, 1: 452
   active materials, 1: 450, 1: 468
      stability, 1: 468
   architectures, 1: 448, 1: 463
   bilayer architecture, 1: 448
   blend cells, 1: 440, 1: 441, 1: 448, 1: 448f, 1: 449, 1: 463
   bulk heterojunctions, 1: 440, 1: 441, 1: 448, 1: 448f, 1: 449, 1: 463
   characteristic values, 1: 449
   current–voltage curves, 1: 449
   deposition, 1: 470
   donor materials, 1: 451
   donor molecules, 1: 440, 1: 448, 1: 451, 1: 457
   down-shifting, 1: 578
   efficiency
      donor molecules, 1: 457
      morphology impacts, 1: 457
      photovoltaic technology, 1: 440, 1: 440t, 1: 450, 1: 457
   electrodes, 1: 456, 1: 466
   encapsulation, 1: 465
   external quantum efficiency, 1: 450
   folded tandem architecture, 1: 464
   future outlooks, 1: 473
   heterojunctions, 1: 440, 1: 441, 1: 448, 1: 448f, 1: 449
   high-voltage devices, 1: 464
   inorganic solar cells, 1: 442
   interfacial layers, 1: 467
   interfacial materials, 1: 453
   interference effects, 1: 463
   internal quantum efficiency, 1: 450
   large-scale production methods, 1: 472
   layer deposition, 1: 470
   lifetime testing, stability, 1: 469
   luminescent down-shifting, 1: 569
   materials, 1: 450
   morphology impacts, efficiency, 1: 457
   nanostructures, 1: 464
   opaque electrodes, photovoltaic technology, 1: 456
   parallel-connected multijunction architecture, 1: 464
   production methods, 1: 470
   quantum efficiency, 1: 450
   roll-to-roll printing, 1: 440, 1: 441, 1: 470

semiconductor physics, **1**: 442
series-connected multijunction architecture, **1**: 463
single devices, **1**: 470
stability, **1**: 465
standards, **1**: 799
tandem architecture, **1**: 463
transparent electrodes, **1**: 456
wrap-through devices, **1**: 465
Organisation for Economic Co-operation and Development (OECD), **2**: 71, **2**: 707
organizational issues:
    developing country photovoltaics, **1**: 119
    Iranian hydropower, **6**: 258
Organization of Petroleum Exporting Countries (OPEC), **2**: 71
organizations: wind energy history, **2**: 71
organosolv, **5**: 238, **5**: 238t
orientation:
    building-integrated photovoltaics, **1**: 700
    collectors, **3**: 441
orifice spillway tunnels, **6**: 485, **6**: 494
origins:
    gases, **7**: 117–118
    geochemistry, **7**: 108
    geothermal fluids, **7**: 108
    photovoltaic/thermal solar collectors, **3**: 256
    wind, **2**: 74
orographic models, **2**: 86
ORS *see* organic solar cells
oscillating water columns (OWC):
    air turbines, **8**: 111, **8**: 113, **8**: 139, **8**: 141
    hydrodynamics, **8**: 141
    linear air turbines, **8**: 142
    nonlinear air turbines, **8**: 145
    ocean wave energy, **8**: 80
    prototype air turbines, **8**: 139
oscillatory baffled reactors (OBR), **5**: 206
OSPREY prototype air turbine, **8**: 139, **8**: 139f
Our common future: geothermal energy, **7**: 273
Outardes river basins, Quebec, Canada, **6**: 161, **6**: 164f, **6**: 167t
outdoor irradiance, **1**: 720
outlet works: Horseshoe Bend scheme, **6**: 474
output power conditioning, **2**: 330, **2**: 331f
output products: solar radiation/meteorological data, **1**: 231
output statistics: numerical weather prediction, **1**: 252
overall control strategies: wind turbines, **2**: 343
overall thermal loss determination, **3**: 133
overshot water wheels, **6**: 31, **6**: 33f
OWC *see* oscillating water columns
ownership: developing country photovoltaics, **1**: 119
oxidants:
    gasifiers, **5**: 139
    microbial fuel cells, **4**: 272
oxidative pretreatments, **5**: 239, **5**: 245
oxide working electrodes, **1**: 490
oxidized dye regeneration, **1**: 485
oxygen:
    corrosion, **7**: 246
    depletion, **5**: 40
    hydropower, **6**: 64
    microcrystalline silicon, **1**: 392
    oxygen-deficient heating, **5**: 357–384
    poisoning, **5**: 40
    proton-exchange membrane fuel cells, **4**: 185
    reservoir water quality, **6**: 64
oxygenation: hydropower, **6**: 61, **6**: 84
ozone, **1**: 230, **3**: 4, **3**: 61

P

packed bed filters, **5**: 145
packed bed storage units, **3**: 215, **3**: 215f, **3**: 227, **3**: 229
packing factor (PF), **3**: 261, **3**: 261f

paddles: wave generation tests, **8**: 89
PAFC *see* phosphoric acid fuel cells
Palagnedra Dam, Switzerland, **6**: 80f, **6**: 81
palm oils, **5**: 104
palm residues, **5**: 58
panchromatic waves, **8**: 80, **8**: 96
panels: photovoltaic design, **1**: 679, **1**: 680
parabolic collectors, **3**: 534, **3**: 587t, **3**: 600, **3**: 602f
parabolic-trough collectors, **3**: 174
    absorbers, **3**: 183
    absorption, **3**: 175
    adjustment, **3**: 185
    agricultural applications, **3**: 571
    characteristics, **3**: 174
    cleaning, **3**: 184
    components, **3**: 175
    construction, **3**: 178
    control, **3**: 177
    drives, **3**: 177
    efficiency, **3**: 178
    error sources, **3**: 178
    heat transfer fluids, **3**: 176
    industrial applications, **3**: 571
    maintenance, **3**: 184
    materials, **3**: 176
    models, **3**: 178
    operation and maintenance, **3**: 184
    performance determination, **3**: 178
    reflection, **3**: 175
    research, **3**: 183
    size, **3**: 176
    solar desalination, **3**: 530f, **3**: 530–531, **3**: 550
    solar thermal systems, **3**: 571
    structure, **3**: 174
    system-specific performance determination, **3**: 178
    tracking systems, **3**: 177
    transmission, **3**: 175
    types, **3**: 176
Paraguay, **6**: 96
parallel biomass cofiring, **5**: 64
parallel-connected multijunction architecture, **1**: 464
parallel solar assisted heat pumps, **3**: 511
parameters:
    crystalline silicon cells, **1**: 363, **1**: 369, **1**: 369t
    luminescent down-shifting, **1**: 569
    passive solar architecture, **3**: 655
    water quality, hydropower reservoirs, **6**: 64
parametric solar radiation models, **1**: 214
Paraná River, **6**: 96, **6**: 108
ParaScan, **3**: 172
Pará, Tucurui project, Brazil, **6**: 101
Parent, Antoine, **2**: 50
Pareto distributions, **8**: 55, **8**: 57
parked conditions: wind turbine loads, **2**: 246
parked turbines, **2**: 268
partial power converters, **2**: 297
particle density, **5**: 373–374
particle size, **5**: 373
particulates:
    engine configuration ranges, **5**: 347, **5**: 349, **5**: 350–351
    environmental impacts, **5**: 51
    syngas contaminants, **5**: 176
part's replacements: high concentration solar collectors, **3**: 185, **3**: 195, **3**: 199
Pasadena Ostrich Farm, **3**: 92, **3**: 92f
pass criteria: photovoltaic reliability, **1**: 793
passenger transport, **4**: 61, **4**: 63–64, **4**: 286
passivated emitter and rear cell (PERC) devices, **1**: 371, **1**: 373
passivation:
    crystalline silicon cells, **1**: 364, **1**: 371
    p-type silicon cells, **1**: 371
passive air-conditioning, **3**: 452
passive control loads: wind turbines, **2**: 251

passive energy storage, **3**: 243
passive heating: history, **3**: 94
passively damped composites, **2**: 713
passive solar architecture, **3**: **637–665**
   see also passive solar technologies
   advanced control, **3**: 657, **3**: 657*t*
   albedo, **3**: 644
   asphalt, **3**: 648
   bilinear models, **3**: 658–659, **3**: 660*f*
   built environment, **3**: **637–665**
   coatings, **3**: 646, **3**: 648
   coloured coatings, **3**: 646
   coloured materials, **3**: 644
   coloured thin-film layers, **3**: 648
   concepts, **3**: 638
   controlled parameters, **3**: 655
   control systems, **3**: 654
   control variables, **3**: 655
   conventional control, **3**: 656
   cooling, **3**: 642, **3**: 644, **3**: 646, **3**: 648
     coloured materials, **3**: 644
   cool materials, **3**: 644, **3**: 646, **3**: 648
   design, **3**: 639
   energy and urbanization, **3**: 637
   future prospects, **3**: 663
   fuzzy logic, **3**: 659, **3**: 661*f*
   green spaces, **3**: 651
   heating, **3**: 639
   historical overviews, **3**: 638
   intelligent control techniques, **3**: 657*t*, **3**: 659
   materials, **3**: 644, **3**: 646, **3**: 648
   online control systems, **3**: 657, **3**: 657*t*
   ON–OFF control, **3**: 655, **3**: 656
   operation, **3**: 639
   phase change materials, **3**: 646
   predictive control, **3**: 658, **3**: 660*f*, **3**: 663
   proportional–integral–derivative, **3**: 655, **3**: 656
   solar cooling, **3**: 642, **3**: 644
     asphalt layers, **3**: 648
     coatings, **3**: 646, **3**: 648
     coloured coatings, **3**: 646
     cool materials, **3**: 644, **3**: 646, **3**: 648
     materials, **3**: 644, **3**: 646, **3**: 648
     phase change materials, **3**: 646
     thermochromic coatings, **3**: 648
     thin-film asphalt layers, **3**: 648
   solar heating, **3**: 639
   thermochromic coatings, **3**: 648
   thin-film asphalt layers, **3**: 648
   urban buildings, **3**: 644, **3**: 651
   urbanization, **3**: 637, **3**: 644
   urban temperatures, **3**: 644
passive solar technologies:
   see also passive solar architecture
   admittance transfer, **3**: 364
   analytical direct gain models, **3**: 369
   Anasazi, **1**: 31, **1**: 32*f*
   building-integrated photovoltaic-thermal systems, **3**: 390
   buildings, **3**: 359, **3**: 361
   cooling loads, **3**: 378
   design, **3**: 359
   direct gain systems, **3**: 360–361, **3**: 361, **3**: 369, **3**: 390
   discrete Fourier series, **3**: 379
   frequency domain, **3**: 362, **3**: 375
   heating loads, direct gain models, **3**: 378
   modeling, **3**: 359
   room models, **3**: 360–361, **3**: 361, **3**: 369, **3**: 390
   room temperatures, **3**: 378
   simulations, **3**: 359
   source models, **3**: 373
   steady-state periodic conditions, **3**: 362, **3**: 373
   temperature analysis, **3**: 361
   thermal analysis, **3**: 361

   time domain solutions, **3**: 374
   transfer admittance, **3**: 364
   transfer functions, **3**: 375, **3**: 377
   transient heat conduction, **3**: 362
   transient response analysis, **3**: 367
   transient thermal analysis, **3**: 367
passive stills, **3**: 589, **3**: 591
PAT *see* pumps as turbines
patents, **1**: 62, **1**: 65, **1**: 580
patterns: hydropower/sediment management, **6**: 362
Paul Scherrer Institute (PSI) system, **1**: 614, **1**: 615
payback periods, **2**: 471
payback ratios, **6**: 6, **6**: 8*f*
payback times, **1**: 436, **2**: 424
PCM *see* phase change materials
PDW *see* pulse width modulation
PE 1 power plant, **3**: 622, **3**: 623*f*
peace issues, **1**: 733, **1**: 734*t*
peak electricity demand, **6**: 286
peak loads, **1**: 190, **3**: 421, **3**: 421*f*, **6**: 40
peak periods: ocean wave energy, **8**: 80
peak power: photovoltaics, **1**: 775
peaks-over-threshold (POT), **8**: 54
pebble-beds, **3**: 402, **3**: 451, **3**: 474, **3**: 474*f*
PECVD *see* plasma-enhanced chemical vapor deposition
PEFC *see* proton-exchange fuel cell
Pelamis, **8**: 21, **8**: 22*t*
pelletizing, **5**: 163
Pelotas River, **6**: 124
Pelton turbines, **6**: 25
PEM *see* proton exchange membranes
PEMFC *see* proton-exchange membrane fuel cells; polymer electrolyte membrane fuel cells
peninsular rivers, **6**: 228, **6**: 231, **6**: 244
penstock developments, **6**: 24
penstock efficiency, **6**: 444
penstock supply, **6**: 445, **6**: 461
PERC *see* passivated emitter and rear cell devices
percentage of people dissatisfied (PPD), **3**: 655–656
Perez model, **3**: 48
perfluoro sulfonic acid (PFSA) membranes, **4**: 186, **4**: 186*f*, **4**: 188
performance:
   advanced Wells air turbine configurations, **8**: 128
   air turbines, **8**: 126, **8**: 131
   alkaline anion exchange membrane fuel cells, **4**: 178
   alkaline fuel cells, **4**: 163
   batteries, **4**: 324
   biological fuel cells, **4**: 264
   cathodes, **4**: 163
   combined heat and power systems, **4**: 251
   concentration photovoltaics, **1**: 760
   concrete structure durability, **6**: 379, **6**: 392
   costs, wind energy, **2**: 474, **2**: 475
   durability design, **6**: 392
   electrochromogenic glazing, **3**: 346
   enzymatic fuel cells, **4**: 264
   flat-type photovoltaic/thermal solar collectors, **3**: 270
   Fresnel collectors, **3**: 196
   geothermal energy power plants, **7**: 235
   high concentration solar collectors, **3**: 168, **3**: 178, **3**: 187, **3**: 196, **3**: 202
   hydrogen technology, **4**: 55
   incentive payments, **1**: 84–85
   intermediate band solar cells, **1**: 623
   low-temperature stationary collectors, **3**: 141
   monitoring
     energy conversion efficiency, **1**: 775, **1**: 776
     energy predictions, **1**: 778
     measurements, **1**: 783
     module energy predictions, **1**: 778
     module yields, **1**: 777, **1**: 781
     performance ratios, **1**: 775, **1**: 777
     photovoltaic yields, **1**: **775–786**, **1**: 10

practical considerations, **1**: 781, **1**: 783, **1**: 784
roller compacted concrete dams, **6**: 480
sensors, **1**: 783
stand-alone photovoltaic systems, **1**: 775, **1**: 777
system efficiency, **1**: 776, **1**: 781, **1**: 783
system yields, **1**: 776, **1**: 781, **1**: 783
wind power, **2**: 429
yields, **1**: **775–786**, **1**: 775
ocean wave energy
revenue, **8**: 162
test phases, **8**: 80, **8**: 81t
wave energy converters, **8**: 30
onshore wind costs, **2**: 475
organic solar cells, **1**: 463
parabolic troughs, **3**: 178
photovoltaics
definitions, **1**: 776
micro-and nanotechnologies, **1**: 515, **1**: 518
standards, **1**: 789
thermal solar collectors, **3**: 269, **3**: 270
yields, **1**: **775–786**, **1**: 10
power plants, geothermal energy, **7**: 235
radiometers, **1**: 224
ratios
desalination, **3**: 529
multieffect distillation, **3**: 533
multistage flash, **3**: 533
photovoltaics, **1**: 775, **1**: 777
solar desalination, **3**: 533, **3**: 547, **3**: 551
receivers, **3**: 187
rotors, wind turbines, **2**: 110
self-rectification air turbines, **8**: 131
solar cells, **1**: 717
solar dishes, **3**: 202
solid oxide fuel cells, **4**: 251
standards
photovoltaic devices, **1**: 789
small wind turbines, **2**: 376
storage, hydrogen technology, **4**: 55
system-specific determination, concentration solar collectors, **3**: 168, **3**: 178, **3**: 187
wave energy converters, **8**: 30
Wells air turbines, **8**: 126
wind energy, costs, **2**: 474, **2**: 475
Peribonka, Quebec, Canada, **6**: 85f, **6**: 162–163, **6**: 166f
perihelion, **3**: 28
periodic operating expenditures: ocean energy, **8**: 159
period parameters: ocean waves, **8**: 14, **8**: 36, **8**: 39
period of record: solar radiation, **1**: 227
permanent joints, **6**: 382
permanent magnets, **2**: 270
permanent magnet synchronous generators, **2**: 337, **2**: 356
permeability: geothermal energy, **7**: 16–18, **7**: 107–108, **7**: 108
permissions: wind power, **2**: 396
permits: bioenergy policy development, **5**: 411, **5**: 416–417, **5**: 420f, **5**: 422
peroxide pathways, **4**: 162
Persian vertical axis designs, **2**: 44
personnel issues:
biomass and biofuel power generation, **5**: 40
wind turbines, **2**: 376
pervaporation, **5**: 211
petrol engine biofuel operation, **5**: 346
petroleum consumption, **5**: 305–306, **5**: 306f
petroleum production, **5**: 305–306, **5**: 306f
PF *see* packing factor
PFR *see* plug flow reactors
PFSA *see* perfluoro sulfonic acid
PGL *see* Pioneer Generation Ltd:
pH:
biochar, **5**: 375, **5**: 383
corrosion rates, **7**: 245
geochemistry, **7**: 129

microbial fuel cells, **4**: 269
phase change: desalination, **2**: 726
phase change materials (PCM):
active energy systems, **3**: 247
passive energy systems, **3**: 243
passive solar architecture, **3**: 646
power conversion, **3**: 609
solar cooling, **3**: 646
solar thermal energy storage, **3**: 211, **3**: 221–222, **3**: 222f, **3**: 223, **3**: 224, **3**: 225t, **3**: 228t, **3**: 229, **3**: 230, **3**: 230f, **3**: 243, **3**: 247, **3**: 249f
phase speed: ocean waves, **8**: 13
phase voltage imbalance, **2**: 594
phenols, **5**: 396
pheophytin, **1**: 657
PHES *see* pumped hydro energy storage
PHOEBUS study, **3**: 629
Phoenix Contact, **2**: 325
phosphoric acid fuel cells (PAFC):
alkaline fuel cells, **4**: 161, **4**: 161t
solid oxide fuel cells, **4**: 243, **4**: 243t, **4**: 246
transport applications, **4**: 282
phosphorus:
diffusion, **1**: 359
glass removal, **1**: 359
indium-phosphide solar cells, **1**: 610
InGaP/GaAs/Ge 3-junction solar cells, **1**: 497, **1**: 503, **1**: 506
reservoir water quality, **6**: 66
photochemical thermodynamics, **1**: 664
photochemical upconversion, **1**: 543
photochromogenics:
chromaticity, **3**: 349, **3**: 349f
device layout/operation, **3**: 346–348, **3**: 348f
glazing, **3**: 316, **3**: 346
photoconductivity, **1**: 404
photoelectrical efficiency, **1**: 540
photoelectric effect, **1**: 34, **1**: 34f
photogrammetry, **3**: 169
photoluminescence intensity, **1**: 500, **1**: 500f, **1**: 572
photon gas approximation, **1**: 316
photonic structures: escape cone losses, **1**: 596
photons:
absorption, **1**: 663
conversion, **1**: **549–561**, **1**: **533–548**
coupling, **1**: **549–561**
management, **1**: 389
property fluxes, **1**: 318
Shockley–Queisser limiting efficiency, **1**: 308
state density, **1**: 306
state occupation, **1**: 307
thermophotovoltaics, **1**: 603, **1**: 604, **1**: 607
thin-film silicon photovoltaics, **1**: 393, **1**: 395
photophysics, **1**: 542
photosynthesis, **1**: **657–677**
artificial antennae, **1**: 669
artificial leaves, **1**: 667, **1**: 669, **1**: 674
electron transfer, **1**: 664
energy storage, **1**: 664
exciton energy transfer, leaves, **1**: 664
fuel-producing solar cell construction, **1**: 674
leaves, **1**: **657–677**
light-harvesting antenna complexes, **1**: 658, **1**: 661
membrane organization, **1**: 661
photochemical thermodynamics, **1**: 664
photon absorption, leaves, **1**: 663
photovoltaics, **1**: **657–677**, **1**: 10, **1**: 657
protein maquettes, **1**: 667
reaction centers, **1**: 657–658, **1**: 659
self-assembled artificial antennae, **1**: 669
solar cell construction, **1**: 674
supercomplex organization, **1**: 660
supramolecular organization, **1**: 660
photosynthetic efficiency, **5**: 297

photothermal (PT) conversion/converters, **1:** 332, **1:** 345, **3: 301–312**
photovoltaic-driven reverse osmosis (PV–RO):
    solar desalination, **3:** 530, **3:** 536, **3:** 553, **3:** 556, **3:** 558, **3:** 560
        brackish water, **3:** 538, **3:** 539*t*, **3:** 556, **3:** 558, **3:** 560, **3:** 560*t*, **3:** 563*f*
        seawater, **3:** 539*t*, **3:** 553, **3:** 558
photovoltaics (PV), **1: 13–30**
    see also concentration photovoltaics; photovoltaic/thermal systems
    2010 global industry overview, **1:** 167
    2020 vision, **1:** 183
    2050 vision, **1:** 185, **1:** 186
    absorption, **1:** 334
    Abu Dhabi desert area, **1:** 690
    acceptor materials, **1:** 452
    acceptor molecules, **1:** 440, **1:** 448, **1:** 452
    active materials, **1:** 450, **1:** 468
    aluminum-alloyed back junctions, **1:** 375
    amorphous silicon, **1:** 8, **1:** 21, **1:** 144, **1:** 389, **1:** 393
    analytical frameworks, **1:** 114
    ancient historical development, **1:** 31
    annihilation statistics, **1:** 543
    antireflective layers, **1:** 520
    architectures, **1:** 448, **1: 697–707**, **1:** 463
    artificial leaves, **1: 657–677**, **1:** 10
    atmospheric processes, **1:** 246
    back contacts, **1:** 432
    backward citation analysis, **1:** 62, **1:** 63
    balance of system, **1:** 685
        batteries, **1:** 687
        charge regulators, **1:** 687
        inverters, **1:** 685
        mounting structures, **1:** 686
    band structure, **1:** 619
    bank funding, **1:** 113, **1:** 121, **1:** 128
    batteries, **1:** 204, **1:** 204*f*, **1:** 206, **1:** 687, **1:** 722
        balance of system, **1:** 687
    beam solar radiation, **1:** 315, **1:** 319, **1:** 325, **1:** 326
    best practice, promotion schemes, **1:** 93
    bilayer architecture, **1:** 448
    bio-inspiration, **1: 657–677**
    blackbodies, **1:** 318, **1:** 321, **1:** 322, **1:** 332
    blend cells
        n-type silicon cells, **1:** 379
        organic solar cells, **1:** 440, **1:** 441, **1:** 448, **1:** 448*f*, **1:** 449, **1:** 463
        silicon photovoltaics, **1:** 393
        thin-film silicon photovoltaic technology, **1:** 393
    boron-diffused back junctions, **1:** 377
    boron-diffused front emitters, **1:** 376
    bottom-up manufacturing, **1:** 67
    breakthroughs, **1:** 61
    bridging power storage technologies, **1:** 206
    building-integrated systems, **1: 697–707**, **1:** 10
    bulk heterojunctions, **1:** 440, **1:** 441, **1:** 448, **1:** 463
    bulk intermediate band solar cells, **1:** 624
    bulk properties, **1:** 368
    cadmium chloride activation, **1:** 431
    cadmium sulphide layers, **1:** 424, **1:** 429
    cadmium telluride thin-films, **1: 423–438**, **1:** 8, **1:** 23, **1:** 515, **1:** 522
        back contacts, **1:** 432
        cadmium chloride activation, **1:** 431
        cadmium sulphide layers, **1:** 424, **1:** 429
        commercial modules, **1:** 424
        device designs, **1:** 424
        disruptive technologies, **1:** 23
        energy-payback times, **1:** 436
        environmental impacts, **1:** 436
        historical overviews, **1:** 423
        industry designs, **1:** 424
        initial commercial modules, **1:** 424
        junctions, **1:** 434
        large-scale deployment considerations, **1:** 434
        layer-specific process descriptions, **1:** 427
        material properties, **1:** 426
        mineral availability, **1:** 436
        payback times, **1:** 436
        reliability, **1:** 435
        technology progress, **1:** 23
    calculating feed-in tariffs, **1:** 94
    Canadian market development, **1:** 184
    capacity, **1:** 161
    capital subsidies, **1:** 125
    carbon financing, **1:** 129
    carbon nanotubes, **1:** 526
    carrier multiplication, **1:** 549
    catalyst development, **1:** 33
    causes, cost reductions, **1:** 48
    cell parameters, **1:** 363, **1:** 369, **1:** 369*t*
    cell technical aspects, **1:** 717
    centralized energy generation, **1:** 189
    chalcopyrite thin films, **1: 399–422**
        crystal structure, **1:** 400
        deposition, **1:** 406
        device properties, **1:** 414
        device structure, **1:** 410
        future outlooks, **1:** 417
        material properties, **1:** 400
        optical properties, **1:** 401
        structure, **1:** 400, **1:** 410
    challenges, **1:** 82, **1:** 89, **1:** 103
    charge regulators, **1:** 687
    cloud motion vectors, **1:** 245, **1:** 249, **1:** 251
    commercial applications, **1:** 580
    commercial banks, **1:** 121
    commercial modules, **1:** 424
    community development, **1: 733–744**
    community participation, **1:** 120
    competiveness, **1:** 181, **1:** 187
    components, **1: 679–695**
    compressed air energy storage, **1:** 210
    compression systems, **3:** 489
    concentration photovoltaics, **1: 745–765**
    concentrators, **1:** 9
    conduction, **1:** 444
    consumer finance/grants, **1:** 121, **1:** 125
    conversion efficiency, **1:** 328, **1: 549–561**
    copper indium diselenide thin films, **1:** 22
    costs, **1: 47–72**, **1:** 5, **1:** 7
        backward citation analysis, **1:** 62, **1:** 63
        bottom-up manufacturing, **1:** 67
        breakthroughs, **1:** 61
        causes, **1:** 48
        demand, **1:** 52
        developing countries, **1:** 116
        drivers, **1:** 49, **1:** 52
        economies of scale, **1:** 50
        expert opinion, **1:** 62, **1:** 65, **1:** 67
        forecasting, **1:** 47, **1:** 54, **1:** 195, **1:** 196
        future demand expectations, **1:** 50
        future directions, **1:** 50, **1:** 69
        future visions, **1:** 195, **1:** 196
        intertechnology spillovers, **1:** 51
        learning from experience, **1:** 51, **1:** 54
        materials, **1:** 51
        micro-and nanotechnologies, **1:** 517
        niche markets, **1:** 49
        non-incremental changes, **1:** 61, **1:** 67
        patent analysis, **1:** 62, **1:** 65
        product attribute changes, **1:** 53
        quality, **1:** 53
        reductions, **1: 47–72**
        research and development, **1:** 49, **1:** 54, **1:** 68
        supply and demand drivers, **1:** 52
    coverage effects, **1:** 647
    crystalline silicon, **1: 353–387**, **1:** 8
        Abu Dhabi desert area, **1:** 691

bulk properties, **1**: 368
cell parameters, **1**: 363, **1**: 369, **1**: 369t
current status, **1**: 355
dielectric surface passivation, **1**: 364
disruptive technologies, **1**: 21
efficiency, **1: 353–387**
evolutionary technologies, **1**: 20
high-efficiency cell structures, **1**: 371, **1**: 375
improvement strategies, **1**: 364
markets, **1**: 353
material parameters, **1**: 363, **1**: 369, **1**: 369t
metallization, **1**: 366
parameter influence, **1**: 363
passivation, **1**: 364, **1**: 371
state-of-the-art technology, **1: 353–387**
surface passivation, **1**: 364
technology progress, **1**: 20, **1**: 21, **1**: 25
crystal structure, **1**: 400
current status, **1**: 181
  crystalline silicon cells, **1**: 355
  developing countries, **1**: 114
  electricity prices, **1**: 181
  grid-connected systems, **1**: 114
  markets, **1**: 180
  module prices, **1**: 181
  off-grid technologies, **1**: 114
  policy support, **1**: 182
  system prices, **1**: 181
  technology development, **1**: 41, **1**: 43
current-voltage analysis, **1**: 449, **1**: 790
data analysis, **1**: 792
decentralized energy generation, **1**: 189, **1**: 191
decentralized storage, **1**: 191
demand cost reductions, **1**: 52
deposition, **1**: 406
design, **1: 679–695**
  artificial leaves, **1**: 666
  modules, **1**: 679, **1**: 680
  panels, **1**: 679, **1**: 680
  system performance, **1**: 679–680, **1**: 692
developing countries, **1: 111–141**
  annual revision finance procedures, **1**: 125
  bank funding, **1**: 113, **1**: 121, **1**: 128
  capital subsidies, **1**: 125
  carbon financing, **1**: 129
  community participation, **1**: 120
  consumer grants, **1**: 125
  costs, **1**: 116
  current status, **1**: 114
  development assistance, **1**: 113
  economics, **1**: 113, **1**: 120
  feed-in tariffs, **1**: 130–131, **1**: 134
  finance, **1**: 113, **1**: 120, **1**: 125, **1**: 130
  financial risk management, **1**: 135
  fiscal incentives, **1**: 128
  funding, **1**: 113, **1**: 120, **1**: 125
  global energy transfer feed-in tariffs, **1**: 128, **1**: 135
  grants, **1**: 125
  guarantees, **1**: 125
  hire purchase, **1**: 126
  import duty reductions, **1**: 128
  incentives, **1: 111–141**
  international funds, **1**: 113
  leasing, **1**: 126
  loans, **1**: 128
  local participation, **1**: 119
  low interest loans, **1**: 128
  market development finance, **1**: 123
  Millennium Development Goals, **1**: 111
  off-grid technologies, **1: 111–141**
  organization, **1**: 119
  ownership, **1**: 119
  poverty alleviation, **1**: 124
  private operators, **1**: 120
  private ownership, **1**: 120
  public finance pools, **1**: 128
  public sector finance, **1**: 124, **1**: 128
  regulation, **1**: 127
  renewable energy premium tariff, **1**: 130
  renewable portfolio standards, **1**: 127
  rural electrification, **1: 111–141**
  rural energy service companies, **1**: 120, **1**: 126, **1**: 132
  small power producer regulation, **1**: 127
  soft loans, **1**: 128
  subsidies, **1**: 125
  support mechanisms, **1: 111–141**
  tariff incentives, **1**: 124
  tariff setting, **1**: 124
  tender systems, **1**: 128
  value added tax reductions, **1**: 128
development, **1: 5–11**
  assistance, **1**: 113
  catalysts, **1**: 33
  global industry overview, **1**: 164
  historical developments, **1: 31–45**
devices
  cadmium telluride thin films, **1**: 424
  chalcopyrite thin films, **1**: 410, **1**: 414
  performance determination standards, **1**: 789
dielectric medium, **1**: 646
dielectric surface passivation, **1**: 364
diesel hybrid systems, **1**: 687
diluted thermal radiation, **1**: 322
direct solar radiation, **1**: 315, **1**: 319, **1**: 325, **1**: 326
discoveries, **1**: 5
disruptive technologies, **1**: 15–16, **1**: 21
donor materials, **1**: 451
donor molecules, **1**: 440, **1**: 448, **1**: 451, **1**: 457
downconversion, **1: 549–561**, **1**: 9, **1**: 549
  carrier multiplication, **1**: 549
  equivalent circuits, **1**: 550
  micro-and nanotechnologies, **1**: 519
  multiple exciton generation, **1**: 549, **1**: 554
  nanotechnologies, **1**: 519
  performance, **1**: 519
  practical applications, **1**: 554
  quantum cutting, **1**: 549, **1**: 555
  singlet fission, **1**: 549, **1**: 559
  space separated quantum cutting, **1**: 555
down-shifting, **1: 563–585**, **1**: 9, **1**: 519
  commercial applications, **1**: 580
  lanthanides, **1**: 566, **1**: 573
  organic dyes, **1**: 578
  patents, **1**: 580
  quantum dots, **1**: 566, **1**: 566–567, **1**: 575
  rare earths, **1**: 566, **1**: 573
  simulation methods, **1**: 571
  spectral response modeling, **1**: 571
driver in cost reductions, **1**: 49, **1**: 52
DSM concept, **1**: 191
dye-sensitized solar cells, **1: 481–496**, **1**: 9, **1**: 26
economics, **1**: 5, **1**: 7, **1**: 113, **1**: 120, **1**: 725, **3**: 269
  developing countries, **1**: 113, **1**: 120
  introduction, **1**: 5, **1**: 7
economies of scale, **1**: 50
effectiveness, support mechanisms, **1**: 78
efficiency
  downconversion, **1: 549–561**
  micro-and nanotechnologies, **1**: 515
  organic solar cells, **1**: 440, **1**: 440t, **1**: 450, **1**: 457
  support mechanisms, **1**: 78
  upconversion, **1: 533–548**
electric double-layer capacitors, **1**: 204, **1**: 204f, **1**: 205
electricity generation, **1**: 162
electricity system changes, **1**: 189
electrification rates, **1**: 114

photovoltaics (PV) (*continued*)
   electrode materials, **1**: 456
   electrodialysis, **3**: 537, **3**: 538*f*, **3**: 540*f*, **3**: 541*f*, **3**: 547
   eligibility, promotion schemes, **1**: 94
   emitters, **1**: 371, **1**: 374, **1**: 380
   energy conversion, **1: 293–313**, **1: 603–618**
     introduction, **1**: 8, **1**: 9
     performance monitoring, **1**: 775, **1**: 776
   energy-payback times, **1**: 147, **1**: 436
   energy performance, standards, **1**: 795
   energy predictions, **1**: 778
   energy rating standards, **1**: 795
   energy storage, **1: 199–212**
     grid impacts, **1**: 199, **1**: 201
     management, **1**: 208
   energy system global industry overview, **1**: 162
   energy technology in rural areas, **1**: 115
   environment
     Abu Dhabi desert area, **1**: 694
     cadmium telluride thin films, **1**: 436
     energy payback times, **1**: 147
     greenhouse gas emissions, **1**: 148
     heavy metal emissions, **1**: 151
     introduction, **1**: 7
     life cycles, **1: 143–159**
       inventory, **1**: 146
       risk analysis, **1**: 153
     pollutants, **1**: 150
     reliability testing, **1**: 794
     risk analysis, **1**: 153
   environmental impacts, **1: 143–159**
   equivalent circuits, **1**: 535, **1**: 550
   European Commission's Joint Research Centre, **1**: 788
   European mainstream power sources, **1**: 183
   European Union
     promotion schemes, **1**: 90, **1**: 93, **1**: 103
     support mechanisms, **1**: 90, **1**: 93, **1**: 103
   evaluation
     power forecasting, **1**: 265, **1**: 271, **1**: 285
     solar irradiance, **1**: 265, **1**: 271, **1**: 285
   evolutionary technologies, **1**: 15, **1**: 19
   exciton generation, **1**: 525
   experience curves, **1**: 54
   expert opinion, **1**: 62, **1**: 65, **1**: 67
   external quantum efficiency, **1**: 450, **1**: 540
   fail criteria, reliability, **1**: 793
   failures, reliability testing, **1**: 793
   feed-in tariffs, **1: 73–109**, **1: 130–131**, **1**: 134
     calculation methodology, **1**: 94
     United States, **1**: 88
   finance, **1**: 7
     Abu Dhabi desert area, **1**: 693
     developing countries, **1**: 113, **1**: 120, **1**: 125, **1**: 130
     fossil-fuels, **1**: 136
     future visions, **1**: 197
     promotion schemes, **1**: 97
     return expectations, **1**: 137
     risk management, **1**: 135, **1**: 136, **1**: 137
     rural areas, **1**: 113, **1**: 120, **1**: 125, **1**: 130
   First Solar LLC, **1**: 169
   fiscal incentives, **1**: 128
   flow batteries, **1**: 208
   flywheels, **1**: 204, **1**: 204*f*, **1**: 205
   forecasting, costs, **1**: 47, **1**: 54
   fossil-fuels, **1**: 136
   funding, **1**: 113, **1**: 120, **1**: 125
   future directions, **1: 47–72**, **1: 179–198**, **1: 353–387**
     centralized energy generation, **1**: 189
     chalcopyrite thin films, **1**: 417
     competiveness, **1**: 181, **1**: 187
     cost reductions, **1**: 50, **1**: 69
     costs, **1: 47–72**, **1**: 195, **1**: 196
     crystalline silicon cells, **1: 353–387**
     decentralized energy generation, **1**: 189, **1**: 191
     decentralized storage, **1**: 191
     demand expectations, **1**: 50
     DSM concept, **1**: 191
     electricity system changes, **1**: 189
     financing, **1**: 197
     generation technology progress, **1**: 15, **1**: 25
     global industry overview, **1**: 175
     global installed capacity, **1**: 185
     grid development, **1**: 187, **1**: 188, **1**: 190, **1**: 192, **1**: 197
     grid infrastructure adaptations, **1**: 188, **1**: 197
     grid management, **1**: 188
     infrastructure adaptations, **1**: 188, **1**: 197
     innovative market designs, **1**: 188
     investments, **1**: 196
     markets, **1**: 183, **1**: 184, **1**: 188, **1**: 191, **1**: 697
       designs, **1**: 188
       development, **1**: 183, **1**: 184, **1**: 188
       segmentation, **1**: 191
     microtechnology, **1**: 528
     module prices, **1**: 193
     multi-junction cells, **1**: 509
     nanotechnology, **1**: 528
     off-grid application share, **1**: 192
     on-grid application share, **1**: 192
     organic solar cells, **1**: 473
     peak loads, **1**: 190
     plasmonics, **1**: 654
     policy recommendations, **1**: 188, **1**: 196
     power distribution systems, **1**: 197
     project investments, **1**: 196
     promotion schemes, **1**: 82, **1**: 89, **1**: 103
     recommendations, **1**: 188, **1**: 196
     regulatory frameworks, **1**: 196
     research and development, **1**: 196, **1**: 197
     signal transmission, **1**: 196
     silicon cells, **1: 353–387**
     smart grids, **1**: 190
     storage, **1**: 191
     sunbelt countries investments, **1**: 197
     super smart grids, **1**: 190
     support regulatory frameworks, **1**: 196
     system prices, **1**: 193
     technological trends, **1**: 192
     technology investments, **1**: 196
     transmission systems, **1**: 197
     United States, **1**: 89, **1**: 184
     upconversion, **1**: 546
     variability management, **1**: 189
     visions, **1: 179–198**
   geometrical factors, **1**: 319
Germany, **1**: 165, **1**: 166, **1**: 168, **1**: 170, **1**: 171, **1**: 172
   promotion/support schemes, **1**: 90, **1**: 93, **1**: 103
giga-watt markets, **1**: 15, **1**: 19
global energy transfer feed-in tariffs, **1**: 128, **1**: 135
global industry overview, **1: 161–177**, **1**: 161, **1**: 162
global installed capacity, **1**: 185
global markets, **1**: 16
grants, **1**: 125
Grätzel cells, **1**: 9, **1**: 26
greenhouse gas emissions, **1**: 148
green power programs, United States, **1**: 86
grids
   current status, **1**: 114
   development, **1**: 187, **1**: 188, **1**: 190, **1**: 192, **1**: 197
   flexibility, **1**: 199
   impacts, **1**: 199, **1**: 201
   infrastructure adaptations, **1**: 188, **1**: 197
   integration, **1**: 241
   management, **1**: 188
   reliability, **1**: 199
group III-V material multi-junction cells, **1**: 9
growth, **1: 13–30**, **1**: 389

guarantees, **1**: 125
health effects, **1**: **143–159**
heavy metal emissions, **1**: 151
heterojunctions
   n-type silicon cells, **1**: 379
   organic solar cells, **1**: 440, **1**: 441, **1**: 448, **1**: 448*f*, **1**: 449, **1**: 463
   silicon photovoltaics, **1**: 393
   thin-films, **1**: 393
high-efficiency cell structures, **1**: 371, **1**: 375
high-efficiency device technology progress, **1**: 24
high-efficiency realization, **1**: **497–514**
hire purchase, **1**: 126
historical overviews
   cadmium telluride thin films, **1**: 423
   costs, **1**: **47–72**
   developments, **1**: **31–45**
   research and development, **1**: **31–45**
   standards, **1**: 787
hot-carriers, **1**: 26, **1**: 525, **1**: 526
hot flashes, **1**: 26
hundred mega-watt plants, **1**: 690
hybrid solar–diesel systems, Mandhoo Island, **1**: 687
IEC, **1**: **787–803**
III–V group compound multi-junction cells, **1**: **497–514**
impact ionization, **1**: 316, **1**: 339
implanted emitters, **1**: 380
import duty reductions, **1**: 128
improvement strategies, **1**: 364
impurity-based approaches, **1**: 624
incentives, **1**: **111–141**
incident light down-shifting, **1**: **563–585**
indium-gallium-phosphorous/gallium-arsenide-based solar cells,
   1: 497, **1**: 503, **1**: 506, **1**: 508
industry
   cadmium telluride thin films, **1**: 424
   introduction, **1**: 7
   overview, **1**: **161–177**, **1**: 7, **1**: 161
   technology progress, **1**: 16
inflation indexation, promotion schemes, **1**: 101
infrastructure adaptations, **1**: 188, **1**: 197
InGaP/GaAs-based multi-junction cells, **1**: 497, **1**: 503, **1**: 508
InGaP/GaAs/Ge 3-junction solar cells, **1**: 497, **1**: 503
initial commercial modules, **1**: 424
innovative market designs, future visions, **1**: 188
inorganic solar cells, **1**: 442
installed system operation, **1**: 8
interfacial materials, **1**: 453
intermediate band solar cells, **1**: **619–639**, **1**: 9
   band structure, **1**: 619
   impurity-based approaches, **1**: 624
   quantum dots, **1**: 623, **1**: 628
   quantum structure nanotechnology, **1**: 527
   structure, **1**: 619
   theoretical models, **1**: 619
internal quantum efficiency, **1**: 450
international funds, **1**: 113
international standards, reliability testing, **1**: 793
intertechnology spillovers, **1**: 51
inverters, **1**: 685
investment incentives, promotion schemes, **1**: 74, **1**: 75–76, **1**: 78,
   1: 106
investments, **1**: 196
ionization, **1**: 316, **1**: 339
irradiance-dependent solar cell performance, g modules, **1**: 681
irradiance power forecasts, **1**: **239–292**
Japan, **1**: 166, **1**: 167, **1**: 170, **1**: 171, **1**: 172, **1**: 184
   global industry overview, **1**: 166, **1**: 167, **1**: 170, **1**: 171, **1**: 172
   market development, **1**: 184
JingAo Solar Co: Ltd, **1**: 170
Joint Research Centre, standards, **1**: 788
Lagrange invariant, **1**: 316, **1**: 325
lanthanides, down-shifting, **1**: 566, **1**: 573
large-scale deployment considerations, **1**: 434

large-scale production methods, **1**: 472
layer-specific process descriptions, **1**: 427
lead–acid batteries, **1**: 206
learning curves, **1**: 47, **1**: 54
learning from experience, **1**: 51, **1**: 54
leasing, developing countries, **1**: 126
leaves, **1**: **657–677**, **1**: 10
life-cycles, **1**: **143–159**
   assessments, **1**: 7
   environmental impacts, **1**: **143–159**
   health effects, **1**: **143–159**
   inventory, **1**: 146
   risk analysis, **1**: 153
lifetimes, reliability testing, **1**: 795
lift-off processing, **1**: 522
light source performance, **1**: 790
light trapping, **1**: 9
lithium–ion batteries, **1**: 207
loans, **1**: 128
localized surface plasmons, **1**: 643
local participation, **1**: 119
low interest loans, **1**: 128
luminescent down-shifting, **1**: **563–585**
luminescent solar concentrators, **1**: **587–601**, **1**: 9
mainstream power sources, future, **1**: 183
managing storage options, **1**: 208
Mandhoo Island, **1**: 687
markets, **1**: **161–177**
   crystalline silicon cells, **1**: 353
   designs, **1**: 188
   developing countries, **1**: 123
   future directions, **1**: 183, **1**: 184, **1**: 188, **1**: 191, **1**: 697
   global industry overview, **1**: **161–177**
   integration design, **1**: 102
   segmentation, **1**: 191
   technology progress, **1**: 16
material properties
   cadmium telluride thin films, **1**: 426
   chalcopyrite thin films, **1**: 400
   plasmonics, **1**: 646
materials
   cost reductions, **1**: 51
   crystalline silicon cells, **1**: 363, **1**: 369, **1**: 369*t*
   organic solar cells, **1**: 450
measurements
   performance determination, **1**: 790, **1**: 791
   standards, **1**: 790, **1**: 791
mega-watt plants, **1**: 690
megawatt-scale, **1**: 690, **1**: **733–744**
mesoporous dye-sensitized solar cells, **1**: **481–496**, **1**: 9
metallization, crystalline silicon cells, **1**: 366
metal nanoparticles, **1**: **641–656**
metal-wrap-through cells, **1**: 372, **1**: 373
microcredits, **1**: 121
micro-silicon thin films, **1**: 21
microtechnology, **1**: **515–531**, **1**: 8, **1**: 9
microwires, **1**: 524
milestone development, **1**: 196
Millennium Development Goals, **1**: 111
mineral availability, **1**: 436
modern history, **1**: 37
modules
   architectural functions, buildings, **1**: 703
   design, **1**: 679, **1**: 680
   energy predictions, **1**: 778
   global industry overview, **1**: 162
   prices, **1**: 193
   yields, **1**: 777, **1**: 781
molecular photophysics, **1**: 542
monochromatic optical efficiency, **1**: 539
monogap solar cells, **1**: 334
Motech Solar, **1**: 170
mounting structures, **1**: 686

photovoltaics (PV) (*continued*)
    multi-exciton generation, **1**: 525
    multi-junction cells, **1**: **497–514**, **1**: **619–639**, **1**: 9, **1**: 24, **1**: 392, **1**: 746, **1**: 746f
    multiple-exciton generation, **1**: 26, **1**: 549, **1**: 554
    nanoarchitectures, **1**: 523
    nanocomposites, **1**: 523
    nanoparticles, **1**: 515, **1**: 517, **1**: 522
    nanoscale metals, **1**: **641–656**
    nano-silicon thin films, **1**: 21
    nanotechnology, **1**: **515–531**
        future outlooks, **1**: 528
        introduction, **1**: 9
        quantum structures, **1**: 525
        technology progress, **1**: 21, **1**: 26
    nanowires, **1**: 524
    narrow band semiconductors, **1**: 340
    national grid extensions, **1**: 192
    natural photosynthesis design, **1**: 657, **1**: 663
    net metering, **1**: 74, **1**: 75–76, **1**: 77, **1**: 86
    niche markets, **1**: 49
    nonbank financing institutions, **1**: 121
    non-incremental cost reductions, **1**: 61, **1**: 67
    Norway, **1**: 171
    n-type silicon cells, **1**: 375
        aluminum-alloyed back junctions, **1**: 375
        boron-diffused back junctions, **1**: 377
        boron-diffused front emitters, **1**: 376
        emitters, **1**: 380
        heterojunctions, **1**: 379
        high-efficiency cell structures, **1**: 375
        implanted emitters, **1**: 380
        polysilicon emitters, **1**: 380
    numerical weather prediction models, **1**: 240–241, **1**: 245, **1**: 248, **1**: 252, **1**: 257, **1**: 271
    off-grid technologies, **1**: **111–141**, **1**: 7, **1**: 192
        application share, **1**: 192
        current status, **1**: 114
        developing countries, **1**: **111–141**
    omnicolor solar convertors, **1**: 345
    one-hand business finance model, **1**: 122
    on-grid application share, **1**: 192
    optical efficiency, **1**: 539
    optical properties, **1**: 401
    organic dyes, down-shifting, **1**: 578
    organic molecules, **1**: 541, **1**: 546
    organic semiconductor physics, **1**: 444
    organic solar cells, **1**: **439–480**
        acceptor materials, **1**: 452
        acceptor molecules, **1**: 440, **1**: 448, **1**: 452
        active materials, **1**: 450, **1**: 468
        architectures, **1**: 448, **1**: 463
        bilayer architecture, **1**: 448
        blend cells, **1**: 440, **1**: 441, **1**: 448, **1**: 448f, **1**: 449, **1**: 463
        bulk heterojunctions, **1**: 440, **1**: 441, **1**: 448, **1**: 463
        characteristic values, **1**: 449
        donor materials, **1**: 451
        donor molecules, **1**: 440, **1**: 448, **1**: 451, **1**: 457
        efficiency, **1**: 440, **1**: 440t, **1**: 450, **1**: 457
        electrode materials, **1**: 456
        external quantum efficiency, **1**: 450
        future outlooks, **1**: 473
        heterojunctions, **1**: 440, **1**: 441, **1**: 448, **1**: 448f, **1**: 449
        inorganic solar cells, **1**: 442
        interfacial materials, **1**: 453
        internal quantum efficiency, **1**: 450
        introduction, **1**: 8–9
        JV curves, **1**: 449
        large-scale production methods, **1**: 472
        materials, **1**: 450
        production methods, **1**: 470
        quantum efficiency, **1**: 450
        roll-to-roll printing, **1**: 440, **1**: 441, **1**: 470
        semiconductor physics, **1**: 442
        stability, **1**: 465
    organization, developing countries, **1**: 119
    ownership, developing countries, **1**: 119
    panel design, **1**: 679, **1**: 680
    parameter influence, crystalline silicon cells, **1**: 363
    pass criteria, reliability, **1**: 793
    passivated emitter and rear cell devices, **1**: 371, **1**: 373
    passivation, **1**: 364, **1**: 371
    patents, **1**: 62, **1**: 65, **1**: 580
    payback times, **1**: 436
    peak loads, future visions, **1**: 190
    performance
        definitions, **1**: 776
        determination standards, **1**: 789
        energy conversion efficiency, **1**: 775, **1**: 776
        energy predictions, **1**: 778
        introduction, **1**: 10
        measurements, **1**: 783
        micro-and nanotechnologies, **1**: 515, **1**: 518
        module energy predictions, **1**: 778
        module yields, **1**: 777, **1**: 781
        monitoring, **1**: **775–786**
        performance ratios, **1**: 775, **1**: 777
        practical considerations, **1**: 781, **1**: 783, **1**: 784
        predictions, **1**: 781
        ratios, **1**: 775, **1**: 777
        sensors, **1**: 783
        stand-alone systems, **1**: 775, **1**: 777
        system efficiency, **1**: 776, **1**: 781, **1**: 783
        system yields, **1**: 776, **1**: 781, **1**: 783
        yields, **1**: **775–786**, **1**: 775
    performance monitoring, **1**: **775–786**
    photochemical upconversion, **1**: 543
    photoelectrical efficiency, **1**: 540
    photon conversion, **1**: **549–561**
    photosynthesis, **1**: **657–677**, **1**: 10
    plant size, tariff differentiation, **1**: 98
    plasmonics, **1**: **641–656**
        applications, **1**: 652
        background, **1**: 642
        coverage effects, **1**: 647
        dielectric medium, **1**: 646
        future outlooks, **1**: 654
        introduction, **1**: 9
        material properties, **1**: 646
        metal nanoparticles, **1**: **641–656**
        quantum structure nanotechnology, **1**: 527
        surface coverage, **1**: 647
        surface plasmons, **1**: 642
    plastics, technology progress, **1**: 26
    plastic solar cells, **1**: **439–480**, **1**: 8–9
    polaritons, **1**: 643
    policies, **1**: 13, **1**: 188, **1**: 196
    pollutants, **1**: 150
    polycrystalline silicon, **1**: 21, **1**: 162, **1**: 173
    polysilicon, **1**: 162, **1**: 173, **1**: 380
    potential, **1**: 8
    poverty alleviation, **1**: 124
    power
        distribution systems, **1**: 197
        evaluation concepts, **1**: 265, **1**: 271, **1**: 285
        irradiance forecasting, **1**: **239–292**
        measurements, **1**: 271
        modeling solar irradiance, **1**: 243
        predicting solar irradiance, **1**: **239–292**
        predictons, **1**: **239–292**
        quality, storage options, **1**: 205
        satellite-based forecasts, **1**: 249, **1**: 275
        simulations, **1**: 262, **1**: 281
        solar irradiance forecasting, **1**: **239–292**
            satellite-based forecasts, **1**: 249, **1**: 275
            simulations, **1**: 262, **1**: 281

statistical methods, 1: 248, 1: 265
storage options, 1: 205
power satellites, 1: **767–774**
practical applications, 1: 540, 1: 554
practical considerations, 1: 781, 1: 783, 1: 784
preconditioning, 1: 790
prices, promotion schemes, 1: 74, 1: 75f, 1: 84
private operators, 1: 120
private ownership, 1: 120
process improvements, 1: 521
product attribute cost reductions, 1: 53
product-integrated photovoltaics, 1: **709–732**, 1: 10
production companies, 1: 169
production methods, 1: 470
prognosis, 1: 13
progress, 1: **13–30**
progress reports, promotion schemes, 1: 98
project investments, 1: 196
promotion schemes, 1: **73–109**
  best practice, 1: 93
  eligibility, 1: 94
  European Union, 1: 90, 1: 93, 1: 103
  feed-in tariffs, 1: **73–109**
  financing mechanisms, 1: 97
  future prospects, 1: 82, 1: 89, 1: 103
  Germany, 1: 90, 1: 93, 1: 103
  inflation indexation, 1: 101
  investment incentives, 1: 74, 1: 75–76, 1: 78, 1: 106
  market integration design, 1: 102
  net metering, 1: 74, 1: 75–76, 1: 77, 1: 86
  prices, 1: 74, 1: 75f, 1: 84
  progress reports, 1: 98
  purchase obligations, 1: 94
  quota-based support, 1: 76
  renewable portfolio standards, 1: 76, 1: 85
  research and development, 1: 74, 1: 75–76, 1: 81
  Singapore, 1: 79, 1: 103
  Spain, 1: 90, 1: 93, 1: 103
  support mechanisms, 1: **73–109**
  tariff calculation methodology, 1: 94
  tariff degression, 1: 99
  tariff payment duration, 1: 97
  tax incentives, 1: 74, 1: 75–76, 1: 78, 1: 87
  tender systems, 1: 74, 1: 75–76, 1: 77
  tradable green certificate schemes, 1: 76
  United States, 1: 83, 1: 103
p-type silicon cells
  emitter passivation, 1: 371
  emitter wrap-through cells, 1: 374
  high-efficiency cell structures, 1: 371
  metal-wrap-through cells, 1: 372, 1: 373
  passivated emitter and rear cell devices, 1: 371, 1: 373
  passivation, 1: 371
  rear cell passivation, 1: 371
public finance pools, 1: 128
public sector finance, 1: 124, 1: 128
pumped hydro energy storage, 1: 208
purchase obligations, 1: 94
Q-Cells AG, 1: 170
quality, cost reductions, 1: 53
quantum cutting, 1: 549, 1: 555
quantum dots
  down-shifting, 1: 566, 1: 566–567, 1: 575
  intermediate band solar cells, 1: 623, 1: 628
  quantum structure nanotechnology, 1: 525, 1: 526, 1: 527
quantum efficiency, 1: 316, 1: 339, 1: 450, 1: 540
quantum structure nanotechnology, 1: 525
quantum wells, 1: 527
quota-based promotion schemes, 1: 76
rare-earths, 1: 533, 1: 540, 1: 546
  down-shifting, 1: 566, 1: 573
rear cell passivation, 1: 371
recent results, 1: 509

recombination processes, 1: 334
recommendations, 1: 188, 1: 196
reference solar devices, 1: 791
reflection losses, 1: 520
regulation, 1: 127, 1: 196
regulatory frameworks, 1: 196
reliability, 1: 199, 1: 435
  testing, 1: 793
renewable energy premium tariff, 1: 130
renewable portfolio standards, 1: 76, 1: 85, 1: 127
research and development
  costs, 1: 49, 1: 54, 1: 68
  future visions, 1: 196, 1: 197
  historical overviews, 1: **31–45**
  promotion schemes, 1: 74, 1: 75–76, 1: 81
  technology progress, 1: **13–30**
resources, 1: 8
retro-materials, 1: 26
return expectations, 1: 137
revolutionary systems, 1: 15, 1: 25
risk analysis, 1: 153
roll-to-roll printing, 1: 440, 1: 441, 1: 470
rural area electrification, 1: **111–141**
  energy technology options, 1: 115
  finance, 1: 113, 1: 120, 1: 125, 1: 130
rural energy service companies, 1: 120, 1: 126, 1: 132
satellites, 1: 36, 1: 36f, 1: **767–774**
scattered solar radiation, 1: 322, 1: 327
scattering, surface plasmons, 1: 644
scientific discoveries, 1: 5
semiconductor physics, 1: 442
sensors, performance monitoring, 1: 783
Sharp Corporation, 1: 170
shifting, 1: 519, 1: 520
Shockley–Queisser model, 1: 338
signal transmission, 1: 196
silicon, 1: **353–387**, 1: **389–398**
  Abu Dhabi desert area, 1: 691
  disruptive technologies, 1: 21
  evolutionary technologies, 1: 19
  global industry overview, 1: 163, 1: 165, 1: 166, 1: 173
  state-of-the-art technology, 1: **353–387**
  technology progress, 1: 19, 1: 20, 1: 21, 1: 25
  thin-film technology, 1: **389–398**
simulation methods, 1: 571
Singapore
  promotion schemes, 1: 79, 1: 103
  solar capability scheme, 1: 79, 1: 80
  support mechanisms, 1: 79, 1: 103
singlet fission, 1: 549, 1: 559
small networks, 1: 243
small power producer regulation, 1: 127
smart grids, 1: 190
snow cover, 1: 283, 1: 286
soft loans, 1: 128
solar capability scheme, 1: 79, 1: 80
solar cell efficiencies, 1: 339
solar cell equation, 1: 337
solar cell production companies, 1: 169
solar concentration, 1: 538
solar cooling systems, 3: 461
solar desalination, 3: 530, 3: 536, 3: 553, 3: 556, 3: 558, 3: 560
  electrodialysis, 3: 537, 3: 538f, 3: 540f, 3: 541f, 3: 547
solar–diesel systems, 1: 687
solar energy conversion principles, 1: **293–313**
solar energy converters, 1: **657–677**
solar irradiance, 1: **239–292**
  atmospheric processes, 1: 246
  cloud motion vectors, 1: 245, 1: 249, 1: 251
  evaluation concepts, 1: 265, 1: 271, 1: 285
  models, 1: 243
  numerical weather prediction models, 1: 240–241, 1: 245, 1: 248, 1: 252, 1: 257, 1: 271

photovoltaics (PV) (*continued*)
    predictions, **1: 239–292**
        snow cover, **1**: 283, **1**: 286
        time series models, **1**: 245, **1**: 248
    solar power satellites, **1**: 36, **1**: 36f, **1: 767–774**
    solar radiation concentration, **1**: 325
    solar radiation resources assessments, **1**: 8, **1**: 218, **1**: 232
    space applications, **1: 767–774**
    space separated quantum cutting, **1**: 555
    Spanish promotion/support schemes, **1**: 90, **1**: 93, **1**: 103
    spectral response modeling, **1**: 571
    stability, **1**: 465
    stand-alone systems
        hybrid wind energy, **2**: 623–624, **2**: 638
        performance monitoring, **1**: 775, **1**: 777
        solar irradiance, **1**: 243
    standards, **1: 787–803**
        data analysis, **1**: 792
        energy performance, **1**: 795
        energy rating, **1**: 795
        European Commission's Joint Research Centre, **1**: 788
        historical overviews, **1**: 787
        IEC TC82, **1: 787–803**
        introduction, **1**: 10–11
        Joint Research Centre, **1**: 788
        measurements, **1**: 790, **1**: 791
        performance determination, **1**: 789
        reference solar devices, **1**: 791
        United States of America, **1**: 787
        working groups, **1**: 788, **1**: 789, **1**: 797
    standard test conditions, **1**: 775, **1**: 776, **1**: 777, **1**: 779–780, **1**: 790
    state-of-the-art silicon cells, **1: 353–387**
    storage, future visions, **1**: 191
    storage options, **1: 199–212**
        grid flexibility, **1**: 199
        grid reliability, **1**: 199
        management, **1**: 208
        power quality, **1**: 205
        reliability, **1**: 199
    stress tests, **1**: 793
    structure
        chalcopyrite thin films, **1**: 400, **1**: 410
        intermediate band solar cells, **1**: 619
    subsidies, **1**: 125
    sunbelt countries investments, **1**: 197
    sunbelt countries market development, **1**: 184
    Suntech Power Co: Ltd:, **1**: 169
    superconducting magnetic energy storage, **1**: 204, **1**: 204f, **1**: 205
    super smart grids, **1**: 190
    supply and demand drivers, **1**: 52
    support mechanisms, **1: 73–109**, **1**: 196, **1: 111–141**
        developing countries, **1: 111–141**
        effectiveness, **1**: 78
        efficiency, **1**: 78
        European Union, **1**: 90, **1**: 93, **1**: 103
        feed-in tariffs, **1: 73–109**
        Germany, **1**: 90, **1**: 93, **1**: 103
        off-grid technologies, **1: 111–141**
        promotion schemes, **1: 73–109**
        Singapore, **1**: 79, **1**: 103
        Spain, **1**: 90, **1**: 93, **1**: 103
        United States, **1**: 83, **1**: 103
    support regulatory frameworks, **1**: 196
    surface coverage, **1**: 647
    surface passivation, **1**: 364
    surface plasmons, **1**: 527, **1**: 642, **1**: 644
    system design, **1: 679–695**
    system efficiency, **1**: 776, **1**: 781, **1**: 783
    system global industry overview, **1**: 162
    system performance, **1**: 679–680, **1**: 692
    system prices, **1**: 193
    system yields, **1**: 776, **1**: 781, **1**: 783

Taiwan, **1**: 167, **1**: 170, **1**: 171, **1**: 172
tariffs
    calculation methodology, **1**: 94
    differencing plant size, **1**: 98
    incentives, **1**: 124
    payment duration, **1**: 97
    setting, **1**: 124
tax incentives, **1**: 74, **1**: 75–76, **1**: 78, **1**: 87
technology
    cadmium telluride thin films, **1**: 23
    copper indium diselenide thin films, **1**: 22
    costs, **1: 47–72**
    crystalline silicon, **1**: 20, **1**: 21, **1**: 25
    current status, **1**: 41, **1**: 43
    future-generation systems, **1**: 15, **1**: 25
    future visions, **1**: 192
    high-efficiency devices, **1**: 24
    introduction, **1: 5–11**
    investments, **1**: 196
    mix, **1**: 168, **1: 5–11**
    progress, **1: 13–30**
    revolutionary systems, **1**: 15, **1**: 25
    silicon, **1**: 19, **1**: 20, **1**: 21, **1**: 25
    standards, **1: 787–803**
tender systems, **1**: 74, **1**: 75–76, **1**: 77, **1**: 128
testing, reliability, **1**: 793
theoretical models, **1**: 619
thermal radiation, **1**: 316, **1**: 328
thermodynamics, **1: 315–352**
    beam solar radiation, **1**: 315, **1**: 319, **1**: 325, **1**: 326
    blackbodies, **1**: 318, **1**: 321, **1**: 322, **1**: 332
    conversion efficiency, **1**: 328
    diluted thermal radiation, **1**: 322
    direct solar radiation, **1**: 315, **1**: 319, **1**: 325, **1**: 326
    geometrical factors, **1**: 319
    impact ionization, **1**: 316, **1**: 339
    introduction, **1**: 7–8, **1**: 8
    ionization, **1**: 316, **1**: 339
    Lagrange invariant, **1**: 316, **1**: 325
    monogap solar cells, **1**: 334
    narrow band semiconductors, **1**: 340
    omnicolor solar convertors, **1**: 345
    quantum efficiency, **1**: 316, **1**: 339
    scattered solar radiation, **1**: 322, **1**: 327
    Shockley–Queisser model, **1**: 338
    solar cell equation, **1**: 337
    solar radiation concentration, **1**: 325
    thermal radiation, **1**: 316, **1**: 328
    voltage, **1**: 340, **1**: 342
thermophotonics, **1**: 26
thermophotovoltaics, **1: 603–618**, **1**: 603
thin-films, **1**: 8
    amorphous silicon, **1**: 8, **1**: 21, **1**: 389, **1**: 393
    cadmium telluride, **1: 423–438**
    chalcopyrite, **1: 399–422**
    current status, **1**: 42–43
    disruptive technologies, **1**: 21, **1**: 22
    evolutionary technologies, **1**: 20
    micro-and nanotechnologies, **1**: 515, **1**: 517, **1**: 522
    nanoparticles, **1**: 515, **1**: 517, **1**: 522
    nanostructures, **1**: 515, **1**: 517, **1**: 522
    silicon, **1: 389–398**
third-generation solar cell plasmonics, **1**: 653
tilted irradiance, **1**: 246, **1**: 247, **1**: 260, **1**: 281
time series models, **1**: 245, **1**: 248
traceability, **1**: 790
tradable green certificate schemes, **1**: 76
transmission systems, **1**: 197
Trina Solar Ltd:, **1**: 170
triple-junction cells, **1**: 24
triplet-triplet annihilation, **1**: 533, **1**: 541–542, **1**: 543
two-hand business finance model, **1**: 123
type approval testing, **1**: 793

United States, **1**: 89, **1**: 184
  feed-in tariffs, **1**: 88
  global industry overview, **1**: 169, **1**: 171
  green power programs, **1**: 86
  promotion schemes, **1**: 83, **1**: 103
  standards, **1**: 787
  support mechanisms, **1**: 83, **1**: 103
upconversion, **1**: **533–548**, **1**: 9, **1**: 533
  annihilation statistics, **1**: 543
  equivalent circuits, **1**: 535
  external quantum efficiency, **1**: 540
  future prospects, **1**: 546
  introduction, **1**: 9
  molecular photophysics, **1**: 542
  monochromatic optical efficiency, **1**: 539
  optical efficiency, **1**: 539
  organic molecules, **1**: 541, **1**: 546
  performance, micro-and nanotechnologies, **1**: 518
  photoelectrical efficiency, **1**: 540
  practical applications, **1**: 540
  quantum efficiency, **1**: 540
  rare-earths, **1**: 533, **1**: 540, **1**: 546
  solar concentration, **1**: 538
  triplet-triplet annihilation, **1**: 533, **1**: 541–542, **1**: 543
urban planning, **1**: **697–707**
value added tax reductions, **1**: 128
variability management, **1**: 189
very large-scale photovoltaics, **1**: **733–744**, **1**: 10
voltage, **1**: 340, **1**: 342
weathering tests, **1**: 793
wind energy, **1**: 203, **2**: 623–624, **2**: 638
working groups, **1**: 788, **1**: 789, **1**: 797
world growth, **1**: 16
world markets, **1**: 16
wrap-through cells, **1**: 374
yields, **1**: **775–786**, **1**: 775
Yingli Green Energy Holding Company Ltd:, **1**: 170
photovoltaic/thermal (PV/T) systems, **3**: **255–300**
  agricultural applications, **3**: 292, **3**: 294
  air circulation, **3**: 257, **3**: 263, **3**: 274, **3**: 276, **3**: 277, **3**: 285
    buildings applications, **3**: 285
      natural airflow, **3**: 274
  air collectors, **3**: 257, **3**: 263, **3**: 274, **3**: 276, **3**: 277, **3**: 285
  airflow rate analysis, **3**: 274
  air heat recovery, **3**: 271
  air-water collectors, **3**: 286
  applications, **3**: 280
  biofuels, **3**: 295
  biomass and biofuels, **3**: 295
  booster diffuse reflectors, **3**: 281
  building applications, **3**: 280, **3**: 282
  buildings, **3**: 280, **3**: 282
  built environment, **3**: 280
  categorization, **3**: 256
  cell electrical performance, **3**: 261
  commercial applications, **3**: 295
  design, **3**: 263, **3**: 267–268, **3**: 276, **3**: 277
  development, **3**: 258
  diffuse reflectors, **3**: 281, **3**: 285f
  early work, **3**: 258
  economics, **3**: 269
  efficiency, **3**: 259, **3**: 261, **3**: 278, **3**: 281
  electrical components, **3**: 271
  electrical conversion, **3**: 259
  electrical performance, **3**: 261
  energy balance equations, **3**: 270, **3**: 272
  energy conversion, **3**: 259
  environmental aspects, **3**: 269
  flat-type solar collectors, **3**: 256–257, **3**: 263
    air heat recovery, **3**: 271
    design principles, **3**: 263
    energy balance equations, **3**: 270, **3**: 272
    heat recovery, **3**: 270, **3**: 271

    liquid heat recovery, **3**: 270
    performance, **3**: 270
    thermal losses, **3**: 271
  Fresnel lenses, **3**: 289
  friction factor, **3**: 275
  geometrical parameters, **3**: 273
  heat recovery, **3**: 270, **3**: 271
  heat transfer coefficients, **3**: 275
  historical overviews, **3**: 258
  hybrid system design, **3**: 277
  illumination effects, **3**: 261
  industrial applications, **3**: 292
  liquid heat recovery, **3**: 270
  modeling, **3**: 379
  natural airflow, **3**: 274
  open-loop models, **3**: 381
  operational parameters, **3**: 273
  origins, **3**: 256
  performance, **3**: 269, **3**: 270
  pressure drop, **3**: 272
  simulations, **3**: 379
  solar collectors, **3**: **255–300**
  temperature, **3**: 261
  temperature effects, **3**: 261
  thermal conversion, **3**: 259
  thermal energy, **3**: 271
  thermal losses, **3**: 271
  thermosonic systems, **3**: 279
  water-air collectors, **3**: 286
  water-cooled modules, **3**: 270, **3**: 282
  water heaters, **3**: 279
  wind energy, **3**: 295
PHS *see* pumped hydro storage
physical basis: wind, **2**: 86
physical constants: solar radiation/resource, **3**: 80
physical dimensions: wind turbines, **2**: 186–187, **2**: 189
physical forecasting models, **2**: 615
physical methods: geothermal energy, **7**: 1
physical models: ocean wave energy, **8**: 84, **8**: 85, **8**: 88
physical postprocessing methods, **1**: 260
physical pretreatment processes, **5**: 240
physical properties:
  biochar, **5**: 373
  biomass cofiring, **5**: 70
  down-shifting, **1**: 566–567
physical storage: hydrogen technology, **4**: 137
physical structure:
  catalyst layers, **4**: 191
  crystalline silicon cells, **1**: 355
  proton-exchange membrane fuel cells, **4**: 191
physical vapor deposition, **3**: 324
physicochemical pretreatments, **5**: 242, **5**: 247t
physicochemical properties:
  alcohol fuels, automotives, **5**: 317
  automotive alcohol fuels, **5**: 317
physics:
  geothermal energy, **7**: **3–50**
  semiconductors, **1**: 294, **1**: 297, **1**: 442
physics-based models: solar radiation, **1**: 225
Pico plant, Azores, Portugal, **8**: 139, **8**: 140f
PID *see* proportional–integral–derivative
Pierson–Moskowitz spectrum, **8**: 91
pilot demonstrations, **2**: 719
pines: feedstocks, **5**: 264, **5**: 274, **5**: 277
Pioneer Generation Ltd: (PGL), **6**: **467–483**
pipelines, **7**: 209, **7**: 210f, **7**: 252
piping:
  compressed gas, **4**: 111–112
  direct heat utilization, **7**: 177, **7**: 178f
PIPV *see* product-integrated photovoltaics
piston engines, **2**: 575
pitch:
  control, **2**: 330, **2**: 331f, **2**: 345, **2**: 358, **2**: 671

pitch: (*continued*)
  stall, **2**: 679
  wind turbine electrical systems, **2**: 271, **2**: 273
pitfalls: wind power, **2**: 413
pit kilns, **5**: 367
pitting corrosion, **7**: 241
pivot arms, **6**: 87
placement considerations: building-integrated photovoltaics, **1**: 702
Planck, Max, **1**: 34, **1**: 35*f*
  Planck equation, **1**: 306, **1**: 307
  Planck's law, **3**: 33
  Planck spacecraft, **4**: 25
planes:
  product-integrated photovoltaics, **1**: 714, **1**: 715*f*
  proton-exchange membrane fuel cells, **4**: 218
planetary gearbox medium speed generators, **2**: 293
planet energy balance:
  consumption, **2**: **11–39**
  electrical generation, **2**: 14
  electrical power, **2**: 14
  fossil fuel status, **2**: 17, **2**: 21
  wind energy, **2**: **11–39**
planned maintenance operating costs: ocean energy, **8**: 159
planning:
  see also urban planning
  building-integrated photovoltaics, **1**: **697–707**
  compressed gas: hydrogen storage, **4**: 135
  electrical networks, wind energy, **2**: 596
  geothermal heat pumps, **7**: 199
  Indian hydropower, **6**: 227
  pumped-storage power plants, **6**: 286
  resettlements, **6**: 210
  urban planning, **1**: **697–707**
  wind energy, **2**: 407, **2**: 596
Planta Solar 10&20 (PS10&20), **3**: 617
plants:
  biomass cofiring, **5**: 64, **5**: 70
  biomass-to-liquids technology, **5**: 184, **5**: 188
  costs, onshore wind, **2**: 476
  desalination, **2**: 726
  hydropower
    economics, **6**: 40
    layouts, **6**: 21, **6**: 22
  life, hydropower economics, **6**: 40
  metabolites, **5**: **385–393**
  onshore wind costs, **2**: 476
  photovoltaic tariff differentiation, **1**: 98
  solar distillation, **3**: 98–99, **3**: 99*t*
  tariff differentiation, **1**: 98
  type, **1**: 99
  wind energy variable costs, **2**: 489
  wind power, **2**: 427
plasma-enhanced chemical vapor deposition (PECVD), **1**: 389, **1**: 390
plasma gasifiers, **5**: 139, **5**: 151, **5**: 169*t*, **5**: 171
plasmonics, **1**: **641–656**, **1**: 9
  coverage effects, **1**: 647
  dielectric medium, **1**: 646
  future outlooks, **1**: 654
  material properties, **1**: 646
  metal nanoparticles, **1**: **641–656**
  photovoltaics, **1**: **641–656**, **1**: 9
    applications, **1**: 652
    background, **1**: 642
  quantum structure nanotechnology, **1**: 527
  scattering, **1**: 644, **1**: 645
  shape effects, **1**: 645
  size effects, **1**: 644
  surface coverage, **1**: 647
  surface plasmons, **1**: 642
  thin-film silicon technology, **1**: 389
  third-generation solar cells, **1**: 653
plasmons: plasmonics for photovoltaics, **1**: 641

plastic-cover-inflated stills, **3**: 100, **3**: 100*f*
plasticity: cracking, **6**: 379
plastics:
  see also organic solar cells
  glazings, **3**: 334
  photovoltaic technology progress, **1**: 26
  solar cells, **1**: **439–480**, **1**: 8–9
  window frames, **3**: 334
platinum group metal catalysts, **4**: 162
plug flow reactors (PFR), **5**: 206
plunge pools, **6**: 485, **6**: 492
PMV *see* predicted mean vote
p-n junctions, **1**: 293, **1**: 301
point-focusing, **3**: 199
poisoning: biomass and biofuel power generation, **5**: 40
polaritons, **1**: 643
polarization, **4**: 245, **5**: 376, **5**: 377*f*, **5**: 378*f*
policy:
  biomass and biofuels
    biomass-to-liquids technology, **5**: 188
    markets, **5**: 75
    wind energy, **2**: 552
  carbon dioxide emission reduction, **2**: 545, **2**: 548
  development
    bioenergy, **5**: **411–429**
    electricity, hydrogen technology, **4**: 69
    hydrogen technology, **4**: 67, **4**: 69
  electricity, wind energy, **2**: 542, **2**: 546, **2**: 552, **2**: 555
  fossil fuels, **2**: 542, **2**: 548, **2**: 552
  future photovoltaic visions, **1**: 188, **1**: 196
  geothermal energy, **2**: 554
  harmonizing support schemes, **1**: 4
  hydraulics, **2**: 553
  hydrogen technology, **4**: 67
  intermittent wind energy sources, **2**: 554
  investment opportunities, **1**: 3
  nuclear options, **2**: 548
  photovoltaics
    costs, **1**: 54
    future visions, **1**: 13, **1**: 188, **1**: 196
  recommendations, photovoltaics, **1**: 188, **1**: 196
  storage, wind energy, **2**: 553
  support schemes, **1**: **1–4**
  wind energy, **2**: **541–568**
    biomass, **2**: 552
    carbon dioxide emission reduction, **2**: 545, **2**: 548
    electricity, **2**: 542, **2**: 546, **2**: 552, **2**: 555
    fossil fuels, **2**: 542, **2**: 548, **2**: 552
    geothermal energy, **2**: 554
    hydraulics, **2**: 553
    intermittent energy sources, **2**: 554
    nuclear options, **2**: 548
    storage, **2**: 553
political objectives: hydropower, Cameroon, Africa, **6**: 135
pollutants/pollution:
  biomass and biofuel power generation, **5**: 31
  costs, wind energy, **2**: 485
  geothermal fluids origins, **7**: 110–111
  hydropower, **6**: 52*t*, **6**: 59
  life cycles, **1**: 150
  photovoltaics, **1**: 150
  reservoirs, **6**: 59
  solar thermal systems, **3**: 3
  wind energy, **2**: 485, **2**: 504
    costs, **2**: 485
    environmental–social benefits/impacts, **2**: 504
poly[2-methoxy-5-(3′,7′-dimethyloctyloxy)-1,4-phenylene vinylene]:phenyl-C_{61}-butyric-acid-methyl ester (MDMO-PPV: PCBM), **1**: 451
polycrystalline materials, **1**: 13
polycrystalline silicon, **1**: 21, **1**: 162, **1**: 173
polycyclic aromatic hydrocarbons, **5**: 407
polyimide substrate structures, **1**: 412

polymer-dispersed liquid crystal switching devices, **3**: 351
polymer electrolyte membrane fuel cells (PEMFC), **4**: 241
polymer fibers, **6**: 394
polymer macromolecules, **1**: 440
polymer matrix enzyme electrodes, **4**: 262
polymer molecules, **1**: 440
polymers: geothermal environments, **7**: 249
polyolefins, **5**: 404
polysilicon:
    emitter n-type cells, **1**: 380
    global industry overview, **1**: 162, **1**: 173
    manufacturers, **1**: 173
    n-type silicon cells, **1**: 380
    photovoltaics, **1**: 162, **1**: 173, **1**: 380
    production processes, **1**: 173
    supply, **1**: 173
polytetrafluoroethylene (PTFE), **4**: 165, **4**: 184
ponds *see* solar ponds
pools: geothermal direct heat utilization, **7**: 169, **7**: 170, **7**: 173*t*
poplars, **5**: 264, **5**: 266–268, **5**: 267*t*, **5**: 268, **5**: 276*f*, **5**: 276–277
population issues:
    desalination, **2**: 727–728, **2**: 728*t*
    energy consumption/planet energy balance, **2**: 12
    hydropower operating strategies, **6**: 87
    passive solar architecture, **3**: 637
pore size, **5**: 374, **5**: 374*f*, **5**: 379–380
pore volumes, **5**: 232
porosity:
    biochar, **5**: 374, **5**: 374*f*
    rock resistivity, **7**: 78, **7**: 79
porous layer models, **7**: 14, **7**: 15
porous materials: hydrogen storage, **4**: 139
porous rock, **7**: 79
porphyrin pigment, **1**: 657
portable applications: proton-exchange membrane fuel cells, **4**: 202
portable electronic systems: fuel cells, **4**: 36
Portuguese wind power, **2**: 665
position effects: metal nanoparticles, **1**: 648
post mills, **2**: 46
postprocessing:
    buoy data, **8**: 28
    numerical weather prediction models, **1**: 257
    ocean wave measurements, **8**: 28
    solar irradiance-photovoltaic power forecasts, **1**: 257, **1**: 283
post-treatments: desalination, **3**: 529
postwar Japanese hydropower history, **6**: 269
postwar wind energy programs, **2**: 58
POT *see* peaks-over-threshold
potential fuels: biomass and biofuel power generation, **5**: 37
potential head, **6**: 31, **6**: 33*f*
potentials:
    hydropower, Cameroon, Africa, **6**: 130
    photovoltaics, **1**: 8, **1**: 187
poverty:
    developing country photovoltaics, **1**: 124
    Millennium Development Goals, **7**: 288
    very large-scale photovoltaics, **1**: 733, **1**: 734*t*
power:
    see also hydropower; powerhouses
    availability, wind energy, **2**: 100
    battery hybrid energy storage, **4**: 318
    beaming, **1**: 768, **1**: 769, **1**: 770, **1**: 773
    biomass combined heat and power, **5**: **87–97**
    capacity, geothermal energy, **7**: 263–264, **7**: 264*t*
    coefficients
        definitions, **2**: 114, **2**: 671
        marine currents, **8**: 2–3
        wind energy, **2**: 102, **2**: 115, **2**: 116*f*, **2**: 135, **2**: 136
    combined heat and power, biomass, **5**: **87–97**
    concentrating solar power conversion, **3**: 600
    conditioning, wind turbines, **2**: 330, **2**: 331*f*
    consumption, product-integrated photovoltaics, **1**: 724
    control, wind turbines, **2**: 272

conversion
    combined cycle solar power, **3**: 605
    concentrating solar power, **3**: 600
    electrical energy storage, **6**: 410
    gas turbines, **3**: 604, **3**: 608–609
    hybridized concentrating solar power, **3**: 605
    micro-and nanophotovoltaic technologies, **1**: 515–516, **1**: 517
    operational hours, **3**: 605
    organic Rankine cycles, **3**: 603
    product-integrated photovoltaics, **1**: 724
    solar dishes, **3**: 605
    solar power systems, **3**: 600
    steam cycles, **3**: 600
    storage, **3**: 609
    wind turbine electrical systems, **2**: 297, **2**: 298
curves
    cubic models, **2**: 130
    energy yields, **2**: 127, **2**: 138
    estimation, **2**: 131
    linear models, **2**: 130
    modeling, **2**: 129
    quadratic models, **2**: 131
    wind turbine energy yields, **2**: 127, **2**: 138
cycle efficiency, **3**: 462, **3**: 462*f*
density, **4**: 184
distribution, future photovoltaics, **1**: 197
dynamic security, wind park design penetration, **2**: 208
electrical control systems, wind turbines, **2**: 272
electronics, **2**: **269–269**, **2**: **329–370**, **4**: **295–329**
    250 kW grid-connected fuel cells, **4**: 300
    bulk converter power loss analysis, **4**: 301
    component specifications, **4**: 325
    condition monitoring schemes, **2**: 364
    converters, **2**: 332, **2**: 332*f*, **2**: 340
    dynamic voltage balancing, **4**: 303
    equivalent circuits, **4**: 327
    experimental studies, **4**: 303
    fault accommodation, **2**: 364
    fuel cells, **4**: **295–329**
    gate-drive circuitry, **4**: 304
    grid-connected fuel cells, **4**: 300
    hardware, **2**: 366
    H-bridge operation, **4**: 305
    hydrogen technology, **4**: **295–329**
    inverter power loss analysis, **4**: 300
    kilowatt grid-connected fuel cells, **4**: 300
    laboratory test environments, **4**: 303
    machine maintenance, **2**: 364
    modeling fuel cells, **4**: 320, **4**: 325
    monitoring wind turbines, **2**: 364
    multiswitch voltage inverters, **4**: 299, **4**: 303
    operating point power, **4**: 302
    power loss analysis, fuel cells, **4**: 300, **4**: 301, **4**: 302
    static voltage balancing, **4**: 303, **4**: 304
    transportation fuel cells, **4**: 320
    two-switch voltage inverters, **4**: 303
    voltage balancing, **4**: 303, **4**: 304, **4**: 305
    voltage inverters, **4**: **295–329**
    voltage regulation systems, **4**: 299
    wind turbines, **2**: **269–269**, **2**: **329–370**
        condition monitoring schemes, **2**: 364
        converters, **2**: 332, **2**: 332*f*, **2**: 340
        fault accommodation, **2**: 364
        hardware, **2**: 366
        machine maintenance, **2**: 364
        maintenance, **2**: 364
        monitoring, **2**: 364
energy, hydropower, **6**: 20
energy yields, wind turbines, **2**: 115, **2**: 116*f*, **2**: 135, **2**: 136
equipment, ocean wave energy, **8**: 8
estimations, ocean waves, **8**: 20
future photovoltaics, **1**: 197

power: (*continued*)
  generation
    biomass and biofuels, **5**: **27–53**
    boilers, **5**: 32, **5**: 34
    bulk density, **5**: 43
    case studies, **5**: **27–53**
    combined heat and power, **5**: 33, **5**: 39
    combustion, **5**: 47
    economics, **5**: 29
    emission limits, **5**: 31, **5**: 33
    environmental impacts, **5**: 51
    finance, **5**: 29
    firing, **5**: 33
    fixed grates, **5**: 33
    fluidized bed boilers, **5**: 34
    fuel cells, **4**: 33
    fuel preparation, **5**: 44
    fuel processing, **5**: 43
    gaseous emissions, **5**: 31, **5**: 33, **5**: 51
    gasification, **5**: 37
    geothermal power plants, **7**: 208, **7**: 209*f*
    grates, **5**: 33
    handling, **5**: 43
    health and safety, **5**: 40
    Horseshoe Bend hydroelectric scheme, **6**: 467
    investment, **5**: 29
    legislation, **5**: 31
    life-cycle analysis, **5**: 29
    liquid biofuels, **5**: 39
    markets, **4**: 200
    material handling, **5**: 43
    moving grates, **5**: 33
    potential fuels, **5**: 37
    prices, **2**: 477, **2**: 481, **5**: 29
    regulation, **5**: 31
    Renewable Obligation, **5**: 32
    solid biofuels, **5**: 37
    storage, **5**: 43
    suspension firing, **5**: 33
    sustainability, **5**: 28
    technology choice availability, **5**: 32
    technology development, **5**: 32
    Three Gorges Project, China, **6**: 183, **6**: 188, **6**: 191, **6**: 206, **6**: 221, **6**: 223
  geographical distribution variability, **2**: 591
  geothermal energy
    corrosion, **7**: **239–257**
    cost and investment factors, **7**: 263–264, **7**: 264*t*
    material selection, **7**: **239–257**
    power plants, **7**: 1, **7**: **207–237**
    scaling, **7**: **239–257**
  houses, Eastmain–Sarcelle–Rupert Diversion Project, Quebec, Canada, **6**: 169, **6**: 170
  integration, wind energy, **2**: 591
  inverter safe operating areas, **4**: 297
  laser beaming, **1**: 770
  loads, solid oxide fuel cells, **4**: 251
  loss analysis, **4**: 300, **4**: 301, **4**: 302
  marine currents, **8**: 2–3
  matrices, **8**: 80
  measurements, ocean wave energy, **8**: 92, **8**: 93, **8**: 94*t*
  micro-photovoltaic technologies, **1**: 515–516, **1**: 517
  microwave beaming, **1**: 768, **1**: 769
  nano-photovoltaic technologies, **1**: 515–516, **1**: 517
  ocean wave energy
    equipment, **8**: 8
    estimations, **8**: 20
    measurements, **8**: 92, **8**: 93, **8**: 94*t*
    revenue, **8**: 166
    takeoff, **8**: **79–110**
  outputs
    alkaline fuel cells, **4**: 161
    ocean energy revenue, **8**: 166

    scale factor variation, **2**: 144
    shape factor variation, **2**: 144
    wind energy potential, **2**: 90
    wind shear, **2**: 140
    wind turbine energy yields, **2**: 140, **2**: 151
  penetration, wind park design, **2**: 183, **2**: 199, **2**: 206, **2**: 208, **2**: 212, **2**: 214, **2**: 216
  performance testing, **2**: 377
  photovoltaics
    concentration photovoltaics, **1**: 750, **1**: 753
    distribution systems, **1**: 197
    future visions, distribution, **1**: 197
    irradiance forecasting, **1**: **239–292**
    product-integrated photovoltaics, **1**: 724
    quality, **1**: 205
    solar irradiance predictions, **1**: **239–292**
    storage options, **1**: 205
  plants
    Cameroon, Africa, **6**: 131, **6**: 135
    commissioning, concentration photovoltaics, **1**: 753
    communication, IEC standards, **2**: 375
    concentrating solar power, **3**: 615
    concentration photovoltaics, **1**: 750, **1**: 753
    construction, **1**: 753
    costs, **7**: 259
    design, **4**: 229
    efficiency ratios, **7**: 207, **7**: 208, **7**: 235
    engineering, **1**: 753
    enhanced geothermal systems, **7**: 207, **7**: 233
    geothermal energy, **7**: 1, **7**: **207–237**
    Goldisthal pumped storage plant, **6**: 406
    IEC standards, **2**: 375
    intake types, **6**: 221
    investment factors, **7**: 259
    molten carbonate fuel cells, **4**: 229, **4**: 231, **4**: 232
    Okinawa, Japan seawater pumped storage, **6**: 418
    performance assessments, **7**: 235
    pumped storage, **6**: 412, **6**: 418
    Spain, **6**: 313
    specific geofluid consumption, **7**: 207, **7**: 235
    testing, wind energy, **2**: 376
    thermal efficiency, **7**: 207, **7**: 235
    thermal energy storage, **3**: 239, **3**: 242
    Three Gorges Project, China, **6**: 191, **6**: 221, **6**: 223
    utilization efficiency ratios, **7**: 208, **7**: 235
    wind energy, testing, **2**: 376
  power-beaming, **1**: 768, **1**: 769, **1**: 770, **1**: 773
  product-integrated photovoltaics, **1**: 724
  production
    concentrating systems, **3**: 95
    energy yields, **2**: 115, **2**: 132
    estimation, wind power, **2**: 403
    geothermal energy, **7**: **239–257**
    loads, wind turbines, **2**: 246, **2**: 254
    scale effects/scaling, **7**: **239–257**
    solar energy history, **3**: 95
    thrust loads, wind turbines, **2**: 254
    wind turbines
      energy yields, **2**: 115, **2**: 132
      loads, **2**: 246, **2**: 254
      thrust loads, **2**: 254
quality
  photovoltaic storage options, **1**: 205
  wind energy testing, **2**: 380
  wind turbines, **2**: 206, **2**: 279
rating, **1**: 798
recovery, **1**: 505, **1**: 505*f*
revenue, **8**: 166
sectors, Cameroon, Africa, **6**: **129–151**
solar cooling cycle efficiency, **3**: 462, **3**: 462*f*
solar energy history, **3**: 92, **3**: 93*f*, **3**: 96, **3**: 96*f*
solar irradiance predictions, **1**: **239–292**
solar power satellites, **1**: **767–774**

solid oxide fuel cell loads, 4: 251
spectrum, wind speeds, 2: 80
subsystems, wind turbines, 2: 270, 2: 272f
supplies, fuel cell current status, 4: 34
systems
   dynamic security, wind park design penetration, 2: 208
   wind energy integration, 2: 591
   wind park design penetration, 2: 208
takeoff, 8: 80
   ocean wave energy, 8: 79–110
Three Gorges Project, China, 6: 183, 6: 188, 6: 191, 6: 206, 6: 221, 6: 223
transmission
   laser beaming, 1: 770
   microwave beaming, 1: 768, 1: 769
   solar power satellites, 1: 768, 1: 769, 1: 770
   wind turbine time evolution, 2: 98
urban electric vehicles, 4: 318
variability, 2: 590, 2: 591
wave energy converters, 8: 20
wind energy
   availability, wind turbines, 2: 100
   integration, 2: 591
   performance testing, 2: 377
   potential, 2: 90
   wind park design penetration, 2: 183, 2: 199, 2: 206, 2: 208, 2: 212, 2: 214, 2: 216
   world market, 2: 25
wind farms, variability, 2: 590
wind speed spectrum, 2: 80
wind turbines
   aggregation variability, 2: 590
   conditioning, 2: 330, 2: 331f
   control systems, 2: 272, 2: 330, 2: 331f
   conversion, 2: 297, 2: 298
   electrical control systems, 2: 272
   electronics, 2: **269–269**, 2: **329–370**
   energy yields, 2: 115, 2: 116f, 2: 135, 2: 136
   loads, 2: 246, 2: 254
   power conversion, 2: 297, 2: 298
   subsystems, 2: 270, 2: 272f
   thrust loads, 2: 254
   wind energy availability, 2: 100
   world market, wind energy, 2: 25
powerhouses:
   Horseshoe Bend hydroelectric scheme, 6: 469
   hydropower essential features, 6: 17
   layouts, 6: 188
   Mekin hydropower project, Cameroon, Africa, 6: 143
   Three Gorges Project, China, 6: 188
Pozo Izquierdo, Gran Canaria Island, 3: 558
PPD *see* percentage of people dissatisfied
PR *see* public relations
practical considerations:
   downconversion, 1: 554
   photovoltaic performance monitoring, 1: 781, 1: 783, 1: 784
   upconversion, 1: 540
prayer wheels, 2: 44
precipitable water, 1: 230
preconditioning: photovoltaic performance, 1: 790
predictability: ocean wave energy, 8: 50
predicted mean vote (PMV), 3: 655–656
prediction projects: wind turbine technology evolution, 2: 717
predictive control: passive solar architecture, 3: 658, 3: 660f, 3: 663
preferential policy: Three Gorges Project, China, 6: 211
preheater analysis, 7: 225
preliminary works: ocean energy, 8: 156
preparation:
   biomass cofiring, 5: 70
   biomass-to-liquids technology, 5: 162, 5: 162f
   catalyst layers, 4: 191
   proton-exchange membrane fuel cells, 4: 191
   tandem stacks, 3: 305
present value:
   ocean energy economics, 8: 153, 8: 154
   wind power design and implementation, 2: 424
preservation: geochemical sampling, 7: 96
pressure:
   air heat recovery, 3: 272
   air turbine oscillation, 8: 113
   balance of plant, 4: 198
   biochar, 5: 370
   cell voltages, 4: 197
   coefficients, 6: 494, 6: 494f
   cycles, binary power plants, 7: 227
   diffusion, 7: 10
   drop, 3: 272
   flash pyrolysis, 5: 370
   fluctuation levels, 6: 413
   geothermal energy physics, 7: 8, 7: 10, 7: 19, 7: 46f
   geothermal wells physics, 7: 19
   head difference, 8: 93
   high concentration solar collectors, 3: 173
   hydrogen safety engineering, 4: 95
   hydropower, 6: 357, 6: 365
   loading, 4: 113
   ocean wave energy, 8: 93
   oscillation, 8: 113
   plate anemometers, 2: 75
   pressure–temperature diagrams, 3: 466, 3: 467f
   proton-exchange membrane fuel cells, 4: 197, 4: 198
   pump-turbine fluctuation levels, 6: 413
   sediment management, 6: 357, 6: 365
   sensors, 6: 494, 6: 494f
   steel vessel loading, 4: 113
   pressure–temperature diagrams, 3: 466, 3: 467f
   tests, 3: 173
   thermal radiation thermodynamics, 1: 328–329
   tube anemometers, 2: 75
   unscheduled releases, 4: 95
   vessels, 4: **111–135**
pressurized air storage, 3: 610
pressurized stacks, 4: 197
pressurized storage water tanks, 3: 217, 3: 217f, 3: 218f
pretreatments:
   bioethanol, 5: 234
   biomass and biofuels, 5: 156, 5: 162f, 5: 163, 5: 166, 5: 167
   biomass-to-liquids technology, 5: 156, 5: 162, 5: 162f, 5: 163, 5: 167
   desalination, 3: 529
   economics, 5: 167
   feedstocks, 5: 162, 5: 162f, 5: 368
   lignocellulosic feedstocks, definitions, 5: 218
   lignocellulosic wastes, 5: 234
prevention:
   alkali–aggregate reaction, 6: 390
   carbonation, 6: 387
   freezing, 6: 387
   geological hazards, 6: 216
   impurity diffusion, 1: 502
   intrusion, 6: 422
   pollution, 5: 31
   seepage scouring, 6: 390
   thawing, 6: 387
prices:
   bioenergy markets, 5: 78–79, 5: 79–80
   bioenergy policy development, 5: 411, 5: 423
   biomass and biofuel power generation, 5: 29
   calculation methods, wind energy, 2: 472
   crude oil, 5: 79–80, 5: 80f
   energy generation, Iran, 6: 253
   future outlook, wind energy, 2: 471
   generation costs, wind energy, 2: 477, 2: 481
   geothermal energy sustainability, 7: 280–281
   incentive support mechanisms, 1: 1
   onshore wind, 2: 478

prices: (*continued*)
    photovoltaic promotion schemes, **1**: 74, **1**: 75*f*, **1**: 84
    power generation, **2**: 477, **2**: 481, **5**: 29
    wind energy
        comparisons in 2020, **2**: 499
        future outlook, **2**: 471
        generation costs, **2**: 477, **2**: 481
        onshore wind, **2**: 478
primary education: Millennium Development Goals, **7**: 288
primary energy:
    consumption, **2**: 12, **6**: 33, **6**: 34*f*, **6**: 34*t*
    definitions, **5**: 109
    hydropower
        historical overviews, **6**: 33, **6**: 34*f*, **6**: 34*t*
        Japanese current status, **6**: 274
        Japanese energy issues, **6**: 280
primary forest residues, **5**: 263, **5**: 283
    collection, **5**: 284
    economics, **5**: 284
    environmental sustainability, **5**: 284
    sustainability, **5**: 284
primary mill residues, **5**: 263, **5**: 286
primary steam separators, **7**: 218
prime movers: solar cooling, **3**: 462
priority issues: Brazilian Sugarcane Industry Association, **5**: 25
prismatic tempered glass, **3**: 111, **3**: 112*f*
private operators: photovoltaics, **1**: 120
private ownership: photovoltaics, **1**: 120
privatization of hydropower, **6**: 129–130, **6**: 138, **6**: 148
probability plots: ocean waves, **8**: 62
process development: biomass-to-liquids technology, **5**: 187
processed wood fuels, **5**: 59
processes:
    biomass-to-liquids technology, **5**: 159, **5**: 187
    desalination, **2**: 726, **2**: 728
    dielectric surface passivation, **1**: 365
    geothermal energy, **7**: 8
    heat pumps, **7**: 192
process improvements: photovoltaics, **1**: 521
processing energy sources: greenhouse gases, **5**: 123
process models: ocean wave energy, **8**: 80, **8**: 81*t*
process safety: biomass and biofuel power generation, **5**: 41
process timescales: biomass-to-liquids technology, **5**: 187
product attribute changes: photovoltaic costs, **1**: 53
product-integrated photovoltaics (PIPV), **1**: 709–732, **1**: 10
    arts, **1**: 714
    batteries, **1**: 722
    business-to-business applications, **1**: 712
    consumer products, **1**: 711
    costs, **1**: 725
    design, **1**: 716, **1**: 723, **1**: 728
    economics, **1**: 725
    electronic conversions, **1**: 724
    energy balance, **1**: 723
    environmental aspects, **1**: 725
    existing technologies, **1**: 711
    future outlooks, **1**: 730
    historical overviews, **1**: 711
    human factors, **1**: 727
    irradiance, **1**: 720, **1**: 724
    lighting products, **1**: 712, **1**: 713*f*, **1**: 721, **1**: 725–726
    manufacturing, design, **1**: 728
    power consumption, **1**: 724
    power conversion, **1**: 724
    rechargeable batteries, **1**: 722
    recreational products, **1**: 713, **1**: 714*f*
    solar cell performance, **1**: 717, **1**: 720
    storage device efficiency, **1**: 724
    system design, **1**: 723
    technical aspects, **1**: 717
    transportation, **1**: 714
    user perception/experiences, **1**: 727
    vehicles, **1**: 714

production:
    automotive biofuels, **5**: 314
    biodiesel, **5**: 3
    bioethanol, **5**: 4
    biomass and biofuels, **5**: 3
        chemical production, **5**: 395–410
        ethics, **5**: 99–108
        intensification, **5**: 205–215
        introduction, **5**: 3
    Cameroon, Africa, hydropower, **6**: 129–151
    companies
        photovoltaics, **1**: 169
        Spanish hydropower, **6**: 315
    concentration photovoltaics, **1**: 760, **1**: 762
    costs, geothermal energy, **7**: 259–270
    crystalline silicon cells, photovoltaics, **1**: 358
    economics, hydrogen technology, **4**: 48
    electricity, Cameroon, Africa, **6**: 132
    estimation, wind turbines, **2**: 115, **2**: 132
    ethics, biofuels, **5**: 99–108
    geochemistry, **7**: 141
    geothermal energy
        costs, **7**: 259–270
        geochemistry, **7**: 141
        potentials, **7**: 22
        sustainability, **7**: 272, **7**: 280
    history of oilseed rape, **5**: 293
    hydrogen
        economics, **4**: 48
        transport applications, **4**: 283
    hydropower, Cameroon, Africa, **6**: 129–151
    incentive support mechanisms, **1**: 1
    industrial crystalline silicon cells, **1**: 358
    inputs, woody biomass feedstocks, **5**: 277
    intensification
        biodiesel, **5**: 205
        bioethanol, **5**: 210
        biofuels, **5**: 205–215
        ethanol, **5**: 210
    methods
        automotive biofuels, **5**: 314
        organic solar cells, **1**: 470
    oilseed rape, **5**: 293–303
        historical overviews, **5**: 293
    operation and maintenance, concentration photovoltaics, **1**: 762
    organic solar cells, **1**: 470
    performance, concentration photovoltaics, **1**: 760
    photovoltaics, **1**: 5, **1**: 6*f*
        concentration photovoltaics, **1**: 760, **1**: 762
        crystalline silicon cells, **1**: 358
        life cycles, **1**: 144, **1**: 145, **1**: 145*f*
        organic solar cells, **1**: 470
        polysilicon, **1**: 173
        silicon, **1**: 173
    polysilicon, **1**: 173
    potentials, geothermal energy, **7**: 22
    processes
        crystalline silicon cells, **1**: 358
        polysilicon, **1**: 173
        silicon, **1**: 173
    results, concentration photovoltaics, **1**: 760
    silicon, **1**: 173
    sugar, **5**: 19
    sustainable geothermal energy, **7**: 272, **7**: 280
    wells, geothermal power, **7**: 251
    wind energy, **2**: 89, **2**: 127
    wind turbine power curves, **2**: 127
productivity: geothermal energy costs/investment factors, **7**: 259
prognosis: photovoltaics, **1**: 13
progress considerations:
    hydroelectricity, **6**: 4

photovoltaics, **1:** **13–30**
   promotion schemes, **1:** 98
   very large-scale systems, **1:** 739
project certification: wind energy standards, **2:** 383, **2:** 386
project construction: Three Gorges Project, China, **6:** 200
project description: wind power documentation, **2:** 425
project design: wind power, **2: 391–391**
project development:
   biomass-to-liquids technology, **5:** 188
   Horseshoe Bend hydroelectric scheme, **6:** 470
   ocean wave energy, **8:** 3, **8:** 3f
   wind power, **2:** 396, **2:** 422
project implementation:
   desalination, **2:** 735
   Indian hydropower, **6:** 240
   wind energy, desalination, **2:** 735
   wind power, **2: 391–391**
project investments: photovoltaics, **1:** 196
project management:
   Horseshoe Bend hydroelectric scheme, **6:** 472
   wind power, **2:** 393
project planning: Indian hydropower, **6:** 240
promotion schemes, **1: 73–109**
   best practice, **1:** 93
   challenges, **1:** 82, **1:** 89, **1:** 103
   common features, **1:** 93
   eligibility, **1:** 94
   European Union, **1:** 90, **1:** 93, **1:** 103
   feed-in tariffs, **1: 73–109**
   financing mechanisms, **1:** 97
   future prospects, **1:** 82, **1:** 89, **1:** 103
   Germany, **1:** 90, **1:** 93, **1:** 103
   inflation indexation, **1:** 101
   investment incentives, **1:** 74, **1:** 75–76, **1:** 78, **1:** 106
   market integration design, **1:** 102
   net metering, **1:** 74, **1:** 75–76, **1:** 77, **1:** 86
   photovoltaics, **1: 73–109**
   prices, **1:** 74, **1:** 75f, **1:** 84
   progress reports, **1:** 98
   purchase obligations, **1:** 94
   quota-based support, **1:** 76
   renewable portfolio standards, **1:** 76, **1:** 85
   research and development, **1:** 74, **1:** 75–76, **1:** 81
   Singapore, **1:** 79, **1:** 103
   Spain, **1:** 90, **1:** 93, **1:** 103
   support mechanisms, **1: 73–109**
   tariff calculation methodology, **1:** 94
   tariff degression, **1:** 99
   tariff payment duration, **1:** 97
   tax incentives, **1:** 74, **1:** 75–76, **1:** 78, **1:** 87
   tender systems, **1:** 74, **1:** 75–76, **1:** 77
   tradable green certificate schemes, **1:** 76
   United States, **1:** 83, **1:** 103
proof of concept: quantum dot intermediate band solar cells, **1:** 631
propane-fueled indoor stoves, **1:** 614
propeller turbines, **6:** 439, **6:** 441–442, **6:** 461, **6:** 461t, **6:** 463t, **6:** 465
properties:
   see also optical properties; thermal properties
   automotive alcohol fuels, **5:** 317
   biochar, **5:** 372, **5:** 374
   biomass cofiring, **5:** 70
   biomass combined heat and power, **5:** 90
   chalcopyrite thin films, **1:** 403, **1:** 405, **1:** 414
   collectors, solar water heating, **3:** 430
   combined heat and power, **5:** 90
   crystalline silicon cells, **1:** 368
   down-shifting, **1:** 566–567
   electrochromogenic devices, **3:** 346, **3:** 347t
   geothermal energy, **7:** 8
   geothermal systems, **7:** 8
   high-temperature geothermal fields, **7:** 240, **7:** 240t
   ocean wave directionality, **8:** 15, **8:** 18, **8:** 25
   organic solar cell efficiency, **1:** 461

plasmonic photovoltaics, **1:** 646
solar water heating systems, collectors, **3:** 430
toughened glass, **3:** 329
proportional–integral–derivative (PID), **3:** 655, **3:** 656
propulsion: space application current status, **4:** 13
propylene glycol, **5:** 399
prospects: wind energy/turbine technology, **2: 671–724**
protected areas: wind power, **2:** 395–396
protection measures: Three Gorges Project, China, **6:** 213
protective coatings, **6:** 249–250, **6:** 250f
protective layers: electrochromogenic materials, **3:** 345
proteins:
   artificial leaf design, **1:** 666
   protein maquettes, **1:** 667
PROTEST project, **2:** 719
proton conducting membranes, **4:** 185, **4:** 189
proton-exchange fuel cell (PEFC) comparisons, **4:** 243, **4:** 243t
proton-exchange membrane fuel cells (PEMFC), **4: 183–225**
   see also solid-polymer fuel
   500W to 5kW power generation markets, **4:** 200
   acid-base complex membranes, **4:** 189
   aerospace industry, **4:** 218
   air-breathing stacks, **4:** 194, **4:** 197, **4:** 199
   air cooling systems, **4:** 199
   airflow, **4:** 194
   air humidity, **4:** 194
   alkaline fuel cells, **4:** 159, **4:** 160, **4:** 161t, **4:** 175
   alternative fuels, **4:** 217
   alternative sulfonated membrane materials, **4:** 188
   anode materials, **4:** 190
   applications, **4: 183–225**
   auxiliary power units, **4:** 200
   backup power systems, **4:** 200
   balance of plant, **4:** 198
   bikes, **4:** 203
   boats, **4:** 218
   buses, **4:** 217
   catalysts, **4:** 190
      physical structure, **4:** 191
      preparation, **4:** 191
      structure, **4:** 191
   cathode materials, **4:** 190
   cell voltages, **4:** 197
   cogeneration, **4:** 208
   conducting membranes, **4:** 185
   cooling, **4:** 199
   direct liquid fuel cells, **4:** 205, **4:** 208
   direct methanol fuel cells, **4:** 185, **4:** 188, **4:** 190, **4:** 196–197, **4:** 200, **4:** 202, **4:** 205
   educational systems, **4:** 202
   electrodes, **4:** 190
   energy storage, **4:** 221
   evaporation, **4:** 194
   external humidification, **4:** 195
   extra humidification systems, **4:** 194
   features, **4:** 185
   fluorinated polymers, **4:** 188
   gas diffusion layers, **4:** 192
   grid-dependent generators, **4:** 202
   high energy dense battery hybrid energy storage, **4:** 317
   high-temperature proton conductors, **4:** 189
   humidification, **4:** 187, **4:** 194
   hybrid vehicles, **4:** 215
   hydrogen
      pressure, **4:** 314
      storage, **4:** 221
      transport applications, **4:** 282, **4:** 282–283
   inlet hydrogen pressure, **4:** 314
   ionic liquid membranes, **4:** 189
   light traction, **4:** 203
   liquid membranes, **4:** 189
   low-power portable applications, **4:** 202
   manufacturers, vehicles, **4:** 189, **4:** 219t

proton-exchange membrane fuel cells (PEMFC) (*continued*)
   marine industry, **4**: 218
   market segments, **4**: 200
   materials
      anodes, **4**: 190
      cathodes, **4**: 190
      membranes, **4**: 185
   membrane features, **4**: 185
   membrane materials, **4**: 185
   mixed-reactant fuel cells, **4**: 205, **4**: 208
   modified membranes, **4**: 188
   motor vehicles, **4**: 203, **4**: 214
   open-circuit voltage, **4**: 184, **4**: 197
   operating temperatures, **4**: 199
   perfluoro sulfonic acid membranes, **4**: 186, **4**: 186*f*, **4**: 188
   physical structure, catalyst layers, **4**: 191
   planes, **4**: 218
   portable applications, **4**: 202
   power generation markets, **4**: 200
   preparation, catalyst layers, **4**: 191
   pressure, **4**: 197, **4**: 198
   pressurized stacks, **4**: 197
   proton conducting membranes, **4**: 185, **4**: 189
   purging, **4**: 314
   rail industry, **4**: 218
   reactant cooling systems, **4**: 199
   reformer methanol fuel cells, **4**: 205, **4**: 208
   road vehicles, **4**: 203, **4**: 214
      manufacturers, **4**: 189, **4**: 219*t*
      test characterization, **4**: 307
   separate reactant cooling systems, **4**: 199
   shipping, **4**: 218
   short-circuits, **4**: 314
   small-scale power generation markets, **4**: 200
   solid oxide fuel cells, **4**: 246
   stack construction, **4**: 192
   stack cooling, **4**: 199
   stationary power, **4**: 208, **4**: 209
   structure of catalyst layers, **4**: 191
   sulfonated membrane materials, **4**: 188
   system design, **4**: 198, **4**: 209
   temperature, **4**: 199
   test characterization, **4**: 307
   traction, **4**: 203
   trains, **4**: 218
   transport, **4**: 203, **4**: 214
   urban electrical vehicles, **4**: 317
   variant technologies, **4**: 205
   vehicles, **4**: 203, **4**: 214
      manufacturers, **4**: 189, **4**: 219*t*
      test characterization, **4**: 307
   water cooling systems, **4**: 199
   water evaporation, **4**: 194
   water management, **4**: 187, **4**: 194
proton exchange membranes (PEM): alkaline fuel cells, **4**: 159, **4**: 160
prototypes:
   air turbines, **8**: 139
   hydrogen vehicles, **4**: 62
   ocean wave energy, **8**: **79–110**, **8**: 4
      conception to demonstration, **8**: **79–110**
      electrical power generation, **8**: 4
      test phases, **8**: 80, **8**: 80–82, **8**: 81*t*
   quantum dot intermediate band solar cells, **1**: 630
provincial hydroelectricity generation, Canada, **6**: **153–178**
Prussian blue, **3**: 345
PS10&PS20 *see* Planta Solar 10&20
PSI *see* Paul Scherrer Institute
PT-1 parabolic trough collectors, **3**: 182
PT *see* photothermal
PTFE *see* polytetrafluoroethylene
p-type semiconductors, **1**: 294
p-type silicon cells:
   emitter passivation, **1**: 371

   emitter wrap-through cells, **1**: 374
   high-efficiency cell structures, **1**: 371
   metal-wrap-through cells, **1**: 372, **1**: 373
   passivated emitter and rear cell devices, **1**: 371, **1**: 373
   photovoltaics, **1**: 371
   rear cell passivation, **1**: 371
public acceptance: wind park design, **2**: 202
public attitude analysis: wind power, **2**: 534, **2**: 535
public consultations: Indian hydropower, **6**: 234, **6**: 236, **6**: 236*f*
public dialogue: wind power, **2**: 397
public finance pools, **1**: 128
public relations (PR), **6**: 423
public sector finance, **1**: 124, **1**: 128
Public Utility Regulatory Policies Act (PURPA), **1**: 84
public utility social responsibilities, **6**: 287
Pueblo: solar energy utilization, **1**: 31, **1**: 32
Puertollano – La Nava power plant, **1**: 750, **1**: 751*t*
pulping liquors, **5**: 264
pulse width modulation (PDW), **2**: 270
pumped hydro energy storage (PHES), **1**: 208
pumped hydro storage (PHS), **2**: 626, **2**: 649–650
pumped-storage hydropower, **1**: 208, **2**: 626, **2**: 649–650, **6**: **405–434**
   benefits, **6**: 284
   characteristics, **6**: 412, **6**: 413
   Coo-Trois Ponts, Belgium, **6**: 431
   design, **6**: **405–434**
   development, **6**: **405–434**
      Japanese current status, **6**: 277
      Japanese history, **6**: 273
      Japanese successful efforts, **6**: 281
      progress, **6**: 7
   examples, **6**: 418
   Goldisthal pumped storage plant, Germany, **6**: 406
   historical overviews, **6**: 412
   Iran, **6**: 259, **6**: 263*f*
   Japan, **6**: 273, **6**: 277, **6**: 294
   Okinawa, Japan Seawater Pumped Storage Power Plant, **6**: 418
   planning, **6**: 286
   power plants, **6**: 412, **6**: 418
   pump-turbine characteristics, **6**: 413
   Tianhuangping, China pumped storage, **6**: 429
pumped storage plants: definitions, **6**: 1, **6**: 16
pump isentropic efficiency ratio, **7**: 207
pumps:
   see also heat...
   direct heat utilization, **7**: 176, **7**: 177*f*
   dry-steam power plants, **7**: 216
   geothermal energy, **7**: 176, **7**: 177*f*
   historical overviews, **2**: 51
   wind energy, **2**: 51
pumps as turbines (PAT), **6**: 440–441
pump-turbines, **6**: 413, **6**: 440–441
   characteristics, **6**: 413
   hydraulic design, **6**: 413
   mechanical design, **6**: 416
   pressure fluctuation levels, **6**: 413
   runner hydraulic design, **6**: 413
purchase costs: wind turbines, **2**: 186–187, **2**: 189
purchase obligations: photovoltaic promotion schemes, **1**: 94
pure battery electric mode fuel cells, **4**: 325
pure cultures: inoculums, **4**: 273
Pure Project case study, **4**: 131
purging: PEM fuel cells, **4**: 314
purification: crude glycerol, **5**: 396
PURPA *see* Public Utility Regulatory Policies Act
purple bacteria, **1**: 661
Putnam, Palmer Cosslett, **2**: 56
PV *see* photovoltaics
PV/T *see* photovoltaic/thermal systems
PV–RO *see* photovoltaic-driven reverse osmosis
pyranometers, **1**: 214, **1**: 219, **1**: 220–221, **1**: 223, **3**: 28
pyrheliometers, **1**: 214, **1**: 220, **1**: 223, **3**: 28

pyrolysis:
   biochar, **5**: **357–384**, **5**: 406
   biomass, **5**: 134, **5**: 135, **5**: 148
   biomass-to-liquids technology, **5**: 156, **5**: 165
   definitions, **5**: 395
   gasification, **5**: 135
   historical development, **5**: 134
   pyrolysis oils, **5**: 406
Pyrovac, Canada, **5**: 148

Q

Q-Cells AG, **1**: 170
QD *see* quantum dots
QDR *see* qualitative design reviews
quadratic models: power curves, **2**: 131
quadruple glazing, **3**: 333
qualitative considerations: wind turbine noise, **2**: 513
qualitative design reviews (QDR): hydrogen safety, **4**: 84–85
qualitative error descriptions: ocean wave models, **8**: 47
quality:
   biodiesel vegetable oil, **5**: 225
   building-integrated photovoltaics, **1**: 705
   concrete structure durability, **6**: 387, **6**: 396
   control
      buoy data, **8**: 28
      geothermal chemistry, **7**: 101
      ocean wave measurements, **8**: 28, **8**: 36, **8**: 37
      photovoltaic power measurements, **1**: 279
      roller compacted concrete dams, **6**: 476
      satellite altimeter data, **8**: 36, **8**: 37
      solar radiation, values, **3**: 49
      Three Gorges Project, China, **6**: 208
      wind power, plant building, **2**: 427
   cost reductions, **1**: 53
   freeze-thaw prevention, **6**: 387
   multi-junction cells, **1**: 498
   photovoltaic cost reductions, **1**: 53
   vegetable oil biodiesel, **5**: 225
quantile plots: ocean waves, **8**: 63
quantitative considerations: wind turbine noise, **2**: 513
quantity-based incentives: support mechanisms, **1**: 1
quantum cutting, **1**: 549, **1**: 555
quantum dots (QD):
   down-shifting, **1**: 566, **1**: 566–567, **1**: 575
   efficiency, **1**: 576, **1**: 631, **1**: 632
   hot carriers, **1**: 525, **1**: 526
   intermediate band photovoltaics, **1**: 623, **1**: 628
   multi-exciton generation, **1**: 525, **1**: 526
   quantum structure photovoltaics, **1**: 525, **1**: 526, **1**: 527
quantum efficiency:
   chalcopyrite thin film photovoltaics, **1**: 414
   dye-sensitized solar cells, **1**: 488
   luminescent down-shifting, **1**: 564, **1**: 568, **1**: 568f, **1**: 570, **1**: 572
   luminescent solar concentrators, **1**: 589
   organic solar cells, **1**: 450
   photovoltaics
      organic solar cells, **1**: 450
         quantum dot intermediate band solar cells, **1**: 631
      thermodynamics, **1**: 316, **1**: 339
      upconversion, **1**: 540
   quantum dots cells, **1**: 631
   thermodynamics, **1**: 316, **1**: 339
   upconversion, **1**: 540
quantum size effects, **1**: 576, **3**: 309
quantum states, **1**: 317
quantum structures, **1**: 525
quantum wells, **1**: 527
quasi-Fermi level concept, **1**: 620
quaternary ammonium, **4**: 159, **4**: 175
Quebec, Canada, **6**: 153, **6**: 161, **6**: 163
Queisser efficiency *see* Shockley–Queisser model

quick economics, **1**: 772
quinone, **1**: 657
quotas:
   bioenergy policy development, **5**: 411, **5**: 416–417, **5**: 420f, **5**: 422
   photovoltaic promotion schemes, **1**: 76

R

R&D *see* research and development
R2R *see* roll-to-roll printing
raceway heating, **7**: 169
radar systems, **2**: 714, **8**: 23
radial-flow self-rectifying impulse air turbines, **8**: 136
radiance predictions, **1**: 240
radiant flux density, **1**: 240
radiation:
   see also infrared…; solar radiation; thermal radiation
   absorption, **3**: 36, **3**: 126, **3**: 128
   anisotropic radiation, **1**: 323–324, **1**: 327, **3**: 48
   definitions, **3**: 1
   exchange, **3**: 130
   hemispherical radiation, **1**: 214, **1**: 216–217, **1**: 224, **1**: 226
   low-temperature stationary collectors, **3**: 126
   ocean wave energy, **8**: 93
   reflection, **3**: 120
   refraction, **3**: 319
   resistance, **1**: 505
   solar thermal systems, **3**: 18
   transmission, **3**: 120, **3**: 319
radiative cooling, **3**: 643, **3**: 643f
radiative generation, **1**: 302
radiative heat transfer, **3**: 383
radiative recombination, **1**: 302
radiative transfer, **1**: 225, **3**: 28, **3**: 40, **3**: 43
radiative transitions, **1**: 574
radioisotope thermophotovoltaics (RTPV), **1**: 613
radiometers/radiometry:
   calibration, **1**: 221, **3**: 67
   performance, **1**: 224
   solar radiation, **3**: 28, **3**: 64, **3**: 78
      resources assessments, **1**: 214, **1**: 219, **1**: 221, **1**: 224
   uncertainties, **1**: 224
radiosity, **3**: 1
rail industry/railways, **2**: 54, **4**: 218, **4**: 285
rainfall, **6**: 232, **6**: 233f
Rainforest Alliance standard, **5**: 106
rainforests, **5**: 21
Range Fuels, **5**: 190
range line method, **6**: 361
Rangit reservoir flushing, **6**: 248, **6**: 248f
Rankine cycles, **7**: 222
RANS *see* Reynolds-averaged Navier–Stokes
rapeseed, **5**: **293–303**, **5**: 388t, **5**: 388–389
rapid economic growth: dams, **6**: 270
rapid erosion: heat flow, **7**: 89
Rapides-des-Coeurs, Quebec, Canada, **6**: 162–163, **6**: 167f
rare-earths:
   down-shifting, **1**: 566, **1**: 573
   efficiency, **1**: 574
   energy transfer, **1**: 574
   nonradiative transitions, **1**: 574
   photovoltaics
      down-shifting, **1**: 566, **1**: 573
      upconversion, **1**: 533, **1**: 540, **1**: 546
   quantum cutting, **1**: 555
   radiative transitions, **1**: 574
   spectroscopy, **1**: 540
   upconversion, **1**: 533, **1**: 540, **1**: 546
rated power:
   ocean energy, **8**: 80, **8**: 162
   wind turbine energy yields, **2**: 114, **2**: 138

rated wind speed, **2**: 370
ratings:
   concentration photovoltaics, **1**: 754
   power, **1**: 798
ratio-based geothermometers, **7**: 59
ratios: concentration/concentrators, **3**: **149–163**, **3**: **165–209**
Rayleigh distribution, **2**: 118
Rayleigh scattering, **3**: 28, **3**: 36, **3**: 44
ray tracing, **1**: 592, **3**: 121, **3**: 121f, **3**: 127, **3**: 128f
RCC *see* roller compacted concrete
RD 1565/2010:, **1**: 92
RD 2366/1994:, **1**: 91
reactant cooling systems, **4**: 199
reaction centers: photosynthesis design, **1**: 657–658, **1**: 659
reaction path calculations: geochemistry, **7**: 128
reaction rates: proton-exchange membrane fuel cells, **4**: 187
reactions: biodiesel production intensification, **5**: 205
reactive extraction, **5**: 208
reactive power, **2**: 370
reactors, **5**: 168, **5**: 180, **5**: 206
real heat system layouts, **3**: 575
realization considerations: hybrid solar–diesel systems, **1**: 689
real-time data acquisition: reservoir water quality, **6**: 70
real-world devices: solar energy conversion principles, **1**: 309
rear cell passivation, **1**: 371
rear-located nanoparticles, **1**: 649
recalcitrance, **5**: 231
receivers, **3**: **149–163**, **3**: **165–209**
   adjustment, **3**: 195
   aim-point strategies, **3**: 187
   analysis, **3**: 172, **3**: 173
   aperture geometry, **3**: 186
   area ratios, **3**: **149–163**, **3**: **165–209**
   beam errors, **3**: 188
   characteristics, **3**: 185
   cleaning, **3**: 174, **3**: 184, **3**: 195
   components, **3**: 186
   control, **3**: 187
   coupling, **3**: 187
   efficiency, **3**: 187
   facets, **3**: 187
   heat transfer fluids, **3**: 186
   heliostats, **3**: 187, **3**: 188, **3**: 190
   high concentration solar collectors, **3**: 172, **3**: 173, **3**: 185, **3**: 199
      aim-point strategies, **3**: 187
      cleaning, **3**: 174, **3**: 184, **3**: 195
      control, **3**: 187
      coupling, **3**: 187
      facets, **3**: 187
      heat transfer fluids, **3**: 186
      heliostats, **3**: 187, **3**: 188, **3**: 190
      kinematics, **3**: 187
      mirrors, **3**: 187
      operation and maintenance, **3**: 195
      optics, **3**: 187, **3**: 189
      performance, **3**: 187
      secondary optics, **3**: 189
      system-specific performance determination, **3**: 187
      tower construction, **3**: 187
   kinematics, **3**: 187
   maintenance, **3**: 195
   markets, **3**: 192
   mirrors, **3**: 187
   operation and maintenance, **3**: 195
   optical losses, **3**: 187
   optics, **3**: 187, **3**: 189
   performance, **3**: 187
   reflection method, **3**: 172
   secondary concentrators, **3**: 189
   secondary optics, **3**: 189
   solar dishes, **3**: 199
   structure, **3**: 185
   system-specific performance determination, **3**: 187

   thermal losses, **3**: 187
   tower construction, **3**: 187
   tower reflectors, **3**: 187, **3**: 189
   tracking accuracy, **3**: 188
   types, **3**: 186
recent developments/results:
   biomass gasification, **5**: 151
   multi-junction cells, **1**: 509
reception issues: feedstocks, **5**: 142
rechargeable batteries, **1**: 722
reciprocating engines, **2**: 575
recombination:
   Auger recombination, **1**: 309, **1**: 315
   carrier-carrier recombination, **1**: 303
   impurity recombination, **1**: 303
   photovoltaic thermodynamics, **1**: 334
   radiative recombination, **1**: 302
   solar energy conversion principles, **1**: 294, **1**: 301
   surface recombination, **1**: 303, **1**: 501, **1**: 570
   thermal recombination, **1**: 302
recommendations: photovoltaic future visions, **1**: 188, **1**: 196
recommended practices: wind energy, **2**: 472
recooling, **3**: 597
recovery ratios: desalination, **3**: 529
recovery times: geothermal energy, **7**: 282
recreational photovoltaics, **1**: 713, **1**: 714f
recuperators: binary power plants, **7**: 226
RED *see* Renewable Energy Directive
redox enzymes, **4**: 260
redox mediator transport, **1**: 486
redox polymers, **4**: 262–263
Red Tractor mark, **5**: 106
reference forecasts: solar irradiance-photovoltaic power forecasts, **1**: 268
reference solar devices: photovoltaic standards, **1**: 791
reference systems:
   definitions, **5**: 109
   greenhouse gas life cycle assessments, **5**: 110
reference yields: photovoltaics, **1**: 775, **1**: 777
reflectance:
   absorber coatings, **3**: 109, **3**: 110f
   selective coatings, **3**: 301
reflection:
   absorber coatings, **3**: 109, **3**: 110f
   building-integrated photovoltaics, **1**: 701
   coatings
      absorber types, **3**: 109, **3**: 110f
      selective types, **3**: 301
      single-glazed windows, **3**: 331
      solar thermal energy, **3**: 320
   glazings, **3**: 320, **3**: 331
   high concentration solar collectors, **3**: 167, **3**: 169, **3**: 175
   losses, **1**: 520
   low-temperature stationary collectors, **3**: 120
   mirrors and solar energy history, **3**: 90, **3**: 91f, **3**: 92
   ocean wave energy, **8**: 93
   parabolic troughs, **3**: 175
   reflectivity, **3**: 170, **3**: 301
   selective coatings, **3**: 301
   single-glazed windows, **3**: 331
   solar energy mirrors, **3**: 90, **3**: 91f, **3**: 92
   solar radiation, **3**: 36
reflector collectors:
   agricultural applications, **3**: 587t
   analysis, **3**: 167, **3**: 169
   concentration photovoltaic/thermal collectors, **3**: 267
   industrial applications, **3**: 571–572, **3**: 572f, **3**: 587t
   shape accuracy, **3**: 167
reformer methanol fuel cells (RMFC), **4**: 205, **4**: 208
reforming: molten-carbonate fuel cells, **4**: 227
reforms: Cameroon, Africa, hydropower, **6**: **129–151**
refraction:
   coatings, **3**: 319

glazings, **3:** 21, **3:** 319
low-temperature stationary collectors, **3:** 109, **3:** 121f
solar radiation, **3:** 21
refrigeration:
see also solar refrigeration
absorption, **3:** 464, **3:** 465, **3:** 471, **3:** 472
adsorption, **3:** 463
agricultural applications, **3:** 592
industrial applications, **3:** 592
lithium–water absorption systems, **3:** 465
solar cooling, **3: 481–494**
absorption, **3:** 464, **3:** 465, **3:** 471, **3:** 472
adsorption, **3:** 463
solar thermal systems, **3:** 592
refueling stations: hydrogen costs, **4:** 54
refuellers: hydrogen technology, **4:** 2, **4:** 8f, **4:** 9f
regeneration:
oxidized dyes, **1:** 485
solar cooling, **3:** 483
regime analysis: wind, **2:** 81
regional developments: wind energy/power, **2:** 3, **2:** 4f, **2:** 507
regional distribution: electricity capacity, **2:** 14
regional photovoltaic power predictions, **1:** 264, **1:** 277
accuracy, **1:** 281
evaluations, **1:** 285
upscaling, **1:** 264, **1:** 284
regression results: geothermal energy, **7:** 265, **7:** 266t, **7:** 267t, **7:** 268t, **7:** 269t
regular waves:
dispersion, **8:** 13
group speed, **8:** 13
mathematical descriptions, **8:** 12
ocean wave energy, **8:** 12, **8:** 13, **8:** 96
phase speed, **8:** 13
speed, **8:** 13
wind turbine loads, **2:** 265
regulation/regulatory frameworks:
biomass and biofuel power generation, **5:** 31
Cameroon, Africa, hydropower, **6:** 148
concentration photovoltaics, **1:** 751
construction management, **6:** 208
developing country, **1:** 127
future photovoltaics, **1:** 196
hydrogen safety engineering, **4:** 82
hydropower, Cameroon, Africa, **6:** 148
photovoltaics, **1:** 127, **1:** 196
power generation, **5:** 31
rehabilitation:
concrete structure durability, **6:** 397
Indian hydropower, **6:** 236, **6:** 239
Reindl model, **3:** 48
reinforced learning, **3:** 657–658
reinforcement: concrete structures, **6:** 382, **6:** 386, **6:** 396
reinjection: geothermal energy, **7:** 39
reinjection well scaling, **7:** 253
rejection issues: wind park design, **2:** 171f
relative permeability, **7:** 16–18
release phenomena: hydrogen safety, **4:** 86, **4:** 95, **4:** 102, **4:** 104
reliability:
cadmium telluride thin films, **1:** 435
experience curves, **1:** 57
grids, **1:** 199
photovoltaics, **1:** 199, **1:** 435
testing, **1:** 793
storage options, **1:** 199
testing, photovoltaics, **1:** 793
wind turbine electrical systems, **2:** 272, **2:** 287f, **2:** 298
RELIAWIND project, **2:** 720
relic protection, **6:** 217
relocation implementation: Three Gorges Project, China **6:** 211
REMAP project, **2:** 716
remediation practices: biochar, **5:** 380

remote consumers: stand alone hybrid wind energy systems, **2: 623–655**
remote onshore wind farms, **2:** 602
remote telecommunication stations, **2:** 740, **2:** 741, **2:** 742
Renaissance: solar energy history, **3:** 87–88
renewability: geothermal energy, physics, **7:** 43
renewable electricity generation: definitions, **2:** 11
Renewable Energy Corporation, **1:** 171, **1:** 174
Renewable Energy Directive (RED), **5:** 100, **5:** 103, **5:** 125
renewable energy premium tariff (RPT), **1:** 130
Renewable Obligations (RO), **5:** 32, **8:** 164
renewable portfolio standards (RPS), **1:** 76, **1:** 85, **1:** 127
renewable targets: carbon dioxide emission reduction, **2:** 546
Renewable Transport Fuel Obligations (RTFO), **5:** 100, **5:** 103
RenovAção Project, **5:** 22
repairs:
concrete structures, **6:** 397, **6:** 398
wind turbine loads, **2:** 246
repayment periods, **2:** 473
REpower, **2:** 317, **2:** 321t
representative designs: axial-flow microhydro turbines, **6:** 438
Republic of Cameroon, Africa: hydropower, **6: 129–151**
RESCO *see* rural energy service companies
research:
biochar, **5:** 357
cell efficiency, **1:** 746, **1:** 747f
concentrating solar power, **3:** 624, **3:** 634
concrete structure durability, **6:** 392
councils, ocean wave energy funding, **8:** 82–83
Fresnel collectors, **3:** 199
high concentration solar collectors, **3:** 183, **3:** 199, **3:** 204
ocean wave energy funding, **8:** 82–83
parabolic troughs, **3:** 183
policies, hydrogen technology, **4:** 70
solar dishes, **3:** 204
solar thermal power plants, **3:** 624
thin-film silicon photovoltaics, **1:** 394
research and development (R&D):
costs, photovoltaics, **1:** 49, **1:** 54, **1:** 68
funding wind turbines, **2:** 708, **2:** 713, **2:** 715
future photovoltaics, **1:** 196, **1:** 197
historical photovoltaics, **1: 31–45**
hydrogen technology policies, **4:** 70
photovoltaics
costs, **1:** 49, **1:** 54, **1:** 68
future visions, **1:** 196, **1:** 197
historical overviews, **1: 31–45**
promotion schemes, **1:** 74, **1:** 75–76, **1:** 81
technology progress, **1: 13–30**
policies, hydrogen technology, **4:** 70
promoting photovoltaic electricity, **1:** 74, **1:** 75–76, **1:** 81
Singapore, **1:** 81
wind energy, **2:** 1
wind turbines, **2:** 518, **2: 671–724**, **2:** 671
reserves:
electricity grids, wind energy policy, **2:** 560
electricity network wind energy variable costs, **2:** 489
energy storage, conventional power systems, **1:** 200
variable costs, wind energy, **2:** 489, **2:** 490
wind energy
policy, **2:** 560
variable costs, **2:** 489, **2:** 490
reservoirs:
bypassing, **6:** 294, **6:** 296, **6:** 298
flood conditions, **6:** 294
Kansai Electric Power Co:, **6:** 294
mitigating floods, **6:** 296, **6:** 298
sediments during flood, **6:** 294
turbid waters, **6:** 294
characteristics, hydropower water quality, **6:** 59
filling management, **6:** 84
Horseshoe Bend hydroelectric scheme, **6:** 469
hydrodynamics, **6:** 59

reservoirs: (*continued*)
   hydropower
      environmental impact management, 6: 58
        India, 6: 237
        sediment management, 6: **355–376**
        water quality, 6: 53, 6: 58
   Indian hydropower, 6: 237
   induced seismicity, 6: 217
   lake stability, 6: 68
   long-term sediment management, 6: 355–376
   morphology, 6: 59
   nutrient dynamics, 6: 66
   operating strategies, 6: 75
   operation schemes, 6: 214
   optimization, 6: 139, 6: 141
   oxygen, water quality, 6: 64
   pollutants, 6: 59
   reservoir-induced seismicity, 6: 217
   rock type effects, 7: 106
   sedimentation, 6: 53, 6: 212
   sediment flushing, 6: 288
   sediment management, 6: **355–376**
   seismicity, 6: 217
   stressors, 6: 59
   surveys, 6: 360
   sustainable hydropower, 6: 355–376
   thermal stratification, 6: 59
   Three Gorges Project, China, 6: **179–227**
   water quality, 6: 70
      autoanalyzers, 6: 70
      autosamplers, 6: 70
      control, 6: 69
      data acquisition, 6: 70
      environmental impact management, 6: 58
      hydropower, 6: 53, 6: 58
      inflow characteristics, 6: 70
      Lake numbers, 6: 68, 6: 70
      lake stability, 6: 68
      models, 6: 70
      monitoring, 6: 69
      multi-layer models, 6: 71, 6: 72
      nutrient dynamics, 6: 66
      one-dimensional models, 6: 70, 6: 71
      oxygen, 6: 64
      temperature models, 6: 70
      thermistor chains, 6: 69
      three-dimensional models, 6: 72
      two-dimensional models, 6: 72
      weather stations, 6: 69
resettlements:
   environment studies, 6: 236
   hydropower, 6: 210, 6: 236, 6: 239, 6: 243*f*
   Indian hydropower, 6: 236, 6: 239, 6: 243*f*
   planning, 6: 210
   relocation implementation, 6: 211
   Three Gorges Project, China, 6: 210
residential grid-connected systems, 1: 396
residential heating, 1: 614, 1: 615
residue processing, 5: 286
resistivity methods:
   electrolytes, 7: 78
   equivalence problem, 7: 63
   geothermal energy exploration techniques, 7: 61
   high-temperature fields, 7: 81
   joint inversion, 7: 71
   Schlumberger soundings, 7: 64, 7: 68
   shift effect, 7: 71
resonance: ocean energy, 8: 80
Resource Atlas, 2: 86, 2: 87
resources:
   assessments
      databases, 1: 229
        energy conversions, 1: **213–237**

        flat plate collectors, 1: 218, 1: 232
        modeling solar radiation, 1: 214
        ocean wave energy, 8: **11–77**
        physics-based solar radiation models, 1: 225
        radiometers, 1: 214, 1: 219
        solar energy collector fuels, 1: 217
      solar radiation
        databases, 1: 229
        energy conversions, 1: **213–237**
        flat plate collectors, 1: 218, 1: 232
        modeling, 1: 214
        physics-based models, 1: 225
        radiometers, 1: 214, 1: 219
        solar energy collector fuels, 1: 217
      sustainability, 1: 219
      terrestrial solar radiation, 1: 214, 1: 215, 1: 216, 1: 217, 1: 226
      wave energy, 8: **11–77**
      wind energy, 2: 709
   consents, hydroelectric schemes, 6: 467, 6: 469, 6: 470
   energy conversion assessments, 1: **213–237**
   geothermal energy heat pumps, 7: 187
   geothermal energy physics, 7: 36
   ocean wave energy assessments, 8: **11–77**
   photovoltaic technology introduction, 1: 8
   wind energy assessments, 2: 709
responses/responsivity:
   buoy measurements, 8: 24
   hydropower, 6: 365
   sediment management, 6: 365
   solar radiation resources assessments, 1: 214
REST2 solar radiation model, 3: 43
restoration considerations:
   land-use, 3: 6
   Okinawa, Japan, 6: 423
retail sector standards, 5: 106
retention times: microbial fuel cells, 4: 269
retro-materials: photovoltaics, 1: 26
RETScreen Clean Energy Project Analysis Software, 1: 691, 1: 692
return expectations: photovoltaic financial risk, 1: 137
return pulses: ocean wave satellite altimeters, 8: 35
return signal noise, 8: 36
return values: peaks-over-threshold method, 8: 58, 8: 64
revegetation: Okinawa, Japan, 6: 423
Revelstoke Complex/Canyon Dam, British Colombia, Canada, 6: 175
revenue:
   ocean energy, 8: 162, 8: 166
   Three Gorges Project, China, 6: 209
   wind park design economics, 2: 210
   wind power design and implementation, 2: 422
reverse flat plate collectors, 3: 150, 3: 152
reverse osmosis:
   definitions, 2: 725, 3: 529
   desalination
      industrial and agricultural applications, 3: 589, 3: 590*f*
      photovoltaics, 3: 530, 3: 536, 3: 547, 3: 553, 3: 556, 3: 558, 3: 560
        brackish water, 3: 538, 3: 539*t*, 3: 556, 3: 558, 3: 560, 3: 560*t*, 3: 563*f*
        seawater, 3: 539*t*, 3: 553, 3: 558
      wind energy, 2: 726, 2: 727*f*, 2: 728, 2: 732, 2: 734, 2: 738
   photovoltaics
      solar desalination, 3: 530, 3: 536, 3: 547, 3: 553, 3: 556
        brackish water, 3: 538, 3: 539*t*, 3: 556, 3: 558, 3: 560, 3: 560*t*, 3: 563*f*
        seawater, 3: 539*t*, 3: 553, 3: 558
   solar desalination, 3: 530, 3: 536, 3: 553, 3: 556, 3: 558, 3: 560
   unit switching, 2: 734
   wind energy, 2: 726, 2: 727*f*, 2: 728, 2: 732, 2: 734, 2: 738
reverse-return array piping, 3: 475–476, 3: 476, 3: 476*f*, 3: 477*f*
reversible cycle heat pumps, 3: 495, 3: 497
revolutionary photovoltaic systems, 1: 15, 1: 25
Reykjavik, Iceland, district heating, 7: 180, 7: 181*f*

Reynolds-averaged Navier–Stokes (RANS) equations, 2: 232–233
Reynolds number, 4: 78, 4: 81
Rhône River, Switzerland, 6: 350
rice husks, 5: 58
Ricobayo dam, Spain, 6: 338, 6: 339f
ride through: wind turbines, 2: 295
rifts: geothermal energy geological explorations, 7: 55
The Rio conference, 7: 273–274, 7: 274, 7: 277
Rio Declaration on Environment and Development, 7: 277
risk:
   see also finance...
   accidents, photovoltaic impacts, 1: 153
   biomass cofiring, 5: 69
   environmental impacts, photovoltaics, 1: 153
   finance, 1: 135, 1: 136, 1: 137
   Horseshoe Bend hydroelectric scheme, 6: **467–483**
   hydrogen safety engineering, 4: 78, 4: 82, 4: 105
   management
      finance
         developing country photovoltaics, 1: 135
         fossil-fuels, 1: 136
         photovoltaics, 1: 135, 1: 136, 1: 137
         return expectations, 1: 137
      finance characterization, 1: 136
      Horseshoe Bend hydroelectric scheme, 6: **467–483**
   ocean wave energy, 8: 80
   photovoltaic environmental impacts, 1: 153
   photovoltaic finance, 1: 135, 1: 136, 1: 137
   wind power design and implementation, 2: 424
rivers:
   Brazilian hydropower plants, 6: **93–127**
   Cameroon, Africa, hydropower, 6: 130
   channel degradation, 6: 212
   closure, Three Gorges Project, China, 6: 206, 6: 223
   debris control, 6: 79
   Iguaçu River hydroelectric project, 6: 108
   Itaipu hydroelectric project, 6: 96
   Japanese hydropower history, 6: 268, 6: 271
   Madeira hydroelectric project, Brazil, 6: 104
   networks, Spanish hydropower, 6: 311
   Rhône River, Switzerland, 6: 350
   Spanish hydropower, 6: 311
   Switzerland, 6: **343–354**
   Three Gorges Project, China, 6: 206, 6: 223
   transport, debris control, 6: 79
   Tucurui hydroelectricity project, Brazil, 6: 101
   Uruguay River hydroelectricity project, 6: 119
RIVM *see* National Institute of Public Health and Environment
RMFC *see* reformer methanol fuel cells
RMSD *see* root mean square deviation; root mean standard deviation
RMSE *see* root mean square error
RO *see* Renewable Obligations
roadside ditch construction, 6: 423
road vehicles:
   see also automotives; vehicles
   battery hybrid energy storage, 4: 317
   biomass and biofuels, 5: **305–342**
   dense battery hybrid energy storage, 4: 317
   fuel cell operation, 4: 322
   hybrid energy storage, 4: 317
   hydrogen fuel cell technology, 4: 287
   hydrogen PEMFCs, 4: 307, 4: 317
   manufacturers, PEMFCs, 4: 189, 4: 219t
   MES-DEA PEMFCs, 4: 308
   operation, fuel cells, 4: 322
   PEMFCs, 4: 203, 4: 214
      dense battery hybrid energy storage, 4: 317
      manufacturers, 4: 189, 4: 219t
      test characterization, 4: 307
   product-integrated photovoltaics, 1: 714, 1: 715f
   test characterization, 4: 307
Robert-Bourassa spillway and dam, Quebec, Canada, 6: 161, 6: 163f

rock-beds, 3: 451, 3: 474, 3: 474f
rock cofferdams, 6: 206, 6: 207
Rocketdyne receivers, 3: 192
rockfill dams, 6: 29, 6: 200
rock matrix: conductivity, 7: 78
rock resistivity, 7: 78, 7: 79
rocks: solar assisted heat pumps, 3: 520
rock storage: solar thermal energy storage, 3: 227, 3: 228t
roll-bond absorbers, 3: 106, 3: 107f
roller compacted concrete (RCC) dams:
   cofferdams, 6: 201
   commissioning, 6: 480
   cross sections, 6: 474, 6: 481f
   geological setting, 6: 473
   handling characteristics, 6: 475
   Horseshoe Bend hydroelectric scheme, 6: 467, 6: 469, 6: 472, 6: 473, 6: 482
   hydrological setting, 6: 473
   hydropower essential features, 6: 30
   mix design, 6: 475
   performance monitoring, 6: 480
   site layouts, 6: 474
   Three Gorges Project, China, 6: 201
roller compacted concrete (RCC) stepped spillways, 6: 485, 6: 489, 6: 491f
roll-to-roll printing (R2R):
   organic solar cells, 1: 440, 1: 441, 1: 470
   thin-film silicon, 1: 396
Romans:
   ship burning, 3: 86
   solar energy utilization history, 1: 31, 1: 32f, 1: 33f
Rondonia, Brazil, 6: 104
roofing louvres, 1: 705
roof-integrated systems, 1: 703, 1: 705
roof-mounted parabolic troughs, 3: 182, 3: 182f
room models: passive solar technologies, 3: 360–361, 3: 361, 3: 369, 3: 390
room temperatures, 3: 378
root mean square deviation (RMSD), 3: 50
root mean square error (RMSE), 1: 240, 3: 50
root mean standard deviation (RMSD), 3: 23
Roscoe Wind Park, Texas, 2: 218
rotation age: woody biomass, 5: 263
rotors:
   aerodynamic analysis, 2: 232, 2: 233
   aerodynamics, 2: 232, 2: 233, 2: 713
   air turbines, 8: 113, 8: 128
   blade-element momentum theory, 2: 236
   blades, 2: 380, 8: 113, 8: 128
   CFD aerodynamic analysis, 2: 232, 2: 233
   definitions, wind turbines, 2: 270
   diameters, wind turbines, 2: 418, 2: 676
   Glauert's optimum rotor method, 2: 227
   performance curves, wind turbines, 2: 110
   small wind turbine electrical systems, 2: 301
   solidity, 8: 127, 8: 128
   technology evolution, 2: 676, 2: 710, 2: 713
   testing, 2: 380
   two-dimensional cascade flow analysis, 8: 113
   wind energy testing, 2: 380
   wind turbines
      aerodynamic analysis, 2: 236
      blade-element momentum theory, 2: 236
      CFD aerodynamic analysis, 2: 232, 2: 233
      electrical systems, 2: 281f, 2: 285, 2: 285f
      financial support, 2: 710
      loads, 2: 255
      performance curves, 2: 110
      technology evolution, 2: 676, 2: 710, 2: 713
roughness:
   change models, 2: 86
   classes, 2: 77
   lengths, 2: 77

roughness: (*continued*)
    selective coatings, **3**: 308
    of terrain, **2**: 409
Round Table on Responsible Soy (RTRS), **5**: 105
Roundtable on Sustainable Palm Oil (RSPO), **5**: 104
routing:
    sediment management, **6**: 366
    ship locks, **6**: 196
Royal Decrees, **1**: 751
RP *see* Renewable Obligation
RPS *see* renewable portfolio standards
RPT *see* renewable energy premium tariff
RSB *see* Roundtable on Sustainable Biofuels
RSPO *see* Roundtable on Sustainable Palm Oil
RTFO *see* Renewable Transport Fuel Obligations
RTPV *see* radioisotope thermophotovoltaics
RTRS *see* Round Table on Responsible Soy
runners:
    damage, Indian hydropower, **6**: 249, **6**: 250*f*
    geometry, **6**: 454
    hydraulic design, **6**: 413
    simplified generic axial-flow microhydro turbines, **6**: 437–438, **6**: 444, **6**: 450, **6**: 453
run-off-river plants:
    Indian hydropower, **6**: 237, **6**: 240, **6**: 242
    Iranian hydropower, **6**: 259, **6**: 261*f*, **6**: 262*f*
Rupert Diversion, Quebec, Canada, **6**: 167
rural area electrification:
    developing country photovoltaics, **1**: **111–141**
    energy technology options, **1**: 115
    financing photovoltaics, **1**: 113, **1**: 120, **1**: 125, **1**: 130
    photovoltaics, **1**: **111–141**
        energy technology options, **1**: 115
        finance, **1**: 113, **1**: 120, **1**: 125, **1**: 130
        support mechanisms, **1**: 114
    rates, **1**: 114
rural energy service companies (RESCO), **1**: 120, **1**: 126, **1**: 132
R-values (inverse heat transfer coefficients), **3**: 322

S

saccharification and fermentation:
    bioethanol, **5**: 248
    enzymes, **5**: 248, **5**: 249
    inhibitors, **5**: 248
    lignocellulosic wastes, **5**: 248, **5**: 249
    substrate-enzyme interactions, **5**: 249
Sadous Riyadh Region, Saudi Arabia, **3**: 558, **3**: 560*t*
safe operating areas: power inverters, **4**: 297
safety:
    automotive alcohol fuels, **5**: 323
    biomass characteristics, **5**: 42
    biomass cofiring, **5**: 68
    biomass power generation, **5**: 40
    certification, wind energy, **2**: 371, **2**: 372, **2**: 383
    compressed gas: hydrogen storage, **4**: 124
    dam breaks, **6**: 220
    engineering, hydrogen technology fuel cells, **4**: **77–109**
    ethanol, **5**: 323
    explosions, **5**: 41, **5**: 42
    fire issues, **4**: **77–109**, **4**: 77, **5**: 41, **5**: 325
    fuel cells, hydrogen technology, **4**: **77–109**
    hydrogen storage, compressed gas, **4**: 124
    hydrogen technology fuel cells, **4**: **77–109**, **4**: 291
    hydropower, **6**: 10
    methanol, **5**: 323
    personnel issues, **5**: 40
    power generation, **5**: 40
    process safety, **5**: 41
    standards
        hydrogen fuel cell technology, **4**: 291
        small wind turbines, **2**: 376

    wind energy, **2**: **371–389**
    testing
        wind energy, **2**: 371, **2**: 376
        wind turbines, **2**: 376
    wind energy, **2**: 525
        certification, **2**: 371, **2**: 372, **2**: 383
        environmental–social benefits/impacts, **2**: 525
        standards, **2**: **371–389**
        testing, **2**: 371, **2**: 376
    wind turbines, **2**: 272, **2**: 376
SAFEWIND *see* Secure Large-Scale Wind Power Integration
sags: voltage variation, **2**: 594
SAIC *see* Science Applications International Corp.
sails: wind energy history, **2**: 41, **2**: 42*f*, **2**: 43*f*, **2**: 44
Sakata Port, Japan, **8**: 139, **8**: 140*f*
Salal dam spillway bucket repairs, **6**: 248, **6**: 249*f*
salinity, **7**: 108, **7**: 143
The Saltire Prize, **8**: 83
Salto Caxias hydroelectricity project, Brazil, **6**: 116
Salto de Moncabril, Spain, **6**: 324, **6**: 325*f*
Salto Osorio hydroelectricity project, Brazil, **6**: 114
Salto Santiago hydroelectric project, Brazil, **6**: 111
Saltos del Sil system, Spain, **6**: 324, **6**: 324*f*
salt tide invasion control, **6**: 214
salvage values: sediment management, **6**: 376
sampling:
    buoy ocean wave measurements, **8**: 28
    gases, **7**: 95
    geothermal energy geochemistry, **7**: 95, **7**: 97
    liquids, **7**: 95
    ocean wave variability, **8**: 28, **8**: 37, **8**: 51
    satellite altimeter data, **8**: 37
    solids, **7**: 97
    vapor phase, **7**: 95
    variability of ocean waves, **8**: 28, **8**: 37, **8**: 51
    wave energy converters, **8**: 51
Sandabotnar springs, **7**: 130
sand discharge outlet structures, **6**: 188
sand heat exchangers, **3**: 611
San Esteban dam, Spain, **6**: 324, **6**: 325*f*
Sangha river, Cameroon, Africa, **6**: 131, **6**: 132, **6**: 137
Santa Eulalia dam, Spain, **6**: 328, **6**: 329*f*
Santamouris model, **3**: 43
Santo Antonio hydroelectric project, Brazil, **6**: 94, **6**: 104*f*, **6**: 105, **6**: 105
SANYO Electric Company, **1**: 172
São Paulo, **6**: 95
SAR *see* synthetic aperture radar
Sarcelle, Quebec, Canada, **6**: 167
satellites:
    see also solar power...
    altimeters, **8**: 23, **8**: 31, **8**: 37
    cloud motion vectors, **1**: 249, **1**: 250
    ocean wave measurements, **8**: 23, **8**: 31, **8**: 37, **8**: 41
    photovoltaics, **1**: 36, **1**: 36*f*, **1**: **767–774**
        power forecasts, **1**: 249, **1**: 275
    solar irradiance forecasts, **1**: 249, **1**: 275
    solar radiation resources assessments, **1**: 215
Saucelle dam, Spain, **6**: 338, **6**: 339*f*
Saudi Arabia solar desalination, **3**: 558, **3**: 560*t*
Saudi Arabia Solar Radiation Network, **3**: 61
saving effectiveness: greenhouse gases, **5**: 200
Savonius rotors, **2**: 44, **2**: 109
Savonius vertical axis wind turbines, **2**: 693–694
saw-damage removal, **1**: 359
sawmill coproducts, **5**: 141
sawtooth diffuse reflectors, **3**: 151–152, **3**: 152*f*
scale effects/scaling:
    biomass combined heat and power, **5**: 95
    biomass-to-liquids technology, **5**: 172, **5**: 172*f*
    combined heat and power, **5**: 95
    corrosion, **7**: 253
    definitions, **7**: 240

gasification, 5: 172, 5: 172f
geothermal energy
    environments, 7: 249
    geochemistry, 7: 143, 7: 151
    power production, 7: **239–257**
    wells, 7: 41, 7: 42, 7: 252, 7: 253
hydraulic modeling, 8: 84
Maopingxi Dam, 6: 200
ocean wave energy, 8: 80, 8: 85
    hydraulic modeling, 8: 84
    physical modeling, 8: 85
    sea trials, 8: 97
physical modeling, ocean wave energy, 8: 85
pipelines, 7: 252
power output parameters, 2: 144
power production
    geothermal energy, 7: **239–257**
    wind turbines, 2: 136, 2: 138
production wells, 7: 251
reinjection wells, 7: 253
sea trials, 8: 97
separators, geothermal power, 7: 252
ship lift, 6: 198
ship locks, 6: 193
simplified generic axial-flow microhydro turbines, 6: 463
Three Gorges Project, China, 6: 182, 6: 186, 6: 188
turbines
    geothermal power, 7: 253
    wind potential, 2: 122
    wind power, 2: 136, 2: 138, 2: 144
underground power plants, 6: 191
wellheads, 7: 252
wells, 7: 41, 7: 42, 7: 252, 7: 253
wind potential evaluation, 2: 122
wind turbines, 2: 114, 2: 122, 2: 136, 2: 138, 2: 144
scanning microscopy, 7: 98
scatter diagrams: ocean wave energy, 8: 80
scattering:
    cloud cover, 1: 231
    definitions, 3: 28
    electron back scatter diffraction, 1: 405, 1: 405f
    Mie scattering, 3: 36, 3: 44
    photovoltaics, 1: 322, 1: 327, 1: 644
    plasmonics, 1: 644
    Rayleigh scattering, 3: 36, 3: 44
    shape effects, 1: 645
    size effects, 1: 644
    surface plasmons, 1: 644
    thermodynamics, 1: 322, 1: 327
    upper bounds, 1: 327
scenarios:
    Abu Dhabi desert area photovoltaic plant, 1: 692
    biochar, 5: 378
scheme evolution: Spanish hydropower, 6: 315
Schlumberger soundings, 7: 64, 7: 68
Schott Solar absorbers, 3: 183
Schwarza River, Germany, 6: 406
Science Applications International Corp: (SAIC), 3: 204
scientific discoveries: photovoltaics, 1: 5
scientific instrument cooling technologies, 4: 24
scientific meetings/conventions: solar energy history, 3: 96
scientific research policies: hydrogen technology, 4: 70
scooters: hydrogen fuel cells, 4: 286
SCOP see solar coefficient of performance
Scotland, 8: 5
scouring, 6: 212, 6: 390
screening: hydropower impact management, 6: 88, 6: 234
screen printing, 1: 360, 1: 472
SCS see solar capability scheme
SD see standard deviation
sealants: glazing, 3: 335
seascape: definitions, wind power, 2: 503
seasonal phenomenon: wind speed time variations, 2: 82

seasonal storage:
    classification, 3: 521
    evaluation, 3: 521
    solar assisted heat pumps, 3: 519, 3: 520, 3: 521
    solar thermal energy storage, 3: 248
seasonal variability: ocean waves, 8: 51
sea surface elevation, 8: 19
sea trials:
    large-scale prototypes, 8: 96
    location, 8: 99, 8: 102
    ocean wave energy, 8: 80, 8: 81t, 8: 96
    scale models, 8: 97
    sites, 8: 99, 8: 102
    test phases, 8: 80, 8: 81t
seawater:
    see also ocean wave energy
    Okinawa, Japan pumped storage hydropower, 6: 418
    solar desalination, 3: 529, 3: 539t, 3: 547, 3: 549, 3: 553, 3: 558
secondary concentrators, 3: 189
secondary optics, 3: 189
second generation biofuels: definitions, 5: 218
second law of thermodynamics, 3: 497
second-stage construction works: Three Gorges Project, China, 6: 202
sector competition: combined heat and power, 5: 92
Secure Large-Scale Wind Power Integration (SAFEWIND), 2: 719
security:
    geothermal energy, 7: 271, 7: **271–295**
    hydrogen fuel cells, 4: 332, 4: 333f
    isolated power systems, 2: 715
    of supply
        automotive biofuels, 5: 305–306
        bioenergy policy development, 5: 424
        very large-scale photovoltaic systems, 1: 733, 1: 734t
    very large-scale photovoltaic systems, 1: 733, 1: 734t
    wind energy policy, 2: **541–568**
    wind park design penetration, 2: 208
    wind turbine operation, 2: 715
SEDC see Solar Energy Development Center
sedimentation:
    see also sediments
    basin stresses, 6: 365
    designing sustainable hydropower, 6: **355–376**
    geothermal energy exploration techniques, 7: 89
    geothermal system classification, 7: 5
    heat flow, 7: 89
    hydropower
        impacts, 6: 363, 6: 367
        India, 6: 244
        responses, 6: 365
        stresses, 6: 365
        sustainability, 6: **355–376**
        upstream impacts, 6: 53
        water quality models, 6: 73
    impacts of hydropower, 6: 363, 6: 367
    rates, 7: 89
    reservoirs, 6: 212
    responses, 6: 365
    sustainable hydropower design, 6: **355–376**
sediments:
    see also sedimentation
    dams, 6: **355–376**
    design, hydropower, 6: **355–376**
    flood conditions, 6: 294
    flushing
        Dashidaira Dam
            consultation issues, 6: 294
            environmental impacts, 6: 294
            major impacts, 6: 291
            mitigation, 6: 291, 6: 292
        flashing facilities, 6: 288
        Japanese successful efforts, 6: 288
        Three Gorges Project, China, 6: 188
    geothermal system classification, 7: 5

sediments: (*continued*)
    hydraulic processes impact management, 6: 74
    hydropower
        bathymetric mapping, 6: 358, 6: 369, 6: 371f, 6: 372f
        dams, 6: **355–376**
        design, 6: **355–376**
        dredging, 6: 366
        Driver, Pressure, State, Impact, Response analytical framework, 6: **355–376**
        driving forces, 6: 357, 6: 365
        environment management, 6: **355–376**
        flushing, 6: 366, 6: 369, 6: 371f, 6: 372f
        hydraulic processes, 6: 74
        impact management, 6: 57, 6: 74, 6: 363, 6: 367
        measurement techniques, 6: 358, 6: 360
        modeling, 6: 361, 6: 367
        numerical modeling, 6: 361, 6: 367
        pressures, 6: 357, 6: 365
        reservoirs, 6: **355–376**
        responses, 6: 365
        state considerations, 6: 362, 6: 366
        stresses, 6: 357, 6: 365
    impact management, hydropower, 6: 57, 6: 74, 6: 363, 6: 367
    Indian hydropower, 6: 244
    management
        Alpine shallow reservoir, 6: 368
        assessments, 6: 370
        bathymetric mapping, 6: 358, 6: 369, 6: 371f, 6: 372f
        dams, 6: **355–376**
        design, 6: **355–376**
        dredging, 6: 366
        Driver, Pressure, State, Impact, Response analytical framework, 6: **355–376**
        driving forces, hydropower, 6: 357, 6: 365
        economic analysis, 6: 370
        environments, hydropower, 6: **355–376**
        flushing, 6: 366, 6: 369, 6: 371f, 6: 372f
        fluvial data, 6: 361
        hydropower
            bathymetric mapping, 6: 358, 6: 369, 6: 371f, 6: 372f
            dams, 6: **355–376**
            design, 6: **355–376**
            dredging, 6: 366
            driving forces, 6: 357, 6: 365
            environment, 6: **355–376**
            flushing, 6: 366, 6: 369, 6: 371f, 6: 372f
            impacts, 6: 57, 6: 74, 6: 363, 6: 367
            measurement techniques, 6: 358, 6: 360
            modeling, 6: 361, 6: 367
            numerical modeling, 6: 361, 6: 367
            pressures, 6: 357, 6: 365
            reservoirs, 6: **355–376**
            responses, 6: 365
            state considerations, 6: 362, 6: 366
            stresses, 6: 357, 6: 365
        impacts of hydropower, 6: 57, 6: 74, 6: 363, 6: 367
        measurement techniques, 6: 358, 6: 360
        modeling, 6: 361, 6: 367
        numerical modeling, 6: 361, 6: 367
        pressures, hydropower, 6: 357, 6: 365
        reservoirs, 6: **355–376**
        responses, hydropower, 6: 365
        shallow reservoirs, 6: 368
        state considerations, 6: 362, 6: 366
        stresses, 6: 357, 6: 365
        surveys, 6: 360
        WOLF modeling system, 6: 368
    reservoirs, 6: **355–376**
        bypassing, 6: 294, 6: 296, 6: 298
        surveys, 6: 360
    Three Gorges Project, China, 6: 188, 6: 212
    transport
        hydropower impact management, 6: 74

Indian hydropower, 6: 244
    turbines, 6: 57
seed numbers, 5: 296, 5: 300
seed size, 5: 296, 5: 297
seepage scouring, 6: 390
SEEWIND *see* South-East Europe Wind Energy Exploitation
segmentation: rifts, 7: 55
Segredo hydroelectric project, Brazil, 6: 110
SEGS power plant, 3: 615, 3: 616f
seismicity, 6: 217, 7: 285
selection techniques:
    axial-flow microhydro turbines, 6: 460
    wind turbines, 2: 158, 2: 416
selective absorbers, 3: **301–312**
    classes, 3: 304
    photovoltaic thermodynamics, 1: 316
selective coatings:
    absorbers, 3: **301–312**
    cermet metal–dielectric composites, 3: 301, 3: 307
    characterization, 3: 309
    classes, 3: 304
    components, 3: **301–312**
    definitions, 3: 302
    high-temperature applications, 3: **301–312**
    interference stacks, 3: 306
    intrinsic materials, 3: 304
    inverse tandem stacks, 3: 305
    mass absorbers, 3: 304
    metal-dielectrics
        composites, 3: 301, 3: 307
        layer interference stacks, 3: 306
        matrices, 3: 302–303, 3: 307
        stacks, 3: 301, 3: 302–303, 3: 306, 3: 307
    multilayer stacks, 3: 306
    optical properties, 3: 303
    photothermal conversion, 3: **301–312**
    quantum size effects, 3: 309
    roughness, 3: 308
    semi-conductor metal tandems, 3: 305
    solar energy conversion, 3: **301–312**
    solar thermal systems, 3: **301–312**
    surface roughness, 3: 308
    tandem stacks, 3: 305
selective emitter materials, 1: 603, 1: 604, 1: 605, 1: 615
selective surfaces: solar energy history, 3: 85, 3: 93
self-assembled artificial antennae, 1: 669
self-assembled donor-acceptor constructs, 1: 672
self-cleaning glazing: coatings, 3: 331
self-compacting concrete, 6: 394
self-generation applications: molten carbonate fuel cells, 4: 233
self-healing concrete, 6: 394
self-heating: health and safety, 5: 42
Self Installing Wind Turbine (SIWT), 2: 716
self-learning algorithms, 3: 657–658, 3: 662–663
self-rectification: ocean energy turbines, 8: 112, 8: 120, 8: 122, 8: 131, 8: 136
semiconductors:
    carrier density, 1: 299
    carrier populations, 1: 298
    doping, 1: 300
    electronic energy levels, 1: 294, 1: 297
    electron state density, 1: 298, 1: 299, 1: 300f
    electron state occupation, 1: 299
    energy bands, 1: 294, 1: 297
    industry, hydrogen technology, 4: 33
    metal tandems, 3: 305
    multiple exciton generation nanostructures, 1: 557
    nanostructures, multiple exciton generation, 1: 557
    organic solar cell physics, 1: 442
    photovoltaic organic solar cells, 1: 442
    physics, 1: 294, 1: 297, 1: 442
    p-n junctions, 1: 301

solar energy conversion principles, 1: 294, 1: 297
very large-scale photovoltaic systems, 1: 737
SenerTrough (SNT-1), 3: 183
sensible heat:
 definitions, 3: 214
 solar thermal energy storage, 3: 211, 3: 214, 3: 225t, 3: 227, 3: 228t, 3: 232, 3: 237, 3: 239, 3: 242
sensors:
 buoy measurements, 8: 24
 control of wind turbines, 2: 366
 hydrogen safety engineering, 4: 103
 hydrophone sensors, 6: 494, 6: 494f
 laser distance sensors, 8: 93–95, 8: 95f
 ocean waves, 8: 24
 photovoltaic performance monitoring, 1: 783
 pressure, 6: 494, 6: 494f
 thermal sensor radiometers, 1: 219
 wind turbine control systems, 2: 366
SEPA: compressed gas: hydrogen storage, 4: 135
separate reactant cooling systems, 4: 199
separation:
 biodiesel production intensification, 5: 206, 5: 209
 desalination, 2: 726
 distances in hydrogen safety engineering, 4: 78, 4: 94, 4: 102
separators:
 geothermal power production, 7: 252
 hydrogen technology, fuel cells, 4: 2, 4: 6f
sequential deposition, 1: 406, 1: 406f, 1: 408
sequestration *see* carbon...
series-connected multijunction organic solar cells, 1: 463
series systems: solar assisted heat pumps, 3: 508
SERIS *see* Solar Energy Research Institute of Singapore
service areas:
 Tokyo Electric Power Co., Inc:, 6: 282
 wind turbines, wind park design, 2: 178
service concessions: renewable energy premium tariff, 1: 132
service hot water, 3: 453
service life: concrete structure durability, 6: 392, 6: 397
service problems: wind turbine energy yields, 2: 152
servo-induced negative damping, 2: 260
SES *see* Stirling Energy Systems
Set For 2020 study, 1: 183
set-up costs: wind parks, 2: 169, 2: 170, 2: 177, 2: 210
sewage sludge, 5: 60
SFOE *see* Swiss Federal Office of Energy
SGS *see* subgrid scales
shading:
 coefficient, 3: 323
 devices, 1: 701, 1: 702, 1: 704, 1: 705
 wind park micro-siting, 2: 191
shadow:
 building-integrated photovoltaics, 1: 701, 1: 702
 flickering, 2: 182, 2: 522
shallow geothermal heat pumps, 7: **187–206**
shallow reservoirs, 6: 368
shallow resource systems, 7: 5
shallow water technology, 2: 431, 2: 441
Shapai Project, 6: 495
shape accuracy: solar collectors, 3: 167, 3: 169
shape effects: plasmonic scattering, 1: 645
shape factor: wind turbine energy yields, 2: 114, 2: 122, 2: 136, 2: 137, 2: 138, 2: 144
Sharp Corporation, 1: 170
Shasta temperature control device, 6: 90
shear: wind shear, 2: 78, 2: 140
shea residues, 5: 58
shelter models: wind energy, 2: 86
Shewanella: microbial fuel cells, 4: 273
SHG *see* solar heat gain
SHGC *see* solar heat gain coefficient
Shibaozhai Camp, Zhong County, 6: 217, 6: 217f
shift effect: geothermal energy resistivity explorations, 7: 71

shifting:
 see also down-shifting
 photovoltaics, 1: 519, 1: 520
 water gas shift, 5: 146
Shi Lianghe key project, 6: 399, 6: 400f
ship lift, 6: 198
ship locks, 6: 193, 6: 197, 6: 207, 6: 223, 6: 224
ships/shipping:
 hydrogen end-use applications, 4: 64, 4: 289
 product-integrated photovoltaics, 1: 714, 1: 714f
 proton-exchange membrane fuel cells, 4: 218
 wind energy, 2: 54, 2: 55f
Shockley–Queisser model:
 photon recycling, 1: 308
 photovoltaic downconversion, 1: 549
 photovoltaic thermodynamics, 1: 338
 photovoltaic upconversion, 1: 533
 solar energy conversion principles, 1: 294, 1: 308, 1: 309, 1: 310f, 1: 312
Shockley–Roosbroeck relationship, 1: 329–330
shore distance considerations: offshore wind costs, 2: 481
short-circuit currents, 1: 294
short-circuits: PEM fuel cells, 4: 314
short-crested waves: ocean wave energy, 8: 80
short-rotation coppice (SRC), 5: 57, 5: 263
short-rotation crops (SRC), 5: 263
short-rotation forestry (SRF), 5: 263, 5: 264
 costs, 5: 277
 production inputs, 5: 277
 sustainability, 5: 281
short-rotation intensive culture (SRIC), 5: 263
short-rotation woody crops (SRWC), 5: 263, 5: 264
 costs, 5: 277
 production inputs, 5: 277
 sustainability, 5: 281
short-term distribution: ocean wave extreme states, 8: 52, 8: 65
short-term reserves: wind energy variable costs, 2: 490
shrinkage: concrete structure durability, 6: 381
Shuman, Frank, 3: 92, 3: 93f
shutdown: wind turbines, 2: 246
SI *see* spark-ignition
Siemens:
 absorbers, 3: 184
 alkaline fuel cells, 4: 174
 offshore wind power, 2: 437
 polysilicon production process, 1: 173
 wind turbine electrical systems, 2: 314
Sierra SunTower Generating Station, 3: 620, 3: 621f
signal noise: ocean wave satellite altimeters, 8: 36
signal transmission: photovoltaic future visions, 1: 196
significant wave height, 8: 37, 8: 80
silica enthalpy models, 7: 138, 7: 138f
silica flume, 6: 393
silica gels, 3: 225, 3: 226t
silica geothermometers, 7: 137, 7: 138, 7: 138f
silica scaling:
 geothermal environments, 7: 249–250, 7: 250
 geothermal geochemistry, 7: 153
 wells, 7: 41, 7: 42
silicon base tandem stack selective coatings, 3: 306
silicon detector radiometers, 1: 219–220
silicon photovoltaics, 1: **353–387**, 1: **389–398**
 see also crystalline silicon
 Abu Dhabi desert area, 1: 691
 amorphous silicon, 1: 8, 1: 21, 1: 144, 1: 389, 1: 393
 amorphous-silicon–carbon-silicon heterojunctions, 1: 393
 blend cells, 1: 379, 1: 393
 carbon-silicon solar cells, 1: 393
 deposition, 1: 389
 disruptive technologies, 1: 21
 environmental impacts, 1: 144
 evolutionary technologies, 1: 19
 fabrication, 1: 395

silicon photovoltaics (*continued*)
   future technologies, **1:** 353–387
   global industry overview, **1:** 163, **1:** 165, **1:** 166, **1:** 173
   heterojunction cells, **1:** 393
   hydrogen plasma, **1:** 389
   light trapping, **1:** 393
   luminescent down-shifting, **1:** 567
   micro-and nanotechnologies, **1:** 522
   microcrystalline silicon thin films, **1:** 389–390, **1:** 391
   module fabrication, **1:** 395
   multijunction solar cells, **1:** 392
   photon management, **1:** 393, **1:** 395
   production processes, **1:** 173
   research challenges, **1:** 394
   solar spectrum, **1:** 746, **1:** 746*f*
   space applications, **1:** 396
   state-of-the-art technology, **1:** 353–387
   technology progress, **1:** 19, **1:** 20, **1:** 21, **1:** 25
   thin-films, **1: 389–398**, **1:** 8
     amorphous silicon, **1:** 8, **1:** 21, **1:** 389, **1:** 393
     amorphous-silicon–carbon-silicon heterojunctions, **1:** 393
     applications, **1:** 396
     carbon-silicon solar cells, **1:** 393
     deposition, **1:** 389
     fabrication, **1:** 395
     heterojunction cells, **1:** 393
     hydrogen plasma, **1:** 389
     light trapping, **1:** 393
     microcrystalline silicon, **1:** 389–390, **1:** 391
     module fabrication, **1:** 395
     multijunction solar cells, **1:** 392
     photon management, **1:** 393, **1:** 395
     research challenges, **1:** 394
     space applications, **1:** 396
silver coatings, **3:** 325
similarity:
   hydrogen safety engineering, **4:** 88
   ocean wave energy, **8:** 84
simplified generic axial-flow microhydro turbines, **6: 435–466**
   blade shape, **6:** 455
   component-level design methods, **6:** 443
   definitions, **6:** 436
   design concepts, **6: 435–466**
   diffusers, **6:** 456, **6:** 460
   direct sizing, **6:** 463
   draft tubes, **6:** 444, **6:** 456
   energy alternatives, **6:** 442
   hydropower design concepts, **6: 435–466**
   inlet volute limits, **6:** 452, **6:** 463
   open flumes, **6:** 449
   penstock supply, **6:** 445
   propeller turbines, **6:** 439, **6:** 441–442, **6:** 461, **6:** 461*t*, **6:** 463*t*, **6:** 465
   representative designs, **6:** 438
   runners, **6:** 437–438, **6:** 444, **6:** 450, **6:** 453
   selection techniques, **6:** 460
   sizing, **6:** 463
   specific speed, **6:** 442, **6:** 455
   speed, **6:** 442, **6:** 455
   swirl, **6:** 450, **6:** 451, **6:** 460
   tangential inlet volute limits, **6:** 452, **6:** 463
   usability, **6:** 438
   volute, **6:** 437, **6:** 444, **6:** 449
   water supply, **6:** 444
   weir supply, **6:** 445
simulations:
   active solar systems, **3:** 396
   building-integrated photovoltaic-thermal systems, **3:** 379
   components of solar thermal systems, **3: 357–417**
   down-shifting, **1:** 571
   passive solar technologies, **3:** 359
   photovoltaics
     down-shifting, **1:** 571
     solar irradiance, **1:** 262, **1:** 281

   thermal systems, **3:** 379
   reservoir water quality, **6:** 72
   solar irradiance, **1:** 262, **1:** 281
   solar thermal systems, **3: 357–417**
   solar water heating design principles, **3:** 438, **3:** 441*f*
   stand alone wind energy hybrid systems, **2:** 651
   wind speed time series, **2:** 88
Singaporean photovoltaics:
   challenges, **1:** 82
   future prospects, **1:** 82
   promotion schemes, **1:** 79, **1:** 103
   solar capability scheme, **1:** 79, **1:** 80
   support mechanisms, **1:** 79, **1:** 103
single crystal research, **1:** 20, **1:** 20*f*
single-effect lithium-bromide–water absorption systems, **3:** 466, **3:** 467*f*, **3:** 468*f*, **3:** 470
single-family housing, **3:** 442
single-flash power plants, **7:** 207, **7:** 217, **7:** 217*f*, **7:** 218, **7:** 231
single glass-type evacuated tube collectors, **3:** 116, **3:** 117*f*
single-glazed stationary collectors, **3:** 124, **3:** 124*t*
single-glazed windows:
   coatings, **3:** 331
   colorants, **3:** 331
   low-emittance coatings, **3:** 331
   reflective coatings, **3:** 331
   self-cleaning glazing, **3:** 331
   tinted glass, **3:** 331
single-junction solar cells, **1:** 497–498
single-organic solar cell device production, **1:** 470
single-stage chalcopyrite thin film deposition, **1:** 406, **1:** 406*f*, **1:** 407
single-stem hardwoods, **5:** 263, **5:** 264, **5:** 268
single-stem softwoods, **5:** 274
single-stem woody crops, **5:** 264, **5:** 268, **5:** 274, **5:** 276
   handling, **5:** 276
   harvesting, **5:** 276
single-step chalcopyrite thin film deposition, **1:** 406, **1:** 406*f*, **1:** 407
single tangential inlet volute limits, **6:** 452, **6:** 463
singlet fission, **1:** 549, **1:** 559
single threshold solar cells (STSC), **1: 549–561**, **1: 533–548**
single-walled carbon nanotubes, **5:** 405
Sinovel: wind turbines, **2:** 324
Siphon propeller turbines, **6:** 439
site investigations: geothermal heat pumps, **7:** 195, **7:** 198
site layouts:
   building-integrated photovoltaics, **1:** 699
   Horseshoe Bend hydroelectric scheme, **6:** 474
   roller compacted concrete dams, **6:** 474
site location: wind power, **2:** 394, **2:** 397, **2:** 398
site remediation: biochar, **5:** 380
site restoration: wind power, **2:** 429
site selection:
   land morphology, **2:** 174
   sea trials, **8:** 99, **8:** 102
   wind park design, **2:** 171
site-specific solar irradiance-photovoltaic power forecasts, **1:** 281
site-to-grid transmission costs, **8:** 157
SIWT *see* Self Installing Wind Turbine
size considerations:
   biomass-to-liquids technology, **5:** 162
   Fischer–Tropsch process, **5:** 162
   Fresnel collectors, **3:** 196
   high concentration solar collectors, **3:** 176, **3:** 196
   parabolic troughs, **3:** 176
   plasmonics, **1:** 644
   scattering, **1:** 644
   wind turbines, **2:** 95, **2:** 416, **2:** 676
sizing:
   axial-flow microhydro turbines, **6:** 463
   stand alone hybrid wind energy systems, **2:** 632
Skartveit–Olseth model, **3:** 48
skill scores, **1:** 269
skin contact: alcohol fuel safety, **5:** 324

Index

Skive, Denmark, **5**: 149
sky imagers: cloud motion vectors, **1**: 245, **1**: 249, **1**: 251
SkyTrough, **3**: 182
sky-glazing, **3**: 130
slag: concrete structures, **6**: 393
sliding: geothermal energy hazards, **7**: 58
slip rings, **2**: 270, **2**: 284
slit buckets, **6**: 485, **6**: 487, **6**: 490f, **6**: 491f
sloped-wall roadside ditch construction, **6**: 423
slopes: ship locks, **6**: 197, **6**: 224
slow pyrolysis, **5**: 366, **5**: 366t, **5**: 373f
sludge pretreatments, **4**: 273
sluicing structures, **6**: 188
slurry bed reactors, **5**: 181
slurry bubble column reactors, **5**: 181
small-scale systems:
    concentrating solar power, **3**: 627
    developing country photovoltaics, **1**: 127
    Horseshoe Bend hydropower scheme, **6: 467–483**
    hydropower, **6**: 346, **6: 467–483**
    noninterconnected power systems, **2**: 211, **2**: 212
    PEMFC power generation markets, **4**: 200
    photovoltaics
        developing countries, **1**: 127
        solar irradiance forecasts, **1**: 243
    power producer regulation, **1**: 127
    solar irradiance forecasts, **1**: 243
    Swiss hydropower, **6**: 346
    wind park design, **2**: 211, **2**: 212
    wind turbines
        certification standards, **2**: 388
        classification, **2**: 301, **2**: 304t
        costs, **2**: 477
        electrical systems, **2**: 301
        IEC standards, **2**: 374
        onshore wind costs, **2**: 477
        technology, **2**: 696, **2**: 713
smart grids, **1**: 190, **2**: 496
Smeaton, John, **2**: 50
SMES *see* superconducting magnetic energy storage
Smith-Putnam Machine, **2**: 56
smock mills, **2**: 47, **2**: 47f
SMR *see* steam methane reforming
SNG *see* synthetic natural gas
snow:
    cover, **1**: 283, **1**: 286
    depth, **1**: 230
    melting, **7**: 169, **7**: 173t
SNT-1 *see* SenerTrough
social issues:
    acceptability
        offshore wind power, **2**: 535
        public attitude analysis, **2**: 534, **2**: 535
        wind farms, **2**: 204f, **2**: 205
        wind park design, **2**: 202, **2**: 204f, **2**: 205
        wind power, **2**: 531, **2**: 534, **2**: 535
    benefits/impacts
        employment, **2**: 507, **2**: 508
        fossil fuel savings/substitution, **2**: 507
        job opportunities, **2**: 507, **2**: 508
        very large-scale photovoltaic systems, **1**: 733, **1**: 734t
        wind power, **2: 503–539**
    benefits/impacts wind power, **2**: 503
    biodiesel from vegetable oil, **5**: 219
    bioenergy policy development, **5**: 417
    bioethanol development, **5**: 21
    developing solar thermal systems, **3**: 6
    employment, **2**: 507, **2**: 508
    fossil fuel savings/substitution, **2**: 507
    geothermal energy sustainable development, **7**: 275, **7**: 282, **7**: 287
    hydropower, **6**: 38, **6**: 210, **6**: 236
        development and progress, **6**: 9
        India, **6**: 251
        sustainability, **6**: 50
    Indian hydropower, **6**: 251
    job opportunities, **2**: 507, **2**: 508
    offshore wind power, **2**: 463, **2**: 535
    public attitude analysis, **2**: 534, **2**: 535
    pumped-storage power plants, **6**: 287
    resettlements, **6**: 210
    responsibility
        bioethanol development, **5**: 21
        pumped-storage power plants, **6**: 287
    socioeconomic development, Indian hydropower, **6**: 251
    solar thermal systems, **3**: 6
    sustainable geothermal energy, **7**: 275, **7**: 282, **7**: 287
    Three Gorges Project, China, **6**: 210, **6**: 211
    vegetable oil biodiesel, **5**: 219
    very large-scale photovoltaic systems, **1**: 733, **1**: 734t
    wind power, **2: 503–539**
        acceptability, **2**: 531, **2**: 534, **2**: 535
        employment, **2**: 507, **2**: 508
        fossil fuel savings/substitution, **2**: 507
        job opportunities, **2**: 507, **2**: 508
        wind farm acceptability, **2**: 204f, **2**: 205
        wind park design acceptability, **2**: 202, **2**: 204f, **2**: 205
    wind turbines, environmental impact reduction, **2**: 687
sodium borohydride fuel, **4**: 180
sodium equivalent: alkali–aggregate reaction, **6**: 389
sodium potassium geothermometers, **7**: 139–140
SOFC *see* solid oxide fuel cells
soft loans, **1**: 128
soft starters: wind turbines, **2**: 296
software:
    geochemistry reaction paths/speciation, **7**: 128
    geothermal energy physics, **7**: 35
    HOMER, **2**: 652, **2**: 653t
    Hybrid2, **2**: 652, **2**: 653t
    reservoir water quality, **6**: 53
    solar thermal systems, **3**: 396, **3**: 411, **3**: 413
    stand alone hybrid wind energy systems, **2**: 651
    TRNSYS simulation, **3**: 396, **3**: 411
    WATSUN simulation, **3**: 396, **3**: 413
soil organic matter (SOM):
    benefits, **5**: 358–359, **5**: 359t
    biochar, **5**: 357, **5**: 358, **5**: 365, **5**: 375, **5**: 379–380
    effects, **5**: 358–359, **5**: 359t
    soil quality, **5**: 358–359, **5**: 359t
soils:
    see also soil organic matter
    biochar, **5: 357–384**
    conditioners, **5**: 357
    contamination, **5**: 383
    fertility, **5**: 358, **5**: 358f, **5**: 362–363, **5**: 365
    geothermal energy sustainable development, **7**: 284
    greenhouse gas life cycle assessments, **5**: 121
    half-lives, **5**: 364
    interaction loads, wind turbines, **2**: 253
    life cycle assessments, **5**: 121
    nitrous oxide emissions, **5**: 121
    quality, **5: 357–384**
    wind turbine interaction loads, **2**: 253
solar access: building-integrated photovoltaics, **1**: 699
solar air heating, **3**: 587
solar angles, **3**: 8
solar architecture *see* passive solar architecture
solar assisted heat pumps, **3: 495–528**
    central heating plant with seasonal storage, **3**: 522, **3**: 525
    classification, **3**: 506
    concepts, **3**: 495
    configurations, **3**: 506
    direct systems, **3**: 507
    dual source systems, **3**: 516
    energy seasonal storage, **3**: 519
    functions, **3**: 506
    ground storage, **3**: 520, **3**: 521
    heat transfer, **3**: 524

solar assisted heat pumps (*continued*)
    mass transfer, **3**: 524
    operation modes, **3**: 495, **3**: 510, **3**: 513, **3**: 515, **3**: 517, **3**: 519
    parallel systems, **3**: 511
    seasonal storage, **3**: 519, **3**: 520, **3**: 521
    series systems, **3**: 508
    underground thermal energy storage, **3**: 495, **3**: 500, **3**: 503–504, **3**: 522
solar atlases, **3**: 28, **3**: 58
solar broadband radiation, **3**: 39
solar capability scheme (SCS), **1**: 79, **1**: 80
solar cells:
    see also multi-junction cells; organic solar cells; photovoltaics
    absorption profiles, **1**: 296
    artificial leaves, **1**: 674
    circuits, **1**: 294
    construction, **1**: 674
    efficiencies, **1**: 339
    equation, **1**: 337
    incident light down-shifting, **1: 563–585**
    intrinsic loss mechanisms, **1**: 294, **1**: 309
    loss mechanisms, **1**: 294, **1**: 309
    materials, thermophotovoltaics, **1**: 608
    mesoporous dye-sensitized solar cells, **1: 481–496**
    optimum voltages, **1**: 342
    performance
        indoor irradiance, **1**: 721
        irradiance, **1**: 720
        outdoor irradiance, **1**: 720
        product-integrated photovoltaics, **1**: 717, **1**: 720
    photosynthesis, **1**: 674
    production capacities, **1**: 162, **1**: 164, **1**: 167
    production companies, **1**: 169
    silicon, **1: 389–398**
    single threshold cells, **1: 549–561**, **1: 533–548**
    solar energy conversion principles
        absorption profiles, **1**: 296
        circuits, **1**: 294
        loss mechanisms, **1**: 294, **1**: 309
    technology, **1: 5–11**
        very large-scale photovoltaic systems, **1**: 737
    thermophotovoltaics, **1**: 608
    thin-film silicon, **1: 389–398**
    upconversion, **1: 533–548**
solar coefficient of performance (SCOP), **3**: 482, **3**: 484, **3**: 488, **3**: 489, **3**: 490
solar collectors *see* collectors
solar Combisystems, **3**: 444, **3**: 446*f*
solar concentration/concentrators:
    luminescence, **1: 587–601**
    photovoltaics, **1**: 9
        luminescence, **1: 587–601**
        upconversion, **1**: 538
    upconversion, **1**: 538
solar constant, **3**: 28, **3**: 32
solar control:
    buildings, **3**: 289
    FRESNEL photovoltaic/thermal solar collectors, **3**: 289
    glazings, **3**: 323
    low-emittance coatings, **3**: 323
solar cooking:
    agricultural applications, **3**: 588
    analysis, **3**: 589
    definitions, **3**: 567
    energy balance, **3**: 589
    industrial applications, **3**: 588
    types, **3**: 588
solar cooling, **3: 449–480**, **3: 481–494**
    absorption, **3**: 461, **3**: 464, **3**: 465, **3**: 471, **3**: 472, **3**: 484, **3**: 612
    adsorption, **3**: 461, **3**: 463, **3**: 486, **3**: 613
    air-conditioning, **3**: 460
    ammonia–water absorption systems, **3**: 471, **3**: 472
    applications, **3**: 492

    asphalt layers, **3**: 648
    best-practice, **3**: 613
    capital cost comparison, **3**: 491
    chillers, **3**: 612, **3**: 613
    coatings, **3**: 646, **3**: 648
    cogeneration, **3**: 611
    coloured coatings, **3**: 646
    coloured thin-film asphalt layers, **3**: 648
    comparisons, **3**: 490
    compression-photovoltaic systems, **3**: 489
    concentrating solar power, **3**: 611
    cool materials, **3**: 644, **3**: 646, **3**: 648
    cost comparisons, **3**: 491
    cost-effectiveness, **3**: 492
    desalination, **3**: 614
    desiccant systems, **3**: 461, **3**: 464, **3**: 482, **3**: 483
    differential temperature controllers, **3**: 478
    ejector cooling systems, **3**: 489
    heat exchangers, **3**: 477
    heat storage, active solar systems, **3**: 473
    history, **3**: 94
    hot water integration, **3**: 492
    life-cycle costs, **3**: 491
    liquid desiccants, **3**: 483
    lithium-bromide–water absorption systems, **3**: 465, **3**: 471*t*
    lithium–water absorption systems, **3**: 465, **3**: 471*t*
    market expectations, **3**: 614
    materials, **3**: 644, **3**: 646, **3**: 648
    mechanical systems, **3**: 462
    need for, **3**: 481
    off-heat usage, **3**: 615
    passive solar architecture, **3**: 642, **3**: 644
        asphalt layers, **3**: 648
        coatings, **3**: 646, **3**: 648
        coloured coatings, **3**: 646
        materials, **3**: 644, **3**: 646, **3**: 648
        phase change materials, **3**: 646
        thermochromic coatings, **3**: 648
        thin-film asphalt layers, **3**: 648
    phase change materials, **3**: 646
    photovoltaic-compression systems, **3**: 489
    prime movers, **3**: 462
    principles, **3**: 612
    refrigeration, **3**: 464, **3**: 465, **3**: 471, **3**: 472
    solar coefficient of performance, **3**: 482, **3**: 484, **3**: 488, **3**: 489, **3**: 490
    solar fraction, **3**: 491
    solar hot water, **3**: 492
    solid desiccants, **3**: 483
    sorption, **3**: 461, **3**: 463, **3**: 464, **3**: 465
    state of the art, **3**: 614
    technologies, **3**: 482, **3**: 490
    thermally driven systems, **3: 481–494**
    thermal storage, **3**: 473
    thermochromic coatings, **3**: 648
    thin-film asphalt layers, **3**: 648
    urban buildings, **3**: 642, **3**: 644
solar declination, **3**: 28
solar dehumidification, **3**: 542
solar desalination, **3: 529–565**
    Abu Dhabi, UAE, **3**: 547
    agricultural applications, **3**: 589
    Almeria, Spain, **3**: 549
    applications, **3**: 547
    Aqaba, Jordan, **3**: 560, **3**: 562*f*, **3**: 563*f*
    basin stills, **3**: 589, **3**: 591
    brackish water, **3**: 529, **3**: 538, **3**: 539*t*, **3**: 556
        reverse osmosis, **3**: 538, **3**: 539*t*, **3**: 556, **3**: 558, **3**: 560, **3**: 560*t*, **3**: 563*f*
    Ceara, Brazil, **3**: 556
    Coité-Pedreiras, Ceara, Brazil, **3**: 556
    collectors, **3**: 530, **3**: 530*f*, **3**: 530–531, **3**: 531, **3**: 531*f*, **3**: 531*t*
    dehumidification, **3**: 542

distillation, 3: 541
economics, 3: 564
electrodialysis, 3: 536, 3: 537, 3: 538f, 3: 540f, 3: 541f, 3: 547
examples, 3: 547
freshwater, 3: **529–565**
history, 3: 85, 3: 97
humidification, 3: 542
industrial applications, 3: 589
Lampedusa Island, Italy, 3: 553
lessons learned, 3: 563
markets, 3: 564
membrane distillation, 3: 543
multieffect distillation, 3: 531, 3: 533, 3: 533f, 3: 534, 3: 534t, 3: 535, 3: 535f, 3: 536f, 3: 547, 3: 549
multistage flash, 3: 531, 3: 532, 3: 532f, 3: 534, 3: 534t
passive stills, 3: 589, 3: 591
photovoltaic-driven systems, 3: 536
    electrodialysis, 3: 537, 3: 538f, 3: 540f, 3: 541f, 3: 547
    reverse osmosis, 3: 530, 3: 536, 3: 553, 3: 556, 3: 558, 3: 560
        brackish water, 3: 538, 3: 539t, 3: 556, 3: 558, 3: 560, 3: 560t, 3: 563f
        seawater, 3: 539t, 3: 553, 3: 558
Pozo Izquierdo, Gran Canaria Island, 3: 558
reverse osmosis, 3: 530, 3: 536, 3: 553, 3: 556, 3: 558, 3: 560
Sadous Riyadh Region, Saudi Arabia, 3: 558, 3: 560t
Saudi Arabia, 3: 558, 3: 560t
seawater, 3: 529, 3: 539t, 3: 547, 3: 549, 3: 553
solar dehumidification, 3: 542
solar energy history, 3: 85, 3: 100
solar humidification, 3: 542
solar membrane distillation, 3: 543
solar stills, 3: 541
solar thermal systems, 3: 529, 3: 530, 3: 547
stills, 3: 541
technology selection guidelines, 3: 546
thermal systems, 3: 529, 3: 530, 3: 547
water production, 3: **529–565**
solar design: building-integrated photovoltaics, 1: 702
solar–diesel systems, 1: 687
solar dishes:
    Brayton engines, 3: 201
    characteristics, 3: 200
    components, 3: 200
    concentrating solar power, 3: 605, 3: 622
    construction, 3: 203
    control, 3: 205
    efficiency, 3: 202
    error sources, 3: 203
    EuroDish, 3: 203
    geometry, 3: 201
    high concentration solar collectors, 3: 199
    Infinia Solar System, 3: 204
    maintenance, 3: 205
    manufacturers, 3: 203
    materials, 3: 201
    models, 3: 203
    operation and maintenance, 3: 205
    performance, 3: 202
    power conversion, 3: 605
    receivers, 3: 199
    research, 3: 204
    Science Applications International Corp:, 3: 204
    Stirling devices, 3: 201, 3: 203
    STM Power, Inc, 3: 204
    structure, 3: 200
    surface characteristics, 3: 201
    system-specific performance determination, 3: 202
    types, 3: 201
    working gases, 3: 202
solar distillation, 3: 85, 3: 97
solar drying:
    agriculture, 3: 579, 7: 169, 7: 173t, 7: 174, 7: 176f, 7: 180, 7: 180f, 7: 181, 7: 182, 7: 183f

analysis, 3: 582
definitions, 3: 568
industrial applications, 3: 579
mathematical models, 3: 582
practical issues, 3: 582
types, 3: 580
solar energy:
    see also solar thermal energy systems
    absorption, 3: 128
    adsorption systems, 3: 248, 3: 250
    air thermal energy storage systems, 3: 215, 3: 227, 3: 228t, 3: 229, 3: 230
    altitude angles, 3: 11
    aquifer thermal energy storage systems, 3: 211, 3: 219
    azimuth angles, 3: 12
    borehole thermal energy storage systems, 3: 211, 3: 219, 3: 237
    chemical reactions, 3: 211, 3: 224
    closed adsorption systems, 3: 248
    collectors
        fuels, resources assessments, 1: 217
        history, 3: 85, 3: 91
    combisystems, 3: 232
    concentrating system history, 3: 95
    concrete, 3: 212, 3: 242
    conversion, 1: **213–237**, 1: **293–313**, 1: **657–677**
        absorption profiles, 1: 296
        below E_g losses, 1: 309, 1: 310
        bio-inspiration, 1: **657–677**
        blackbody radiation, 1: 295, 1: 296
        Boltzmann losses, 1: 309, 1: 311
        Carnot losses, 1: 309, 1: 311
        carrier-carrier generation, 1: 303
        carrier-carrier recombination, 1: 303
        carrier density, 1: 299
        carrier populations, 1: 298
        chemical energy, thermal energy, 1: 304
        circuits, solar cells, 1: 294
        current extraction, 1: 305
        detailed balance, 1: 308
        doping semiconductors, 1: 300
        E_g losses, 1: 309, 1: 310
        electron state density, 1: 298, 1: 299, 1: 300f
        electron state occupation, 1: 299
        emission losses, 1: 309, 1: 311
        energy bands, 1: 294, 1: 297
        fuels, solar energy potential, 1: **213–237**
        fundamental principles, 1: **293–313**
        generalized Planck equation, 1: 305
        generation, 1: 301
        geometrical factor, 1: 306
        impurity generation, 1: 303
        impurity recombination, 1: 303
        intrinsic loss mechanisms, 1: 294, 1: 309
        loss mechanisms, solar cells, 1: 294, 1: 309
        photon state density, 1: 306
        photon state occupation, 1: 307
        photovoltaics, 1: **293–313**, 1: **657–677**
        Planck equation, 1: 305
            geometrical factor, 1: 306
            photon state density, 1: 306
            photon state occupation, 1: 307
        p-n junctions, 1: 301
        principles, 1: **293–313**
        radiative generation, 1: 302
        radiative recombination, 1: 302
        recombination, 1: 301
        selective absorber coatings, 3: **301–312**
        semiconductors, 1: 294, 1: 297
            carrier density, 1: 299
            carrier populations, 1: 298
            doping, 1: 300
            electron state density, 1: 298, 1: 299, 1: 300f
            electron state occupation, 1: 299

solar energy: (*continued*)
    energy bands, **1**: 294, **1**: 297
    p-n junctions, **1**: 301
    Shockley–Queisser limiting efficiency, **1**: 308, **1**: 309, **1**: 310*f*, **1**: 312
    solar cells
        absorption profiles, **1**: 296
        circuits, **1**: 294
        loss mechanisms, **1**: 294, **1**: 309
    solar energy potential, fuels, **1: 213–237**
    solar resource, **1**: 295
    surface generation, **1**: 303
    surface recombination, **1**: 303
    thermal energy, chemical energy, **1**: 304
    thermal generation, **1**: 302
    thermalization losses, **1**: 309, **1**: 311
    thermal recombination, **1**: 302
  cooling *see* solar cooling
  day lengths, **3**: 12
  declination angle, **3**: 10
  desalination, **3**: 85, **3: 529–565**, **3**: 97
  designing thermal energy storage, **3**: 213
  distillation, **3**: 85, **3**: 97
  early times history, **3**: 86
  economics of thermal energy storage, **3**: 228
  energy savings of thermal storage, **3**: 227
  engine history, **3**: 85, **3**: 91
  environmental characteristics, **3**: 7
  equation of time, **3**: 8
  evacuated-tube solar collectors, **3**: 85, **3**: 96, **3**: 100, **3**: 101*f*
  flat-plate solar collectors, **3**: 85, **3**: 92, **3**: 93, **3**: 93*f*
  heating, history, **3**: 94, **3**: 97
  heat pipes, **3**: 85, **3**: 97
  heat pumps, **3**: 505–506
  history, **3: 85–102**
    China, **3**: 87, **3**: 88*f*
    collectors, **3**: 85, **3**: 91
    concentrating systems, **3**: 95
    cooling, **3**: 94
    desalination, **3**: 85, **3**: 97
    distillation, **3**: 85, **3**: 97
    early times, **3**: 86
    engines, **3**: 85, **3**: 91
    evacuated-tube solar collectors, **3**: 85, **3**: 96, **3**: 100, **3**: 101*f*
    flat-plate solar collectors, **3**: 85, **3**: 92, **3**: 93, **3**: 93*f*
    heating, **3**: 94, **3**: 97
    heat pipes, **3**: 85, **3**: 97
    Middle Ages, **3**: 87
    scientific meetings/conventions, **3**: 96
    selective surfaces, **3**: 85, **3**: 93
    solar collectors, **3**: 85, **3**: 91
    solar distillation, **3**: 85, **3**: 97
    solar-driven desalination, **3**: 85, **3**: 100
    solar engines, **3**: 85, **3**: 91
    space cooling, **3**: 94
    Sun, **3**: 86
    twentieth century, **3**: 91
  hour angle, **3**: 11
  hydropower multibenefit solutions, **6**: 43
  incidence angles, **3**: 12, **3**: 13
  latent heat, **3**: 211, **3**: 221, **3**: 225*t*, **3**: 227, **3**: 228*t*, **3**: 229, **3**: 230, **3**: 230*f*, **3**: 231
  liquid media, **3**: 216, **3**: 219, **3**: 227, **3**: 228*t*, **3**: 232, **3**: 239
  longitude correction, **3**: 8
  Middle Ages, history, **3**: 87
  moving surface incidence angles, **3**: 12, **3**: 13
  open adsorption systems, **3**: 250
  phase change materials, **3**: 211, **3**: 221–222, **3**: 222*f*, **3**: 223, **3**: 224, **3**: 225*t*, **3**: 228*t*, **3**: 229, **3**: 230, **3**: 230*f*, **3**: 243, **3**: 247, **3**: 249*f*
  potential fuels, **1: 213–237**
  renewable portfolio standards, **1**: 76, **1**: 85, **1**: 127
  rock storage, **3**: 227, **3**: 228*t*
  scientific meetings/conventions, **3**: 96
  seasonal storage, **3**: 248
  selective surfaces, **3**: 85, **3**: 93
  sensible heat, **3**: 211, **3**: 214, **3**: 225*t*, **3**: 227, **3**: 228*t*, **3**: 232, **3**: 237, **3**: 239, **3**: 242
  solar angles, **3**: 8
  solar engines, **3**: 85, **3**: 91
  sorption systems, **3**: 224, **3**: 248, **3**: 250
  space cooling, **3**: 94, **3: 449–480**
  space heating, **3**: 94, **3: 449–480**
  standards, renewable portfolios, **1**: 76, **1**: 85, **1**: 127
  Sun, history, **3**: 86
  sun path diagrams, **3**: 17
  sun rise/set times, **3**: 12
  thermal energy storage, **3: 211–253**
    adsorption systems, **3**: 250
    air systems, **3**: 215, **3**: 227, **3**: 228*t*, **3**: 229, **3**: 230
    chemical reactions, **3**: 211, **3**: 224
    closed adsorption systems, **3**: 248
    combisystems, **3**: 232
    concrete, **3**: 212, **3**: 242
    design, **3**: 213
    economics, **3**: 228
    energy savings, **3**: 227
    latent heat, **3**: 211, **3**: 221, **3**: 225*t*, **3**: 227, **3**: 228*t*, **3**: 229, **3**: 230, **3**: 230*f*, **3**: 231, **3**: 243, **3**: 247
    liquid media, **3**: 216, **3**: 219, **3**: 227, **3**: 228*t*, **3**: 232, **3**: 239
    open adsorption systems, **3**: 250
    phase change materials, **3**: 211, **3**: 221–222, **3**: 222*f*, **3**: 223, **3**: 224, **3**: 225*t*, **3**: 228*t*, **3**: 229, **3**: 230, **3**: 230*f*, **3**: 243, **3**: 247, **3**: 249*f*
    rock storage, **3**: 227, **3**: 228*t*
    seasonal storage, **3**: 248
    sensible heat, **3**: 211, **3**: 214, **3**: 225*t*, **3**: 227, **3**: 228*t*, **3**: 232, **3**: 237, **3**: 239, **3**: 242
    sorption systems, **3**: 224, **3**: 248, **3**: 250
    thermochemical heat, **3**: 211, **3**: 224
    thermoeconomics, **3**: 228
    water storage, **3**: 216, **3**: 227, **3**: 228*t*, **3**: 232
  thermochemical heat, **3**: 211, **3**: 224
  thermoeconomics, **3**: 228
  twentieth century history, **3**: 91
  underground thermal energy storage, **3**: 211, **3**: 219, **3**: 237
  water storage, **3**: 216, **3**: 227, **3**: 228*t*, **3**: 232
Solar Energy Development Center (SEDC), **3**: 628
Solar Energy Research Institute of Singapore (SERIS), **1**: 79, **1**: 81
solar engines: history, **3**: 85, **3**: 91
solar fraction, **3**: 491, **3**: 568
solar furnaces, **3**: 87
SolarGenix collectors, **3**: 180
solar geometry, **1**: 215, **3**: 28
solar-geothermal hybrid power plants, **7**: 230
solar heat, **3: 419–447**, **3: 449–480**, **3: 567–594**
solar heat gain coefficient (SHGC), **3**: 323
solar heat gain (SHG), **3**: 322
solar heating: passive solar architecture, **3**: 639
solar hot water:
  cost-effectiveness, **3**: 492
  design principles, **3**: 438
  domestic water, **3: 419–447**
  heating systems, **3: 419–447**
  solar cooling, **3**: 492
  technologies, **3**: 420, **3**: 420*f*, **3**: 425
solar humidification, **3**: 542
solar industrial process heat: definitions, **3**: 568
solar irradiance:
  atmospheric processes, **1**: 246
  characteristics, **1**: 246
  cloud motion vectors, **1**: 245, **1**: 249, **1**: 251
  coatings, **3**: 316
  European Centre for Medium-Range Weather Forecasts, **1**: 245, **1**: 252, **1**: 254
  evaluation concepts, **1**: 265, **1**: 271, **1**: 285

forecasting, **1**: 246
glazings, **3**: 316
grid integration, **1**: 241
measurements, **1**: 271
mesoscale models, **1**: 256
models, photovoltaic power, **1**: 243, **1**: 256
module plane, **1**: 260
numerical weather prediction, **1**: 240–241, **1**: 245, **1**: 248, **1**: 252, **1**: 257, **1**: 271, **1**: 273, **1**: 275
photovoltaic power
    cloud motion vectors, **1**: 245, **1**: 249, **1**: 251
    evaluation concepts, **1**: 265, **1**: 271, **1**: 285
    forecasting, **1**: **239–292**
    models, **1**: 243
    numerical weather prediction, **1**: 240–241, **1**: 245, **1**: 248, **1**: 252, **1**: 257, **1**: 271, **1**: 273
    predictions, **1**: **239–292**
    satellite-based forecasts, **1**: 249, **1**: 275
    simulations, **1**: 262, **1**: 281
    snow cover, **1**: 283, **1**: 286
    statistical methods, **1**: 248, **1**: 265
    time series models, **1**: 245, **1**: 248
power predictions, **1**: **239–292**
regional photovoltaic power predictions, **1**: 264, **1**: 277
satellite-based forecasts, **1**: 249, **1**: 275
simulations, **1**: 262, **1**: 281
small networks, **1**: 243
snow cover, **1**: 283, **1**: 286
stand-alone systems, **1**: 243
statistical methods, **1**: 248, **1**: 265
time series models, **1**: 245, **1**: 248
solar machines: history, **3**: 85
solar membrane distillation, **3**: 543
Solarmundo, **3**: 198
Solar One power plant, **3**: 624
Solar Pathfinder, **3**: 63
solar photovoltaic electricity *see* photovoltaics
solar ponds:
    agricultural applications, **3**: 572, **3**: 587*t*
    history, **3**: 92, **3**: 93
    industrial applications, **3**: 572, **3**: 587*t*
    solar assisted heat pumps, **3**: 520
    thermal energy storage, **3**: 217
solar power:
    concentrating solar power, **3**: 600
    history, **3**: 92, **3**: 93*f*, **3**: 96, **3**: 96*f*
    power conversion systems, **3**: 600
    satellites, **1**: **767–774**
        apertures, **1**: 768, **1**: 770
        atmospheric factors, **1**: 771
        dirty economics, **1**: 772
        economics, **1**: 772
        future evolution, **1**: 771
        geosynchronous orbits, **1**: 772
        historical overviews, **1**: 767
        laser beaming, **1**: 770
        microwave beaming, **1**: 768, **1**: 769
        microwave transmission efficiency, **1**: 768
        photovoltaics
            historical developments, **1**: 36, **1**: 36*f*
        power-beaming, **1**: 768, **1**: 769, **1**: 770, **1**: 773
        power requirements, **1**: 768, **1**: 769, **1**: 770
        power transmission, **1**: 768, **1**: 769, **1**: 770
        quick economics, **1**: 772
        spot diameters, **1**: 768
        sunlight factors, **1**: 771
        sun pointing, **1**: 771
        transmission efficiency, **1**: 768, **1**: 770
    wind turbine technology evolution, **2**: 715
Solar Power Group (SPG), **3**: 197
solar radiation, **1**: **213–237**, **1**: 214
    absorption, **3**: 36, **3**: 126
    aerosol optical depth, **1**: 214, **1**: 231

application-specific data conversions, **1**: 226
atmospheric effects, **3**: 36
atmospheric filters, **1**: 216
attenuation, **3**: 36
broadband radiation, **1**: 214, **1**: 217, **1**: 231
calculation tools, **3**: 62
coatings, **3**: 316, **3**: 318
coefficient of determination, **3**: 52
collector configurations, **1**: 231, **1**: 233*t*
concentrating collectors, **1**: 232
concentration, **1**: 325
conversion factors, **3**: 80
databases, **1**: 229
data conversions, **1**: 226
data elements, **1**: 227, **1**: 228
data set properties, **1**: 227
data sources, **1**: 227, **1**: 228
definitions, **3**: 2, **3**: 28
diffuse hemispherical radiation, **1**: 214, **1**: 216, **1**: 219, **1**: 224, **1**: 227
direct beam irradiance, **1**: 214, **1**: 216, **1**: 224, **1**: 226
direct normal irradiance, **1**: 214, **1**: 216, **1**: 220, **1**: 224, **1**: 226, **1**: 227
Earth's atmosphere interference, **3**: 34
electrical conversion, **3**: 259
empirical models, **1**: 214
energy conversions, **1**: **213–237**, **1**: 214
evaluation models, **3**: 49
exergy, **1**: 316, **1**: 328
flat plate collectors, **1**: 218, **1**: 232
fundamentals, **1**: 215
future directions, **1**: 234
Geographical Information Systems, **1**: 226
geothermal energy, shallow systems, **7**: 189, **7**: 189*f*
glazing, **3**: 21, **3**: 318
glazings, **3**: 316
horizontal surfaces, **3**: 39
index of agreement, **3**: 52
instrumentation, **3**: 64
interference, **3**: 34
laws, **3**: 318
low-temperature stationary collectors, **3**: 126
mean bias error, **3**: 51
measurements, **1**: 219, **1**: 227, **3**: 64
meteorological data, **1**: 230
Mie scattering, **3**: 36
modeling
    coefficient of determination, **3**: 52
    evaluation models, **3**: 49
    index of agreement, **3**: 52
    mean bias error, **3**: 51
    net solar radiation, **3**: 54
    resources assessments, **1**: 214, **1**: 227
    root mean square error, **3**: 50
    standard deviation, **3**: 50
    t-tests, **3**: 51
optical air mass, **3**: 35, **3**: 80*t*
parametric models, **1**: 214
period of record, **1**: 227
photovoltaic technologies, **1**: 218, **1**: 232
physical constants, **3**: 80
physics-based models, **1**: 225
pyranometers, **1**: 214, **1**: 219, **1**: 220–221, **1**: 223
pyrheliometers, **1**: 214, **1**: 220, **1**: 223
radiative transfer models, **3**: 28, **3**: 40, **3**: 43
radiometry, **1**: 214, **1**: 219, **1**: 221, **1**: 224, **3**: 64, **3**: 78
Rayleigh scattering, **3**: 36
reflection, **3**: 36
refraction, **3**: 21
resources assessments
    databases, **1**: 229
    energy conversions, **1**: **213–237**, **1**: 214
    flat plate collectors, **1**: 218, **1**: 232

solar radiation (*continued*)
    fundamentals, **1**: 215
    modeling, **1**: 214
        physics-based models, **1**: 225
        radiometers, **1**: 214, **1**: 219
        solar energy collector fuels, **1**: 217
    root mean square error, **3**: 50
    satellite-based models, **1**: 215
    solar collector configurations, **1**: 231, **1**: 233*t*
    solar energy collector fuels, **1**: 217
    solar geometry, **1**: 215
    solar radiometers, **3**: 64
    solar resource
        horizontal surfaces, **3**: 39
        spectral distribution, **3**: 67
        tilted surfaces, **3**: 39
    solar thermal flat panels, **1**: 218
    solar thermal systems
        components and applications, **3**: 18
        resources assessments, **1**: 218, **1**: 219
    solar water heating systems, **3**: 438, **3**: 439*f*, **3**: 440*f*
    spatial coverage, **1**: 227, **1**: 228
    spectral considerations, **1**: 216
    spectral distribution, **3**: 67
    spectral models, **3**: 54
    standard deviation, **3**: 50
    station networks, **3**: 58
    sustainable resource assessments, **1**: 219
    temporal resolution, **1**: 227, **1**: 228
    thermal conversion, **3**: 259
    thermal flat panels, **1**: 218
    tilt, **1**: 226, **1**: 246, **1**: 247, **1**: 260, **1**: 281, **3**: 39
    traceability, **1**: 222
    transparent plates, **3**: 21
    t-tests, **3**: 51
    uncertainties, **1**: 224, **1**: 227, **1**: 229
    utility calculation tools, **3**: 62
    values, **3**: 49
    World Radiometric Reference, **1**: 221, **3**: 67
Solar Radiation Network (SolRad-Net), **3**: 60–61
solar radiometry, **3**: 64, **3**: 78
    error corrections, **3**: 67
    solar resource, **3**: 64
    terminology, **3**: 36*t*
    units, **3**: 36*t*
solar reflectance:
    coating/glazing properties, **3**: 317–318, **3**: 318
    passive solar architecture, **3**: 644, **3**: 645
solar refrigeration, **3**: 592
Solar Research Facility Unit power plant, **3**: 628
SolarReserve, **3**: 192, **3**: 633
solar resources, **3**: 27–84
    broadband solar radiation, **3**: 39
    calculation tools, **3**: 62
    conversion factors, **3**: 80
    evaluation models, **3**: 49
    horizontal surfaces, **3**: 39
    meteorological radiation model, **3**: 43
    meteorological year, **3**: 22
    modeling, **3**: 39, **3**: 49
    net solar radiation, **3**: 54
    optical air mass, **3**: 35
    photovoltaic technology introduction, **1**: 8
    physical constants, **3**: 80
    radiometry, **3**: 64, **3**: 78
    solar atlases, **3**: 58
    solar constant, **3**: 32
    solar energy conversion principles, **1**: 295
    solar radiation
        horizontal surfaces, **3**: 39
        spectral distribution, **3**: 67
        station networks, **3**: 58
        tilted surfaces, **3**: 39

    solar radiometry, **3**: 64
    solar spectrum, **3**: 33
    solar thermal systems, **3**: 22
    spectral distribution, **3**: 67
    spectral radiation models, **3**: 54
    Sun—Earth astronomical relations, **3**: 29
    tilted surfaces, **3**: 39
    typical meteorological year, **3**: 22, **3**: 23
    utility calculation tools, **3**: 62
solar service water heating, **3**: 403
solar space cooling systems, **3**: **449–480**
solar space heating, **3**: **449–480**
    see also space heating systems
    active solar systems, **3**: **449–480**
    array design, **3**: 475
    auxiliary sources, **3**: 458
    differential temperature controllers, **3**: 478
    domestic hot water, **3**: 456
    heat exchangers, **3**: 450, **3**: 452*f*, **3**: 454, **3**: 454*f*, **3**: 477
    heat pumps, **3**: 459
    history, **3**: 94
    module design, **3**: 475
    storage tanks, **3**: 458, **3**: 473
    thermal storage, **3**: 473
    water heating systems, **3**: 458, **3**: 459
solar spectrum:
    multijunction cells, **1**: 746, **1**: 746*f*
    Planck's law, **3**: 33
    silicon cells, **1**: 746, **1**: 746*f*
    solar resource, **3**: 33
    Stefan–Boltzmann law, **3**: 20, **3**: 34, **3**: 303
    Wien's displacement law, **1**: 605, **1**: 605*f*, **3**: 33
solar stills, **3**: 541
solar thermal collectors, **1**: 218, **1**: 219
solar thermal energy systems, **3**: **1–25**
    see also solar energy
    absorbers, **3**: 571
    acid rain, **3**: 4
    active systems
        cooling, **3**: **449–480**
        heating, **3**: **449–480**
        modeling, **3**: 396
        simulations, **3**: 396
        space heating, **3**: **449–480**
        water heating, **3**: 449, **3**: 453, **3**: 461
    agricultural applications, **3**: **567–594**
        absorbers, **3**: 571
        air heating, **3**: 587
        characteristics, **3**: 568
        collectors, **3**: 569
        component layouts, **3**: 573
        cooking, **3**: 588
        desalination, **3**: 589
        design, **3**: 577
        direct solar gain, **3**: 587
        drying, **3**: 579, **7**: 169, **7**: 173*t*, **7**: 174, **7**: 176*f*, **7**: 180, **7**: 180*f*, **7**: 181, **7**: 182, **7**: 183*f*
        economics, **3**: 569
        energy storage, **3**: 569
        evacuated tube collectors, **3**: 571, **3**: 587*t*
        flat-plate collectors, **3**: 570, **3**: 571, **3**: 587*t*
        generic process system layouts, **3**: 573
        greenhouses, **3**: 586
        heating buildings, **3**: 587
        heat system design, **3**: 577
        heat system layouts, **3**: 573
        hot water, **3**: 577
        line-axis collectors, **3**: 571, **3**: 587*t*
        operational limits, **3**: 576
        parabolic trough collectors, **3**: 571
        real heat system layouts, **3**: 575
        refrigeration, **3**: 592
        solar ponds, **3**: 572, **3**: 587*t*

Index

stationary collectors, 3: 570, 3: 571, 3: 572, 3: 587t
stills, 3: 589
system layouts, 3: 573
temperature requirements, 3: 568, 3: 569t
thermal energy storage, 3: 569
ventilation, 3: 587
water heating, 3: 577
air heating, 3: 452, 3: 455, 3: 587
air systems, 3: 402
air water heating systems, 3: 452, 3: 455
buildings, coatings/glazings, 3: **313–355**
characteristics, 3: 568
chromogenic materials, 3: 316, 3: 342
climate change, 3: 5
coatings, 3: **313–355**
   modern windows, 3: 316
   optical analysis, 3: 319
   optical properties, 3: 316
   thermal properties, 3: 316
collectors, 3: 329
   agricultural applications, 3: 569
   high concentration solar collectors, 3: **165–209**
   industrial applications, 3: 569
   photovoltaic/thermal solar collectors, 3: **255–300**
components
   high concentration solar collectors, 3: **165–209**
   introduction, 3: **1–25**
   layouts, 3: 573
   modeling, 3: **357–417**
   photovoltaic/thermal solar collectors, 3: **255–300**
   selective coatings, 3: **301–312**
   simulations, 3: **357–417**
   thermal energy storage, 3: **211–253**
concentrating solar power, 3: **595–636**
cooking, 3: 588
cooling systems, 3: **449–480**, 3: **481–494**
desalination, 3: 529, 3: 530, 3: 547, 3: 589
direct circulation systems, 3: 449, 3: 451f
direct solar gain, 3: 587
drying, 3: 579, 7: 169, 7: 173t, 7: 174, 7: 176f, 7: 180, 7: 180f, 7: 181, 7: 182, 7: 183f
economics, 3: 6, 3: 569
electrochromic glazing/windows, 3: 314, 3: 316, 3: 336, 3: 338, 3: 342, 3: 343
energy-related environmental problems, 3: 3
energy storage, 3: **211–253**, 3: 569
environmental characteristics, 3: 7
environmental problems, 3: 3, 3: 5
evacuated glazing, 3: 314, 3: 336
evacuated tube collectors
   agricultural applications, 3: 571, 3: 587t
   industrial applications, 3: 571, 3: 587t
f-chart method, 3: 396, 3: 408, 3: 411
   air systems, 3: 402
   heat exchanger size corrections, 3: 401, 3: 410
   liquid systems, 3: 400
   storage capacity corrections, 3: 401, 3: 402, 3: 410
   water heating, 3: 403
   water systems, 3: 400
flat-plate collectors, 3: 570, 3: 571, 3: 587t
float glass, 3: 314, 3: 315, 3: 327
gasochromogenics, 3: 316, 3: 350
generic process system layouts, 3: 573
glass glazings, 3: 315, 3: 321, 3: 327
glass solar collectors, 3: 329
glazings
   buildings, 3: **313–355**
   chromogenic materials, 3: 316, 3: 342
   electrochromogenic devices/materials, 3: 314, 3: 316, 3: 336, 3: 338, 3: 342, 3: 343
   float glass, 3: 314, 3: 315, 3: 327
   gasochromogenics, 3: 316, 3: 350
   glass, 3: 315, 3: 321, 3: 327

low-emittance coatings, 3: 314, 3: 316, 3: 323
metal hydride switchable mirrors, 3: 350
optical analysis, 3: 319
optical properties, 3: 316
photochromogenics, 3: 316, 3: 346
thermal properties, 3: 316
thermogenics, 3: 316, 3: 350
toughened glass, 3: 328
windows, 3: 315, 3: 321, 3: 327
global climate change, 3: 5
greenhouse effect, 3: 5
greenhouses, 3: 230, 3: 231, 3: 586
heat exchanger size corrections, 3: 401, 3: 410
heating, 3: **449–480**
   air-conditioning, 3: 360–361, 3: 362, 3: 391
   buildings, 3: 587
   ventilation, 3: 360–361, 3: 362, 3: 391
   water, 3: **419–447**, 3: 577
     active systems, 3: 449, 3: 453, 3: 461
     agricultural applications, 3: 577
     f-chart method, 3: 400, 3: 403
     industrial applications, 3: 577
heat storage, 3: 473
heat system
   design, 3: 577
   layouts, 3: 573
high concentration solar collectors, 3: **165–209**
high-temperature selective coatings, 3: **301–312**
hot water, 3: **419–447**, 3: 577
industrial applications, 3: **567–594**
   absorbers, 3: 571
   air heating, 3: 587
   characteristics, 3: 568
   collectors, 3: 569
   component layouts, 3: 573
   cooking, 3: 588
   desalination, 3: 589
   design, 3: 577
   direct solar gain, 3: 587
   drying, 3: 579
   economics, 3: 569
   energy storage, 3: 569
   evacuated tube collectors, 3: 571, 3: 587t
   flat-plate collectors, 3: 570, 3: 571, 3: 587t
   generic process system layouts, 3: 573
   greenhouses, 3: 586
   heating buildings, 3: 587
   heat system design, 3: 577
   heat system layouts, 3: 573
   hot water, 3: 577
   line-axis collectors, 3: 571, 3: 587t
   operational limits, 3: 576
   parabolic trough collectors, 3: 571
   real heat system layouts, 3: 575
   refrigeration, 3: 592
   solar ponds, 3: 572, 3: 587t
   stationary collectors, 3: 570, 3: 571, 3: 572, 3: 587t
   stills, 3: 589
   system layouts, 3: 573
   temperature requirements, 3: 568, 3: 569t
   thermal energy storage, 3: 569
   ventilation, 3: 587
   water heating, 3: 577
line-axis collectors, 3: 571, 3: 587t
liquid systems, 3: 400
low concentration ratio solar collectors, 3: **149–163**
low-emittance coatings, 3: 314, 3: 316, 3: 323
low-energy homes, 3: 389
low-temperature stationary collectors, 3: **103–147**
metal hydride switchable mirrors, 3: 350
modeling components, 3: **357–417**
   active solar systems, 3: 396
modern window coatings, 3: 316

solar thermal energy systems (*continued*)
   multiple-glazed windows, **3:** 314, **3:** 332
   near-optimal design, **3:** 389
   numerical models, **3:** 358, **3:** 368, **3:** 374, **3:** 379, **3:** 383, **3:** 411
   operational limits, **3:** 576
   optical analysis, **3:** 316, **3:** 319
   optical properties, **3:** 316
   ozone layer depletion, **3:** 4
   parabolic trough collectors, **3:** 571
   passive solar architecture, **3: 637–665**
   photochromogenics, **3:** 316, **3:** 346
   photothermal conversion, **3: 301–312**
   photovoltaic/thermal solar collectors, **3: 255–300**
   pollution, **3:** 3
   quadruple glazing, **3:** 333
   radiation components and applications, **3:** 18
   real heat system layouts, **3:** 575
   refrigeration, **3:** 592
   renewable energy environmental problems, **3:** 5
   selective absorbers, **3: 301–312**
   selective coatings, **3: 301–312**
   simulations, **3: 357–417**
   social development, **3:** 6
   software, **3:** 396, **3:** 411, **3:** 413
   solar assisted heat pumps, **3: 495–528**
   solar cooling, **3: 449–480**, **3: 481–494**
   solar desalination, **3:** 529, **3:** 530, **3:** 547
   solar hot water heating systems, **3: 419–447**
   solar ponds, **3:** 572, **3:** 587t
   solar radiation
     components and applications, **3:** 18
     resources assessments, **1:** 218, **1:** 219
   solar resources, **3:** 22, **3: 27–84**
   space cooling, **3: 449–480**
   space heating, **3: 449–480**
   spectrally selective coatings, **3: 301–312**
   stationary collectors, **3:** 570, **3:** 571, **3:** 572, **3:** 587t
   stills, **3:** 589
   storage
     active solar systems, **3:** 473
     agricultural applications, **3:** 569
     air systems, **3:** 215, **3:** 227, **3:** 228t, **3:** 229, **3:** 230, **3:** 402
     capacity corrections, **3:** 401, **3:** 402, **3:** 410
     components, **3: 211–253**
     industrial applications, **3:** 569
   Sun, components and applications, **3:** 2
   system layouts, **3:** 573
   temperature requirements, **3:** 568, **3:** 569t
   thermal properties, **3:** 316
   thermal radiation components and applications, **3:** 18
   thermogenics, **3:** 316, **3:** 350
   toughened glass, **3:** 328
   transparent insulation, **3:** 314, **3:** 339
   triple glazing, **3:** 314, **3:** 333
   TRNSYS simulation software program, **3:** 396, **3:** 411
   utilizability method, **3:** 396, **3:** 404, **3:** 408
   ventilation, **3:** 587
   water heating, **3: 419–447**
     active systems, **3:** 449, **3:** 453, **3:** 461
     agricultural applications, **3:** 577
     f-chart method, **3:** 400, **3:** 403
     industrial applications, **3:** 577
   WATSUN simulation software program, **3:** 396, **3:** 413
   windows/glazings, **3:** 315, **3:** 321, **3:** 327
solar thermal flat panels, **1:** 218
solar thermophotovoltaics (STPV), **1:** 612, **3:** 287
solar transmittance, **3:** 317, **3:** 318
Solar Two power plant, **3:** 625
solar water heating systems, **3: 419–447**
   active systems, **3: 449–480**
   advanced thermal storage technologies, **3:** 435, **3:** 436f
   apartment housing, **3:** 443
   auxiliary heat sources, **3:** 436, **3:** 458
   centralized solar thermal systems, **3:** 435
   circuits, collectors, **3:** 431
   circulation, **3:** 426, **3:** 428f
   collectors, **3:** 420, **3:** 422–423, **3:** 424f, **3:** 426
     circuits, **3:** 431
     efficiency, **3:** 430, **3:** 431f
     inclination, **3:** 441
     integration, **3:** 430, **3:** 432f
     new developments, **3:** 431
     orientation, **3:** 441
     properties, **3:** 430
   combined heating systems, **3:** 444, **3:** 446f
   components, **3:** 420, **3:** 426, **3:** 428f
   concepts, **3:** 426
   decentralized solar thermal systems, **3:** 435
   deployment, **3:** 420, **3:** 420f, **3:** 422
   design principles, **3:** 438, **3:** 441f
   developing countries, **3:** 422, **3:** 422f
   distribution by application, **3:** 423
   domestic hot water, **3: 419–447**
     apartment housing, **3:** 443
     circulation, **3:** 426, **3:** 428f
     components, **3:** 420, **3:** 426, **3:** 428f
     design principles, **3:** 438
     forced circulation, **3:** 426
     households, **3:** 442
     multi-family housing, **3:** 443
     natural circulation, **3:** 426, **3:** 428f
     single-family housing, **3:** 442
   economics, **3:** 436, **3:** 438f
   flat-plate collectors, **3:** 420, **3:** 426, **3:** 429
   forced circulation, **3:** 426
   future aspects, **3: 419–447**
   heat management, **3:** 440
   heat sources, **3:** 436
   heat storage, **3:** 434
   high-performance flat-plate collectors, **3:** 429
   hot water tanks, **3:** 434
   households, **3:** 442
   hydraulic principles, **3:** 440, **3:** 442f
   hygienic aspects, **3:** 437
   inclination of collectors, **3:** 441
   integrating collectors, **3:** 430, **3:** 432f
   market deployment, **3:** 420, **3:** 420f, **3:** 422
   market development, **3:** 420, **3:** 420f, **3:** 422–423, **3:** 424f
   meteorological conditions, **3:** 438
   multi-family housing, **3:** 443
   natural circulation, **3:** 426, **3:** 428f
   new developments, collectors, **3:** 431
   orientation of collectors, **3:** 441
   properties of collectors, **3:** 430
   simulation tools, **3:** 438, **3:** 441f
   single-family housing, **3:** 442
   solar Combisystems, **3:** 444, **3:** 446f
   solar system, **3:** 440, **3:** 442f
   space heating systems, **3:** 444, **3:** 446f
   state of the art, **3: 419–447**
   storage, **3:** 431, **3:** 434, **3:** 440
   sustainable energy, **3:** 419
   tanks, **3:** 434
   technologies, **3:** 420, **3:** 420f, **3:** 425
   thermal storage, **3:** 434
   water storage, **3:** 434
   worldwide distribution, **3:** 423
Solar World AG, **1:** 171
SolFocus – Almoguera power plant, **1:** 751, **1:** 751t, **1:** 752f
solid biofuels, **5:** 37, **5:** 406
solid deposition, **7:** 245
solid desiccants, **3:** 483
solid electrolytes, **4:** 185
solid fuel recovery, **5:** 140, **5:** 142t
solid hydrocarbon gasification, **4:** 50
solidity: air turbines, **8:** 127, **8:** 128

solid media:
    biomass cofiring, **5**: 57, **5**: 58, **5**: 59
    geothermal chemistry, **7**: 97
    sampling, **7**: 97
    solar energy storage, **3**: 212, **3**: 242, **3**: 609
solid oxide fuel cells (SOFC), **4**: **241–257**
    250 kW grid-connected fuel cells, **4**: 300
    advantages over other cells, **4**: 246
    anodes, **4**: 247
    cathodes, **4**: 247
    combined heat and power systems, **4**: 249
        durability, **4**: 252
        efficiency, **4**: 250, **4**: 252
        heat-to-power ratio, **4**: 253, **4**: 254
        performance characteristics, **4**: 251
    comparisons, **4**: 243, **4**: 243t
    components, **4**: 246
    durability, **4**: 252
    efficiency, **4**: 250, **4**: 252
    electrolytes, **4**: 246
    example systems, **4**: 249
    heat-to-power ratio, **4**: 253, **4**: 254
    hydrogen technology, **4**: **241–257**
        anodes, **4**: 247
        cathodes, **4**: 247
        combined heat and power systems, **4**: 249
        components, **4**: 246
        efficiency, **4**: 250, **4**: 252
        electrolytes, **4**: 246
        interconnects, **4**: 248
        materials, **4**: **241–257**
        Nernst equation, **4**: 244, **4**: 245
        operation principles, **4**: 246
        theory, **4**: **241–257**
        thermodynamics, **4**: 243, **4**: 245
        transport applications, **4**: 282
    interconnects, **4**: 248
    materials, **4**: **241–257**
    micro combined heat and power systems, **4**: 251
    Nernst equation, **4**: 244, **4**: 245
    operation principles, **4**: 246
    performance characteristics, **4**: 251
    theory, **4**: **241–257**
    thermodynamics, **4**: 243, **4**: 245
solid polymer electrolytes, **4**: 175
solid-polymer fuel cells (SPFC) *see* proton-exchange membrane fuel cells
solid residuals: combustion/environmental impacts, **5**: 51
solid-state dehydrogenation, **4**: 143
solid-state surfaces: interfacing proteins, **1**: 666
SolRad-nET *see* Solar Radiation Network
solstice, **3**: 28
solubility: geochemistry, **7**: 143
solute geothermometers, **7**: 135–137
solvents:
    binary systems, **1**: 461
    bioethanol, **5**: 212
    organic solar cells, **1**: 458
    vapor annealing, **1**: 461
SOM *see* soil organic matter
Song Loulou plant, Cameroon, Africa, **6**: 132, **6**: 133f, **6**: 133t, **6**: 134, **6**: 134t, **6**: 137
sonic anemometers, **2**: 76
sorghum stalks, **5**: 59
sorption:
    desiccants, **3**: 461, **3**: 464
    solar cooling systems, **3**: 461, **3**: 463, **3**: 464, **3**: 465
    solar thermal energy storage, **3**: 224, **3**: 248, **3**: 250
    thermochemical heat, **3**: 224
Soultz-sous-Forêts, Upper Rhine graben, France, **7**: 233, **7**: 234f, **7**: 234f
sound measurements, **2**: 379
    see also acoustics; noise

sourcing renewable energy:
    biochar, **5**: 366
    bioethanol, **5**: 231
    desalination, **3**: **529–565**
    heat pumps, **3**: 502
    lignocellulosic wastes, **5**: 231
    passive solar technologies, **3**: 373
    solar desalination, **3**: **529–565**
South American hydroelectricity, **6**: **93–127**
South-East Europe Wind Energy Exploitation (SEEWIND), **2**: 716
soy biofuel ethics, **5**: 105
space applications:
    alkaline fuel cells, **4**: 172
    Apollo, **4**: 26
    astronaut environmental control, **4**: 24
    astronaut life support, **4**: 24
    battery power, **4**: 22
    cooling instruments, **4**: 24
    current status, **4**: 13
    energy storage, **4**: 22
    fuel cells, **4**: 26
    Gemini spacecraft, **4**: 26
    hydrogen technology
        astronaut environmental control, **4**: 24
        astronaut life support, **4**: 24
        battery power, **4**: 22
        current status, **4**: 13
        energy storage, **4**: 22
        instrument cooling technologies, **4**: 24
        propulsion, **4**: 13
        scientific instrument cooling technologies, **4**: 24
    industrial PEMFCs, **4**: 218
    InGaP/GaAs/Ge 3-junction solar cells, **1**: 506
    instrument cooling technologies, **4**: 24
    liquid electrolytes, **4**: 172
    nickel hydrogen batteries, **4**: 22
    PEMFCs, **4**: 218
    photovoltaics
        InGaP/GaAs/Ge 3-junction solar cells, **1**: 506
        satellites, **1**: **767–774**
        solar power satellites, **1**: **767–774**
        thin-film silicon, **1**: 396
    propulsion current status, **4**: 13
    scientific instrument cooling technologies, **4**: 24
    solar power satellites, **1**: **767–774**
    space shuttle, **4**: 17, **4**: 29
    thin-film silicon photovoltaics, **1**: 396
    wide-field infrared survey explorer, **4**: 24
space cooling:
    see also cooling
    active solar systems, **3**: **449–480**
    array design, **3**: 475
    differential temperature controllers, **3**: 478
    geothermal energy, **7**: 1–2, **7**: 169, **7**: 173t
    heat storage, **3**: 473
    history, **3**: 94
    module design, **3**: 475
    solar energy history, **3**: 94
    storage tanks, **3**: 473
space heating:
    see also solar space heating
    active solar systems, **3**: **449–480**
    air water heating systems, **3**: 455
    array design, **3**: 475
    differential temperature controllers, **3**: 478
    direct heat utilization, **7**: 169, **7**: 171, **7**: 173t, **7**: 174f, **7**: 180, **7**: 181f, **7**: 182, **7**: 184, **7**: 184f
    flat-plate solar collectors, **3**: 95
    geothermal energy, **7**: 1–2, **7**: 169, **7**: 171, **7**: 173t, **7**: 174f, **7**: 180, **7**: 181f, **7**: 182, **7**: 184, **7**: 184f
    heat exchangers, **3**: 450, **3**: 452f, **3**: 454, **3**: 454f, **3**: 477
    heat storage, **3**: 473
    history, **3**: 94

space heating: (*continued*)
    hot water, **3**: 453
    module design, **3**: 475
    service hot water, **3**: 453
    solar energy history, **3**: 94
    solar thermal systems, **3**: **449–480**
    solar water heating systems, **3**: 444, **3**: 446*f*
    storage tanks, **3**: 473
    thermal storage, **3**: 473
    water heating systems, **3**: 452, **3**: 453, **3**: 455
    wind energy, **2**: 497
space requirements: building-integrated photovoltaics, **1**: 702
spacer layers: plasmonics for photovoltaics, **1**: 641, **1**: 650
spacers: glazing, **3**: 335
space separated quantum cutting, **1**: 555
space variations: hydropower, **6**: 358
spa heating, **7**: 169, **7**: 170, **7**: 173*t*
Spain, **6**: **309–341**
    1890–1940, **6**: 317
    1940–1960, **6**: 323
    1960–1975, **6**: 327
    1970's onwards, **6**: 333
    civil war, **6**: 323
    companies, **6**: 315
    concentrating solar power, **3**: 192
    desalination, **2**: 739
    development of hydropower, **6**: **309–341**
    Duero System, **6**: 336
    electricity, **6**: 309
    future hydropower directions, **6**: 339
    high concentration solar collector markets, **3**: 192
    historical hydropower development, **6**: 309, **6**: 315
    hydroelectric power, **6**: 309
    hydrology, **6**: 311
    hydropower, **6**: **309–341**
    market development, **2**: 663
    ocean wave energy funding, **8**: **83–84**
    photovoltaics
        promotion/support, **1**: 90, **1**: 93, **1**: 103
        solar irradiance-photovoltaic power forecasts, **1**: 273
    power plants, **6**: 313
    production companies, **6**: 315
    promoting photovoltaics, **1**: 90, **1**: 93, **1**: 103
    river networks, **6**: 311
    scheme evolution of hydropower, **6**: 315
    solar irradiance-photovoltaic power forecasts, **1**: 273
    strategic importance of hydropower, **6**: 310
    supporting photovoltaics, **1**: 90, **1**: 93, **1**: 103
    twentieth century hydropower, **6**: 315
    wind power market development, **2**: 663
spark-ignition (SI) engines, **5**: 319
spatial averaging: weather predictions, **1**: 259
spatial coverage: solar radiation, **1**: 227, **1**: 228
spatial distribution: hydropower, **6**: 258
spatial modeling: sediment management, **6**: 362
spatial planning: wind turbines, **2**: 709
speciation: geothermal energy chemistry, **7**: 128
species changes: hydropower reservoir water quality, **6**: 62
specifications: Horseshoe Bend hydroelectric scheme, **6**: 468
specific energy yields: wind turbines, **2**: 677–679, **2**: 678*f*
specific geofluid consumption, **7**: 207, **7**: 235
specific impulse magnetoplasma rockets, **4**: 19
specific speed: microhydro turbines, **6**: 442, **6**: 455
spectral distribution: solar radiation, **3**: 67
spectrally selective coatings, **3**: **301–312**
spectral models:
    ocean waves, **8**: 45
    solar radiation, **3**: 54
spectral radiance/radiation:
    bandgap materials, **1**: 318
    blackbodies, **1**: 318
    models, **3**: 54
    resources assessments, **1**: 216

spectral range extensions, **1**: 596
spectral reflectance, **3**: 301
spectral response:
    down-shifting, **1**: 571
    efficiency, **1**: 571
    solar cells, **1**: 719, **1**: 719*t*
spectrometers, **3**: 28
spectroscopy:
    deep level transient spectroscopy, **1**: 505, **1**: 506*f*
    energy-dispersive X-ray spectroscopy, **7**: 99
    Fourier transform infrared spectroscopy, **5**: 375–376, **5**: 376*f*
    nuclear magnetic spectroscopy, **5**: 376, **5**: 377*f*, **5**: 378*f*
    rare-earths, **1**: 540
specular reflectivity, **3**: 167
speed:
    axial-flow microhydro turbines, **6**: 442, **6**: 455
    dynamic studies, wind energy, **2**: 87
    regular ocean waves, **8**: 13
    wind energy
        dynamic studies, **2**: 87
        mathematical representation, **2**: 83
        time variations, **2**: 81
        turbine control systems, **2**: 330, **2**: 331*f*
        variation with time, **2**: 81
        wind energy potential, **2**: 75
SPFC *see* solid-polymer fuel cells
SPG *see* Solar Power Group
spherical bowl reflector collectors, **3**: 587*t*
spillways:
    Chinese hydropower projects, **6**: **485–505**
    debris control, **6**: 77
    Horseshoe Bend hydroelectric scheme, **6**: 474
    Itaipu hydroelectric project, **6**: 99
    Mekin hydropower project, Cameroon, Africa, **6**: 143
    retrofit solutions, **6**: 77
    Tucurui project, Brazil, **6**: 102
spindle mills, **5**: 45
spinning blades shading effect, **2**: 194
spinning reserve, **6**: 408
spiral case structures, **6**: 191, **6**: 221
spiral wound membrane distillation modules, **3**: 543, **3**: 543*f*
split heat pump systems, **3**: 501
spontaneous combustion/fires: biomass cofiring, **5**: 68
spontaneous ignition: hydrogen safety engineering, **4**: 81
spontaneous mutations: yield improvement potentials, **5**: 301
spot diameters, **1**: 768
SPP-5 power plant, **3**: 629
SPR *see* surface plasmon resonance
spraying: Chinese hydraulic research, **6**: 485, **6**: 499
sputtering:
    chemical methods, **3**: 314
    glazings, **3**: 324
    organic solar cells, **1**: 471–472
    selective coatings, **3**: 301
squirrel-cage generators, **2**: 282, **2**: 340, **2**: 353, **2**: 354
SRC *see* short-rotation coppice; short-rotation crops
SRF *see* short-rotation forestry
SRIC *see* short-rotation intensive culture
SRWC *see* short-rotation woody crops
ST *see* steam turbines
stability:
    micro-and nanotechnology photovoltaics, **1**: 517
    organic solar cells, **1**: 465
    rotor blades, **2**: 713
    wind energy, **2**: 74
stable economic growth: dams, **6**: 270
stable isotopes, **7**: 108–109, **7**: 141
stacks:
    alkaline fuel cells, **4**: 170
    construction, **4**: 192
    cooling, **4**: 199
    liquid electrolytes, **4**: 170

metal-dielectric selective coatings, **3**: 301, **3**: 302–303, **3**: 306, **3**: 307
proton-exchange membrane fuel cells, **4**: 192, **4**: 199
staged construction: Three Gorges Project, China, **6**: 201
stainless steels, **7**: 240, **7**: 247
stakeholder acceptance: wind park design, **2**: 202
stall: wind turbines, **2**: 276, **2**: 671, **2**: 679
stamped absorbers, **3**: 104, **3**: 105f
stand-alone systems, **2**: 1, **2**: **623–655**, **2**: 623
   auxiliary electronic equipment, **2**: 632
   biomass power plant unit trends, **5**: 28
   complementary electric generator units, **2**: 632
   contribution to wind energy, **2**: 626
   design, **2**: 649, **2**: 651
   diesel–wind energy, **2**: 623–624, **2**: 636, **2**: 639f
   electricity generation, **2**: 623–655
   electronic equipment, **2**: 632
   energy storage, **2**: 647
   evaluating wind energy, **2**: 651
   historical development, **2**: 624
   hybrid wind energy systems, **2**: **623–655**
   hydrogen–wind energy, **2**: 645, **2**: 650
   hydropower–wind energy, **2**: 643, **2**: 649–650
   performance monitoring, **1**: 775, **1**: 777
   photovoltaics
      components, **1**: 679
      design and components, **1**: 679
      performance monitoring, **1**: 775, **1**: 777
      solar irradiance, **1**: 243
      wind energy, **2**: 623–624, **2**: 638
   simulations, wind energy, **2**: 651
   software tools, **2**: 651
   solar irradiance forecasts, **1**: 243
   storage system units, **2**: 632, **2**: 647
   system configurations, **2**: 629, **2**: 632
   unit trends, biomass power plants, **5**: 28
   wind energy, **2**: 1, **2**: **623–655**
standard days, **1**: 796
standard deviation (SD), **2**: 120, **3**: 50
standard hydrogen electrodes, **4**: 10
standardization:
   concentration photovoltaics, **1**: 749
   wind energy, **2**: **371–389**
      historical overviews, **2**: 371
      technology-specific issues, **2**: 372
standard offer contracts, **1**: 84
standards:
   biodiesel, **5**: 225
   biofuel production ethics, **5**: **99–108**
   CEN standards, **5**: 105
   certification, wind energy, **2**: 371, **2**: 383
   compressed gas, **4**: 116
   concentration photovoltaics, **1**: 797
   data analysis, photovoltaics, **1**: 792
   design, wind turbines, **2**: 373
   Det Norske Veritas-OS-J101 standard, **2**: 376
   energy performance/ratings, **1**: 795
   ethics in biofuel production, **5**: **99–108**
   European Commission, **1**: 788
   historical overviews
      photovoltaics, **1**: 787
      wind turbines, **2**: 371
   hydrogen safety engineering, **4**: 82, **4**: 101
   International Electrotechnical Commission, **1**: **787–803**, **2**: 372, **2**: 373, **2**: 374
   ISO wind energy standards, **2**: 373
   EC Joint Research Centre, **1**: 788
   measurements, photovoltaics, **1**: 790, **1**: 791
   performance, photovoltaic devices, **1**: 789
   photovoltaics, **1**: **787–803**
      data analysis, **1**: 792
      device performance determination, **1**: 789
      energy performance, **1**: 795

      energy rating, **1**: 795
   European Commission's Joint Research Centre, **1**: 788
   historical overviews, **1**: 787
   IEC, **1**: **787–803**
   IEC TC82, **1**: 788
   introduction, **1**: 10–11
   Joint Research Centre, **1**: 788
   measurements, **1**: 790, **1**: 791
   performance determination, **1**: 789
   reference solar devices, **1**: 791
   United States of America, **1**: 787
   working groups, **1**: 788, **1**: 789, **1**: 797
   power rating, **1**: 798
   reference solar devices, **1**: 791
   renewable portfolio standards, **1**: 76, **1**: 85, **1**: 127
   retail sector, **5**: 106
   safety
      hydrogen fuel cell technology, **4**: 291
      small wind turbines, **2**: 376
   tanks, **4**: 117
   testing, wind energy, **2**: 371, **2**: 376
   turbine design requirements, **2**: 373
   USA photovoltaics, **1**: 787
   vegetable oil, **5**: 225
   wind energy, **2**: **371–389**
      certification, **2**: 371, **2**: 383
      IEC, **2**: 372, **2**: 373, **2**: 374
      international standards, **2**: 372
      ISO standards, **2**: 373
      testing, **2**: 371, **2**: 376
   wind turbines, **2**: 371, **2**: 373, **2**: 383
   working groups, photovoltaics, **1**: 788, **1**: 789, **1**: 797
standard shapes: ocean waves, **8**: 15, **8**: 18, **8**: 19
standard test conditions (STC):
   photovoltaics
      concentration photovoltaics, **1**: 755
      modules, **1**: 679, **1**: 683
      performance determination, **1**: 790
      performance monitoring, **1**: 775, **1**: 776, **1**: 777, **1**: 779–780
stars: solar radiation resources assessments, **1**: 214
start-up conditions: wind turbines, **2**: 246
STATCOM *see* static compensators
State Compensatory Afforestation Fund Management and Planning Authority (State CAMPA), **6**: 235
state considerations: hydropower sediment management, **6**: 362, **6**: 366
state-of-the-art:
   crystalline silicon cells, **1**: **353–387**
   evacuated glazing, **3**: 337
   hydrogen safety engineering, **4**: **77–109**
   joints, concrete structure durability, **6**: 382
   ocean wave energy, electrical power, **8**: **1–6**
   passive solar cooling, **3**: 643–644
   photovoltaic crystalline silicon cells, **1**: **353–387**
   solar cooling, **3**: 614
   solar water heating systems, **3**: **419–447**
static compensators (STATCOM), **2**: 585
static modeling: geothermal energy, **7**: 30
static voltage balancing, **4**: 303, **4**: 304
stationary collectors, **3**: 570, **3**: 571, **3**: 572, **3**: 587t
   see also low-temperature...
stationary engines:
   biodiesel, **5**: 348
   biofuels, **5**: 348
   biomass gaseous fuels, **5**: 351
   bio-oils, **5**: 348
   dual fuel operation, **5**: 350
   fossil fuel blends, **5**: 348
   gaseous biofuels, **5**: 351
   vegetable oils, **5**: 349
stationary power:
   electricity, **4**: 334
   fuel cells, **4**: 334

stationary power: (*continued*)
   hydrogen technology, **4**: 59, **4**: 334
   proton-exchange membrane fuel cells, **4**: 208, **4**: 209
   system design, **4**: 209
station networks: solar radiation, **3**: 58
stations: hydrogen technology, **4**: 2, **4**: 10*f*
statistic: definitions, **3**: 28
statistical effects: cloud cover, **1**: 231
statistical mechanics: solar energy conversion, **1**: 308
statistical methods:
   error measures, **1**: 266
   forecasting, **1**: 248, **1**: 265, **2**: 615
   photovoltaic power forecasting, **1**: 248, **1**: 265
   solar energy conversion principles, **1**: 308
   solar irradiance forecasting, **1**: 248, **1**: 265
   surveys, **2**: 202, **2**: 204*f*
   wind energy forecasting, **2**: 615
   wind park design, **2**: 202, **2**: 204*f*
stator winding assemblies, **2**: 280*f*
STC *see* standard test conditions
steady-state:
   aerodynamics, **2**: 249
   building-integrated photovoltaic-thermal systems, **3**: 381
   energy balance, **3**: 129
   low-temperature flat-plate stationary collectors, **3**: 129
   open-loop building-integrated photovoltaic-thermal models, **3**: 381
   passive solar technologies, **3**: 362, **3**: 373
   periodic passive solar technologies, **3**: 362, **3**: 373
   voltage level fluctuations, **2**: 207
   wind turbines, **2**: 207, **2**: 249
steam cycles, **3**: 600, **5**: 87, **5**: 88
steam engines, **2**: 51
steam explosion, **5**: 242
steam geothermal power plants, **7**: 207, **7**: 209
steam methane reforming (SMR), **4**: 49, **4**: 49*t*, **4**: 49–50
steam turbines (ST), **5**: 88, **5**: 90, **5**: 94, **5**: 95
steels: geothermal environment power production, **7**: 247
steel structures, **6**: 187, **6**: 198, **6**: 226
steel vessels:
   compressed gas: hydrogen storage, **4**: 112
   dished ends, **4**: 115
   materials, **4**: 112
   nozzles, **4**: 115
   openings, **4**: 115
   pressure loading, **4**: 113
Stefan–Boltzmann law, **3**: 20, **3**: 34, **3**: 303
step-by-step design: building-integrated photovoltaics, **1**: 702
step-change methods: hydrogen infrastructure, **4**: 54
Stevin, Simon, **2**: 49
stilling basin damage, **6**: 248, **6**: 248*f*
stills, **3**: 541, **3**: 589
Stirling dishes, **3**: 605, **3**: 622
Stirling Energy Systems (SES), **3**: 204
Stirling engines, **3**: 90, **3**: 90*f*, **5**: 88, **5**: 89
Stirling high concentration solar collectors, **3**: 201, **3**: 203
STJ power plant, **3**: 619, **3**: 627
STM Power, Inc, **3**: 204
stochastic loads: wind turbines, **2**: **243–268**
stochastic modeling: wind speeds, **2**: 88
Stockholm conference, **7**: 277
stoker combustion, **5**: 61
storage:
   see also carbon capture and storage; energy storage; thermal energy storage; water…
   alkali amidoboranes, **4**: 144
   alkaline earth amidoboranes, **4**: 144
   amidoboranes, **4**: 144
   amine-hydride combinations, **4**: 147*t*, **4**: 149
   ammonia borane, **4**: 140
   biomass and biofuels
      cofiring, **5**: 70
      combined heat and power, **5**: 89

      power generation, **5**: 43
   borohydrides, **4**: 147
   capacity corrections
      air-based solar thermal systems, **3**: 402
      f-chart method, **3**: 401, **3**: 402, **3**: 410
      liquid solar thermal systems, **3**: 401
      pebble-beds, **3**: 402
      solar thermal systems, **3**: 401, **3**: 402, **3**: 410
   chemical hydrides, **4**: 139, **4**: 153
   chemical methods, **4**: **137–157**
   cofiring biomass, **5**: 70
   combined heat and power, **5**: 89
   complex hydrides, **4**: 147, **4**: 153
   compressed air energy storage, **1**: 210, **2**: 649, **2**: 650, **4**: **111–135**
   compressed gas: hydrogen storage, **4**: **111–135**
   concentrating solar power, **3**: 609
   dams, **6**: 134, **6**: 137
   desalination, **2**: 733, **2**: 734
   design parameters, **2**: 649
   economics, hydrogen technology, **4**: 55
   efficiency, **1**: 724
   electrical energy storage, **6**: 406
   future photovoltaics, **1**: 191
   geothermal energy, **7**: 10–11
   grid flexibility, **1**: 199
   grid reliability, **1**: 199
   heat, **3**: 434, **3**: 473, **3**: 524
   high energy dense battery hybrid energy storage, **4**: 317
   high-temperature storage, **3**: 522, **3**: 523
   hydrides, **4**: 139, **4**: 147, **4**: 153
   hydrogen, **4**: **111–135**, **4**: **137–157**, **4**: 57
      alkali amidoboranes, **4**: 144
      alkaline earth amidoboranes, **4**: 144
      amidoboranes, **4**: 144
      amine-hydride combinations, **4**: 147*t*, **4**: 149
      ammonia borane, **4**: 140
      automotives, **5**: 312
      borohydrides, **4**: 147
      chemical hydrides, **4**: 139, **4**: 153
      chemicals, **4**: **137–157**
      complex hydrides, **4**: 147, **4**: 153
      compressed gas, **4**: **111–135**
      economics, **4**: 55
      hydrides, **4**: 139, **4**: 147, **4**: 153
      liquids, **4**: **137–157**
      metal hydrides, **4**: 139
      pending issues, **4**: 153
      performance, **4**: 55
      safety engineering, **4**: 105
      transport applications, **4**: 285
   hydropower
      Cameroon, Africa, **6**: 134, **6**: 137
      India, **6**: 233*f*, **6**: 233–234, **6**: 242
      Iran, **6**: 259, **6**: 260*f*, **6**: 263*f*
      pumped-storage, **1**: 208, **2**: 626, **2**: 649–650, **6**: **405–434**
   Indian hydropower, **6**: 233*f*, **6**: 233–234, **6**: 242
   liquid methods, **4**: **137–157**
   management, photovoltaics, **1**: 208
   mass transfer, **3**: 524
   metal hydrides, **4**: 139
   ocean wave energy, **8**: 9
   organic media storage, **3**: 609
   packed bed storage units, **3**: 215, **3**: 215*f*, **3**: 227, **3**: 229
   passive energy storage, **3**: 243
   pebble-beds, **3**: 402
   performance, hydrogen technology, **4**: 55
   phase change materials, **3**: 211, **3**: 221–222, **3**: 222*f*, **3**: 223, **3**: 224, **3**: 225*t*, **3**: 228*t*, **3**: 229, **3**: 230, **3**: 230*f*, **3**: 243, **3**: 247, **3**: 249*f*
   photovoltaics, **1**: **199–212**
      future visions, **1**: 191
      grid flexibility, **1**: 199
      grid reliability, **1**: 199
      management, **1**: 208

power quality, **1**: 205
reliability, **1**: 199
physical methods, **4**: 137
plants
   hydroelectricity development and progress, **6**: 7
   Iranian hydropower, **6**: 259, **6**: 260f, **6**: 263f
   pumped storage, **6**: **405–434**
policy, wind energy, **2**: 553
power conversion, **3**: 609
power generation, biomass and biofuels, **5**: 43
power quality, photovoltaics, **1**: 205
pressurized air storage, **3**: 610
pressurized storage water tanks, **3**: 217, **3**: 217f, **3**: 218f
product-integrated photovoltaics, **1**: 724
proton-exchange membrane fuel cells, **4**: 221, **4**: 317
pumped-storage hydropower, **1**: 208, **2**: 626, **2**: 649–650, **6**: **405–434**
reliability, photovoltaics, **1**: 199
seasonal, **3**: 248, **3**: 519, **3**: 520, **3**: 521
solar assisted heat pumps, **3**: 520, **3**: 521
solar thermal energy components, **3**: **211–253**
solar water heating systems, **3**: 431, **3**: 434, **3**: 440
solid media, solar power, **3**: 212, **3**: 242, **3**: 609
stand alone hybrid wind energy systems, **2**: 632, **2**: 647, **2**: 649
tanks
   cooling systems, **3**: 473
   hydrogen technology, **4**: 2, **4**: 7f
   parallel solar assisted heat pumps, **3**: 514
   solar space heating, **3**: 458, **3**: 473
   space cooling systems, **3**: 473
   space heating, **3**: 473
   water tanks, **3**: 217, **3**: 217f, **3**: 218f, **3**: 458
thermocline tanks, **3**: 550
water heating systems, **3**: 217, **3**: 217f, **3**: 218f, **3**: 431, **3**: 434, **3**: 440, **3**: 458
water tanks, **3**: 217, **3**: 217f, **3**: 218f
wind energy
   desalination, **2**: 733, **2**: 734
   mitigating variable costs and effects, **2**: 495
   policy, **2**: 553
   repercussions, **2**: 599
   stand alone hybrid systems, **2**: 632, **2**: 647
storativity: geothermal energy, **7**: 11
storms: ocean wave heights, **8**: 70
stoves:
   biochar, **5**: 358, **5**: 381f
   thermophotovoltaic energy conversion, **1**: 614
STPV see solar thermophotovoltaics
StraflowMatrix/HydroMatrix turbine units, **6**: 438
strategic planning: building-integrated photovoltaics, **1**: 702
stratified water tanks, **3**: 216, **3**: 217f
straw: biomass cofiring, **5**: 59
stress:
   concrete structure durability, **6**: 380
   corrosion cracking, **7**: 243
   hydropower/reservoir water quality, **6**: 59
   hydropower, sediment management, **6**: 357, **6**: 365
   sulfide stress cracking, **7**: 244
   tests, **1**: 793
structural design: concrete structure durability, **6**: 391, **6**: 395
structural options: hydropower impact management, **6**: 87
structure:
   see also infrastructure; nanostructures; support structures
   Cameroon, Africa institutional reforms, **6**: **129–151**
   catalyst layers, **4**: 191
   chalcopyrite thin films, **1**: 400, **1**: 410
   concrete structure durability, **6**: **377–403**
   crystalline silicon cells, **1**: 355
   dye-sensitized solar cells, **1**: 482, **1**: 483f, **1**: 487, **1**: 487f
   electrical power systems, **2**: 571
   electrochromogenic devices, **3**: 343, **3**: 343f, **3**: 343–344
   Fresnel collectors, **3**: 195
   geological explorations, **7**: 55

high concentration solar collectors, **3**: 169, **3**: 174, **3**: 185, **3**: 195, **3**: 200
hydropower impact management, **6**: 87
institutional reforms, **6**: **129–151**
intermediate band solar cells, **1**: 619
mapping, **7**: 55
Mekin hydropower project, Cameroon, Africa, **6**: 142
Memve'Élá hydro plant project, Cameroon, Africa, **6**: 140
parabolic troughs, **3**: 174
photovoltaics, **1**: 400, **1**: 410, **1**: 619
proton-exchange membrane fuel cells, **4**: 191
quantum photovoltaics, **1**: 525
receivers, **3**: 185
solar dishes, **3**: 200
STSC see single threshold solar cells
Stykkishólmur, Snæfellsnes peninsula, west Iceland, **7**: 90
sub-band gap losses, **1**: 516–517
subgrid scales (SGS): wind turbines, **2**: 232–233
sub-kilowatt turbines, **6**: 440
subsidies:
   bioenergy trade barriers, **5**: 81
   developing country photovoltaics, **1**: 125
   geothermal energy, **7**: 285
   high concentration solar collectors, **3**: 206
substations: offshore wind power, **2**: 450
substrates:
   chalcopyrite thin films, **1**: 410
   enzyme interactions, **5**: 249
   lattice matching, **1**: 500, **1**: 503, **1**: 504
   multi-junction cells, **1**: 500, **1**: 503, **1**: 504
   thermophotovoltaics, **1**: 610
subsurface mapping, **7**: 55
subsurface resistivity, **7**: 61
subsystems: electrical energy storage, **6**: 410
suction bucket foundations, **2**: 445, **2**: 446f
sugarcane, **5**: **15–26**, **5**: 59
sugar production, **5**: 19
sugars:
   cellulose conversion, **5**: 400
   chemical production, **5**: 400
   levunic acid, **5**: 401
sugar trade, **5**: 19
sulfates, **6**: 388, **7**: 247
sulfide scaling, **7**: 249–250, **7**: 251
sulfide stress cracking, **7**: 244
sulfonated membrane materials, **4**: 188
sulfur:
   biomass gasification, **5**: 146
   geothermal energy geochemistry, **7**: 132
   oxides, **5**: 51, **5**: 348
   syngas contaminants, **5**: 173
Sun, **1**: 214, **3**: 2
   see also solar…
   blackbodies, **3**: 79
Sun–Earth relationship, **1**: 215, **3**: 2, **3**: 2f, **3**: 29
sunbelt countries, **1**: 184, **1**: 197
Sun Earth Solar Power Co: Ltd:, **1**: 172
SunEye, **3**: 63
sunlight factors, **1**: 771
sun path diagrams, **3**: 2, **3**: 17
sun pointing, **1**: 771
SunPower Corporation, **1**: 171
sun rise/set times, **3**: 12
sunshape, **3**: 168
Sunshine power plant, **3**: 629
sunspaces: architecture, **3**: 640–641, **3**: 641f
Suntech Power Co: Ltd:, **1**: 169
SunTracker, **3**: 63
supercapacitors, **2**: 650
supercomplex organization, **1**: 660
superconducting magnetic energy storage (SMES), **1**: 204, **1**: 204f, **1**: 205, **2**: 650
supercritical fluid technology, **5**: 245

supercritical reactions: biodiesel, **5**: 208
SuperGen Marine, **8**: 83
supergrids: wind energy, **2**: 496
supersaturation, **6**: 73, **6**: 75
super smart grids, **1**: 190
superstrate devices, **1**: 427
supervision:
   Three Gorges Project construction, **6**: 208
   wind power plant building, **2**: 427
   wind turbines, **2**: 332, **2**: 332*f*
supplementary equipment: offshore wind power, **2**: 450
supply:
   bioenergy policy development, **5**: 414
   biomass and biofuels
      biomass-to-liquids technology, **5**: 187–188
      cofiring, **5**: 70
      feedstocks, **5**: 278
      woody biomass feedstocks, **5**: 278
   biomass cofiring, **5**: 70
   biomass-to-liquids technology, **5**: 187–188
   and demand, **1**: 52, **6**: 282
   energy crops, **5**: 278
   polysilicon, **1**: 173
   security of supply, **1**: 733, **1**: 734*t*, **5**: 305–306, **5**: 424
   wind power plant building, **2**: 427
   wind turbines, **2**: 418
Support for Large Scale Integration of Wind Power (SUPWIND), **2**: 717
support mechanisms:
   analytical frameworks, **1**: 114
   assessments, **1**: 78
   deployment impact, **1**: 3
   developing country photovoltaics, **1**: **111–141**
   effectiveness, **1**: 78
   efficiency, **1**: 78
   European Union photovoltaics, **1**: 90, **1**: 93, **1**: 103
   external costs, **2**: 486
   feed-in tariffs, **1**: **73–109**
   German photovoltaics, **1**: 90, **1**: 93, **1**: 103
   harmonization, **1**: 4
   incentives, **1**: **1–4**
   investment opportunities, **1**: 3, **1**: 74, **1**: 75–76, **1**: 78, **1**: 106
   net metering, **1**: 74, **1**: 75–76, **1**: 77, **1**: 86
   off-grid technologies, **1**: **111–141**
   photovoltaics, **1**: **73–109**, **1**: 196, **1**: **111–141**
      analytical frameworks, **1**: 114
      assessments, **1**: 78
      effectiveness, **1**: 78
      efficiency, **1**: 78
      European Union, **1**: 90, **1**: 93, **1**: 103
      Germany, **1**: 90, **1**: 93, **1**: 103
      investment incentives, **1**: 74, **1**: 75–76, **1**: 78, **1**: 106
      net metering, **1**: 74, **1**: 75–76, **1**: 77, **1**: 86
      quota-based support, **1**: 76
      renewable portfolio standards, **1**: 76, **1**: 85
      Singapore, **1**: 79, **1**: 103
      Spain, **1**: 90, **1**: 93, **1**: 103
      tax incentives, **1**: 74, **1**: 75–76, **1**: 78, **1**: 87
      tender systems, **1**: 74, **1**: 75–76, **1**: 77
      United States, **1**: 83, **1**: 103
   policy, **1**: **1–4**
   promotion schemes, **1**: **73–109**
   quota-based support, **1**: 76
   regulatory frameworks, **1**: 196
   renewable portfolio standards, **1**: 76, **1**: 85
   Singaporean photovoltaics, **1**: 79, **1**: 103
   Spanish photovoltaics, **1**: 90, **1**: 93, **1**: 103
   tax incentives, **1**: 74, **1**: 75–76, **1**: 78, **1**: 87
   tender systems, **1**: 74, **1**: 75–76, **1**: 77
   United States photovoltaics, **1**: 83, **1**: 103
   wind energy external costs, **2**: 486
support structures:
   cabling, **2**: 451

Det Norske Veritas-OS-J101 standard, **2**: 376
floating technology, **2**: 449
offshore wind power, **2**: 431
   cabling, **2**: 451
   Det Norske Veritas-OS-J101 standard, **2**: 376
   floating technology, **2**: 449
   shallow water technology, **2**: 441
   supplementary equipment, **2**: 450
   transitional water technology, **2**: 446
   underwater cabling, **2**: 451
regulatory frameworks, **1**: 196
shallow water technology, **2**: 441
supplementary equipment, **2**: 450
transitional water technology, **2**: 446
underwater cabling, **2**: 451
wind farms, **2**: 441, **2**: 444*f*
supramolecular organization, **1**: 660
SUPWIND *see* Support for Large Scale Integration of Wind Power
surface activity: geothermal systems, **7**: 28
surface area:
   biochar, **5**: 374
   lignocellulosic wastes, **5**: 232
surface characteristics: high concentration solar collectors, **3**: 201
surface chemistry: biochar, **5**: 375, **5**: 379–380
surface coverage: plasmonic photovoltaics, **1**: 647
surface elevation: ocean waves, **8**: 19
surface functionality: biochar, **5**: 375
surface generation: solar energy conversion principles, **1**: 303
surface mapping: geological explorations, **7**: 54
surface passivation: crystalline silicon cells, **1**: 364
surface plasmon resonance (SPR), **1**: 527
surface plasmons:
   material properties, **1**: 646
   photovoltaics, **1**: 527, **1**: 642, **1**: 644
   plasmonics, **1**: 642
   polaritons, **1**: 643
   scattering, **1**: 644
surface properties: chalcopyrite thin films, **1**: 405
Surface Radiation Budget Network (SURFRAD), **3**: 61
surface recombination, **1**: 303, **1**: 501, **1**: 570
surface rock: geothermal energy, **7**: 1
surface roughness: coatings, **3**: 308
surface waters: heat pumps, **3**: 505
SURFRAD *see* Surface Radiation Budget Network
surge: hydropower, **6**: 56, **6**: 370, **6**: 375*f*
surpluses:
   electricity life cycle assessments, **5**: 111, **5**: 125
   wind energy high-penetration levels, **2**: 492
surveys:
   reservoir sediment management, **6**: 360
   wind park design, **2**: 202, **2**: 204*f*
suspended particle switching devices, **3**: 351
suspended solids: corrosion rates, **7**: 245
suspension firing, **5**: 33
sustainability:
   see also sustainable development
   additional value extraction, **5**: **385–393**
   automotives alcohol fuels, **5**: 335
   biofuel ethics, **5**: 99, **5**: 103, **5**: 104, **5**: 105
   biomass and biofuels
      additional value extraction, **5**: **385–393**
      biomass-to-liquids technology, **5**: 203
      power generation, **5**: 28
      woody biomass feedstocks, **5**: 281, **5**: 284
   Canadian, hydropower, **6**: **153–178**
   climate change and geothermal energy, **7**: 272, **7**: 283, **7**: 290
   Eastmain–Sarcelle–Rupert Diversion Project, Quebec, Canada, **6**: 173
   ethics, **5**: 99, **5**: 103, **5**: 104, **5**: 105
   extracting additional value feedstocks, **5**: **385–393**
   feedstocks, **5**: **385–393**
   geothermal energy, **7**: **271–295**, **7**: 272
      climate change, **7**: 272, **7**: 283, **7**: 290

greenhouse gases, **7**: 272, **7**: 283, **7**: 290
  heat pumps, **7**: 203
  physics, **7**: 43
  production, **7**: 272, **7**: 280
guidelines, hydropower, **6**: 12
hydrogen fuel cells, **4**: **331–340**
hydropower
  Canada, **6**: **153–178**
  dams, **6**: **355–376**
  design, **6**: **355–376**
  environmental impact management, **6**: 50
  guidelines, **6**: 12
  reservoirs, **6**: **355–376**
  sediment management, **6**: **355–376**
index, **7**: 272
investment, **7**: 261, **7**: 262f
La Romaine Complex, Quebec, Canada, **6**: 165
management systems, **5**: 99
organic fuels, **5**: 335
portfolio standards, **1**: 76, **1**: 85, **1**: 127
power generation, **5**: 28
primary forest residues, **5**: 284
production of geothermal energy, **7**: 272, **7**: 280
resources assessments, **1**: 219
Revelstoke Complex, British Colombia, Canada, **6**: 177
short-rotation forestry/woody crops, **5**: 281
solar radiation resources assessments, **1**: 219
solar water heating systems, **3**: 419
very large-scale photovoltaic systems, **1**: 741
sustainable development:
  see also sustainability
  atmosphere, geothermal energy, **7**: 283
  bioenergy policy development, **5**: 416
  clean development mechanisms, **7**: 290, **7**: 291
  conferences, **7**: 273
  current geothermal energy status, **7**: 286
  direct-use geothermal energy applications, **7**: 279
  economics, geothermal energy, **7**: 274, **7**: 280, **7**: 286
  environmental impacts, **3**: 3
    geothermal energy, **7**: 276, **7**: 278, **7**: 283, **7**: 287, **7**: 289
  equity, geothermal energy, **7**: 282
  geothermal energy, **7**: **271–295**, **7**: 272
    atmosphere, **7**: 283
    clean development mechanisms, **7**: 290, **7**: 291
    conferences, **7**: 273
    current status, **7**: 286
    definitions, **7**: 277
    direct-use applications, **7**: 279
    economics, **7**: 274, **7**: 280, **7**: 286
    environmental impacts, **7**: 276, **7**: 278, **7**: 283, **7**: 287, **7**: 289
    equity, **7**: 282
    global partnerships, **7**: 290
    goals, **7**: 272, **7**: 274, **7**: 277, **7**: 287
    health, **7**: 287
    heat pumps, **7**: 279
    historical overviews, **7**: 276, **7**: 286
    Iceland, **7**: 286
    indicators, **7**: 277, **7**: 278
    indirect-use applications, **7**: 279
    Kyoto Protocol, **7**: 290, **7**: 291
    Millennium Development Goals, **7**: 272, **7**: 274, **7**: 287
    security, **7**: **271–295**, **7**: 272
    social issues, **7**: 275, **7**: 282, **7**: 287
    water impacts, **7**: 285
  global partnerships, **7**: 290
  goals, **7**: 272, **7**: 274, **7**: 277, **7**: 287
  health, **7**: 287
  heat pumps, **7**: 279
  historical overviews, **7**: 276, **7**: 286
  Iceland, **7**: 286
  indicators, **7**: 277, **7**: 278
  indirect-use applications, geothermal energy, **7**: 279
  Kyoto Protocol, **7**: 290, **7**: 291

Millennium Development Goals, **7**: 272, **7**: 274, **7**: 287
  social issues, **7**: 275, **7**: 282, **7**: 287
  water impacts, **7**: 285
Suzion, **2**: 314
Sway concept, **2**: 305, **2**: 306f
Sweden:
  bioenergy policy development, **5**: 427
  offshore wind power, **2**: 433, **2**: 437, **2**: 439
swells: wind turbines, **2**: 594
swimming pools, **7**: 169, **7**: 170, **7**: 173t
swirl: microhydro turbines, **6**: 450, **6**: 451, **6**: 460
Swiss Federal Office of Energy (SFOE), **6**: 346
switchable glazing, **3**: 314, **3**: 316, **3**: 336, **3**: 338, **3**: 342, **3**: 343
switchable mirrors, **3**: 350
switch generators: wind turbines, **2**: 293, **2**: 293f
switch voltage balance implementation, **4**: 304
Switzerland, **6**: **343–354**
  Cleuson-Dixence hydroelectricity project, **6**: 351
  dams, **6**: 346
  Dixence hydroelectricity project, **6**: 350
  Grande-Dixence hydroelectricity project, **6**: 350
  Hongrin Léman Plus hydroelectricity project, **6**: 354
  hydroelectricity, **6**: **343–354**
  large hydropower plants, **6**: 345
  Linthal 2015 hydroelectricity project, **6**: 353
  Nant de Dranse hydroelectricity project, **6**: 352
  new hydropower plants, **6**: 349
  small-scale hydropower plants, **6**: 346
  solar irradiance-photovoltaic power forecasts, **1**: 273
sycamore, **5**: 268
synchronous generators:
  voltage control, **2**: 586
  wind turbines, **2**: 279–280, **2**: 280f, **2**: 285, **2**: 337, **2**: 356
syndiesel, **5**: 128–129, **5**: 156
synergies: biochar, **5**: 378
syngas, **5**: **155–204**, **5**: 156
  alkaline compounds, **5**: 176
  alternative options, **5**: 183
  biochar, **5**: 366t, **5**: 371, **5**: 379
  biomass combined heat and power, **5**: 89
  biomass gasification, **5**: 144, **5**: 144f, **5**: 144t
  biomass-to-liquids technology, **5**: **155–204**, **5**: 156
    alternative options, **5**: 183
    contaminants, **5**: 172
    economics, **5**: 191
    gasification, **5**: 168
    implementation, **5**: 188
    methanation, **5**: 186
  cleanup, **5**: 172
  combined heat and power, **5**: 89
  conditioning, **5**: 177
  contaminants, **5**: 172, **5**: 173
  economics, **5**: 191
  gasification, **5**: 168
  implementation, **5**: 188
  methanation, **5**: 186
  particulate contaminants, **5**: 176
  quality, **5**: 144, **5**: 144f, **5**: 144t
  tar contaminants, **5**: 176
synoptic variability: ocean waves, **8**: 51
synthesis:
  see also photosynthesis
  biomass-to-liquids technology, **5**: 158, **5**: 162f, **5**: 183f, **5**: 185
synthetic aperture radar (SAR), **2**: 714, **8**: 23
synthetic natural gas (SNG):
  biomass combined heat and power, **5**: 89–90, **5**: 96
  biomass-to-liquids technology, **5**: 156, **5**: 171, **5**: 177, **5**: 183, **5**: 186, **5**: 203
system achievements: alkaline fuel cells, **4**: 172
system balance: photovoltaic life cycles, **1**: 147
system boundaries:
  definitions, **5**: 109
  life cycle assessments, **5**: 110

system configurations:
    molten carbonate fuel cells, **4**: 228
    stand alone hybrid wind energy systems, **2**: 629, **2**: 632
system design:
    alkaline fuel cells, **4**: 170
    liquid electrolytes, **4**: 170
    luminescent solar concentrators, **1**: 594
    photovoltaics, **1**: **679–695**
    pressure selection, **4**: 198
    product-integrated photovoltaics, **1**: 723
    proton-exchange membrane fuel cells, **4**: 198, **4**: 209
    stationary power, **4**: 209
system efficiency:
    luminescent solar concentrators, **1**: 588–589, **1**: 595
    photovoltaic performance monitoring, **1**: 776, **1**: 781, **1**: 783
    thermophotovoltaics, **1**: 604
system layouts: solar applications, **3**: 573
system location: electrical energy storage, **6**: 407
system optimization: stand alone hybrid wind energy systems, **2**: 632
system performance:
    Fresnel collectors, **3**: 196
    high concentration solar collectors, **3**: 168, **3**: 178, **3**: 187, **3**: 196, **3**: 202
    parabolic troughs, **3**: 168, **3**: 178
    photovoltaic design, **1**: 679–680, **1**: 692
    receivers, **3**: 187
    solar dishes, **3**: 202
    wind turbines, **2**: 96
system prices: photovoltaics, **1**: 181, **1**: 193
systems:
    thermal energy storage integration, **3**: 214
    Three Gorges Project construction, **6**: 208
system safety: photovoltaic standards, **1**: 799
systems analysis:
    binary power plants, **7**: 224, **7**: 225
    dry-steam power plants, **7**: 211
    flash-steam power plants, **7**: 217
system sizing: stand alone hybrid wind energy systems, **2**: 632
system storage: wind energy variable costs and effects, **2**: 495
system yields: photovoltaic performance, **1**: 776, **1**: 781, **1**: 783

T

tailrace: hydropower, **6**: 17, **6**: 223
Taiwan photovoltaics, **1**: 167, **1**: 170, **1**: 171, **1**: 172
Tajo de la Encantada reversible pumping plant, Spain, **6**: 333, **6**: 334f
Tajo project, Spain, **6**: 330, **6**: 331f
Talam dam, Spain, **6**: 321, **6**: 321f
tall oils, **5**: 60
tallow, **5**: 60
Tanakpur Hydroelectric Project, **6**: 249, **6**: 250f
tandem solar cells *see* multi-junction cells
tandem stacks, **3**: 305, **3**: 306
tangential inlet volute limits, **6**: 452, **6**: 463
tank-in-tank heat exchangers, **3**: 454, **3**: 454f
tanks:
    cooling systems, **3**: 473
    design, hydrogen storage, **4**: 128
    exchangers, **3**: 454, **3**: 454f
    hot water, **3**: 434
    hydrogen technology, **4**: 2, **4**: 7f, **4**: 128
    multiple tank storage, **3**: 217, **3**: 218f
    parallel solar assisted heat pumps, **3**: 514
    pressurized storage water tanks, **3**: 217, **3**: 217f, **3**: 218f
    solar assisted heat pumps, **3**: 519
    solar desalination, **3**: 550
    solar space heating, **3**: 458, **3**: 473
    solar water heating systems, **3**: 434
    space cooling, **3**: 473
    space heating, **3**: 473
    standards, **4**: 117
    stratified water tanks, **3**: 216, **3**: 217f
    tank-in-tank heat exchangers, **3**: 454, **3**: 454f
    testing
        hydrogen storage, **4**: 130
        ocean wave energy, **8**: 84
    thermocline storage tanks, **3**: 550
    unpressurized storage water tanks, **3**: 218f
    water heating systems, **3**: 458
    water tanks, **3**: 217, **3**: 217f, **3**: 218f, **3**: 519
tariffs:
    see also feed-in-tariffs
    annual revision tariffs, **1**: 125
    bioenergy policy development, **5**: 411, **5**: 423
    bioenergy trade barriers, **5**: 81
    calculation methodology, **1**: 94
    degression, **1**: 99
    differentation, **1**: 98, **1**: 99
    incentives, **1**: 124
    payment duration, **1**: 97
    renewable energy premium tariff, **1**: 130
    setting, **1**: 124
tars:
    biochar, **5**: 379
    removal/destruction, **5**: 146
    syngas contaminants, biomass-to-liquids technology, **5**: 176
taxation: biofuel sustainability, **5**: 337–338
tax incentives:
    photovoltaic promotion schemes, **1**: 74, **1**: 75–76, **1**: 78, **1**: 87
    support mechanisms, **1**: 1, **1**: 2t
TC *see* technical committees
TCO *see* transparent conducting oxide layers
TCR-FC *see* thyristor-controlled reactor-fixed capacitors
technical aspects:
    availability
        wind energy, **2**: 1
        wind turbine energy yields, **2**: 114, **2**: 151, **2**: 153, **2**: 155
    biomass cofiring, **5**: 57, **5**: 69
    costs
        offshore wind, **2**: 478, **2**: 480
        wind energy, **2**: **469–501**
    desalination, **2**: 734
    Eastmain–Sarcelle–Rupert Diversion Project, Quebec, Canada, **6**: 168
    economics
        offshore wind, **2**: 478, **2**: 480
        onshore wind, **2**: 475
        wind energy, **2**: **469–501**
    electricity generation costs, wind energy, **2**: **469–501**
    embedded generation benefits, **2**: 484, **2**: 486
    evaluating wind energy
        costs, **2**: **469–501**
        economics, **2**: **469–501**
        electricity generation costs, **2**: **469–501**
        financial issues, **2**: **469–501**
        generation costs, **2**: **469–501**
        total costs, **2**: 493, **2**: 497
    external wind energy costs, **2**: 483, **2**: 484
    financial issues
        offshore wind, **2**: 478, **2**: 480
        onshore wind, **2**: 475
        wind energy, **2**: **469–501**
    generation costs, **2**: **469–501**
    hydropower, Iran, **6**: 257
    La Romaine Complex, Quebec, Canada, **6**: 164
    offshore wind costs/economics, **2**: 478, **2**: 480
    onshore wind economics, **2**: 475
    product-integrated photovoltaics, **1**: 717
    Revelstoke Complex, British Colombia, Canada, **6**: 176
    Three Gorges Project, China, **6**: 221
    total costs, wind energy, **2**: 493, **2**: 497
    variability costs, wind energy, **2**: 487, **2**: 494

wind energy
   costs, **2**: **469–501**
   desalination, **2**: 734
   economics, **2**: **469–501**
   electricity generation costs, **2**: **469–501**
   embedded generation benefits, **2**: 484, **2**: 486
   external costs, **2**: 483, **2**: 484
   financial issues, **2**: **469–501**
   generation costs, **2**: **469–501**
   total costs, **2**: 493, **2**: 497
   variability costs, **2**: 487, **2**: 494
wind turbines
   energy yields, **2**: 151, **2**: 153, **2**: 155
   wind park design, **2**: 186–187
Wuskwatim Generating Station Project, Manitoba, Canada, **6**: 159
technical committees (TC):
   hydrogen safety engineering, **4**: 83
   photovoltaic standards, **1**: **787–803**
   wind energy standards, **2**: 374
technology aspects:
   bioenergy policy development, **5**: 419
   biomass combined heat and power, **5**: 93
   biomass-to-liquids technology, **5**: 188, **5**: 203
   blades, **2**: 682, **2**: 710, **2**: 713
   cadmium telluride thin films, **1**: 23
   choice availability, biomass and biofuels, **5**: 32
   combined heat and power, biomass, **5**: 93
   concentration photovoltaics, **1**: 17, **1**: 24
   copper indium diselenide thin films, **1**: 22
   costs, photovoltaics, **1**: **47–72**
   crystalline silicon, **1**: 20, **1**: 21, **1**: 25
   development
      biomass and biofuel power generation, **5**: 32
      concentration photovoltaics, **1**: 763
      current status of photovoltaics, **1**: 41, **1**: 43
      desalination, **2**: 740
      electrical power generation, **8**: 3
      ocean wave energy, **8**: 3
      photovoltaics, **1**: 41, **1**: 43, **1**: 763
      power generation, **5**: 32
      wind energy, **2**: 48, **2**: 740
   evolution
      blades, **2**: 682, **2**: 710, **2**: 713
      forecasting, **2**: 710, **2**: 714
      mapping, **2**: 710, **2**: 714
      rotors, **2**: 676, **2**: 710, **2**: 713
      small wind turbines, **2**: 696
      vertical axis wind turbines, **2**: 672, **2**: 693
      wind turbines, **2**: **671–724**
         blades, **2**: 682, **2**: 710, **2**: 713
         forecasting, **2**: 710, **2**: 714
         mapping, **2**: 710, **2**: 714
         rotors, **2**: 676, **2**: 710, **2**: 713
         vertical axis, **2**: 672, **2**: 693
   forecasting, **2**: 710, **2**: 714
   future-generation systems, **1**: 15, **1**: 25
   future photovoltaics, **1**: 192
   high-efficiency devices, **1**: 24
   hydrogen economics, **4**: 46
   hydrogen energy chain, **4**: 47
   investments, future photovoltaics, **1**: 196
   mapping, **2**: 710, **2**: 714
   mix, photovoltaics, **1**: 168
   niches, hydrogen economics, **4**: 46
   ocean wave energy, readiness levels, **8**: 3, **8**: 80
   photovoltaics, **1**: **13–30**, **1**: **5–11**
      cadmium telluride thin films, **1**: 23
      copper indium diselenide thin films, **1**: 22
      costs, **1**: **47–72**
      crystalline silicon, **1**: 20, **1**: 21, **1**: 25
      future-generation systems, **1**: 15, **1**: 25
      future visions, **1**: 192

      global industry overview, **1**: 168
      high-efficiency devices, **1**: 24
      mix, **1**: 168
      revolutionary systems, **1**: 15, **1**: 25
      silicon, **1**: 19, **1**: 20, **1**: 21, **1**: 25
      very large-scale systems, **1**: 737
   properties, combined heat and power, **5**: 90
   readiness levels, ocean wave energy, **8**: 3, **8**: 80
   revolutionary systems, **1**: 15, **1**: 25
   rotors, **2**: 676, **2**: 710, **2**: 713
   selection criteria
      biomass and biofuels, **5**: 32
      grid capacity, **3**: 206
      high concentration solar collectors, **3**: 205
      location issues, **3**: 205
      net systems, **3**: 206
      solar desalination, **3**: 546
   silicon, **1**: 19, **1**: 20, **1**: 21, **1**: 25
   small wind turbines, **2**: 696
   solar cooling, **3**: 482, **3**: 490
   solar water heating systems, **3**: 420, **3**: 420f, **3**: 425
   solutions
      biomass and biofuels, **5**: 5, **5**: 6
      novel feedstocks, **5**: **263–291**
      waste materials, **5**: **217–261**
      woody biomass, **5**: **263–291**
   standardization, wind energy, **2**: 372
   thermophotovoltaics, **1**: 26
   turbines, **2**: **671–724**
   vertical axis wind turbines, **2**: 672, **2**: 693
   very large-scale photovoltaic systems, **1**: 737
   wind energy, **2**: **1–10**
      safety, **2**: 372
      standardization, **2**: 372
   wind turbines, **2**: **671–724**
      blades, **2**: 682, **2**: 710, **2**: 713
      forecasting, **2**: 710, **2**: 714
      mapping, **2**: 710, **2**: 714
      rotors, **2**: 676, **2**: 710, **2**: 713
Technology Strategy Board (TSB), **8**: 83
telecommunications: wind energy, **2**: 624, **2**: 740, **2**: 741, **2**: 742
Telkes, Maria, **3**: 98, **3**: 99f
TEM *see* transient electromagnetic resistivity methods
temperature:
   agricultural solar applications, **3**: 568, **3**: 569t
   alkaline fuel cells, **4**: 161t
   cell electrical performance, **3**: 261
   chalcopyrite thin film photovoltaics, **1**: 416
   concentration photovoltaic/thermal solar collectors, **3**: 266–267, **3**: 268
   control
      dam concrete construction, **6**: 224
      hydropower impact management, **6**: 90
   corrosion rates, **7**: 245
   current-voltage analysis, **1**: 416
   dam concrete construction, **6**: 224
   electrical performance, **3**: 261
   entropy diagrams, **7**: 213, **7**: 219–220, **7**: 223f, **7**: 224, **7**: 224f
   exploration techniques, **7**: 58
   geochemistry, **7**: 103, **7**: 141
   geothermal energy
      exploration techniques, **7**: 58
      geochemistry, **7**: 103, **7**: 141
   hydropower impact management, **6**: 70, **6**: 90
   Indian hydropower development, **6**: 232, **6**: 232f
   industrial solar applications, **3**: 568, **3**: 569t
   lift, thermal energy storage, **3**: 226
   microbial fuel cells, **4**: 268
   open-loop building-integrated photovoltaic-thermal models, **3**: 383
   passive solar technologies, **3**: 361
   photovoltaic/thermal solar collectors, **3**: 261
   proton-exchange membrane fuel cells, **4**: 199
   reservoir water quality, **6**: 70

temperature: (*continued*)
    solar thermal system applications, **3**: 568, **3**: 569*t*
    superstrate cadmium telluride thin films, **1**: 428
    urban buildings, **3**: 644
    wind power planning tools, **2**: 413
temporal averages: ocean waves, **8**: 28
temporal interpolations: weather predictions, **1**: 259
temporal resolution: solar radiation, **1**: 227, **1**: 228
temporary effects: heat flow, **7**: 88
temporary joints: concrete structure durability, **6**: 382
temporary structures: Three Gorges Project, China, **6**: 206
Temps–Coulson model, **3**: 48
tender systems:
    developing country photovoltaics, **1**: 128
    promoting photovoltaics, **1**: 74, **1**: 75–76, **1**: 77
    support mechanisms, **1**: 1
tension leg spars (TLS), **2**: 258
tents: product-integrated photovoltaics, **1**: 713, **1**: 714*f*
tenure issues/arrangements, **6**: 470, **6**: 482
TEPCO *see* Tokyo Electric Power Co., Inc.
ternerary blends: gasoline displacement, **5**: 333
terrain roughness, **2**: 409
terra preta, **5**: 358, **5**: 358*f*, **5**: 359, **5**: 360, **5**: 361*f*
terrestrial applications:
    alkaline fuel cells, **4**: 173
    hydrogen technology, **4**: 296
    liquid electrolytes, **4**: 173
    photovoltaic technology, **1**: 506
terrestrial solar radiation, **1**: 214, **1**: 215, **1**: 216, **1**: 217, **1**: 226
TES *see* thermal energy storage
test case specifications, **1**: 265
testing:
    acoustic noise measurements, **2**: 379
    anemometry, **2**: 377
    concentration photovoltaics, **1**: 755
    electrical characteristics, **2**: 380
    facilities, MES-DEA PEM fuel cells, **4**: 310
    hydrogen PEM fuel cells, **4**: 307
    international standards, **2**: 372
    measurement, wind energy, **2**: 376, **2**: 382
    mechanical load measurements, **2**: 378
    MES-DEA PEM fuel cells, **4**: 311
    noise measurements, **2**: 379
    ocean wave energy, **8**: 84, **8**: 88, **8**: 96
    PEM fuel cells, **4**: 307, **4**: 311
    photovoltaic reliability, **1**: 793
    photovoltaic/thermal solar collectors, **3**: 278
    physical models, ocean wave energy, **8**: 84, **8**: 88
    power plants, wind energy, **2**: 376
    power quality measurements, **2**: 380
    reliability, photovoltaics, **1**: 793
    road vehicle applications, **4**: 307
    rotor blades, **2**: 380
    safety, wind energy, **2**: 371, **2**: 376
    sound measurements, **2**: 379
    standards, wind energy, **2**: 371, **2**: 376
    tanks, hydrogen storage, **4**: 130
    test-bedding program, **1**: 81
    test rigs, air turbines, **8**: 125
    turbine safety, **2**: 376
    wind energy, **2**: 371, **2**: 376
        acoustic noise measurements, **2**: 379
        anemometry, **2**: 377
        electrical characteristics, **2**: 380
        measurement, **2**: 376, **2**: 382
        mechanical load measurements, **2**: 378
        noise measurements, **2**: 379
        power plants, **2**: 376
        power quality measurements, **2**: 380
        rotor blades, **2**: 380
        safety, **2**: 371, **2**: 376
        sound measurements, **2**: 379
        standards, **2**: 371, **2**: 376

wind turbines, **2**: 376, **2**: 719
tetrawatt hours (TWh), **6**: 1, **6**: 16
tetrawatt photovoltaic markets, **1**: 15
Teviot River, Central Otago, New Zealand, **6**: **467–483**
texturing: crystalline silicon cells, **1**: 359
TGP *see* Three Gorges Project (TGP), China
TGV *see* tradable green certificate
Thanet Wind Park, United Kingdom, **2**: 220, **2**: 437–438
thawing, **6**: 387
Theistareykir, NE Iceland, **7**: 155
Themis power plant, **3**: 627
theory:
    see also individual theories
    alkaline fuel cells, **4**: **159–182**
    geothermal energy
        exploration techniques, **7**: 84
    hydrogen technology, solid oxide fuel cells, **4**: **241–257**
    intermediate band solar cells, **1**: 619
    luminescent solar concentrators, **1**: 588
    molten carbonate fuel cells, **4**: **227–239**
    photovoltaic intermediate band solar cells, **1**: 619
    pitch control, **2**: 276
    solid oxide fuel cells, **4**: **241–257**
    wind energy, historical overviews, **2**: 49
    wind turbine energy yields, **2**: 140
thermal analysis:
    air systems, **3**: 216
    compound parabolic collectors, **3**: 154
    flat-plate collectors, **3**: 129
    high concentration solar collectors, **3**: 169, **3**: 173, **3**: 174, **3**: 187
    low concentration ratio solar collectors, **3**: 154
    low-temperature stationary collectors, **3**: 129
    passive solar technologies, **3**: 361
    water storage, **3**: 219
thermal annealing, **1**: 459
thermal capacity, **3**: 145, **6**: 132, **6**: 134*t*
thermal conductivity, **7**: 85, **7**: 195, **7**: 198
thermal conversion, **3**: 259
thermal effectiveness: solar cooling, **3**: 483
thermal efficiency:
    building-integrated photovoltaic-thermal systems, **3**: 388
    geothermal power plants, **7**: 207, **7**: 235
thermal energy:
    chemical energy, **1**: 304
    photovoltaic/thermal solar collectors, **3**: 271
    solar energy conversion principles, **1**: 304
thermal energy storage (TES):
    see also thermal storage
    active energy systems, **3**: 247
    adsorption systems, **3**: 248, **3**: 250
    agricultural applications, **3**: 569
    air systems, **3**: 215, **3**: 227, **3**: 228*t*, **3**: 229, **3**: 230, **3**: 402, **3**: 474
        solar energy, **3**: 215, **3**: 227, **3**: 228*t*, **3**: 229, **3**: 230
    boreholes, **3**: 211, **3**: 219, **3**: 237
    capital investment, solar energy, **3**: 231
    case studies, **3**: 232
    chemical reactions, **3**: 211, **3**: 224
    closed adsorption systems, **3**: 248
    combisystems, solar energy, **3**: 232
    components, **3**: **211–253**, **3**: 211
    concrete, **3**: 212, **3**: 242
    costs, **3**: 230
    definitions, **3**: 212
    design, **3**: 213
    economics, **3**: 227, **3**: 228
    energy savings, **3**: 227
    exergy analysis, **3**: 222, **3**: 230, **3**: 230*f*
    greenhouses, **3**: 230, **3**: 231
    high-temperature solar power plants, **3**: 239
    industrial applications, **3**: 569
    integration, **3**: 214
    latent heat
        exergy analysis, **3**: 222

solar energy, **3**: 211, **3**: 221, **3**: 225t, **3**: 227, **3**: 228t, **3**: 229, **3**: 230, **3**: 230f, **3**: 231, **3**: 243, **3**: 247
    liquid media, **3**: 216, **3**: 219, **3**: 227, **3**: 228t, **3**: 232, **3**: 239
    methods, **3**: 214
    molten salts, **3**: 239
    open adsorption systems, **3**: 250
    passive energy systems, **3**: 243
    phase change materials
        active energy systems, **3**: 247
        passive energy systems, **3**: 243
        solar energy, **3**: 211, **3**: 221-222, **3**: 222f, **3**: 223, **3**: 224, **3**: 225t, **3**: 228t, **3**: 229, **3**: 230, **3**: 230f, **3**: 243, **3**: 247, **3**: 249f
    power plants
        molten salts, **3**: 239
        solid media, **3**: 242
    rock storage, **3**: 227, **3**: 228t
    seasonal storage, solar energy, **3**: 248
    sensible heat, **3**: 211, **3**: 214, **3**: 225t, **3**: 227, **3**: 228t, **3**: 232, **3**: 237, **3**: 239, **3**: 242
    solar applications, **3**: 569
    solar energy, **3**: 250
        adsorption systems, **3**: 248, **3**: 250
        air systems, **3**: 215, **3**: 227, **3**: 228t, **3**: 229, **3**: 230
        chemical reactions, **3**: 211, **3**: 224
        closed adsorption systems, **3**: 248
        combisystems, **3**: 232
        components, **3: 211-253**, **3**: 211
        concrete, **3**: 212, **3**: 242
        design, **3**: 213
        economics, **3**: 228
        energy savings, **3**: 227
        latent heat, **3**: 211, **3**: 221, **3**: 225t, **3**: 227, **3**: 228t, **3**: 229, **3**: 230, **3**: 230f, **3**: 231, **3**: 243, **3**: 247
        liquid media, **3**: 216, **3**: 219, **3**: 227, **3**: 228t, **3**: 232, **3**: 239
        open adsorption systems, **3**: 250
        phase change materials, **3**: 211, **3**: 221-222, **3**: 222f, **3**: 223, **3**: 224, **3**: 225t, **3**: 228t, **3**: 229, **3**: 230, **3**: 230f, **3**: 243, **3**: 247, **3**: 249f
        rock storage, **3**: 227, **3**: 228t
        seasonal storage, **3**: 248
        sensible heat, **3**: 211, **3**: 214, **3**: 225t, **3**: 227, **3**: 228t, **3**: 232, **3**: 237, **3**: 239, **3**: 242
        sorption systems, **3**: 224, **3**: 248, **3**: 250
        thermochemical heat, **3**: 211, **3**: 224
        thermoeconomics, **3**: 228
        water storage, **3**: 216, **3**: 227, **3**: 228t, **3**: 232
    solid media, **3**: 212, **3**: 242
    sorption systems, **3**: 224, **3**: 248, **3**: 250
    system integration, **3**: 214
    thermochemical heat, **3**: 211, **3**: 224
    thermoeconomics, solar energy, **3**: 228
    underground systems, **3**: 211, **3**: 219, **3**: 237, **3**: 495, **3**: 500, **3**: 503-504, **3**: 522
    water storage, **3**: 216, **3**: 227, **3**: 228t, **3**: 232
thermal evaporation, **3**: 324
thermal expansion, **1**: 428
thermal exploration techniques, **7**: 83
thermal flat panels, **1**: 218
thermal generation: solar energy conversion principles, **1**: 302
thermal infrared radiation (TIR), **3**: 302
thermal insulation, **3**: 323, **3**: 333, **3**: 336
thermalization, **1**: 294
thermal losses:
    low-temperature stationary collectors, **3**: 133
    photovoltaics, **1**: 516-517, **3**: 271
    receivers, **3**: 187
    solar energy conversion principles, **1**: 309, **1**: 311
thermally driven cooling, **3: 481-494**, **3**: 611-612, **3**: 612
thermal management: concentration photovoltaics, **1**: 747, **1**: 756, **1**: 756f
thermal power plants, **2**: 573, **2**: 574
thermal power stations: definitions, **2**: 11
thermal pressure relief devices, **4**: 79, **4**: 79f, **4**: 80f

thermal priority operation (TPO), **3**: 261
thermal properties:
    coatings, **3**: 316
    definitions, **3**: 317
    energy evaluation, **3**: 321
    frames, **3**: 334
    glazings
        energy evaluation, **3**: 321
        frames, **3**: 334
        heat transfer coefficients, **3**: 321, **3**: 322, **3**: 330, **3**: 330t, **3**: 332, **3**: 332f, **3**: 334, **3**: 334t
        solar thermal energy, **3**: 316
        window frames, **3**: 334
    heat transfer coefficients, **3**: 321, **3**: 322, **3**: 330, **3**: 330t, **3**: 332, **3**: 332f, **3**: 334, **3**: 334t
    mid-pane values, **3**: 330, **3**: 330t
    solar thermal energy, **3**: 316
    transparent insulation, **3**: 339
    window energy evaluation, **3**: 321
    window frames, **3**: 334
    window glazing coatings, **3**: 330, **3**: 330t
thermal radiation:
    blackbodies, **1**: 318, **1**: 321
    coatings, **3**: 318
    continuous spectrum approximation, **1**: 317
    energy conversion, **1**: 328
    geometrical factors, **1**: 319
    glazings, **3**: 318
    laws, **3**: 318
    photon gases, **1**: 316
    photovoltaics, **1**: 316, **1**: 328
    solar thermal systems, **3**: 18
    upper bounds, **1**: 328
    work, **1**: 328
thermal recombination, **1**: 302
thermal response tests, **7**: 195, **7**: 196
thermal sensor radiometers, **1**: 219
thermal solar desalination, **3**: 529, **3**: 530, **3**: 547
thermal storage:
    see also thermal energy storage
    active solar systems, **3**: 473
        air systems, **3**: 474
        liquid systems, **3**: 474
        water, **3**: 474
    air systems, **3**: 474
    cooling systems, **3**: 473
    liquid systems, **3**: 474
    passive solar technologies, **3**: 359, **3**: 361
    solar cooling systems, **3**: 473
    solar space heating systems, **3**: 473
    solar thermal systems, **3**: 473
    solar water heating systems, **3**: 434
    space heating systems, **3**: 473
    water heating systems, **3**: 474
thermal stratification, **6**: 59
thermal stress, **6**: 380
thermistor chains, **6**: 69
thermochemical heat, **3**: 211, **3**: 224
    chemical reactions, **3**: 224
    definitions, **3**: 224
    sorption systems, **3**: 224
thermochemical processes:
    biochar, **5: 357-384**
    biomass-to-liquids technology, **5: 155-204**
thermochromic coatings, **3**: 648
thermocline storage tanks, **3**: 550
thermocouples, **3**: 173, **3**: 174
thermodynamics, **1: 315-352**
    alkaline fuel cells, **4**: 162
    beam solar radiation, **1**: 315, **1**: 319, **1**: 325, **1**: 326
    blackbodies, **1**: 318, **1**: 321, **1**: 322, **1**: 332
    continuous spectrum approximation, **1**: 317
    conversion efficiency, photovoltaics, **1**: 328

thermodynamics (*continued*)
    diluted thermal radiation, 1: 322
    direct solar radiation, 1: 315, 1: 319, 1: 325, 1: 326
    efficiency limits, 1: 589
    geometrical factors, 1: 319
    heat pumps, 3: 497
    hydrogen technology, 4: 243, 4: 245
    impact ionization, 1: 316, 1: 339
    ionization, 1: 316, 1: 339
    Lagrange invariant, 1: 316, 1: 325
    lithium–water absorption systems, 3: 466
    luminescent solar concentrators, 1: 589, 1: 590
    monogap solar cells, 1: 334
    narrow band semiconductors, 1: 340
    omnicolor solar convertors, photovoltaics, 1: 345
    photon gases, 1: 316
    photovoltaics, 1: **315–352**, 1: 7–8, 1: 8
    quantum efficiency, 1: 316, 1: 339
    scattered solar radiation, 1: 322, 1: 327
    Shockley–Queisser model, 1: 338
    solar cell equation, 1: 337
    solar radiation concentration, 1: 325
    solid oxide fuel cells, 4: 243, 4: 245
    thermal radiation, 1: 316, 1: 317, 1: 328
        geometrical factors, 1: 319
        photon gases, 1: 316
    voltage, 1: 340, 1: 342
thermoeconomics, 3: 228
thermogenics, 3: 316, 3: 350
thermography, 3: 173
thermometry, 7: 58, 7: 59, 7: 134
thermophotonics, 1: 26
thermophotovoltaics (TPV), 1: **603–618**, 1: 9, 1: 603
    emitter materials, 1: 603, 1: 604, 1: 615
    energy conversion, 1: **603–618**, 1: 9, 1: 603
    filters, 1: 604, 1: 607, 1: 610
    future outlook, 1: 616
    gallium-antimonide solar cells, 1: 608, 1: 614
    germanium, 1: 611
    heat source, 1: 604, 1: 605
    indium-gallium-antimonide solar cells, 1: 608, 1: 610
    indium-gallium-arsenide-antimonide-phosphide solar cells, 1: 611
    indium-gallium-arsenide solar cells, 1: 610, 1: 611
    indium-phosphide solar cells, 1: 610
    market potential, 1: 616
    materials, 1: 608
    Midnight Sun®, 1: 614
    Paul Scherrer Institute system, 1: 614, 1: 615
    photons, 1: 603, 1: 604, 1: 607
    residential heating, 1: 614, 1: 615
    selective emitter materials, 1: 603, 1: 604, 1: 605, 1: 615
    solar cells, 1: 608
    substrates, 1: 610
    system efficiency, 1: 604
    technology progress, 1: 26
thermopile detector pyranometers, 1: 219–220, 1: 220*f*
thermoplastics, 3: 334
thermosonic systems, 3: 279
thickness:
    blades, 8: 120
    hydrogen storage, 4: 130
thin-films:
    amorphous silicon, 1: 8, 1: 21, 1: 389, 1: 393
    asphalt layers, 3: 648
    cadmium telluride, 1: **423–438**, 1: 8, 1: 23, 1: 515, 1: 522
        back contacts, 1: 432
        buffer layers, 1: 428
        cadmium chloride activation, 1: 431
        commercial modules, 1: 424
        device designs, 1: 424
        energy-payback times, 1: 436
        environmental impacts, 1: 436
        historical overviews, 1: 423
        industry designs, 1: 424
        initial commercial modules, 1: 424
        junctions, 1: 434
        large-scale deployment considerations, 1: 434
        layer-specific process descriptions, 1: 427
        material properties, 1: 426
        microtechnologies, 1: 515, 1: 517, 1: 522
        mineral availability, 1: 436
        nanotechnologies, 1: 515, 1: 517, 1: 522
        payback times, 1: 436
        reliability, 1: 435
        transparent conducting oxide layers, 1: 424, 1: 428
    chalcopyrite, 1: **399–422**, 1: 8
        absorption coefficients, 1: 401
        back contacts, 1: 412
        barrier layers, 1: 412
        buffer layers, 1: 412
        copper indium diselenide thin films, 1: 22
        crystal structure, 1: 400
        deposition, 1: 406
        device properties, 1: 414
        device structure, 1: 410
        electrical properties, 1: 403
        front contacts, 1: 414
        future outlooks, 1: 417
        glass substrate structures, 1: 410
        grain boundaries, 1: 405
        material properties, 1: 400
        metal substrate structures, 1: 411
        optical properties, 1: 401
        polyimide substrate structures, 1: 412
        sequential deposition, 1: 406, 1: 406*f*, 1: 408
        single-step deposition, 1: 406, 1: 406*f*, 1: 407
        structure, 1: 400, 1: 410
        substrate structure, 1: 410
        surface properties, 1: 405
    copper indium diselenide, 1: 22, 1: **399–422**
    copper (indium, gallium) selenide$_2$, 1: 22, 1: **399–422**
    copper (indium, gallium) (selenide, sulfur)$_2$, 1: 22, 1: 515, 1: 517, 1: 522
    current status, 1: 42–43
    disruptive technologies, 1: 21, 1: 22
    environmental impacts, 1: **143–159**
    evolutionary technologies, 1: 20
    global industry overview, 1: 166, 1: 168
    life cycles, environmental impacts, 1: **143–159**
    lift-off processing, 1: 522
    microtechnology photovoltaics, 1: 8, 1: 515, 1: 517, 1: 522
        crystalline silicon, 1: 389–390, 1: 391
    nanotechnology photovoltaics, 1: 515, 1: 517, 1: 522
    photovoltaics, 1: 8
        amorphous silicon, 1: 8, 1: 21, 1: 389, 1: 393
        cadmium telluride, 1: **423–438**, 1: 8, 1: 515, 1: 522
        chalcopyrite, 1: **399–422**, 1: 8
        copper indium diselenide, 1: 22, 1: **399–422**
        copper (indium, gallium) selenide$_2$, 1: 22, 1: **399–422**
        copper (indium, gallium) (selenide, sulfur)$_2$, 1: 22, 1: 515, 1: 517, 1: 522
        current status, 1: 42–43
        disruptive technologies, 1: 21, 1: 22
        environmental impacts, 1: **143–159**
        evolutionary technologies, 1: 20
        global industry overview, 1: 166, 1: 168
        life cycles, 1: **143–159**
        microtechnology, 1: 8, 1: 515, 1: 517, 1: 522
            crystalline silicon, 1: 389–390, 1: 391
        nanotechnology, 1: 515, 1: 517, 1: 522
        silicon, 1: **389–398**
    silicon, 1: **389–398**, 1: 8
        amorphous silicon, 1: 8, 1: 21, 1: 389, 1: 393
        amorphous-silicon–carbon-silicon heterojunctions, 1: 393
        applications, 1: 396

carbon-silicon solar cells, **1**: 393
   challenges, **1**: 394
   deposition, **1**: 389
   fabrication, **1**: 395
   heterojunction cells, **1**: 393
   hydrogen plasma, **1**: 389
   light trapping, **1**: 393
   microcrystalline silicon, **1**: 8, **1**: 391
   module fabrication, **1**: 395
   multijunction solar cells, **1**: 392
   photon management, **1**: 393, **1**: 395
   research challenges, **1**: 394
   space applications, **1**: 396
  very large-scale photovoltaic systems, **1**: 737
third-generation solar cells, **1**: 653
third-stage construction works: Three Gorges Project, China, **6**: 203, **6**: 206, **6**: 207
three bladed systems, **2**: 61
three-dimensional (3-D):
   axial-flow air turbines, **8**: 123
   reservoir water quality, **6**: 72
Three Gorges Project (TGP), China, **6**: **179–227**
   achievements, **6**: 210
   aqua-ecosystems, **6**: 214
   Baidi City, **6**: 219, **6**: 219*f*
   Baiheliang inscriptions and carvings, **6**: 217, **6**: 218*f*
   biodiversity, **6**: 213
   carp, **6**: 216
   cautious decisions, **6**: 200
   challenges, **6**: 210
   clean water discharging, **6**: 212
   cofferdams, **6**: 201, **6**: 206, **6**: 223
   concrete cofferdams, **6**: 201
   concrete gravity dams, **6**: 184
   conduit systems, **6**: 190, **6**: 193, **6**: 195*f*, **6**: 197
   construction
     quality control, **6**: 208
     technology, **6**: 200, **6**: 223
   cultural relic protection, **6**: 217
   dams, **6**: 184, **6**: 200, **6**: 219
     break analysis, **6**: 219
     concrete construction, **6**: 224
     toe power plants, **6**: 188
   debris sluicing structures, **6**: 188
   decision making, **6**: 200
   deep water cofferdam construction, **6**: 223
   degradation issues, **6**: 212
   demonstration, **6**: 200
   discharge structures, **6**: 186, **6**: 188, **6**: 212
   dissipation structures, **6**: 186
   diversion schemes, **6**: 205, **6**: 206, **6**: 207
   double-line ship lock, **6**: 223
   downstream scouring, **6**: 212
   dual-way five-step ship locks, **6**: 193
   earthquakes, **6**: 217
   economic development, **6**: 211
   ecosystem protection, **6**: 213
   energy dissipation structures, **6**: 186
   financing control, **6**: 209
   first-stage construction works, **6**: 201, **6**: 206
   fish, **6**: 216
   five-step ship locks, **6**: 193, **6**: 223
   floating debris sluicing structures, **6**: 188
   flood control, **6**: 183, **6**: 220
   flood discharging, **6**: 187
   flushing structures, **6**: 188
   full demonstration, **6**: 200
   geological hazards, **6**: 216
   geology, **6**: 181
   gravity dams, **6**: 184
   greenhouse gas emissions, **6**: 221
   hydraulic complex structures, **6**: 183
   hydraulic steel structures, **6**: 187, **6**: 198, **6**: 226
   hydraulic structure design, **6**: 221
   hydroelectric turbine generation units, **6**: 191, **6**: 192*t*, **6**: 193*t*, **6**: 194*t*
   hydrometeorology, **6**: 180
   hydropower, **6**: **179–227**
   intake types, **6**: 221
   inundated practicality index, **6**: 210
   investment control, **6**: 210, **6**: 211
   key features, **6**: 182
   layouts, **6**: 188, **6**: 193, **6**: 195*f*, **6**: 196
   location, **6**: 180, **6**: 181*f*
   Maopingxi Dam, **6**: 200
   natural condition, **6**: 180
   navigation, **6**: 183, **6**: 193, **6**: 205, **6**: 207, **6**: 221
   objectives, **6**: 182
   open diversion channels, **6**: 206
   power generation, **6**: 183, **6**: 188, **6**: 191, **6**: 206, **6**: 221, **6**: 223
   powerhouses, **6**: 188
   power plants, **6**: 191, **6**: 221, **6**: 223
   project construction, **6**: 200
   quality control in construction, **6**: 208
   relic protection, **6**: 217
   reservoir-induced seism, **6**: 217
   reservoir operating strategies, **6**: 75
   resettlements, **6**: 210
   revenue, **6**: 209
   river channel degradation, **6**: 212
   river closure, **6**: 206, **6**: 223
   roller-compacted concrete cofferdams, **6**: 201
   salt tide invasion control, **6**: 214
   sand discharge outlet structures, **6**: 188
   scale issues, **6**: 182, **6**: 186, **6**: 188
   scouring, **6**: 212
   second-stage construction works, **6**: 202
   sediment, **6**: 188, **6**: 212
   seismic activity, **6**: 217
   ship lift, **6**: 198
   ship locks, **6**: 193, **6**: 197, **6**: 207, **6**: 223, **6**: 224
   sluicing structures, **6**: 188
   social development, **6**: 211
   social issues, **6**: 210
   spiral case structures, **6**: 191, **6**: 221
   staged construction, **6**: 201
   steel structures, **6**: 187, **6**: 198, **6**: 226
   supervised construction, **6**: 208
   tailrace tunnels, **6**: 223
   technical advancements, **6**: 221
   temporary structures, **6**: 206
   third-stage construction works, **6**: 203, **6**: 206, **6**: 207
   trash way outlets, **6**: 188
   turbine generation units, **6**: 191, **6**: 192*t*
   underground power plants, **6**: 191, **6**: 223
   vertical ship lift, **6**: 198
   water discharge, **6**: 186, **6**: 212
   water diversion, **6**: 205, **6**: 207
   water quality, **6**: 213
   Zhangfei Temple, **6**: 218
three-stage chalcopyrite thin film deposition, **1**: 407
thresholds:
   peaks-over-threshold, **8**: 54
   single threshold solar cells, **1**: **549–561**, **1**: **533–548**
thrust loads, **2**: 254
thyristor-controlled reactor-fixed capacitors (TCR-FC), **2**: 585
Tianhuangping, China pumped storage hydropower, **6**: 429, **6**: 430
tidal currents, **8**: **1–6**
tidal energy, **8**: **7–9**
tidal stream systems, **8**: 152
TIGAS *see* Topsoe integrated gasoline synthesis
tilt:
   irradiance power predictions, **1**: 246, **1**: 247, **1**: 260, **1**: 281
   solar radiation, **1**: 226, **1**: 246, **1**: 247, **1**: 260, **1**: 281, **3**: 39
timber drying, **7**: 181, **7**: 183*f*

time considerations:
    biomass-to-liquids technology, **5**: 160, **5**: 161*f*, **5**: 187, **5**: 189*f*
    electricity capacity, planet energy balance, **2**: 14
    fossil fuel depletion, **2**: 22
    geochemistry, **7**: 108
    geological explorations, **7**: 55
    geothermal energy, **7**: 55, **7**: 108
    hydropower, **6**: 359
    mechanical-dynamic loads, **2**: 244, **2**: 254
    ocean energy revenue, **8**: 163
    ocean wave energy, **8**: 104, **8**: 108
    passive solar technologies, **3**: 374
    photovoltaic power forecasting, **1**: 245, **1**: 248
    primary energy consumption, **2**: 12
    sediment management, **6**: 359
    solar energy environmental characteristics, **3**: 8
    solar irradiance forecasting, **1**: 245, **1**: 248
    vertical axis wind turbines, **2**: 672
    wind energy
        wind parks design, **2**: 169, **2**: 170, **2**: 181, **2**: 186–187, **2**: 189
        wind power installed capacity, **2**: 3, **2**: 3*f*
        wind speed time variations, **2**: 81, **2**: 82
        world market, **2**: 27, **2**: 31
    wind turbines, **2**: 93, **2**: **671–724**
        mechanical-dynamic loads, **2**: 244, **2**: 254
        size, **2**: 2–3, **2**: 3*f*
        wind park design, **2**: 186–187, **2**: 189
    world-wide wind energy markets, **2**: 27, **2**: 31
time domains: ocean wave energy, **8**: 80
tinted glass, **3**: 331
tip correction, **2**: 229
tip speed ratio, **2**: 102, **2**: 270, **2**: 671
TIR *see* thermal infrared radiation
von Tischirnhaus, Ehrenfried Walther, **3**: 88, **3**: 89*f*
titanium and it's alloys, **7**: 249
Tjæreborg turbines, **2**: 237
TLS *see* tension leg spars
TMY *see* typical meteorological year
Tocantins River, Brazil, **6**: 101
Tokuyama Corporation, **1**: 175
Tokyo Electric Power Co., Inc (TEPCO), **6**: 281
tomato drying, Greece, **7**: 180, **7**: 180*f*
toolbox concept: dye-sensitized solar cells, **1**: 489
TOPFARM project, **2**: 715
top heat loss coefficients, **3**: 134
top-of-the-atmosphere: definitions, **3**: 28
topography:
    geothermal energy geological explorations, **7**: 54
    geothermal system physics, **7**: 27
    heat flow, **7**: 88
Topsoe integrated gasoline synthesis (TIGAS) process, **5**: 158, **5**: 183*f*, **5**: 185
Torfajökull high-temperature fields, Iceland, **7**: 60
Tormes development, Spain, **6**: 336–337
torque:
    air turbines, **8**: 112
    alcohol fuels, **5**: 320
    coefficients, **2**: 102
torrefaction:
    biochar, **5**: 366*t*, **5**: 368, **5**: 373*f*
    biomass-to-liquids technology, **5**: 156, **5**: 164
torrefied wood, **5**: 59
total costs of wind energy, **2**: 493, **2**: 497
total solar adsorption, **3**: 318
total solar energy rejected, **3**: 323
total solar reflectance, **3**: 317–318
total solar transmittance, **3**: 317
total variability costs: wind energy, **2**: 493, **2**: 497
TOUGH2 code, **7**: 35
toughened glass, **3**: 328, **3**: 329
tourism, **2**: 194, **6**: 144
towers:
    construction, **3**: 187
    shadow, **2**: 255, **2**: 256*f*, **2**: 257*f*
    tower mills, **2**: 46
    tower reflectors, **3**: 187, **3**: 189
    wind farms, **2**: 441
toxic emissions, **5**: 325
TPO *see* thermal priority operation
TPV *see* thermophotovoltaics
traceability:
    photovoltaic performance determination, **1**: 790
    solar radiation measurements, **1**: 222
tracers:
    geothermal energy physics, **7**: 42–43
    geothermal fluids origins, **7**: 108
tracking:
    accuracy, **3**: 169, **3**: 188
    agricultural applications, **3**: 570*f*, **3**: 571–572, **3**: 572*f*, **3**: 587*t*
    concentration photovoltaics, **1**: 748, **1**: 799, **3**: 267
    Fresnel collectors, **3**: 196
    high concentration solar collectors, **3**: 169, **3**: 177, **3**: 188, **3**: 196
    industrial applications, **3**: 570*f*, **3**: 571–572, **3**: 572*f*, **3**: 587*t*
    losses, **8**: 37
    moving surface incidence angles, **3**: 13
    parabolic troughs, **3**: 177
    satellite altimeter data, **8**: 37
traction: PEMFCs, **4**: 203
tradable green certificate (TGC) schemes, **1**: 76
tradable permits, **5**: 411, **5**: 416–417, **5**: 420*f*, **5**: 422
trade:
    bioenergy global markets, **5**: **75–85**
    sugar, Brazil, **5**: 19
traditional charcoal making, **5**: 366
traditional inverter safe operating areas, **4**: 297
traffic: wind energy impacts, **2**: 524
Traidcraft, **5**: 106
training *see* education
trains, **2**: 54, **4**: 218, **4**: 285
Tranco del Diablo, Spain, **6**: 335, **6**: 336*f*
transesterification, **5**: 208, **5**: 218, **5**: 219, **5**: 223, **5**: 228
transfer admittance, **3**: 364
transfer functions: passive solar technologies, **3**: 375, **3**: 377
transfers: wind power, **4**: 428
transformers: wind turbines, **2**: 270
transient air-based photovoltaic-thermal systems, **3**: 381
transient building-integrated photovoltaic-thermal systems, **3**: 381
transient electromagnetic (TEM) resistivity methods, **7**: 61, **7**: 62, **7**: 65, **7**: 68
transient heat conduction, **3**: 362
transient open-loop photovoltaic-thermal systems, **3**: 381
transient response analysis: direct gain systems, **3**: 367
transients: wind turbines, **2**: 207
transient thermal analysis, **3**: 367
transitional water technology, **2**: 431, **2**: 446
transitions:
    fuel cells and hydrogen technology, **4**: **331–340**
    momentum-to-buoyancy jet releases, **4**: 90
transit times: offshore work vessels, **8**: 162
transmission:
    capital costs, **8**: 157
    coatings, **3**: 319
    conventional power systems, **1**: 201
    electricity
        Cameroon, Africa, **6**: 134*t*
        energy storage, **1**: 201, **6**: 408
        Japanese hydropower history, **6**: 266
        wind energy, **2**: 602
    future visions, photovoltaics, **1**: 197
    glazings, **3**: 319
    high concentration solar collectors, **3**: 175
    laser beaming, **1**: 770
    luminescent solar concentrators, **1**: 589
    microwave beaming, **1**: 768
    parabolic troughs, **3**: 175

photovoltaic future visions, **1**: 197
radiation, **3**: 120
simplified generic axial-flow microhydro turbines, **6**: 444
solar power satellites, **1**: 768, **1**: 770
upgrades deferral, **6**: 408
variable costs, **2**: 492
wind energy, **2**: 492, **2**: 602
transmittance:
   absorptance product, **3**: 127, **3**: 128f
   cloud cover, **1**: 231
   definitions, **3**: 2
transmitted ocean waves, **8**: 93
transparent conducting oxide (TCO) layers, **1**: 390, **1**: 424, **1**: 428
transparent conductive electrochromogenic films, **3**: 343–344, **3**: 344
transparent electrodes, **1**: 456
transparent insulation:
   aerogel glazing, **3**: 340
   flat-plate collectors, **3**: 112f, **3**: 112–113, **3**: 113f
   glass capillary structures, **3**: 341
   granular aerogels, **3**: 340
   historical development, **3**: 339
   materials, **3**: 340
   monolithic silica aerogels, **3**: 341
   optical properties, **3**: 339
   solar thermal energy, **3**: 314, **3**: 339
   thermal properties, **3**: 339
transparent plates, **3**: 21
transpired air heating collectors, **3**: 114, **3**: 115f
transport:
   biofuel and biomass CEN standards, **5**: 105
   Cameroon, Africa, hydropower, **6**: **129–151**
   CEN standards, **5**: 105
   charge transport, **1**: 444, **1**: 445, **1**: 661
   decarbonization, **4**: 65
   distance costs, **5**: 167, **5**: 167f
   end-use hydrogen applications, **4**: 61, **4**: 62, **4**: 63
   ethanol-diesel blends, **5**: 344
   fossil fuel blends, **5**: 343
   fuel cells, hydrogen technology, **4**: 333, **4**: **281–293**
   greenhouse gases, **5**: 167, **5**: 167f, **5**: 168f
   heat
      geothermal energy exploration techniques, **7**: 84
      high concentration solar collectors, **3**: 173
   hydrogen
      decarbonization, **4**: 65
      end-use applications, **4**: 61, **4**: 62, **4**: 63
      fuel cells, **4**: 333, **4**: **281–293**
      policy development, **4**: 68
      production, **4**: 283
      solid oxide fuel cells, **4**: 243f
   hydropower, Cameroon, Africa, **6**: **129–151**
   number, **4**: 184
   passenger transport, **4**: 61, **4**: 63–64, **4**: 286
   phosphoric acid fuel cells, **4**: 282
   policy development, **4**: 68
   proton-exchange membrane fuel cells, **4**: 203, **4**: 214
   redox mediator transport, **1**: 486
   Renewable Transport Fuel Obligations, **5**: 100, **5**: 103
   sediments, **6**: 74, **6**: 244
   solid oxide fuel cells, **4**: 243f
   wind turbines, **2**: 177, **2**: 246
transportation:
   electricity, Cameroon, Africa, **6**: 132
   fuel cell power electronics, **4**: 320
   hydrogen storage, **4**: 130
   offshore wind farms, **2**: 456
   power electronics, **4**: 320
   product-integrated photovoltaics, **1**: 714
   wind energy, **2**: 177, **2**: 456, **2**: 524
   wind turbine installation, **2**: 177
   wood fuel markets, **5**: 78
trash way outlets, **6**: 188

trees:
   additional value extraction, **5**: 390, **5**: 391f, **5**: 392, **5**: 392f
   building-integrated photovoltaics, **1**: 701
   wind power planning, **2**: 413
trends:
   stand-alone biomass power plants, **5**: 28
   wind power global markets, **2**: **657–669**
   wind turbines, **2**: 164, **2**: **671–724**
trickle bed reactors, **5**: 181
tri flex-fuel vehicles, **5**: 332
Trina Solar Ltd:, **1**: 170
Tripile structures, **2**: 448
triple glazing, **3**: 314, **3**: 333
triple-junction cells, **1**: 24
triplet-triplet annihilation, **1**: 533, **1**: 541–542, **1**: 543
tripod foundations, **2**: 443f, **2**: 447
TRNSYS simulation software program, **3**: 396, **3**: 411
Trombe walls, **3**: 640, **3**: 641f
trophic status assessments, **6**: 63
trunnions, **6**: 87
TSA project, **3**: 193
t-tests, **3**: 51
tube absorbers, **3**: 104, **3**: 105f, **3**: 107f, **3**: 153, **3**: 154f
tube-ball mills, **5**: 45
Tucurui hydroelectric project, **6**: 101
tungsten oxide, **3**: 344
tunnel inlets, **6**: 469
tunnel junctions, **1**: 502
tunnel outlets, **6**: 473
turbidity routing, **6**: 366
turbid water reservoir bypassing, **6**: 294, **6**: 296, **6**: 298
turbines:
   see also air turbines; wind turbines
   aerodynamic analysis, **2**: **225–241**
   aesthetics, **2**: 518, **2**: 687
   blade construction, **2**: 682
   blade design, **2**: 682
   blade numbers, **2**: 61, **2**: 64
   building-integrated systems, **2**: 699
   California wind rush, **2**: 66
   control systems, **2**: **329–370**
   costs, **2**: 702, **2**: 709
   current concepts, **2**: 675
   derating, **2**: 735
   desalination, **2**: 733, **2**: 735
   design requirement standards, **2**: 373
   development, **2**: 711, **2**: 714
   double-flash geothermal power plants, **7**: 208
   dry-steam power plants, **7**: 209, **7**: 211f, **7**: 212
   dynamic analyses, **2**: 244
   efficiency, **6**: 444
   energy yields, **2**: **113–168**
   environmental impacts, **2**: 687
   evolution, **2**: **671–724**
   financial support, **2**: 708, **2**: 710, **2**: 713, **2**: 715, **2**: 718
   Gedser machine, **2**: 60
   historical overviews, **2**: 54, **2**: 55, **2**: 55f, **2**: 56, **2**: 71, **2**: 624
   Horseshoe Bend hydroelectric scheme, **6**: 467
   hydropower, **6**: 24, **6**: 57
      axial-flow microhydro turbines, **6**: **435–466**
      bank turbines, **6**: 26, **6**: 28f
      cross-flow turbines, **6**: 26, **6**: 28f
      Francis turbines, **6**: 25, **6**: 28f
      generic axial-flow microhydro turbines, **6**: **435–466**
      Hydraulienne siphon turbines, **6**: 27
      Kaplan turbines, **6**: 25, **6**: 26f
      Omega siphon turbines, **6**: 27
      Pelton turbines, **6**: 25
      sedimentation impacts, **6**: 57
      simplified generic axial-flow microhydro turbines, **6**: **435–466**
      water turbine types, **6**: 24

turbines: (*continued*)
   industry, **2**: **671–724**
   innovation, **2**: **671–724**
   integration projects, **2**: 711, **2**: 714
   isentropic efficiency ratio, **7**: 208
   loads, **2**: **243–268**
   management, **2**: 711, **2**: 714
   medium-sized systems, **2**: 713
   Mekin hydropower project, Cameroon, Africa, **6**: 143
   modeling, **2**: 333
   noise impacts, **2**: 513
   ocean wave energy, **8**: 8, **8**: **111–149**, **8**: 8–9
   offshore wind power, **2**: **431–468**, **2**: 688, **2**: 713
   postwar programs, **2**: 58
   power electronics, **2**: **329–370**
   propeller turbines, **6**: 439, **6**: 441–442, **6**: 461, **6**: 461*t*, **6**: 463*t*, **6**: 465
   prospects, **2**: **671–724**
   pumps as turbines, **6**: 440–441
   pump-turbines, **6**: 413, **6**: 440–441
   research and development, **2**: **671–724**
   rotor aerodynamics, **2**: 232, **2**: 233, **2**: 713
   safety, testing, **2**: 376
   scale effects/scaling, **2**: 136, **2**: 138, **2**: 144
   scaling, **7**: 253
   sediments, **6**: 57
   selection, **2**: 416, **6**: 460
   simplified generic axial-flow microhydro turbines, **6**: **435–466**
   size evolution, **2**: 676
   sizing, **6**: 463
   small systems, **2**: 696, **2**: 713
   Smith-Putnam Machine, **2**: 56
   stand alone hybrid wind energy systems, **2**: 624, **2**: 626, **2**: 631
   standards, **2**: 373
   steam turbines, **5**: 88, **5**: 90, **5**: 94, **5**: 95
   sub-kilowatt turbines, **6**: 440
   technology evolution, **2**: 93, **2**: **671–724**
   testing, safety, **2**: 376
   three bladed systems, **2**: 61
   Three Gorges Project, China, **6**: 191, **6**: 192*t*
   time evolution, **2**: **671–724**
   trends, **2**: **671–724**
   two bladed systems, **2**: 61, **2**: 64
   types, **6**: 24
   upgrading, **2**: 415, **2**: 416
   vertical axis designs, **2**: 71
   visual impacts, wind energy, **2**: 518
turbulence:
   constant loads, **2**: 256, **2**: 257*f*
   inflow noise, **2**: 238
   offshore wind turbines, **2**: 259
   wind power, **2**: 406
   wind speed profiles, **2**: 78
   wind turbine loads, **2**: 256, **2**: 257*f*, **2**: 259
twentieth century history, **3**: 91, **6**: 315
twin glass-type evacuated tube collectors, **3**: 117*f*, **3**: 117–118, **3**: 118*f*, **3**: 119*f*
twin unidirectional impulse air turbines, **8**: 137
two bladed systems, **2**: 61, **2**: 64
two-dimensional (2-D):
   cascade flow analysis, **8**: 113
   concentration photovoltaic/thermal solar collectors, **3**: 268
   reservoir water quality, **6**: 72
two-hand business finance model, **1**: 123
two-phase regions/systems: geothermal energy, **7**: 15
two-pump reservoirs, **6**: 429
two-stage chalcopyrite thin film deposition, **1**: 407
two-step transesterification, **5**: 222
two-switch voltage inverters, **4**: 303
type approval testing: photovoltaics, reliability testing, **1**: 793
typical meteorological year (TMY), **1**: 228, **3**: 22, **3**: 23

U

UAV *see* unmanned air vehicles
UCC *see* Union Carbide Corporation
UK *see* United Kingdom
Ultimate Trough collectors, **3**: 181
ultracapacitors, **2**: 277*f*, **2**: 327
ultrahigh thermal insulation, **3**: 333
ultrasonication, **5**: 224
ultraviolet radiation, **3**: 61
ultraviolet transmittance, **3**: 318
Umm Al Nar Power and Desalination Station, **3**: 547
unburnt carbon, **5**: 49, **5**: 51
uncertainty:
   hindcast ocean wave data, **8**: 66
   radiometers, **1**: 224
   solar irradiance-photovoltaic power forecasts, **1**: 270
   solar radiation, **1**: 224, **1**: 227, **1**: 229
   solar radiometers, **3**: 67
   wind power, **2**: 412
uncoated single-glazed windows, **3**: 331
underexpanded jets, **4**: 78, **4**: 86, **4**: 86*f*, **4**: 89
underground power plants, **6**: 191, **6**: 223
underground thermal energy storage (UTES), **3**: 211, **3**: 219, **3**: 237, **3**: 495, **3**: 500, **3**: 503–504, **3**: 522
underwater cabling, **2**: 451
UNEP *see* United Nations Environment Programme
uneven settlement, **6**: 381
UNFCC *see* United Nations Framework Convention on Climate Change
UNGA *see* United Nations General Assembly
UNICA *see* Brazilian Sugarcane Industry Association
unidirectional flow turbines, **8**: 111, **8**: 137
unidirectional impulse air turbines, **8**: 137
unified omnicolor solar convertors, **1**: 349
uniform corrosion, **7**: 241
unignited releases, **4**: 86, **4**: 95
uninterruptible power supplies (UPS), **4**: 59
Union Carbide Corporation (UCC) system, **4**: 173
unitary systems: heat pumps, **3**: 501
unit costs: offshore work vessels, **8**: 160
United Kingdom (UK):
   bioenergy policy development, **5**: 426
   biomass cofiring, **5**: 66
   borehole thermal energy storage office buildings, **3**: 237
   climate change levees, **2**: 486, **8**: 164
   heat loads, **4**: 251
   ocean wave energy, **8**: 7, **8**: 83–84, **8**: 163, **8**: 164
   offshore wind power
      activity, **2**: 436–437, **2**: 437–438
      historical overviews, **2**: 433
      market development, **2**: 667
      Robin Rigg project, **2**: 441, **2**: 444*f*
   renewable obligation certificates, **8**: 164
   small wind turbines, **2**: 376, **2**: 388
   solid oxide fuel cells, **4**: 251
   wind power market development, **2**: 664–665
United Nations Environment Programme (UNEP), **5**: 415
United Nations Framework Convention on Climate Change (UNFCC), **5**: 412–413
United States of America (USA):
   biomass cofiring, **5**: 64
   challenges, photovoltaics, **1**: 89
   concentrating solar power, **3**: 631
   feed-in tariffs, **1**: 88
   green power programs, **1**: 86
   high concentration solar collector markets, **3**: 192
   hydropower, **6**: 36, **6**: 37*f*, **6**: 37*t*
   net metering, photovoltaics, **1**: 86
   offshore wind power, **2**: 440, **2**: 689
   photovoltaics
      challenges, **1**: 89
      feed-in tariffs, **1**: 88

future directions, **1**: 89, **1**: 184
global industry overview, **1**: 169, **1**: 171
green power programs, **1**: 86
market development, **1**: 184
net metering, **1**: 86
promotion schemes, **1**: 83, **1**: 103
renewable portfolio standards, **1**: 85
standards, **1**: 787
support mechanisms, **1**: 83, **1**: 103
tax incentives, **1**: 87
promotion schemes, **1**: 83, **1**: 103
renewable portfolio standards, **1**: 85
small wind turbines, **2**: 376, **2**: 388
standards, **1**: 787
supporting photovoltaics, **1**: 83, **1**: 103
tax incentives, **1**: 87
wind power market development, **2**: 665
wind pump historical overviews, **2**: 51
wind turbine manufacturers, **2**: 669
United States solar atlas (USSRA), **3**: 61–62
unit service concessions, **1**: 132
unit switching: reverse osmosis, **2**: 734
unit values: ocean energy revenue, **8**: 163
univariant geothermometers, **7**: 59, **7**: 138
universal primary education, **7**: 288
unmanned air vehicles (UAV), **4**: 290
unplanned maintenance operating costs, **8**: 159
unpredictability: wind energy, **2**: 586
unpressurized storage water tanks, **3**: 218f
unscheduled hydrogen releases, **4**: 95
unsteady aerodynamics: wind turbines, loads, **2**: 249
unsteady flows, **6**: 74, **6**: 86
unsteady Reynolds-averaged Navier–Stokes (URANS) equations, **2**: 232–233
Unsworth–Monteith turbidity, **3**: 39
UN Work Programme on Indicators of Sustainable Development, **7**: 278
upconversion:
    annihilation statistics, **1**: 543
    efficiency, **1**: **533–548**
    equivalent circuits, **1**: 535
    external quantum efficiency, **1**: 540
    future prospects, **1**: 546
    molecular photophysics, **1**: 542
    monochromatic optical efficiency, **1**: 539
    optical efficiency, **1**: 539
    organic molecules, **1**: 541, **1**: 546
    photoelectrical efficiency, **1**: 540
    photovoltaics, **1**: **533–548**, **1**: 9, **1**: 533
    practical applications, **1**: 540
    quantum efficiency, **1**: 540
    rare-earths, **1**: 533, **1**: 540, **1**: 546
    single threshold solar cells, **1**: **533–548**, **1**: 533
    solar concentration, **1**: 538
    triplet-triplet annihilation, **1**: 533, **1**: 541–542, **1**: 543
upconverters: definitions, **1**: 533
update issues: solar radiation/meteorological data, **1**: 227, **1**: 232
updraft fixed bed gasifiers, **5**: 136, **5**: 150
upgrading wind turbines, **2**: 415, **2**: 416
upper bounds:
    direct solar radiation, **1**: 326
    scattered solar radiation, **1**: 327
    thermal radiation, **1**: 328
Upper Krishna Project, **6**: 244, **6**: 246f
UPS *see* uninterruptible power supplies
upscaling photovoltaics, **1**: 264, **1**: 284
upstream impacts: hydropower, **6**: 53
upstream sectional elevations, **6**: 480, **6**: 480f
UPWIND *see* Integrated Wind Turbine Design
upwind rotor configurations, **2**: 255
URANS *see* unsteady Reynolds-averaged Navier–Stokes
urban buildings:
    albedo, **3**: 644
    cooling, **3**: 642, **3**: 644
    green spaces, **3**: 651
    passive solar architecture, **3**: 637
    photovoltaic planning, **1**: **697–707**
    solar cooling, **3**: 642, **3**: 644
urban electrical vehicles:
    see also electrical vehicles
    battery hybrid energy storage, **4**: 317
    energy requirements, **4**: 318
    hydrogen PEM fuel cells, **4**: 317
    power requirements, **4**: 318
urban heat islands: definitions, **3**: 637
urbanization: passive solar architecture, **3**: 637, **3**: 644
urban planning: building-integrated photovoltaics, **1**: **697–707**
urban residue feedstocks, **5**: 263, **5**: 264, **5**: 286
urban temperatures, **3**: 644
urea formaldehyde, **5**: 404
Uruguay River hydroelectricity project, **6**: 119
USA *see* United States of America
user perception/experiences: photovoltaics, **1**: 727
USSRA *see* United States solar atlas
US Windpower company, **2**: 66, **2**: 67, **2**: 70f
UTES *see* underground thermal energy storage
utility calculation tools, **3**: 62
utility demand: wind turbines, **2**: 186–187
utilization:
    active solar thermal systems, **3**: 396, **3**: 404, **3**: 408
    efficiency ratios, **7**: 208, **7**: 235
    geothermal energy
        geochemistry, **7**: **95–168**
        physics, **7**: 22, **7**: 43
        sustainability, **7**: 281, **7**: 282
U-tubes, **3**: 117f, **3**: 117–118, **3**: 118f, **3**: 119f
UVE river, Cameroon, Africa, **6**: 146

V

Vab Krevelen plots, **5**: 373f
vacuum hydrogen absorption, **3**: 173
vacuum tube collectors, **3**: 116
valance bands, **1**: 619
Valdecañas dam, Spain, **6**: 328, **6**: 329f
valence bands, **1**: 294
validation:
    ocean wave energy test phases, **8**: 80, **8**: 81t
    satellite altimeters, **8**: 37
valley breezes, **2**: 82
valuations: wind energy economics, **2**: 470
value added tax reductions, **1**: 128
value chains: concentration photovoltaics, **1**: 764
valve-controlled air flow, **8**: 146
vanadium pentoxide, **3**: 345
vaneless turbines, **6**: 440
vanes: wind direction measurements, **2**: 76
vapor compression cycles, **3**: 497
vapor compression systems, **3**: 590–591
vapor deposition, **3**: 324, **3**: 324–325
vapor permeation, **5**: 211
vapor phase sampling, **7**: 95
vapor pressure, **5**: 320–321, **5**: 321f
variability:
    see also variable costs
    desalination, **2**: 735
    ocean wave energy, **8**: 28, **8**: 37, **8**: 50
    peaks-over-threshold method, ocean waves, **8**: 65
    photovoltaic future visions, **1**: 189
    wave energy converters, **8**: 50
    wind energy, **2**: 586, **2**: 588, **2**: 735
variable costs:
    see also variability
    assimilations, **2**: 489
    backup reserves, **2**: 489, **2**: 491, **2**: 492

variable costs: (*continued*)
  capacity credit, **2**: 491
  carbon dioxide savings, **2**: 491
  characteristics, **2**: 489
  electricity networks, **2**: 488
  extra short-term reserves, **2**: 490
  mitigation, **2**: 494
  reserves, **2**: 489, **2**: 490
  short-term reserves, **2**: 490
  technical evaluation, **2**: 487, **2**: 494
  transmission constraints, **2**: 492
  wind energy
    assimilations, **2**: 489
    backup reserves, **2**: 489, **2**: 491, **2**: 492
    capacity credit, **2**: 491
    carbon dioxide savings, **2**: 491
    characteristics, **2**: 489
    electricity networks, **2**: 488
    extra short-term reserves, **2**: 490
    mitigation, **2**: 494
    reserves, **2**: 489, **2**: 490
    short-term reserves, **2**: 490
    technical evaluation, **2**: 487, **2**: 494
    transmission constraints, **2**: 492
variable-pitch rotors, **8**: 129
variable-specific impulse magnetoplasma rockets, **4**: 19
variable-speed controls, **2**: 330, **2**: 331*f*
variable-speed direct-grid coupling generators, **2**: 287
variable-speed indirect-grid coupling generators, **2**: 289
variable-speed machines, **6**: 427
variable-speed power systems, **2**: 297
variance spectrum: ocean wave energy, **8**: 80
variants:
  PEMFCs, **4**: 205
  Wells air turbines, **8**: 114
vegetable oils:
  additional value extraction, **5**: 388*t*, **5**: 388–389
  biodiesel, **5**: 218, **5**: 228
    challenges, **5**: 219
    economics, **5**: 218
    emission characteristics, **5**: 227
    engine performance, **5**: 226
    environmental factors, **5**: 218
    enzymatic transesterification, **5**: 223
    ethical issues, **5**: 219
    management, **5**: 218
    oil collection, **5**: 219
    optimization, **5**: 219
    quality, **5**: 225
    social issues, **5**: 219
    standards, **5**: 225
    transesterification, **5**: 219, **5**: 228
    ultrasonication, **5**: 224
  biomass and biofuels, **5**: 218, **5**: 228, **5**: 388*t*, **5**: 388–389
  collection, **5**: 219
  combustion, **5**: 351
  dual fuel operation, **5**: 351
  economics, **5**: 218
  emission characteristics, **5**: 227
  engine configuration ranges, **5**: 349
  engine performance, **5**: 226
  environmental factors, **5**: 218
  ethical issues, **5**: 219
  frying oil effects, **5**: 219
  historical perspectives, **5**: 12
  management, **5**: 218
  oil collection, **5**: 219
  optimization, **5**: 219
  quality, **5**: 225
  social issues, **5**: 219
  standards, **5**: 225
  stationary engines, **5**: 349
  transesterification, **5**: 219, **5**: 228

  ultrasonication, **5**: 224
vegetation impacts:
  geothermal energy direct heat utilization, **7**: 180
  wind park design, **2**: 171, **2**: 173, **2**: 174*f*
vehicles:
  see also automotives; electrical vehicles; road vehicles
  batteries, **4**: 322, **4**: 324, **4**: 327
  biomass and biofuels, **5**: 305–342
  Brazilian bioethanol development, **5**: 17, **5**: 18
  costs
    hydrogen
      consumer costs, **4**: 62
      delivery infrastructure, **4**: 52
      refueling stations, **4**: 54
    wind energy, **2**: 496
  drive trains, **4**: 63
  energy requirements, **4**: 318
  flex-fuel vehicles, **5**: 17, **5**: 332
  fuel cells
    battery performance, **4**: 324
    current status, **4**: 36
    hydrogen, **4**: 284, **4**: 333
  hydrogen
    consumer costs, **4**: 62
    delivery infrastructure costs, **4**: 52
    drive trains, **4**: 63
    fuel cells, **4**: 284, **4**: 333
    market opportunities, **4**: 63
    PEM fuel cells, **4**: 317
    prototypes, **4**: 62
    refueling station costs, **4**: 54
    storage performance, **4**: 55
  market opportunities, **4**: 63
  power requirements, **4**: 318
  product-integrated photovoltaics, **1**: 714
  proton-exchange membrane fuel cells, **4**: 189, **4**: 203, **4**: 214, **4**: 219*t*
  prototype hydrogen technology, **4**: 62
  storage performance, **4**: 55
  traction batteries, **4**: 322, **4**: 327
  unmanned air vehicles, **4**: 290
  wind energy, costs, **2**: 496
  ZEBRA technology, **4**: 322, **4**: 327
velocity:
  head, **6**: 31
  wind energy, **2**: 74
VEM wind turbines, **2**: 324
ventilation:
  agricultural solar thermal applications, **3**: 587
  building-integrated photovoltaics, **1**: 701
  industrial solar applications, **3**: 587
  Mekin hydropower project, Cameroon, Africa, **6**: 144
  passive solar cooling, **3**: 643, **3**: 643*f*
Venturi phenomenon, **2**: 175
verification: wind resources, **2**: 394, **2**: 396
vertical axis wind turbines (VAWT), **2**: 44, **2**: 71, **2**: 104, **2**: 106, **2**: 672, **2**: 693
vertical cyclone separators, **7**: 218
vertical ship lift, **6**: 198
vertical spindle mills, **5**: 45
very large-scale photovoltaics (VLS-PV), **1**: 733–744, **1**: 10
  benefits, **1**: 733
  capital costs, **1**: 737
  climate change, **1**: 741
  community development, **1**: 733–744
  costs, **1**: 736, **1**: 739
  definitions, **1**: 733
  deployment strategies, **1**: 734
  DESERTEC, **1**: 739
  ecological impacts, **1**: 738
  economics, **1**: 733, **1**: 734*t*, **1**: 736, **1**: 739
  emerging initiatives, **1**: 739
  energy potential, **1**: 734

environmental impacts, **1**: 733, **1**: 734*t*, **1**: 737, **1**: 741
Europe, the Middle East, and North Africa regions, **1**: 739
evaluation, **1**: 734
future prospects, **1**: 741
generation costs, **1**: 736
initiatives, **1**: 739
life cycle analysis, **1**: 737
Middle East, and North Africa regions, **1**: 739
multibenefits, **1**: 733
North Africa, **1**: 739
progress considerations, **1**: 739
roadmaps, **1**: 743
semiconductor technologies, **1**: 737
solar cell technology, **1**: 737
sustainability issues, **1**: 741
technology aspects, **1**: 737
visions/roadmaps, **1**: 743
vessels:
  compressed gas: hydrogen storage, **4**: **111–135**
  flash geothermal power plants, **7**: 218, **7**: 219
  ocean energy economics, **8**: 160
  offshore work, **8**: 160
Vestas, **2**: 306, **2**: 308*t*, **2**: 437
vibration:
  Chinese hydraulic research, **6**: 499
  wind turbines, **2**: 365
Victorville 2 project, **3**: 631–632
Villarino power plant, Spain, **6**: 338–339, **6**: 340*f*
Villora project, Spain, **6**: 319, **6**: 319*f*
Vina du Nord river, Cameroon, Africa, **6**: 145, **6**: 145*t*
vinyl glazings/window frames, **3**: 334
virgin biomass feedstocks, **5**: 141, **5**: 142*t*
visible light properties, **3**: 318
visual impacts:
  geothermal energy sustainable development, **7**: 284
  offshore wind power, **2**: 463, **2**: 503, **2**: 527
  wind energy, **2**: 518, **2**: 527
  wind turbines, **2**: 518
visual inspections: concrete structure durability, **6**: 397
VLH turbines, **6**: 439–440
VLS-PV *see* very large-scale photovoltaics
VOC *see* volatile organic compounds
volatile constituents: water, **7**: 100
volatile hazards: biomass cofiring, **5**: 69
volatile organic compounds (VOC), **5**: 51
volcanoes:
  geothermal classification, **7**: 5, **7**: 6–7
  geothermal energy hazard assessments, **7**: 56
voltage:
  see also current-voltage analysis
  balancing, **4**: 303, **4**: 304, **4**: 305
  capacitance voltage measurements, **1**: 404
  cell voltages, **4**: 197
  control, wind energy integration, **2**: 585
  flicker, **2**: 594
  fluctuations/variations, wind turbines, **2**: 207, **2**: 594
  high-voltage direct current transmission systems, **6**: 157
  high-voltage organic solar cells, **1**: 464
  inverters, **4**: **295–329**
  multi-junction cells, **1**: 501
  open-circuit voltage, **1**: 340, **1**: 416, **4**: 184, **4**: 197
  open-current voltages, **4**: 245
  phase voltage imbalance, **2**: 594
  photovoltaic thermodynamics, **1**: 340, **1**: 342
  regulation, **4**: 299, **6**: 408
  solar cells in circuits, **1**: 294
  static voltage balancing, **4**: 303, **4**: 304
volume:
  geothermal energy physics, **7**: 30
  hydrogen technology fuel cells, **4**: 2
voluntary observing ships (VOS), **8**: 23
volute: microhydro turbines, **6**: 437, **6**: 444, **6**: 449, **6**: 451
von Tischirnhaus, Ehrenfried Walther, **3**: 88, **3**: 89*f*

vortices:
  shaft spillway tunnels, **6**: 485, **6**: 495
  wind turbine aerodynamic analysis, **2**: 231
VOS *see* voluntary observing ships

W

Wacker Polysilicon AG, **1**: 174
wafer-based technologies, **1**: 168, **1**: 737
wakes:
  wind turbines
    blade-element momentum theory, **2**: 230
    computational fluid dynamics, **2**: 234
    energy yields, **2**: 149
    loads, **2**: 249
    technology evolution, **2**: 717
walls: admittance transfer, **3**: 364
warranties: hydrogen storage, **4**: 129
washing: biodiesel, **5**: 210
Waste Incineration Directive (WID), **5**: 31
waste materials, **5**: **217–261**
  biochar, **5**: 357
  biodiesel, **5**: 218, **5**: 228
  biofuels, **5**: **217–261**
  biomass cofiring, **5**: 58
  biomass feedstocks, **5**: **217–261**
    gasification, **5**: 140, **5**: 142*t*
      mixed wood, **5**: 140
      solid fuel recovery, **5**: 140, **5**: 142*t*
      wood, **5**: 140
    mixed wood gasification, **5**: 140
    solid fuel recovery, **5**: 140, **5**: 142*t*
    wood gasification, **5**: 140
  hydropower multibenefit solutions, **6**: 41, **6**: 41*t*
  vegetable oils, **5**: 218, **5**: 228
water:
  see also hydropower; ocean wave energy
  active solar systems, **3**: 474
  air collectors, **3**: 286
  air heat pumps, **3**: 391
  air systems thermal storage, **3**: 474
  biomass gasification, **5**: 146, **5**: 147
  boiling points, **7**: 16
  characteristics, **6**: 57
  classification, **7**: 101
  consumption, **2**: 505
  conveyance structures, **6**: 16
  cooled photovoltaic/thermal solar collectors, **3**: 256–257, **3**: 263, **3**: 270, **3**: 282
  cooling
    binary power plants, **7**: 224, **7**: 224*f*
    dry-steam power plants, **7**: 209–210, **7**: 211*f*, **7**: 215
    proton-exchange membrane fuel cells, **4**: 199
  dams, Cameroon, Africa, **6**: 135, **6**: 136*t*
  demand, desalination, **2**: 726, **2**: 732
  depth, offshore wind costs, **2**: 481
  desalination, **3**: **529–565**
  direct heat utilization, **7**: 179
  discharge, Three Gorges Project, China, **6**: 186, **6**: 212
  diseases, **3**: 437, **6**: 63
  diversion, Three Gorges Project, China, **6**: 205, **6**: 207
  electrolysis, **4**: 45, **4**: 48
  evaporation, **4**: 194
  f-chart method, **3**: 400
  gas shift, **5**: 146
  geothermal chemistry, **7**: 101
  geothermal energy, **7**: 179, **7**: 285
  geothermal system physics, **7**: 28, **7**: 40, **7**: 44–45
  heating
    see also hot water
    active solar systems, **3**: **449–480**
    agricultural solar thermal systems, **3**: 577

314 Index

water: (*continued*)
    air systems, **3:** 452, **3:** 455
    auxiliary sources, **3:** 458
    components, **3:** 420, **3:** 426, **3:** 428*f*
    direct circulation systems, **3:** 449, **3:** 451*f*
    f-chart method, **3:** 403
    heat pumps, **3:** 459
    indirect active solar systems, **3:** 450, **3:** 452
    industrial solar thermal systems, **3:** 577
    integrated collector storage systems, **3:** 159
    photovoltaic/thermal solar collectors, **3:** 279
    solar heating systems, **3: 419–447**
    solar space heating systems, **3:** 453, **3:** 455, **3:** 458, **3:** 459
    solar thermal systems, **3:** 403, **3:** 577
    storage tanks, **3:** 458
    thermal storage, **3:** 474
    thermosonic systems, **3:** 279
    wind energy costs and effects, **2:** 497
  heat pumps, **3:** 391, **3:** 505
  hydrogen technology, **4:** 2, **4:** 6*f*
  Indian hydropower, **6:** 230, **6:** 230*t*
  MES-DEA PEM fuel cells, **4:** 310
  mills, **2:** 42, **2:** 43*f*
  pollution, **7:** 110–111
  power, **2:** 42, **2:** 43*f*, **8:** 93
  production, desalination, **3: 529–565**
  proton-exchange membrane fuel cells, **4:** 187, **4:** 194
  pumping systems, **2:** 742, **2:** 744
  quality
    environmental impact management, **6:** 53, **6:** 58
    eutrophication, **6:** 61, **6:** 72
    geothermal energy, **7:** 285
    impact management, **6:** 53, **6:** 58
    lake stability, **6:** 68
    nitrogen, **6:** 66
    nutrient dynamics, **6:** 66
    oxygenation, **6:** 61
    parameters, **6:** 64
    phosphorus, **6:** 66
    reservoirs, **6:** 53, **6:** 58, **6:** 66, **6:** 68
    Three Gorges Project, China, **6:** 213
    upstream impacts, **6:** 53
  related diseases, **3:** 437, **6:** 63
  simplified generic axial-flow microhydro turbines, **6:** 444
  solar assisted heat pumps, **3:** 519, **3:** 523
  solar desalination, **3: 529–565**
  solar thermal systems, **3:** 400
  splitting, **4:** 51
  storage
    heat exchangers, **3:** 216
    solar energy, **3:** 216, **3:** 227, **3:** 228*t*, **3:** 232
    solar water heating systems, **3:** 434
    thermal analysis, **3:** 219
    thermal energy storage, **3:** 216, **3:** 227, **3:** 228*t*, **3:** 232
  supply, **6:** 221, **6:** 444
  surface elevation, **8:** 93
  sustainable geothermal energy, **7:** 285
  tanks, **3:** 217, **3:** 217*f*, **3:** 218*f*, **3:** 519
  thermal storage, **3:** 474
  Three Gorges Project, China, **6:** 221
  treatments
    biomass gasification, **5:** 146, **5:** 147
    hydrogen technology, fuel cells, **4:** 2, **4:** 6*f*
  turbines, **6:** 24, **8:** 8–9
  volatile constituents, **7:** 100
  wind energy
    environmental–social benefits/impacts, **2:** 505
    power, **2:** 42, **2:** 43*f*
    pumping systems, **2:** 742, **2:** 744
WATES *see* Wave and Tidal Energy Scheme
WATSUN simulation software program, **3:** 396, **3:** 413
wave basin tests, **8:** 89
wave climate data, **8:** 31
wave conditions: mean wind loads, **2:** 262
wave currents, **8: 1–6**
wave energy conversion/converters, **8: 11–77, 8: 79–110**
  climatic variability, **8:** 51
  commercial demonstration, **8: 79–110**
  device development, **8: 79–110**
  historical overviews, **8: 7–9**
  initial conception, **8: 79–110**
  interannual variability, **8:** 51
  mathematical descriptions, **8:** 12
  numerical models, **8:** 49, **8:** 50
  ocean waves
    climatic variability, **8:** 51
    interannual variability, **8:** 51
    numerical models, **8:** 49, **8:** 50
    performance assessments, **8:** 30
    power estimations, **8:** 20
    predictability, **8:** 50
    sampling variability, **8:** 51
    seasonal variability, **8:** 51
    synoptic variability, **8:** 51
    variability, **8:** 50
  performance assessments, **8:** 30
  power estimations, ocean waves, **8:** 20
  predictability, **8:** 50
  resource assessments, **8: 11–77**
  sampling variability, **8:** 51
  seasonal variability, **8:** 51
  synoptic variability, **8:** 51
  variability, **8:** 50
wave evaluation: wind farms, **2:** 454
wave farm development: ocean wave energy, **8:** 4
wave flume tests, **8:** 89
wave generation tests: ocean wave energy, **8:** 89
wave height, **8:** 37, **8:** 52, **8:** 54, **8:** 70
Wave Hub, **8:** 4–5, **8:** 5*f*, **8:** 102
wave-induced loads: wind turbines, **2:** 258
wavemakers: ocean wave energy, **8:** 90
wave parameters:
  frequency domain, **8:** 105
  time domain, **8:** 108
wave period: ocean waves, **8:** 36, **8:** 39
Waveplam, **8:** 84
wave prediction: wind turbines, **2:** 717
wave spectrum: ocean waves, **8:** 13
wave stream systems: ocean energy, **8:** 152
wave theory: wind turbines, **2:** 265
Wave and Tidal Energy Scheme (WATES), **8:** 83
Wave and Tidal-stream Energy Demonstration Scheme, **8:** 102–103
WaveTrain2:, **8:** 84
weak networks: wind power penetration, **2:** 208
weak systems: wind park design, **2:** 183, **2:** 206
weather conditions:
  passive solar technologies, **3:** 369, **3:** 371*f*
  wind turbine energy yields, **2:** 152, **2:** 153
weather forecasting: wind energy, **2:** 616
weathering tests, **1:** 793
weather prediction, **1:** 240, **1:** 240–241, **1:** 245, **1:** 248, **1:** 252, **1:** 257, **1:** 271, **1:** 273, **1:** 275
weather protection, **3:** 330
weather stations, **6:** 69
Wedderburn number, **6:** 68
wedge absorbers, **3:** 153, **3:** 154*f*
weeping: gas diffusion electrodes, **4:** 169
WEG *see* Wind Energy Group
WEH refueller nozzles, **4:** 2, **4:** 8*f*
Weibull distribution:
  wind potential evaluation, **2:** 184, **2:** 186*f*, **2:** 197, **2:** 197*f*, **2:** 198, **2:** 198*t*
  wind speed, **2:** 84, **2:** 117, **2:** 120, **2:** 124, **2:** 144
Weier pitch motors, **2:** 276*f*
Weier wind turbines, **2:** 324

weighting factors:
  meteorological year, **3**: 23
  thermal capacity, **3**: 145, **3**: 145*t*
weir supply, **6**: 445
welding integrity, **4**: 129
wellheads, **7**: 209, **7**: 210*f*, **7**: 252
wells:
  geothermal energy
    physics, **7**: 18
    scale effects/scaling, **7**: 41, **7**: 42, **7**: 252, **7**: 253
Wells, Allan A, air turbines:
  advanced configurations, **8**: 128
  biplane rotors, **8**: 128
  contra-rotating rotors, **8**: 129
  impulse turbines, **8**: 122
  ocean energy, **8**: 111, **8**: 112, **8**: 112*f*, **8**: 114, **8**: 122, **8**: 125, **8**: 126, **8**: 139
  performance, ocean energy, **8**: 126
  prototypes, **8**: 139
  testing, ocean energy, **8**: 125
  variable-pitch rotors, **8**: 129
  variants, **8**: 114
WERATLAS, **8**: 8
Western United States: hydropower hydraulic process impacts, **6**: 75
wet chemical analysis, **7**: 99
wet cooling systems, **3**: 597
wet oxidation, **5**: 245
wet scrubbers, **5**: 145
WG *see* working groups
wheat, **5**: 386, **5**: 386*f*, **5**: 387–388, **5**: 389
whole-energy-system hydrogen technology, **4**: 65
wholesale wind energy markets, **2**: 557
WID *see* Waste Incineration Directive
wide bandgap back-surface-field layers, **1**: 501
wide bandgap tunnel junction, **1**: 503, **1**: 504
wide-field infrared survey explorer (WISE), **4**: 24
Wien's displacement law, **1**: 605, **1**: 605*f*, **3**: 33
wildlife impacts:
  geothermal direct heat utilization, **7**: 180
  offshore wind power, **2**: 463
  wind energy, **2**: 522, **2**: 528, **2**: 529
  wind park design, **2**: 182
Willmott model, **3**: 48
willow coppice crops, **5**: 264, **5**: 277
wind:
  see also offshore wind power; onshore wind; wind energy; wind farms; wind parks; wind potential; wind power; wind speed; wind turbines
  atlas method, **2**: 407, **2**: 411
  classes, **2**: 418
  climate, **2**: 403, **2**: 418
  data
    wind power, **2**: 403, **2**: 406, **2**: 426
    wind speed, **2**: 403
  driven ocean waves, **8**: 1
  electricity penetration, **1**: 201
  evaluation, wind farms, **2**: 454
  frequency distribution, **2**: 82, **2**: 404
  gust determination, **2**: 81, **2**: 126
  height, **2**: 404
  induced loads, **2**: 254, **2**: 258
  maps
    electricity production maximization, **2**: 171–172
    wind park design, **2**: 171–172, **2**: 197
    wind potential evaluation, **2**: 184, **2**: 184–186, **2**: 186*f*, **2**: 187*f*
    wind resources, **2**: 394, **2**: 396, **2**: 414
  measurements, wind power, **2**: 406, **2**: 412
  ocean waves, **8**: 1
  prediction, **2**: 717
  pumps, **2**: 51
  resources, **2**: 86, **2**: 87, **2**: 394, **2**: 396, **2**: 414
  rose, **2**: 76, **2**: 184, **2**: 185*f*
  shear, **2**: 78, **2**: 140

stream power losses, **2**: 114
theory, **2**: 263
turbines, **2**: 364
velocity, **2**: 174
wakes, wind power, micro-siting, **2**: 398
wind energy:
  2020 price comparisons, **2**: 499
  access issues, **2**: 524
  acoustic noise measurements, **2**: 379
  advantages, **2**: 3
  aerodynamic analysis, **2**: **225–241**
  aesthetics, **2**: 182, **2**: 194, **2**: 205, **2**: 463, **2**: 518, **2**: 687
  air pollution, **2**: 504
  American wind pumps, **2**: 51
  amortization periods, **2**: 472
  anemometry, **2**: 75, **2**: 377
  archaeology, **2**: 524
  artificial neural networks, **2**: 88
  assessments, **2**: 511
  assimilations, **2**: 489
  Atlas Models, **2**: 86, **2**: 87
  auxiliary electronic equipment, **2**: 632
  axial momentum theory, **2**: 90
  backup requirements, **2**: 734
  backup reserves, **2**: 489, **2**: 491, **2**: 492
  balance of plant costs, **2**: 474
  balancing costs, **2**: 484
  Bayesian adaptive combination, **2**: 88
  Bayesian model averaging, **2**: 89
  benefits, **2**: 611
  biomass policy, **2**: 552
  birds, **2**: 182, **2**: 205, **2**: 529, **2**: 687–688
  blade construction, **2**: 682
  blade design, **2**: 682
  blade numbers, **2**: 61
  British Wind Energy Association, **2**: 65, **2**: 71
  building-integrated systems, **2**: 699
  calculating energy prices, **2**: 472
  California wind rush, **2**: 66
  capacity credit, **2**: 491
  carbon dioxide emissions, **2**: 504, **2**: 545, **2**: 548
  carbon dioxide savings, **2**: 491
  carbon taxes, **2**: 485
  carbon trading, **2**: 485
  case studies, **2**: **169–223**
  causes, **2**: 74
  certification, **2**: 371, **2**: 372, **2**: 383, **2**: 388
  characteristics, **2**: 74, **2**: 489, **2**: 586
  charge rates, **2**: 473
  climate change levy, **2**: 486
  complementary electric generator units, **2**: 632
  component certificates, standards, **2**: 388
  condition monitoring systems, **2**: 388
  contribution of stand alone hybrid systems, **2**: 626
  control systems, **2**: **329–370**
  conventional electrical power systems, **2**: 592
  costs
    balancing, **2**: 474, **2**: 484
    desalination, **2**: 736
    electrical networks, **2**: 612
    electricity generation, **2**: **469–501**, **2**: 612
    inputs, **2**: 471
    integration, **2**: 612
    performance issues, **2**: 474, **2**: 475
    pollution, **2**: 485
    technical evaluation, **2**: **469–501**
    time evolution, **2**: 702
    turbine technology, **2**: 702, **2**: 709
  cultural heritage, **2**: 524
  cup anemometers, **2**: 75
  current concepts, **2**: 675
  current implemented forecasting tools, **2**: 616
  current status, **2**: **1–10**, **2**: 477

316　Index

wind energy: (*continued*)
　　data mining forecasting models, **2**: 615
　　decentralized generation, **2**: 496
　　dedicated storage, **2**: 495
　　definitions, **2**: 1
　　demand management, **2**: 494
　　desalination, **2**: **725–747**, **2**: 729
　　　backup requirements, **2**: 734
　　　costs, **2**: 736
　　　design issues, **2**: 733
　　　economics, **2**: 736
　　　energy requirements, **2**: 729
　　　examples, **2**: 738
　　　future trends, **2**: 740
　　　hybrid energy systems, **2**: 735, **2**: 740
　　　integrated systems, **2**: 732
　　　membranes, **2**: 726, **2**: 727*f*, **2**: 728, **2**: 733
　　　operational issues, **2**: 734, **2**: 735
　　　plants, **2**: 726
　　　project implementation, **2**: 735
　　　reverse osmosis, **2**: 726, **2**: 727*f*, **2**: 728, **2**: 732, **2**: 734, **2**: 738
　　　storage, **2**: 733, **2**: 734
　　　technological developments, **2**: 740
　　　turbines, **2**: 733, **2**: 735
　　　water demand, **2**: 732
　　design
　　　desalination, **2**: 733
　　　stand alone hybrid systems, **2**: 649, **2**: 651
　　diesel, **2**: 623–624, **2**: 636, **2**: 639*f*
　　direction, **2**: 74, **2**: 76
　　disadvantages, **2**: 3
　　distribution networks, **2**: 602
　　dynamic studies, speed, **2**: 87
　　early science, **2**: 49
　　economics, **2**: 542, **2**: 555
　　　desalination, **2**: 736
　　　electricity production, **2**: **469–501**, **2**: 555
　　　embedded generation benefits, **2**: 484, **2**: 486
　　　planet energy balance, **2**: **11–39**
　　　technical evaluation, **2**: **469–501**
　　economies of scale, **2**: 488
　　electrical characteristics, testing, **2**: 380
　　electric cars, mitigating variable costs and effects, **2**: 496
　　electricity
　　　costs, **2**: **469–501**, **2**: 612
　　　distribution networks, **2**: 602
　　　economics, **2**: **469–501**, **2**: 555
　　　energy balance, **2**: 3, **2**: 4*f*
　　　generation, **2**: **469–501**, **2**: 555
　　　historical overviews, **2**: 52, **2**: 54
　　　integration, **2**: **569–622**
　　　markets, policy, **2**: 542, **2**: 546
　　　microgrids, **2**: 571, **2**: 592–593, **2**: 600, **2**: 607
　　　network integration, **2**: **569–622**
　　　operation, **2**: 581, **2**: 596
　　　planning, **2**: 596
　　　policy, **2**: 542, **2**: 546, **2**: 552, **2**: 555
　　　production economics, **2**: **469–501**, **2**: 555
　　　repercussions, **2**: 596
　　　requirements, **2**: 613
　　　space heating, **2**: 497
　　　transmission networks, **2**: 602
　　　variability, **2**: 588
　　　variability costs, **2**: 488
　　　water heating, **2**: 497
　　electronic equipment, **2**: 632
　　embedded generation benefits, **2**: 484, **2**: 486
　　energy balance, **2**: **11–39**
　　environmental impacts, **2**: **503–539**
　　　air pollution, **2**: 504
　　　assessments, **2**: 511
　　　birds, **2**: 182, **2**: 205, **2**: 529, **2**: 687–688

　　　carbon dioxide emissions, **2**: 504
　　　fauna, **2**: 522, **2**: 528
　　　flora, **2**: 522
　　　pollutants, **2**: 504
　　　social benefits/impacts, **2**: **503–539**
　　　turbine technology, **2**: 687
　　　water consumption, **2**: 505
　　　wildlife, **2**: 522, **2**: 528, **2**: 529
　　European history, **2**: 44
　　European supergrids, **2**: 496
　　European Wind Energy Association, **2**: 65, **2**: 71
　　evaluation, **2**: **469–501**, **2**: 651
　　experiment, historical overviews, **2**: 49
　　external costs
　　　climate change levy, **2**: 486
　　　embedded generation benefits, **2**: 484, **2**: 486
　　　market solutions, **2**: 485
　　　support mechanisms, **2**: 486
　　　technical evaluation, **2**: 483, **2**: 484
　　extra short-term reserves, **2**: 490
　　fauna, **2**: 522, **2**: 528
　　finance, **2**: **469–501**, **2**: 708, **2**: 710, **2**: 713, **2**: 715, **2**: 718
　　fish, **2**: 528
　　flora, **2**: 522
　　forecasting, **2**: 31, **2**: 494, **2**: 616, **2**: 710, **2**: 714, **2**: 719
　　fossil fuel policy, **2**: 542, **2**: 548, **2**: 552
　　fuel prices, **2**: 498
　　fundamental causes, **2**: 74
　　future price trends, **2**: 471, **2**: 498
　　future prospects, **2**: **1–10**, **2**: 35
　　Gedser machine, **2**: 60, **2**: 63*f*
　　generation costs, **2**: **469–501**
　　geothermal energy policy, **2**: 554
　　global market energy balance, **2**: **11–39**
　　greenhouse gas reduction, **2**: **541–568**
　　grid networks, **2**: 496
　　health and safety, **2**: 525
　　high-penetration level surpluses, **2**: 492
　　historical overviews, **2**: **41–72**
　　　American wind pumps, **2**: 51
　　　blade numbers, **2**: 61
　　　British Wind Energy Association, **2**: 65, **2**: 71
　　　California wind rush, **2**: 66
　　　early science, **2**: 49
　　　electrical power, **2**: 52, **2**: 54
　　　Europe, **2**: 44
　　　European Wind Energy Association, **2**: 65, **2**: 71
　　　experiment, **2**: 49
　　　Gedser machine, **2**: 60, **2**: 63*f*
　　　horizontal axis machines, **2**: 45
　　　Hütter, Ulrich, **2**: 61, **2**: 63, **2**: 64*f*
　　　International Energy Agency, **2**: 71
　　　large machines, **2**: 54
　　　organizations, **2**: 71
　　　Persian vertical axis designs, **2**: 44
　　　post mills, **2**: 46
　　　postwar programs, **2**: 58
　　　pumps, **2**: 51
　　　sails, **2**: 41, **2**: 42*f*, **2**: 43*f*, **2**: 44
　　　Smith-Putnam Machine, **2**: 56
　　　stand alone hybrid systems, **2**: 624
　　　standardization, **2**: 371
　　　technological developments, **2**: 48
　　　theory, **2**: 49
　　　three bladed systems, **2**: 61
　　　tower mills, **2**: 46
　　　two bladed systems, **2**: 61, **2**: 64
　　　vertical axis designs, **2**: 44, **2**: 71
　　　wind pumps, **2**: 51
　　　wind turbines, **2**: 54, **2**: 55, **2**: 55*f*, **2**: 56, **2**: 71
　　horizontal axis machines, **2**: 45
　　Hütter, Ulrich, **2**: 61, **2**: 63, **2**: 64*f*
　　hybrid energy desalination, **2**: 735, **2**: 740

Index

hybrid stand alone systems, 2: 1, 2: **623–655**
hydraulics policy, 2: 553
hydrogen, stand alone hybrid systems, 2: 645, 2: 650
hydropower, stand alone hybrid systems, 2: 643, 2: 649–650
IEC, 2: 372, 2: 373, 2: 374
industry and markets, 2: **657–669**
integrated desalination systems, 2: 732
integrated resource planning, 2: 485
integration
    conventional electrical power system overviews, 2: 571
    costs, 2: 612
    electrical networks, 2: **569–622**
    future trends, 2: 617
    power systems, 2: 591
interest rates, 2: 472, 2: 473
intermittent energy sources, 2: 554
internal rate of return, 2: 472
internal standards, 2: 372
International Energy Agency, 2: 71
introduction, 2: **1–10**
land occupation, 2: 182, 2: 688
land-use, 2: 174, 2: 182, 2: 395, 2: 688
large machines, 2: 54
loads, 2: **243–268**, 2: 244
losses, 2: 114, 2: 412
markets and industry, 2: 485, 2: **657–669**
measurements, 2: 75, 2: 377
mechanical loads, 2: **243–268**, 2: 378
membrane desalination, 2: 726, 2: 727f, 2: 728, 2: 733
meteorology, 2: 74
microclimate impacts, 2: 523, 2: 530
microgrids, 2: 571, 2: 592–593, 2: 600, 2: 607
mitigation, 2: 398, 2: 494, 2: 530
motor vehicles, 2: 496
net present value, 2: 471
neural networks, 2: 1, 2: 88
noise impacts, 2: 513, 2: 525, 2: 526
noise measurements, 2: 379
nuclear options, 2: 548
operational costs, 2: 474
operational issues
    desalination, 2: 734, 2: 735
    electrical networks, 2: 581, 2: 596
organizations, 2: 71
origins, 2: 74
orographic models, 2: 86
payback period, 2: 471
performance, costs, 2: 474, 2: 475
Persian vertical axis designs, 2: 44
photovoltaics
    stand alone hybrid systems, 2: 623–624, 2: 638
    storage integration, 1: 203
    thermal solar collectors, 3: 295
physical basis, 2: 86
physical forecasting models, 2: 615
planet energy balance, 2: **11–39**
planning, 2: 407, 2: 596
policy, 2: **541–568**
    biomass, 2: 552
    carbon dioxide emission reduction, 2: 545, 2: 548
    electricity, 2: 542, 2: 546, 2: 552, 2: 555
    fossil fuels, 2: 542, 2: 548, 2: 552
    geothermal energy, 2: 554
    greenhouse gases, 2: **541–568**
    hydraulics, 2: 553
    intermittent energy sources, 2: 554
    markets, 2: 542, 2: 546
    nuclear options, 2: 548
    security, 2: **541–568**
    storage, 2: 553
pollutants/pollution, 2: 485, 2: 504
post mills, 2: 46
postwar programs, 2: 58

prices, 2: 470, 2: 471, 2: 472
    calculation methods, 2: 472
    comparisons in 2020, 2: 499
    electricity generation costs, 2: 477, 2: 481
    future outlook, 2: 471, 2: 498
    generation costs, 2: 477, 2: 481
    onshore wind, 2: 478
problems with microgrids, 2: 612
production, 2: 89, 2: 127
project certification, 2: 383, 2: 386
project implementation, 2: 735
prospects, turbine technology, 2: **671–724**
pumps, 2: 51
recommended practices, 2: 472
regime analysis, 2: 81
remote telecommunication stations, 2: 740, 2: 741, 2: 742
repayment periods, 2: 473
research and development, 2: **671–724**
reserve variable costs, 2: 489, 2: 490
Resource Atlas, 2: 86, 2: 87
reverse osmosis, 2: 726, 2: 727f, 2: 728, 2: 732, 2: 734, 2: 738
rotor blades, 2: 380
roughness change models, 2: 86
safety, 2: **371–389**
    certification, 2: 371, 2: 372, 2: 383
    environmental–social benefits/impacts, 2: 525
    testing, 2: 371, 2: 376
sails, 2: 41, 2: 42f, 2: 43f, 2: 44
security, 2: **541–568**
shadow flickering, 2: 522
shelter models, 2: 86
short-term reserves, 2: 490
simulations, 2: 651
smart grids, 2: 496
Smith-Putnam Machine, 2: 56
social benefits/impacts, 2: **503–539**
software tools, 2: 651
sound measurement testing, 2: 379
sources, electrical energy variability, 2: 588
space heating, 2: 497
special power applications, 2: **725–747**
stability models, 2: 74
stand alone hybrid systems, 2: 1, 2: **623–655**, 2: 623
    auxiliary electronic equipment, 2: 632
    complementary electric generator units, 2: 632
    contribution, 2: 626
    design, 2: 649, 2: 651
    diesel, 2: 623–624, 2: 636, 2: 639f
    electronic equipment, 2: 632
    energy storage, 2: 647
    evaluation, 2: 651
    historical development, 2: 624
    hydrogen, 2: 645, 2: 650
    hydropower, 2: 643, 2: 649–650
    photovoltaics, 2: 623–624, 2: 638
    simulations, 2: 651
    software tools, 2: 651
    solar photovoltaic energy, 2: 623–624, 2: 638
    storage system units, 2: 632, 2: 647
    system configurations, 2: 629, 2: 632
standardization, 2: **371–389**
    historical overviews, 2: 371
    technology-specific issues, 2: 372
standards, 2: **371–389**
    certification, 2: 371, 2: 383
    IEC, 2: 372, 2: 373, 2: 374
    testing, 2: 371, 2: 376
statistical forecasting models, 2: 615
steam engines, 2: 51
storage
    desalination, 2: 733, 2: 734
    mitigating variable costs and effects, 2: 495
    policy, 2: 553

318 Index

wind energy: (*continued*)
    repercussions, 2: 599
    stand alone hybrid systems, 2: 632, 2: 647
  supergrids, 2: 496
  support mechanisms, external costs, 2: 486
  surpluses, 2: 492
  system configurations, 2: 629, 2: 632
  system storage, 2: 495
  technical evaluation
    costs, 2: **469–501**
    economics, 2: **469–501**
    electricity generation costs, 2: **469–501**
    embedded generation benefits, 2: 484, 2: 486
    external costs, 2: 483, 2: 484
    financial issues, 2: **469–501**
    total costs, 2: 493, 2: 497
    variability costs, 2: 487, 2: 494
  technology-specific issues
    desalination, 2: 740
    historical overviews, 2: 48
    introduction, 2: **1–10**
    safety, 2: 372
    standardization, 2: 372
  telecommunications, 2: 624, 2: 740, 2: 741, 2: 742
  testing, 2: 371, 2: 376
    acoustic noise measurements, 2: 379
    anemometry, 2: 377
    electrical characteristics, 2: 380
    measurement, 2: 376
    mechanical load measurements, 2: 378
    noise measurements, 2: 379
    power plants, 2: 376
    power quality measurements, 2: 380
    rotor blades, 2: 380
    safety, 2: 371, 2: 376
    sound measurements, 2: 379
    standards, 2: 371, 2: 376
  theory, historical overviews, 2: 49
  three bladed systems, 2: 61
  time evolution of world markets, 2: 27, 2: 31
  total costs, 2: 493, 2: 497
  tower mills, 2: 46
  traffic, 2: 524
  transmission constraints, 2: 492
  transmission networks, 2: 602
  transportation, 2: 177, 2: 456, 2: 524
  two bladed systems, 2: 61, 2: 64
  unpredictability, 2: 586
  valuations, economics, 2: 470
  variability, characteristics, 2: 586, 2: 588
  variable costs
    assimilations, 2: 489
    backup reserves, 2: 489, 2: 491, 2: 492
    capacity credit, 2: 491
    carbon dioxide savings, 2: 491
    characteristics, 2: 489
    electricity networks, 2: 488
    extra short-term reserves, 2: 490
    mitigation, 2: 494
    reserves, 2: 489, 2: 490
    short-term reserves, 2: 490
    technical evaluation, 2: 487, 2: 494
    transmission constraints, 2: 492
  vehicles, 2: 496
  velocity, 2: 74
  visual impacts, 2: 518, 2: 527
  water consumption, 2: 505
  water heating, 2: 497
  water pumping systems, 2: 742, 2: 744
  weather forecasting, 2: 616
  wildlife, 2: 522, 2: 528, 2: 529
  wind pumps, 2: 51
  world-wide markets, 2: 25, 2: 27, 2: 31
  yields, 2: **113–168**
Wind Energy Group (WEG), 2: 65, 2: 68*f*, 2: 71
Wind Energy Network project, 2: 714
Wind Energy Technology Platform Secretariat (WINDSEC), 2: 716
wind farms:
  assembly processes, 2: 456
  currents, 2: 454
  definitions, 2: 1
  design, 2: 452
  development, 2: 711, 2: 714
  environmental impacts, 2: 510, 2: 530
  equipment selection requirements, 2: 452
  geographical distribution, 2: 591
  gravity foundations, 2: 441, 2: 443*f*, 2: 445
  installation, 2: 452
  jacket foundations, 2: 443*f*, 2: 447
  layouts, 2: 399
  loading sources, 2: 454
  maintenance, 2: 452
  management, 2: 711, 2: 714
  micro-siting, 2: 431
  monopile foundations, 2: 441
  offshore wind power
    activity, 2: 434
    basic features, 2: 440
    design, 2: 452
    equipment selection requirements, 2: 452
    installation, 2: 452
    maintenance, 2: 452
  operation and maintenance, 2: 458
  Roscoe Wind Park, Texas, 2: 218
  shallow water technology, 2: 441
  siting, 2: 530
  size issues, 2: 475
  social acceptance, 2: 204*f*, 2: 205
  support structures, 2: 441, 2: 444*f*
  towers, offshore power, 2: 441
  transportation, 2: 456
  tripod foundations, 2: 443*f*, 2: 447
  turbine technology, 2: 711, 2: 714
  wave evaluation, 2: 454
  wind evaluation, 2: 454
Windflow, 2: 322
wind generators: definitions, 2: 270
WINDGRID *see* Wind on the Grid
Wind on the Grid (WINDGRID), 2: 716
windmills, 2: **41–72**
  Europe, 2: 44
  steam engines, 2: 51
windows:
  built environment, 3: 330
  emerging technologies, 3: 316, 3: 336, 3: 339, 3: 342
  energy evaluation, 3: 321
  frames, 3: 333
    aluminum, 3: 333
    composite wood products, 3: 333
    fiberglass, 3: 334
    hybrid materials, 3: 334
    plastics, 3: 334
    thermal properties, 3: 334
    thermoplastics, 3: 334
    vinyls, 3: 334
    wood, 3: 333
  glazings, 3: 333
    aluminum, 3: 333
    coatings, 3: 330, 3: 330*t*
    composite wood products, 3: 333
    emerging technologies, 3: 316, 3: 336, 3: 339, 3: 342
    fiberglass, 3: 334
    hybrid materials, 3: 334
    plastics, 3: 334
    sealants, 3: 335
    solar thermal energy, 3: 315, 3: 321, 3: 327

spacers, 3: 335
   thermal properties, 3: 334
   thermoplastics, 3: 334
historical development, 3: 315
passive solar technologies, 3: 359
sealants, 3: 335
solar thermal energy glazings, 3: 315, 3: 321, 3: 327
spacers, 3: 335
thermal properties, 3: 321
wood, 3: 333

wind parks:
   aesthetics, 2: 182, 2: 194, 2: 205
   annual electricity production calculations, design, 2: 196
   annual expenses, 2: 211
   case studies, 2: **169–223**
   characteristics, 2: 211
   connections, 2: 209
   construction, 2: 512*t*, 2: 512–513
   costs, 2: 169, 2: 170, 2: 177, 2: 210
   definitions, 2: 1
   design case studies, 2: **169–223**
   economic analysis, 2: 169, 2: 170, 2: 177, 2: 210
   economic indexes, 2: 211
   efficiency, 2: 402
   electricity network connection, 2: 209
   electricity production calculations, 2: 196
   electricity production maximization, 2: 169, 2: 169–170, 2: 171
   environmental impacts, 2: 512*t*, 2: 512–513, 2: 513*t*, 2: 514*t*, 2: 536
   expenses, 2: 211
   funding schemes, 2: 210
   future trends, 2: 536
   installation site selection, 2: 171
   integrating local networks, 2: 206
   investment annual net profits, 2: 211
   investment annual revenue calculations, 2: 210
   large sized noninterconnected power systems, 2: 211, 2: 216
   local network integration, 2: 206
   micro-siting, 2: 188–189, 2: 190
   net profits, 2: 211
   noninterconnected power systems, 2: 211, 2: 212, 2: 216
   offshore wind energy projects, 2: 190, 2: 211, 2: 220
   onshore wind energy projects, 2: 211, 2: 218
   operation phase, 2: 512–513, 2: 513*t*
   power penetration, 2: 183, 2: 199, 2: 206, 2: 208, 2: 212, 2: 214, 2: 216
   revenue calculations, 2: 210
   set-up costs, 2: 169, 2: 170, 2: 177, 2: 210
   site selection, 2: 171
   small sized noninterconnected power systems, 2: 211, 2: 212
   social approval/attitude, 2: 202
   time minimization, 2: 169, 2: 170, 2: 181
   weak systems, 2: 183, 2: 206
   wind power penetration, 2: 183, 2: 199, 2: 206, 2: 208, 2: 212, 2: 214, 2: 216
windpods, 2: 686
wind potential, 2: **73–92**
   Barsch index, 2: 173, 2: 173*t*
   calm spell determination, 2: 125
   energy yields, 2: 117
   evaluation, 2: 183
   Griggs-Putnam index, 2: 173, 2: 173*t*
   gust determination, 2: 81, 2: 126
   long-term studies, 2: 124
   maps, 2: 171–172
   micro-siting, 2: 191, 2: 194
   scale impacts, 2: 122
   shape factor variation, 2: 122
   Weibull distribution, 2: 184, 2: 186*f*, 2: 197, 2: 197*f*, 2: 198, 2: 198*t*
   wind gust determination, 2: 81, 2: 126
   wind turbines, 2: 117, 2: 189

wind power:
   acceptance issues, 2: 396
   access roads, 2: 421
   activity creation, 2: 507
   appeals, 2: 398
   Asia, 2: 666
   availability, 2: 100
   benefits, 2: **503–539**
   budgeting, 2: 426
   building phase, 2: 427
   business models, 2: 429
   capital costs, 2: 422, 2: 424
   China, 2: 666
   coefficients, 2: 102
   commissioning, 2: 428
   condition monitoring, 2: 428
   conflicting interests, 2: 395, 2: 403
   construction, 2: 427
   contracts, 2: 427
   costs, 2: 420
   decommissioning, 2: 429
   definitions, 2: 1
   depreciation, 2: 422
   design, 2: 178, 2: **391–391**, 2: 421
   developing global markets, 2: **657–669**
   developing projects, 2: 396
   documentation, 2: 425
   economics, 2: 420, 2: **469–501**, 2: 422, 2: 423, 2: 426
   electronics, 2: **329–370**
   employment, 2: 507, 2: 508
   energy rose, 2: 399, 2: 411
   energy storage, 2: 599
   environmental–social benefits/impacts, 2: 397, 2: **503–539**, 2: 426
   error sources, 2: 412
   estimating power production, 2: 403
   Europe, 2: 662
   farm layouts, 2: 399
   feasibility studies, 2: 394
   financing, 2: 420, 2: 425, 2: 426
   fingerprints, 2: 411
   forests, 2: 413
   fossil fuel savings/substitution, 2: 507
   foundations, 2: 421
   friction, 2: 409
   future trends, 2: 536
   generation reserve capacity, 2: 598
   Germany, 2: 662
   global market development, 2: **657–669**
   grid connections, 2: 395, 2: 421
   hills, planning tools, 2: 409
   hydropower multibenefit solutions, 6: 43
   impacts, 2: **503–539**
   implementation, 2: **391–391**
   industry and markets, 2: **657–669**
   installed capacity, 2: 3, 2: 3*f*
   integration projects, 2: 711, 2: 714
   internal rate of return, 2: 424
   investment, 2: 421
   job opportunities, 2: 507, 2: 508
   land issues, 2: 395
   land lease, 2: 397, 2: 422
   layouts, 2: 399, 2: 415*f*, 2: 416*f*
   leasing, 2: 397, 2: 422
   local acceptance, 2: 396
   long-term wind climate, 2: 403
   losses, planning tools, 2: 412
   maintenance, 2: 422, 2: 423, 2: 428
   managing projects, 2: 393
   market development, 2: **657–669**
      Asia, 2: 666
      China, 2: 666
      Europe, 2: 662

wind power: (*continued*)
    Germany, 2: 662
    North America, 2: 665
    Spain, 2: 663
    United States, 2: 665
  micro-siting, 2: 188–189, 2: 190, 2: 397, 2: 398, 2: 455–456
  mitigation, 2: 398, 2: 530
  monitoring, 2: 428
  neighbor issues, 2: 395, 2: 397
  North America, 2: 665
  obstacles issues, 2: 190, 2: 409
  operation, 2: 422, 2: 423, 2: 428
  opposing interests, 2: 395, 2: 403
  optimization, micro-siting, 2: 397, 2: 401
  output potential, 2: 90
  park efficiency, 2: 402
  penetration
    dynamic security, 2: 208
    weak networks, 2: 208
    wind park design, 2: 183, 2: 199, 2: 206, 2: 208, 2: 212, 2: 214, 2: 216
  performance monitoring, 2: 429
  performance testing, 2: 377
  permission, 2: 396
  pitfalls, 2: 413
  planning tools, 2: 407
  plant, 2: 376, 2: 381, 2: 427
  present value, 2: 424
  production estimation, 2: 403
  project design, 2: **391–391**
  project development, 2: 396, 2: 422
  project implementation, 2: **391–391**
  project management, 2: 393
  public attitude analysis, 2: 534, 2: 535
  public dialogue, 2: 397
  quality control, 2: 427
  quality measurements, 2: 380
  revenue, 2: 422
  risk assessments, 2: 424
  roughness of terrain, 2: 409
  scale effects/scaling, 2: 136, 2: 138, 2: 144
  site location, 2: 394, 2: 397, 2: 398
  site restoration, 2: 429
  social benefits/impacts, 2: **503–539**
    acceptability, 2: 531, 2: 534, 2: 535
    activity creation, 2: 507
    employment, 2: 507, 2: 508
    fossil fuel savings, 2: 507
    fossil fuel substitution, 2: 507
    job opportunities, 2: 507, 2: 508
  Spain, 2: 663
  status, world market, 2: 25
  supervision, 2: 427
  suppliers, 2: 427
  system integration, 2: 591
  temperatures, 2: 413
  terrain roughness, planning tools, 2: 409
  transfers, 2: 428
  trees, 2: 413
  turbulence, 2: 406
  uncertainty, 2: 412
  United States, 2: 665
  variability, 2: 590, 2: 591
  wakes, 2: 398
  wind atlas method, 2: 407, 2: 411
  wind climate, 2: 403
  wind data, 2: 403, 2: 406, 2: 426
  wind farm layouts, 2: 399
  wind measurements, 2: 406, 2: 412
  wind park design, 2: 183, 2: 199, 2: 206, 2: 208, 2: 212, 2: 214, 2: 216
  wind resources, 2: 394, 2: 396, 2: 414
  wind speed, 2: 403, 2: 413

wind turbines
  design and implementation, 2: 415, 2: 416
  integration projects, 2: 711, 2: 714
  scale effects/scaling, 2: 136, 2: 138, 2: 144
  selection, 2: 416
  upgrading, 2: 415
Windpower's yaw mechanism, 2: 278*f*, 2: 279
wind pumping: definitions, 2: 725
Wind Resource Atlas, 2: 86, 2: 87
WinDrive generators, 2: 287
wind speed:
  artificial neural networks, 2: 88
  distribution, 2: 117, 2: 120, 2: 124
  dynamic studies, 2: 87
  energy yields, 2: 117, 2: 120, 2: 124
  forecasting, 2: 88
  installed costs, 2: 475
  mathematical representation, 2: 83
  measurements, 2: 398
  Rayleigh distribution, 2: 118
  time variations, 2: 81, 2: 82
  variation with time, 2: 81
  Weibull distribution, 2: 117, 2: 120, 2: 124, 2: 144
  wind data, 2: 403
  wind energy potential, 2: 75, 2: 77
  wind power, 2: 403, 2: 413
  wind turbine energy yields, 2: 117, 2: 120, 2: 124, 2: 144
wind turbines, 2: **1–10**, 2: **93–111**, 2: **225–241**
  see also offshore wind power
  ABB company, 2: 324, 2: 325*f*
  Acciona, electrical systems, 2: 317, 2: 320*f*, 2: 321*t*
  active-stall systems, 2: 276, 2: 679
  actuators, 2: 366
  advanced modeling, 2: 231
  aerodynamics, 2: **225–241**
    advanced modeling, 2: 231
    blade-element momentum theory, 2: 225, 2: 228, 2: 236
    computational fluid dynamics, 2: 232, 2: 233
    Glauert's optimum rotor method, 2: 227
    loads, 2: 247
    momentum theory, 2: 226, 2: 236
    noise, 2: 238
    one-dimensional momentum theory, 2: 226
    optimum rotor method, 2: 227
    vortex models, 2: 231
  aesthetics, 2: 518, 2: 687
  aggregation, 2: 590
  air density variation, 2: 146
  airfoil drag, 2: 102
  airfoil lift, 2: 102
  Alstom, 2: 323
  annual wind energy production estimates, 2: 134, 2: 138
  asynchronous generators, 2: 279, 2: 281, 2: 339, 2: 340, 2: 353, 2: 354
  AVANTIS, 2: 324
  basic principles, 2: 100
  blade-element momentum theory, 2: 225, 2: 228, 2: 236
  blade numbers, 2: 61, 2: 64
  blades
    construction, 2: 682
    definition, 2: 270
    design, 2: 682
    financial support, 2: 710
    technology evolution, 2: 682, 2: 710, 2: 713
  building-integrated systems, 2: 699
  California wind rush, 2: 66
  capacitor banks, electrical systems, 2: 296
  capacity factors, 2: 1, 2: 135, 2: 153–154, 2: 677–679, 2: 678*f*
  categorization, 2: 330, 2: 331*t*
  certification, 2: 383
  classification, 2: 104, 2: 272, 2: 273*f*
  Clipper Windpower, 2: 322
  computational fluid dynamics, 2: 232, 2: 233

Index

condition monitoring schemes, **2**: 364
contribution, stand alone hybrid wind energy systems, **2**: 626
control loads, **2**: 251
control systems, **2: 329–370**
   actuators, **2**: 366
   electrical systems, **2**: 272
   generators, **2**: 330, **2**: 352, **2**: 358
   grid connections, **2**: 330, **2**: 331*f*, **2**: 358, **2**: 362
   hardware, **2**: 366
   mechanical modeling, **2**: 334
   modeling, **2**: 333
   pitch, **2**: 330, **2**: 331*f*, **2**: 345, **2**: 358
   sensors, **2**: 366
   time evolution, **2**: 98
   yaw, **2**: 330, **2**: 331*f*, **2**: 360
converters, **2**: 332, **2**: 332*f*, **2**: 336, **2**: 340
costs, **2**: 477, **2**: 702, **2**: 709
coupled pitch—generator control systems, **2**: 358
current concepts, **2**: 675
current loads, **2**: 253
Darrieus rotors, **2**: 107
definitions, **2**: 1
desalination, **2**: 733, **2**: 735
design, **2**: 246, **2**: 373, **2**: 440
development, **2**: 659
direct-drive systems, **2**: 680
disturbances, **2**: 593
downwind rotor configurations, **2**: 255
drag, **2**: 102
dynamic analyses, **2**: 244
economic evolution, **2**: 100
electrical component modeling, **2**: 336
electrical networks
   disturbances, **2**: 593
   frequency variations, **2**: 593
   harmonics, **2**: 595
   interaction disturbances, **2**: 593
   phase voltage imbalance, **2**: 594
   voltage flicker, **2**: 594
   voltage variations, **2**: 594
electrical systems, **2: 269–269**
   control, **2**: 272
   electricity production, **2**: 279
   generators, **2**: 279, **2**: 281
   industry, **2**: 306
   manufacturers, **2**: 306
   power control, **2**: 272
   reliability, **2**: 272, **2**: 287*f*, **2**: 298
electromagnetic communication systems, **2**: 524
electromagnetic induction generators, **2**: 279, **2**: 281
electromagnetic interference, **2**: 182
Enercon, **2**: 275*f*, **2**: 290, **2**: 309, **2**: 309*f*, **2**: 310*f*
energy production estimation, **2**: 115, **2**: 132
energy yields, **2: 113–168**
   air density variation, **2**: 146
   annual wind energy production estimates, **2**: 134, **2**: 138
   energy production estimation, **2**: 115, **2**: 132
   estimation, **2**: 131, **2**: 153
   hub heights, **2**: 144
   instantaneous power output, **2**: 132
   material failure, **2**: 152, **2**: 153
   mean power coefficients, **2**: 135, **2**: 136
   power coefficients, **2**: 115, **2**: 116*f*, **2**: 135, **2**: 136
   power curves, **2**: 127, **2**: 138
   power output parameters, **2**: 140, **2**: 151
   power production estimation, **2**: 115, **2**: 132
   selection techniques, **2**: 158
   shape factor variation, **2**: 122, **2**: 136, **2**: 137, **2**: 138, **2**: 144
   technical availability impacts, **2**: 151
   theoretical distributions, **2**: 140
   wake effect impacts, **2**: 149
   wind potential evaluation, **2**: 117
   wind speed distribution, **2**: 117, **2**: 120, **2**: 124, **2**: 144

environmental condition loads, **2**: 246–247, **2**: 262
environmental impacts, **2**: 687
erection, **2**: 180
estimating energy yields, **2**: 131, **2**: 153
European financial support, **2**: 710
European Standard EN 50308, **2**: 376
evolution, **2**: 93, **2: 671–724**
fault accommodation, **2**: 364
financial support, **2**: 708, **2**: 710, **2**: 713, **2**: 715, **2**: 718
fixed speed power systems, **2**: 295
forecasting, **2**: 710, **2**: 714
foundations, **2**: 178
frequency/fluctuations variations, **2**: 207, **2**: 593
Fuhrländer AG, **2**: 323
function testing, **2**: 381
funding, **2**: 708, **2**: 710, **2**: 713, **2**: 715, **2**: 718
future outlooks, **2**: 303
Gamesa, **2**: 310, **2**: 311*t*, **2**: 312*f*, **2**: 313*f*
gearbox systems, **2**: 680
Gedser machine, **2**: 60
GE energy, **2**: 313, **2**: 313*f*, **2**: 314*f*, **2**: 315*t*
generators
   control systems, **2**: 330, **2**: 352, **2**: 358
   electrical systems, **2**: 279, **2**: 281
   modeling, **2**: 336
   stand alone hybrid wind energy systems, **2**: 631
Glauert's optimum rotor method, **2**: 227
Goldwind, electrical systems, **2**: 322
gravitational loads, **2**: 251
grid compatibility, **2**: 418
grid connections, **2**: 330, **2**: 331*f*, **2**: 358, **2**: 362
hardware control systems/power electronics, **2**: 366
harmonics, **2**: 207, **2**: 295, **2**: 595
historical overviews, **2**: 54, **2**: 55, **2**: 55*f*, **2**: 56, **2**: 71, **2**: 624
   standards, **2**: 371
horizontal axis, **2**: 45, **2**: 104, **2**: 440
hub heights, **2**: 144
hydrodynamic loads, **2**: 249
ice loads, **2**: 253
IEC 61400 categorization, **2**: 330, **2**: 331*t*
induction generators, **2**: 279, **2**: 281
industry, **2: 671–724**
   electrical systems, **2**: 306
inertial loads, **2**: 251
Ingeteam, **2**: 325, **2**: 327*f*
innovation, **2: 671–724**
installation issues, **2**: 177
installed capacity growth, **2**: 94
instantaneous power output, **2**: 132
integrated time domain analysis, **2**: 244, **2**: 254
integration projects, **2**: 711, **2**: 714
interaction disturbances, **2**: 593
interference, electromagnetic communication systems, **2**: 524
introduction, **2: 1–10**
investment, **2**: 421
irregular wave theory, **2**: 266
lift, **2**: 102
lightening protection, **2**: 272, **2**: 287*f*, **2**: 298
loads, **2: 243–268**
   design analysis, **2**: 246
   dynamic analyses, **2**: 244
   environmental conditions, **2**: 246–247, **2**: 262
   offshore wind turbines, **2**: 247, **2**: 258
   onshore wind turbines, **2**: 254
   power production, **2**: 246, **2**: 254
   turbulence, **2**: 256, **2**: 257*f*, **2**: 259
   wave theory, **2**: 265
   wind theory, **2**: 263
loss assessments, **2**: 114
maintenance, **2**: 246, **2**: 364
manufacturers, **2**: 306, **2**: 667
mapping, **2**: 710, **2**: 714
market share, **2**: 303

wind turbines (*continued*)
  Maxwell Technologies, 2: 327
  mean power coefficients, 2: 135, 2: 136
  mean wind loads, wave conditions, 2: 262
  mechanical components, 2: 333
  mechanical-dynamic loads, 2: **243–268**
    design analysis, 2: 246
    dynamic analyses, 2: 244
    integrated time domain analysis, 2: 244, 2: 254
    time domain analysis, 2: 244, 2: 254
    wave theory, 2: 265
  mechanical modeling, 2: 334
  medium-sized systems, 2: 713
  modeling, 2: 333
    control systems, 2: 333
    converters, 2: 336
    electrical components, 2: 336
    generators, 2: 336
    mechanical components, 2: 333
    wind park design, 2: 186
  modified linear wave theory, 2: 266
  momentum theory, 2: 226, 2: 236
  monitoring, power electronics, 2: 364
  noise, 2: 238, 2: 513, 2: 518
  nominal power, 2: 186–187, 2: 188, 2: 418
  Nordex, 2: 317
  offshore wind power, 2: **431–468**
    catenary moored spars, 2: 258
    design, 2: 440
    Det Norske Veritas-OS-J101 standard, 2: 376
    hydrodynamic damping, 2: 259
    IEC standards, 2: 375
    loads, 2: 247, 2: 258
    mechanical-dynamic loads, 2: 247, 2: 258
    servo-induced negative damping, 2: 260
    support structures, 2: 376
    technology evolution, 2: 688
    tension leg spars, 2: 258
    turbulence, 2: 259
    wave-induced loads, 2: 258
    wind-induced loads, 2: 258
    wind parks, 2: 190, 2: 688, 2: 713
  one-dimensional momentum theory, 2: 226
  onshore wind, 2: 254
    costs, 2: 477
    downwind rotor configurations, 2: 255
    loads, 2: 254
    rotor configurations, 2: 255
    small-scale systems, 2: 477
    thrust loads, 2: 254
    tower shadow, 2: 255, 2: 256f, 2: 257f
    upwind rotor configurations, 2: 255
    wind-induced loads, 2: 254
  optimum rotor method, 2: 227
  overall control strategies, 2: 343
  performance curves, rotors, 2: 110
  personnel safety, 2: 376
  phase voltage imbalance, 2: 594
  Phoenix Contact, 2: 325
  pitch
    control systems, 2: 330, 2: 331f, 2: 345, 2: 358
    electrical systems, 2: 271, 2: 273
    stall, 2: 679
  postwar programs, 2: 58
  power
    aggregation variability, 2: 590
    coefficients, 2: 102, 2: 115, 2: 116f, 2: 135, 2: 136
    conditioning, 2: 330, 2: 331f
    control systems, 2: 272, 2: 330, 2: 331f
    conversion, 2: 297, 2: 298
    curves, 2: 127, 2: 138
    electrical control systems, 2: 272
    electronics, 2: **269–269**, 2: **329–370**
      condition monitoring schemes, 2: 364
      converters, 2: 332, 2: 332f, 2: 340
      fault accommodation, 2: 364
      hardware, 2: 366
      maintenance, 2: 364
      monitoring, 2: 364
    energy yields, 2: 115, 2: 116f, 2: 135, 2: 136
    loads, 2: 246, 2: 254
    output, 2: 90
    output parameters, 2: 140, 2: 151
    production estimation, energy yields, 2: 115, 2: 132
    production loads, 2: 246, 2: 254
    quality
      electrical systems, 2: 279
      wind park design, 2: 206
    subsystems, 2: 270, 2: 272f
    thrust loads, 2: 254
    transmission advancements, 2: 98
    wind energy availability, 2: 100
  principles, 2: 100
  production estimation, 2: 115, 2: 132
  prospects, 2: **671–724**
  qualitative and quantitative noise considerations, 2: 513
  reducing environmental impacts, 2: 687
  regular wave theory, 2: 265
  reliability, 2: 272, 2: 287f, 2: 298
  REpower, 2: 317, 2: 321t
  research and development, 2: 518, 2: **671–724**
  ride through, 2: 295
  rotors
    aerodynamic analysis, 2: 236
    blade-element momentum theory, 2: 236
    CFD aerodynamic analysis, 2: 232, 2: 233
    configurations, 2: 255
    diameter, 2: 418
    electrical systems, 2: 281f, 2: 285, 2: 285f
    financial support, 2: 710
    loads, 2: 255
    performance curves, 2: 110
    technology evolution, 2: 676, 2: 710, 2: 713
  safety
    electrical systems, 2: 272
    standards, 2: 376
    testing, 2: 376
  Savonius rotors, 2: 109
  scale effects/scaling, 2: 122, 2: 136, 2: 138, 2: 144
  security, 2: 715
  selection techniques, 2: 158, 2: 416
  sensors, 2: 366
  service areas, 2: 178
  Siemens, 2: 314
  Sinovel, 2: 324
  size
    technology trends, 2: 676
    time evolution, 2: 2–3, 2: 3f, 2: 95
    wind power design and implementation, 2: 416
  small-scale systems, 2: 696, 2: 713
    certification standards, 2: 388
    classification, 2: 301, 2: 304t
    costs, 2: 477
    electrical systems, 2: 301
    IEC standards, 2: 374
    onshore wind costs, 2: 477
    technology, 2: 696, 2: 713
  Smith-Putnam Machine, 2: 56
  social issues, 2: 687
  soft starter devices, 2: 296
  soil interaction loads, 2: 253
  solar power, 2: 715
  spatial planning, 2: 709
  specific energy yields, 2: 677–679, 2: 678f

speed, **2**: 330, **2**: 331f
squirrel-cage generators, **2**: 282, **2**: 340, **2**: 353, **2**: 354
stall, **2**: 276, **2**: 679
stand alone hybrid wind energy systems, **2**: 624
standards, **2**: 371, **2**: 373, **2**: 383
start-up conditions, **2**: 246
steady-state voltage level fluctuations, **2**: 207
stochastic loads, **2**: **243–268**
subgrid scales, **2**: 232–233
supervision, **2**: 332, **2**: 332f
suppliers, **2**: 418
Suzion, electrical systems, **2**: 314
swells, **2**: 594
synchronous generators, **2**: 279–280, **2**: 280f, **2**: 285, **2**: 337, **2**: 356
system performance, **2**: 96
technical availability impacts, energy yields, **2**: 151
technology
    blades, **2**: 682, **2**: 710, **2**: 713
    evolution, **2**: 93, **2**: **671–724**
    forecasting, **2**: 710, **2**: 714
    mapping, **2**: 710, **2**: 714
    problems, **2**: 709
    rotors, **2**: 676, **2**: 710, **2**: 713
telecommunication stations, **2**: 741
testing, **2**: 376, **2**: 719
theoretical distributions, **2**: 140
three bladed systems, **2**: 61
thrust loads, **2**: 254
time domain analysis, **2**: 244, **2**: 254
time evolution, **2**: 93, **2**: **671–724**
tip speed ratio, **2**: 102
torque coefficients, **2**: 102
tower shadow, **2**: 255, **2**: 256f, **2**: 257f
transients, **2**: 207
transport, **2**: 177, **2**: 246
trends, **2**: 164, **2**: **671–724**
turbulence, **2**: 256, **2**: 257f, **2**: 259
two bladed systems, **2**: 61, **2**: 64
types, **2**: 417
ultracapacitors, **2**: 277f, **2**: 327
upgrading, **2**: 415, **2**: 416
upwind rotor configurations, **2**: 255
variable-speed power systems, **2**: 297
VEM, electrical systems, **2**: 324
vertical axis, **2**: 44, **2**: 71, **2**: 104, **2**: 106, **2**: 672, **2**: 693
Vestas, **2**: 306, **2**: 308t
visual impacts, **2**: 518
voltage flicker, **2**: 594
voltage fluctuations/variations, **2**: 207, **2**: 594
vortex models, **2**: 231
wakes
    blade-element momentum theory, **2**: 230
    computational fluid dynamics, **2**: 234
    effect impacts, **2**: 149
    loads, **2**: 249
    technology evolution, **2**: 717
wave conditions, **2**: 262
wave-induced loads, **2**: 258
wave prediction, **2**: 717
wave theory, **2**: 265
Weier, **2**: 324
wind classes, **2**: 418
wind climate, **2**: 418
wind farms, **2**: 711, **2**: 714
Windflow, **2**: 322
wind potential evaluation, **2**: 117
wind power
    design and implementation, **2**: 415, **2**: 416
    integration projects, **2**: 711, **2**: 714
    scale effects/scaling, **2**: 136, **2**: 138, **2**: 144
    selection, **2**: 416
    upgrading, **2**: 415
wind speed distribution, **2**: 117, **2**: 120, **2**: 124, **2**: 144
wind theory, loads, **2**: 263
WinWind, **2**: 322
yaw
    control systems, **2**: 330, **2**: 331f, **2**: 360
    electrical systems, **2**: 271, **2**: 277
winnowing, **2**: 41
WinWind, **2**: 322
wiring: building-integrated photovoltaics, **1**: 701
WISE *see* wide-field infrared survey explorer
WOLF modeling system, **6**: 368
women empowerment: Millennium Development Goals, **7**: 276
woodchip: gasification, **5**: 141
wood composite window frames, **3**: 333
wooden window frames: glazings, **3**: 333
wood fuels:
    2000's markets, **5**: 78
    bioenergy markets, **5**: 77
    biomass cofiring, **5**: 57, **5**: 59
    development, **5**: 77
    finance, markets, **5**: 78
    gasification, **5**: 140, **5**: 141, **5**: 142t
    international trade, **5**: 77
    markets, **5**: 77
    transportation, **5**: 78
    virgin biomass feedstocks, **5**: 141, **5**: 142t
    waste biomass feedstocks, **5**: 140
wood pellets, **5**: 59
wood processing residues, **5**: 286
woody biomass, **5**: 7, **5**: **263–291**
    coppice crops, **5**: 263, **5**: 264
    forestland-derived resources, **5**: 263, **5**: 282
    forest residues, **5**: 263, **5**: 283
    fuelwood, **5**: 286
    loblolly pine, **5**: 264, **5**: 274
    pines, **5**: 264, **5**: 274
    primary forest residues, **5**: 263, **5**: 283
    residue processing, **5**: 286
    short-rotation woody crops, **5**: 263, **5**: 264
    single-stem woody crops, **5**: 264, **5**: 268, **5**: 274, **5**: 276
    urban residues, **5**: 263, **5**: 264, **5**: 286
    willow coppice crops, **5**: 264
    wood processing residues, **5**: 286
work:
    blackbodies, **1**: 332
    enclosed thermal radiation, **1**: 328
    free thermal radiation, **1**: 330
    hydropower, **6**: 17
    thermal radiation, **1**: 328
work conditions in Brazil, **5**: 23
workers: Brazilian bioethanol development, **5**: 22, **5**: 23
working gases, **3**: 202
working groups (WG): photovoltaic standards, **1**: 788, **1**: 789, **1**: 797
working mechanisms: carbonation, **6**: 386
working principles:
    inorganic semiconductor physics, **1**: 445
    microbial fuel cells, **4**: 266
    organic semiconductor physics, **1**: 445
Work Programme on Indicators of Sustainable Development, **7**: 278
World banks, **6**: 229
World Commission on Environment and Development, **7**: 273
World Radiometric Reference (WRR), **1**: 221, **3**: 67
World Summit on Sustainable Development, **7**: 274
world-wide considerations:
    see also individual countries
    alkali–aggregate reaction, **6**: 389
    biomass cofiring trends, **5**: 56, **5**: 64

world-wide considerations: (*continued*)
    commissioning dams, 6: 355–356, 6: 356f
    geothermal energy utilization, 7: 187, 7: 188f
    hydropower, 6: 33, 6: 43, 6: 44, 6: 258
        Cameroon, Africa, 6: **129–151**
        Canada, 6: **153–178**
        Indian development trends, 6: **227–252**
        Japan, 6: **265–307**
        New Zealand, 6: **467–483**
        pumped storage developments, 6: 412–413, 6: 414t
        Spain, 6: **309–341**
        Three Gorges Project, China, 6: **179–227**
    offshore wind power projects, 2: **431–468**
    photovoltaic markets, 1: 16
    solar water heating systems, 3: 423
    wind energy markets, 2: 25, 2: 27, 2: 31
wound rotor doubly fed induction generators, 2: 353
wrap-through devices, 1: 465
WRF mesoscale models, 1: 243
WRR *see* World Radiometric Reference
Wuskwatim Generating Station Project, Manitoba, Canada, 6: 159
    environmental aspects, 6: 160
    location, 6: 159
    technical aspects, 6: 159

X

X-band marine radar, 8: 23
Xiaolangdi Project, 6: 499–500, 6: 500f
Xiaowan project, 6: 499, 6: 499f, 6: 500f
Xiluodu Hydropower Project, 6: 495, 6: 496f
Xingu River, 6: 124
X-ray diffraction, 7: 98
X-ray fluorescence: geothermal chemistry, 7: 99
X-ray solids characterization, 7: 98
XTL *see* X to liquids family
X to liquids (XTL) family, 5: **155–204**

Y

Yang model, 3: 43
Yangtze River, China, 6: **179–227**
    natural condition, 6: 180
    navigation structures, 6: 183, 6: 193
Yangzte estuary, 6: 214
yaw:
    control systems, 2: 330, 2: 331f, 2: 360
    correction, 2: 230
    definitions, 2: 270
    electrical systems, 2: 271, 2: 277
yields:
    biomass feedstocks, 5: **293–303**
    Brassica breeders, 5: 300
    canola, 5: **293–303**
    crops, 5: **293–303**
    feedstocks, 5: **293–303**
    genetics, 5: 299, 5: 300
    improvement potentials, 5: **293–303**
    oilseed rape, 5: **293–303**
    photovoltaic performance monitoring, 1: **775–786**
    rapeseed, 5: **293–303**
    wind turbine energy yields, 2: **113–168**
Yingli Green Energy Holding Company Ltd:, 1: 170
ytterbium oxide emitters, 1: 606, 1: 615
Yueniao turbines, 6: 440

Z

ZEBRA technology, 4: 322, 4: 327
zenith angles, 1: 214, 1: 215, 1: 240, 3: 2
zeolites, 3: 225, 3: 225t, 3: 228t
Zhangfei Temple, 6: 218
Zhejiang, 6: 429
Zigui County resettlement, 6: 211, 6: 211f
zoning: urban planning, 1: 701